CAREER PREP

CSK 100 - Study Skills

CMF 95 - Math Fundamentals

CAT 150 - Anatomy, Physiology, and Terminology

Taken from:

Medical Terminology: A Living Language, Fourth Edition
by Bonnie F. Fremgen and Suzanne S. Frucht

Keys to Success: Building Analytical, Creative, and Practical Skills, Brief Fifth Edition
by Carol Carter, Joyce Bishop, and Sarah Lyman Kravits

Math Basics for the Health Care Professional, Third Edition
by Michele Benjamin Lesmeister

PIMA MEDICAL INSTITUTE

Custom Publishing

New York Boston San Francisco
London Toronto Sydney Tokyo Singapore Madrid
Mexico City Munich Paris Cape Town Hong Kong Montreal

Front Cover Photo Credit: Photo by Bill Cronin, Copyright Pima Medical Institute.

Back Cover Photo Credit: Image from *Anatomie normale du corps humain* courtesy of the National Library of Medicine, illustration by Sigismond Balicki.
Stock photography provided by *www.comstock.com* <http://www.comstock.com/> .
All other images copyright Pima Medical Institute.

Taken from:

Medical Terminology: A Living Language, Fourth Edition
by Bonnie F. Fremgen and Suzanne S. Frucht
Copyright © 2009 by Pearson Education, Inc.
Published by Prentice Hall
Upper Saddle River, New Jersey 07458

Keys to Success: Building Analytical, Creative, and Practical Skills, Brief Fifth Edition
by Carol Carter, Joyce Bishop, and Sarah Lyman Kravits
Copyright © 2009, 2006, 2003, 2001, 1999 by Pearson Education, Inc.
Published by Prentice Hall

Math Basics for the Health Care Professional, Third Edition
by Michele Benjamin Lesmeister
Copyright © 2009 by Pearson Education, Inc.
Published by Prentice Hall

This special edition published in cooperation with Pearson Custom Publishing.

Printed in the United States of America

10 9 8 7 6 5 4

2007280108

DC

Pearson Custom Publishing is a division of

PEARSON

www.pearsonhighered.com

ISBN 10: 0-536-36877-5
ISBN 13: 978-0-536-36877-5

Contents

Medical Terminology: A Living Language

by Bonnie F. Fremgen and Suzanne S. Frucht

CSK 100
Study Skills

Taken From:
Keys to Success: Building Analytical, Creative, and Practical Skills, Brief Fifth Edition
by Carol Carter, Joyce Bishop, and Sarah Lyman Kravits

WELCOME TO
Opening Do
Your Goals
D

COLLEGE
to Success

1

"Successfully intelligent people . . . have a can-do attitude. They realize that the limits to what they can accomplish are often in what they tell themselves they cannot do, rather than in what they really cannot do."

ROBERT STERNBERG

You and your fellow students are embarking on a new phase of life—one that offers ideas, information, and skills in exchange for hard work and dedication. The tools you acquire in college will help you succeed in an ever-changing world where technology and the global marketplace are transforming the way you live and work. *Keys to Success* will help you learn successfully, graduate, and reap the personal and professional rewards of a solid education. This chapter gets you started with an overview of how being a "successfully intelligent," responsible, and forward-thinking student will help you face challenges head-on and achieve more than you ever imagined.

In this chapter you explore answers to the following questions:

- Where are you now—and where can college take you? 4
- How can successful intelligence help you achieve your goals? 7
- What actions will prepare you for college success? 11
- How can you work effectively with others? 20
- How can the things you learn now promote life success? 24
- Successful Intelligence Wrap-Up 26

Chapter 1's Successful Intelligence Skills

Analytical

- Evaluating your starting point as you begin college
- Analyzing how successful intelligence can help you achieve goals
- Considering how specific actions promote success in college

Creative

- Creating new ideas about college goals
- Developing a fresh understanding of your ability to grow
- Creating ways to benefit from failure

Practical

- How to follow the code of academic integrity
- How to work with others effectively
- How to become a lifelong learner

Where Are You Now—And Where Can College Take You?

Reflect on the road that brought you to this day. You completed high school or its equivalent. You may have built life skills from experience as a partner or parent. You may have been employed in one or more jobs or completed a tour of duty in the armed forces. You have enrolled in college, found a way to pay for it, signed up for courses, and shown up for class. And, in deciding to pursue a degree, you chose to believe in your ability to accomplish goals. You have earned this opportunity to be a college student!

To make the most of college, first understand its value. College is the ideal time to acquire skills that will serve you in the **global marketplace**, where workers in the United States work seamlessly with people in other parts of the world. Thomas Friedman, author of *The World Is Flat*, explains how the digital revolution has transformed the working environment you will enter after college: "It is now possible for more people than ever to collaborate and compete in real time with more other people on more different kinds of work from more different corners of the planet and on a more equal footing than in any previous time in the history of the world—using computers, e-mail, networks, teleconferencing, and dynamic new software."[1]

GLOBAL MARKETPLACE
An interconnected marketplace, where companies do business without regard to time zones and boundaries, and where companies from all over the world compete directly for business.

This means that you may be doing *knowledge work* and other jobs in conjunction with, or in competition with, highly trained and motivated people from around the world. Reaching your potential has never been

REAL QUESTIONS

How can I make the transition to college easier?

I grew up in a diverse community and am in the first generation of my family to attend college. In high school, making friends and fitting in was very easy for me. However, I am nervous about the college experience. One reason is that I don't have role models in my family for what college is all about, and another is that the student body at my college has a different cultural makeup than my high school and community. When I tried meeting people on campus the first day I visited, I didn't feel like I made any real connections. What can I do to make the change easier?

Kevin Abreu
Montclair State University
Montclair, New Jersey

PRACTICAL ANSWERS

Jennifer Joralmon
American Sign Language Instructor
Paradise Valley Community College,
Phoenix, Arizona

Forge connections with organizations, role models, and fellow students.

You're asking questions and that's the best first step. I think one of the fastest ways to feel more a part of college is to visit your Student Affairs office to find a list of clubs and activities. Pick a couple that pique your interest and check them out. Meeting people who share your interests will help you feel more connected. Also, assess your academic strengths and weaknesses. If you're strong in a certain subject, such as a second language or math, visit the on-campus tutoring center and apply to become a tutor. Or, if you're weak in a subject, get the extra help early. You'll meet other students—both tutors and those who are seeking help.

Another way to ease the transition is to seek out an adult role model. As you attend your classes, find an instructor you feel comfortable with—or talk to a counselor or advisor. Ask that person questions about how to navigate college, such as how to withdraw from a class or what to do if the bookstore has run out of the text you need. Many schools, such as mine, have peer or student leadership programs where you can find an older student to explain the ins and outs of college, including which teachers and courses to seek out and which to avoid.

Above all, stick with it and remember that you're not the only one feeling awkward. I see so many students start school that way who end up having a great experience. Try some of these suggestions and experiment with your own. In fact, try introducing yourself to the person next to you in class. Who knows? That student may be feeling the same way you are.

more crucial to your success. You will be up to the task of succeeding in the global marketplace if you do the following:

- Acquire solid study skills
- Commit to lifelong learning and job training
- Persevere despite obstacles
- Perform high-quality work on a consistent basis
- Embrace change as a way of life

KEY 1.1

More education is likely to mean more income.

Median annual income of persons with income 25 years old and over, by gender and highest level of education, 2002

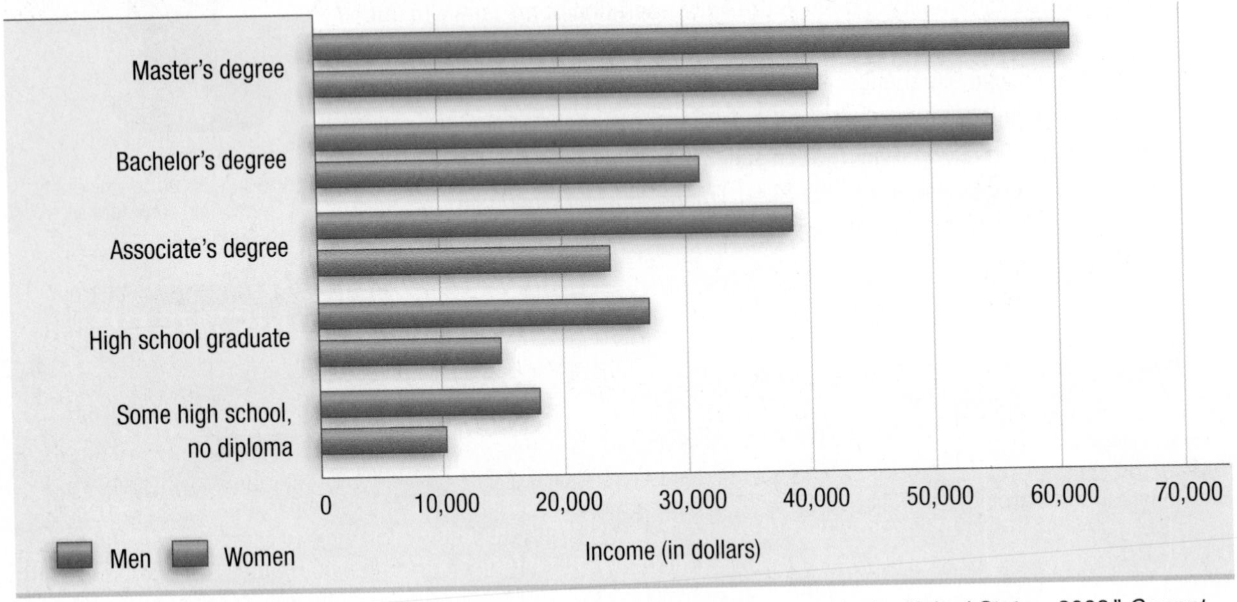

Source: U.S. Census Bureau, "Income, Poverty, and Health Insurance Coverage in the United States, 2003," *Current Population Reports*, Series P60-226, August 2004.

On a more personal level, college can help you achieve overarching "life success goals":

Life Success Goal: Increased employability and earning potential. Getting a degree greatly increases your chances of finding and keeping a highly skilled, well-paying job. College graduates earn, on average, around $20,000 more per year than those with just a high school diploma (see Key 1.1). Furthermore, the unemployment rate for college graduates is less than half that of high school graduates (see Key 1.2).

Life Success Goal: Preparation for career success. Your course work will give you the knowledge and hands-on skills you need to achieve your career goals. It will also expose you to a variety of careers and areas of academic specialty, many of which you may not have even heard of. Completing college will open career doors that are closed to those without a degree.

Life Success Goal: Smart personal health choices. The more educated you are, the more likely you are to take care of your physical and mental health. A college education prepares you with health-related information and attitudes that you will use over your lifetime, helping you to practice wellness through positive actions and to avoid practices with the potential to harm.

Life Success Goal: Active community involvement and an appreciation of different cultures. Going to college prepares you to understand complex

KEY 1.2

More education is likely to mean more consistent employment.

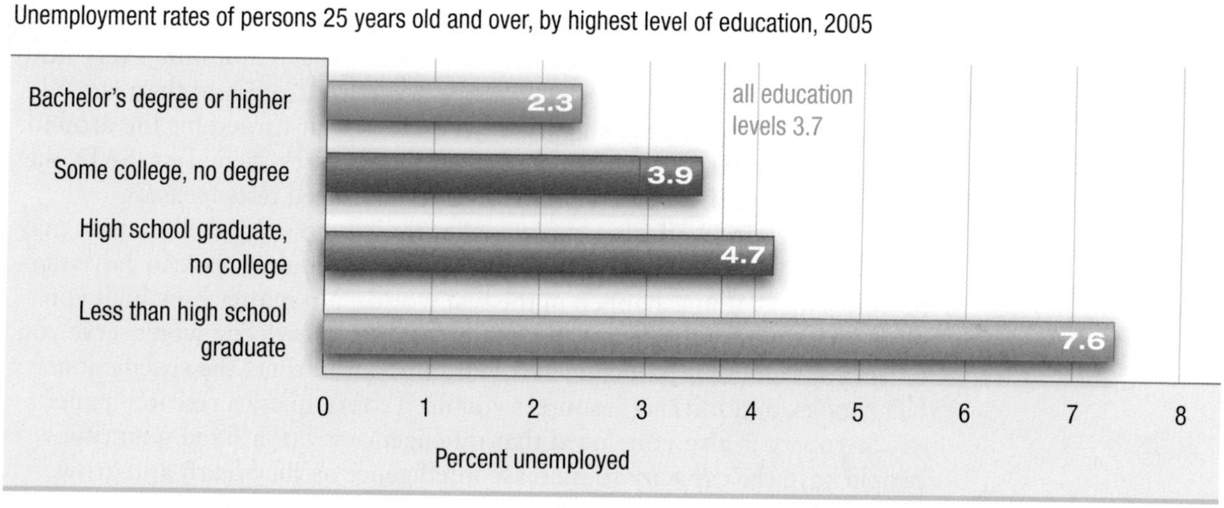

Source: U.S. Department of Labor, Bureau of Labor Statistics, Office of Employment and Unemployment Statistics, "Employment and Earnings," January 2005.

political, economic, and social forces that affect you and others. This understanding is the basis for good citizenship and encourages community involvement. Your education also exposes you to the ways in which people and cultures are different and how these differences affect world affairs. As a worker likely to encounter many cultures in the global marketplace, this knowledge will help you succeed.

Life Success Goal: Self-knowledge. Being in college gets you thinking about yourself on a big-picture level. What do you do well? What do you want out of life? What can you improve? College gives you the chance to evaluate where you are and decide where you want to be.

This course and *Keys to Success* provide the tools you need to kick off this exploration. Especially crucial is your ability to use *successful intelligence*—your most important goal-achievement tool, and the theme of this text.

How Can Successful Intelligence Help You Achieve Your Goals?

Think about how you define *intelligence.* Many people view an intelligent person as someone with "book smarts," someone who will excel in high-level analytical courses and go on to a brilliant career in a challenging profession such as science or law. Traditionally, many people have also believed that each individual is born with a fixed amount of intelligence, and that this has a significant effect on success. Another fairly common belief is that standardized tests, such as IQ (intelligence quotient) tests, accurately measure a person's intelligence and are predictors of success.

Psychologist Robert J. Sternberg has an entirely different view of intelligence. His life experiences convinced him that traditional intelligence measurements lock people into poor performances and often do not accurately reflect their potential for life success. When test anxiety caused Sternberg to score poorly on IQ and other standardized tests during elementary school, he delivered exactly what was expected of him—very little. In the fourth grade, when a teacher expected more from him than he had ever shown he could give, she provided a spark that turned his life around.

INERT INTELLIGENCE
Passive recall and analysis of learned information rather than goal-directed thinking linked to real-world activities.

Sternberg asserts that IQ tests, the Scholastic Assessment Test (SAT), the American College Test (ACT), and other standardized tests measure **inert intelligence**. He further explains that those who score well on tests may have strong recall and analytical skills, but they do not necessarily have the power to make things happen in the real world.[2] No matter how high you score on a library science test, for example, your knowledge won't serve you unless you can use it to locate, in a short amount of time, the specific journals, books, and Internet resources you need to complete a research paper.

Sternberg is also convinced that intelligence is *not* a fixed quantity; people have the capacity to increase intelligence as they learn and grow. Recent studies support this perspective, showing that the brain continues to develop throughout life if you continue to learn new things.[3] To make this development happen, you need to actively challenge yourself and believe in your ability to grow. Psychologist Carol Dweck says that "people with a growth mindset thrive when they're stretching themselves."[4] Conversely, people who shy away from challenge will experience less growth. Challenge yourself, and your value to yourself and to others will grow.

Defining Successful Intelligence

In his book *Successful Intelligence: How Practical and Creative Intelligence Determine Success in Life*, Sternberg focuses on what he calls *successful intelligence*—"the kind of intelligence used to achieve important goals."[5] Successful intelligence better predicts life success than any IQ test because it focuses largely on actions—what you *do* to achieve your goals—instead of just on recall and analysis.

Sternberg uses this story to illustrate the impact of successful intelligence:

Two boys are walking in a forest. They are quite different. The first boy's teachers think he is smart, his parents think he is smart, and as a result, he thinks he is smart. He has good test scores, good grades, and other good paper credentials that will get him far in his scholastic life.

Few people consider the second boy smart. His test scores are nothing great, his grades aren't so good, and his other paper credentials are, in general, marginal. At best, people would call him shrewd or street smart.

As the two boys walk along in the forest, they encounter a problem—a huge, furious, hungry-looking grizzly bear, charging straight at them. The first boy, calculating that the grizzly bear will overtake them in 17.3 seconds, panics. In this state, he looks at the second boy, who is calmly taking off his hiking boots and putting on his jogging shoes.

The first boy says to the second boy, "You must be crazy. There is no way you are going to outrun that grizzly bear!"

The second boy replies, "That's true. But all I have to do is outrun you!"[6]

This story shows that successful problem solving and decision making require more than book smarts. When confronted with a problem, using *only* analytical thinking put the first boy at a disadvantage. On the other hand, the second boy thought in different ways; he analyzed the situation, creatively considered the options, and took practical action. He asked and answered questions. He knew his purpose. And he lived to tell the tale.

Sternberg breaks successful intelligence into three parts or abilities:

- *Analytical thinking*—commonly known as *critical thinking*—involves analyzing and evaluating information, often in order to work through a problem or decision. Analytical thinking is largely responsible for school success and is measured through traditional testing methods.
- *Creative thinking* involves generating new and different ideas and approaches to problems and, often, viewing the world in ways that disregard convention.
- *Practical thinking* means putting what you've learned into action in order to solve a problem or make a decision—and carrying what you learn from the experience with you to use with future situations. Practical thinking enables you to accomplish goals despite obstacles.

Learning is not the only benefit of engaging successful intelligence. Using practical and creative skills also contributes to relationship building and a sense of fun in the classroom.

Together, these abilities move you toward a goal, as Sternberg explains:

> Analytical thinking is required to solve problems and to judge the quality of ideas. Creative intelligence is required to formulate good problems and ideas in the first place. Practical intelligence is needed to use the ideas and their analysis in an effective way in one's everyday life.[7]

Here are two examples that illustrate how this works.

Successful intelligence in a study group—reaching for the goal of helping each other learn:

- *Analyze* the concepts you must learn, including how they relate to what you already know.
- *Create* humorous memory devices to help you remember key concepts.
- *Think practically* about who in the group does what best, and assign tasks accordingly.

Successful intelligence regarding academics—reaching for the goal of declaring a major:

- *Analyze* what you do well and like to do. Then analyze the course offerings in your college catalog until you come up with one or more that seem to mesh with your strengths.

- *Create* a dream career, then come up with majors that support it. For example, if you want to be a science writer, consider majoring in biology and minoring in journalism.
- *Think practically* about your major by talking with students and instructors in the department, looking at course requirements, and interviewing professionals in fields of interest.

Why is successful intelligence your key to success? It helps you understand how learning propels you toward goals, boosting your desire to learn. It gives you ways to move toward those goals, increasing your willingness to work hard. It helps you to maximize strengths and compensate for weaknesses, leading to a greater ability to capitalize on who you are and what you can do. It also increases your value in school and on the job: *People with highly developed critical, creative, and practical thinking skills are in demand because they can apply what they know to new situations, innovate, and accomplish their goals.*

The three elements of successful intelligence can give all kinds of learners a more positive outlook on their abilities. Students who have trouble with tests and other analytical skills can see that creative and practical thinking also play a significant role in success. Students who test well but have trouble using their knowledge to innovate and make things happen can develop a team approach to success as they work to improve their creative and practical skills. Everyone can find room, and ways, to grow.

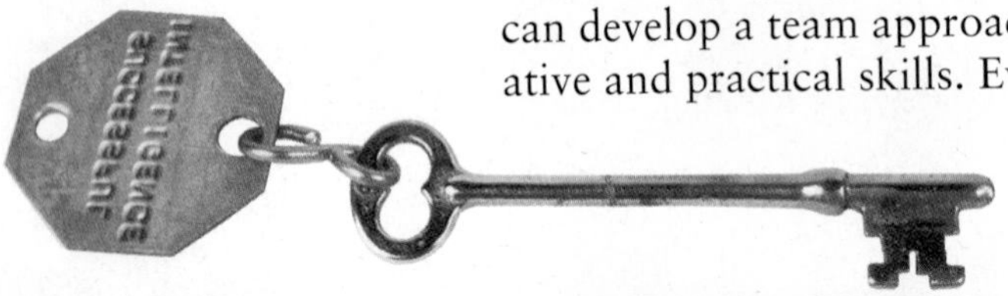

How This Book Helps You Build Successful Intelligence

Keys to Success is designed to help you build the analytical, creative, and practical thinking skills that will get you where you want to go in school and in life.

Chapter Content

Each chapter incorporates successful intelligence with the following:

- A visual overview of the analytical, creative, and practical tools that you will gather in the chapter
- Contextual connections to analytical, creative, and practical thinking
- Accounts and examples from students, professors, and professionals that show how people use various analytical, creative, and practical skills to accomplish goals
- A *Successful Intelligence Wrap-Up* that summarizes the analytical, creative, and practical skills you have explored

In addition, chapter 4—the chapter on thinking—goes into more detail about all three skills.

In-Chapter Activities

Within the text of each chapter, you will find three activities that help you build your successful intelligence skills:

- *Get Analytical* gives you an opportunity to develop your own analytical skills through your analysis of a chapter topic.

- *Get Creative* prompts you to develop your own creative skills as you think innovatively about chapter material.
- *Get Practical* provides a chance to develop your own practical skills through the experience of applying an idea from the chapter.

In this chapter, these exercises take the form of mini-assessments—tools that will help you get to know yourself as an analytical, creative, and practical thinker. With self-knowledge as the starting point, you will develop your successful intelligence throughout this book. Chapter 8 will provide an opportunity for you to assess yourself once again and consider how you have grown in each area.

End-of-Chapter Exercises

Here you have the opportunity to combine what you have learned and apply it to important tasks in several ways, as follows:

- *Successful Intelligence: Think, Create, Apply* unites the three aspects of successful intelligence.
- *Teamwork: Create Solutions Together* encourages you to apply various successful intelligence elements to a group setting.
- *Writing: Journal and Put Skills to Work* provides an opportunity to put analysis, creative thoughts, and practical ideas down in words.
- *Personal Portfolio: Prepare for Career Success* builds practical skills and a portfolio of information that promote career success.

Whereas successful intelligence is the overarching framework of how you will achieve college and life goals, many specific elements move you toward those goals day by day. Explore attitudes and actions that prepare you for success.

What Actions Will Prepare You for College Success?

Preparing for college success is as much a state of mind as it is making sure you take specific actions. The following section points to the basics you need—in actions as well as attitude—to achieve your goals. Always remember that you are your own manager, in charge of meeting your obligations and making decisions that move you toward your goals.

Be Responsible and Accountable

Your primary responsibility as a student is to pursue academic excellence—to do your very best in every course so that you come away with knowledge and marketable skills. The theme of *responsibility* stands out in how two New Mexico State University students describe the struggle to adjust to college life:[8]

Angie Miller (majoring in Biology): The hardest part of my [freshman] courses was that I had to do all my work myself with nobody telling me every day that my homework was due. . . . Also, I felt that there was more

GET ANALYTICAL!

Assess Yourself as an Analytical Thinker

For each statement, circle the number that feels right to you, from 1 for "not at all true for me" to 5 for "very true for me."

1. I recognize and define problems effectively.	1 2 3 4 5
2. I see myself as "a thinker," "analytical," "studious."	1 2 3 4 5
3. When working on a problem in a group setting, I like to break down the problem into its components and evaluate them.	1 2 3 4 5
4. I need to see convincing evidence before accepting information as fact.	1 2 3 4 5
5. I weigh the pros and cons of plans and ideas before taking action.	1 2 3 4 5
6. I tend to make connections among pieces of information by categorizing them.	1 2 3 4 5
7. Impulsive, spontaneous decision making worries me.	1 2 3 4 5
8. I like to analyze causes and effects when making a decision.	1 2 3 4 5
9. I monitor my progress toward goals.	1 2 3 4 5
10. Once I reach a goal, I evaluate the process to see how effective it was.	1 2 3 4 5
Total your answers here:	28

If your total ranges from 38–50, you consider your analytical thinking skills to be *strong*.
If your total ranges from 24–37, you consider your analytical thinking skills to be *average*.
If your total ranges from 10–23, you consider your analytical thinking skills to be *weak*.

Remember that you can improve your analytical thinking skill with focus and practice.

material covered in a shorter time period, so it was more study time than in high school.

Daniel Estrada (majoring in Latin American History and Spanish): I find that . . . the [classes are] more to my interest since I picked [them].

Now the catch is that it is not up to the instructor to keep you on task. . . . It is left unsaid that it is our responsibility to keep up with the reading, homework, and actually showing up for class.

As a student, you show responsibility by taking a series of small but important actions that are the building blocks of academic success:

- Read assigned material before it is discussed in class.
- Attend class on time and with a positive attitude.
- Complete assignments on schedule.
- Listen attentively, take notes, and participate in discussions.
- Study for exams, either on your own or with others.
- Communicate with instructors and students, and seek help from them if you need it.

A critical responsibility in each class is to thoroughly read your **syllabus** and refer to it frequently throughout the term. You will receive a syllabus at the first class meeting of each of your courses. Consider each syllabus as a "contract" between you and your instructor, outlining what your instructor expects of you (such as readings, assignments, and class participation) as well as what you can expect from your instructor (availability, schedule of topics, clarification of grading system).

Your syllabus will answer questions about course focus, required and optional reading, schedule of coverage, dates of exams and due dates for assignments, the components of your final grade, and more. Marking up your syllabus in your own way will help remind you of responsibilities, as will "backdating"—in other words, noting in your datebook, calendar, or PDA the interim goals you have to achieve by particular dates in order to complete more involved assignments. For example, if you have a 15-page paper due on October 15, you would enter dates in September and October for goals like choosing a topic, research, first draft, and final draft. Key 1.3 shows a portion of an actual syllabus with important items noted.

Finally, in all of your daily academic tasks, persist until you know exactly what you need to accomplish so that you can complete your work on time. **Persistence** is the responsible student's master key.

SYLLABUS

A comprehensive outline of course topics and assignments.

PERSISTENCE

The act of continuing steadfastly in a course of action, even in the face of obstacles or challenges.

Get Motivated

Success is a process, not a fixed mark. **Motivation** is what keeps the process in motion. Successfully intelligent people find ways to motivate themselves to learn, grow, and work toward what they want. Your challenge as you begin college is to identify and activate the forces that move you forward. These *motivators*—grades, love of a subject, the drive to earn a degree—can change with time and situations.

The primary key to motivation is to continually remind yourself of what you stand to gain from achieving your most important goals. A nursing student at Palo Alto College in San Antonio, Texas, understands how goals relate to motivation: "To stay motivated I will always remember that I am doing this to better myself and to learn what I need to in order to be the best nurse that I can be. Making a commitment and staying true to it is not easy, but I know that an uncommitted person will never finish anything."[9]

MOTIVATION

A goal-directed force that moves a person to action.

KEY 1.3

A syllabus helps you stay on schedule and fulfill responsibilities.

ENG 122 Spring 2007

How to connect with the instructor

Instructor: Jennifer Gessner
Office Hours: Tue & Thur 12:30–1:30 (or by appointment) in DC 305
Phone: 303-555-2222
E-mail: jg@abc.xyz

Books and materials to get ASAP

Required Texts: *Good Reasons with Contemporary Arguments,* Faigley and Selzer
A Writer's Reference, 5th ed., Diana Hacker

Required Materials:

- a notebook with lots of paper
- a folder for keeping everything from this class
- an active imagination and critical thinking

Course coverage, expectations, responsibilities

Course Description: This course focuses on argumentative writing and the researched paper. Students will practice the rhetorical art of argumentation and will gain experience in finding and incorporating researched materials into an extended paper.

Writer's Notebook: All students will keep, and bring to class, a notebook with blank paper. Throughout the semester, you will be given writing assignments to complete in this book. You must bring to class and be prepared to share any notebook assignment. Notebook assignments will be collected frequently, though sometimes randomly, and graded only for their completeness, not for spelling, etc.

How grades are determined for this course

Grading:

- Major Writing Assignments worth 100 points each.
- Final Research Project worth 300 points.
- Additional exercises and assignments range from 10 to 50 points each.
- Class participation: Based on the degree to which you complete the homework and present this in a thoughtful, meaningful manner in class.
- Attendance: Attendance is taken daily and students may miss up to three days of class without penalty, but will lose 5 points for each day missed thereafter.
- Late work: All work will lose 10% of earned points per class day late. No work will be accepted after five class days or the last class meeting.

Final Grade: The average of the total points possible (points earned divided by the total possible points). 100–90% = A; 89–80% = B; 79–70% = C (any grade below 70% is not passing for this class).

Reflects school's academic integrity policy

Academic Integrity: Students must credit any material used in their papers that is not their own (including direct quotes, paraphrases, figures, etc.). Failure to do so constitutes plagiarism, which is illegal, unethical, always recognizable, and a guaranteed way to fail a paper. The definition of plagiarism is "to steal and use (the writings or ideas of another) as one's own."

Week 4

Topics of that day's class meeting

Notice of due date for paper draft

2/1 The Concise Opinion.
HW: Complete paper #1 Rough Draft (5–7 pages double-spaced)

Notice of reading assignments to complete

2/3 How Professionals Argue
HW: Read Jenkins Essay (p 501 of *Good Reasons) and* Rafferty Essay (p 525); compare argumentative style, assess and explain efficacy of arguments.

Week 5

Notice of quiz

2/15 Developing an Argument
Essay Quiz on Jenkins and Rafferty Essays
HW: Chap 5 of *Good Reasons;* based on components of a definition of argument, write a brief explanation of how your argument might fit into this type.

Notice of final due date for paper

2/17 Library Workday: Meet in Room 292
PAPER #1 DUE

Source: Jennifer Gessner, Community College of Denver.

Low self-esteem and fear can stall your motivation. Here are some ideas about how to overcome these roadblocks and keep moving ahead.

Successful Intelligence Connections Online

Listen to author Sarah Kravits describe how to use analytical, creative, and practical intelligence to build and sustain motivation.

Go to the *Keys to Success* Companion Website at www.prenhall.com/carter to listen or download as a podcast.

Build Self-Esteem

When people have faith in themselves, their **self-esteem** fuels their motivation to succeed. Belief, though, is only half the game. The other half is the action and effort that help you feel that you have earned your self-esteem, as basketball coach Rick Pitino explains: "Self-esteem is directly linked to deserving success. If you have established a great work ethic and have begun the discipline that is inherent with that, you will automatically begin to feel better about yourself."[10]

SELF-ESTEEM
Belief in one's value as a person that builds as you achieve your goals.

Although thinking positively sets the tone for success, taking action gets you there. In order to get moving in a positive direction, create personal guidelines that support your success—for example, "I turn in assignments on deadline." Then, follow up your guideline with the action you've promised to take—in this case, always turning in your assignments on time.

Face Your Fears

Everyone experiences fear. Anything unknown—starting college, meeting new people, encountering new challenges—can be frightening. The following steps will help you work through fear with courage and reignite your motivation to succeed:

1. *Acknowledge fears.* Naming your fear begins to lessen its hold on you. Be specific.
2. *Examine fears.* Sometimes one fear hides a larger one. Do you fear a test, or the fact that if you pass it you will have to take a tougher class next?
3. *Develop and implement a plan.* Come up with ways to overcome your fear, and put them to work. For example, if reading a play by William Shakespeare intimidates you, you might ask an instructor for advice, rent a film adaptation, or listen to an audio version on your iPod.

Practice Academic Integrity

Having **academic integrity** means valuing education and learning over grades. Academic integrity promotes learning and ensures a quality education based on *ethics* (your sense of what is right to do) and hard work. Read your school's code of honor, or academic integrity policy, in your student handbook. When you enrolled, you agreed to abide by it.

ACADEMIC INTEGRITY
Following a code of moral values, prizing honesty and fairness in all aspects of academic life—classes, assignments, tests, papers, projects, and relationships with students and faculty.

What Academic Integrity Is

The Center for Academic Integrity, part of the Kenan Institute for Ethics at Duke University, defines academic integrity as a commitment to five fundamental values:[11]

- *Honesty.* Honesty defines the pursuit of knowledge and implies a search for truth in your classwork, papers and lab reports, and teamwork with other students.

- *Trust.* Trust means being true to your word. Mutual trust—between instructor and student, as well as among students—makes possible the exchange of ideas that is essential for learning.
- *Fairness.* Instructors must create a fair academic environment where students are judged against clear standards and in which procedures are well defined.
- *Respect.* In a respectful academic environment, both students and instructors accept and honor a wide range of opinions, even if the opinions are contrary to core beliefs.
- *Responsibility.* You are responsible for making choices that will provide you with the best education—choices that reflect fairness and honesty.

Unfortunately, the principles of academic integrity are frequently violated on college campuses. In a recent survey, three of four college students admitted to cheating at least once during their undergraduate careers.[12] Violations of academic integrity—turning in previously submitted work, using unauthorized devices during an exam, providing unethical aid to another student, or downloading passages or whole papers from the Internet—aren't worth the price. Consequences of violations vary from school to school and include participation in academic integrity seminars, grade reduction or course failure, suspension, or expulsion.

Why Academic Integrity Is Worth It

Choosing to act with integrity has the following positive effects:

- *Increased self-esteem.* Self-esteem is tied to respectful and honorable action.
- *Acquired knowledge.* Honest work is more likely to result in knowledge that lasts.
- *Effective behavioral patterns.* When you play fair now, you set a positive pattern.
- *Mutual respect.* Respecting the work of others will encourage others to respect your work.

The risk to students who violate standards of integrity is growing because cheating is now easier to discover. Make a commitment to uphold the highest standards of academic integrity.

Understand and Manage Learning Disabilities

The following will help you understand learning disabilities and, should you be diagnosed with one, give you the tools to manage your disability successfully.

The National Center for Learning Disabilities (NCLD) defines learning disabilities as follows:[13]

- They are neurological disorders that interfere with one's ability to store, process, and produce information.
- They do *not* include mental retardation, autism, behavioral disorders, impaired vision, hearing loss, or other physical disabilities.

- They do *not* include attention deficit disorder and attention deficit hyperactivity disorder, although these problems may accompany learning disabilities.[14]
- They often run in families and are lifelong, although people with learning disabilities can use specific strategies to manage and even overcome areas of weakness.
- Persons with a disability must be diagnosed by professionals in order to receive federally funded aid.

How can you determine if you should be evaluated for a learning disability? According to the NCLD, persistent problems in any of the following areas may indicate a learning disability:[15]

- Reading or reading comprehension
- Math calculations, understanding language and concepts
- Social skills or interpreting social cues
- Following a schedule, being on time, meeting deadlines
- Reading or following maps
- Balancing a checkbook
- Following directions, especially on multistep tasks
- Writing, sentence structure, spelling, and organizing written work

For an evaluation, contact your school's learning center or student health center for a referral to a licensed professional. If you are diagnosed with a learning disability, focused action will help you manage it and maximize your ability to learn and succeed.

Be informed about your disability. Search the library and the Internet—try NCLD at www.ncld.org or LD Online at www.ldonline.org (other Web sites are listed at the end of the chapter). Or call NCLD at 1-888-575-7373. Make sure you understand your individualized education program (IEP)—the document describing your disability and recommended strategies.

Seek assistance from your school. Speak with your advisor about specific accommodations that will help you learn. Services mandated by law for students who have learning disabilities include extended time on tests, note-taking assistance, assistive technology devices (such as tape recorders or laptop computers), alternative assessments and test formats, tutoring, and study skills assistance.

Be a dedicated student. Be in class and on time. Read assignments before class. Sit where you can focus. Review notes soon after class. Spend extra time on assignments. Ask for help.

Build a positive attitude. See your accomplishments in light of how far you have come. Rely on people who support you. Know that help will give you the best possible chance to learn and grow.

Learn from Failure and Celebrate Success

Even the most successful people make mistakes and experience failures. In fact, failure is one of the greatest teachers. Failure provides an opportunity to realize what you didn't know so that you can improve.

Learning from Failure

Learning from your failures and mistakes involves careful thinking.

Analyze what happened. For example, imagine that after a long night of studying for a chemistry test, you forgot to complete an American history paper due the next day. Your focus on the test caused you to overlook other tasks. Now you may face a lower grade on your paper if you turn it in late, plus you may be inclined to rush it and turn in a product that isn't as good as it could be.

Come up with creative ways to improve the situation and change for the future. In the present, you can request an appointment with the instructor to discuss the paper. For the future, you can make a commitment to note deadlines in a bright color in your planner and to check due dates more often.

Put your plan into action. Do what you have decided to do—and keep an eye on how it is working. Talk with the instructor and see if you can hand in your paper late. If you decide to be better about noting deadlines, in the future you might work backwards from your paper due date, setting dates for individual tasks related to the paper and planning to have it done two days before it is due in order to have time for last-minute corrections.

Sometimes, however, you can't get motivated to turn things around. Here are some ways to boost your outlook when failure gets you down:

- Believe you are a capable person. Focus on your strengths and know you can try again.
- Share your disappointment with others. Blow off steam and exchange creative ideas that can help you learn from what happened.
- Look on the bright side. At worst, you got a lower grade because your paper was late. At best, you learned lessons that will help you avoid the same mistake in the future.

Your value as a human being does not diminish when you make a mistake. People who can manage failure demonstrate to themselves and others that they have the courage to take risks and learn. Employers often value risk takers more than people who always play it safe.

Celebrating Success

Take a moment to acknowledge what you accomplish, whether it is a good grade, a job offer, or any personal victory. Let your success fuel your confidence that you can do it again. Don't forget to reward yourself when you succeed. Take the kind of break you like best—see a movie, socialize with some friends, read a book for fun, declare a no-work day. Enjoy what college has to offer outside of the classroom.

Finally, being a motivated, responsible, ethical, and committed student is no easy feat. Don't hesitate to reach out for support throughout your college experience.

get creative!

Assess Yourself as a Creative Thinker

For each statement, circle the number that feels right to you, from 1 for "not at all true for me" to 5 for "very true for me."

1. I tend to question rules and regulations.	1 2 3 4 5
2. I see myself as "unique," "full of ideas," "innovative."	1 2 3 4 5
3. When working on a problem in a group setting, I generate a lot of ideas.	1 2 3 4 5
4. I am energized when I have a brand-new experience.	1 2 3 4 5
5. If you say something is too risky, I'm ready to give it a shot.	1 2 3 4 5
6. I often wonder if there is a different way to do or see something.	1 2 3 4 5
7. Too much routine in my work or schedule drains my energy.	1 2 3 4 5
8. I tend to see connections among ideas that others do not.	1 2 3 4 5
9. I feel comfortable allowing myself to make mistakes as I test out ideas.	1 2 3 4 5
10. I'm willing to champion an idea even when others disagree with me.	1 2 3 4 5

Total your answers here: 29

If your total ranges from 38–50, you consider your creative thinking skills to be *strong.*

If your total ranges from 24–37, you consider your creative thinking skills to be *average.*

If your total ranges from 10–23, you consider your creative thinking skills to be *weak.*

Remember that you can improve your creative thinking skill with focus and practice.

How Can You Work Effectively with Others?

A century ago it was possible to live an entire lifetime surrounded only by people from your own culture. Not so today. American society consists of people from a multitude of countries and cultural backgrounds. In fact, in the 2000 census, American citizens described themselves in terms of 63 different racial categories, compared with only 5 in 1990.[16] Cable television, the Internet, and the global marketplace add to our growing cultural awareness, linking people from all over the world in ways that were unimaginable less than a decade ago.

Your success at school and at work will depend on your ability to cooperate with diverse people in a team setting. Valuing diversity and knowing how to work in groups are two keys to developing this ability.

Value Diversity

What does *diversity* mean?

Diversity means differences among people. On an interpersonal level, diversity refers to the differences between ourselves and others, between the groups we belong to and the groups we are not part of. Differences in gender, skin color, ethnicity and national origin, age, physical characteristics and abilities, and sexual orientation are most obvious in this level of diversity. Differences in cultural and religious beliefs and practices, education, socioeconomic status, family background, and marital and parental status are less visible but no less significant in how they define people and affect relationships.

In college you are likely to meet classmates and instructors who reflect America's growing diversity, including people in the following demographic groups:

- Biracial or multiracial individuals
- People from families with more than one religious tradition
- Non-native English speakers who may have emigrated from outside the United States
- People older than "traditional" 18- to 22-year-old students
- Persons living with various kinds of disabilities
- Persons practicing different lifestyles—often expressed in the way they dress, their interests, their sexual orientation, or their leisure activities

Being able to appreciate and adjust to differences among people is crucial to your success at school and prepares you for success in life. Former University of Michigan student Fiona Rose describes the benefits of a positive approach to diversity this way:

> My years at U-M have been enhanced by relationships with men and women from all cultures, classes, races, and ethnicities. Such interac-

tions are essential to an education. While courses teach us the history and academic value of diversity, friendships prepare us to survive and thrive in our global community. Good institutions consider not only what a potential student will gain from classes and course work, but what he or she will bring to the campus community.[17]

Diversity refers to the differences within people. Another layer of diversity lies within each person. Among the factors that define this layer are personality traits, learning style, strengths and weaknesses, and natural talents and interests. No one else has been or will ever be exactly like you.

Chapter 3 will go into more detail about diversity and communication as well as about how people learn—a less visible but no less important aspect of personal diversity. Additionally, in chapter 4 you will explore differences in analytical, creative, and practical abilities.

Develop Emotional and Social Intelligence

Successful relationships in a diverse world depend on competencies that go beyond intellectual and career skills. All relationships depend on what psychologist Daniel Goleman calls **emotional intelligence** and **social intelligence.**

EMOTIONAL INTELLIGENCE
The ability to perceive, assess, and manage one's own emotions as well as understand the emotions of others.

SOCIAL INTELLIGENCE
Having an understanding of the complexity of social interaction and using that understanding to manage relationships effectively.

Emotional Intelligence

Your emotional intelligence quotient (EQ) is a set of competencies that involves knowing yourself, mastering your feelings, and understanding how to manage those feelings when interacting with others.[18] Goleman divides these competencies into two categories (see Key 1.4):[19]

- *Personal competence:* How you manage yourself—your self-awareness, self-regulation, and motivation
- *Social competence:* How you handle relationships with others, including awareness of the needs and feelings of others and ability to encourage others to do things

Social Intelligence

When someone close to you is happy, sad, or fearful, you probably tend to experience some of the same feelings out of concern or friendship. New research shows that the human brain is hardwired to connect with other brains around it. On an MRI brain scan, the area of your friend's brain that lights up during an emotional experience also lights up in your brain as you "share" the emotion. Your nervous system has what are called "mirror neurons" that mimic an observed emotion, allowing you to "participate" in the feeling even though you did not originate it. These capacities of your nervous system are involved in social intelligence.

Goleman defines *social intelligence* as a combination of two key categories: "social awareness, what we sense about others—and social facility, what we then do with that awareness" (see Key 1.5).[20]

- *Social awareness* ranges from just sensing other peoples' emotions on a basic level to actively working to understand how other people feel. It

KEY 1.4 Become more emotionally intelligent by developing these qualities.

PERSONAL COMPETENCE	SOCIAL COMPETENCE
Self-Awareness	**Social Awareness**
• I know my emotions and how they affect me. • I understand my strengths and my limits. • I am confident in my abilities. • I am open to improvement.	• I sense the feelings and perspectives of others. • I help others improve themselves. • I know how to relate to people from different cultures. • I can sense how to serve the needs of others.
Self-Management	**Social Skills**
• I can control my emotions and impulses. • I can delay gratification when there is something more important to be gained. • I am trustworthy. • I can adapt to change and new ideas. • I persist toward my goals despite obstacles.	• I know how to work in a team. • I can inspire people to act. • I understand how to lead a group. • I know how to persuade people. • I can make positive change happen.

Source: Based on Daniel Goleman, *Working with Emotional Intelligence*, New York: Bantam Books, 1998, pp. 26–27.

also includes knowledge of how the social world works (with different understandings for different settings). Active, attuned listening is a key component.

- *Social facility* is the active and most practical component, where you put your social awareness to work to achieve a goal. It involves smooth nonverbal interaction, presenting yourself in ways appropriate to individual situations, actively shaping the course of social interactions, and acting on your sense of what others need.

Emotional and social intelligence influence your ability to communicate and maneuver in social environments and achieve your goals. You will see more about these topics in chapter 4, chapter 8, and throughout the text.

Know How to Work with Others in Groups

A real-world application of diversity in action is likely to occur in the study group setting. Students taking the same course may form a study group that meets one or more times a week or right before exams. Instructors sometimes initiate student study groups, commonly for math

KEY 1.5

Become more socially intelligent through awareness and action.

Social Awareness	Social Facility
I sense nonverbal signals about how others are feeling.	My nonverbal body language is appropriate to the situation and communicates what I am feeling.
I listen fully and tune in carefully to others.	Considering what I hear and sense from others, I present myself verbally and physically in ways that make a desired impression.
I make an effort to understand what others feel, think, and intend.	I put my understanding of others to work by using tact and self-control to shape the outcome of my interactions.
I have a sense of how the social world works, how people interact with one another.	I use my sense of the social world to note when people need support and to help them in appropriate and needed ways.

Source: Based on Daniel Goleman, *Social Intelligence: The New Science of Human Relationships*, New York: Bantam Books, 2006, p. 84.

or science courses, known as *peer-assisted study sessions* or *supplemental instruction.*

Don't wait until crunch time to benefit from studying with others. As you begin to get to know students in your classes, start now to exchange phone numbers and e-mails, form groups, and schedule meetings. When you study with one or more people, you will gain benefits like these:

- *Shared and solidified knowledge.* When students share their knowledge with one another in a group, the effort takes less time and energy than when students learn all of the material alone. Furthermore, when you discuss concepts or teach them to others, you solidify what you know and strengthen your critical thinking.
- *Increased motivation.* Knowing that you are accountable to others and that they will see your level of work and preparation, you may be more motivated to work hard.
- *Increased teamwork ability.* The more you understand the dynamics of working with a group and the more

Having a sense of how to relate to others—in other words, drawing on your social intelligence—promotes positive and productive relationships on campus.

experience you have with teamwork, the more your interpersonal skills will grow.

- *Increased awareness and understanding of diversity.* Teams gain strength from the intellectual diversity of their members. When you work with others, you are bound to come up with ideas and solutions you never would have thought of on your own.

Strategies for Study Group Success

Every study group is unique. The way a group operates depends on members' personalities, the subject you study, the location of the group, and the size of the group. No matter what your particular group's situation, though, a few general strategies apply.

Set long-term and short-term goals. At your first meeting, determine what the group wants to accomplish. At the start of each meeting, have one person compile a list of questions to address.

Determine a regular schedule and leadership rotation. Determine what your group needs and what the members' schedules can handle. Try to meet weekly or, at the least, every other week. Rotating the leadership among members willing to lead helps all members take ownership of the results.

Create study materials for one another and help one another learn. Give each group member the task of finding a piece of information to compile, photocopy, and review for the other group members. Have group members teach pieces of information, make up quizzes for each other, or go through flash cards together.

Share the workload and pool your note-taking resources. The most important factor is a willingness to work, not knowlege level. Compare notes with group members and fill in information you don't have. Try different note-taking styles (see chapter 6 for a discussion of note taking).

Know how to be an effective leader. As a leader, you need a broad perspective that allows you to envision how different aspects of a project will come together. You must define projects, assign work, and set schedules. You also set meeting and project agendas, focus the group, keep people moving ahead, set a positive tone, and evaluate results.

Know how to be an effective participant. Participants are "part owners" of the team process with a responsibility for, and a stake in, the outcome. Let people know your ideas and your opinions about decisions. Be organized and willing to discuss. Fulfill the tasks you promise to do.

As you think about your tools and how you plan to use them to achieve your goals, you may be a bit uneasy about the road ahead and its inevitable stumbling blocks. You can give yourself the best possible chance to succeed if you remind yourself of the connection between your work in school and your ability to achieve goals in your life beyond graduation.

get practical!

Assess Yourself as a Practical Thinker

For each statement, circle the number that feels right to you, from 1 for "not at all true for me" to 5 for "very true for me."

1. I can find a way around any obstacle. 1 2 3 4 5
2. I see myself as a "doer," the "go-to" person; I "make things happen." 1 2 3 4 5
3. When working on a problem in a group setting, I like to figure out who will do what and when it should be done. 1 2 3 4 5
4. Because I learn well from experience, I don't tend to repeat a mistake. 1 2 3 4 5
5. I finish what I start and don't leave loose ends hanging. 1 2 3 4 5
6. I pay attention to my emotions in academic and social situations to see if they help or hurt me as I move toward a goal. 1 2 3 4 5
7. I can sense how people feel, and can use that knowledge to interact with others effectively in order to achieve a goal. 1 2 3 4 5
8. I manage my time effectively. 1 2 3 4 5
9. I find ways to adjust to the teaching styles of my instructors and the communication styles of my peers. 1 2 3 4 5
10. When involved in a problem-solving process, I can shift gears as needed. 1 2 3 4 5

Total your answers here: 32

If your total ranges from 38–50, you consider your practical thinking skills to be *strong.*

If your total ranges from 24–37, you consider your practical thinking skills to be *average.*

If your total ranges from 10–23, you consider your practical thinking skills to be *weak.*

Remember that you can improve your practical thinking skill with focus and practice.

How Can the Things You Learn Now Promote Life Success?

In his book *Techno Trends—24 Technologies That Will Revolutionize Our Lives*, futurist Daniel Burrus describes a tomorrow that is linked to continuing education: "The future belongs to those who are capable of being retrained again and again," he says. "Think of it as periodically upgrading your human assets throughout your career. . . . Humans are infinitely upgradeable, but it does require an investment" in lifelong learning.[21]

The vast majority of Americans see lifelong learning as important in their own lives. In a survey of workers aged 18 to 24, conducted by the AFL-CIO, the country's leading labor union, 85% of respondents viewed education and training as the nation's top economic priority, and 9 out of 10 believed that the key to career advancement is ongoing education and training.[22]

In other words, you will need to continue to learn and grow in order to succeed. As a college student, you are making sacrifices—including a significant investment of time and money as well as a dramatic lifestyle change—to achieve success throughout your life. You are building the analytical, creative, and practical intelligence you need to cope with a world that is changing in many ways:

- *Knowledge in nearly every field is doubling every two to three years.* That means that if you stop learning, for even a few years, your knowledge base will be inadequate to keep up with the changes in your career.
- *Technology is changing how you live and work.* The Internet and technology will shape communications and improve knowledge and productivity during the next 20 years—and will require continual learning.
- *The global economy is moving from a product and service base to a knowledge and talent base.* Jobs of the past are being replaced by knowledge-based jobs, in the United States and abroad, that ask workers to think critically to come up with solutions.
- *Workers are changing jobs and careers more frequently.* The National Research Bureau reports that currently the average employee changes jobs every three to four years, and it is estimated that a 22-year-old college graduate in the year 2000 will have an average of eight employers in his or her first 10 years in the workplace.[23] Every time you decide to start a new career, you need new knowledge and skills.

LIFELONG LEARNERS
Individuals who continue to build knowledge and skills as a mechanism for improving their lives and careers.

All of these signs point to the need to become **lifelong learners**. Through successful intelligence, you will maintain the kind of flexibility that will enable you to adapt to the demands of the global marketplace. If you analyze what is happening, come up with creative approaches for handling it, and make a practical plan to put your ideas into motion, you can stay on track toward your goals. Or, you may decide to shift direction toward a new goal that never occurred to you before the change. Facing change means taking risks.

Successful Intelligence Wrap-Up

You have the power to engage your successful intelligence to pursue goals that are most important to you. Although college presents challenges and risks to everyone, persistent and motivated learners can manage them effectively. Here's how you have built skills in chapter 1:

Analytical

By completing the three self-assessments, you analyzed where you are now in analytical, creative, and practical intelligence. At the beginning and end of the chapter, you explored how learning—in college and throughout life—can promote success. In learning about the theory of successful intelligence, you considered how it can enable you to reach important goals.

Creative

Reading about the global marketplace may have inspired new ideas of what you want out of college. Thinking about the three parts of successful intelligence helped to provide a new perspective of your potential as a student. Exploring strategies about learning from failure, working with others in a team, and facing fears may have helped you see connections among these topics that you didn't see before.

Practical

You examined specific practical actions that are the building blocks of college success: how to work with academic integrity, fulfill day-to-day academic responsibilities, stay motivated, and learn from failure. You also investigated emotional and social intelligence, two highly practical skills that allow you to work effectively with others. Finally, you considered specific, practical actions to take when working in a project team or study group.

Egyszer volt budán kutyavásár

(edge-zehr volt bu-darn ku-tcho-vah-shahr)

This unusual Hungarian phrase, translated literally, means "There was a dog-market in Buda only once." In modern English, you would interpret this to be a favorable opportunity that comes along only once—something that you should grasp with both hands, lest you regret not taking advantage of it later.[24]

For you, this opportunity has arrived. Make the most of all your college has to offer, and gather learning skills that you will use throughout your life. By taking the initiative to use your time well, you can build the successful intelligence that will help you realize your dreams.

"There is no elevator to success. You have to take the stairs."

UNKNOWN

Building World-Class Skills for College, Career, and Life Success

SUCCESSFUL INTELLIGENCE

Think, Create, Apply

Activate yourself. Robert Sternberg found that successfully intelligent people, despite differences in thinking and personal goals, have 20 particular characteristics in common. He calls these characteristics *self-activators*—things that get you moving and keep you going.[25]

Step 1. Think it through: ***Analyze where you are now.*** Use this self-assessment to see how developed you perceive your self-activators to be *right now.*

1	2	3	4	5
Not at All Like Me	Somewhat Unlike Me	Not Sure	Somewhat Like Me	Definitely Like Me

Please circle the number that best represents your answer:

1. I motivate myself well.	1 2 3 4 5
2. I can control my impulses.	1 2 3 4 5
3. I know when to persevere and when to change gears.	1 2 3 4 5
4. I make the most of what I do well.	1 2 3 4 5
5. I can successfully translate my ideas into action.	1 2 3 4 5
6. I can focus effectively on my goal.	1 2 3 4 5
7. I complete tasks and have good follow-through.	1 2 3 4 5
8. I initiate action—I move people and projects ahead.	1 2 3 4 5
9. I have the courage to risk failure.	1 2 3 4 5
10. I avoid procrastination.	1 2 3 4 5
11. I accept responsibility when I make a mistake.	1 2 3 4 5
12. I don't waste time feeling sorry for myself.	1 2 3 4 5

13. I independently take responsibility for tasks. 1 2 3 4 5

14. I work hard to overcome personal difficulties. 1 2 3 4 5

15. I create an environment that helps me to concentrate on my goals. 1 2 3 4 5

16. I don't take on too much work or too little. 1 2 3 4 5

17. I can delay gratification in order to receive the benefits. 1 2 3 4 5

18. I can see both the big picture and the details in a situation. 1 2 3 4 5

19. I am able to maintain confidence in myself. 1 2 3 4 5

20. I can balance my analytical, creative, and practical thinking skills. 1 2 3 4 5

Step 2. Think out of the box: *Brainstorm over time.* Looking at the self-assessment, choose five self-activators that you most want to develop throughout the term. Then, pretend you are an instructor recommending yourself for a scholarship or a job. Write yourself a short e-mail about how strong you are in the areas of those five self-activators. Save the e-mail as a reminder of what you would like such a person to be able to truly say about you.

Step 3. Make it happen: *Prepare yourself for action.* Let this self-assessment direct your decisions about how you approach the material in this course. If you wish to procrastinate less, for example, pay special attention to the time-management information in chapter 2. To jump-start your focus, look at the self-assessment again and circle or highlight the five self-activators that you most want to concentrate on at this point.

In the last chapter of this book you will revisit this self-assessment and get more specific about actions you have taken, and plan to take, to promote personal growth.

TEAMWORK

Create Solutions Together

Motivators. Gather in a group of three to five. Together, brainstorm motivation blockers—situations or things that most often kill your motivation to succeed in school. When you have as many problems as you have group members, each person should choose one problem and write it at the top of a blank sheet of paper.

Look at the motivation blocker on your page. Under it, write one practical idea you have about how to overcome it. When everyone is finished, pass the pages to the person on the left. Then write an idea about the new blocker at the top of the page you've received. If you can't think of anything, pass the page as is. Continue this way until your page comes back to you. Then discuss the ideas as a group, analyzing which ideas might work better than others. Add other ideas to the lists if you think of them.

The last step: On your own, keeping in mind your group discussion, list three specific actions that you commit to taking in order to keep motivation high when the going gets rough.

1. ____

2. ____

3. ____

WRITING

Journal and Put Skills to Work

Record your thoughts on a separate piece of paper, in a journal, or on a computer file.

Journal entry: Reasons for college. Think about why you are here. Why did you decide to attend college, and what do you want out of the experience? What sacrifices—in terms of time, hard work, finances—are you willing to make in your quest for success?

Real-life writing: Initial impressions. Although you have not been in school for long, you already have some sense of your instructors, their style, and how classes are likely to proceed. Compare and contrast your initial impressions of two of your instructors and the courses they teach. Discuss teaching style, course expectations, degree of difficulty, how the classroom is run, and any other factor that is significant to you. Finally, note any changes you think you should make—in your in-class or study approach—based on these impressions.

PERSONAL PORTFOLIO

Prepare for Career Success

This is the first of eight portfolio assignments you will complete, one for each chapter. By the end of the term, you will have built skills that promote success in pursuing any career as you compile a portfolio of documents that will help you achieve career goals.

Type your work and store the documents electronically in one file folder. Use loose paper for assignments that ask you to draw or make collages.

Setting career goals. Whether you have a current career, have held a few different jobs, or have not yet entered the workplace, college is an ideal time to take stock of your career goals. The earlier in your college education that you consider career goals, the more you can take advantage of how college can help prepare you for work, in both job-specific and general ways. Having a strong vision of where you wish to go will also be a powerful motivator as you face some of the inevitable challenges of the next few years.

Take some time to think about your working life. Spend 15 minutes brainstorming everything that you wish you could be, do, have, or experience in your career 10 years from now—the skills you want to have, money you want to earn, benefits, experiences, travel, anything you can think of. List your wishes, draw them, depict them using cutouts from magazines, or combine these ideas—whatever you like best.

Now, look at your list. To discover how your wishes relate to one another, group them in order of priority. Label three computer pages or three pieces of paper Priority 1, Priority 2, and Priority 3. Write each wish where it fits, with Priority 1 being the most important, Priority 2 the second most important, and Priority 3 the third.

Look at your priority lists. What do they tell you about what is most important to you? What wishes are you ready to work toward right now? Circle or highlight the three highest-priority wishes (they will most likely appear on your Priority 1 page). Write down the trade-offs you may have to make today to make these wishes come true. Don't let yourself off the hook—be realistic and direct. You may want to look back at these materials at the end of the term to see what changes may have taken place in your priorities.

Suggested Readings

Friedman, Thomas L. *The World Is Flat: A Brief History of the Twenty-first Century*. New York: Farrar, Straus & Giroux, 2006.

Jeffers, Susan. *Feel the Fear . . . and Do It Anyway*. New York: Ballantine Books, 2006.

Kadar, Andrew. *College Life 102: The No-Bull Guide to a Great Freshman Year*. Lincoln, NE: iUniverse, 2006.

Newport, Cal. *How to Win at College: Surprising Secrets for Success from the Country's Top Students*. New York: Broadway Books, 2005.

Simon, Linda. *New Beginnings: A Reference Guide for Adult Learners*, 3rd ed. Upper Saddle River, NJ: Prentice Hall, 2005.

Sternberg, Robert. *Successful Intelligence: How Practical and Creative Intelligence Determine Success in Life*. New York: Plume, 1997.

Students Helping Students. *Navigating Your Freshman Year: How to Make the Leap to College Life*. New York: Penguin, 2005.

Tyler, Suzette. *Been There, Should've Done That II: More Tips for Making the Most of College*. Lansing, MI: Front Porch Press, 2001.

Internet and Podcast Resources

The Center for Academic Integrity: **www.academicintegrity.org**

Motivation on the Run podcasts: **http://podcasts.yahoo.com/series?s=ed9231d7be13524016aeb51d5f40e2d1**

NPR, "For Workers, 'The World Is Flat,'" April 14, 2005, broadcast of *Fresh Air from WHYY*: **www.npr.org/templates/story/story.php?storyId=4600258**

Student.Com—The Student Center: **www.student.com**

StudentNow—College Life, Fun, & Resources: **www.studentnow.com**

Prentice Hall Student Success SuperSite: **www.prenhall.com/success**

Success Stories: **www.prenhall.com/success/Stories/index.html**

Check your college Web site for podcasts produced by your school.

Endnotes

[1] Thomas Friedman, *The World Is Flat,* New York: Farrar, Straus & Giroux, 2006, p. 8.

[2] Robert J. Sternberg, *Successful Intelligence: How Practical and Creative Intelligence Determine Success in Life*, New York: Plume, 1997, p. 11.

[3] Lawrence F. Lowery, *"The Biological Basis of Thinking and Learning,"* 1998, Full Option Science System, University of California at Berkeley (http://lhsfoss.org/newsletters/archive/pdfs/FOSS_BBTL.pdf).

[4] Carol Dweck, *Mindset: The New Psychology of Success*, New York: Random House, 2006, p. 22.

[5] Sternberg, *Successful Intelligence,* p. 12.

[6] Ibid., p. 127.

[7] Ibid., pp. 127–128.

[8] "Are the Classes Really That Much Harder Than High School?" New Mexico State University, June 1999 (https://www.nmsu.edu/aggieland/students/faq_classes.html).

[9] From student essay submitted by the First Year Experience students of Patty Parma, Palo Alto College, San Antonio, Texas, January 2004.

[10] Rick Pitino, *Success Is a Choice,* New York: Broadway Books, 1997, p. 40.

[11] *The Fundamental Values of Academic Integrity*, Center for Academic Integrity, Kenan Institute for Ethics, Duke University, October 1999 (www.academicintegrity.org/fundamental.asp).

[12] From "Facts About Plagiarism," 2007, Plagiarism.org (www.plagiarism.org/facts.html).

[13] "LD at a Glance," 2007, National Center for Learning Disabilities (www.ncld.org/index.php?option=content&task=view&id=448).

[14] *LD Advocates Guide,* n.d., National Center for Learning Disabilities (www.ncld.org/index.php?option=content&task=view&id=291).

[15] National Center for Learning Disabilities, "Adult Learning Disabilities: A Learning Disability Isn't Something You Outgrow—It's Something You Learn to Master" (pamphlet), New York: National Center for Learning Disabilities.

[16] "For 7 Million, One Census Race Category Wasn't Enough," *New York Times*, March 13, 2001, pp. A1, A14.

[17] Media Watch, *Diversity Digest,* Fall 1997 (www.diversityweb.org/Digest/F97/mediawatch.html#top).

[18] Daniel Goleman, *Emotional Intelligence: Why It Can Matter More Than IQ,* New York: Bantam Books, 1995.

[19] Daniel Goleman, *Working with Emotional Intelligence,* New York: Bantam Books, 1998, pp. 26–27.

[20] Quote and material for the following section are from Daniel Goleman, *Social Intelligence: The New Science of Human Relationships,* New York: Bantam Books, 2006, pp. 84–97.

[21] Cited in Colin Rise and Malcolm J. Nicholl, *Accelerated Learning for the 21st Century,* New York: Dell, 1997, pp. 5–6.

[22] Study cited in Susan Rosenblum, "Young Workers Name Lifelong Learning as Top Need for Economy of Future," *Nation's Cities Weekly*, September 6, 1999, p. 1.

[23] Jay Palmer, "Marry Me a Little," *Barron's*, July 24, 2000, p. 25.

[24] Christopher J. Moore, *In Other Words: A Language Lover's Guide to the Most Intriguing Words Around the World,* New York: Walker, 2004, p. 43.

[25] List and descriptions based on Sternberg, *Successful Intelligence,* pp. 251–269.

VALUES, GOALS, AND TIME

Managing Yourself

2

"Successfully intelligent people are well aware of the penalties for procrastination. They schedule their time so that the important things get done—and done well."

ROBERT STERNBERG

This chapter divides the indispensable skill of self-management into three parts: using values to guide your goal setting, working through a process to achieve goals, and managing time in a way that propels you toward your goals and helps you manage stress. It also provides ideas about how to think through the important goal of choosing a major or concentration. Your ability to manage yourself will help you cope with what you encounter, achieve your goals, and build skills that fuel your success now and in the future.

In this chapter you explore answers to the following questions:

Chapter 2's Successful Intelligence Skills

Analytical

- Examining values
- Analyzing how you manage time
- Considering what goals are most important to you

Creative

- Developing ideas for how to reach a goal
- Creating ways to avoid procrastination
- Brainstorming what majors interest you

Practical

- How to set effective goals
- How to achieve a goal
- How to manage a schedule

Why Is It Important to Know What You Value?

VALUES

Principles or qualitites that you consider important.

You make life choices—what to do, what to believe, what to buy, how to act—based on your personal **values.** Your choice to pursue a degree, for example, reflects that you value the personal and professional growth that come from a college education. Being on time for your classes shows that you value punctuality. Paying bills regularly and on time shows that you value financial stability.

Values play a key role in your drive to achieve important goals, because they help you to do the following:

- *Understand what you want out of life.* Your most meaningful goals should reflect what you value most.
- *Build "rules for life."* Your values form the foundation for your decisions and behavior. You will return repeatedly to them for guidance, especially in unfamiliar territory.
- *Find people who inspire you.* Spending time with people who share similar values will help you clarify how you want to live and find support for your goals.

Your value system is complex, built piece by piece over time. Many forces affect your values—family, friends, culture, media, school, work, neighborhood, religious beliefs, world events. No matter how powerful these external influences may be, however, it is your decision whether or not to adopt a value. Making this decision involves answering questions like the following to evaluate whether a given value is right for you:

- Where did the value come from?
- What other different values could I consider?

REAL QUESTIONS

How can I choose a major that is right for me?

I've just started college and my school requires that all students choose a major right away, as entering freshmen. I know this is a very important decision because it could chart the direction of the rest of my life, so I want to make sure I find what's right for me.

I've always loved being outdoors, reading, and learning other languages—and I think I would make a great teacher, but I want to do more than just teach. I see myself going toward humanitarian aid or international affairs, and then later going back to school to get an advanced degree and become a professor some day. What kind of major should I look for that will make me a marketable candidate for a fulfilling and challenging career?

Courtney Mellblom
California Polytechnic State University
San Luis Obispo, California

PRACTICAL ANSWERS

Antoine Pickett
Resident Engineer, Federal Aviation Administration
Aurora Air Traffic Control Center, Aurora, Illinois

Explore the possibilities carefully and follow your heart.

Many college freshmen ask this type of question. It is not an easy decision to make at such a young age. Fortunately, you seem to have a sense of what direction you want to move in. Although many people go for the quick or big bucks, the most marketable candidate for a job is one who shows a great interest and desire in what they have studied. If you follow your heart in your studies you will not go wrong.

First, I suggest that you find out more about courses that could help you explore your interest in the international arena. In fact, you could consider a major that would allow you to focus on your humanitarian interests, such as international affairs or international relations. Becoming proficient in a foreign language would also tend to make you more marketable.

Second, work backwards. Examine potential careers in the area of international affairs, talk to people who have international experience, and from there try to gain work or intern experience while you are in college to see if it truly interests you. Your proactive research should inform your decision about what major to choose.

If your eventual goal is to become a college professor, many colleges require graduate and doctoral work but do not require a teaching certificate. Later, if you decide you don't want to become a professor, you can still pursue a certificate. Your experience in the working world will make you a better teacher. As someone once said, "The error of youth is to believe that intelligence is a substitute for experience, while the error of age is to believe that experience is a substitute for intelligence." Any experience you gain will help you learn and grow.

- What might happen as a result of adopting this value?
- Have I made a personal commitment to this choice? Have I told others about it?
- Do my life goals and day-to-day actions reflect this value?

Your values often shift to fit new circumstances as you grow. For example, a student who benefits from the support of friends and family while recovering from an auto accident may place greater value on relationships than he did before.

How Values Affect Your Educational Experience

The fact that you are here in college means that you value education. Making education a priority is a practical choice that will help you do the following:

- *Keep going when the going gets tough.* "Success takes much hard work and dedication," says a student at Palo Alto College. "Since I have a hard time with writing, and I can't understand algebra, I've made a commitment to write in a journal every day and attend math tutoring at least three times a week."[1]
- *Choose your major and a career direction.* If you've always been an environmentalist, then you may choose to specialize in environmental science. If you feel fulfilled when you help people, then you might consider a career in social work.
- *Choose friends and activities that enrich your life.* Having friends who share your desire to succeed in school will increase your motivation and reduce your stress. Joining organizations whose activities reflect your values will broaden your educational experience.
- *Choose what you want to get out of school.* What kinds of skills and knowledge do you wish to build? Are you focused on building the foundation for a successful career? Your values will help you determine what you are willing to do to achieve academic goals.

Values and Cultural Diversity

At college, you may meet people who seem different in unexpected ways. Unfamiliar attitudes and behaviors are rooted in unique cultures. A *culture* is a unique set of values, behaviors, tastes, knowledge, attitudes, and habits shared by a specific group of people.

Cultural misunderstandings can interfere with relationships. As someone who accepts and appreciates diversity, your goal is to develop **cultural competence**.[2] Chapter 3 will go into more detail about how to be a culturally competent communicator.

CULTURAL COMPETENCE

The ability to understand and appreciate differences and to respond to people of all cultures in a way that values their worth, respects their beliefs and practices, and builds communication and relationships.

As you continue to read *Keys to Success*, think of the wisdom of cultural diversity consultant Helen Turnbull on turning differences into strengths:

> We must suspend our judgment. We should not judge others negatively because they are indirect, or their accents aren't clear, or their tone of voice is tentative, or they avoid eye contact. We must learn patience and suspend judgment long enough to realize these differences don't make one of us right and the other wrong. They simply mean that we approach communication from a different frame of reference and, many times, a different value system.[3]

Although clarifying your values will help you choose your educational path, goal-setting and goal-achievement skills will turn values into tools that help you travel that path to the end.

GET ANALYTICAL!

Explore Your Values

Rate each of the values in the list on a scale from 1 to 5, with 1 being least important to you and 5 being most important.

_______ Knowing yourself
_______ Being liked by others
_______ Reading
_______ Self-improvement
_______ Taking risks
_______ Time to yourself
_______ Improving physical/mental health
_______ Time for fun/relaxation
_______ Lifelong learning
_______ Leadership and teamwork skills
_______ Staying fit through exercise
_______ Competing and winning
_______ Getting a good job
_______ Pursuing an education
_______ Spiritual/religious life
_______ Making a lot of money
_______ Good relationships with family
_______ Community involvement
_______ Creative/artistic pursuits
_______ Helping others
_______ Keeping up with the news
_______ Being organized
_______ Financial stability
_______ Other (write below)
____

Write your top three values here:

1. ____

2. ____

3. ____

Now connect your values to educational goals. (*Example:* A student who values helping others chooses to study nursing.) Choose one top value that is a factor in an educational choice you have made. Explain the choice and how the value is involved:

____

____

Name an area of study that you think would help you live according to this value:

____

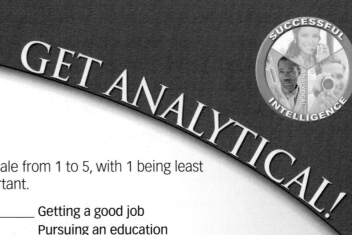

How Do You Set and Achieve Goals?

GOAL

An end toward which effort is directed; an aim or intention.

When you identify something that you want, you set a **goal.** Achieving goals, whether they are short term or long term, involves the careful formulation and execution of a goal-achievement plan. Think of this plan as a map that defines your route to destinations nearby and far away.

Set Long-Term Goals

Start by setting *long-term goals*—objectives that you want to achieve in the next six months, year, or more. As a student, your long-term goals may include earning a degree or certificate and starting a career.

Some long-term goals have an open-ended time frame. This is especially the case with goals that involve creative expression, which depend on the time and freedom to consider different paths. For example, if your goal is to become the best jazz trombonist you can be, you will work at it over your entire life and use different methods to improve your technique. Other goals, such as completing the general education requirements at your school, have a shorter scope, a more definite end, and often fewer options for getting from A to Z.

Writing out a long-term goal statement can help you clarify the goal. Here's one example of a goal that would take forethought and years to reach:

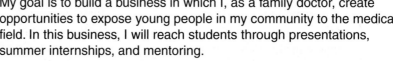

© Paul Murphy—Fotolia.com

> My goal is to build a business in which I, as a family doctor, create opportunities to expose young people in my community to the medical field. In this business, I will reach students through presentations, summer internships, and mentoring.

For a student two years away from college graduation who is pursuing this long-term goal, here is a supporting set of one-year long-term goals:

> Design courses for the year to make sure I am on track for premed course completion. Find medical practices in the area that could serve as a model for my business. Research medical schools for application next year.

Just as this set of goals is tailored to one student's personality, abilities, and values, your goals should reflect your uniqueness. To determine your long-term goals, think about what you think is important to accomplish while you are in school and after you graduate. Here are some linkages between personal values and professional goals:

- **Values:** Health and fitness, helping others

  Goal: To work for a company that produces organic foods
- **Values:** Independence, financial success

  Goal: To obtain a degree in business and start a company

Basing your long-term goals on your values increases your motivation to succeed. The more your goals focus on what is most important to you, the greater your drive to reach them.

Set Short-Term Goals

Short-term goals are smaller steps that move you toward a long-term goal. Lasting as short as an hour or as long as a few months, these goals help you manage broader aspirations as they narrow your focus and encourage progress. If you had a long-term goal of graduating with a degree in nursing, for example, you may want to accomplish the following short-term goals in the next six months:

- I will learn the names, locations, and functions of every human bone and muscle.
- I will work with a study group to understand the musculoskeletal system.

These goals can be broken down into even smaller parts, such as the following one-month goals:

- I will work with on-screen tutorials of the musculoskeletal system until I understand and memorize the material.
- I will spend three hours a week with my study partners.

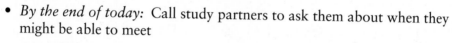

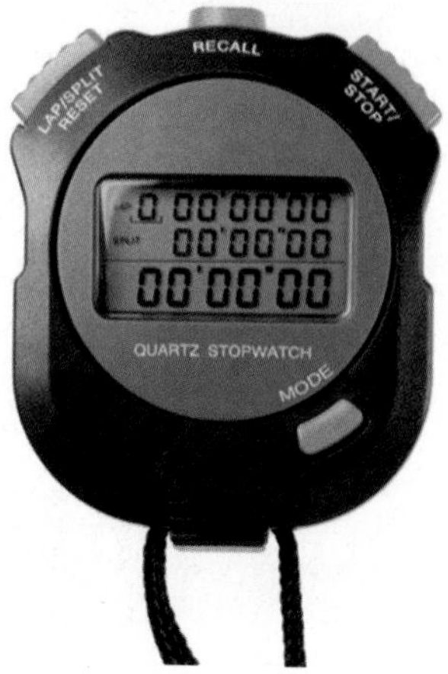

© VisualField—Fotolia.com

In addition to monthly goals, you may have short-term goals that extend for a week, a day, or even a couple of hours in a given day. To support your monthlong goal of regularly meeting with your study partners, you may wish to set the following short-term goals:

- *By the end of today:* Call study partners to ask them about when they might be able to meet
- *One week from now:* Have scheduled each of our weekly meetings this month
- *Two weeks from now:* Have had our first meeting
- *Three weeks from now:* Type and distribute notes from first meeting; have second meeting

Your motivation is at its peak when you begin to move toward a goal and when you are about to achieve that goal. For that reason, try to pay special attention to goals that fall in the middle—for example, one-month or one-term goals on the way to a yearlong goal. If you work hard to stay motivated through the whole journey, you will have a better result.

As you consider your long- and short-term goals, notice how all of your goals are linked to one another. As Key 2.1 shows, your long-term goals establish a context for the short-term goals. In turn, your short-term goals make the long-term goals seem clearer and more reachable.

At any given time, you will be working toward goals of varying importance. Setting priorities helps you decide where and when to focus your energy and time.

Prioritize Goals

When you **prioritize**, you evaluate everything you are working toward, decide which goals are most important, and plan how to achieve them. Prioritizing helps you avoid impulsive decisions that waste energy and time. What should you consider as you prioritize?

PRIORITIZE

To arrange or deal with in order of importance.

- *Your values.* Think about what you value to establish your top goals—for example, graduating in four years or developing a strong network of personal contacts.
- *Your personal situation.* Are you going to school and working part-time? Are you taking three classes or five classes? Are you a parent with

KEY 2.1

Goals reinforce one another.

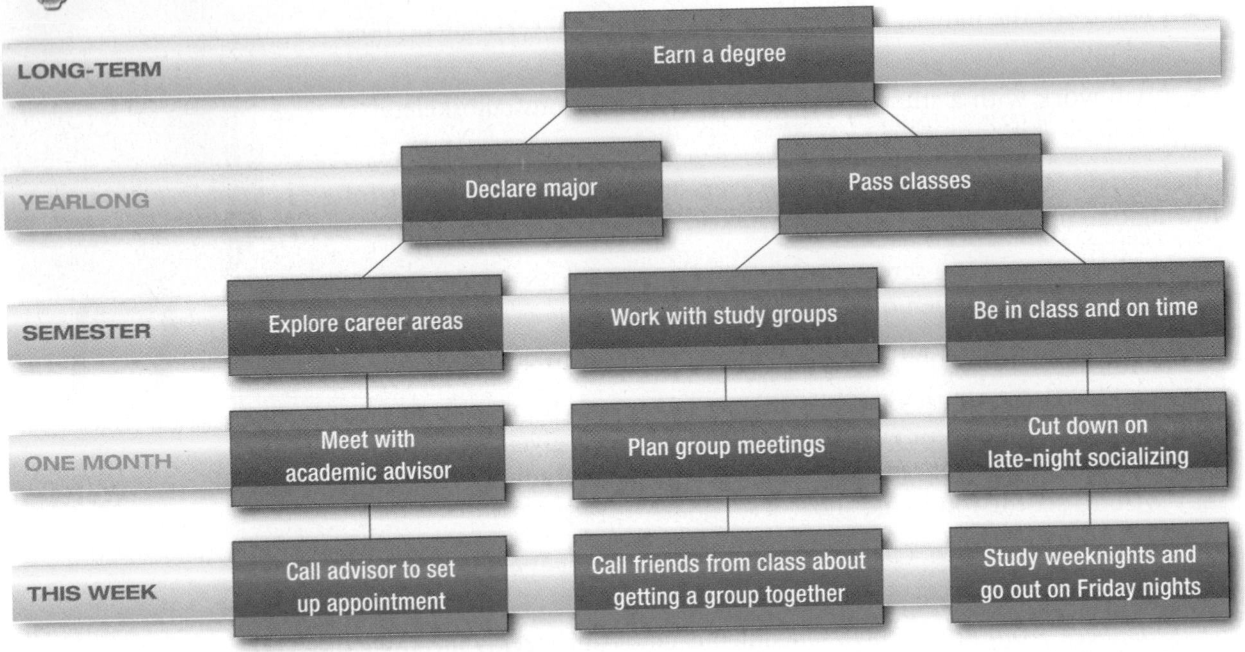

young children? Are you an athlete on a sports team? Every individual situation requires unique priorities and scheduling.

- *Your time commitments.* Hours of your day may already be committed to class, team practices, a part-time job, or sleep. Your challenge is to make sure these commitments reflect what you value and to establish priorities for the remaining hours. As you will see later in the chapter, setting clear priorities will help you manage your time and accomplish more.

Work to Achieve Goals

Being practical will help you achieve your goals. Remember, the more specific your plans, the more likely you are to fulfill them.

- *Define your goal-setting strategy: How do you plan to reach your goal?* Brainstorm different paths that might get you there. Choose one; then map out its steps and strategies. Focus on specific behaviors and events that are under your control and that are measurable.
- *Set a timetable: When do you want to accomplish your goal?* Set a realistic time line that includes specific deadlines for each step and strategy you have defined. Charting your progress will help you stay on track.
- *Be accountable for your progress: What safeguards will keep you on track?* Define a personal reporting or buddy system that makes accountability a priority.
- *Get unstuck: What will you do if you hit a roadblock?* Define two ways to get help with your efforts if you run into trouble. Be ready to pursue more creative ideas if those don't work.

get creative!

Map Out a Personal Goal

Working backwards can help you find an interesting path toward an important goal.

Name one important personal goal you have for this year:

____

Now imagine that you have achieved your goal and an impressed friend asks you to describe how you did it. Write three important steps you took first:

1. ____________________________________
2. ____________________________________
3. ____________________________________

Briefly describe how you followed the rest of the plan:

____

____

____

Finally, tell your friend what positive results have come from achieving your goal:

____

____

You just created a potential plan. Consider putting it—or a plan similar to it—to work. As you begin, let the image of the success you created in this exercise motivate and inspire you.

How Can You Begin to Explore Majors?

At some point near the completion of your general education requirements, you will be asked to declare a **major or concentration** (for the sake of simplicity, the term *major* will appear throughout the rest of the text). Although you likely have plenty of time to make this decision, start early to

MAJOR (OR CONCENTRATION)
An academic subject area chosen as a field of specialization, requiring a specific course of study.

narrow down possibilities so you can match your talents, skills, and dreams with a concrete curriculum. Choosing a major is one of the most important decisions you'll make in college because your major largely determines the courses you will take, what you will learn, and with whom you will spend school time. Your major may also influence your future career.

Thinking practically, exploring your course emphasis early on can save you time and money. Because many of the courses that fulfill requirements in one major may not count toward another, changing your major might mean that you stay in college longer and spend additional money on courses, especially if you make the change in your junior or senior year. Having a sense of what you do or do not want to specialize in will make your course selection more efficient.

With what you know about setting and achieving goals, envision declaring a major as a long-term goal made up of the multiple steps (short-term goals) that follow. Start the process now even if, as is true of many students, you don't yet know what you want to study.

Short-Term Goal #1: Use Self-Assessments to Identify Interests and Talents

When you identify your interests and talents and choose a major that focuses on them, you are likely to have a positive attitude and perform at your highest level. You may still be figuring out what inspires you, or you may have sensed a career direction since you were young. This was the case with University of Illinois student Brian DeGraff, whose interests were mechanical:

> I am amazed by how things work. The way a car can turn a tank of greasy, smelly, toxic liquid into my ride to school. People always say stop and smell the roses, but I'd rather stop and wonder why the roses smell. It was this passion that drove me to want to be an engineer.[4]

To pinpoint the areas that spark your interest, consider the following questions:

- What are my favorite courses? What do these courses have in common?
- What subjects interest me when I read?
- What activities do I look forward to?
- Am I a "natural" in any academic or skill area?
- What do people say I do well?
- How do I learn most effectively? (see chapter 3)

Short-Term Goal #2: Explore Academic Options

Next, find out about the academic choices available at your school.

Learn what's possible. Consult your college catalog for guidelines on declaring (and changing) your major. Find answers to these questions:

- When do I have to declare a major? (Generally this is required at the end of the second year for four-year programs, or earlier for associate or certificate programs.)

- What are my options in majoring? (You may consider double majors, minors, *interdisciplinary majors* incorporating more than one discipline and designed with the help of an advisor.)
- What majors are offered at my school?

If a major looks interesting, explore it further by answering these questions:

- What minimum grade point average (GPA), if any, does the department require before it will accept me as a major?
- What GPA must I maintain in the courses included in the major?
- What preparatory courses (prerequisites) are required?
- What courses will I be required to take and in what sequence? How many credits do I need to graduate in the major?
- Should I consider a minor in this academic area? (A minor has fewer requirements than a major. Many students choose a minor suited for a career. For example, a sociology major who wants to work in an inner-city hospital might consider a minor in Spanish.)

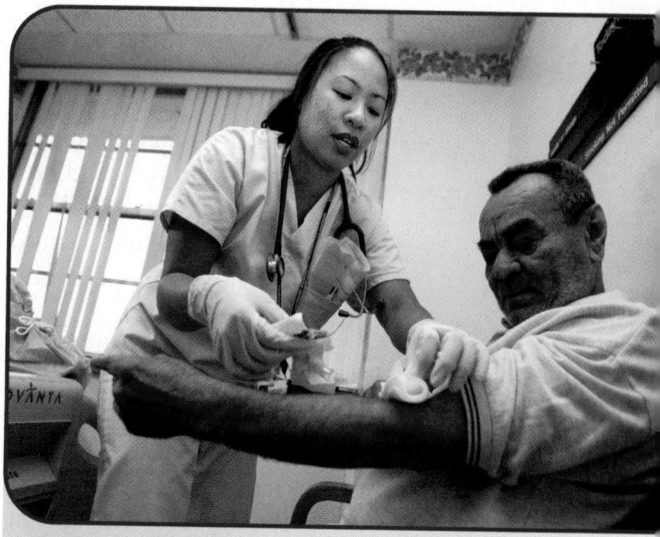

Exploring career-related interests early on can help you find a major that will support your career goals. Students interested in nursing might consider majoring in one of the sciences.

Talk to people who can help. Early on, begin discussing your major with your advisor; he or she can help you evaluate different options. You also may want to ask students who are a year or two ahead of you to describe their experiences with the courses, the workload, and the instructors.

Visit the department. When considering a major, analyze your comfort with the academic department as well as with the material. Ask the department secretary for information, sit in on a class, and consider asking an instructor in the department for an appointment. When Ashiana Esmail decided to major in Ethnic Studies at the University of California at Berkeley, she did so in part because she felt that working with a close-knit department "was better than an A+" in helping to build academic momentum.[5]

Short-Term Goal #3: Establish Your Academic Schedule

Map out your time frame. How many years do you plan to study as an undergraduate or graduate student? Do you plan to attend graduate school? If so, do you plan to go there directly after graduation or take time off? From there, get more specific about scheduling.

Set timing for short-term goals. Work with your academic advisor to pinpoint when to accomplish the short-term goals that lead to graduation. What are the deadlines for completing core requirements or declaring a major? Although you won't need to plan out your entire course load right

CURRICULUM

The particular set of courses required for a degree.

now, drafting a tentative **curriculum**—both within and outside your major—can help clarify where you are heading. Remember, you are not expected to do this alone. Your academic advisor is there to help you succeed.

Identify dates connected to your goal fulfillment. Pay attention to academic dates (you will find an academic calendar in each year's college catalog and on the college's Web site). Such dates include registration dates, final date to declare a major, final date to drop a course, and so forth. Plan ahead so you don't miss a deadline.

Be Flexible as You Come to a Decision

Flexibility is essential when defining any important goal. Many students change their minds as they consider majors; some declare a major and then change it one or more times before finding a good fit. Once you have considered a change carefully, act on it right away by informing your advisor, completing required paperwork, and redesigning your schedule to reflect your choice.

Through this process, you will often be thinking about how well you are using your time. In fact, being able to achieve any significant goal is directly linked to effective time management.

How Can You Effectively Manage Your Time?

Although everyone has the same 24 hours every day, on some days you may feel like you have hours to spare, while on others the clock becomes your worst enemy. Thinking about time before you act empowers you to make smart choices. Consider each day as a jigsaw puzzle: You have the pieces in a pile, and your task is to form a picture of how you want your day to look.

Successful time management starts with identifying your time-related needs and preferences. This self-knowledge sets the stage for building and managing your schedule, avoiding procrastination, and being flexible in the face of change. Finally, understanding the connection between time and stress will help you keep stress levels under control.

Identify Your Time-Related Needs and Preferences

Body rhythms and habits affect how each person deals with time. Some people are night owls; others function best in the morning. Some people are chronically late; others get everything done with time to spare. Being aware of factors like these will help you create a schedule that maximizes your strengths and cuts down on stress. If you are a morning person, for example, look for sections of required courses that meet early in the day. If you work best at night, schedule most of your study time at a library that stays open late.

Take the following steps to identify your time-related needs and preferences:

Create a personal time "profile." Ask yourself these questions: At what time of day do I have the most energy? The least energy? Do I tend to be early, on time, or late? Do I focus well for long stretches or need regular breaks? Your answers will help you find your best schedule.

Evaluate the effects of your profile. Which of your time-related habits and preferences will have a positive impact on your success at school? Which are likely to cause problems?

Establish the schedule preferences that suit your profile best. Make a list of these preferences—or even map out an ideal schedule as a way of illustrating them. For example, one student's preference list might read: "Classes bunched together on Mondays, Wednesdays, and Fridays. Tuesdays and Thursdays free for studying and research. Study time primarily during the day."

Next, build a schedule that takes this information into account. Your goal should be to maximize your strengths and compensate for your weaker time-management areas.

Successful Intelligence Connections Online

Listen to author Sarah Kravits describe how to use analytical, creative, and practical intelligence to define your personal time profile.

Go to the *Keys to Success* Companion Website at www.prenhall.com/carter to listen or download as a podcast.

Build a Schedule

Schedules help you gain control of your life in two ways: They provide segments of time for goal-related tasks and they remind you of tasks, events, due dates, responsibilities, and deadlines.

Use a Planner

A planner is a tool for managing your time. Use it to keep track of events and commitments, schedule goal-related tasks, and rank tasks according to priority. Time-management expert Paul Timm says that "rule number one in a thoughtful planning process is: Use some form of a planner where you can write things down."[6]

There are two types of planners. One is a book or notebook where you can note commitments. If you write detailed daily plans, look for the kind that devotes a page to each day. If you prefer to see more days at a glance, try the kind that shows a week's schedule on a two-page spread. Some planners contain sections for monthly and yearly goals.

© Iryna Petrenko—Fotolia.com

The other option is an electronic planner or personal digital assistant (PDA) such as a Palm Pilot, BlackBerry, or Sidekick. Basic PDA functions allow you to schedule days and weeks, note due dates, make to-do lists, perform mathematical calculations, and create and store an address book. You can also transfer information to and from a computer.

Though electronic planners are handy and have a large data capacity, they cost more than the paper versions, and their small size means they can be easily lost. Analyze your preferences and options, and decide which tool you are most likely to use every day. A blank notebook, used conscientiously, may work as well for some people as a top-of-the-line PDA.

Keep Track of Events and Commitments

Your planner is designed to help you schedule and remember events and commitments. A quick look at your notations will remind you when items are approaching. Your class syllabus is also a tool for keeping track of reading and homework assignments and test dates (see the sample syllabus on page 14).

Putting your schedule in writing will help you think ahead to prepare for crunch times. For example, if you see that you have three tests and a presentation coming up all in one week, you may have to rearrange your schedule during the preceding week to create extra study time.

Among the events and commitments worth noting in your planner are the following:

- Test and quiz dates; due dates for papers, projects, and presentations
- Details of your academic schedule, including term and holiday breaks
- Club and organizational meetings
- Personal items—medical appointments, due dates for bills, birthdays, social events
- Milestones toward a goal, such as due dates for sections of a project

It's important to include class prep time—reading and studying, writing and working on assignments and projects—in the planner. According to one reasonable formula, you should schedule at least two hours of preparation for every hour of class—that is, if you take 15 credits, you should study about 30 hours a week, making your total classroom and preparation time 45 hours.

Getting adequate study time means thinking creatively about when and where to study. This student takes time to get some work done between races at a track meet.

Surveys have shown, however, that most students study 15 or fewer hours per week, and some study even less—often not enough to master the material. As a freshman at Boston College, William Imbriale had priorities other than course work. "I got a D on my first philosophy paper," said William. "That woke me up, big time." When a professor helped him plan his time more effectively, William increased his study time and received an A− on the final paper.[7]

Working students have to fit study time in where they can. Lisa Marie Webb, a University of Utah student, prepares for class while commuting to and from her job. Athletes, too, have to work hard to fit everything in. "I get up at 6:30, go to study hall from 7:30 to 9, have class from 9:30 to 1:15, then have practice at 2," said Ohio State defensive back A. J. Hawk.[8] Situations like these demand creative time management and attention to your schedule.

Schedule Tasks and Activities That Support Your Goals

Linking day-to-day events in your planner to your broader goals will give meaning to your efforts, bring order to your schedule, and keep you motivated. Planning study time for an economics test, for example, will mean more to you if you link the hours you spend to your goal of being accepted into business school. Here is how a student might translate his goal of entering business school into action steps over a year's time:

- *This year:* Complete enough courses to meet curriculum requirements for business school and maintain class standing.
- *This term:* Complete my economics class with a B average or higher.
- *This month:* Set up economics study group schedule to coincide with quizzes and tests.
- *This week:* Meet with study group; go over material for Friday's test.
- *Today:* Go over chapter 3 in econ text.

The student can then arrange his time to move him in the direction of his goal. He schedules activities that support his short-term goal of doing well on the test and writes them in his planner as shown in the example below. Achieving his overarching long-term goal of doing well in a course he needs for business school is the source of his motivation.

Monday	Tuesday	Wednesday	Thursday	Friday	Saturday	Sunday
9 AM: Economics class Talk with study group members to schedule meeting.	3–5 PM: Study econ chapter 3.	9 AM: Economics class Drop by instructor's office hours to ask question about test	6 PM: Go over chapter 3 7–9 PM: Study group meeting.	9 AM: Economics class—Test 3:30 PM: Meet w/advisor to discuss GMAT and other business school requirements	Sleep in—schedule some down time	5 PM: Go over quiz questions with study partner

Before each week begins, remind yourself of your long-term goals and what you can accomplish over the next seven days to move you closer to them. Key 2.2 shows parts of a daily schedule and a weekly schedule.

Indicate Priority Levels

Just as your goals have varying degrees of importance, so too do your daily and weekly tasks. Prioritizing these items helps you to identify your most important tasks so you can focus the bulk of your energy and time on them. It also helps you plan when in your day to get things done. Because many top-priority items (classes, work) occur at designated times, prioritizing helps you lock in these activities and schedule less urgent items around them.

Indicate level of importance using three different categories. You can identify these categories with any code that makes sense to you—some people use numbers, some use letters (A, B, C), and some use different-colored pens. The three categories are as follows:

- *Priority 1* items are the most crucial. They may include attending class, completing school assignments, working at a job, picking up a child from day care, and paying bills. Enter Priority 1 items on your planner first, before scheduling anything else.

KEY 2.2 Note daily and weekly tasks.

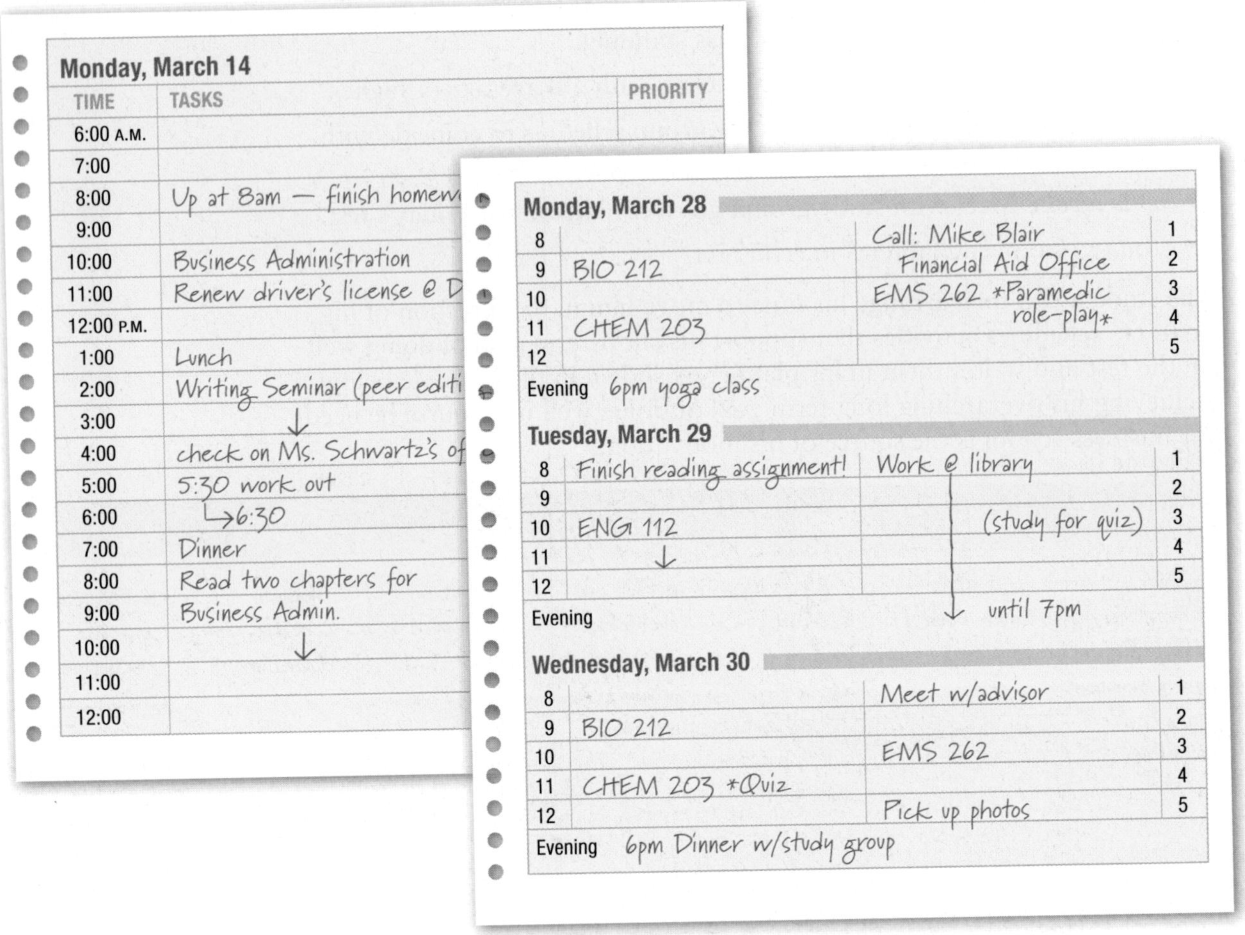

- *Priority 2* items are important but more flexible parts of your routine. Examples include library study time, completing an assignment for a school club, and working out. Schedule these around Priority 1 items.
- *Priority 3* items are least important—the "it would be nice if I could get to that" items. Examples include phoning a friend, downloading a dozen new songs onto your iPod, and cleaning out a closet. Many people don't enter Priority 3 tasks in their planners until they know they have time for them. Others keep a separate list of these tasks so that when they have free time they can choose what they want to accomplish.

Use Scheduling Techniques

The following strategies will help you turn your scheduling activities into tools that move you closer to your goals:

Plan regularly. Set aside a regular time each day, and perhaps a longer time at the end of each week, to plan out your schedule. Being methodical about scheduling will help you reduce stress and save the hassle that might result if you forget something important. Your planner can help you only if you use it—so keep it with you and check it throughout the day.

Make and use to-do lists. Use a to-do list to record the things you want to accomplish on a given day or week. Write your to-do items on a separate piece of paper so you can set priorities. Then transfer the items you plan to accomplish each day to open time periods in your planner. To-do lists are critical time-management tools for exam week and major projects. They will help you rank your responsibilities so that you get things done in order of importance.

Post monthly and yearly calendars at home. Keeping track of your major commitments on a monthly wall calendar will give you the overview you need to focus on responsibilities and upcoming events. Key 2.3 shows a monthly calendar. If you live with family or friends, create a group calendar to stay aware of each other's plans and avoid scheduling conflicts.

Avoid time traps. Try to stay away from situations that eat up time unnecessarily. Say no graciously if you don't have time for a project; curb excess social time; declare your cell phone off-limits when you study, delegate chores. Rein in the time you spend surfing the Internet and instant-messaging with friends, because these activities can eat up hours before you know it.

Schedule down time. Leisure time is more than just a nice break—it's essential to your health and success. Even a half-hour of down time a day will

KEY 2.3

Keep track of your time with a monthly calendar.

MARCH

SUNDAY	MONDAY	TUESDAY	WEDNESDAY	THURSDAY	FRIDAY	SATURDAY
	1 WORK	2 Turn in English paper topic	3 Dentist 2pm	4 WORK	5	6
7 Frank's birthday	8 Psych Test 9am WORK	9	10 6:30 pm Meeting @ Student Ctr.	11 WORK	12	13 Dinner @ Ryan's
14	15 English paper due WORK	16 Western Civ paper—Library research	17	18 Library 6 pm WORK	19 Western Civ makeup class	20
21	22 WORK	23 2 pm meeting, psych group project	24 Start running program: 2 miles	25 WORK	26 Run 2 miles	27
28 Run 3 miles	29 WORK	30 Western Civ paper due	31 Run 2 miles			

refresh you and improve your productivity when you get back on task. Fill the time with whatever relaxes you—reading, watching television, chatting online, playing a game or sport, walking, writing, or just doing nothing.

Fight Procrastination

PROCRASTINATION
The act of putting off a task until another time.

It's human, and common for busy students, to leave difficult or undesirable tasks until later. If taken to the extreme, however, **procrastination** can develop into a habit that causes serious problems, often because a procrastinator may not think through the consequences of putting something off.

This excerpt from the Study Skills Library at California Polytechnic State University at San Luis Obispo illustrates how procrastination can quickly turn into a destructive pattern:

> The procrastinator is often remarkably optimistic about his ability to complete a task on a tight deadline. . . . For example, he may estimate that a paper will take only five days to write; he has fifteen days; there is

SUCCESSFUL INTELLIGENCE

get practical!

Make a To-Do List

Reduce stress by accomplishing practical goals. Make a to-do list for what you have to do on your busiest day this week. Include all the tasks and events you know about, including attending class and study time, and the activities you would like to do (working out at the gym, watching your favorite TV show) if you have extra time. Then prioritize your list using the coding system of your choice.

Date: ______________

1. ______________	7. ______________
2. ______________	8. ______________
3. ______________	9. ______________
4. ______________	10. ______________
5. ______________	11. ______________
6. ______________	12. ______________

After examining this list, record your daily schedule in your planner (if you have a busy day, you may want to list Priority 3 items separately to complete if time permits). At the end of the day, evaluate this system. Did the list help you to manage your time and tasks effectively? If you liked it, use this exercise as a guide for using to-do lists regularly.

> plenty of time, no need to start. Lulled by a false sense of security, time passes. At some point, he crosses over an imaginary starting time and suddenly realizes, "Oh no! I am not in control! There isn't enough time!"
>
> At this point, considerable effort is directed toward completing the task, and work progresses. This sudden spurt of energy is the source of the erroneous feeling that "I work well only under pressure." Actually, at this point you are making progress only because you haven't any choice. . . . Progress is being made, but you have lost your freedom.
>
> Barely completed in time, the paper may actually earn a fairly good grade; whereupon the student experiences mixed feelings: pride of accomplishment (sort of), scorn for the professor who cannot recognize substandard work, and guilt for getting an undeserved grade. But the net result is *reinforcement:* The procrastinator is rewarded positively for his poor behavior ("Look what a decent grade I got after all!"). As a result, the counterproductive behavior is repeated time and time again.[9]

Among the reasons people procrastinate are the following:

- *Perfectionism.* According to Jane B. Burka and Lenora M. Yuen, authors of *Procrastination: Why You Do It, What to Do About It,* habitual procrastinators often gauge their self-worth solely by their ability to achieve. In other words, "an outstanding performance means an outstanding person; a mediocre performance means a mediocre person."[10] To the perfectionist procrastinator, not trying at all is better than an attempt that falls short of perfection.
- *Fear of limitations.* Some people procrastinate in order to avoid the truth about what they can achieve. "As long as you procrastinate, you never have to confront the real limits of your ability, whatever those limits are,"[11] say Burka and Yuen. If you procrastinate and fail, you can blame the failure on waiting too long, not on any personal shortcoming.
- *Being unsure of the next step.* If you get stuck and don't know what to do, sometimes it seems easier to procrastinate than to make the leap to the next level of your goal.
- *Facing an overwhelming task.* Some big projects create immobilizing fear. If a person facing such a task fears failure, she may procrastinate in order to avoid confronting the fear.

Although it can bring relief in the short term, avoiding tasks almost always causes problems, such as a buildup of responsibilities and less time to complete them, work that is not up to par, the disappointment of others who are depending on your work, and stress brought on by the weight of the unfinished tasks. The following strategies can help you avoid procrastination and the problems associated with it:

- *Analyze the effects.* What may happen if you continue to put off a responsibility? Chances are you will benefit more in the long term from facing the task head-on.
- *Set reasonable goals.* Unreasonable goals can intimidate and immobilize you. Set manageable goals and allow enough time to complete them.
- *Break tasks into smaller parts.* If you concentrate on achieving one small step at a time, setting time limits for each step, the task may become less burdensome.

- *Get started whether or not you "feel like it."* The motivation techniques from chapter 1 might help you take the first step. Once you start, you may find it easier to continue.
- *Ask for help.* Once you identify what's holding you up, see who can help you face the task. Another person may come up with an innovative way to get you moving.
- *Don't expect perfection.* People learn by starting at the beginning, making mistakes, and learning from those mistakes. It's better to try your best than to do nothing at all.
- *Reward yourself.* Find ways to boost your confidence when you accomplish a particular task. Remind yourself—with a break, a movie, some kind of treat—that you are making progress.

Be Flexible

Change is a part of life. No matter how well you think ahead and plan your time, sudden changes—ranging from a room change for a class to a medical emergency—can upend your plans. However, you have some control over how you handle your circumstances. Your ability to evaluate situations, come up with creative options, and put practical plans to work will help you manage changes.

Small changes—for instance, the need to work an hour overtime at your after-school job, or a meeting that runs late—can result in priority shifts that jumble your schedule. For changes that occur frequently, think through a backup plan ahead of time. For surprises, the best you can do is to keep an open mind about possibilities and rely on your internal and external resources.

When change involves serious problems—your car breaks down and you have no way to get to school, or you fail a class and have to consider summer school—use problem-solving skills to help you through (see chapter 4). There are resources available at your college to help you throughout this process. Your academic advisor, counselor, dean, financial aid advisor, and instructors may have ideas and assistance.

Manage Stress by Managing Time

STRESS

Physical or mental strain or tension produced in reaction to pressure.

If you are feeling more stress in your everyday life as a student, you are not alone. Stress levels among college students have increased dramatically.[12] Stress factors for college students include being in a new environment, facing increased work and difficult decisions, and juggling school, work, and personal responsibilities.

Dealing with the stress of college life is, and will continue to be, one of your biggest challenges. But here's some good news: *Every time-management strategy you have read in this chapter contributes to your ability to cope with stress.* Remember that stress refers to how you react to pressure. When you create and follow a schedule that gets you places on time and helps you take care of tasks and responsibilities, you reduce pressure. Less pressure, less stress.

Analyze, and adjust if necessary, the relationship between stress and your time-management habits. For example, if you're a night person with early classes and are consistently stressed about waking up in time, use strategies such as going to bed earlier a few nights a week, napping in the afternoon, exercising briefly before class to boost energy, or exploring how to schedule later classes next term. Reduce anxiety by thinking before you act.

Following are some practical strategies for coping with stress through time management. You will find more detail on stress in chapter 8.

Be realistic about time commitments. For example, many students attempting to combine work and school find that they have to trim one or the other to reduce stress and promote success. Overloaded students often fall behind and experience high stress levels that can lead to dropping out. Determine what is reasonable for you; you may find that taking longer to graduate is a viable option if you need to work while in school.

Put sleep and down time on your schedule. Sleep-deprived bodies and minds have a harder time handling pressure effectively. Figure out how much sleep you need and do your best to get it. When you pull an all-nighter, make sure you play catch-up over the days that follow. Also, with time for relaxation in whatever form you choose, your mind will be better able to manage stress.

Actively manage your schedule. The most detailed datebook page or PDA entry can't help you unless you look at it. Get in the habit of checking at regular intervals throughout the day. Also, try not to put off tasks. If you can get it done ahead of time, get it done.

Focus on one assignment at a time. Stress is at its worst when you have five pressing assignments in five different classes all due in the next week. Focus on one at a time, completing it to the best of your ability as quickly as you can, then move to the next and the next until you're through.

Check things off. Use a physical action to indicate that you have completed a task—check off the item, delete it from your PDA task list, crumple up the Post-it Note. A physical act can relieve stress and highlight the confidence that comes from getting something done.

Sometimes stress freezes you in place and blocks you from finding answers. At those times, remember that taking even a small step is a stress-management strategy because it begins to move you ahead.

Successful Intelligence Wrap-Up

Self-management is about making well-examined choices—and you are the manager who does the choosing. Think intelligently about what you value, what goals are important to you, and how to best manage your time. Here's how you have built skills in chapter 2:

Analytical

In the *Get Analytical* exercise, you explored what you value and how your values inform educational goals. As you read the section on goals, you broke down the goal-setting process into its step-by-step parts. While exploring the topic of time management, you thought about who you are as a time manager and how that affects your scheduling and procrastination habits.

Creative

With the *Get Creative* exercise to motivate you, you came up with ideas about how to pursue an important personal goal. What you read about majors may have inspired new ideas about what you want to major in or how to construct your major. Exploring the importance of flexibility in time management showed you the key role of creativity in the face of change.

Practical

You explored the practical action of mapping out and pursuing goals step-by-step, and considered how this process applies to declaring a major. In the section on time management, you examined practical strategies for getting in control of your schedule, and created a to-do list tailored to an upcoming busy day in the *Get Practical* exercise. At the end of the chapter, you gathered practical, time-related techniques for managing the stress that all students encounter.

paseo

(pass-eh-o)

This Spanish word refers to an activity that traditionally takes place in Spanish towns in the time of evening after the afternoon *siesta*, or rest. At this late afternoon hour, families often dress up and enjoy a *paseo*—a walk outdoors in the town, to be seen and to socialize.[13]

The relaxed pace of traditional life in many European countries holds a lesson for the overscheduled, harried student. Like many other students, you may feel like you just can't afford to take a break when there is so much to do. However, you also might not be able to afford the negative effects of the stress that results when you *don't* take a break. When you manage your time effectively, you will be able to make time for relaxation, which is critical for stress reduction. So find your version of the *paseo*—a walk on the campus, a coffee shop visit, a game of soccer—and make it part of your life.

"Goals are dreams with deadlines."

DIANA SCHARF HUNT

Building World-Class Skills for College, Career, and Life Success

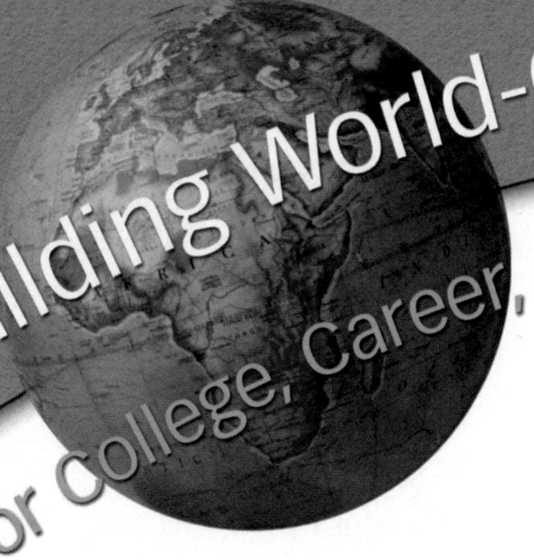

SUCCESSFUL INTELLIGENCE

Think, Create, Apply

Make your first term count. Campus resources, clubs, student activity groups, and other organizations can enrich your college experience. To benefit from what your school has to offer, set a goal to get involved sooner rather than later.

Step 1. Think it through: ***Analyze your college self.*** Making connections with people and groups in college starts with understanding who you are as a student, both alone and in relation to your school's student body. On a separate sheet of paper, describe your particular circumstances, opinions, and needs in a short paragraph, using questions like these to think through your description:

- How would you describe yourself in terms of culture, ethnicity, gender, age, and lifestyle?
- How would you describe your student status—traditional or returning, full- or part-time?
- How long are you planning to be in your current college? Is it likely that you will transfer?
- What family and work obligations do you have?
- What is your current living situation?
- What do you feel are your biggest challenges in college?
- What do you like to study, and why does it interest you?

Step 2. Think out of the box: ***Brainstorm your ideal extracurriculars.*** On a second piece of paper, write ideas about how you want to spend your time outside of class. To inspire creative ideas, try using one or more of the following questions as a starting point:

- If you had no fear, what horizon-broadening experience would you sign up for?
- When you were in elementary school, what were your favorite activities? Which activities might translate into current interests and pursuits?

- What kinds of organizations, activities, groups, experiences, or people make you think, "Wow, I want to do that"?
- Think about the people who bring out the best in you. What do you like to do with them? What kinds of things are they involved with?

Step 3. Make it happen: ***Take practical steps toward the activities you like.*** First, look in your student handbook at the resources and organizations your school offers. These may include some or all of the following:

Academic centers (reading, writing, etc.)
Academic organizations
Adult education center
Arts clubs (music, drama, dance, etc.)
Fraternities/sororities
International student groups
Minority student groups
On-campus work opportunities
Disabled student groups
Religious organizations
School publications
School TV/radio stations
Sports clubs
Student associations
Student government
Volunteer groups

Taking your analysis of yourself and your creative ideas into consideration, use the left-hand column on the grid that follows to list the three offices or organizations you most want to check out this term. Then—through your school publications and/or a little legwork—fill in the grid, answering the questions shown across the top for each item. The last column requires action—fill it in when you have made contact with each office or organization. Finally, if you wish to become more involved after your initial contact, go for it.

Office or Organization	Location	Hours, or times of meetings	What it offers	Phone number or e-mail	*Initial contact—date and what happened*

TEAMWORK

Create Solutions Together

Multiple paths to a goal. In a group of three or four, brainstorm important academic goals that can reasonably be accomplished in the course of one year in college. Write your ideas on a piece of paper. From that list, pick out one goal to explore together.

Each group member takes two minutes alone to think about this goal in terms of the first goal-achievement step on page 42—defining a strategy. In other words, answer the question "How would I do it?" Each person writes down all the paths he or she can think of.

The group then gathers and everyone shares their strategies. The group evaluates strategies and chooses one that seems effective. Finally, as a group, brainstorm the rest of the goal-achievement process, based on the chosen strategy or path:

- **Set a timetable.** When do you plan to reach your goal? Discuss different time frames and how each might change the path.
- **Be accountable.** What safeguards will keep you on track? Talk about different ways to make sure you are moving ahead consistently.
- **Get unstuck.** What will you do if you hit a roadblock? Brainstorm the roadblocks that could get in the way of this particular goal. For each, come up with ways to overcome the obstacle.

At the end of the process, you should have a wealth of ideas for how to approach one particular academic goal—and an appreciation for how many paths you could take in order to get there.

WRITING

Journal and Put Skills to Work

Use the tables here to record data. Answer questions and write additional thoughts on a separate piece of paper, in a journal, or on a computer file.

Journal entry: Discover how you spend your time. In the table on the following page, estimate the total time you think you spend per week on each listed activity. Then, add the hours. If your number is over 168 (the number of hours in a week), rethink your estimates and recalculate so that the total equals 168.

Now, spend a week recording exactly how you spend your time. The chart on pages 61–62 has blocks showing half-hour increments. As you go through the week, write in what you do each hour, indicating when you started and when you stopped. Don't forget activities that don't feel like "activities"—such as sleeping, relaxing, or watching TV. Finally, be sure to record your *actual* activities instead of how you want or think you should have spent your time. There are no wrong answers.

After a week, go through your filled-in chart and add up how many hours you spent on the activities for which you previously estimated your

Activity	Estimated Time Spent	Activity	Estimated Time Spent
Class		Chores and personal business	
Work		Friends and important relationships	
Studying		Communication time (phone, computer)	
Sleeping		Leisure/entertainment	
Eating		Spiritual life	
Family time/child care		Other	
Commuting/traveling		TOTAL	

hours. Tally the hours in the boxes in the table on page 63 using straight tally marks; round off to half hours and use a short tally mark for each half hour. In the third column, total the hours for each activity. Leave the "Ideal Time in Hours" column blank for now.

Add the totals in the third column to find your grand total. Compare your grand total to your estimated grand total; compare your actual activity hour totals to your estimated activity hour totals. Use a separate sheet of paper to answer the following questions:

- What matches and what doesn't? Describe the most interesting similarities and differences.
- Where do you waste the most time? What do you think that is costing you?

Now evaluate what kinds of changes might improve your ability to achieve goals. Analyze what you do daily, weekly, and monthly. Go back to the table on page 63 and fill in the "Ideal Time in Hours" column. Consider the difference between actual hours and ideal hours. Ask yourself questions:

- On what activities do you think you should spend more or less time?
- What are you willing to do to change, and why?

Finally, write a short paragraph describing two key time-management changes in detail. Describe what goal you are aiming for, and map out how you plan to put the changes into action.

Real-life writing: Examine two areas of academic specialty. Use your course catalog to identify two academic areas that look interesting. Write a short report comparing and contrasting the majors or concentrations in these areas, being sure to note GPA requirements, number of courses, relevance to career areas, campus locations of departments, "feel" of the departments, other requirements, and any other relevant characteristics. Conclude your report with observations about how this comparison and evaluation process has refined your thinking.

Monday		Tuesday		Wednesday		Thursday	
TIME	ACTIVITY	TIME	ACTIVITY	TIME	ACTIVITY	TIME	ACTIVITY
6:00 A.M.		6:00 A.M.		6:00 A.M.		6:00 A.M.	
6:30 A.M.		6:30 A.M.		6:30 A.M.		6:30 A.M.	
7:00 A.M.	Get up	7:00 A.M.	Get up	7:00 A.M.	Get up	7:00 A.M.	Get up
7:30 A.M.		7:30 A.M.		7:30 A.M.		7:30 A.M.	
8:00 A.M.	Study	8:00 A.M.		8:00 A.M.		8:00 A.M.	
8:30 A.M.		8:30 A.M.		8:30 A.M.		8:30 A.M.	
9:00 A.M.		9:00 A.M.		9:00 A.M.		9:00 A.M.	
9:30 A.M.		9:30 A.M.		9:30 A.M.		9:30 A.M.	
10:00 A.M.		10:00 A.M.	Study at home	10:00 A.M.	Cleaned House	10:00 A.M.	helped someone with taxes
10:30 A.M.	Cleaned House	10:30 A.M.		10:30 A.M.		10:30 A.M.	
11:00 A.M.		11:00 A.M.		11:00 A.M.		11:00 A.M.	
11:30 A.M.		11:30 A.M.		11:30 A.M.		11:30 A.M.	
12:00 P.M.		12:00 P.M.		12:00 P.M.		12:00 P.M.	
12:30 P.M.		12:30 P.M.		12:30 P.M.		12:30 P.M.	
1:00 P.M.		1:00 P.M.		1:00 P.M.	Study	1:00 P.M.	
1:30 P.M.		1:30 P.M.		1:30 P.M.		1:30 P.M.	
2:00 P.M.		2:00 P.M.		2:00 P.M.		2:00 P.M.	
2:30 P.M.		2:30 P.M.		2:30 P.M.		2:30 P.M.	Library
3:00 P.M.		3:00 P.M.		3:00 P.M.		3:00 P.M.	
3:30 P.M.		3:30 P.M.		3:30 P.M.		3:30 P.M.	
4:00 P.M.	leave for School	4:00 P.M.	leave for School	4:00 P.M.		4:00 P.M.	
4:30 P.M.		4:30 P.M.		4:30 P.M.		4:30 P.M.	
5:00 P.M.		5:00 P.M.		5:00 P.M.		5:00 P.M.	
5:30 P.M.		5:30 P.M.		5:30 P.M.		5:30 P.M.	
6:00 P.M.		6:00 P.M.		6:00 P.M.		6:00 P.M.	
6:30 P.M.		6:30 P.M.		6:30 P.M.		6:30 P.M.	
7:00 P.M.		7:00 P.M.		7:00 P.M.		7:00 P.M.	
7:30 P.M.		7:30 P.M.		7:30 P.M.		7:30 P.M.	
8:00 P.M.		8:00 P.M.		8:00 P.M.		8:00 P.M.	
8:30 P.M.		8:30 P.M.		8:30 P.M.		8:30 P.M.	
9:00 P.M.		9:00 P.M.		9:00 P.M.		9:00 P.M.	
9:30 P.M.		9:30 P.M.		9:30 P.M.		9:30 P.M.	
10:00 P.M.		10:00 P.M.		10:00 P.M.		10:00 P.M.	
10:30 P.M.	Bed	10:30 P.M.	Bed	10:30 P.M.	Bed	10:30 P.M.	Bed
11:00 P.M.		11:00 P.M.		11:00 P.M.		11:00 P.M.	
11:30 P.M.		11:30 P.M.		11:30 P.M.		11:30 P.M.	
12–6 A.M.		12–6 A.M.		12–6 A.M.		12–6 A.M.	

Friday		Saturday		Sunday		Notes
TIME	ACTIVITY	TIME	ACTIVITY	TIME	ACTIVITY	
6:00 A.M.		6:00 A.M.		6:00 A.M.		
6:30 A.M.		6:30 A.M.		6:30 A.M.		
7:00 A.M.		7:00 A.M.		7:00 A.M.		
7:30 A.M.		7:30 A.M.		7:30 A.M.		
8:00 A.M.		8:00 A.M.		8:00 A.M.		
8:30 A.M.		8:30 A.M.		8:30 A.M.		
9:00 A.M.		9:00 A.M.		9:00 A.M.		
9:30 A.M.		9:30 A.M.		9:30 A.M.		
10:00 A.M.		10:00 A.M.		10:00 A.M.		
10:30 A.M.		10:30 A.M.		10:30 A.M.		
11:00 A.M.		11:00 A.M.		11:00 A.M.		
11:30 A.M.		11:30 A.M.		11:30 A.M.		
12:00 P.M.		12:00 P.M.		12:00 P.M.		
12:30 P.M.		12:30 P.M.		12:30 P.M.		
1:00 P.M.		1:00 P.M.		1:00 P.M.		
1:30 P.M.		1:30 P.M.		1:30 P.M.		
2:00 P.M.		2:00 P.M.		2:00 P.M.		
2:30 P.M.		2:30 P.M.		2:30 P.M.		
3:00 P.M.		3:00 P.M.		3:00 P.M.		
3:30 P.M.		3:30 P.M.		3:30 P.M.		
4:00 P.M.		4:00 P.M.		4:00 P.M.		
4:30 P.M.		4:30 P.M.		4:30 P.M.		
5:00 P.M.		5:00 P.M.		5:00 P.M.		
5:30 P.M.		5:30 P.M.		5:30 P.M.		
6:00 P.M.		6:00 P.M.		6:00 P.M.		
6:30 P.M.		6:30 P.M.		6:30 P.M.		
7:00 P.M.		7:00 P.M.		7:00 P.M.		
7:30 P.M.		7:30 P.M.		7:30 P.M.		
8:00 P.M.		8:00 P.M.		8:00 P.M.		
8:30 P.M.		8:30 P.M.		8:30 P.M.		
9:00 P.M.		9:00 P.M.		9:00 P.M.		
9:30 P.M.		9:30 P.M.		9:30 P.M.		
10:00 P.M.		10:00 P.M.		10:00 P.M.		
10:30 P.M.	Go tob	10:30 P.M.		10:30 P.M.		
11:00 P.M.		11:00 P.M.		11:00 P.M.		
11:30 P.M.		11:30 P.M.		11:30 P.M.		
12–6 A.M.		12–6 A.M.		12–6 A.M.		

Activity	Time Tallied over One-Week Period	Total Time in Hours	Ideal Time in Hours
Example: Class	卌 卌 卌 ||	16.5	
Class			
Work			
Studying			
Sleeping			
Eating			
Family time/child care			
Commuting/traveling			
Chores and personal business			
Friends and important relationships			
Telephone time			
Leisure/entertainment			
Spiritual life			
Other			

PERSONAL PORTFOLIO

Prepare for Career Success

Complete the following in your electronic portfolio or on separate sheets of paper.

Knowledge, skills, and attitudes. No matter what career goals you ultimately pursue, certain knowledge, skills, and attitudes are useful in any career area. Consider this list of what employers look for in people they hire:

Acceptance
Critical thinking
Leadership
Communication
Flexibility

Positive attitude

Continual learning

Goal setting

Teamwork

Creativity

Integrity

Choose and circle three of these that you want to focus on developing this year.

Map out a plan for your progress by indicating a series of smaller goals that will lead you toward developing these skills. For example:

Skill: Teamwork

Long-term goal: To be comfortable and effective working with others

Short-term goal: I will join, or form, a study group for my economics class.

Short-term goal: I will participate in a short-term volunteering opportunity for which I am required to work in a team with others.

Short-term goal: When looking into courses with my advisor, I will consider teamwork opportunities (small group work, small seminar courses) as one of my criteria.

Suggested Readings

Allen, David. *Getting Things Done: The Art of Stress-Free Productivity.* New York: Penguin, 2003.

Burka, Jane B., and Lenora M. Yuen. *Procrastination.* Reading, MA: Perseus Books, 1990.

Charlesworth, Edward A., and Ronald G. Nathan. *Stress Management: A Comprehensive Guide to Wellness.* New York: Ballantine Books, 2004.

College Board. *The College Board Book of Majors,* 2nd ed. New York: Author, 2006.

Covey, Stephen. *The Seven Habits of Highly Effective People.* New York: Simon & Schuster, 2004.

Emmett, Rita. *The Procrastinator's Handbook: Mastering the Art of Doing It Now.* New York: Walker, 2000.

Fogg, Neeta, Paul Harrington, and Thomas Harrington. *The College Majors Handbook with Real Career Paths and Payoffs: The Actual Jobs, Earnings, and Trends for Graduates of 60 College Majors.* Indianapolis: Jist Works, 2004.

Gleeson, Kerry. *The Personal Efficiency Program: How to Get Organized to Do More Work in Less Time,* 2nd ed. New York: Wiley, 2000.

Hallowell, Edward M. *Crazy Busy: Overstretched, Overbooked, and About to Snap! Strategies for Handling Your Fast-Paced Life.* New York: Ballantine Books, 2007.

Phifer, Paul. *College Majors and Careers: A Resource Guide for Effective Life Planning,* 4th ed. Chicago: Ferguson, 2003.

Sapadin, Linda, and Jack Maguire. *Beat Procrastination and Make the Grade: The Six Styles of Procrastination and How Students Can Overcome Them.* New York: Penguin, 1999.

Simon, Sydney B. *In Search of Values: 31 Strategies for Finding Out What Really Matters Most to You.* New York: Warner Books, 1993.

Timm, Paul R. *Successful Self-Management, Revised Edition: Increasing Your Personal Effectiveness.* Los Altos, CA: Crisp Publications, 1993.

Internet and Podcast Resources

About.com—Stress Management (resources, including a variety of self-assessments): **http://stress.about.com/**

Mind Tools—Time Management: **http://mindtools.com/pages/main/newMN_HTE.htm**

Time Management Secrets with Ruth Klein podcasts: **http://odeo.com/audio/633014/view**

Top Achievement (goal-setting and self-improvement resources): **www.topachievement.com**

Troubled With (help with stress management and personal issues): **www.troubledwith.com**

Riley Guide—Values Inventories (self-assessment resources): **www.rileyguide.com/assess.html#values**

"Stress Cops" episodes on Podcast.net: **www.podcast.net/show/22377**

Prentice Hall Student Success SuperSite: **www.prenhall.com/success**

Look to your college Web site for school-specific information on declaring a major.

Endnotes

[1]Student essay submitted by the First Year Experience students of Patty Parma, Palo Alto College, San Antonio, Texas, January 2004.

[2]Mark A. King, Anthony Sims, and David Osher, "How Is Cultural Competence Integrated in Education?" March 2007, Center for Effective Collaboration and Practice (http://cecp.air.org/cultural/Q_integrated.htm#def).

[3]Cited in Louis E. Boone and David L. Kurtz, *Contemporary Business Communication*, Upper Saddle River, NJ: Prentice Hall, 1994, p. 643.

[4]Students Speak: Excerpts from *Your Educational Experience Essays,* University of Illinois, October 2, 2001 (http://ae3_cen_uiuc_edu/stessay/StudentsSpeak; no longer available).

[5]Cited in Terry Strathman, "What Do Students Want?" April 15, 2002, L & S Colloquium on Undergraduate Education (http://ls.berkeley.edu/?q=about-college/l-s-divisions/undergraduate-division/colloquium-undergraduate-education/april-2002).

[6]Paul Timm, *Successful Self-Management: A Psychologically Sound Approach to Personal Effectiveness*, Los Altos, CA: Crisp Publications, 1987, pp. 22–41.

[7]Jeffrey R. Young, "'Homework? What Homework?' Students Seem to Be Spending Less Time Studying Than They Used To," *Chronicle of Higher Education,* December 6, 2002 (http://chronicle.com/weekly/v49/i15/15a03501.htm).

[8]Welch Suggs, "How Gears Turn at a Sports Factory: Running Ohio State's $79-Million Athletics Program Is a Major Endeavor, with Huge Payoffs and Costs," *Chronicle of Higher Education*, November 29, 2002 (http://chronicle.com/weekly/v49/i14/14a03201.htm).

[9]William E. Sydnor, "Procrastination," from the California Polytechnic State University Study Skills Library (www.sas.calpoly.edu/asc/ssl/procrastination.html). Based on *Overcoming Procrastination* by Albert Ellis. Used with permission.

[10]Jane B. Burka and Lenora M. Yuen, *Procrastination. Why You Do It, What to Do About It*, Reading, MA: Perseus Books, 1983, pp. 21–22.

[11]Ibid.

[12]Jodi Wilgoren, "Survey Shows High Stress Levels in College Freshmen," *New York Times*, January 23, 2000, p. NA.

[13]Christopher J. Moore, *In Other Words: A Language Lover's Guide to the Most Intriguing Words Around the World*, New York: Walker, 2004, pp. 36–37.

DIVERSITY MATTERS

How You Learn and Communicate

3

"Successfully intelligent people figure out their strengths and their weaknesses, and then find ways to capitalize on their strengths—make the most of what they do well—and to correct for or remedy their weaknesses—find ways around what they don't do well, or make themselves good enough to get by."

ROBERT STERNBERG

Diversity exists both within each person and among all people. The layers of diversity *within you*—physical being, personality, talents, skills, and thinking abilities—include your unique way of learning and communicating. This chapter builds your awareness of diversity within and without—helping you to identify how you learn, how you put your knowledge to work, how you can relate to others in a culturally competent way, and how you can practice communication strategies that will help you build successful relationships in school and elsewhere.

In this chapter you explore answers to the following questions:

- Why explore who you are as a learner? 68
- What tools can help you assess how you learn and interact with others? 70
- How can you use your self-knowledge? 80
- How can you develop cultural competence? 87
- How can you communicate effectively? 92
- Successful Intelligence Wrap-Up 98

Chapter 3's Successful Intelligence Skills

Analytical

- Analyzing your eight multiple intelligences
- Investigating how you relate to others
- Evaluating the assumptions that underlie prejudice and stereotypes

Creative

- Creating new ways to develop your abilities
- Developing a new vision of yourself as a learner
- Creating new ideas about what diversity means

Practical

- How to choose and use your best study strategies
- How to adjust to an instructor's teaching style
- How to relate to others with cultural competence

Why Explore Who You Are as a Learner?

Have you ever thought about yourself as a learner? Most students, even those who do well in the areas traditionally valued by schools (verbal and mathematical skills), conclude that "this high (or low) GPA is who I am. I am intelligent (or not)." More often than not, decisions stretching throughout a lifetime are made based on that self-assessment.

© Jaimie Duplass—Fotolia.com

Your Unique Intelligence Can Change and Develop

Each person in the world is unique, with an individual blend of characteristics. Likewise, each person has a particular way in which his or her mind receives and processes information. Everyone is also born with particular levels of ability and potential in different areas. For example, some musicians can play anything they hear. Your natural abilities, plus effort and environmental influences, combine to create a recipe for the achievement level you can attain.

Picture a bag of a variety of rubber bands. Some are thick, some are thin; some are long, some are short. *But all of them can stretch*. A small rubber band, stretched out, can reach the length of a larger one that lies unstretched. In other words, with effort and focus, you can grow to some extent whatever raw material you

REAL QUESTIONS

How can I maximize what I do well?

How can I make the most of my strengths in a course if the professor doesn't use teaching methods that I can relate to? For example, I'm an artist and I tend to connect with information visually. I tend to rely on written notes, maps, and diagrams to absorb information. When I have professors who only lecture, I find it very hard to listen and take notes at the same time—but I need the notes to look at later for studying. How can I deal with this situation?

Cheryl Whitley
Florida Community College
at Jacksonville

PRACTICAL ANSWERS

Darren Love
Midwestern University,
Phoenix, Arizona

Use what you do well to adapt to what challenges you.

I know firsthand that it takes time and some training to adapt to a different teaching style than you're used to. When I began college, I was mostly a visual learner, and I quickly learned that I had to either adapt to different styles or be left behind. I became more flexible with practice as I tried new study techniques. As the years passed, I discovered I could adjust to whatever format I encountered in the classroom, including lecture and group-based learning.

Try using techniques in an area of strength to compensate for an area of weakness. I know that you are a visual learner (strength) but most of your courses are lecture-based (weakness). Using visually focused techniques will help you adjust to lectures and ultimately integrate the two styles. First, ask your professor if you can videotape or audiotape the lectures so that you will always have the lecture material. Second, when you write your notes, fold your paper in half. On one side, write the notes in pencil or one color of pen; then, when you go home, complement the partial notes that you took earlier by consulting your text and writing text notes in pen (if you used pencil) or a different color of pen (if you used pen) on the other side of the paper. Third, use the audio or videotape of the lecture and convert the material to something that is more visual, such as charts, graphs, or a picture. Fourth, try writing your notes in shorthand, using your visual strength to convert words to symbols or pictures to represent the professor's words.

Now I am in grad school, where one course is often taught by several professors, each with a different style of lecturing. I am adapting once again, accenting my strengths in visual and interpersonal learning to manage the challenges I face in lecture-based classrooms. Over time, as you emphasize your strength, the confidence you build will help you face styles less natural to you.

have at the start. *To reach your individual potential is your most worthy goal, and the most you can ask of yourself.*

Studies of the brain, showing that humans of any age are able to build new neuropathways and thereby learn new ideas and skills, support Sternberg's theory that intelligence can change over time.[1] Set aside the notion that your intelligence has a "fixed" level as you continue through this chapter, through college, and into your life after college. Work instead to understand your strengths—to define the characteristics of your rubber band and stretch it to the limit.

Assessments Can Help You Learn About Yourself

POTENTIALS

Abilities that may be developed.

INTELLIGENCE

As defined by Howard Gardner, an ability to solve problems or create products that are of value in a culture.

An assessment, as professor and psychologist Howard Gardner puts it, is "the obtaining of information about a person's skills and **potentials**... providing useful feedback to the person."[2] With the information you gain from the two assessments you will take in this chapter—*Multiple Pathways to Learning* and the *Personality Spectrum*—you will learn more about what your strengths and weaknesses are, leading you to the ability to maximize those strengths and compensate for those weaknesses as a successfully intelligent learner. (You will learn about these **intelligences** and other characteristics later in the chapter.)

Understanding yourself as a learner will also help you to see and appreciate how people differ. In a study group or classroom, each person is taking in the material in a unique way. What you know about how others learn can help you improve communication and teamwork.

Self-knowledge is a key to personal power. With self-knowledge, you can work toward controlling how you respond to circumstances as you and your environment change, making adjustments that will help you cope and grow. Use these assessments to help you look at the present—and plan for the future—by asking questions: "Who am I right now?" "How does this compare with who I want to be?"

Compare the process of responding to the assessment questions to the experience of trying on new eyeglasses to correct blurred vision. The glasses will not create new paths and possibilities, but they will help you see more clearly the ones that exist today.

What Tools Can Help You Assess How You Learn and Interact with Others?

This chapter presents two assessments designed to help you get a closer look at your learning capacities and favored modes of interaction with others. The first—*Multiple Pathways to Learning*—focuses on eight areas of potential and is based on Howard Gardner's Multiple Intelligences theory. The second—the *Personality Spectrum*—is based on the Myers-Briggs Type Indicator® (MBTI) and helps you evaluate how you react to people and situations.

Following each assessment is information about the typical traits of each intelligence or personality spectrum dimension. As you will see from your scores, you have abilities in all areas, though some are more developed than others.

Assess your Multiple Intelligences with *Multiple Pathways to Learning*

In 1983, Howard Gardner changed the way people perceive intelligence and learning with his Multiple Intelligences theory. Like Robert Sternberg,

Gardner had developed the belief that the traditional view of intelligence—based on mathematical, logical, and verbal measurements comprising an "intelligence quotient" or IQ—did not comprehensively reflect the spectrum of human ability. Whereas Sternberg focused on the spectrum of actions that help people achieve important goals, Gardner honed in on the idea that humans possess a number of different areas of natural ability and potential:

> I believe that we should . . . look . . . at more naturalistic sources of information about how peoples around the world develop skills important to their way of life. Think, for example, of sailors in the South Seas, who find their way around hundreds, or even thousands, of islands by looking at the constellations of stars in the sky, feeling the way a boat passes over the water, and noticing a few scattered landmarks. A word for intelligence in a society of these sailors would probably refer to that kind of navigational ability.[3]

The Theory of Multiple Intelligences

Gardner's reading and research in biology, neuropsychology, and other disciplines led him to believe that there are eight unique "intelligences," or areas of ability. These include the areas traditionally associated with the term *intelligence*—logic and verbal skills—but go beyond, to encompass a wide range of potentials of the human brain. Note that these intelligences almost never function in isolation. Gardner emphasizes that, with few exceptions, "intelligences always work in concert," and adults will almost always use several of them for any significant role or task.[4]

Look at Key 3.1 for descriptions of each intelligence. To further illustrate the intelligences, the table lists examples of people who have unusually high levels of ability in each intelligence. Although few people will have the verbal-linguistic intelligence of William Shakespeare or the interpersonal intelligence of Oprah Winfrey, everyone has some level of ability in each intelligence. Your goal is to identify what your levels are and to work your strongest intelligences to your advantage.

Gardner defines *an intelligence* as "a biophysical potential to process information that can be activated in a cultural setting to solve problems or create products that are of value in a culture."[5] Restated more simply, an intelligence is an ability that is valued by a group of people for what it can produce. This definition takes the concept of intelligence beyond what a standard IQ test can measure. As Tibetan mountain natives prize the bodily-kinesthetic ability of a top-notch Himalayan mountain guide, so the Detroit auto manufacturing community appreciates the visual-spatial talents of a master car designer.

Your Own Eight Intelligences

You have your own personal "map" of abilities, which is a combination of what you are born with and what you work to develop. Gardner believes that all people possess some capacity in each of the eight

KEY 3.1

Each intelligence is linked to specific abilities.

INTELLIGENCE	DESCRIPTION	HIGH-ACHIEVING EXAMPLE
Verbal-Linguistic	Ability to communicate through language; listening, reading, writing, speaking	Playwright William Shakespeare
Logical-Mathematical	Ability to understand logical reasoning and problem solving; math, science, patterns, sequences	Microsoft founder Bill Gates
Bodily-Kinesthetic	Ability to use the physical body skillfully and to take in knowledge through bodily sensation; coordination, working with hands	Ice skating champion Michelle Kwan
Visual-Spatial	Ability to understand spatial relationships and to perceive and create images; visual art, graphic design, charts and maps	Architect Frank Gehry
Interpersonal	Ability to relate to others, noticing their moods, motivations, and feelings; social activity, cooperative learning, teamwork	Telejournalist Oprah Winfrey
Intrapersonal	Ability to understand one's own behavior and feelings; self-awareness, independence, time spent alone	The Dalai Lama
Musical	Ability to comprehend and create meaningful sound; sensitivity to music and musical patterns	Singer and musician Alicia Keys
Naturalist	Ability to identify, distinguish, categorize, and classify species or items, often incorporating high interest in elements of the natural environment	Conservationist Steve Irwin

intelligences, and that every person has developed some intelligences more fully than others. When you find a task or subject easy, you are probably using a more fully developed intelligence. When you have trouble, you may be using a less developed intelligence.[6] Furthermore, Gardner believes your levels of development in the eight intelligences can grow or recede throughout your life, depending on your efforts and experiences, reflecting how the brain grows with learning and slows without it.

The *Multiple Pathways to Learning* assessment helps you determine the levels to which your eight intelligences are developed. Key 3.2, immediately following the assessment, describes specific skills associated with the eight intelligences. Finally, the *Multiple Intelligence Strategies* grids in chapters 5 through 8 will demonstrate how to apply your knowledge to key college success skills and to specific areas of study.

MULTIPLE PATHWAYS TO LEARNING

Each intelligence has a set of numbered statements. Consider each statement on its own. Then, on a scale from 1 (lowest) to 4 (highest), rate how closely it matches who you are right now and write that number on the line next to the statement. Finally, total each set of six questions.

rarely	sometimes	usually	always
1	2	3	4

1. 3 I enjoy physical activities.
2. 2 I am uncomfortable sitting still.
3. 3 I prefer to learn through doing.
4. 2 When sitting, I move my legs or hands.
5. 2 I enjoy working with my hands.
6. 2 I like to pace when I'm thinking or studying.

14 TOTAL for **BODILY–KINESTHETIC**

1. 1 I enjoy telling stories.
2. 2 I like to write.
3. 4 I like to read.
4. 2 I express myself clearly.
5. 2 I am good at negotiating.
6. 3 I like to discuss topics that interest me.

14 TOTAL for **VERBAL–LINGUISTIC**

1. 1 I use maps easily.
2. 1 I draw pictures/diagrams when explaining ideas.
3. 2 I can assemble items easily from diagrams.
4. 2 I enjoy drawing or photography.
5. 1 I do not like to read long paragraphs.
6. 1 I prefer a drawn map over written directions.

8 TOTAL for **VISUAL–SPATIAL**

1. 2 I like math in school.
2. 2 I like science.
3. 2 I problem-solve well.
4. 2 I question how things work.
5. 2 I enjoy planning or designing something new.
6. 2 I am able to fix things.

12 TOTAL for **LOGICAL–MATHEMATICAL**

1. 3 I listen to music.
2. 2 I move my fingers or feet when I hear music.
3. 2 I have good rhythm.
4. 1 I like to sing along with music.
5. 1 People have said I have musical talent.
6. 1 I like to express my ideas through music.

10 TOTAL for **MUSICAL**

1. 3 I need quiet time to think.
2. 3 I think about issues before I want to talk.
3. 3 I am interested in self-improvement.
4. 2 I understand my thoughts and feelings.
5. 3 I know what I want out of life.
6. 2 I prefer to work on projects alone.

16 TOTAL for **INTRAPERSONAL**

1. 2 I like doing a project with other people.
2. 3 People come to me to help settle conflicts.
3. 2 I like to spend time with friends.
4. 2 I am good at understanding people.
5. 3 I am good at making people feel comfortable.
6. 4 I enjoy helping others.

16 TOTAL for **INTERPERSONAL**

1. 2 I like to think about how things, ideas, or people fit into categories.
2. 3 I enjoy studying plants, animals, or oceans.
3. 2 I tend to see how things relate to, or are distinct from, one another.
4. 1 I think about having a career in the natural sciences.
5. 2 As a child I often played with bugs and leaves.
6. 2 I like to investigate the natural world around me.

12 TOTAL for **NATURALISTIC**

Source: Developed by Joyce Bishop, Ph.D., Golden West College, Huntington Beach, CA. Based on Howard Gardner, *Frames of Mind: The Theory of Multiple Intelligences,* New York: HarperCollins, 1993.[8]

SCORING GRID FOR MULTIPLE PATHWAYS TO LEARNING

For each intelligence, shade the box in the row that corresponds with the range where your score falls. For example, if you scored 17 in Bodily–Kinesthetic intelligence, you would shade the middle box in that row; if you scored a 13 in Visual–Spatial, you would shade the last box in that row. When you have shaded one box for each row, you will see a "map" of your range of development at a glance.

A score of 20–24 indicates a high level of development in that particular type of intelligence, 14–19 a moderate level, and below 14 an underdeveloped intelligence.

	20-24 (Highly Developed)	14-19 (Moderately Developed)	Below 14 (Underdeveloped)
Bodily-Kinesthetic			
Visual-Spatial			
Verbal-Linguistic			
Logical-Mathematical			
Musical			
Interpersonal			
Intrapersonal			
Naturalistic			

KEY 3.2

Particular abilities and skills are associated with each intelligence.

Verbal-Linguistic		• Analyzing own use of language • Remembering terms easily • Explaining, teaching, learning, using humor • Understanding syntax and word meaning • Using writing or speech to convince someone to do or believe something
Musical		• Sensing tonal qualities • Creating/enjoying rhythms, melodies • Being sensitive to sounds and rhythms • Using an understanding of musical patterns to hear music • Understanding the symbols and structure of music
Logical-Mathematical		• Recognizing abstract patterns • Using facts to support an idea, and generating ideas based on evidence • Discerning relationships and connections • Performing complex calculations • Reasoning scientifically (formulating and testing a hypothesis)
Visual-Spatial		• Perceiving and forming objects accurately • Recognizing relationships between objects • Representing something graphically • Manipulating images • Finding one's way in space
Bodily-Kinesthetic		• Strong mind–body connection • Controlling and coordinating body movement • Improving body functions • Expanding body awareness to all senses • Using the body to create products or express emotion
Intrapersonal		• Accessing one's internal emotions • Understanding feelings and using them to guide behavior • Evaluating own thinking • Understanding self in relation to others • Forming a comprehensive self-concept
Interpersonal		• Seeing things from others' perspectives • Noticing moods, intentions, and temperaments of others • Cooperating within a group • Communicating verbally and nonverbally • Creating and maintaining relationships
Naturalistic		• Ability to categorize something as a member of a group or species • Ability to distinguish items in a group from one another • Understanding of relationships among natural organisms • Appreciation of the delicate balance in nature • Deep comfort with, and respect for, the natural world

Source: Adapted from David Lazear, *Seven Pathways of Learning,* Tucson: Zephyr, 1994.

Assess Your Style of Interaction with the *Personality Spectrum*

The multiple intelligences assessment focuses on your potential in areas of ability. In contrast, personality assessments help you understand how you respond to the world around you, including people, work, and school. They also can help guide you as you explore majors and careers.

The concept of dividing human beings into four basic personality types goes as far back as Aristotle and Hippocrates, ancient Greek philosophers. Psychologist and philosopher Carl Jung, working in the early half of the 20th century, got more specific about personality **typology.** He defined the following:[7]

TYPOLOGY
A systematic classification or study of types.

- **An individual's preferred "world."** Jung said that *extroverts* tend to prefer the outside world of people and activities, while *introverts* tend to prefer the inner world of thoughts, feelings, and fantasies.
- **Different ways of dealing with the world, or "functions."** Jung said that we all use the same ones, but in different proportions. He laid out four: *sensing* (learning through what your senses take in), *thinking* (evaluating information rationally), *intuiting* (learning through an instinct that comes from many integrated sources of information), and *feeling* (evaluating information through emotional response).

Katharine Briggs and her daughter, Isabel Briggs Myers, developed an assessment based on Jung's typology. This Myers-Briggs Type Indicator®, or MBTI, is one of the most widely used personality inventories in the world. People completing the MBTI will find that they fall into one of 16 possible types (each a unique combination of the four dimensions). David Keirsey and Marilyn Bates combined the Myers-Briggs types into four temperaments, and developed a corresponding assessment called the Keirsey Sorter.

The *Personality Spectrum* assessment in this chapter is based on the Keirsey Sorter as well as on the MBTI. It adapts and simplifies the material into four personality types—Thinker, Organizer, Giver, and Adventurer—and was developed by Joyce Bishop, one of the authors of *Keys to Success*.

Like the assessments on which it is based, the *Personality Spectrum* assessment helps you identify the kinds of interactions that are most, and least, comfortable for you. As with multiple intelligences, personality results may change over time in reaction to new experiences, effort, and practice. Key 3.3, on page 79, shows skills that are characteristic of each personality type.

PERSONALITY SPECTRUM

STEP 1. Rank-order all four responses to each question from most like you (4) to least like you (1) so that for each question you use the numbers 1, 2, 3, and 4 one time each. Place numbers in the boxes next to the responses.

4	**3**	**2**	**1**
most like me	more like me	less like me	least like me

1. I like instructors who

   a. [14] tell me exactly what is expected of me.

   b. [23] make learning active and exciting.

   c. [41] maintain a safe and supportive classroom.

   d. [32] challenge me to think at higher levels.

2. I learn best when the material is

   a. [14] well organized.

   b. [32] something I can do hands-on.

   c. [23] about understanding and improving the human condition.

   d. [41] intellectually challenging.

3. A high priority in my life is to

   a. [14] keep my commitments.

   b. [41] experience as much of life as possible.

   c. [23] make a difference in the lives of others.

   d. [32] understand how things work.

4. Other people think of me as

   a. [14] dependable and loyal.

   b. [41] dynamic and creative.

   c. [23] caring and honest.

   d. [32] intelligent and inventive.

5. When I experience stress I would most likely

   a. [32] do something to help me feel more in control of my life.

   b. [41] do something physical and daring.

   c. [14] talk with a friend.

   d. [23] go off by myself and think about my situation.

6. I would probably not be close friends with someone who is

   a. [23] irresponsible.

   b. [41] unwilling to try new things.

   c. [14] selfish and unkind to others.

   d. [32] an illogical thinker.

7. My vacations could be described as

   a. [23] traditional.

   b. [41] adventuresome.

   c. [32] pleasing to others.

   d. [14] a new learning experience.

8. One word that best describes me is

   a. [23] sensible.

   b. [41] spontaneous.

   c. [14] giving.

   d. [32] analytical.

STEP 2. Add up the total points for each letter.

TOTAL FOR **a.** Organizer **b.** Adventurer **c.** Giver **d.** Thinker

STEP 3. Plot these numbers on the brain diagram on page 78.

SCORING DIAGRAM FOR PERSONALITY SPECTRUM

Write your scores from page 77 in the four squares just outside the brain diagram—Thinker score at top left, Giver score at top right, Organizer score at bottom left, and Adventurer score at bottom right.

Each square has a line of numbers that go from the square to the center of the diagram. For each of your four scores, place a dot on the appropriate number in the line near that square. For example, if you scored 15 in the Giver spectrum, you would place a dot between the 14 and 16 in the upper right-hand line of numbers. If you scored a 26 in the Organizer spectrum, you would place a dot on the 26 in the lower left-hand line of numbers.

THINKER

Technical
Scientific
Mathematical
Dispassionate
Rational
Analytical
Logical
Problem-solving
Theoretical
Intellectual
Objective
Quantitative
Explicit
Realistic
Literal
Precise
Formal

Connect the four dots to make a four-sided shape. If you like, shade the four sections inside the shape using four different colors.

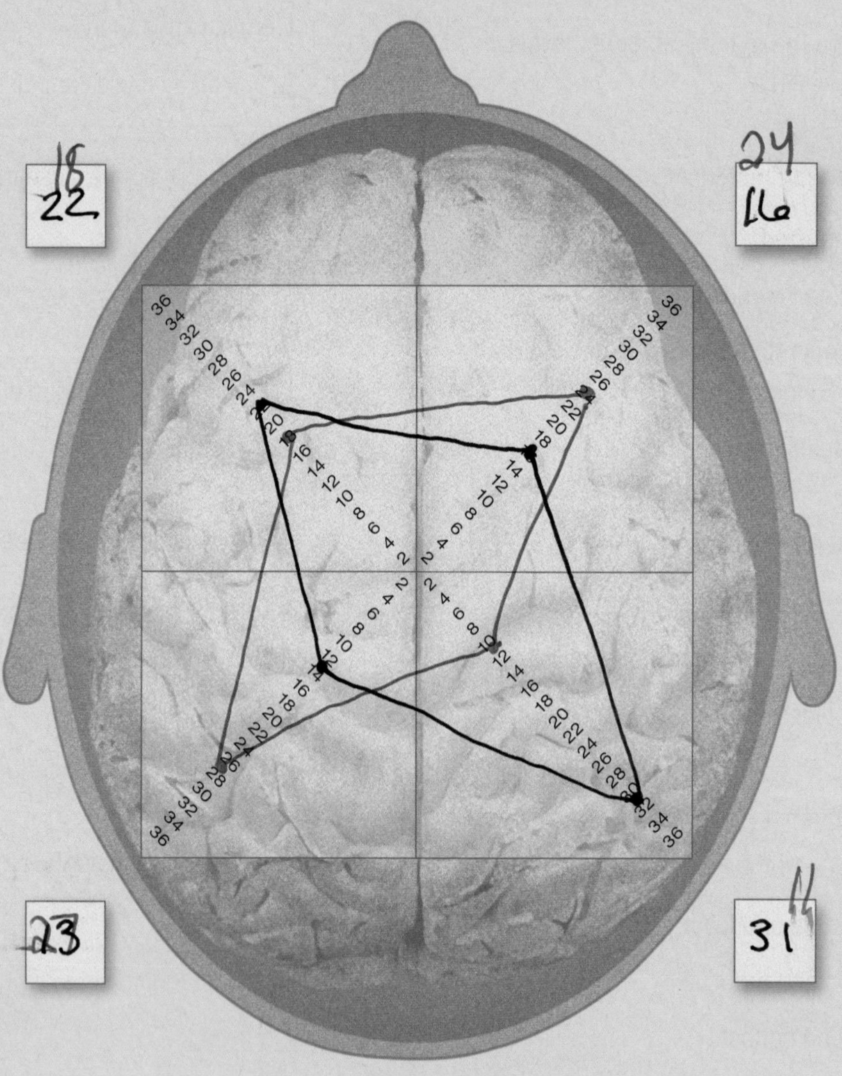

GIVER

Interpersonal
Emotional
Caring
Sociable
Giving
Spiritual
Musical
Romantic
Feeling
Peacemaker
Trusting
Adaptable
Passionate
Harmonious
Idealistic
Talkative
Honest

ORGANIZER

Tactical
Planning
Detailed
Practical
Confident
Predictable
Controlled
Dependable
Systematic
Sequential
Structured
Administrative
Procedural
Organized
Conservative
Safekeeping
Disciplined

For the *Personality Spectrum,*
26–36 indicates a strong tendency in that dimension,
14–25 a moderate tendency,
and below 14 a minimal tendency.

Source for brain diagram: Understanding Psychology, 3rd ed. by Morris, © 1996. Adapted by permission of Prentice-Hall, Inc., Upper Saddle River, NJ.

ADVENTURER

Active
Visual
Risking
Original
Artistic
Spatial
Skillful
Impulsive
Metaphoric
Experimental
Divergent
Fast-paced
Simultaneous
Competitive
Imaginative
Open-minded
Adventuresome

KEY 3.3 **Particular abilities and skills are associated with each Personality Spectrum dimension.**

Thinker

© Tracy Martinez—Fotolia.com

- Solving problems
- Developing models and systems
- Analytical and abstract thinking
- Exploring ideas and potentials
- Ingenuity
- Going beyond established boundaries
- Global thinking—seeking universal truth

Organizer

© mckryak—Fotolia.com

- Responsibility, reliability
- Operating successfully within social structures
- Sense of history, culture, and dignity
- Neatness and organization
- Loyalty
- Orientation to detail
- Comprehensive follow-through on tasks
- Efficiency
- Helping others

Giver

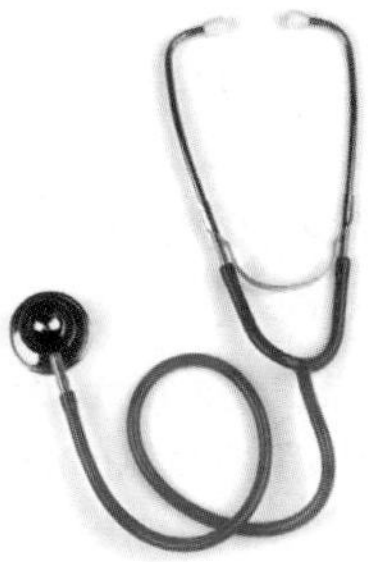

© James Steidl—Fotolia.com

- Honesty, authenticity
- Successful, close relationships
- Making a difference in the world
- Cultivating potential of self and others
- Negotiation; promoting peace
- Openness
- Helping others

Adventurer

© Howard Sandler—Fotolia.com

- High ability in a variety of fields
- Courage and daring
- Hands-on problem solving
- Living in the present
- Spontaneity and action
- Ability to negotiate
- Nontraditional style
- Flexibility
- Zest for life

Source: © 2001, Joyce Bishop, in *Keys to Success*, 3rd ed., Upper Saddle River, NJ: Pearson Prentice Hall, 2001.

How Can You Use Your Self-Knowledge?

The lecture format is most common in the college classroom. Students who find it challenging can make the most of a lecture-based course using strategies that suit their strenghts.

Now that you've completed your assessments, how can you apply what you learned about yourself to promote success? Generally, self-knowledge helps you make choices that maximize your strengths and manage your weaknesses. In completing the assessments, you have explored your levels of potential in eight abilities as well as how you tend to interact with others. This section of the chapter focuses on how you can use this new picture to choose—and most importantly, *use*—effective strategies inside the classroom, during study time, and in the workplace.

Classroom Benefits

Instructors have a range of teaching styles, reflecting their learning strengths and preferred styles of interaction. How you prefer to learn may work well with some instructors and be a mismatch with others. After several class meetings, you should be able to assess an instructor's teaching styles (see Key 3.4). Then you can use what you know about your most effective ways to learn to creatively get the most out of any instructor's teaching style.

Although presentation styles vary, the standard lecture is still the norm in most classrooms. For this reason, the traditional college classroom is generally a happy home for the verbal or logical learner and the Thinker and the Organizer. However, many students learn best when interacting with other students more than a traditional lecture allows. What can you do when your preferences don't match up with how your instructor teaches? Here are three suggestions:

- **Play to your strengths.** For example, a musical learner with an instructor who delivers material in a random way might record lecture highlights digitally and listen to them on an MP3 player as a study tool. Likewise, a Giver taking a straight lecture course with no student-to-student contact might be motivated by meeting with a study group to go over the details and fill in factual gaps.
- **Work to strengthen weaker areas.** While a visual learner is reviewing notes from a structured lecture course, he could use logical-mathematical strategies such as outlining notes or thinking about cause-and-effect relationships within the material. An Organizer, studying for a test from notes delivered by an instructor who used a random presentation, could find ways to organize the material (for example, by creating notes in a table format).

KEY 3.4 **Instructors often prefer one or more teaching styles.**

TEACHING STYLE	WHAT TO EXPECT IN CLASS
Lecture, verbal focus	Instructor speaks to the class for the entire period, with little class interaction. Lesson is taught primarily through words, either spoken or written on the board, overhead projector, handouts, or text.
Lecture with group discussion	Instructor presents material but encourages class discussion.
Small groups	Instructor presents material and then breaks class into small groups for discussion or project work.
Visual focus	Instructor uses visual elements such as PowerPoint slides, diagrams, photographs, drawings, transparencies, and videos.
Logical presentation	Instructor organizes material in a logical sequence, such as by steps, time, or importance.
Random presentation	Instructor tackles topics in no particular order, and may jump around a lot or digress.
Conceptual presentation	Instructor spends the majority of time on the big picture, focusing on abstract concepts and umbrella ideas.
Detailed presentation	Instructor spends the majority of time, after introducing ideas, on the details and facts that underlie them.
Experience-based presentation	Instructor uses demonstrations, experiments, props, and class activities to show key points.

- **Ask your instructor for additional help.** If you are having trouble with course work, take the initiative to communicate with your instructor through e-mail or during office hours. This is especially important in large lectures where you are anonymous unless you speak up. A visual learner, for example, might ask the instructor to recommend graphs, figures, or videos that illustrate the lecture.

No instructor can give every student in a diverse group of learners exactly what each one needs. The flexibility that helps you manage how you adjust to instructors' teaching styles is a tool for career and life success. Just as you can't hand-pick your instructors, you will rarely, if ever, be able to choose your work colleagues or their work styles. When there are many different instructors teaching sections of a course, ask other students about the instructors' teaching styles and how the courses are structured.

Get Analytical, Creative, Practical!

Maximize Your Classroom Experience

Consider first what you know about yourself as a learner. Then, reflect on your instructors' teaching styles this term. Analyze which instructors mesh well with how you learn, and which don't as much. Make notes here about the situation that you think is the most challenging.

Course: ________________ Instructor style: ____________________________

Your analysis of the problem: ____

____

Next, brainstorm at least three ideas about actions you can take to improve the situation:

1. ____
2. ____
3. ____

Finally, choose one action and put it to practical use. Briefly note what happened: Were there improvements as a result? ________________________

____

Study Benefits

First, when you can, use what you know about yourself to choose study techniques that capitalize on your strengths. For example, if you tend to learn successfully from a linear, logical presentation, you can look for order (for example, a *chronology*—information organized sequentially according to event dates—or a problem–solution structure) as you review notes. If you are strong in interpersonal intelligence, you can try to work in study groups whenever possible.

When you are faced with a task or topic that challenges your weaknesses, use strategies that may boost your ability in those areas. An Adventurer who does *not* respond well to linear information, for example, has two choices when faced with logical presentations: She can apply her strengths to the material—for example, she might find a hands-on approach— or she can focus on developing study skills that work well for Thinker-dominant learners.

KEY 3.5

Particular study techniques maximize each intelligence.

Verbal-Linguistic

- Reading text; highlighting selectively
- Using a computer to retype and summarize notes
- Outlining chapters
- Teaching someone else
- Reciting information or writing scripts/debates

Musical-Rhythmic

- Creating rhythms out of words
- Beating out rhythms with hand or stick while reciting concepts
- Writing songs or raps that help you learn concepts
- Writing out study material to fit into a wordless tune you have on a CD or MP3 player; chanting or singing the material to the tune as you listen
- Taking music breaks

Logical-Mathematical

- Organizing material logically; if it suits the topic, using a spreadsheet program
- Explaining material sequentially to someone
- Developing systems and finding patterns
- Writing outlines
- Analyzing and evaluating information

Visual-Spatial

- Developing graphic organizers for new material
- Drawing mind maps and think links
- Using a computer to develop charts and tables
- Using color in notes to organize
- Linking material in your mind with items or places that you can visualize (method of loci)

Bodily-Kinesthetic

- Moving while you learn; pacing and reciting
- Using tangible items as memory devices
- Rewriting or retyping notes to engage "muscle memory"
- Designing and playing games to learn material
- Acting out scripts of material

Intrapersonal

- Reflecting on personal meaning of information
- Visualizing information
- Keeping a journal
- Studying in quiet areas
- Imagining essays or experiments before beginning

Interpersonal

- Studying in a group
- As you study, discussing information over the phone or sending instant messages
- Using flash cards with others
- Teaching someone else the material
- Making time to discuss assignments and tests with your instructor

Naturalistic

- Breaking down information into categories
- Looking for ways that items fit or don't fit together
- Looking for relationships among ideas, events, facts
- Studying in a natural setting if it helps you to focus
- Forming study groups of people with similar interests

Source: Adapted from David Lazear, *Seven Pathways of Learning,* Tucson: Zephyr, 1994.

KEY 3.6 Particular study techniques maximize each Personality Spectrum dimension.

Thinker

© Tracy Martinez—Fotolia.com

- Finding time to reflect independently on new information
- Learning through problem solving
- Designing new ways of approaching issues
- Converting material into logical charts, flow diagrams, and outlines
- Trying to minimize repetitive tasks
- Looking for opportunities to work independently

Organizer

© mckryak—Fotolia.com

- Defining tasks in concrete terms so that you know what is required
- Looking for a well-structured study environment
- Requesting feedback from instructors and classmates via e-mail or phone
- Using a planner or PDA to schedule tasks and dates
- Organizing material by rewriting and summarizing class and/or text notes
- Using flash cards
- Highlighting materials and notes carefully

Giver

© James Steidl—Fotolia.com

- Studying with others in person, on the phone, or using instant messages
- Teaching material to others
- Seeking out tasks, groups, and subjects that involve helping people
- Expressing thoughts and feelings clearly and honestly
- Prioritizing your most important academic relationships

Adventurer

© Howard Sandler—Fotolia.com

- Looking for environments/courses that encourage nontraditional approaches
- Finding hands-on ways to learn
- Seeking instructors and students whom you find stimulating
- Using or developing games and puzzles to help memorize terms
- Fighting boredom by asking to do something extra or performing a task in a more active way

When you study with others, an understanding of diverse learning styles will help you assign tasks effectively and learn more comprehensively, as these suggestions show:

- An Interpersonal learner could take the lead in teaching material to others.
- An Organizer could coordinate the group schedule.
- A Naturalistic learner might organize facts into categories that solidify concepts.

Successful Intelligence Connections Online

Listen to author Sarah Kravits discuss analytical, creative, and practical ideas for how to choose your best setting for successful studying.

Go to the *Keys to Success* Companion Website at http://www.prenhall.com/carter to listen or download as a podcast.

Key 3.5 shows study strategies that suit each intelligence, and Key 3.6 shows study strategies that suit each Personality Spectrum dimension. Because you have some level of ability in each area, and because there will be times that you need to boost your ability in a weaker area, you may find useful suggestions under any of the headings. Try different techniques, analyze how effective they are, and use what works best for you.

Workplace Benefits

The self-knowledge you build throughout this chapter has practical application on the job and for career planning. A self-aware employee, or job candidate, can expect many benefits.

Better Performance and Teamwork

Knowing how you learn and interact with others will help you work more effectively. When you understand your strengths, you can find ways to use them on the job more readily. For tasks that require you to use less developed skills, you will be more able to find ways to compensate, such as seeking help. In addition, you will be better able to find ways to work with others effectively. For example, if you are a Giver you might enjoy helping new hires adjust to the people and environment. Or a team leader assigning tasks to an intrapersonal team member might offer the chance to take material home to think about before a meeting.

This biology researcher engages her naturalistic intelligence and strength in the Thinker dimension on a daily basis as she studies the sensory organs of alligators and crocodiles.

Better Career Planning

Exploring ways to use your strengths in school will help you make better choices about what internships, jobs, or careers will suit you. For instance, a love of math combined with strong interpersonal intelligence might guide you toward activities—such as math tutoring—that inform future career goals (teaching math, working with a research group in a lab).

For most college students, internships and majors are more immediate steps on the road to a career. A strength in one or more intelligences might lead you to particular internships and majors that may make sense for you. Key 3.7 shows some possibilities for majors and internships that link

KEY 3.7 Multiple intelligences may open doors to majors and internships.

Multiple intelligence	Consider majoring in . . .	Think about an internship at a . . .
Bodily-Kinesthetic 	Massage or Physical Therapy Kinesiology Construction Engineering Sports Medicine Dance or Theater	Sports physician's office Physical or massage therapy center Construction company Dance studio or theater company Athletic club
Intrapersonal 	Psychology Finance Computer Science Biology Philosophy	Accounting firm Biology lab Pharmaceutical company Publishing house Computer or Internet company
Interpersonal 	Education Public Relations Nursing Business Hotel/Restaurant Management	Hotel or restaurant Social service agency Public relations firm Human Resources department Charter school
Naturalistic 	Geology Zoology Atmospheric Sciences Agriculture Environmental Law	Museum National park Environmental law firm Zoo Geological research firm
Musical 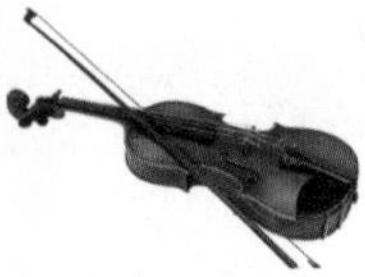	Music Music Theory Voice Composition Performing Arts	Performance hall Radio station Record label or recording studio Children's music camp Orchestra or opera company
Logical-Mathematical 	Math Physics Economics Banking/Finance Computer Science	Law firm Consulting firm Bank Information technology company Research lab
Verbal-Linguistic 	Communications Marketing English/Literature Journalism Foreign Languages	Newspaper or magazine PR/marketing firm Ad agency Publishing house Network TV affiliate
Visual-Spatial 	Architecture Visual Arts Multimedia Design Photography Art History	Photo or art studio Multimedia design firm Architecture firm Interior design firm Art gallery

to the eight intelligences. This list is by no means complete; rather, it represents only a fraction of the available opportunities. Use what you see here to inspire thought and spur investigation. See Key 8.8 on pages 276–277, in the section on careers in chapter 8, for ideas about how intelligences may link to particular careers.

Being sensitive to your unique way of learning will benefit you in ways beyond your education and career. A better understanding of your learning strengths and preferences and personality traits will help you identify, appreciate, and adapt to the diversity among people.

How Can You Develop Cultural Competence?

Interacting successfully with all kinds of people is the goal of *cultural competence*. As you learned in chapter 2, cultural competence refers to the ability to understand and appreciate differences among people and adjust your behavior in ways that enhance, rather than detract from, relationships and communication. According to the National Center for Cultural Competence, to develop cultural competence you must act upon the following five steps:[9]

1. Value diversity.
2. Identify and evaluate personal perceptions and attitudes.
3. Be aware of opportunities and challenges that occur when different cultures interact.

KEY 3.8

Approaching diversity with an open mind builds relationships.

Your role	Situation	Closed-minded actions	Open-minded actions
Fellow student	For an assignment, you are paired with a student old enough to be your mother.	You assume the student will be clueless about the modern world. You think she might preach to you about how to do the assignment.	You get to know the student as an individual. You stay open to what you can learn from her experiences and knowledge.
Friend	You are invited to dinner at a friend's house. When he introduces you to his partner, you realize that he is gay.	You are turned off by the idea of two men in a relationship. You make an excuse to leave early. You avoid your friend after that.	You have dinner with the two men and make an effort to get to know more about them, individually and as a couple.
Employee	Your new boss is of a different racial and cultural background from yours.	You assume that you and your new boss don't have much in common. You think he will be distant and uninterested in you.	You rein in your stereotypes. You pay close attention to how your new boss communicates and leads. You adapt to his style and make an effort to get to know him better.

4. Build knowledge about other cultures.
5. Use what you learn to adapt to diverse cultures as you encounter them.

As you develop cultural competence, you heighten your ability to analyze how people relate to one another. Most important, you become better equipped to connect to others by bridging the gap between who you are and who they are.[10]

Value Diversity

Valuing diversity means having a basic respect for, and acceptance of, the differences among people. Every time you meet someone new, you have a choice about how to interact. You won't like everyone you meet, but if you value diversity, you will choose to treat people with tolerance and respect, avoiding assumptions about them and granting them the right to think, feel, and believe without being judged. Being open-minded in this way will help your relationships thrive, as shown in Key 3.8.

Identify and Evaluate Personal Perceptions and Attitudes

Whereas people may value the *concept* of diversity, attitudes and emotional responses may influence how they act when they confront the *reality* of diversity in their own lives. As a result, many people have prejudices that lead to damaging stereotypes.

Prejudice

PREJUDICE

A preconceived judgment or opinion formed without just grounds or sufficient knowledge.

Almost everyone has some level of **prejudice** resulting in the prejudging of others, usually on the basis of characteristics such as gender, race, sexual orientation, disability, or religion. People judge others without knowing anything about them because of factors like these:

- **Influence of family and culture.** Children learn attitudes, including intolerance, superiority, and hate, from their parents, peers, and community.
- **Fear of differences.** It is human to fear the unfamiliar and to make assumptions about it.
- **Experience.** One bad experience with a person of a particular race or religion may lead someone to condemn all people with the same background.

Stereotypes

STEREOTYPE

A standardized mental picture that represents an oversimplified opinion or uncritical judgment.

Prejudice is usually based on **stereotypes**—assumptions made, without proof or critical thinking, about the characteristics of a person or group of people. Stereotyping emerges from factors such as these:

- **Desire for patterns and logic.** People often try to make sense of the world by using the labels, categories, and generalizations that stereotypes provide.
- **Media influences.** The more people see stereotypical images—the airhead beautiful blonde, the jolly fat man—the easier it is to believe that stereotypes are universal.

KEY 3.9 Both positive and negative stereotypes mask uniqueness.

Positive stereotype	Negative stereotype
Women are nurturing.	Women are too emotional for business.
African Americans are great athletes.	African Americans struggle in school.
Hispanic Americans are family oriented.	Hispanic Americans have too many kids.
White people are successful in business.	White people are cold and power hungry.
Gay men have a great sense of style.	Gay men are sissies.
People with disabilities have strength of will.	People with disabilities are bitter.
Older people are wise.	Older people are set in their ways.
Asian Americans are good at math and science.	Asian Americans are poor leaders.

- **Laziness.** Labeling group members according to a characteristic they seem to have in common takes less energy than asking questions that illuminate the qualities of individuals.

Stereotypes derail personal connections and block effective communication, because pasting a label on a person makes it hard for you to see the real person underneath. Even stereotypes that seem positive may be untrue and may get in the way of perceiving uniqueness. Key 3.9 shows some positive and negative stereotypes.

Use your analytical abilities to question your own ideas and beliefs, weed out the narrowing influence of prejudice and stereotyping, and discover problems that need addressing. Giving honest answers to questions like the following is an essential step in the development of cultural competence:

- How do I react to differences?
- What prejudices or stereotypes come to mind when I see people, in real life or the media, who are a different color than I am? From a different culture? Making different choices?
- Where did my prejudices and stereotypes come from?
- Are these prejudices fair? Are these stereotypes accurate?
- What harm can having these prejudices and believing these stereotypes cause?

With the knowledge you build as you answer these questions, move on to the next stage: Looking carefully at what happens when people from different cultures interact.

Be Aware of Opportunities and Challenges That Occur When Cultures Interact

Interaction among people from different cultures can promote learning, build mutual respect, and broaden perspectives. However, as history has shown, such interaction can also produce problems caused by lack of understanding, prejudice, and stereotypical thinking. At their mildest, these problems create roadblocks that obstruct relationships and communication. At their worst, they set the stage for acts of discrimination and hate crimes.

Discrimination

Federal law says that you cannot be denied basic opportunities and rights because of your race, creed, color, age, gender, national or ethnic origin, religion, marital status, potential or actual pregnancy, or potential or actual illness or disability (unless the illness or disability prevents you from performing required tasks and unless accommodations are not possible). Despite these legal protections, **discrimination** is common and often appears on college campuses. Students may not want to work with students of other races. Members of campus clubs may reject prospective members because of religious differences. Outsiders may harass students attending gay and lesbian alliance meetings. Instructors may judge students according to their weight, accent, or body piercings.

DISCRIMINATION

Actions that deny people equal employment, educational, and housing opportunities, or treat people as second-class citizens.

Hate Crimes

When prejudice turns violent, it often manifests itself in *hate crimes*—crimes motivated by a hatred of a specific characteristic thought to be possessed by the victim—usually directed at people based on their race, ethnicity, religion, or sexual orientation. Because hate-crime statistics include only reported incidents, they tell just a part of the story—many more crimes likely go unreported by victims fearful of what might happen if they contact authorities.

Focusing on the positive aspect of intercultural interaction starts with awareness of the ideas and attitudes that lead to discrimination and hate crimes. With this awareness, you will be better prepared to push past negative possibilities and open your mind to positive ones.

Build Cultural Knowledge

The thinking response to discrimination and hate, and the next step in your path toward cultural competence, is to gather knowledge. You have a personal responsibility to learn about people who are different from you, including those you are likely to meet on campus.

What are some practical ways to begin?

- *Read* newspapers, books, magazines, and Web sites that expose you to different perspectives.
- *Ask questions* of all kinds of people, about themselves and their traditions.
- *Observe* how people behave, what they eat and wear, how they interact with others.
- *Travel internationally* to unfamiliar places where you can experience different ways of living.
- *Travel locally* to equally unfamiliar, but nearby, places that are home to a variety of people.
- *Build friendships* with fellow students or coworkers you would not ordinarily approach.

Building knowledge also means exploring yourself. Talk with family, read, seek experiences that educate you about your own cultural heritage. Then share what you know with others.

Adapt to Diverse Cultures

Here's where you take everything you have gathered—your value of diversity, your self-knowledge, your understanding of how cultures interact, your information about different cultures—and put it to work with practical actions. As you question, you can define actions and solutions that improve how you relate to others, and perhaps even change how people relate to one another on a larger scale. Choose actions that feel right to you, that cause no harm, and that may make a difference, however small.

Dr. Martin Luther King Jr. believed that careful thinking could change attitudes. As he put it:

> The tough-minded person always examines the facts before he reaches conclusions: in short, he postjudges. The tender-minded person reaches conclusions before he has examined the first fact; in short, he prejudges and is prejudiced. . . . There is little hope for us until we become tough minded enough to break loose from the shackles of prejudice, half-truths, and down-right ignorance.[11]

Let the following suggestions inspire your own creative ideas about what you can do to improve how you relate to others.

Look past external characteristics. If you meet a woman with a disability, get to know her. She may be an accounting major, a daughter, and a mother. She may love baseball, politics, and science fiction novels. These characteristics—not just her physical person—describe who she is.

Put yourself in other people's shoes. Attend a meeting about an issue that people in your community face but that is unfamiliar to you. Ask questions about what other people feel, especially if there's a conflict. Offer information and friendship to someone new who is adjusting to your school community.

Adjust to cultural differences. When you understand someone's way of being and put it into practice, you show respect and encourage communication. If a friend's family is formal at home, dress appropriately and behave formally when you visit. If an instructor maintains a lot of personal space, keep a respectful distance when you visit during office hours. If a study group member takes offense at a particular kind of language, avoid it when you meet.

Help others in need. When you see or uncover a problem, do what you can to help solve it. Newspaper columnist Sheryl McCarthy wrote about an African American who, in the midst of the 1992 Los Angeles riots, saw an Asian American man being beaten and helped him to safety: "When asked why he risked grievous harm to save an Asian man he didn't even know, the African-American man said, 'Because if I'm not there to help someone else, when the mob comes for me, will there be someone there to save me?' "[12]

Stand up against prejudice, discrimination, and hate. When you hear a prejudiced remark or notice discrimination taking place, ask yourself questions about how to encourage a move in the right direction. Then act. You may choose to make a comment, or to get help by approaching an authority such as an instructor or dean. Sound the alarm on hate crimes—let authorities know if you suspect that a crime is about to occur, join campus protests, support organizations that encourage tolerance.

Recognize that people everywhere have the same basic needs. Everyone loves, thinks, hurts, hopes, fears, and plans. When you are trying to find common ground with diverse people, remember that you are united first through your essential humanity.

Diversity also occurs in the way people communicate. Understanding who you are and how you learn, and how people differ from one another, will promote successful communication.

How Can You Communicate Effectively?

Spoken communication that is clear promotes success at school, at work, and in personal relationships. Successfully intelligent communicators analyze and adjust to communication styles, learn to give and receive criticism, analyze and make practical use of body language, and work through communication problems.

Adjust to Communication Styles

When you speak, your goal is for listeners to receive the message as you intended. Problems arise when one person has trouble "translating" a message coming from someone using a different communication style. Your knowledge of the Personality Spectrum dimensions will help you understand and analyze the ways diverse people communicate.

Identify Your Styles

Following are some communication styles that tend to be associated with the four dimensions in the Personality Spectrum. No one style is better than another. Successful communication depends on understanding your personal style and becoming attuned to the styles of others.

Thinker-dominant communicators focus on facts and logic. As speakers, they tend to rely on logical analysis to communicate ideas and prefer quantitative concepts to those that are conceptual or emotional. As listeners, they often do best with logical messages. Thinkers may also need time to process what they have heard before responding. Written messages—on paper or via e-mail—are often useful for these individuals because writing can allow for time to put ideas together logically.

Organizer-dominant communicators focus on structure and completeness. As speakers, they tend to deliver well-thought-out, structured messages that fit into an organized plan. As listeners, they often appreciate a well-organized message that defines practical tasks in concrete terms. As with Thinkers, a written format is often an effective form of communication to or from an Organizer.

Giver-dominant communicators focus on concern for others. As speakers, they tend to cultivate harmony, analyzing what will promote closeness in relationships. As listeners, they often appreciate messages that emphasize personal connection and address the emotional side of an issue. Whether speaking or listening, Givers often favor in-person talks over written messages.

When you share an interest with someone, you may find that communication flows and personal differences fade into the background. These students, both interested in television, work together to learn how to operate broadcasting equipment.

Adventurer-dominant communicators focus on the present. As speakers, they focus on creative ideas, tending to convey a message as soon as the idea arises and then move on to the next activity. As listeners, they appreciate up-front, short, direct messages that don't get sidetracked. Like Givers, Adventurers tend to communicate and listen more effectively in person.

What is your style? Use this information as a jumping-off point for your self-exploration. Just as people tend to demonstrate characteristics from more than one Personality Spectrum dimension, communicators may demonstrate different styles.

Put Your Knowledge of Communication Style to Use

Analyze your style by thinking about the communication styles associated with your dominant Personality Spectrum dimensions. Compare them to how you tend to communicate and how others seem to respond to you. Then, use creative and practical thinking skills to decide what works best for you as a communicator.

Speakers adjust to listeners. Listeners may interpret messages in ways you never intended. Think about practical solutions to this kind of problem as you read the following example involving a Giver-dominant instructor and a Thinker-dominant student (the listener):

> *Instructor:* Your essay didn't communicate any sense of your personal voice.
>
> *Student:* What do you mean? I spent hours writing it. I thought it was on the mark.

- **Without adjustment:** The instructor ignores the student's need for detail and continues to generalize. Comments like "You need to elaborate" "Try writing from the heart" or "You're not considering your audience" might confuse or discourage the student.
- **With adjustment:** Greater logic and detail will help. For example, the instructor might say, "You've supported your central idea clearly, but

you didn't move beyond the facts into your interpretation of what they mean. Your essay reads like a research paper. The language doesn't sound like it is coming directly from you."

Listeners adjust to speakers. As a listener, improve understanding by being aware of stylistic differences and translating the message into one that makes sense to you. The following example of an Adventurer-dominant employee speaking to an Organizer-dominant supervisor shows how adjusting can pay off:

Employee: I'm upset about the e-mail you sent me. You never talked to me directly and you let the problem build into a crisis. I haven't had a chance to defend myself.

- **Without adjustment:** If the supervisor is annoyed by the employee's insistence on direct personal contact, he or she may become defensive: "I told you clearly what needs to be done. I don't know what else there is to discuss."
- **With adjustment:** In an effort to improve communication, the supervisor responds by encouraging the in-person exchange that is best for the employee: "Let's meet after lunch so you can explain to me how you believe we can improve the situation."

Although adjusting to communication styles helps you speak and listen more effectively, you also need to understand, and learn how to effectively give and receive, criticism.

Know How to Give and Receive Criticism

CONSTRUCTIVE CRITICISM

Criticism that promotes improvement or development.

Criticism can be either *constructive* or *unconstructive*. **Constructive criticism** is a practical problem-solving strategy, involving goodwill suggestions for improving a situation. In contrast, unconstructive criticism focuses on what went wrong, doesn't offer alternatives that might help solve the problem, and is often delivered negatively, creating bad feelings.

When offered constructively, criticism can help bring about important changes. Consider a case in which someone has continually been late to study group sessions. The group leader can comment in one of two ways. Which comment would encourage you to change your behavior?

- **Constructive.** The group leader talks privately with the student, saying, "I've noticed that you've been late a lot. We count on you, because our success depends on what each of us contributes. Is there a problem that is keeping you from being on time? Can we help?"
- **Unconstructive.** The leader watches the student arrive late and says, in front of everyone, "If you can't start getting here on time, there's really no point in your coming."

At school, instructors criticize classwork, papers, and exams. On the job, criticism may come from supervisors, coworkers, or customers. No matter the source, constructive comments can help you grow as a person. Be open to what you hear, and remember that most people want you to succeed.

Offering Constructive Criticism

When offering constructive criticism, use the following strategies to be effective:

- **Criticize the behavior rather than the person.** Avoid personal attacks. "You've been late to five group meetings" is much preferable to "You're lazy."
- **Define the problematic behavior specifically.** Try to focus on the facts, substantiating with specific examples and minimizing emotions. Avoid additional complaints—people can hear criticisms better if they are discussed one at a time.
- **Suggest new approaches and offer help.** Talk about ways of handling the situation. Work with the person to develop creative options. Help the person feel supported.
- **Use a positive approach and hopeful language.** Express the conviction that changes will occur and that the person can turn the situation around.

Receiving Criticism

When you are on criticism's receiving end, use the following techniques to handle it constructively:

- **Analyze the comments.** Listen carefully, then evaluate what you heard. What does it mean? What is the intent? Try to let unconstructive comments go without responding.
- **Request suggestions on how to change your behavior.** Ask, "How would you like me to handle this in the future?"
- **Summarize the criticism and your response to it.** Make sure everyone understands the situation.
- **Use a specific strategy.** Use problem-solving skills to analyze the problem, brainstorm ways to change, choose a strategy, and take action to make it happen.

One of the biggest barriers to successful communication is conflict, which can result in anger and even violence. With effort, you can successfully manage conflict and stay away from those who cannot.

Manage Conflict

Conflicts, both large and small, arise when there is a clash of ideas or interests. You may have small conflicts with a housemate over a door left unlocked. You may have major conflicts with your partner about finances or with an instructor about a failing grade. Conflict, as unpleasant as it can be, is a natural element in the dynamic of getting along with others. Prevent it when you can—and when you can't, use problem-solving strategies to resolve it.

Conflict-Prevention Strategies

The following two strategies can help you to prevent conflict from starting in the first place.

KEY 3.10

Assertiveness fosters successful communication.

AGGRESSIVE	ASSERTIVE	PASSIVE
Blaming, name-calling, and verbal insults: "You have created this mess!"	Expressing oneself and letting others do the same: "I have thoughts about this—first, what is your opinion?"	Feeling that one has no right to express anger: "No, I'm fine."
Escalating arguments: "You'll do it my way, no matter what it takes."	Using "I" statements to defuse arguments: "I am uncomfortable with that choice and want to discuss it."	Avoiding arguments: "Whatever you want to do is fine."
Being demanding: "Do this."	Asking and giving reasons: "Please consider doing it this way, and here's why . . ."	Being noncommittal: "You don't have to do this unless you really want to . . ."

Send "I" messages. "I" messages help you communicate your needs rather than attacking someone else. Creating these messages involves some simple rephrasing: "You didn't lock the door!" becomes "I felt uneasy when I came to work and the door was unlocked." Similarly, "You never called last night" becomes "I was worried when I didn't hear from you last night."

"I" statements soften the conflict by highlighting the effects that the other person's actions have on you, rather than focusing on the other person or the actions themselves. These statements help the receiver feel freer to respond, perhaps offering help and even acknowledging mistakes.

Be assertive. Most people tend to express themselves in one of three ways—aggressively, assertively, or passively. *Aggressive* communicators focus primarily on their own needs and can become impatient when needs are not satisfied. *Passive* communicators focus primarily on the needs of others and often deny themselves power, causing frustration. *Assertive* communicators are able to declare and affirm their opinions while respecting the rights of others to do the same. Assertive behavior strikes a balance between aggression and passivity and promotes the most productive communication. Key 3.10 contrasts the characteristics of these three.

What can aggressive and passive communicators do to move toward a more assertive style? Aggressive communicators might take time before speaking, use "I" statements, listen to others, and avoid giving orders. Passive communicators might acknowledge anger, express opinions, exercise the right to make requests, and know that their ideas and feelings are important.

Conflict Resolution

All too often, people deal with conflict through *avoidance* (a passive tactic that shuts down communication) or *escalation* (an aggressive tactic that often leads to fighting). Conflict resolution demands calm communication, motivation, and careful thinking. Use your thinking skills to apply the problem-solving approach you will learn in chapter 4.

Your ability to communicate and manage conflict has a major impact on your relationships with friends and family. Successful relationships are built on self-knowledge, good communication, and hard work.

Manage Communication Technology

Modern technology has revolutionized the way people communicate with one another. You can call or text on a mobile phone; you can send a note via e-mail or instant message, from a computer or a PDA such as a BlackBerry or Treo; you can communicate through Internet-based venues such as blogs and chat rooms; and you can learn about one another by frequenting social networking sites such as MySpace or Facebook.

Communication technologies have many advantages. You can communicate faster, more frequently, and with more people at one time than ever before. However, there are drawbacks. It's easy to misunderstand the tone or meaning of instant messages (IMs), e-mails, and text messages. Many of these communication methods are addictive—you might look up at the clock and realize you've spent hours of study time IM-ing your friends. In addition, revealing too much about yourself on social networking sites may come back to haunt you. Increasingly, employers are checking MySpace and Facebook for information about prospective job candidates.[13] Before posting words or images, remember that once this information is in cyberspace, you cannot pull it back.

The best way for you to create your ideal communication "recipe" is to analyze situations carefully, think creatively, and make practical decisions about how to move forward. How do you prefer to communicate with others? What are the effects? Use moderation, letting modern communication methods *enhance* in-person interaction rather than replace it.

Choose Communities That Enhance Your Life

© Andres Rodriguez—Fotolia.com

Personal relationships often take place within *communities*, or groups that include people who share your interests—for example, sororities and fraternities, athletic clubs, and political groups. The presence of the Internet has added chat rooms, blogs, and newsgroups to the scope of social communities available to you. Some colleges even put their facebooks online and have school-sponsored online communities.

So much of what you accomplish in life is linked to your network of personal contacts. If you affiliate with communities that are involved in positive activities, you are more likely to surround yourself with responsible and character-rich people who may become your friends and colleagues. You may find among them your future spouse or partner, your best friend, a person who helps you land a job, your doctor, accountant, real estate agent, and so on. Finding and working with a community of people with similar interests can have positive effects in personal relationships and in workplace readiness.

If you find yourself drawn toward groups that encourage negative and even harmful behavior—such as gangs, organizations that haze pledges, or mean-spirited online communities—stop and think. Analyze why you are drawn to these groups. Resist the temptation to join in. If you are already involved and want out, stand up for yourself and be determined.

Successful Intelligence Wrap-Up

Think back to chapter 1, and to Robert Sternberg's definition of successful intelligence—"the kind of intelligence used to achieve important goals." Knowing who you are and how you learn, and using that knowledge to communicate successfully with all kinds of people in a variety of situations, are keys to your successful pursuit of goals that are important to you. Here's how you have built skills in chapter 3:

Analytical

With the two self-assessments, you analyzed your levels of ability in the eight intelligences and examined how you relate to people and the world around you. In the *Maximize Your Classroom Experience* exercise, you examined how your instructors' teaching styles relate to how you learn. In the section about cultural competence, you gathered the tools you need to analyze your attitudes toward people, cultures, and values that differ from yours. You explored the ways in which you and others communicate and the effects of various styles.

Creative

As you read about the multiple intelligences and the personality spectrum, you may have developed new ideas about your abilities and talents and how you relate to others. In the *Maximize Your Classroom Experience* exercise, you brainstormed ideas about how to improve a situation where how you learn doesn't match up well with how an instructor teaches. You expanded your range of ideas for how to accept and support different people and cultures and how to communicate in ways that promote understanding.

Practical

In the *Maximize Your Classroom Experience* exercise, you put an action to practical use in trying to improve your experience in a classroom where you have trouble with the teaching style. Reading Keys 3.5 and 3.6 gave you practical study strategies relating to each intelligence and Personality Spectrum dimension. You considered practical strategies for avoiding prejudice, stereotyping, and discrimination, keeping in mind what experience has taught you in those areas.

Oruko lonro ni

(o-roo-ko lon-ro nee)

In the language of the Yoruba, an ethnic group living primarily in Nigeria and other West African countries, *oruko lonro ni* translates as "names affect behavior." This belief, common among the Yoruba people, refers to the idea that people live up to the names given to them by others or even chosen by themselves.[14] As Robert Sternberg learned when he found himself living up to the "lackluster" label given to him as an elementary school student, names and labels have enormous power.

As you think about how you learn and relate to others, use this idea to understand, and rise above, the confines of the names and labels that you give yourself and others or that others give to you. Find new and culturally competent ways to interact with those around you in ways that transcend labels. Know that you have potential for change.

"... no two selves, no two consciousnesses, no two minds are exactly alike. Each of us is therefore situated to make a unique contribution to the world."

HOWARD GARDNER, PSYCHOLOGIST AND EDUCATOR

PERSONAL TRIUMPH CASE STUDY

KNOWING YOURSELF AS A LEARNER

DR. JOYCE BISHOP
PROFESSOR OF PSYCHOLOGY, GOLDEN WEST COLLEGE, HUNTINGTON BEACH, CALIFORNIA

Dr. Bishop, the creator of the assessments in this chapter, has a passion for learning that was inspired by her ordeal as a college student with a learning disability. As it did with her, knowing who you are as a learner can help you surmount the obstacles that come your way. Read the account; then answer the questions on page 101.

I have difficulty understanding words I hear, which made listening to lectures in college very hard. No one would know I had this difficulty because I learned how to compensate for it. In fact, I didn't know it myself until years after I graduated. It is a learning disability in the area of auditory discrimination.

College was confusing for me. I did well in some classes and felt totally lost in others. The hardest were the lecture-based classes. When I wasn't familiar with the information or the words, I couldn't make sense of what I was hearing.

If I read the material ahead of time, I could make visual pictures in my mind that would help me absorb the material. I could also look up words and research concepts I didn't understand. Then the lectures made more sense.

I read lips and facial expressions well, so I did well in small classes where I could consistently see the teacher's face. The disadvantage for me in small classes was that, because I heard voices around me as much as I heard the speaker, I had trouble blocking the extra noise. In an attempt to make lecture classes easier to understand, I would drag a tape recorder to class so that I could play back the lecture a number of times later. I found, however, that it didn't really help when I re-listened to the tapes. After that, I bargained with my classmates to borrow their notes in exchange for typing their term papers. Typing is bodily-kinesthetic and helped me to internalize what I was learning.

What helped me get by in college was that I am strong in logical-mathematical intelligence. School is primarily taught in the verbal-linguistic and logical-mathematical learning styles. I am also a strong visual learner. Science classes were easiest for me because they are more visual. I switched from sociology to biology my freshman year; it was easier for me to remember the visual biology material as opposed to the more verbal liberal arts classes. Without my commitment to my education and my will to succeed, I probably would not have graduated.

Twelve years after graduating, I pursued my master's in public health. Part of why I waited so long was that I needed to heal from the trauma of my own learning process. My graduate classes were much more hands-on, but there was still a great deal of reading. One day my eye doctor expressed concern about the stress my school work was causing my eyes and suggested that I get tested for a learning problem. He sent me to a center that usually tests small children for learning disabilities. The person giving the test said words and I was to spell out the words with blocks. I couldn't get some of the words right. I would consistently confuse or mistake words with close sounds. It was determined that I processed language on a fourth-grade level, a condition that has not changed in my adult life.

"How far did you go through school?" asked the therapist conducting the test.

"How far do you think I went?" I asked.

After thinking for a moment, she answered, "The tenth grade." I shared that I was just completing my master's degree. Her eyes got big and she said, "You work really hard in school, don't you?"

At that moment my head flooded with memories of report cards saying "Doesn't pay attention in class" and "Isn't working up to potential." I started to cry. An explanation for what had brought years of pain and struggle had finally come to the surface.

Now that I know what the problem is, I use strategies that allow me to deal with the way I learn. This is why I am so passionate about the power of knowing how you learn. We all have our strengths and weaknesses; the way we work to manage those weaknesses while maximizing our strengths makes all the difference.

Matthew Denman, the student artist who created this drawing, brings his unique eye to each subject he draws. Like Joyce, Matthew was diagnosed with a disability that affects his learning—autism. With the help of family and teachers, he discovered that he had an eye for structure, which has helped him in his academic career and beyond. Currently, he is attending Boulder Technical College. For more of Matthew's story, please visit www.prenhall.com/carter.

Building World-Class Skills for College, Career, and Life Success

SUCCESSFUL INTELLIGENCE

Think, Create, Apply

Learn from the experiences of others. Look back to Joyce Bishop's Personal Triumph on page 100. After you've read her story, relate her experience to your own life by completing the following on a separate sheet of paper or on a computer file:

Step 1. Think it through: ***Analyze your experience and compare it to Joyce's.*** How do you feel "different" in the classroom? What is a consistent academic challenge for you, and how does this relate to Joyce's experience? How might this be explained by your knowledge of how you learn?

Step 2. Think out of the box: ***Imagine ways of advising.*** You are an advisor to a student identical to yourself. Be a harsh advisor—how would you criticize your performance as a student? Then be a wise advisor, focused on tapping into information about intelligences and the Personality Spectrum dimensions—how would you identify challenges and suggest ways to handle them?

Step 3. Make it happen: ***Head off your own challenges with practical strategies.*** You have named a consistent challenge—and you have imagined what you would say as your own advisor. Now identify steps that will help you face your challenge (choosing particular courses, meeting with an advisor or instructor who can give you ideas, approaching work in particular ways).

TEAMWORK

Create Solutions Together

Ideas about personality types. Divide into groups according to the four types of the *Personality Spectrum* assessment—Thinker-dominant students in one group, Organizer-dominant students in another, Giver-dominant students in a third, and Adventurer-dominant students in the fourth. If you have scored the same in more than one of these types, join whatever group is smaller. With your group, brainstorm the following lists for your type:

1. The strengths of this type
2. The struggles it brings
3. The stressors (things that cause stress) for this type
4. Career areas that tend to suit this type
5. Career areas that are a challenge for this type
6. People who clash with this type the most (often because they are strong in areas where this type needs to grow)

If there is time, each group can present this information to the entire class; this will boost understanding and acceptance of diverse ways of relating to information and people.

WRITING

Journal and Put Skills to Work

Record your thoughts on a separate piece of paper, in a journal, or on a computer file.

Journal entry: Personal diversity. Being able to respond to people as individuals requires that you become more aware of the diversity that is not always on the surface. Start by examining your own uniqueness. Write down, and expand upon if you wish, 10 words or phrases that describe you. The challenge: Keep references to your ethnicity or appearance (brunette, Cuban American, wheelchair-dependent, and so on) to a minimum, and fill the rest of the list with characteristics others can't see at a glance (laid-back, only child, 24 years old, drummer, marathoner, interpersonal learner, and so on).

Real-life writing: Improve communication. Few students make use of the wealth of ideas and experience that academic advisors can offer. Think of a question you have—regarding a specific course, major, or academic situation—that your advisor might help you answer. Craft an e-mail in appropriate language to your advisor, and send it. Then, to stretch your communication skills, rewrite the same e-mail twice more: once in a format you would send to an instructor, and once in a format appropriate for a friend. Send either or both of these if you think the response would be valuable to you.

PERSONAL PORTFOLIO

Prepare for Career Success

Complete the following on separate sheets of paper or electronically (if you can use a graphics program).

Self-portrait. Because self-knowledge helps you to make the best choices about your future, a self-portrait is an important step in your career exploration. Use this exercise to synthesize everything you have been exploring about yourself into one comprehensive self-portrait. Design your portrait in "think link" style, using words and visual shapes to describe your dominant multiple intelligences, Personality Spectrum dimensions, values, abilities and interests, personal characteristics, and anything else that you have discovered through self-exploration.

A *think link* is a visual construction of related ideas, similar to a map or web, which represents your thought process. Ideas are written inside geometric shapes, often boxes or circles, and related ideas and facts are attached to those ideas by lines that connect the shapes (see the note-taking section in chapter 6 for more about think links).

If you want to use the style shown in the example in Key 3.11, create a "web" of ideas coming off your central shape. Then, spreading out from each of those ideas (interests, values, and so forth), draw lines connecting

KEY 3.11

One example of a self-portrait.

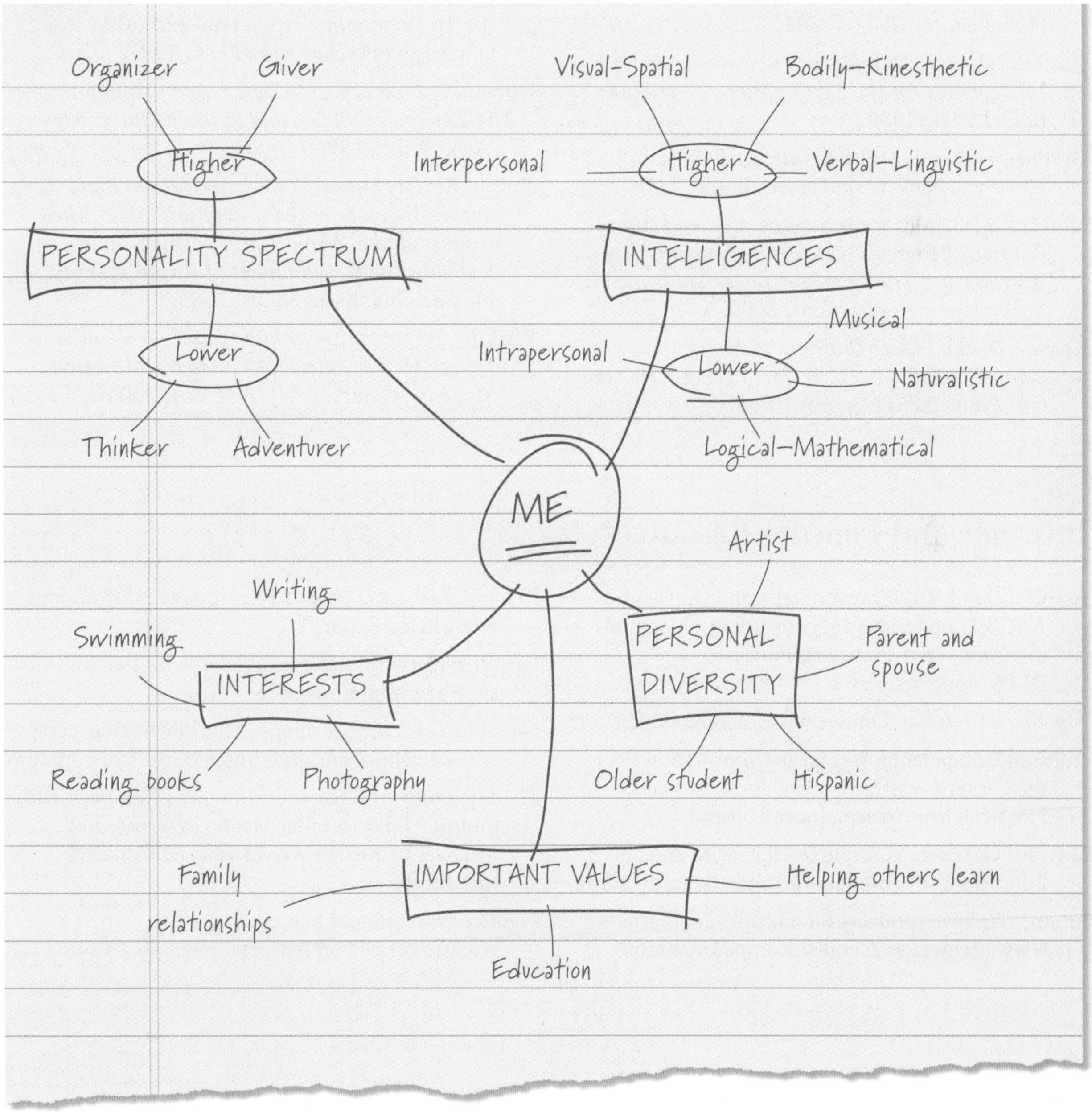

the thoughts that go along with that idea. Connected to "Interests," for example, might be "Singing," "Stock market," and "History."

You don't have to use the wheel image, however. You might design a treelike think link, a line of boxes with connecting thoughts, or some other format. Let your design reflect who you are, just as what you write does. You may want to look back at it at the end of the term to see how you have changed and grown from the self-image you have today.

Suggested Readings

Dublin, Thomas, ed. *Becoming American, Becoming Ethnic: College Students Explore Their Roots.* Philadelphia: Temple University Press, 1996.

Furlong, Gary. *The Conflict Resolution Toolbox.* Hoboken, NJ: Wiley, 2005.

Gardner, Howard. *Intelligence Reframed: Multiple Intelligences for the 21st Century*. New York: Basic Books, 2000.

Gardner, Howard. *Multiple Intelligences: New Horizons*. New York: Perseus Books, 2006.

Howard, Kim, and Annie Stevens. *Out and About Campus: Personal Accounts by Lesbian, Gay, Bisexual and Transgender College Students*. New York: Alyson Publications, 2000.

Keirsey, David. *Please Understand Me II: Temperament, Character, Intelligence*. Del Mar, CA: Prometheus Nemesis, 1998.

Levine, Mel. *A Mind at a Time*. New York: Simon & Schuster, 2003.

Pearman, Roger R., and Sarah C. Albritton. *I'm Not Crazy, I'm Just Not You: The Real Meaning of the 16 Personality Types*. Palo Alto, CA: Consulting Psychologists Press, 1997.

Qubein, Nido R. *How to Be a Great Communicator: In Person, on Paper, and at the Podium*. New York: Wiley, 1996.

Tatum, Beverly Daniel. *"Why Are All the Black Kids Sitting Together in the Cafeteria?" and Other Conversations About Race: A Psychologist Explains the Development of Racial Identity.* Philadelphia: Basic Books, 2003.

Watkins, Boyce D. *Everything You Ever Wanted to Know About College: A Guide for Minority Students*. Camillus, NJ: Blue Boy, 2004.

Internet and Podcast Resources

Association of American Colleges and Universities—AAC&U Podcasts (podcasts about on-campus diversity): **www.aacu.org/Podcast/DL06_podcasts.cfm**

The Black Collegian Online: **www.black-collegian.com**

Cultural Competency Web page (information from the Center for Effective Collaboration and Practice): **http://cecp.air.org/cultural**

Howard Gardner, Multiple Intelligences, and Education: **www.infed.org/thinkers/gardner.htm**

Internet Archive (podcast on multiple intelligences): **www.archive.org/details/dcampdaraabrams**

Keirsey Sorter and other Myers-Briggs information: **www.keirsey.com**

Latino USA (with podcasts available on the Web site): **www.latinousa.org**

New Horizons for Learning—Multiple Intelligences: **www.newhorizons.org/strategies/mi/front_mi.htm**

The Sociology of Race and Ethnicity (Web page with multiple links to other resources, created by Michael C. Kearl): **www.trinity.edu/mkearl/race.html**

Prentice Hall Student Success SuperSite: **www.prenhall.com/success**

Endnotes

[1]One such study is K. Warner Schaie, "The Seattle Longitudinal Studies of Adult Intelligence," in *Essential Papers on the Psychology of Aging,* M. Powell Lawton and Timothy A. Salthouse, eds., New York: New York University Press, 1998, pp. 263–271. Also available online (www.memory-key .com/Seniors/longitudinal_study.htm).

[2]Howard Gardner, *Multiple Intelligence: New Horizons,* New York: Basic Books, 2006, p. 180.

[3]Howard Gardner, *Multiple Intelligences: The Theory in Practice,* New York: HarperCollins, 1993, pp. 5–49.

[4]Gardner, *Multiple Intelligence: New Horizons,* p. 8.

[5]Howard Gardner, *Intelligence Reframed,* New York: Basic Books, 1999, pp. 33–34.

[6]Gardner, *Multiple Intelligences: The Theory in Practice,* p. 7.

[7]C. George Boeree, "Personality Theories: Carl Jung," 2006 (http://webspace.ship.edu/cgboer/ jung.html).

[8]Developed by Joyce Bishop, Ph.D., Golden West College, Huntington Beach, CA. Based on Howard Gardner, *Frames of Mind: The Theory of Multiple Intelligences,* New York: HarperCollins, 1993.

[9]"Conceptual Frameworks/Models, Guiding Values and Principles," National Center for Cultural Competence, 2002 (www11.georgetown.edu/ research/gucchd/nccc/foundations/ frameworks.html).

[10]Information in the sections on the five stages of building competency is based on Mark A. King, Anthony Sims, and David Osher, "How Is Cultural Competence Integrated in Education?" n.d., Center for Effective Collaboration and Practice (http://cecp.air.org/cultural/ Q_integrated.htm).

[11]Martin Luther King Jr., from his sermon "A Tough Mind and a Tender Heart," *Strength in Love,* Philadelphia: Fortress Press, 1986, p. 14.

[12]Sheryl McCarthy, *Why Are the Heroes Always White?* Kansas City, MO: Andrews McMeel, 1995, p. 137.

[13]Betsy Israel, "The Overconnecteds," *New York Times* Education Life, November 5, 2006, p. 20.

[14]Christopher J. Moore, *In Other Words: A Language Lover's Guide to the Most Intriguing Words Around the World,* New York: Walker, 2004, p. 78.

get focused!

time and test preparation

Prepare with a Study Plan and Schedule

Because some instructors may schedule exams early and often in the term, begin now to develop strategies for test success. The material in this segment is designed to help you organize yourself and manage time efficiently as you prepare for exams. When you reach chapter 7, "Test Taking: Showing What You Know," you will study test taking in depth, including test preparation, test anxiety, general test-taking strategies, strategies for handling different types of test questions, and learning from test mistakes.

Decide on a Study Plan

Start your test preparation by deciding what you will study. Go through your notes, texts, related primary sources, and handouts, and set aside materials you don't need. Then prioritize the remaining materials. Your goal is to focus on information that is most likely to be on the exam. Use the test-preparation tips on pages 220–225 in chapter 7 and the material on studying your text in chapter 5 to boost your effectiveness as you prepare.

Create a Study Schedule and Checklist

Next, use the time-management and goal-setting skills from chapter 2 to prepare a schedule. Consider all of the relevant factors—your study materials, the number of days until the test, and the time you can study each day. If you establish your schedule ahead of time and write it in a planner, you are more likely to follow it.

A comprehensive checklist like the one on the facing page will help you organize and stay on track as you prepare. Use a checklist to assign specific tasks to particular study times and sessions. That way, not only do you know when you have time to study, but you also have defined goals for each study session.

Decide How Well These Techniques Work for You

Now put these studying and scheduling techniques into action by using them every time you prepare for an exam. Make extra copies of the checklist so that they're ready to fill out as soon as an exam is announced.

Prepare for a Test

Complete the following checklist for each exam to define your study goals, get organized, and stay on track:

Course: ______________________ Instructor: ______________________

Date, time, and place of test: ______________________

Type of test (Is it a midterm or a minor quiz?): ______________________

What instructor said about the test, including types of test questions, test length, and how much the test counts toward your final grade:

____

____

Topics to be covered on the test, in order of importance (information should also come from your instructor):

1. ______________________
2. ______________________
3. ______________________
4. ______________________
5. ______________________

Study schedule, including materials you plan to study (texts, class notes, homework problems, and so forth) and dates you plan to complete each:

Material	**Completion Date**
1. ______________	______________
2. ______________	______________
3. ______________	______________
4. ______________	______________
5. ______________	______________

Materials you are expected to bring to the test (textbook, sourcebook, calculator, etc.):

____

____

____

Special study arrangements (such as planning study group meeting, asking the instructor for special help, getting outside tutoring):

____

____

____

Life-management issues (such as rearranging work hours):

____

____

____

Source: Adapted from Ron Fry, *"Ace" Any Test,* 3rd ed., Franklin Lakes, NJ: Career Press, 1996, pp. 123–124.

After you use these strategies one or more times, answer the following questions:

- How did this approach help you organize your time before an exam?

____

____

____

____

- How did this approach help you organize your study material so that you remembered to cover every topic?

____

____

____

____

- Can you think of ways to change the checklist to improve your test-prep efficiency? If you can, list the ways here and incorporate them into the checklist.

____

____

____

____

PART II

Developing Skills for School and Life

CRITICAL, CREATIVE, AND PRACTICAL THINKING

Solving Problems and Making Decisions

4

"Successfully intelligent people define problems correctly and thereby solve those problems that really confront them, rather than extraneous ones. . . . [They] carefully formulate strategies for problem solving. In particular, they focus on long-range planning rather than rushing in and then later having to rethink their strategies."

ROBERT STERNBERG

To serve you successfully, your education must do more than fill your head with facts and figures: It must also give you the tools to work through problems and decisions. These tools take the form of analytical, creative, and practical thinking skills and are at the heart of *successful intelligence*.

This chapter will help you build your ability to analyze information, come up with creative ideas, and put a practical plan into action. As you build these skills, you will become a better problem solver and decision maker, moving ever more effectively toward your goals.

In this chapter you explore answers to the following questions:

- What does it mean to think with successful intelligence? 112
- How can you improve your analytical thinking skills? 115
- How can you improve your creative thinking skills? 120
- How can you improve your practical thinking skills? 124
- How can you use successful intelligence to solve problems and make decisions? 130
- Successful Intelligence Wrap-Up 135

Chapter 4's Successful Intelligence Skills

Analytical	Creative	Practical
• Evaluating fact, opinion, assumptions, and perspectives • Analyzing whether examples support ideas • Evaluating potential and actual solutions and choices	• Brainstorming • Taking risks and promoting a creative environment • Developing potential solutions and choices	• How to identify problems and decisions • How to use a plan to work through problems and decisions • How to adapt to your environment and learn from experience

What Does It Mean to Think with Successful Intelligence?

Some tasks primarily engage one thinking skill at a time. You might use analytical thinking (also known as *critical thinking*) to complete a quiz, creative thinking to write a poem, or practical thinking to get errands done on a busy day. However, when you need to solve a problem or make a decision, combining your analytical, creative, and practical thinking skills gives you the greatest chance of moving forward successfully.[1] These three skills give you myriad ways to connect to material in school and out (see Key 4.1).

Successfully Intelligent Thinking Means Asking and Answering Questions

What is thinking? According to experts, it is what happens when you ask questions and move toward the answers.[2] "To think through or rethink anything," says Dr. Richard Paul, director of research at the Center for Critical Thinking, "one must ask questions that stimulate our thought. Questions define tasks, express problems, and delineate issues. . . . Only students who have questions are really thinking and learning."[3]

As you answer questions, you transform raw data into information that you can use to achieve goals. A *Wall Street Journal* article titled "The Best Innovations Are Those That Come from Smart Questions" relays the story of a cell biology student, William Hunter, whose professor told him that "the difference between good science and great science is the quality of the

REAL QUESTIONS

How can I succeed in college if I don't test well?

Parisa Malekzadeh
University of Arizona
Major: Undeclared

My grades were good in high school, and I was also involved in extracurricular activities such as the freshman mentor program and tae kwon do (I am a black belt and instructor). My family and my teachers always told me that I will do well in college.

But I am not so sure. I have a hard time with multiple-choice tests and I did not do well on the SAT and ACT. I worry that maybe I am just not smart enough, even though I can express myself well in essays and conversation. How can I do better on these tests, and how can I make the most of what I already do well?

PRACTICAL ANSWERS

Benjamin E. Victorica,
MD Professor Emeritus,
Pediatric Cardiology
University of Florida

Strive to improve your skills, and know that your other strengths will lead you to success.

To accomplish goals, one must remain focused on the objectives and maintain perseverance. You have already demonstrated that you can focus and persevere by your academic performance and level of expertise in tae kwon do. These qualities will prove more important to your success than test scores.

I had a similar experience with multiple-choice testing. At the time of my medical education in Argentina, all my tests were oral. In order to continue my postgraduate education in this country, I had to pass the ECFMG examination, which is almost entirely multiple-choice. Since I knew the medical material, I learned how to properly answer multiple-choice questions by reviewing and taking sample tests. The majority of my wrong answers occurred because I was quickly glancing at the questions instead of reading carefully. With more focus, I passed the test and was able to continue my training.

My success as a physician has come from combining analytical work (analyzing the key signs and symptoms of a condition and correlating them to clinical and laboratory findings) with creativity (thinking through situations comprehensively) and practical ability (discussing the diagnosis with the patient, applying the appropriate treatment, and monitoring the results). Work hard to improve testing and analytical skills, but value and build your practical and creative skills just as much, knowing that the combination will help you reach your goals.

questions posed."[4] Now a physician, Dr. Hunter asks questions about new ways to use drugs. His questions have led to the promotion of a revolutionary product—a drug-coated mesh used to strengthen vessels in limbs that are threatened by late-stage arterial disease. Through seeking answers to probing questions, Dr. Hunter reached a significant goal.[5]

You use questions in order to analyze ("How bad is my money situation?"), come up with creative ideas ("How can I earn more money?"), and apply practical solutions ("Who do I talk to about getting a job on campus?"). Later in the chapter, in the sections on analytical, creative, and

KEY 4.1

Successful intelligence helps you achieve goals in any discipline.

DISCIPLINE	ANALYTICAL THINKING	CREATIVE THINKING	PRACTICAL THINKING
Behavioral Science	Comparing one theory of child development with another	Devising a new theory of child development	Applying child development theories to help parents and teachers understand and deal with children more effectively
Literature	Examining the development of the main character in a novel	Writing alternative endings to the novel	Using the experience of the main character to better understand and manage one's own life situations
History	Considering similarities and differences between World War I and World War II	Imagining yourself as a German citizen dealing with economic depression after WWI	Seeing what WWI and WWII lessons can be applied to current Middle East conflicts
Sports	Taking a close look at the opposing team's strategy on the soccer field	Coming up with innovative ways to move the ball downfield	Using tactics to hide your strategy from an opposing team—or a competing company

Source: Adapted from Robert J. Sternberg, *Successful Intelligence,* New York: Plume, 1996, p. 149.

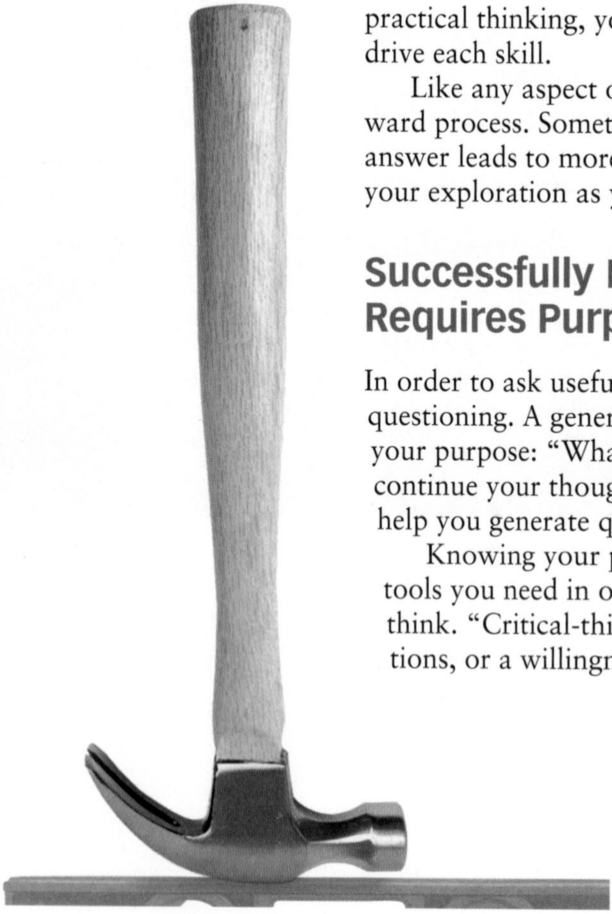

practical thinking, you will find examples of the kinds of questions that drive each skill.

Like any aspect of thinking, questioning is usually not a straightforward process. Sometimes the answer doesn't come right away. Often the answer leads to more—and more specific—questions. Patience is key in your exploration as you search for results.

Successfully Intelligent Thinking Requires Purpose and Drive

In order to ask useful questions, you need to know *why* you are questioning. A general question can be your starting point for defining your purpose: "What am I trying to accomplish, and why?" As you continue your thought process, you will find more specific purposes that help you generate questions along the way.

Knowing your purpose helps you with one of the most important tools you need in order to activate your thinking powers: The *drive* to think. "Critical-thinking skills are different from critical-thinking dispositions, or a willingness to deploy these skills," says cognitive psychologist D. Alan Bensley of Frostburg State University in Maryland. In other words, having the skills isn't enough—you also have to want to use them. Skilled thinkers not motivated to use their thinking skills are likely to make decisions in ways similar to those who don't have the skills to deploy.[6]

The bottom line is that the three skills, or aspects, of successful intelligence are useful to you only if you activate them. As Sternberg says, "It is more important to know when and how to use these aspects of successful intelligence than just to have them."[7] If you know and understand your purpose, you are more likely to be willing to use your skills.

Begin by exploring the analytical thinking skills that you'll need to solve problems and make decisions effectively.

How Can You Improve Your Analytical Thinking Skills?

Analytical thinking is the process of gathering information, analyzing it in different ways, and evaluating it for the purposes of gaining understanding, solving a problem, or making a decision. The first step in analytical thinking is to define your purpose by asking what you want to analyze, and why. Then you gather the necessary information, analyze and clarify the ideas, and evaluate what you've found. Throughout the process, you will formulate new questions that may take you in unforeseen directions or even change your purpose.

Gather Information

Information is the raw material for thinking. Choosing what to gather requires analyzing how much information you need, how much time to spend gathering it, and whether it is relevant. Say, for instance, that you have to write a paper on one aspect of the media (TV, radio, Internet) and its influence on a particular group. If you gathered every available resource on the topic, the course would be over long before you got to the writing stage.

Here's how you might use analysis to effectively gather information for that paper:

You will rarely use just one aspect of successful intelligence at a time. This instructor and student are gathering data (analytical intelligence) as they work hands-on with terrapins in a bayside marsh (practical intelligence).

- Reviewing the assignment, you learn that the paper should be approximately 10 pages and describe at least three significant points of influence.
- At the library and online, you find thousands of articles on the topic. After an hour, you decide to focus your paper on how the Internet influences young teens (ages 13–15).
- You get an overview from six comprehensive articles that lead you to three in-depth sources.

In this way you achieve a subgoal—a selection of useful materials—on the way to your larger goal of writing a well-crafted paper.

Analyze and Clarify Information

Once you've gathered the information, the next step is to analyze it to determine whether the information is reliable and useful in helping you answer your questions.

Break Information into Parts

When analyzing information, you break information into parts and examine the parts so that you can see how they relate to each other and to information you already know. The following strategies help you break down information into pieces and set aside what is unclear, unrelated, or unimportant, resulting in a deeper and more reliable understanding:

Separate the ideas. If you are reading about how teens aged 13–15 use the Internet, you might discuss method of access, popular Web sites, and how they interact via instant message or blogs.

Compare and contrast. Look at how things are similar to, or different from, each other. You might explore how different young teen subgroups (boys versus girls, for example) have different purposes for setting up pages on sites such as Facebook or MySpace.

Examine cause and effect. Look at the possible reasons why something happened (possible causes) and its consequences (effects, both positive and negative). You might examine the effect that Internet use has on how young teens spend their time outside of school.

An important caution: Analyze carefully to seek out *true causes*—some apparent causes may not be actual causes (often called *false causes*). For example, changes in this group since the Internet became popular may have been the result of a number of different factors, including increased or decreased parental and school pressure and the impact of other media such as film and television.

Look for themes, patterns, and categories. Note connections that form as you look at how bits of information relate to one another. For example, you might see patterns of Internet use that link young teens from particular cultures or areas of the country together into categories.

© David Davis—Fotolia.com

Once the ideas are broken down, you can examine whether examples support ideas, separate fact from opinion, consider perspective, and investigate hidden assumptions.

Examine Whether Examples Support Ideas

When you encounter an idea or claim, examine how it is supported with examples or *evidence* (facts, expert opinion, research findings, personal experience, and so on). How useful an idea is to your work may depend on whether, or how well, it is backed up with solid evidence or made concrete with examples. Be critical of the information you gather; don't take it at face value.

For example, a blog written by a 12-year-old may make statements about what kids do on the Internet. The word of one person, who may or may not be telling the truth, is not adequate support. On the other hand, a study of kids' technology use by the Department of Commerce under the provisions of the Children's Internet Protection Act may be more reliable. Whenever you see an **argument** in written materials, you use questioning to judge the quality of the evidence, whether it supports the central idea, and whether examples and ideas connect logically.

ARGUMENT
A set of connected ideas, supported by examples, made by a writer to prove or disprove a point.

Finding credible, reliable information with which to answer questions and come up with ideas enables you to separate fact from opinion.

Distinguish Fact from Opinion

A *statement of fact* is information presented as objectively real and verifiable ("The Internet is a research tool"). In contrast, a *statement of opinion* is a belief, conclusion, or judgment that is inherently difficult, and sometimes impossible, to verify ("The Internet is always the best and most reliable research tool"). When you critically evaluate materials that you read, looking carefully at whether an argument is based on fact or opinion will help you determine how reliable it is. Key 4.2 defines important characteristics of fact and opinion.

Even though facts may seem more solid, you can also make use of opinions if you determine that they are backed up with facts. However, it is important to examine opinions for their underlying perspectives and assumptions.

KEY 4.2

Examine how fact and opinion differ.

Facts include statements that . . .	Opinions include statements that . . .
. . . *deal with actual people, places, objects, or events.* Example: "In 2002, the European Union introduced the physical coins and banknotes of a new currency—the euro—that was designed to be used by its member nations."	. . . *show evaluation.* Any statement of value indicates an opinion. Words such as *bad, good, pointless,* and *beneficial* indicate value judgments. Example: "The use of the euro has been beneficial to all the states of the European Union."
. . . *use concrete words or measurable statistics.* Example: "The charity event raised $50,862."	. . . *use abstract words.* Hard-to-define words like *misery* or *success* usually indicate a personal opinion. Example: "The charity event was a smashing success."
. . . *describe current events in exact terms.* Example: "Mr. Barrett's course has 378 students enrolled this semester."	. . . *predict future events.* Statements about future occurrences are often opinions. Example: "Mr. Barrett's course is going to set a new enrollment record this year."
. . . *avoid emotional words and focus on the verifiable.* Example: "Citing dissatisfaction with the instruction, 7 out of the 25 students in that class withdrew in September."	. . . *use emotional words.* Emotions are unverifiable. Words such as *delightful* or *miserable* express an opinion. Example: "That class is a miserable experience."
. . . *avoid absolutes.* Example: "Some students need to have a job while in school."	. . .*use absolutes.* Absolute *qualifiers,* such as *all, none, never,* and *always,* often express an opinion. Example: "All students need to have a job while in school."

Source: Adapted from Ben E. Johnson, *Stirring Up Thinking,* New York: Houghton Mifflin, 1998, pp. 268–270.

Examine Perspectives and Assumptions

PERSPECTIVE

A characteristic way of thinking about people, situations, events, and ideas.

A **perspective** can be broad, such as a generally optimistic or pessimistic view of life. Or it can be more focused, such as an attitude about whether students should commute or live on campus.

Perspectives are associated with **assumptions.** For example, the perspective that there are many successful ways to handle the issue of media exposure leads to assumptions such as "Parents can control children's exposure to the Internet" and "Children can access the Internet without being exposed to inappropriate content." Having a particular experience with children and the Internet can build or reinforce a perspective.

ASSUMPTION

A judgment, generalization, or bias influenced by experience and values.

Assumptions often hide within questions and statements, blocking you from considering information in different ways. Take this classic puzzler as an example: "Which came first, the chicken or the egg?" Thinking about this question, most people assume that the egg is a chicken egg. If you think past that assumption and come up with a new idea—such as, the egg is a dinosaur egg—then the obvious answer is that the egg came first!

Examining perspectives and assumptions enables you to judge whether material is reliable and free of **bias,** what particular perspective and intent the author may have, and what assumptions underlie the material. It also helps you identify whether your own perspectives and assumptions are clouding your judgment.

BIAS

A preference or inclination, especially one that prevents evenhanded judgment.

Perspectives and assumptions in information. Perspectives and assumptions permeate nearly everything you read. Being able to separate them from the facts will help you identify bias and evaluate information effectively. For example, the conclusions in two articles on Internet advertising may differ if one appears on the Web site of a company that advertises on the Internet and one appears in a publication that wants the Internet to be an advertising-free zone. Another example: A historical Revolutionary War document that originated in the colonies may assume that the rebellion against the British was entirely justified and leave out information to the contrary.

Personal perspectives and assumptions. Your perspective affects how accurately you view information. A student who thinks that the death penalty is wrong, for example, may have a hard time analyzing arguments that defend it, or when researching may focus on materials that support his perspective. Try to set aside perspectives and assumptions when you analyze information. "Anticipate your reactions and prejudices and then consciously resist their influence," says Colby Glass, professor of information research and philosophy at Palo Alto College.[8]

There's an added benefit to opening yourself to new perspectives: It will give you more information to work with as you encounter life's problems. Come to the classroom ready to hear and read new ideas, think about their merits, and make informed decisions about what you believe. Says Sternberg: "We need to . . . see issues from a variety of viewpoints and, especially, to see how other people and other cultures view issues and problems facing the world."[9]

Evaluate Information

You've gathered and analyzed your information. You examined its components, its evidence, its validity, its perspective, and any underlying assumptions. Now, based on an examination of evidence and careful analysis, you *evaluate* whether an idea or piece of information is important or unimportant, applicable or trivial, strong or weak, and why. You then set aside what is not useful and use the rest to form an opinion, possible solution, or decision.

In preparing your paper on young teens and the Internet, for example, you gathered pertinent information, came up with an idea you wanted to write about, researched information and materials, and analyzed how your research applied to your position. You then drafted your paper, presenting what you learned in an organized, persuasive way.

See Key 4.3 for some questions you can ask to build and use analytical thinking skills.

KEY 4.3

Ask questions like these in order to analyze.

To gather information, ask:	• What kinds of information do I need to meet my goal? • What information is available? Where and when can I get to it? • Of the sources I found, which ones will best help me achieve my goal?
To analyze, ask:	• What are the parts of this information? • What is similar to this information? What is different? • What are the reasons for this? Why did this happen? • What ideas, themes, or conclusions emerge from this material? • How would you categorize this information?
To see if evidence or examples support an idea, ask:	• Does the evidence make sense? • How do the examples support the idea/claim? • Are there examples that might disprove the idea/claim?
To distinguish fact from opinion, ask:	• Do the words in this information signal fact or opinion? • What is the source of this information? Is the source reliable? • If this is an opinion, is it supported by facts?
To examine perspectives and assumptions, ask:	• What perspectives might the author have, and what may be emphasized or deemphasized as a result? • What assumptions might lie behind this statement or material? • How could I prove, or disprove, an assumption? • How might my perspective affect the way I see this material?
To evaluate, ask:	• What information will support what I'm trying to prove or accomplish? • Is this information true or false, and why? • How important is this information?

Source: Adapted from "Questions That Probe Reasons and Evidence" (www-ed.fnal.gov/trc/tutorial/taxonomy.html), based on Richard Paul, *Critical Thinking: How to Prepare Students for a Rapidly Changing World,* Santa Rosa, CA: Center for Critical Thinking, 1993; and from Barbara Fowler, "Bloom's Taxonomy and Critical Thinking," 1996, Longview Community College (http://mcckc.edu/longview/ctac/blooms.htm).

GET ANALYTICAL!

Analyze a Statement

Consider this statement; then analyze it by answering the questions that follow.

"The Internet is the best place to find information about any topic."

Is this statement fact or opinion? Why?

____

____

What examples can you think of that support or negate this statement?

____

____

What perspectives are guiding this statement?

____

____

What assumptions underlie the statement? Pose a problem: What negative effects might result from accepting these assumptions and therefore agreeing with the statement?

____

____

As a result of your critical thinking, what is your evaluation of this statement?

____

____

Pursuing your goals, in school and in the workplace, requires not just analyzing information but also thinking creatively about how to use what you've learned from your analysis.

How Can You Improve Your Creative Thinking Skills?

What is creativity?

- Some researchers define *creativity* as combining existing elements in an innovative way to create a new purpose or result (using a weak adhesive to mark pages in a book, a 3M scientist created Post-it Notes).

- Others see creativity as the ability to generate new ideas from looking at how things are related (noting what ladybugs eat inspired organic farmers to bring them in to consume crop-destroying aphids).[10]
- Still others, including Sternberg, define it as the ability to make unusual connections—to view information in quirky ways that bring about unique results.

To think creatively is to generate new ideas that may bring change. Here's an example of how creativity can work in the classroom: Working with study group partners, Smith College junior Meghan E. Taugher devised a solar-powered battery for a laptop for their class on electrical circuits:

> We took the professor's laptop, put all the parts together, and sat outside watching it with a little device to see how much power it was saving. When it fully charged the battery, it was one of those times I felt that what I was learning was true, because I was putting it to use in real life.[11]

Meghan's experience led her to generate an idea of a new major and career—engineering.

Even though some people seem to have more or better ideas than others, creative thinking is a skill that can be developed. Creativity expert Roger von Oech highlights mental flexibility. "Like race-car drivers who shift in and out of different gears depending on where they are on the course," he says, you can enhance creativity by learning to "shift in and out of different types of thinking depending on the needs of the situation at hand."[12]

The following actions will help you make those shifts and build your ability to think creatively. Because ideas often pop up randomly, get in the habit of writing them down as they arise. Keep a pen and paper by your bed, your PDA in your pocket, a notepad in your car, or a tape recorder in your backpack so that you can grab ideas before they fade.

Brainstorm

BRAINSTORMING

Letting your mind free-associate to come up with different ideas or answers.

Brainstorming is also referred to as *divergent thinking:* You start with a question and then let your mind diverge—go in many different directions—in search of solutions. Brainstorming is *deliberate* creative thinking. When you brainstorm, try to generate ideas without thinking about how useful they are; evaluate their quality later. Brainstorming works well in groups because group members can become inspired by, and make creative use of, one another's ideas.[13]

One way to inspire ideas when brainstorming is to think of similar situations—in other words, to make *analogies* (comparisons based on a resemblance of things otherwise unlike). For example, Velcro is a product of analogy: When imagining how two pieces of fabric could stick to each other, the inventor thought of the similar situation of a burr sticking to clothing.

When you are brainstorming ideas, don't get hooked on finding the one right answer. Questions may have many "right answers"—or many answers that have degrees of usefulness. The more possibilities you generate, the better your chance of finding the best one. Also, don't stop the process when you think you have the best answer—keep going until you are out of steam. You never know what may come up in those last gasps of creative energy.[14]

Take a New and Different Look

If no one ever questioned established opinion, people would still think the sun revolved around the earth. Here are some ways to change how you look at a situation or problem:

Challenge assumptions. In the late 1960s, conventional wisdom said that school provided education and television provided entertainment. Jim Henson, a pioneer in children's television, asked, "Why can't we use TV to educate young children?" From that question, the characters of Sesame Street, and eventually a host of other educational programs, were born.

Shift your perspective. Try on new perspectives by asking others for their views, reading about new ways to approach situations, or deliberately going with the opposite of your first instinct.[15] Then use those perspectives to inspire creativity. For a political science course, for example, craft a position paper for a senatorial candidate. For a fun example of how looking at something in a new way can unearth a totally different idea, look at the perception puzzles in Key 4.4.

Ask "what if" questions. Set up hypothetical environments in which new ideas can grow—for example, "What if I had unlimited money or time?" The founders of Seeds of Peace, faced with generations of conflict in the Middle East, asked: What if Israeli and Palestinian teens met at a summer camp in Maine so that the next generation has greater understanding and

KEY 4.4 Use perception puzzles to experience a shift in perspective.

There are two possibilities for each image. What do you see?
(See page 143 for answers.)

Source of middle puzzle: "Sara Nadar" illustration from *Mind Sights* by Roger Shepard. Copyright © 1990 by Roger Shepard. Reprinted by permission of Henry Holt and Company, LLC.

respect? And what if follow-up programs and reunions are set up to cement friendships so that relationships change the politics of the Middle East? Based on the ideas that came up, they created an organization that helps teenagers from the Middle East develop leadership and communication skills.

Set the Stage for Creativity

Use these strategies to give yourself the best possible chance at generating creative ideas:

Choose, or create, environments that free your mind. Find places that energize you. Play music that moves you. Seek out people who inspire you.[16]

Be curious. Try something new and different: Take a course outside of your major, listen to a new genre of music, read a book on an unfamiliar topic. Try something you don't think you would like in order to see if you had misjudged your reaction. Seeking out new experiences will broaden your knowledge, giving you more raw materials with which to build creative ideas.[17]

Give yourself time to "sit" with a question. American society values speed, so much so that we equate being "quick" with being smart.[18] In fact, however, creative ideas often come when you give your brain permission to "leave the job" for a while.[19] Take breaks when figuring out a problem—get some exercise, nap, talk with a friend, work on something else, do something fun.

Take Risks

Creative breakthroughs can come from sensible risk taking.

Fly in the face of convention. Entrepreneur Michael Dell turned tradition on its ear when he took a "tell me what you want and I will build it for you" approach to computer marketing instead of a "build it and they will buy it" approach. The possibility of failure did not stop him from risking money, time, energy, and reputation to achieve a truly unique and creative goal.

Let mistakes be okay. Open yourself to the learning that comes from not being afraid to mess up. When a pharmaceutical company failed to develop a particular treatment for multiple sclerosis, the CEO said, "You have to celebrate the failures. If you send the message that the only road to career success is experiments that work, people won't ask risky questions, or get any dramatically new answers."[20]

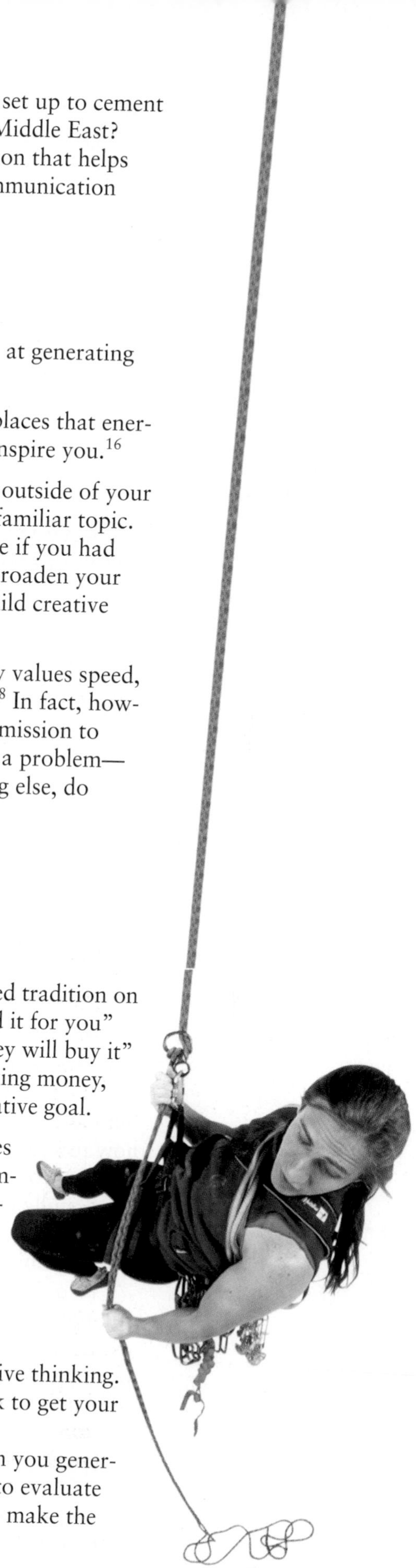

As with analytical thinking, asking questions powers creative thinking. See Key 4.5 for examples of the kinds of questions you can ask to get your creative juices flowing.

Creativity connects analytical and practical thinking. When you generate ideas, solutions, or choices, you need to think analytically to evaluate their quality. Then, you need to think practically about how to make the best solution or choice happen.

KEY 4.5 Ask questions like these in order to jump-start creative thinking.

To brainstorm, ask:	• What do I want to accomplish? • What are the craziest ideas I can think of? • What are 10 ways that I can reach my goal? • What ideas have worked before, and how can I apply them?
To shift your perspective, ask:	• How has this always been done—and what would be a different way? • How can I approach this task or situation from a new angle? • How would someone else do this or view this? • What if . . . ?
To set the stage for creativity, ask:	• Where, and with whom, do I feel relaxed and inspired? • What music helps me think out of the box? • When in the day or night am I most likely to experience a flow of creative ideas? • What do I think would be new and interesting to try, to see, to read?
To take risks, ask:	• What is the conventional way of doing this? What would be a totally different way? • What would be a risky approach to this problem or question? • What is the worst that can happen if I take this risk? What is the best? • What have I learned from this mistake?

How Can You Improve Your Practical Thinking Skills?

You've analyzed a situation. You've brainstormed ideas. Now, with your practical skill, you make things happen and learn from your actions.

Practical thinking does incorporate "common sense" or "street smarts" but has a broader reach. When you take practical action, you figure out how to adapt to your environment, or shape or change your environment to adapt to you, in order to pursue important goals. Think again about the successfully intelligent boy in the story in chapter 1: He quickly sized up his environment (bear and slower boy) and adapted (got ready to run) in order to pursue his goal (to escape becoming the bear's dinner).

Here is another example: Your goal is to pass your required freshman composition course. You are a visual learner. To achieve your goal, you can use the instructor's PowerPoints or other visual media to enhance your learning (adapt to your environment) or enroll in an Internet course that is primarily visual (change your environment to adapt to you)—or both.

Why Practical Thinking Is Important

Although the traditional classroom tends to focus on analytical thinking, real-world problems and decisions require you to move beyond analysis

get creative!

Activate Your Creative Powers

First, think about the past month; then, list three creative acts you performed.

1. In order to study, I ____________________
2. In my personal life, I ____________________
3. At work or in the classroom, I ____________________

Now think of a problem or situation that is on your mind. Brainstorm one new idea for how to deal with it.

____

____

Write down a second idea—but focus on the risk-taking aspect of creativity. What would be a risky way to handle the situation? How do you hope it would pay off?

____

____

Finally, sit with the question—then write down one more idea *only* after you have been away from this page for at least 24 hours.

____

____

Keep these in mind. You may want to use one soon!

alone. Your success in a sociology class, for example, usually is not just a product of your academic work—it may depend in part on adapting to your instructor's style or personality as well. Similarly, the way you solve a personal financial dilemma has a more significant impact on your life than how you work through a problem in an accounting course.

Furthermore, academic knowledge on its own isn't enough to bring you success in the workplace. You need to be able to actively apply what you know to problems and decisions that come up periodically. For example, while students majoring in elementary education may successfully quote child development facts on an exam, it won't mean much to their career success unless they can adapt to the classroom by evaluating and addressing real children's needs. Successfully solving real-world problems demands a practical approach.[21]

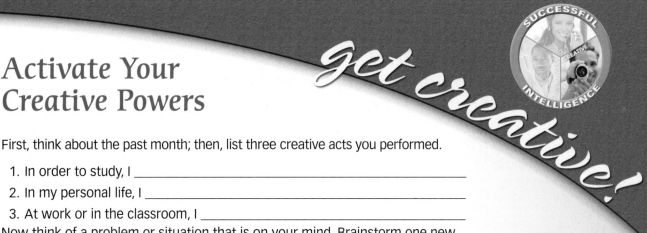

The accomplishments of David Hosei, a finance and entrepreneurship major at Indiana University, show how practical thinking helps you bridge the gap between being a successful student and achieving real-world success. Pursuing a goal to help others, Hosei formed HELP (Help Educate Lots of People), a nonprofit organization, to teach peers about money management. In addition, he organizes an annual fund-raiser—the IU Battle of the Bands—to raise money for Jill's House, a refuge for families seeking cancer treatments at a local medical center.[22] Achieving any important goal requires you to put practical skill into play.

Through Experience You Acquire Emotional and Social Intelligence

You gain much of your ability to think practically from personal experience, rather than from formal lessons.[23] What you learn from experience answers "how" questions—how to talk, how to behave, how to proceed.[24] For example, after completing several papers for a course, you may learn what your instructor expects and deliver it. Following a couple of conflicts with a partner, you may learn how to avoid sore spots when the conversation heats up. See Key 4.6 for ways in which this kind of knowledge can be shown in "if-then" statements.

Experience teaches you how to "navigate" personal emotions and social interactions. The emotional and social intelligence you gain as a result of life experiences are essential tools for achieving personal and professional goals.

- *Emotional intelligence.* As you learned in chapter 1, *emotional intelligence* is defined by psychologist Daniel Goleman as the ability to

KEY 4.6 Here is one way to map out what you learn from experience.

Goal: You want to talk to the soccer coach about your status on the team.

IF the team has had a good practice and IF you've played well during the scrimmage and IF the coach isn't rushing off somewhere, THEN grab a moment with him right after practice ends.

perceive, assess, and manage one's own emotions and understand the emotions of others. This ability helps you to notice what emotions arise in others in reaction to what you say or do, make choices about how to respond to those emotions, and assess what results from your choices. This sequence results in a greater ability to choose appropriate practical actions in future situations.

- *Social intelligence.* The concept of *social intelligence,* also introduced in chapter 1, involves understanding social interactions and using that understanding to maximize your relationships. If you pay attention to how things work in social situations at school, at home, and at work, experience can provide continual practical lessons about which actions to take.

Social intelligence skills, such as sensing what others feel and making a desired impression through what you say verbally and nonverbally, will help you make the most out of your interactions with instructors.

Look closely at what happens among the social players as well as within your emotional landscape, and consider what will promote success. Say, for example, that you receive a disappointing grade on a paper, and you are angry about it. An emotionally and socially intelligent response involves these practical actions:

- Cooling off before you schedule a meeting with the instructor
- Calmly making your point at the meeting
- Listening carefully to what your instructor says in response
- Politely requesting what is possible (a rewrite, for example)

With this course of action, you maximize the likelihood that your instructor will be receptive and helpful (social intelligence), and you maximize your ability to manage your own emotions and use them effectively to work toward your goal (emotional intelligence).

Practical Thinking Means Action

Action is an extension of practical thinking. Basic student success strategies that promote action—staying motivated, making the most of your strengths, learning from failure, managing time, taking the initiative to seek help from instructors and advisors, and believing in yourself—will keep you moving toward your goals.[25]

The key to making practical knowledge work is to use what you discover, assuring that you will not have to learn the same lessons over and over again. As Sternberg says, "What matters most is not how much experience you have had but rather how much you have profited from it—in other words, how well you apply what you have learned."[26]

See Key 4.7 for some questions you can ask in order to apply practical thinking to your problems and decisions.

KEY 4.7 **Ask questions like these to activate practical thinking.**

To learn from experience, ask:	• What worked well, or not so well, about my approach? My timing? My tone? My wording? • What did others like or not like about what I did? • What did I learn from that experience, conversation, event? • How would I change things if I had to do it over again? • What do I know I would do again?
To apply what you learn, ask:	• What have I learned that would work here? • What have I seen others do, or heard about from them, that would be helpful here? • What does this situation have in common with past situations I've been involved in? • What has worked in similar situations in the past?
To boost your ability to take action, ask:	• How can I get motivated and remove limitations? • How can I, in this situation, make the most of what I do well? • If I fail, what can I learn from it? • What steps will get me to my goal, and what trade-offs are involved? • How can I manage my time more effectively?

get practical!

Take a Practical Approach to Building Successful Intelligence Skills

Use the wheel on the facing page to get a big-picture look at how you perceive your skills in all three aspects of successful intelligence. In the appropriate sections of the circle, write your self-assessment scores from *Get Analytical* (page 12), *Get Creative* (page 19), and *Get Practical* (page 25) in chapter 1. Then, in each of the three areas of the wheel, draw a curved line approximately at the level of the number of your score and fill in the wedge below that line. Look at what the wheel says about how balanced you perceive your three aspects of successful intelligence to be. If it were a real wheel, would it roll?

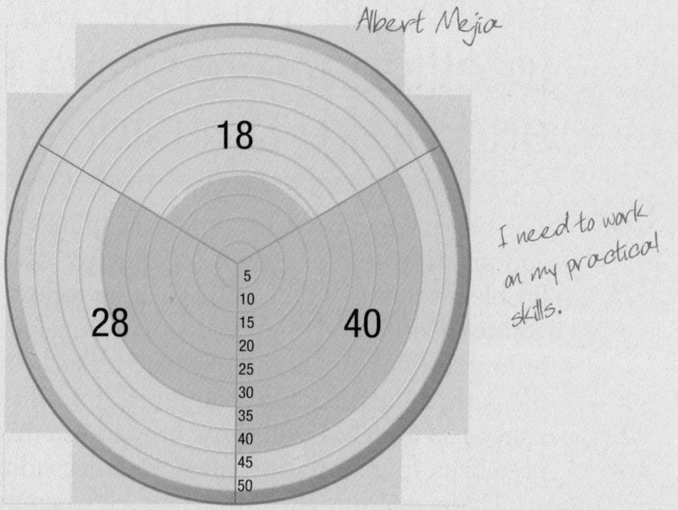

Sample Wheel

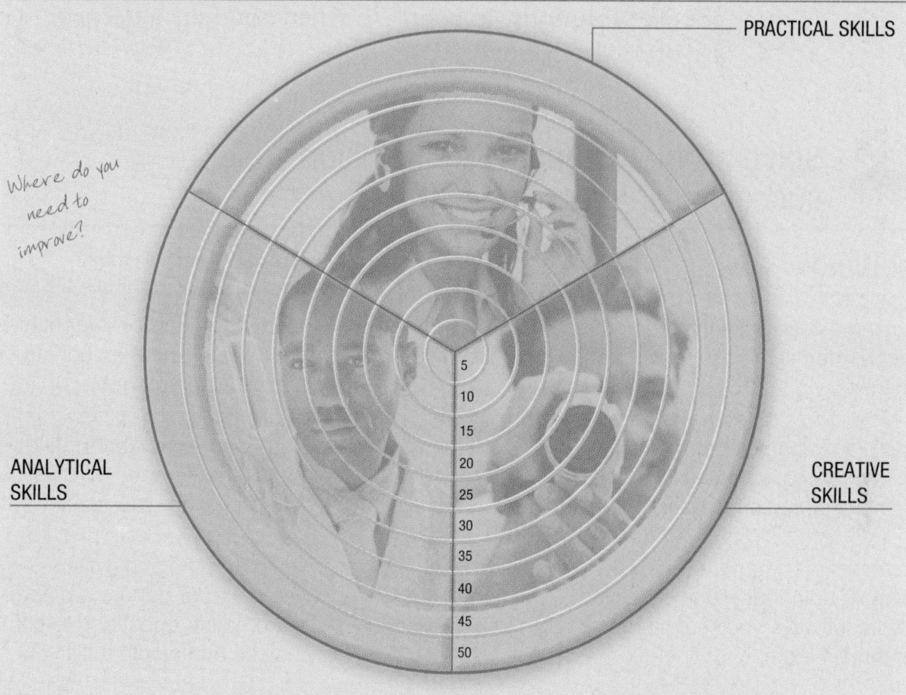

Source: Based on "The Wheel of Life" model developed by the Coaches Training Institute. © Co-Active Space 2000.

Based on looking at your wheel, in which area do you most want to build strength?

____

Write down two practical actions you can take that will improve your skills in that area. For example, someone who wants to be more creative could take a course focused on creativity; someone who wants to be more practical could work on paying attention to social cues; someone who wants to be more analytical could decide to analyze one newspaper article every week.

____

____

How Can You Use Successful Intelligence to Solve Problems and Make Decisions?

The best problem solvers and decision makers put their analytical, creative, and practical thinking skills together to solve problems and make decisions. Problem solving and decision making follow similar paths, both requiring you to identify and analyze a situation, generate possibilities, choose one, follow through on it, and evaluate its success. Key 4.8 gives an overview of the path, indicating how you think at each step. Keys 4.10 and 4.11 on pages 133 and 134 will show how to use this path, and provide a visual organizer, to map out problems and decisions effectively.

Understanding the differences between problem solving and decision making will help you know how to proceed:

- Problem solving generally requires more focus on coming up with possible solutions. In contrast, when you face a decision, your choices are often determined.

KEY 4.8 **Solve problems and make decisions using successful intelligence.**

PROBLEM SOLVING	THINKING SKILL	DECISION MAKING
Define the problem—recognize that something needs to change, identify what's happening, look for true causes.	STEP 1 DEFINE	Define the decision—identify your goal (your need) and then construct a decision that will help you get it.
Analyze the problem—gather information, break it down into pieces, verify facts, look at perspectives and assumptions, evaluate information.	STEP 2 ANALYZE	Examine needs and motives—consider the layers of needs carefully, and be honest about what you really want.
Generate possible solutions—use creative strategies to think of ways you could address the causes of this problem.	STEP 3 CREATE	Name and/or generate different options—use creative questions to come up with choices that would fulfill your needs.
Evaluate solutions—look carefully at potential pros and cons of each, and choose what seems best.	STEP 4 ANALYZE (EVALUATE)	Evaluate options—look carefully at potential pros and cons of each, and choose what seems best.
Put the solution to work—persevere, focus on results, and believe in yourself as you go for your goal.	STEP 5 TAKE PRACTICAL ACTION	Act on your decision—go down the path and use practical strategies to stay on target.
Evaluate how well the solution worked—look at the effects of what you did.	STEP 6 ANALYZE (REEVALUATE)	Evaluate the success of your decision—look at whether it accomplished what you had hoped.
In the future, apply what you've learned—use this solution, or a better one, when a similar situation comes up again.	STEP 7 TAKE PRACTICAL ACTION	In the future, apply what you've learned—make this choice, or a better one, when a similar decision comes up again.

- A problem exists when a situation has negative effects, and problem solving aims to remove or counteract those effects. In contrast, decision making aims to fulfill a need.

See Key 4.9 for some examples. Remember, too, that whereas all problem solving involves decision making, only some decision making requires you to solve a problem.

Solving a Problem

Use these strategies as you move through the problem-solving process outlined in Key 4.8.

Use probing questions to define problems. Focus on causes. If you are not happy in a class, for example, you could ask questions like these:

- What do I think about when I feel unhappy?
- Do my feelings involve my instructor? My classmates? School in general?
- Is the subject matter difficult? The volume of work too much?

Chances are that how you answer one or more of these questions may lead to a clear definition—and ultimately to the right solution.

Analyze carefully. Gather information for a comprehensive examination. Consider how the problem is similar to, or different from, other problems. Clarify facts. Note your own perspective, and ask others for theirs. Make sure your assumptions are not clouding your analysis.

Generate possible solutions based on causes, not effects. Addressing a cause provides a lasting solution, whereas "fixing" an effect cannot. Say, for example, that your shoulder hurts when you use your computer. Getting a friend to massage it is a helpful but temporary solution, because the pain returns whenever you go back to work. Changing the height of your keyboard and mouse is a better idea, because it eliminates the cause of your pain.

KEY 4.9

Examine how problems and decisions differ.

Situation	You have a problem if . . .	You need to make a decision if . . .
Planning summer activities	Your low GPA means you need to attend summer school—and you've already accepted a summer job.	You've been accepted into two summer abroad internship programs.
Declaring a major	It's time to declare, but you don't have all the prerequisites for the major you want.	There are three majors that appeal to you and you qualify for them all.
Handling communications with instructors	You are having trouble following the lecture style of a particular instructor.	Your psychology survey course has seven sections taught by different instructors; you have to choose one.

Successful Intelligence Connections Online

Listen to author Sarah Kravits discuss some additional ways to boost your creativity.

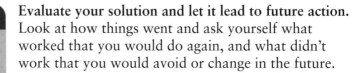

Go to the *Keys to Success* Companion Website at www.prenhall.com/carter to listen or download as a podcast.

Evaluate your solution and let it lead to future action. Look at how things went and ask yourself what worked that you would do again, and what didn't work that you would avoid or change in the future.

What happens if you don't work through a problem comprehensively? Take, for example, a student having an issue with an instructor. The student may get into an argument with the instructor, stop showing up to class, or take a quick-and-dirty approach to assignments. All of these choices have negative consequences. Now look at how the student might work through this problem using analytical, creative, and practical thinking skills. Key 4.10 shows how his effort can pay off.

Making a Decision

As you use the steps in Key 4.8 to make a decision, remember these strategies:

Look at the given options—then try to think of more. Some decisions have a given set of options. For example, your school may allow you to major, double major, or major and minor. However, you may be able to brainstorm with an advisor to come up with more options, such as an interdisciplinary major. As with problem solving, consider similar situations you've been in or heard about, what decisions were made, and what resulted from those decisions.

Think about how your decision affects others. What you choose might have an impact on friends, family, and others around you. Your conclusions about that impact may affect what decision you ultimately make.

Gather perspectives. Talk with others who have made similar decisions. There are more ways of doing things than one brain can possibly imagine on its own.

Look at the long-term effects. As with problem solving, a final evaluation is crucial. For important decisions, do a short-term evaluation and another evaluation after a period of time. Examine whether your decision has sent you down a path that has continued to bring positive effects or whether you should rethink your choice.

Consider all of the factors. Psychologists who study decision making realize that many random factors influence the choices people make. For example, you may choose a major, not because you love the subject, but because you think your parents will approve of it. The goal is to make well-considered decisions despite factors that may derail your thinking.

What happens when you make important decisions too quickly? Consider the student trying to decide whether to transfer schools. If she makes her decision based on a reason that ultimately is not the most important one for her (for example, a boyfriend or close friends go to the other school), she may regret her choice later. Key 4.11 shows how she worked through the analytical, creative, and practical parts of the process.

KEY 4.10 Working through a problem relating to an instructor.

DEFINE PROBLEM HERE:

I don't like my Freshman Composition instructor

ANALYZE THE PROBLEM

We have different views and personality types—
I don't feel respected or heard.
I'm not interested in being there and my grades are suffering from my lack of motivation.

Use boxes below to list possible solutions:

POTENTIAL POSITIVE EFFECTS	SOLUTION	POTENTIAL NEGATIVE EFFECTS
List for each solution: Don't have to deal with that instructor Less stress	**SOLUTION #1** Drop the course	*List for each solution:* Grade gets entered on my transcript I'll have to take the course eventually; it's required for my major
Getting credit for the course Feeling like I've honored a commitment	**SOLUTION #2** Put up with it until the end of the semester	Stress every time I'm there Lowered motivation Probably not such a good final grade
A chance to express myself Could get good advice An opportunity to ask direct questions of the instructor	**SOLUTION #3** Schedule meetings with advisor and instructor	Have to face instructor one-on-one Might just make things worse

Now choose the solution you think is best—circle it and make it happen.

ACTUAL POSITIVE EFFECTS	PRACTICAL ACTION	ACTUAL NEGATIVE EFFECTS
List for chosen solution: Got some helpful advice from advisor Talking in person with the instructor actually promoted a fairly honest discussion I won't have to take the course again	I scheduled and attended meetings with both advisor and instructor, and opted to stick with the course.	*List for chosen solution:* The discussion was difficult and sometimes tense I still don't know how much learning I'll retain from this course

FINAL EVALUATION: Was it a good or bad solution?

The solution has improved things. I'll finish the course, and even though the instructor and I aren't the best of friends, we have a mutual understanding now. I feel more respected and more willing to put my time into the course.

Source: Based on heuristic created by Frank T. Lyman Jr. and George Eley, 1985.

KEY 4.11 Making a decision about whether to transfer schools.

DEFINE THE DECISION

Whether or not to transfer schools

EXAMINE NEEDS AND MOTIVES

I attend a small private college. My father has changed jobs and can no longer afford my tuition. My goal is to become a physical therapist, so I need a school with a full physical therapy program. My family needs to cut costs. I need to transfer credits.

Use boxes below to list possible choices:

POTENTIAL POSITIVE EFFECTS	CHOICE	POTENTIAL NEGATIVE EFFECTS
List for each solution:	**CHOICE #1**	*List for each solution:*
No need to adjust to a new place or new people Ability to continue course work as planned	Continue at the current college	Need to finance most of my tuition and costs on my own Difficult to find time for a job Might not qualify for aid
Opportunity to connect with some high school friends Cheaper tuition and room costs Credits will transfer	**CHOICE #2** Transfer to a state college	Need to earn some money or get financial aid Physical therapy program is small and not very strong
Many physical therapy courses available School is close so I could live at home and save room costs Reasonable tuition; credits will transfer	**CHOICE #3** Transfer to the community college	No personal contacts there that I know of Less independence if I live at home No bachelor's degree available

Now choose the one you think is best—circle it and make it happen.

ACTUAL POSITIVE EFFECTS	PRACTICAL ACTION	ACTUAL NEGATIVE EFFECTS
List for chosen solution:		*List for chosen solution:*
Money saved Opportunity to spend time on studies rather than on working to earn tuition money Availability of classes I need	Go to community college for two years; then transfer to a four-year school to get a B.A. and complete physical therapy course work.	Loss of some independence Less contact with friends

FINAL EVALUATION: Was it a good or bad choice?

I'm satisfied with the decision. It can be hard being at home at times, but my parents are adjusting to my independence and I'm trying to respect their concerns. With fewer social distractions, I'm really getting my work done. Plus the financial aspect of the decision is ideal.

Source: Based on heuristic created by Frank T. Lyman Jr. and George Eley, 1985.

Keeping Your Balance

No one has equal strengths in analytical, creative, and practical thinking. Successfully intelligent thinkers are able to analyze their abilities, come up with creative ideas about how to maximize their strengths and build their weaknesses, and put them to use with practical action. Staying as balanced as possible requires that you do the following:

- Use what you've learned in this chapter and the rest of the text to maximize your analytical, creative, and practical abilities.
- Reflect on what you do well, and focus on strengthening weaker skills.
- Combine all three thinking skills to accomplish your goals, knowing when and how to apply your analytical, creative, and practical abilities.
- Believe in your skills as a thinker.

"Successfully intelligent people," says Sternberg, "defy negative expectations, even when these expectations arise from low scores on IQ or similar tests. They do not let other people's assessments stop them from achieving their goals. They find their path and then pursue it, realizing that there will be obstacles along the way and that surmounting these obstacles is part of the challenge."[27] Let the obstacles come, as they will for everyone, in all aspects of life. You can face and overcome them with the power of your successfully intelligent thinking.

Successful Intelligence Wrap-Up

With the power of successful intelligence, you can identify your most significant goals, devise ways to pursue them, and most importantly, take concrete actions to attain them. In addition, you can move beyond a fixed view of your intelligence. Here's how you have built skills in chapter 4:

Analytical

You explored the steps and parts of analytical thinking in the section on analytical thinking skills, including crucial topics such as fact vs. opinion, perspective, and how examples support an idea. In the *Get Analytical* exercise, you honed your skills by analyzing a statement. At the end of the chapter, you considered how to use your analytical skills to evaluate potential ideas and choices in the problem-solving and decision-making processes.

Creative

You developed a detailed understanding of creative thinking as you read the section on creative thinking skills. You learned of some creativity-boosting strategies and probably thought of more. In the *Get Creative* exercise, you brainstormed creative acts as well as new ideas about how to deal with a problem. In the section on problem solving and decision making, you explored ways to brainstorm solutions and choices.

Practical

You broadened your concept of practical thinking as you read the section on practical thinking skills, including developing more specific ideas of how to apply your emotional and social intelligence. In the *Get Practical* exercise, you built a picture of how you see your successful intelligence and generated practical ideas about how to improve. When reading about problem solving and decision making, you explored practical ways to put solutions and choices to work.

kunnskaping

(kun-skahp-ping)

This Norwegian word is a creative combination of *kunnskap* (meaning "knowledge") and *verdiskaping* (meaning "value creation"). It translates loosely as "knowledging," which can be read as developing knowledge and meaning that are of use in school and work.[28] In the global marketplace described by Thomas Friedman (see chapter 1), knowledge as a tool and product is more important than ever before.

Think of this concept as you use your analytical, creative, and practical thinking skills to solve problems, make decisions, innovate, and question. Successful intelligence enables you to put knowledge to work as you strive toward your goals. It also empowers you to be creative, in much the same way that some clever Norwegian was when he or she coined *kunnskaping* and made it part of the language.

"I am enough of an artist to draw freely upon my imagination. Imagination is more important than knowledge. Knowledge is limited. Imagination encircles the world."

ALBERT EINSTEIN, MATHEMATICIAN AND SCIENTIST

Building World-Class Skills for College, Career, and Life Success

SUCCESSFUL INTELLIGENCE

Think, Create, Apply

Make an important decision. Put the decision-making process to work on something that matters to you. You will apply your analytical, creative, and practical thinking skills. Use a separate sheet of paper for steps 2, 3, and 5.

Step 1. Analyze: ***Define the decision.*** Write an important long-term goal that you have, and define the decision that will help you fulfill it. Example: "My goal is to become a nurse. My decision: What to specialize in."

Step 2. Analyze: ***Examine needs and concerns.*** What are your needs, and how do your values come into play? What is most needed in the health market, and how can you fulfill that need? What roadblocks might be involved? List everything you come up with. For example, the prospective nurse might list needs like these: "I need to feel that I'm helping people. I intend to help with the shortage of perinatal or geriatric nurses. I need to make a good living."

Step 3. Be creative: ***Generate options.*** Ask questions to imagine what's possible. Where might you work? What might be the schedule and pace? Who might work with you? What would you see, smell, and hear on your job? What would you do every day? List, too, all of the options you know of. The prospective nurse, for example, might list perinatal surgery, neonatal intensive care unit, geriatric nursing in a hospital or in a retirement community, and so forth.

Step 4. Analyze: ***Evaluate options.*** Think about how well your options will fulfill your needs. For two of your options, write potential positive and negative effects (pros and cons) of each.

Option 1:

____

Potential pros:

____

Potential cons:

Option 2:

Potential pros:

Potential cons:

Step 5. Get practical: ***Imagine acting on your decision.*** Describe one practical course of action, based on your thinking so far, that you might follow. List the specific steps you would take. For example, the prospective nurse might list actions that help him determine what type of nursing suits him best, such as interning, summer jobs, academic goals, and talking to working nurses.

An additional practical action is to go where the job is and talk to people. The prospective nurse might go to a hospital, a clinic, and a health center at a retirement community. Get a feel for what the job is like day-to-day so that can be part of your decision.

TEAMWORK

Create Solutions Together

Powerful group problem solving. On a 3-by-5 card or a plain sheet of paper, each student in the class writes a school-related problem—this could be a fear, a challenge, a sticky situation, or a roadblock. Students hand these in without names. The instructor writes the list on the board.

Divide into groups of two to four. Each group chooses one problem to work on (try not to have two groups working on the same problem). Use the problem-solving flowchart (Key 4.12) on page 139 to fill in your work.

Analyze: ***Define and examine the problem.*** As a group, look at the negative effects and state your problem specifically. Write down the causes and examine them to see what's happening. Gather information from all group members, verify facts, and go beyond assumptions.

Create: ***Generate possible solutions.*** From the most likely causes of the problem, derive possible solutions. Record all the ideas that group members offer. After 10 minutes or so, each group member should choose one possible solution to evaluate independently.

Analyze: ***Evaluate each solution.*** In thinking independently through the assigned solution, each group member should (1) weigh the positive and negative effects, (2) consider similar problems, and (3) describe how the solution affects the causes of the problem. Will your solution work?

Get practical: ***Choose a solution.*** Group members then come together, share observations and recommendations, and then take a vote: Which solution is the best? You may have a tie or may want to combine two different solutions. Try to find the solution that works for most of the group. Then, together, come up with a plan for how you would put your solution to work.

KEY 4.12

Work through a problem using this flowchart.

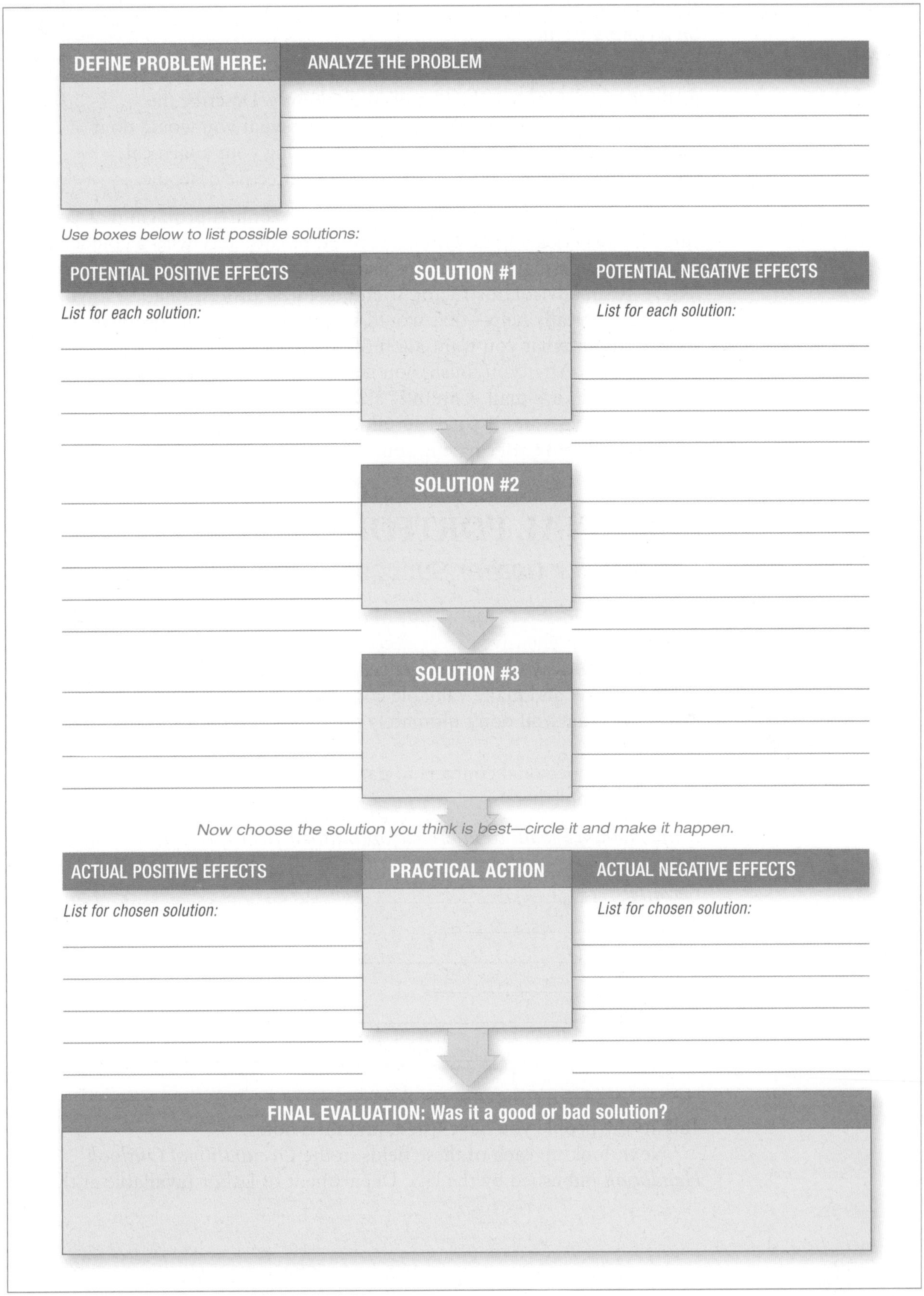

Source: Based on heuristic created by Frank T. Lyman Jr. and George Eley, 1985.

WRITING

Journal and Put Skills to Work

Record your thoughts on a separate piece of paper, in a journal, or on a computer file.

Journal entry: Make a wiser choice. Think about a decision you made that you wish you had handled differently. Describe the decision and its consequences. Then, describe what you would do if you could approach the decision again, applying your analytical, creative, and practical skills to reach a more effective outcome.

Real-life writing: Address a problem. Think about a problem that you are currently experiencing in school—it could be difficulty with a course, a scheduling nightmare, or perhaps a conflict with a classmate. Write a letter—to an advisor, instructor, friend, medical professional, or anyone else who may logically help—that would solicit input on your problem. Be specific about what you want and how the person to whom you are writing can help you. After you finish, you may want to consider sending your letter via mail or e-mail. Carefully assess the potential effects that your letter may have—and if you determine that it is likely to help more than harm, send it only after having someone you trust review it for you.

PERSONAL PORTFOLIO

Prepare for Career Success

Generating ideas for internships. Pursuing internships is part of a comprehensive career decision-making process. It's a practical way to get experience, learn what you like and don't like, and make valuable connections. Even if you intern in a career area that you don't ultimately pursue, you build skills that are useful in any career.

First, use personal contacts to gather information about career fields. List three people here:

People whom I want to interview about their fields/professions, and why:

1. ____________________ *Field:* ____________________

Because: ____

2. ____________________ *Field:* ____________________

Because: ____

3. ____________________ *Field:* ____________________

Because: ____

____

____

Talk to the people you have listed, and take notes.

Next, look up each of these fields in the *Occupational Outlook Handbook* published by the U.S. Department of Labor (available at the library, or online at http://stats.bls.gov/oco/home.htm). To get a better idea of whether you would want to intern in these fields, read OOH categories for each—such as Nature of the Work, Training, Working Conditions, Advancement, Job Outlook, Earnings, and so on. Take notes and compare the fields based on what you've learned.

Finally, consult someone in your school's career office about local companies that offer internships. Get specific information about internship job descriptions, timing (during the term, summer), and whether there is any pay involved.

Analyze what you have learned from your reading, your interviews, and the career office information. Write here in what field or fields you would like to intern and why, and describe what practical action you plan to take to secure an internship within the next two years:

Suggested Readings

Cameron, Julia, with Mark Bryan. *The Artist's Way: A Spiritual Path to Higher Creativity,* 10th ed. New York: Putnam, 2002.

deBono, Edward. *Lateral Thinking: Creativity Step by Step*. New York: Perennial Library, 1990.

Goleman, Daniel. *Emotional Intelligence: Why It Can Matter More Than IQ, 10th Anniversary Edition*. New York: Bantam Books, 2006.

Goleman, Daniel. *Social Intelligence: The New Science of Social Relationships*. New York: Bantam Books, 2006.

Moscovich, Ivan. *1000 Playthinks*. New York: Workman, 2001.

Noone, Donald J. *Creative Problem Solving*. New York: Barron's, 1998.

SARK. *Make Your Creative Dreams Real: A Plan for Procrastinators, Perfectionists, Busy People, and People Who Would Rather Sleep All Day*. New York: Fireside, 2004.

von Oech, Roger. *A Kick in the Seat of the Pants*. New York: Harper & Row, 1986.

von Oech, Roger. *A Whack on the Side of the Head*. New York: Warner Books, 1998.

Internet and Podcast Resources

Creativity at Work (resources for workplace creativity): **www.creativityatwork.com**

Creativity for Life (tips and strategies for creativity): **www.creativityforlife.com**

Free Management Library—Problem Solving: **www.managementhelp.org/prsn_prd/prob_slv.htm**

"Get Creative" podcast from Podcast Alley, on the topic of problem solving and creativity: **www.podcastalley.com/search.php?searchterm=problem+solving**

"LSAT Logic in Everyday Life" podcasts on thinking, from the *Princeton Review:* **www.princetonreview.com/podcasts/lsat.asp**

Mind Tools—Decision Making Techniques:
www.mindtools.com/pages/main/newMN_TED.htm

Roger von Oech's Creative Think Web site:
www.creativethink.com

Prentice Hall Student Success Supersite:
www.prenhall.com/success

Endnotes

[1]Matt Thomas, "What Is Higher-Order Thinking and Critical/Creative/Constructive Thinking?" n.d., Center for Studies in Higher-Order Literacy (http://a-s.clayton.edu/tparks/What%20is%20Higher%20Order%20Thinking.doc).

[2]Vincent Ruggiero, *The Art of Thinking*, 2001, quoted in "Critical Thinking," Oregon State University (http://success.oregonstate.edu/criticalthinking.html).

[3]From "The Role of Socratic Questioning in Thinking, Teaching, and Learning," n.d., The Critical Thinking Community, Foundation for Critical Thinking (www.criticalthinking.org/page.cfm?PageID=522&CategoryID=71), based on Richard W. Paul, Douglas Martin, and Ken Adamson, *Critical Thinking Handbook: High School,* 1989, Foundation for Critical Thinking.

[4]"The Best Innovations Are Those That Come from Smart Questions," *Wall Street Journal*, April 12, 2004, p. B1.

[5]Angiotech Pharmaceuticals, "Angiotech Submits Application for European Regulatory Approval for Its Vascular Wrap Product," news release, November 16, 2006 (www.angiotech.com/news/press-releases/?id=709).

[6]Sharon Begley, "Critical Thinking: Part Skill, Part Mindset and Totally Up to You," *Wall Street Journal*, October 20, 2006, p. B1.

[7]Robert J. Sternberg, *Successful Intelligence,* New York: Plume, 1996, p. 128.

[8]Colby Glass, "Strategies for Critical Thinking," March 1999 (www.criticalthink.info/Phil1301/ctstrategies.htm).

[9]Sternberg, *Successful Intelligence,* p. 49.

[10]Charles Cave, "Definitions of Creativity," August 1999 (http://members.optusnet.com.au/~charles57/Creative/Basics/definitions.htm).

[11]Elizabeth F. Farrell, "Engineering a Warmer Welcome for Female Students: The Discipline Tries to Stress Its Social Relevance, an Important Factor for Many Women," *Chronicle of Higher Education*, February 22, 2002 (http://chronicle.com/weekly/v48/i24/24a03101.htm).

[12]Roger von Oech, *A Kick in the Seat of the Pants*, New York: Harper & Row, 1986, pp. 5–21.

[13]Dennis Coon, *Introduction to Psychology: Exploration and Application*, 6th ed., St. Paul: West, 1992, p. 295.

[14]Roger von Oech, *A Whack on the Side of the Head,* New York: Warner Books, 1990, pp. 11–168.

[15]J. R. Hayes, *Cognitive Psychology: Thinking and Creating,* Homewood, IL: Dorsey, 1978.

[16]Sternberg, *Successful Intelligence,* p. 219.

[17]Adapted from T. Z. Tardif and R. J. Sternberg, "What Do We Know About Creativity?" in *The Nature of Creativity*, R. J. Sternberg, ed., London: Cambridge University Press, 1988.

[18]Sternberg, *Successful Intelligence,* p. 212

[19]Hayes, *Cognitive Psychology.*

[20]"The Best Innovations," p. B1.

[21]Sternberg, *Successful Intelligence,* pp. 229–230.

[22]"Amazing Student, David Hosei—Entrepreneur with a Heart," 2003 Indiana University (http://excellence.indiana.edu/hosei; no longer available).

[23]Sternberg, *Succesful Intelligence,* p. 236.

[24]Robert J. Sternberg and Elena L. Grigorenko, "Practical Intelligence and the Principal," Yale University: Publication Series No. 2, 2001, p. 5.

[25]Sternberg, *Successful Intelligence,* pp. 251–269.

[26]Ibid., p. 241.

[27]Ibid., p. 128.

[28]Christopher J. Moore, *In Other Words: A Language Lover's Guide to the Most Intriguing Words Around the World,* New York: Walker, 2004, p. 61.

Answers to perception puzzles on page 122

First puzzle: A duck or a rabbit

Second puzzle: A face or a musician

Third puzzle: Lines or the letter E

READING AND STUDYING

Focusing on Content

5

"Successful intelligence is most effective when it balances all three of its analytical, creative, and practical aspects. It is more important to know when and how to use these aspects of successful intelligence than just to have them."

ROBERT J. STERNBERG

Your ability to read—and to understand, analyze, and use what you read—is the cornerstone of college learning. Taking a step-by-step approach to reading linked to analytical, creative, and practical thinking techniques will help you master content, whether you are getting ahead of the game with a stack of summer reading or staying up late studying for finals. This chapter introduces strategies to increase your efficiency and depth of understanding so that every hour you spend reading will be more valuable.

In this chapter you explore answers to the following questions:

Chapter 5's Successful Intelligence Skills

Analytical

- Identifying steps to improve comprehension
- Mastering SQ3R
- Building vocabulary by mastering roots, prefixes, and suffixes
- Critically evaluating reading passages

Creative

- Creating an environment that encourages concentration
- Adapting SQ3R to your unique studying needs
- Using colors and notations to highlight text and take text notes

Practical

- How to study word parts to build vocabulary
- How to make SQ3R a personal tool
- How to put highlighting and note-taking systems into action

What Will Improve Your Reading Comprehension?

Reading is an analytical process that requires you, the reader, to make meaning from written words. You do this by connecting what you know to what you read. Your understanding is affected by your familiarity with a subject, your cultural background and life experiences, and the way you interpret words and phrases.

Because these factors are different for every person, your reading experiences are uniquely your own. If, for example, your family owns a hardware store where you worked during summers, you will read a retailing chapter in a business text from the perspective of your work in the store. While you are comparing text concepts to your family's business practices, your classmates may be reading for basic ideas and vocabulary.

Improving your reading comprehension is especially important in college because assignments are generally longer, more difficult, and require a lot of independent work. In addition, what you learn from introductory-level texts is the foundation for your understanding in advanced courses. When you struggle through and master concepts that you considered impossible the first time you read them, you'll be proud of your ability to overcome obstacles instead of giving up. This pride will motivate you every time you read.

REAL QUESTIONS

How can I improve my reading and studying despite my learning disabilities?

Darrin Estepp
Ohio State University,
Columbus, Ohio

In elementary school I needed extra help with reading. By high school, I was having a hard time keeping up, and a test showed I had dyslexia. Study assistance helped, but I attended high school for an extra year to improve my record.

I learn best by hearing, seeing, and doing all at once. If I just hear something, it doesn't sink in. I keep hanging in there though. Eventually, when I have a career, I would like to help others. I can see myself being on the lookout for early signs of disabilities like mine. What suggestions do you have that will help me cope with my learning disabilities?

PRACTICAL ANSWERS

Morgan Paar
Graduate Student,
Academy of Art College
San Francisco, California

One thing I learned in college is that there is more than one way to succeed, even when I had trouble keeping up with the reading.

First, I attended every single class without exception. Second, if I got behind in my note taking (and I often did), I would borrow a friend's notes and rewrite mine, combining the two versions. Third, I made friends with my teachers, and they would help me during their office hours.

One incident showed me that anything is possible. A friend worked for a newspaper and asked me to write a story. I laughed—I said I could barely spell my name, never mind write an article. I labored through it; my friend loved the writing (despite my "creative grammar"), and it appeared as a two-part story in the travel section. I have since had 17 articles published.

It never gets easy—but one route to success is to do something you love. I write travel stories because I love traveling and sharing stories. I am now a filmmaker, and I am studying film in graduate school so I can someday teach it. Darrin, you already know the skills you need to achieve your goals, though maybe they are deep in your subconscious mind. I was 27 years old before I knew what I really wanted to do. Just keep following your passions, never give up, figure out what you need to do to achieve your goals, and know that there is more than one path to your destination.

Set Your Expectations

On any given day, you may be faced with reading assignments like this:

- A 10-page textbook chapter on the history of South African apartheid (world history)
- An original research study on the relationship between sleep deprivation and the development of memory problems (psychology)
- The first three chapters in John Steinbeck's classic novel, *The Grapes of Wrath* (American literature)
- A technical manual on the design of computer antivirus programs (computer science, software design)

get creative!

See the Movie—Read the Book

Movies from *Gone With the Wind* to *The Devil Wears Prada* are based on popular books. The Mid-Continent Public Library (www.mcpl.lib.mo.us/readers/movies/year.cfm) compiles a yearly list of movies made from books. Search this list, choose a movie you would like to see (or see again), and then watch it on video. List the name of the movie here:

____

On a separate sheet or computer file, jot down your thoughts about the plot and characters and describe your reaction. Hold on to these thoughts for later.

During a school break, when you have time to read for pleasure, *read the book* on which the movie is based and write a similar page of reflections.

Then compare what you thought of the movie version to what you thought of the book. List three major differences here:

1. ______________________________
2. ______________________________
3. ______________________________

Describe what you gained from reading the book that you *did not* get from watching the movie.

____

____

Based on this experience, are you likely to make the movie–book connection again? Why or why not?

____

____

How might you use another work as a starting point for your own creative effort?

____

____

____

This material is rigorous by anyone's standards. You can help yourself handle it by setting higher expectations—*know at the start that you will read more than you ever did in high school*—and by challenging yourself to handle more complex ideas.

To get through it all—and master what you read—you need a systematic approach that taps into your analytic and practical thinking skills. Without one, you may face problems similar to those of a student at a large northeastern university, who explains:

> I did not get off to a great start because I had never really learned to study this enormous amount of material in a systematic way. I tended to do one subject for a big span of time and then neglect it for a week. Then I moved on to another subject, and forgot about that for a week. So there was no continuity within each course. That had a lot to do with it. Finally I figured it out. This year, I'm pushing myself to spend a little bit of time every day on each subject.[1]

Take an Active Approach to Difficult Texts

Because college texts are generally written to challenge the intellect, even those that are well written may be tough going, especially when you encounter new concepts and terms. This is often the case when assignments are from *primary sources*—original documents, including academic journal articles and scientific studies—rather than from *secondary sources*—other writers' interpretations of these documents.

The following strategies will help you take an active, positive approach to reading difficult material:

Think positively. Instead of telling yourself that you cannot understand, think positively. Tell yourself: *I can learn this material. I am a good reader. I can succeed.*

Have an open mind. Be careful not to prejudge assignments as impossible or boring or a waste of time and energy before you begin.

Look for order and meaning in seemingly chaotic reading materials. Use SQ3R and the critical reading strategies introduced later in this chapter to discover patterns and connections.

Don't expect to master material on the first pass. Instead, create a multistep plan: On your first reading, your goal is to gain an overview of key concepts and interrelationships. On subsequent readings, you grasp ideas and relate them to what you already know. By your last reading, you master concepts and details and can apply the material to problems.

Know that some texts require extra work and concentration. If new material doesn't click, scan background material—including the text you used last term—for information that will help you understand. Set a goal to make your way through the material, whatever it takes. *If you want to learn, you will.*

Define unclear concepts and words. Use your practical intelligence as you consult resources—instructors, study group partners, tutors, and reference materials—for help. Build a library of texts in your major and minor areas of study and refer to them when needed, and bookmark helpful Web sites.

Ask yourself questions. Put on your analytical thinking cap as you engage in an internal question-and-answer session before reading a chapter. Look at the chapter headings and think about what the material means and why it is being presented in this way. Write down your thoughts. Then read the chapter summary to see if your questions are answered. (Questioning is at the heart of the SQ3R study system that you will learn later in this chapter.)

Be honest with yourself. Ask yourself: Do I understand what I just read? Are ideas and supporting evidence clear? Am I able to explain the material to someone else?

Choose the Right Setting

Find the right place and time to focus on your reading:

Select the right company (or no company at all). If you prefer to read alone, find an out-of-the-way spot at the library. Even if you don't mind activity nearby, try to minimize distractions.

Select the right location. Many students study at a desk or in a comfortable chair. Still others like to spread out papers on the floor. Be careful about studying in bed—some students tend to fall asleep.

Select a time when you are alert and focused. Eventually, you will associate certain times with focused reading. Pay attention to your natural body rhythms and study when your energy is high. While night owls are productive when everyone else is sleeping, morning people have a hard time working during late-night sessions. Knowing yourself is a key to emotional intelligence.

Students with young children face the additional challenge of keeping their family busy while they work. Key 5.1 explores some ways that parents or others caring for children can maximize their study efforts.

Learn to Concentrate

When you focus your attention on one thing and one thing only, you are engaged in the act of **concentration**. Following are active learning methods for remaining focused as you study. Many involve tapping your emotional and social intelligence.

CONCENTRATION

The act of applying all your mental energy and focus to your academic work.

Be intensely involved. Tell yourself that what you are doing is important and needs your full attention—no matter what is going on around you. It might help to place a purpose statement at the top of your desk. For example: "I'm concentrating on the U.S. Constitution because it is the basis for our laws and because it will be on Friday's exam."

Banish extraneous thoughts onto paper. Don't let unrelated thoughts block your efforts. When such thoughts come up, write them down and deal with them later. Keeping a monthly calendar of classes, appointments, and events will help you stay organized.

Deal with internal distractions. Internal distractions—for example, personal worries or even hunger—can get in the way of work. Taking a break to deal with what's bothering you (a sign of emotional intelligence) will make you more efficient. Physical exercise may relax and focus you; studying while listening to music may relieve stress; and a snack break will reduce hunger.

KEY 5.1

Use these techniques to manage children while studying.

KEEP THEM UP-TO-DATE ON YOUR SCHEDULE

Let them know when you have a big test or project due and when you are under less pressure, and what they can expect of you in each case.

EXPLAIN WHAT YOUR EDUCATION ENTAILS

Tell them how it will improve your life and theirs. This applies, of course, to older children who can understand the situation and compare it with their own schooling.

FIND HELP

Ask a relative or friend to watch your children or arrange for a child to visit a friend. Consider trading baby-sitting hours with another parent, hiring a sitter to come to your home, or using a day care center.

KEEP THEM ACTIVE WHILE YOU STUDY

Give them games, books, or toys. If there are special activities that you like to limit, such as watching videos or TV, save them for your study time.

STUDY ON THE PHONE

You might be able to have a study session with a fellow student over the phone while your child is sleeping or playing quietly.

OFFSET STUDY TIME WITH FAMILY TIME AND REWARDS

Children may let you get your work done if they have something to look forward to, such as a movie night or a trip for ice cream.

SPECIAL NOTES FOR INFANTS

- Study at night if your baby goes to sleep early, or in the morning if your baby sleeps late.
- Study during nap times if you aren't too tired yourself.
- Lay your notes out and recite information to the baby. The baby will appreciate the attention, and you will get work done.
- Put baby in a safe and fun place while you study, such as a playpen, motorized swing, or jumping seat.

Compartmentalize your life. Social invitations may be easier to resist if you have a policy of separating study time from play time. Tell yourself: "I will be able to go out with my friends on Saturday because I'm finishing this assignment on Friday so I won't have to work over the weekend."

Analyze your environment to see if it helps or hurts concentration. Think about your last study session. How long did you *try to* concentrate and how long did you *actually* concentrate? If you spent more than 10% of

Different people respond better to some reading environments than to others. This student chose to live in a substance-free dormitory and prefers to study in her room.

your time blocking out distractions (people, things going on around you), try another location.

Don't let technology distract you. Don't Web-surf, e-mail, instant-message, or download songs onto your iPod while you are trying to read. Get into the habit of turning off your cell phone, and check voice mail and text messages only after you finish your work.

Structure your study session so you know the time you will spend and the material you will study. No one can concentrate for unlimited periods, so set realistic goals and a specific plan for dividing your time. Tell yourself: "I'm going to answer these 15 questions and then eat lunch with my friends for 45 minutes."

Plan a reward. Make sure you have something to look forward to, because you deserve it!

The strongest motivation to concentrate comes from within—not from the fear of failing a test or disappointing a teacher. When you see the connection between what you study and your short- and long-term goals, you will be better able to focus, to remember, to learn, and to apply.

Become Emotionally Involved

You are more likely to remember material that evokes an emotional response than material that does not affect you, as student success expert Eric Jensen explains:

> The stronger you feel about something you read the more likely you are to remember it and make sense out of it. The good thing about this is that it works both ways; hating something or disagreeing with something works just as well as liking something or strongly agreeing with it.[2]

This is easy to do with controversial material, but how do you surround normally "dry" text chapters with emotions? These suggestions might help:

- Stop and think about your reaction to ideas, to the author's point of view and writing style, to chapter features and text design, and even to the chapter order.
- Discuss specific points with classmates, and have a heated discussion when you disagree. This will also help you understand the material.
- Think through the implications of a concept when it is applied in the real world.

Define Your Reading Purpose

When you define your purpose, you ask yourself *why* you are reading particular material. One way to do this is by completing this sentence: "In reading this material, I intend to define/learn/answer/achieve . . ." *Write down your goal before you begin and look at it whenever you lose focus or get bogged down in details.* With a clear purpose, you can decide how much time and effort to expend on various assignments. This is particularly important in college where you may be overwhelmed by assignments unless you prioritize. Later in this chapter, you will find suggestions for prioritizing the readings on your plate.

Purpose Determines Reading Strategy

Following are four reading purposes. You may have one or more for any "reading event."

- *Purpose 1: Read for understanding.* Here you read to comprehend concepts and details. Details help explain or support general concepts, and concepts provide a framework for details.
- *Purpose 2: Read to evaluate analytically.* Analytical evaluation requires that you approach material with an open mind as you examine causes and effects, evaluate ideas, and ask questions that test arguments and assumptions. Analytical reading brings a level of understanding that goes beyond basic information recall (see pages 166–167 for more on this topic).
- *Purpose 3: Read for practical application.* Here you gather usable information to apply to a specific goal. When you read an instruction booklet for new software or a lab manual for chemistry, your goal is to learn how to do or use something. Reading and action usually go hand in hand.
- *Purpose 4: Read for pleasure.* Some materials you read for entertainment, such as *Sports Illustrated* magazine or a mystery or romance novel.

Use your class syllabus to help define your purpose for each assignment. If, for example, you know that the topic of inflation will be discussed in your next economics class, read the assigned chapter, targeting what your instructor will expect you to know and do with the material. He may expect you to master definitions, economic models, causes and consequences, government intervention strategies, and historical examples—and be able to apply your knowledge to economic problems. In this case, depending on what your instructor expects, you may have three reading purposes—understanding, critical evaluation, and practical application. If you are confused about your purpose, e-mail your instructor for clarification. He is likely to be impressed with your motivation to stay on top of your assignments.

Spend Enough Time

You'll need more than good intentions to finish assignments on schedule. You'll have to put in hours of work every day. One formula for success is this: *For every hour you spend in the classroom each week, spend at least two hours preparing for the class.* For example, if you are carrying a course load of 15 credit hours, you should spend 30 hours a week studying outside of class. Students who fall far short of this goal are likely to have trouble keeping up. Check your syllabus for the dates reading assignments are due, and give yourself enough time to complete them. (The syllabus on page 14 specifies reading assignments and due dates.)

Use Special Strategies with Math and Science Texts

Math and science readings present unique challenges to many students. Try some of the following analytical, creative, and practical thinking techniques to succeed:

- *Interact with the material critically as you go.* Math and science texts are problem-and-solution based. Keep a pad nearby to solve problems and take notes. Draw sketches to help visualize material. Try not to move on until you understand the example and how it relates to the central ideas. Write down questions for your instructor or classmates.
- *Note formulas.* Make sure you understand the principle behind every formula—why it works—before memorizing it.
- *Use memory techniques.* Science textbooks are packed with specialized vocabulary. To learn these new words, use mnemonic devices, flash cards, and rehearsing aloud or silently (for more on memory techniques, see chapter 6). Selective highlighting and summarizing your readings in table format will also help.

Develop Strategies to Manage Learning Disabilities

Students with reading-related learning disabilities may need to engage their practical thinking skills and emotional and social intelligence to manage reading assignments. Roxanne Ruzic of the Center for Applied Special Technology explored the strategies used by two LD students at an urban college in the Northeast:

- Danielle received an A in her Art History survey course, in part because she chose some courses with heavy reading requirements and some with light requirements. This allowed her to complete all her assignments on time. In addition, she frequently sought instructors' advice about what they wanted her to learn from assigned texts and used tutors whenever she needed extra help.
- Chloe received an A in her Introduction to Psychology course, in part because she met twice weekly with a tutor who helped her prioritize reading assignments and keep on top of her work. She also learned to tailor the amount of time she spent on different text sections to the importance of the material on upcoming tests. Finally, when she felt comfortable with text concepts, she read them quickly or skipped them entirely, but when she had trouble with the material, she did extra reading or sought help.[3]

If you have a learning disability, think of these students as you investigate the services your college offers through reading centers and tutoring programs. Remember: *The ability to succeed is often linked to the willingness to ask for help.* (See chapter 1 for more on learning disabilities and support services.)

Expand Your Vocabulary

As reading materials become more complex, your vocabulary influences how much you comprehend—and how readily you do it. Use the following techniques to learn unfamiliar words as you encounter them.

Analyze Word Parts

If you understand part of a word, you often can figure out the entire word. This is true because many English words combine Greek and Latin prefixes, roots, and suffixes. *Prefixes* are word parts that are added to the beginning of a root. The **root** is the central part or basis of a word around which prefixes and/or suffixes are added to produce different words. *Suffixes* are added to the end of the root.

ROOT

The central part or basis of a word around which prefixes and suffixes can be added to produce different words.

Key 5.2 contains just a few of the prefixes, roots, and suffixes you will encounter as you read. Taking the time to memorize these verbal building blocks will help you grow your vocabulary. (Keep in mind that although prefixes, roots, and suffixes are reliable tools, they do not always apply to words with complex origins.)

Use a Dictionary

When reading a textbook, the first "dictionary" to search is the end-of-book glossary that explains technical words and concepts. Those definitions are usually limited to the meanings used in the text.

Standard dictionaries provide broader information such as word origin, pronunciation, part of speech, synonyms, antonyms, and multiple meanings. Buy a standard dictionary, keep it nearby, and consult it to learn unfamiliar words. You may even want to invest in an electronic handheld dictionary or, if you prefer an online version, investigate Web sites like Dictionary.com (http://dictionary.reference.com). The following suggestions will help you make the most of your dictionary:

Read every meaning, not just the first. Think critically about which meaning suits the context of the word in question, and choose the one that makes the most sense to you.

Say the word out loud—then write it down to make sure you can spell it. Check your pronunciation against the dictionary symbols as you say each word, or listen to the pronunciation on a handheld electronic or online dictionary. (Merriam-Webster Online, at http://merriamwebster.com, has a pronunciation feature.) Speaking and writing new words will boost recall.

Restate the definition in your own words. When you can do this with ease, you know that you understand the meaning and are not merely parroting a dictionary definition.

Try to use the word in conversation in the next 24 hours. Not only does this demonstrate that you know how the word is used, but it also aids memorization.

Learn Specialized Vocabulary

As you learn a subject, you will encounter specialized, unfamiliar vocabulary (see Key 5.3 for examples from four college texts). Even if you

KEY 5.2

Build your vocabulary with common prefixes, roots, and suffixes.

PREFIX	PRIMARY MEANING	EXAMPLE
a-, ab-	from	abstain, avert
ad-, af-, at-	to	adhere, affix, attain
con-, cor-, com-	with, together	convene, correlate, compare
di-	apart	divert, divorce
il-	not	illegal, illegible
ir-	not	irresponsible
post-	after	postpone, postpartum
pro-	before	prologue
sub-, sup-	under	subordinate, suppose
ROOT	**PRIMARY MEANING**	**EXAMPLE**
-logue	to speak	dialogue
-com	fill	incomplete
-strict	bind	restriction
-cept	take	receptacle
-chron	time	synchronize
-ann	year	biannual
-sper	hope	desperate
-clam	cry out	proclamation
-voc	speak, talk	convocation
SUFFIX	**PRIMARY MEANING**	**EXAMPLE**
-able	able	recyclable
-arium	place for	aquarium, solarium
-cule	very small	molecule
-ist	one who	pianist
-meter	measure	thermometer
-ness	state of	carelessness
-sis	condition of	hypnosis
-y	inclined to	sleepy

feel like you are diving into a foreign language, know that continual exposure will lead to mastery.

Apply a basic vocabulary-building approach to learn these terms. Understand words in the context of the chapter; then turn to the glossary for a review, record definitions in your notes, create vocabulary flash cards, use terms in your own sentences, and more. Instead of rushing through unfamiliar words, look them up, ask other students about them, and relate them to what you already know.

KEY 5.3

Every text includes specialized vocabulary.

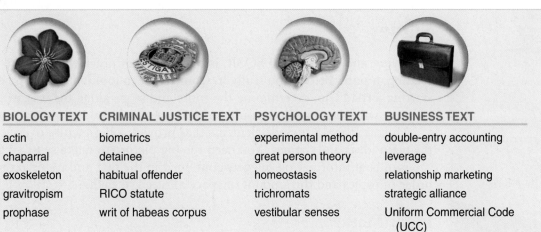

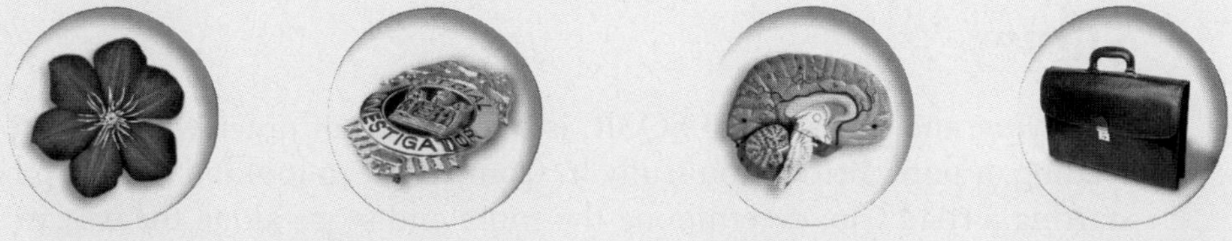

BIOLOGY TEXT	CRIMINAL JUSTICE TEXT	PSYCHOLOGY TEXT	BUSINESS TEXT
actin	biometrics	experimental method	double-entry accounting
chaparral	detainee	great person theory	leverage
exoskeleton	habitual offender	homeostasis	relationship marketing
gravitropism	RICO statute	trichromats	strategic alliance
prophase	writ of habeas corpus	vestibular senses	Uniform Commercial Code (UCC)

Your instructors will test you on your ability to define and use course-specific vocabulary, so make sure you understand terms well enough to define them correctly on short-answer tests and to use them on essay exams.

Use Memory Aids to Ensure Recall

Most students find that their most important vocabulary-building tool is the simple but very practical flash card. Your efforts will pay off if you study several cards a day and push yourself to use your new words in conversation and writing. Memorization tools, including mnemonic devices and flash cards, are discussed in chapter 6.

How Can SQ3R Help You Master Content?

SQ3R stands for *Survey, Question, Read, Recite*, and *Review*. Developed more than 60 years ago by Francis Robinson, the technique is still used today because it works.[4]

As you move through the stages of SQ3R, you will skim and scan your text. **Skimming** refers to the rapid reading of such chapter elements as section introductions and conclusions, boldfaced or italicized terms, pictures and charts, and summaries. The goal of skimming is a quick construction of the main ideas. In contrast, **scanning** involves a careful search for specific information. You might use scanning during the SQ3R review phase to locate particular facts.

SKIMMING

Rapid, superficial reading of material to determine central ideas and main elements.

SCANNING

Reading material in an investigative way to search for specific information.

Approach SQ3R as a *flexible framework* on which to build your study method. When you bring your personal learning styles and study preferences to the system, it will work better than if you follow it rigidly. For example, you and another classmate may focus on elements in a different order when you survey, write different types of questions, or favor different sets of

review strategies. Explore different strategies, evaluate what works, and then make the system your own. (Note that SQ3R is not appropriate for literature.)

Survey

Surveying, the first stage in SQ3R, is the process of previewing, or pre-reading, a book before you study it. Compare it to looking at a map before starting a road trip; determining the route and stops along the way in advance will save time and trouble while you travel.

Most textbooks include elements that provide a big-picture overview of the main ideas and themes. You need the big picture to make sense of the thousands of information nuggets contained in the text and to learn the order of topics and the amount of space allotted to each.

Front Matter

Skim the *table of contents* for the chapter titles, the main chapter topics, and the order in which they will be covered, as well as special features. Then skim the *preface,* which is a note from the author that tells you what the book will cover and its point of view. For example, the preface for the American history text *Out of Many* states that it highlights "the experiences of diverse communities of Americans in the unfolding story of our country."[5] This tells you that cultural diversity is a central theme.

Chapter Elements

Generally, every chapter includes structural elements that highlight important content:

- Chapter title, which establishes the topic and often the author's perspective
- Chapter introduction, outline, list of objectives, or list of key topics
- First, second, and third level headings
- Information in the margins including definitions, quotes, questions, and exercises
- Tables, charts, photographs, and captions that express important concepts
- Side-bar boxed features that are connected to text-wide themes
- Particular styles or arrangements of type (**boldface,** *italics*, underlining, larger fonts, bullet points, boxed text) that call attention to vocabulary or concepts
- An end-of-chapter summary that reviews chapter content
- Review questions and exercises that help you analyze and master content

In Key 5.4, a typical page from the college textbook *Psychology: An Introduction* by Charles G. Morris and Albert A. Maisto, how many elements do you recognize? How do these elements help you grasp the subject even before reading it?[6]

KEY 5.4

Various survey elements are included on this text page.

186 **Chapter 5** • Learning

Classical (or Pavlovian) conditioning The type of learning in which a response naturally elicited by one stimulus comes to be elicited by a different, formerly neutral stimulus.

Unconditioned stimulus (US) A stimulus that invariably causes an organism to respond in a specific way.

Unconditioned response (UR) A response that takes place in an organism whenever an unconditioned stimulus occurs.

Conditioned stimulus (CS) An originally neutral stimulus that is paired with an unconditioned stimulus and eventually produces the desired response in an organism when presented alone.

Conditioned response (CR) After conditioning, the response an organism produces when only a conditioned stimulus is presented.

you are experiencing insight. When you imitate the steps of professional dancers you saw last night on television, you are demonstrating observational learning. Like conditioning, cognitive learning is one of our survival strategies. Through cognitive processes, we learn which events are safe and which are dangerous without having to experience those events directly. Cognitive learning also gives us access to the wisdom of people who lived hundreds of years ago, and it will give people living hundreds of years from now some insight into our experiences and way of life.

Our discussion begins with *classical conditioning.* This simple kind of learning serves as a convenient starting point for examining what learning is and how it can be observed.

Classical Conditioning

How did Pavlov's discovery of classical conditioning help to shed light on learning?

Ivan Pavlov (1849–1936), a Russian physiologist who was studying digestive processes, discovered classical conditioning almost by accident. Because animals salivate when food is placed in their mouths, Pavlov inserted tubes into the salivary glands of dogs to measure how much saliva they produced when they were given food. He noticed, however, that the dogs salivated before the food was in their mouths: The mere sight of food made them drool. In fact, they even drooled at the sound of the experimenter's footsteps. This aroused Pavlov's curiosity. What was making the dogs salivate even before they had the food in their mouths? How had they learned to salivate in response to the sound of the experimenter's approach?

To answer these questions, Pavlov set out to teach the dogs to salivate when food was not present. He devised an experiment in which he sounded a bell just before the food was brought into the room. A ringing bell does not usually make a dog's mouth water but, after hearing the bell many times just before getting fed, Pavlov's dogs began to salivate as soon as the bell rang. It was as if they had learned that the bell signaled the appearance of food, and their mouths watered on cue even if no food followed. The dogs had been conditioned to salivate in response to a new stimulus—the bell—that would not normally have prompted that response (Pavlov, 1927). Figure 5–1, shows one of Pavlov's procedures in which the bell has been replaced by a touch to the dog's leg just before food is given.

Elements of Classical Conditioning

Generally speaking, **classical (or Pavlovian) conditioning** involves pairing an *involuntary* response (for example, salivation) that is usually evoked by one stimulus with a different, formerly neutral stimulus (such as a bell or a touch on the leg). Pavlov's experiment illustrates the four basic elements of classical conditioning. The first is an **unconditioned stimulus (US)**, such as food, which invariably prompts a certain reaction—salivation, in this case. That reaction—the **unconditioned response (UR)**—is the second element and always results from the unconditioned stimulus: Whenever the dog is given food (US), its mouth waters (UR). The third element is the neutral stimulus—the ringing bell—which is called the **conditioned stimulus (CS).** At first, the conditioned stimulus is said to be "neutral" with respect to the desired response (salivation), because dogs do not salivate at the sound of a bell unless they have been conditioned to react in this way by repeatedly presenting the CS and US together. Frequent pairing of the CS and US produces the fourth element in the classical conditioning process: the **conditioned response (CR).** The conditioned response is the behavior that the animal has learned in response to the conditioned stimulus. Usually, the unconditioned response and the conditioned

Source: Psychology: An Introduction, 12th ed., by Morris/Maisto, © 2005. Reprinted by permission of Pearson/Prentice Hall, Upper Saddle River, NJ.

Back Matter

Some texts include a *glossary* that defines text terms, an *index* to help you locate topics, and a *bibliography* that lists additional readings.

GET ANALYTICAL!

Survey a Text

Practice will improve your surveying skills. So start now with this text or another you are currently using.

- Skim the front matter, including the table of contents and preface. What does this material tell you about the theme? About the book's approach and point of view?

- Are there unexpected topics listed in the table of contents? Are there topics you expected to see that are missing?

- Now look at a typical chapter. List the devices that organize the structure and content of the material.

- After skimming the chapter, what do you know about the material? What elements helped you skim quickly?

- Finally, skim the back matter. What elements can you identify?

- How do you plan to use each of the elements you identified in your text survey when you begin studying?

Question

Your next step is to *ask questions* about your assignment. This process leads you to discover knowledge on your own, which is the essence of critical thinking (see chapter 4). As you pose questions and discover the answers in your text, you teach yourself the material.

Step 1: Ask Yourself What You Know About the Topic

Before you begin reading, summarize in writing what you already know about the topic, if anything. As you perform this task, you delve into your knowledge base, preparing yourself to apply what you know to new material.

Thinking about your current knowledge is especially important in your major, where the concepts you learn in one course prepare you for subsequent courses. For example, while your first business course may introduce the broad concept of marketing research, an upper-level marketing course may explore how marketing research analyzes consumer behavior according to age, education, income and economic status, and attitudes. Learning this advanced material depends on understanding the basics.

Step 2: Write Questions Linked to Chapter Headings

Next, examine the chapter headings and, on a separate page or in the text margins, write questions linked to them. For an assignment without headings, divide the material into logical sections, and then develop questions based on what you think is the main idea of each section.

Key 5.5 shows how this works. The column on the left contains primary- and secondary-level headings from a section of *Out of Many*. The column on the right rephrases these headings in question form.

KEY 5.5

Create questions from headings.

HEADING	QUESTION
The Meaning of Freedom	What did freedom mean for both slaves and citizens in the United States?
Moving About	Where did African Americans go after they were freed from slavery?
The African American Family	How did freedom change the structure of the African American family?
African American Churches and Schools	What effect did freedom have on the formation of African American churches and schools?
Land and Labor after Slavery	How was land farmed and maintained after slaves were freed?
The Origins of African American Politics	How did the end of slavery bring about the beginning of African American political life?

There is no "correct" set of questions. Given the same headings, you could create different questions. Your goal is to engage the material as you begin to think critically about it.

Use Bloom's Taxonomy to Formulate Questions

Educational psychologist Benjamin Bloom developed Bloom's taxonomy because he believed that not all questions are created equal and that the greatest learning results from rigorous inquiry.[7] While some questions ask for a simple recall, said Bloom, others ask for higher levels of thinking. Key 5.6 shows the six levels of questions identified by Bloom: knowledge, understanding, application, analysis, synthesis, and evaluation. It also identifies verbs that are associated with each level. As you read, using these verbs to formulate specific questions will help you learn. Recognizing these verbs on essay tests will help you answer effectively.

KEY 5.6 **Use Bloom's taxonomy to formulate questions at different cognitive levels.**

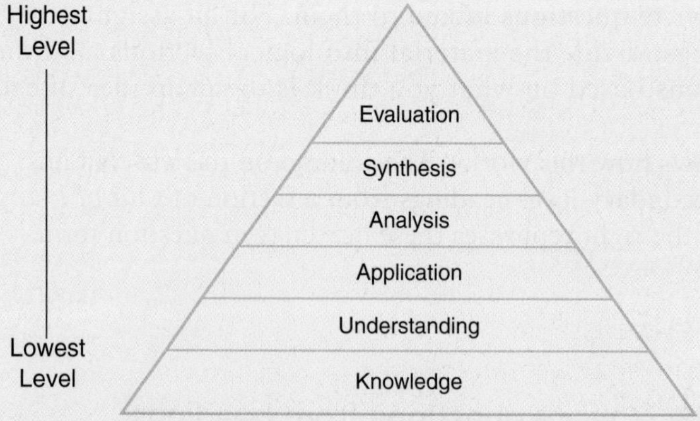

Verbs That Indicate Each Level

1. ***Knowledge:*** average, define, duplicate, label, list, memorize, name, order, recognize, relate, recall, repeat, reproduce, state.
2. ***Understanding:*** classify, describe, discuss, explain, express, identity, indicate, locate, recognize, report, restate, review, select, translate.
3. ***Application:*** apply, choose, demonstrate, dramatize, employ, illustrate, interpret, operate, practice, schedule, sketch, solve, use, write.
4. ***Analysis:*** analyze, appraise, calculate, categorize, compare, contrast, criticize, differentiate, discriminate, distinguish, examine, experiment, question, test.
5. ***Synthesis:*** arrange, assemble, collect, compose, construct, create, design, develop, formulate, manage, organize, plan, prepare, propose, set up, write.
6. ***Evaluation:*** appraise, argue, assess, attach, choose, compare, defend, estimate, judge, predict, rate, score, select, support, value, evaluate.

Read

Your text survey and questions give you a starting point for *reading*, the first R in SQ3R. Retaining what you read requires an active approach, as follows:

- *Focus on the key points of your survey.* Pay special attention to points raised in headings, in italics and boldface type, in chapter objectives, and in the summary.
- *Focus on your Q-stage questions.* Read the material with the purpose of answering each question. Write down or highlight ideas and examples that relate to your questions.
- *Mark up your text and take text notes.* Write notes in the margins or on separate paper, circle critical ideas, or highlight key points to focus on what's important. These cues will help you study for exams. Text-marking and note-taking techniques will be examined later in the chapter.
- *Create text tabs.* Place plastic index tabs or adhesive notes at the start of different chapters so you can flip back and forth with ease.

Find the Main Idea

Understanding what you read depends on your ability to recognize *main ideas* and link other ideas to them. Here are places you are likely to find these core ideas:

- In a topic sentence at the beginning of the paragraph, stating the topic of the paragraph and what about that topic the author wants to communicate, followed by support
- At the end of the paragraph, following supporting details that lead up to it
- Buried in the middle of the paragraph, sandwiched between supporting details
- In a compilation of ideas from various sentences, each of which contains a critical element, leaving it up to you to piece together these elements to find the main idea

When the main idea of a passage is unclear, use a three-step approach to decide what it is:[8]

1. *Search for the topic of the paragraph.* The topic of the paragraph is not the same as the main idea. Rather, it is the broad subject being discussed—for example, Apple CEO Steve Jobs, hate crimes on campus, or binge drinking on campus.
2. *Identify the aspect of the topic that is the paragraph's focus.* If the general topic is Steve Jobs, the author may focus on any of thousands of aspects of that topic, such as his cofounding of Apple Computer in 1976, his role in the Pixar computer animation company, or his role in the development of the iPod portable music player.
3. *Find what the author wants you to know about that specific aspect; this is the main idea.* The main idea of a paragraph dealing with Jobs's role in the development of the iPod may be this:

    In his role as CEO of Apple, Steve Jobs oversaw the creation of the iPod portable music player, which changed the way the world listens to and purchases music.

Prioritize Your Reading Assignments

Ask yourself what is important and what you have to remember. According to Adam Robinson, cofounder of the *Princeton Review,* successful students can tell the difference between information worthy of study, information they should know in a general way, and information they should ignore. Says Robinson: "The only way you can effectively absorb the relevant information is to ignore the irrelevant information. . . . Trying to digest and understand all the information in a textbook is . . . an excellent way to become quickly and hopelessly confused."[9]

The following questions will help you determine if text material is important enough to study in depth:

- Is the material stressed in headings, charts, tables, captions, key terms, and definitions? In mid-chapter and end-of-chapter exercises? In the chapter introduction and summary? (Surveying before reading will help you answer these questions.)
- Is the material a definition, a crucial concept, an example, an explanation of a variety or type, a critical relationship or comparison?
- Does it spark questions and reactions as you read?
- Does it surprise or confuse you?
- Did your instructor stress the material in class? Does your assignment ask you to focus on something specific?

When trying to figure out what to study and what to skim, ask yourself whether your instructor would expect you to know the material. If you are unsure and if the topic is not on your syllabus, e-mail your instructor and ask for clarification.

Recite

Once you finish reading a topic, stop and answer the questions you raised in the Q stage of SQ3R. *Even if you have already done this during the reading phase, do it again now—with the purpose of learning and committing the material to memory.*

You may decide to *recite* each answer aloud, silently speak the answers to yourself, "teach" the answers to another person, or write your ideas and answers in note form. Whatever recitation method you choose, make sure you know how ideas connect to one another and to the general concept being discussed.

Writing is the most effective way to learn new material. Using your own words to explain new concepts gives you immediate feedback: When you can do it effectively, you know the material. When you can't, you still need to work with the text or a study partner. Whatever you do, don't get discouraged. Just go back and search for what you missed.

Writing comprehensive responses at this stage can save time later. As you respond to your Q-stage questions, you can compare what you write to the text and make adjustments. Your responses then become a study tool for review.

Keep your learning styles in mind when you explore different strategies (see chapter 3). For example, an intrapersonal learner may prefer writing, while an interpersonal learner may choose to recite answers aloud to a classmate. A logical-mathematical learner may benefit from organizing material into detailed outlines or charts, while a musical learner might want to chant information aloud to a rhythm.

When do you stop to recite? Waiting for the end of a chapter is too late; stopping at the end of a paragraph is too soon. The best plan is to recite at the end of each text section, right before a new text heading. Repeat the question-read-recite cycle until you complete the chapter.

If you find yourself fumbling for thoughts, you have not mastered the ideas. Reread the section that's giving you trouble until you know it cold.

Review

Reviewing, both immediately and periodically in the days and weeks after you read, will help you learn and memorize material. If you close the book after reading it once, chances are that you will forget almost everything—which is why students who read material for the first time right before a test often do poorly. *Reviewing is your key to learning.*

Reviewing the same material over time will also help you identify knowledge gaps. It's natural to forget material between study sessions, especially if it's confusing or complex. When you come back after a break, you can focus on your deficits.

Here are some reviewing techniques. Try them all, and use the ones that work best:

- Reread your notes. Then summarize them from memory.
- Review and summarize in writing the text sections you highlighted or bracketed. Try to condense the material so that you can focus on key ideas.
- Answer the end-of-chapter review, discussion, and application questions.
- Reread the preface, headings, tables, and summary.
- Recite important concepts to yourself, or record and play them back on a tape player.
- Listen to audio recordings of your text and other reading materials on your MP3 player.
- Make flash cards with a word or concept on one side and a definition, examples, or other related information on the other. Test yourself.
- Quiz yourself, using the questions you raised in the Q stage. If you can't answer a question, scan the text for the answer.
- Discuss the concepts with a classmate or in a study group. Use each other's Q-stage questions to help one another learn.
- Finally, ask your instructor for help with difficult material. Define exactly what you want to discuss and then schedule a meeting during office hours or e-mail your questions.

Reviewing material with a classmate nearby can give you the opportunity to discuss and clarify ideas together.

KEY 5.7

Use SQ3R to become an active reader and learn new concepts.

STAGE OF SQ3R	DESCRIPTION
Survey	Pre-reading a book before studying it—involves skimming and scanning as you examine the front matter, chapter elements, and back matter for clues about text content and organization.
Question	Developing questions linked to chapter headings and to what you already know about the topic. Questioning engages your critical thinking skills.
Read	Reading the material to answer the questions formulated in the Q stage and find main ideas. You can take notes as you read or highlight key ideas and information in your text.
Recite	Recitation involves answering—perhaps for a second time—your Q-stage questions. You may decide to recite the answers aloud or silently to yourself, teach them to a study partner, or record them in writing.
Review	Using various techniques to learn the material before an exam. Become actively involved with the material through summarizing notes, answering study questions, writing outlines or think links, reciting concepts, using flash cards, thinking critically, and so on.

All this effort takes time, but the potential payoff is huge if you're motivated to work hard. Although at times it may be tempting to photocopy a classmate's text notes instead of reading and taking your own notes, you will learn only if you do the work yourself.

Refreshing your knowledge is easier and faster than learning the first time. Make a review schedule—for example, every three days—and stick to it until you're sure of your knowledge. Use different reviewing techniques as you work toward mastery.

Key 5.7 summarizes how SQ3R turns you into an active reader.

How Can You Respond Critically to What You Read?

Think of the reading process as an archaeological dig. The first step is to excavate a site and uncover the artifacts. The second step is to investigate your findings, evaluate meaning, and derive knowledge from your discoveries. Critical reading is comparable to this crucial second step.

Critical reading, like critical thinking, taps your analytical intelligence (see chapter 4). Instead of simply *accepting* what you read, seek *understanding* by questioning material as you move from idea to idea. The best critical readers question every statement for accuracy, relevance, and logic.

Use Knowledge of Fact and Opinion to Evaluate Arguments

Critical readers evaluate arguments to determine whether they are accurate and logical. In this context, the word *argument* refers to a persuasive case—a set of connected ideas supported by examples—that a writer makes to prove or disprove a point.

It's easy—and common—to accept or reject an argument outright, according to whether it fits with your point of view. If you ask questions, however, you can determine the argument's validity and understand it in greater depth. Evaluating an argument involves looking at these factors:

- The quality of the evidence
- Whether the evidence fits the concept
- The logical connections

EVIDENCE

Facts, statistics, and other materials that are presented in support of an argument.

When quality evidence combines with tight logic, the argument is solid.

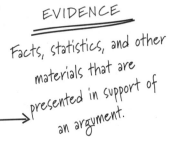

What is the quality of the evidence? Ask the following questions to evaluate the evidence:

- What is the source?
- Is the source reliable and free of bias?
- Who wrote this and with what intent?
- What assumptions underlie this material?
- Is the argument based on opinion?
- How does the evidence compare with evidence from other sources?

How well does the evidence support the idea? Ask these questions to determine whether the evidence fits the concept:

- Is there enough evidence to support the central idea?
- Do examples and ideas logically connect to one another?
- Is the evidence convincing? Do the examples build a strong case?
- What different and perhaps opposing arguments seem just as valid?

Approach every argument with healthy skepticism. Have an open mind in order to assess whether you are convinced or have serious questions.

In addition to the foregoing critical reading strategies, transforming your textbook into a valuable work tool through highlighting and notes will help you make the most of study time as you set the stage for review.

How Do You Customize Your Text with Highlighting and Notes?

Textbooks are designed and written with students in mind, but they are not customized to meet your unique reading and studying needs. It is up to you

Successful Intelligence Connections Online

Listen to author Sarah Kravits describe how to use analytical, creative, and practical intelligence to customize your text with highlighting and notes.

Go to the *Keys to Success* Companion Website at www.prenhall.com/carter to listen or download as a podcast.

to do that for yourself through text highlighting and notes. Your goal is to transform your texts into very personal study tools.

How to Highlight a Text

Highlighting involves the use of special markers or regular pens or pencils to flag important passages. When used correctly, highlighting is an essential study technique. The following techniques will help you make highlighting a learning tool:

- *Develop a highlighting system and stick to it.* For example, use your creative intelligence to decide if you will use different colored markers for different elements, brackets for long passages, or pencil underlining. Make a key that identifies each notation.
- *Consider using a regular pencil or pen instead of a highlighter pen.* The copy will be cleaner and look less like a coloring book than a textbook.
- *Read an entire paragraph before you begin to highlight, and don't start until you have a sense of what is important.* Only then put pencil or highlighter to paper as you pick out key terms, phrases, and ideas.
- *Avoid overmarking.* A phrase or two in any paragraph is usually enough. Enclose long passages with brackets rather than marking every line. Avoid underlining entire sentences, when possible. The less color the better.
- *Highlight supporting evidence.* Mark examples that explain important ideas.

Although these techniques will help you highlight effectively, they won't help you learn the material and, ironically, they may actually obstruct learning as you diligently add color to the page. Experts agree that you will not learn what you highlight unless you *interact* with the material through surveying, questioning, reciting, and review. Without this interaction, all you are doing is marking your book.

How to Take Text Notes

When you combine highlighting with marginal notes or text flags, you remind yourself what a particular passage is about and why you consider it important. This combination customizes your text, which helps you study for exams. Going a step further by taking a full set of text notes is an excellent way to commit material to memory.

As you will also see in chapter 6, note taking on texts and in class is critical because material is cumulative—that is, what you learn today builds on what you learned yesterday and the day before since the beginning of the term.

Taking Marginal Notes

Here are some tips for taking marginal notes right on the pages of your text:

- Use pencil so you can erase comments or questions that are answered as you read.

- Write your Q questions from SQ3R in the margins right next to text headings.
- Mark critical sections with marginal notations such as "def." for definition, "e.g." for helpful example, or "concept" for an important concept.
- Write notes at the bottom of the page connecting the text to what you learned in class or in research. You can also attach adhesive notes with your comments.

Key 5.8 shows how to underline effectively and take marginal notes in an introduction to business textbook that introduces the concept of target marketing and market segmentation.

Your customized text will be uniquely yours; no one else will highlight or take text notes as you do because no one else has your knowledge, learning style, or study techniques. Because text customization is so important to learning, you may find it hard to use previously owned texts that are heavily highlighted or filled with marginal notations. Even if the prior owner was a good student, he or she is not you—and that fact alone will affect your ability to master content.

Creating Full-Text Summaries

Taking a full set of notes on assigned readings helps you learn as you summarize main ideas in your own words. Taking notes makes you an active participant as you think about how material fits into what you already know and how to capture key points.

To construct a summary, focus on the main ideas and examples that support them. Don't include your own ideas or evaluations at this point. Your summary should simply condense the material, making it easier to focus on concepts and interrelationships when you review.

Here are suggestions for creating effective full-text summaries:

- Try to use your own words, because repeating the author's words may mean parroting concepts you do not understand. When studying a technical subject with precise definitions, you may have little choice but to use text wording.
- Try to make your notes simple, clear, and brief. Include what you need to understand about the topic, while eliminating less important details.
- Consider outlining the text so you can see how ideas relate to one another.
- Before you write, identify the main idea of a passage.
- Once that idea ends and another begins, begin taking notes from memory, using your own words. Go back into the text, as needed, to cull information that you didn't get on first reading.
- Take notes on tables, charts, photographs, and captions; these visual presentations may contain information presented nowhere else in the text.
- Use shorthand symbols to write quickly (see chapter 6).
- Create notes in visual form:
  - Construct your own charts, tables, and diagrams to depict written concepts.

KEY 5.8

Underlining and taking marginal notes help you master content.

Chapter 10: Understanding Marketing Processes and Consumer Behavior 297

How does target marketing and market segmentation help companies sell product?

TARGET MARKETING AND MARKET SEGMENTATION

Marketers have long known that products cannot be all things to all people. Buyers have different tastes, goals, lifestyles, and so on. The emergence of the marketing concept and the recognition of consumer needs and wants led marketers to think in terms of **target markets**—groups of people with similar wants and needs. Selecting target markets is usually the first step in the marketing strategy.

Target marketing requires **market segmentation**—dividing a market into categories of customer types or "segments." Once they have identified segments, companies may adopt a variety of strategies. Some firms market products to more than one segment. General Motors *(www.gm.com)*, for example, offers compact cars, vans, trucks, luxury cars, and sports cars with various features and at various price levels. GM's strategy is to provide an automobile for nearly every segment of the market.

In contrast, some businesses offer a narrower range of products, each aimed toward a specific segment. Note that segmentation is a strategy for analyzing consumers, not products. The process of fixing, adapting, and communicating the nature of the product itself is called *product positioning.*

Definitions

target market
Gr... of people that has similar ... ds and that can be ... w interest in the sa...

Chap...

← GM eg

market segmentation
Pro... ss of dividing a market into c... stomer types

Mar... have...

GM makes cars for diff. market segments

How do companies identify market segments?

Identifying Market Segments

By definition, members of a market segment must share some common traits that affect their purchasing decisions. In identifying segments, researchers look at several different influences on consumer behavior. Three of the most important are *geographic, demographic,* and *psychographic variables.*

What effect does geography have on segmentation strategies?

Geographic Variables Many buying decisions are affected by the places people call home. The heavy rainfall in Washington State, for instance, means that people there buy more umbrellas than people in the Sun Belt. Urban residents don't need agricultural equipment, and sailboats sell better along the coasts than on the Great Plains. **Geographic variables** are the geographical units, from countries to neighborhoods, that may be considered in a segmentation strategy.

These patterns affect decisions about marketing mixes for a huge range of products. For example, consider a plan to market down-filled parkas in rural Minnesota. Demand will be high and price competition intense. Local newspaper ads may be

Buying decisions influenced by where people live

geographic variables
Geo... aphical units that may be c... eveloping a ... rategy

by d... affec... diffe...

— good eg — selling parkas in Minnesota

Thought
Geographical variables change with the seasons

Source: Business Essentials, 5th ed., by Ebert/Griffin, © 2005. Reprinted by permission of Pearson/Prentice Hall, Upper Saddle River, NJ.

- Devise a color-coding system to indicate level of importance of different ideas, and then mark up your notes with these colors.
- Devise symbols and numbers and use them consistently to indicate the level of importance of different ideas. Write these in different-colored pens.

Mark Up a Page to Learn a Page

get practical!

Below, the text material in Key 5.8 continues. Put your own pencil to paper as you highlight concepts and take marginal notes. Compare your efforts to those of your classmates to see how each of you approached the task and what you can learn from their methods.

effective, and the best retail location may be one that is easily reached from several small towns.

Although the marketability of some products is geographically sensitive, others enjoy nearly universal acceptance. Coke, for example, gets more than 70 percent of its sales from international markets. It is the market leader in Great Britain, China, Germany, Japan, Brazil, and Spain. Pepsi's international sales are about 15 percent of Coke's. In fact, Coke's chief competitor in most countries is some local soft drink, not Pepsi, which earns 78 percent of its income at home.

demographic variables
Characteristics of populations that may be considered in dev... 298 segmentation strategy

Demographic Variables Demographic v**ariables** describe populations by identifying such traits as age, income, gender, ethnic background, marital status, race, religion, and social class. For example, several general consumption characteristics can be attributed to certain age groups (18–25, 26–35, 36–45, and so on). A marketer can, thus, divide markets into age groups. Table 10.1 lists some possible demographic breakdowns. Depending on the marketer's purpose, a segment can be a single classification (*aged* 20–34) or a combination of categories (*aged* 20–34, *married with children, earning* \$25,000–\$34,999). Foreign competitors, for example, are gaining market share in U.S. auto sales by appealing to young buyers (under age 30) with limited incomes (under \$30,000). Whereas companies such as Hyundai ***(www.hyundai.net)***, Kia *(www.kia.com)*, and Daewoo *(www.daewoous.com)* are winning entry-level customers with high quality and generous warranties, Volkswagen *(www.vw.com)* targets under-35 buyers with its entertainment-styled VW Jetta.[4]

psychographic variables
Consumer characteristics, such as lifestyles, opinions, intere... attitudes, that may be con... developing a segmentatio...

Psychographic Variables Markets can also be segmented according to such **psychographic variables** as lifestyles, interests, and attitudes. Take, for example, Burberry ***(www.burberry.com)***, whose raincoats have been a symbol of British tradition since 1856. Burberry has repositioned itself as a global luxury brand, like Gucci *(www.gucci.com)* and Louis Vuitton *(www.vuitton.com)*. The strategy, which recently resulted in a 31-percent sales increase, calls for attracting a different type of customer—the top-of-the-line, fashion-conscious individual—who shops at such stores as Neiman Marcus and Bergdorf Goodman.[5]

Psychographics are particularly important to marketers because, unlike demographics and geographics, they can be changed by marketing efforts. For example, Polish companies have overcome consumer resistance by promoting the safety and desirability of using credit rather than depending solely on cash. One product of changing attitudes is a booming economy and the emergence of a robust middle class.

TABLE 10.1
Demographic Variables

Age	Under 5, 5–11, 12–19, 20–34, 35–49, 50–64, 65+
Education	Grade school or less, some high school, graduated high school, some college, college degree, advanced degree
Family life cycle	Young single, young married without children, young married with children, older married with children under 18, older married without children under 18, older single, other
Family size	1, 2–3, 4–5, 6+
Income	Under \$9,000, \$9,000–\$14,999, \$15,000–\$24,999, \$25,000–\$34,999, \$35,000–\$45,000, over \$45,000
Nationality	African, American, Asian, British, Eastern European, French, German, Irish, Italian, Latin American, Middle Eastern, Scandinavian
Race	Native American, Asian, Black, White
Religion	Buddhist, Catholic, Hindu, Jewish, Muslim, Protestant
Sex	Male, female

MULTIPLE INTELLIGENCE STRATEGIES

FOR READING

APPLY DIFFERENT INTELLIGENCES TO CONCEPTS IN SOCIOLOGY.

INTELLIGENCE	USE MI STRATEGIES *to become a better reader*	APPLY MI READING STRATEGIES *to learn about social groups for your introduction to sociology course*
 Verbal-Linguistic	• Use the steps in SQ3R, focusing especially on writing Q-stage questions, summaries, and so on. • Make marginal text notes as you read.	• Summarize in writing the technical differences among social groups, categories, and crowds.*
 Logical-Mathematical	• Logically connect what you are reading with what you already know. Consider similarities, differences, and cause-and-effect relationships. • Draw charts showing relationships and analyze trends.	• Create a table comparing and contrasting the characteristics of primary and secondary social groups.
 Bodily-Kinesthetic	• Use text highlighting to take a hands-on approach to reading. • Take a hands-on approach to learning experiments by trying to re-create them yourself.	• Create an experiment that might turn a crowd of strangers into a social group joined together by a common problem.
 Visual-Spatial	• Make charts, diagrams, or think links illustrating difficult ideas you encounter as you read. • Take note of photos, tables, and other visual aids in the text.	• Create a visual aid showing four primary mechanisms through which people with shared experiences, loyalties, and interests meet—for example, through school and business—and how initial contacts may lead to deep social group relationships.
Interpersonal 	• Discuss reading material and clarify concepts in a study group. • Talk to people who know about the topic you are studying.	• Interview people who shared a difficult experience with a crowd of strangers—for example, people stuck in an elevator or train for an extended period—about how relationships changed as focus turned to a common problem.
 Intrapersonal	• Apply concepts to your own life; think about how you would manage. • Try to understand your personal strengths and weaknesses to lead a study group on the reading material.	• After reading about the nature of primary groups, think about the nature of your personal family relationships and the degree to which family members are your key support system.
Musical 	• Recite text concepts to rhythms or write a song to depict them. • Explore relevant musical links to the material.	• Listen to a rock concert that was performed in front of a live crowd. Then listen to the same music recorded in a studio. Think about performance differences that might link to the presence or absence of a crowd.
Naturalistic 	• Tap into your ability to notice similarities and differences in objects and concepts by organizing reading materials into relevant groupings.	• Over the next few weeks, ask some close friends if you can have dinner with them and their families. After the visits, try to identify characteristics that all the families share. Create a chart to report your findings.

*For information on social groups, see John J. Macionis, *Sociology,* 11th ed., Upper Saddle River, NJ: Prentice Hall, 2007.

Successful Intelligence Wrap-Up

Reading and studying are the tools you will use over and over again to acquire information in your personal and community life and career. After college, you will be figuring out almost everything on your own—your 401(k) retirement plan, a new office-wide computer system, or even the fine print in a cell phone contract. Your reading success may depend on your ability to use successful intelligence. Here's how you have built skills in chapter 5:

Analytical

You explored an analytical approach to reading comprehension, taking a close look at reading environment, reading purpose, and vocabulary. In the *Get Analytical* exercise, you used surveying skills to analyze the front matter and one chapter of a textbook. Within the section on critical reading, you examined how to consider fact and opinion, how arguments are supported, and perspectives in your approach to reading materials.

Creative

In the *Get Creative* exercise, you generated ideas from reading a book and then seeing a movie made from the same story. Reading about concentration may have inspired ideas about how to create a reading environment that suits you best. When exploring the SQ3R reading method, you may have adopted different ideas about how to implement it into a blend that is uniquely your own.

Practical

You discovered practical actions that can build your knowledge of roots, prefixes, and suffixes. You explored how emotional involvement can deepen your reading experience. You saw examples of how to put the practical steps of the SQ3R reading system into action. In the *Get Practical* exercise, you applied your knowledge of how to highlight and mark up text to a specific textbook page, solidifying your understanding of what strategies work best for you.

yokomeshi

(yo-ko-meh-shi)

Reading your college textbooks may feel at times like what this Japanese word literally means: "eating a meal sideways" (*meshi* means "boiled rice" and *yoko* means "horizontal"). The Japanese use this word to describe how difficult it is to learn a foreign language, since Japanese characters are vertical while most other world languages are horizontal. When the Japanese use this word to describe a difficult intellectual task, they force themselves to laugh at the image, which decompresses the stress.

If you feel overwhelmed by the new concepts and specialized vocabulary in your readings, just think of the challenge of eating a meal sideways. Then take heart in the certainty that you are not alone in trying to figure out what things mean. You will succeed by taking as many deep breaths as you need, by keeping your sense of humor, and by committing yourself to using the strategies suggested in this chapter to meet new reading challenges.[10]

"Somewhere, something incredible is waiting to be known."

CARL SAGAN, ASTRONOMER

Building World-Class Skills for College, Career, and Life Success

SUCCESSFUL INTELLIGENCE

Think, Create, Apply

Studying a text page. The following page is from the chapter "Groups and Organizations" in the sixth edition of John J. Macionis's *Sociology*.[11] Apply SQ3R as you read the excerpt. Using what you learned in this chapter about study techniques, complete the questions that follow (some questions ask you to mark the page itself).

Step 1. Think it through: ***Gather information and analyze it.*** Skim the excerpt. Identify the headings on the page and the relationships among them. Mark primary-level headings with a #1, secondary headings with a #2, and tertiary (third-level) headings with a #3. Then analyze:

Which heading serves as an umbrella for the rest?

____

What do the headings tell you about the content of the page?

____

What are three concepts that seem important to remember?

1. ____
2. ____
3. ____

Step 2. Think out of the box: ***Create useful study questions.*** Based on the three concepts you pulled out, write three study questions that you can review with an instructor, a teaching assistant, or a fellow student:

1. ____
2. ____
3. ____

Step 3. Make it happen: ***Read and remember.*** Read the excerpt, putting SQ3R to work. Using a marker, highlight key phrases and sentences. Write

SOCIAL GROUPS

Virtually everyone moves through life with a sense of belonging; this is the experience of group life. A **social group** refers to *two or more people who identify and interact with one another.* Human beings continually come together to form couples, families, circles of friends, neighborhoods, churches, businesses, clubs, and numerous large organizations. Whatever the form, groups encompass people with shared experiences, loyalties, and interests. In short, while maintaining their individuality, the members of social groups also think of themselves as a special "we."

Groups, Categories, and Crowds

People often use the term "group" imprecisely. We now distinguish the group from the similar concepts of category and crowd.

Category. A *category* refers to people who have some status in common. Women, single fathers, military recruits, homeowners, and Roman Catholics are all examples of categories.

Why are categories not considered groups? Simply because, while the individuals involved are aware that they are not the only ones to hold that particular status, the vast majority are strangers to one another.

Crowd. A *crowd* refers to a temporary cluster of individuals who may or may not interact at all. Students sitting in a lecture hall do engage one another and share some common identity as college classmates; thus, such a crowd might be called a loosely formed group. By contrast, riders hurtling along on a subway train or bathers enjoying a summer day at the beach pay little attention to one another and amount to an anonymous aggregate of people. In general, then, crowds are too transitory and impersonal to qualify as social groups.

The right circumstances, however, could turn a crowd into a group. People riding in a subway train that crashes under the city streets generally become keenly aware of their common plight and begin to help one another. Sometimes such extraordinary experiences become the basis for lasting relationships.

Primary and Secondary Groups

Acquaintances commonly greet one another with a smile and the simple phrase, "Hi! How are you?" The response is usually a well scripted, "Just fine, thanks, how about you?" This answer, of course, is often more formal than truthful. In most cases, providing a detailed account of how you are *really* doing would prompt the other person to beat a hasty and awkward exit.

Sociologists classify social groups by measuring them against two ideal types based on members' genuine level of personal concern. This variation is the key to distinguishing *primary* from *secondary* groups.

According to Charles Horton Cooley (1864–1929), a **primary group** is a *small social group whose members share personal and enduring relationships.* Bound together by primary relationships, individuals in primary groups typically spend a great deal of time together, engage in a wide range of common activities, and feel that they know one another well. Although not without periodic conflict, members of primary groups display sincere concern for each other's welfare. The family is every society's most important primary group.

Cooley characterized these personal and tightly integrated groups as *primary* because they are among the first groups we experience in life. In addition, the family and early play groups also hold primary importance in the socialization process, shaping attitudes, behavior, and social identity.

short marginal notes to help you review the material later. After reading this page thoroughly, write a short summary paragraph:

____

____

____

Step 4. Tap your multiple intelligences: ***Use MI strategies to improve your reading.*** The Multiple Intelligence Strategies table in this chapter (see page 172) encourages you to use different reading strategies to study the topic of social groups. Identify the strategies that work best for you and incorporate them into your studying routine.

TEAMWORK

Create Solutions Together

Organizing a study group. Organize a study group with three or four members of your class. At the group's first meeting do the following:

- **Set a specific goal**—to prepare for an upcoming test, for example—and create a weekly schedule. Write everything down and give everyone a copy.
- **Talk about the specific ways you will work together.** Discuss which of the following methods you want to try in the group: pooling your notes; teaching each other difficult concepts; making up, administering, and grading quizzes for each other; creating study flash cards; using SQ3R to review required readings. Set specific guidelines for how group members will be held accountable.

As an initial group exercise, try the following:

- **Review the study questions that you wrote for the *Sociology* excerpt in the previous exercise.** Each person should select one question to focus on while reading (no two people should have the same question). Group members should then reread the excerpt individually, thinking about their questions as they read and answering them in writing.
- **When you finish reading critically, gather as a group.** Each person should take a turn presenting the question, the response or answer that was derived through critical reading, and other thoughts. Other members may then add to the discussion. Continue until everyone presents a concept.

Over several weeks, evaluate the different methods as a group, singling out those that were most helpful. Then incorporate them into your ongoing study sessions.

WRITING

Journal and Put Skills to Work

Record your thoughts on a separate piece of paper, in a journal, or on a computer file.

Journal entry: Reading challenges. Which of the courses you are currently taking presents your most difficult reading challenge? What makes the reading tough—the type of material, the length of the assignments, the level of difficulty? Describe techniques you learned in this chapter that you will use to meet your reading challenge. Describe why you think they will help.

Real-life writing: Asking for help. Self-help plans often involve reaching out to others. Draft an e-mail to your instructor that describes the difficulties you are facing in the course you wrote about in the journal entry and that details the specific help you need in order to move to the next step.

To accomplish your goal while also coming across as a respectful, diligent student, make sure that your message is clear and accurate; that your grammar, spelling, and punctuation are correct; and that your tone is appropriate. (See Quick Start to College at the front of the book for guidelines for communicating with instructors.) Whether or not you send the e-mail is up to you. In either case, writing it will help you move forward in your reading improvement plan.

PERSONAL PORTFOLIO

Prepare for Career Success

Complete the following in your electronic portfolio or on separate paper.

Reading skills on the job. Excellent reading skills are a requirement for almost every 21st century job. Employers expect that you will read independently to master new skills and keep up with change. Whether it is in print or electronic form, on-the-job reading will challenge you as much—if not more—than college reading. For example, although taking sociology courses involves reading textbooks, journals, and case studies, actually working in the field requires that you keep on top of case reports, government regulations, court documents, and an unending stream of work-related e-mails.

Prepare yourself for what's ahead by honestly assessing your practical skills *right now*. Use the following list to rate your ability on a scale of 1 to 10, with 10 being the highest:

- Ability to concentrate, no matter the distractions
- Ability to use emotional triggers to learn and remember material
- Ability to define your reading purpose and use it to guide your focus and pace
- Ability to use specific vocabulary-building techniques to improve comprehension
- Ability to use every aspect of SQ3R to master content
- Ability to skim and scan
- Ability to use analytical thinking skills when reading
- Ability to use highlighting and notes to help you master content

For the two skill areas in which you rated yourself lowest, think about how you can improve. Make a problem-solving plan for each (you may want to use a flowchart like the one on page 139). Check your progress in one month and at the end of the term. Finally, write down the ways in which you anticipate using the reading skills you learned in this chapter in your chosen career.

Suggested Readings

Armstrong, William H., and M. Willard Lampe II. *Barron's Pocket Guide to Study Tips: How to Study Effectively and Get Better Grades.* New York: Barron's, 2004.

Chesla, Elizabeth. *Reading Comprehension Success: In 20 Minutes a Day*, 2nd ed. Florence, KY: Thomson Delmar Learning, 2002.

Cutler, Wade E. *Triple Your Reading Speed*, 4th ed. New York: Pocket Books, 2003.

Labunski, Richard E. *The Educated Student: Getting the Most Out of Your College Years.* Versailles, KY: Marley and Beck, 2003.

Luckie, William R., Wood Smethurst, and Sarah Beth Huntley. *Study Power Workbook: Exercises in Study Skills to Improve Your Learning and Your Grades.* Cambridge, MA: Brookline Books, 1999.

Olsen, Amy E. *Active Vocabulary: General and Academic Words*, 3rd ed. New York: Longman, 2006.

Silver, Theodore. *The Princeton Review Study Smart: Hands-On, Nuts and Bolts Techniques for Earning Higher Grades.* New York: Villard Books, 1996.

Internet and Podcast Resources

Academictips.org (study tips and links): **www.academictips.org**

College Tutor Study Guide: **www.amelox.com/study.htm**

HowToStudy.com (study advice with valuable links): **www.howtostudy.com**

Improve Your Study Skills (tips from SoYouWanna.com): **www.soyouwanna.com/site/syws/studyskills/studyskills.html**

Lesson Tutor—Good Study Habits: **www.lessontutor.com/studygeneralhome.html**

Merriam-Webster's Word of the Day (free word of the day in audio form available on the Internet or as podcasts): **www.merriam-webster.com/cgi-bin/mwwod.pl**

Princeton Review Vocab Minute (free vocabulary-building podcasts using songs to help you remember): **RobinR@Review.com**

Study Guides and Strategies: **www.studygs.net**

Taking College Courses: **www.math.usf.edu/~mccolm/Aclasses.html**

Prentice Hall Student Success SuperSite: **www.prenhall.com/success**

Endnotes

[1]Richard J. Light, *Making the Most of College: Students Speak Their Minds,* Cambridge, MA: Harvard University Press, 2001, pp. 23–24. Copyright © 2001 by Richard J. Light. Reprinted by permission of the publisher.

[2]Eric Jensen, *Student Success Secrets*, 5th ed., New York: Barron's, 2003, p. 88.

[3]Roxanne Ruzic, "Lessons for Everyone: How Students with Reading-Related Learning Disabilities Survive and Excel in College Courses with Heavy Reading Requirements," paper presented at the Annual Meeting of the American Educational Research Association, Seattle, April 13, 2001 (http://iod.unh.edu/EE/articles/lessons_for_everyone.html).

[4]Francis P. Robinson, *Effective Behavior,* New York: Harper & Row, 1941.

[5]John Mack Faragher, Mari Jo Buhle, Daniel Czitrom, and Susan H. Armitage, *Out of Many: A History of the American People*, 3rd ed., Upper Saddle River, NJ: Prentice Hall, p. xxxvii.

[6]Charles G. Morris and Albert A. Maisto, *Psychology: An Introduction,* 12th ed., Upper Saddle River, NJ: Pearson/Prentice Hall, 2005, p. 186.

[7]Benjamin S. Bloom, *Taxonomy of Educational Objectives, Handbook I: The Cognitive Domain,* New York: McKay, 1956.

[8]Ophelia H. Hancock, *Reading Skills for College Students,* 5th ed., Upper Saddle River, NJ: Prentice Hall, 2001, pp. 54–59.

[9]Adam Robinson, *What Smart Students Know,* New York: Three Rivers Press, 1993, p. 82.

[10]Christopher J. Moore, *In Other Words: A Language Lover's Guide to the Most Intriguing Words Around the World,* New York: Walker, 2004, p. 87.

[11]John J. Macionis, *Sociology,* 6th ed., Upper Saddle River, NJ: Prentice Hall, 1997, p. 174.

LISTENING, NOTE TAKING, AND MEMORY

Taking In, Recording, and Remembering Information

6

"Successfully intelligent people find their path and then pursue it, realizing that there will be obstacles along the way and that surmounting these obstacles is part of their challenge."

ROBERT J. STERNBERG

College exposes you daily to all kinds of information—and your job as a student is to take it in, write it down, and keep what is important. This chapter shows you how to accomplish this by building your skills in the area of listening (taking in information), note-taking (recording what's important), and memory (remembering information). Each process engages your analytical, creative, and practical abilities and helps you build knowledge you can use.

In this chapter you explore answers to the following questions:

Chapter 6's

Successful Intelligence Skills

Analytical

- Understanding the listening process and the challenge of good listening
- Evaluating the importance of class notes and different note-taking systems
- Analyzing the nature of memory and why memory strategies work

Creative

- Constructing active listening strategies that help you learn
- Personalizing note-taking systems and strategies
- Thinking of and using mnemonic devices to boost recall

Practical

- How to overcome distractions to listen actively
- How to use note-taking systems and shorthand and craft a master note set
- How to use mnemonics to learn

How Can You Become a Better Listener?

LISTENING

A process that involves sensing, interpreting, evaluating, and reacting to spoken messages.

The act of hearing is not the same as the act of listening. *Hearing* refers to sensing spoken messages from their source. **Listening** involves a complex process of communication. Successful listening occurs when the listener understands the speaker's intended message. In school and at work, poor listening may cause communication breakdowns, while skilled listening promotes success. The good news is that listening is a teachable—and learnable—skill that engages analytical and practical abilities.

Know the Stages of Listening

Listening is made up of four stages that build on one another: sensing, interpreting, evaluating, and reacting. These stages take the message from the speaker to the listener and back to the speaker (see Key 6.1), as follows:

- During the *sensation* stage (also known as *hearing*) your ears pick up sound waves and transmit them to the brain. For example, you are sitting in class and hear your instructor say, "The only opportunity to make up last week's test is Tuesday at 5 p.m."
- In the *interpretation* stage, you attach meaning to a message: You understand what is said and link it to what you already know. You relate this message to your knowledge of the test, whether you need to make it up, and what you are doing on Tuesday at 5:00.

REAL QUESTIONS

How can I improve my memory?

Shyama Parikh
DePaul University
Chicago, Illinois

When I took a memory test in a psychology class, I discovered that my classmates and I are better at remembering a full definition to a word rather than reading the definition and remembering the word. We would have thought that it would be easier to recall a word than an entire definition, but that was not the case.

Sometimes I find memorization work difficult, even though I know I have the ability. For instance, I know I have the material written down in my notes, down to the exact page, but then on the test, I sometimes can't remember the answers.

I try to incorporate mnemonic devices as I study, but that doesn't always work. I know that rereading and repetition reinforce learning, but it's hard to devote enough time to retaining information for five classes. I've just been accepted to law school, and I'm concerned because law requires learning technical terms. Can you suggest ways for me to improve my memory?

PRACTICAL ANSWERS

Stephen Beck
Director, Learn-to-Learn Company
Winston-Salem,
North Carolina

Understanding material will help you memorize and retain information.

Understanding what you study and grasping the way material is organized are crucial memory tools. The definitions exercise you took in your psychology class illustrates that you are more likely to remember a sentence of 30 words than a list of 15 random words because the sentence has meaning for you. Similarly, if a system of categorizing biology terms makes sense, you are more likely to understand and remember the terms. Mentally placing information in logical categories enhances recall, as do mnemonic devices.

Take the time to scope out the organization of a text or chapter before you start reading. Read the table of contents, preface, and chapter section and subsection titles. Look at chapter objectives and summaries. This overview will help you form meaningful connections and will set the stage for learning the details.

As you study, be an active participant by continually asking yourself whether information makes sense. If it doesn't, try to figure out why you're stuck—what strand of understanding is missing. To reinforce reading comprehension, pause at good stopping points and take notes from memory. Your notes are proof that you can recall and understand the material. How do you know if you have memorized a list? Write it down to find out exactly what you do and do not know.

This active pause-reflect-and-write technique is critical for learning new material.

- In the *evaluation* stage, you evaluate the message as it relates to your needs and values. If the message goes against your values or does not fulfill your needs, you may reject it, stop listening, or argue in your mind with the speaker. In this example, if you need to make up the test but have to work Tuesday at 5:00, you may evaluate the message in an unfavorable way.

KEY 6.1

The listening process moves messages along a listening loop.

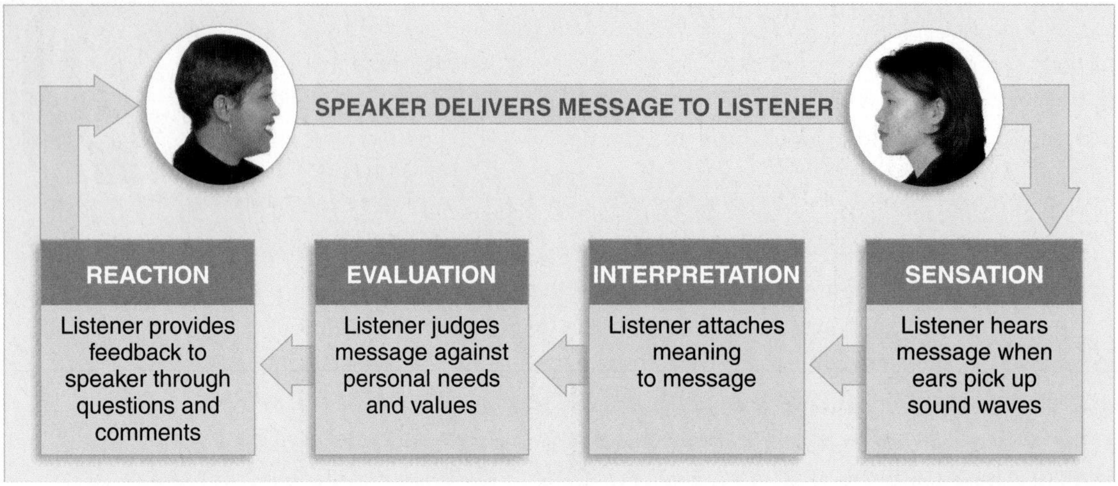
SPEAKER DELIVERS MESSAGE TO LISTENER
REACTION
Listener provides feedback to speaker through questions and comments
EVALUATION
Listener judges message against personal needs and values
INTERPRETATION
Listener attaches meaning to message
SENSATION
Listener hears message when ears pick up sound waves

- The final stage of listening is a *reaction* to the message in the form of direct feedback. In a classroom, direct feedback often comes in the form of questions and comments. Your reaction, in this case, may be to ask the instructor if she can schedule another test time.

You will become a better listener by learning to recognize and manage listening challenges and becoming actively involved with the material.

Manage Listening Challenges

Classic studies have shown that immediately after listening, students are likely to recall only half of what was said. This low retention rate is due, in part, to the following listening challenges.[1]

Divided Attention and Distractions

Internal and external distractions often divide your attention. *Internal distractions* include anything from hunger to headache to personal worries. Something the speaker says may also trigger a recollection that may cause your mind to drift. In contrast, *external distractions* include factors outside yourself, such as noise and excessive heat or cold. They also involve sending and receiving text messages on your cell phone, instant-messaging friends, or surfing the Internet on your laptop.

Use practical strategies that tap your emotional and social intelligence to reduce distractions as they arise: Try your best to put your worries aside during class; sit near the front of the room; move away from chatting classmates; ban technology for social uses during class; get enough sleep to stay alert; and eat enough to avoid hunger.

Listening Lapses

Your instructors are responsible for communicating information, but they cannot make you listen. That responsibility is in your hands. If you decide that a subject is too difficult or uninteresting, you may tune out and miss the foundation for what comes next. You may also fall into the trap of focusing on specific points and shutting out the rest of the message. If you experience a listening lapse, try to refocus quickly instead of worrying about what you missed. After class, look at a classmate's notes to fill in the gaps.

Preventing listening lapses starts with having the right attitude. Remind yourself that what your instructors say is valuable and that they often present material in class that is not in the text. If you work to take in the whole message, you will be able to read over your notes later, combine your class and text notes, and think critically about what is important.

The Rush to Judgment

It is common for people to stop listening when they hear something they don't like. Their focus turns to their personal reactions and away from the message. Students who disagree during a lecture often spend valuable class time thinking about their reaction.

Judgments also involve reactions to the speakers themselves. If you do not like your instructors or have preconceived notions about their ideas or background, you may dismiss their message. Anyone whose words have ever been ignored because of race, ethnicity, gender, physical characteristics, or disability understands how prejudice interferes with listening. Although it is human nature to stop listening at times in reaction to a speaker or message, this tendency can get in the way of your education. Use your analytical intelligence to overcome the tendency to rush to judgment. It will make you more socially and emotionally competent.

Partial Hearing Loss and Learning Disabilities

If you have a hearing loss, seek out special services, including tutoring and equipment, that can help you listen in class. For example, listening to a taped lecture at a higher-than-normal volume can help you hear things you missed. Ask your instructors if digitalized recordings are available, which you can download onto your computer or MP3 player. Meeting with your instructor outside of class to clarify your notes may also help, as will sitting near the front of the room.

Other disabilities, such as attention deficit disorder (ADD) or a problem with processing spoken language, can add to listening difficulties. People with these problems may have trouble paying attention or understanding what they hear. If you have a disability that creates a listening challenge, seek help through the services available at your college.

Active listening means being in class and connecting with the material by taking notes and asking questions. These students benefit from a visual aid as they take notes in an anatomy class.

Become an Active Listener

On the surface, listening seems like a passive activity: You sit back as someone else speaks. In reality, effective listening is an active process that involves the following factors:

Be There

Being an active listener requires that you show up on time—preferably a few minutes before class begins. Instructors often make important announcements in the first few minutes and may also summarize the last lecture.

Set Purposes for Listening

Before every class, use your analytical intelligence to establish what you want to achieve, such as understanding difficult concepts or mastering a task. Many instructors start a lecture with a statement of purpose, so listen carefully to their introductory words. Then write them at the top of your notes to help you focus.

Accomplishing your purpose requires that you read assignments before class and review your notes from the previous class. This preparation will set the stage for you to follow the lecture and will help you tell the difference between important and unimportant material. Without it, you may find yourself scrambling to take down every word.

Making your purpose for listening *personal* will motivate you to listen closely. As you prepare for class, ask yourself how the material relates to your academic goals. With the mind-set that what you hear will help *you*, you will be more able to make listening a top priority in class.

Focus on Understanding

Rather than taking notes on everything, record information only when you can say to yourself, "I get it!" If you miss important material, leave holes in your notes and return later. Your instructor may repeat the point you missed, or another comment may help you piece it together.

Ask Questions

Active listeners ask analytical questions to clarify their understanding and to associate new ideas with what they already know. Questions like "What is this part of?" or "How is it similar to yesterday's topic?" signal active involvement. Get into the habit of jotting down your questions and coming back to them during a discussion period so they don't interfere with listening.

VERBAL SIGNPOSTS Spoken words or phrases that call attention to information that follows.

Pay Attention to Verbal Signposts

Instructors' choice of words may tell you what they consider important and help you predict test questions. For example, an idea described as "new and exciting" or "classic" is more likely to be on a test than one described as "interesting." **Verbal signposts**—words or phrases that call attention to what comes next—help organize information, connect ideas, and indicate what is important and what is not (see Key 6.2). Use your practical intelligence to pay attention to these signals and to become more socially attuned.

KEY 6.2

Pay attention to verbal signposts.

SIGNALS POINTING TO KEY CONCEPTS	SIGNALS OF SUPPORT
A key point to remember . . .	A perfect example . . .
Point 1, point 2, etc. . . .	Specifically . . .
The impact of this was . . .	For instance . . .
The critical stages in the process are . . .	Similarly . . .
SIGNALS POINTING TO DIFFERENCES	**SIGNALS THAT SUMMARIZE**
On the contrary . . .	From this you have learned . . .
On the other hand . . .	In conclusion . . .
In contrast . . .	As a result . . .
However . . .	Finally . . .

Expect the Unexpected

Active listening requires opening your mind to diverse points of view and to the heated classroom debates that may result. When the literature students in the following example listened actively, where the discussion led surprised them:

> The professor said she had attended a symposium where the author Ward Just said: "In my books, I always make sure readers know by about page 35 how each of the key characters earns their living. I just think this is critical to help each reader put all the characters in my writing in a context."
>
> My instructor then assigned two books for us to read. One was by Ward Just, and it was organized exactly as promised. The other was by a different writer, who . . . obviously couldn't care less whether readers ever learned how characters earned their living. Each of us was asked to come prepared to either agree or disagree with Mr. Just's idea. . . . It was clear the professor was hoping for some disagreement.
>
> Well, she got it. Three of us took the same position as Mr. Just. The other five strongly disagreed. And about a half-hour into the discussion, which was as spirited as we had all semester, one of the women said she couldn't help noticing that the three who shared Mr. Just's view just happened to be the three men in the class, while the five who disagreed happened to be the five women. "Does that imply anything?" she wondered. Which, as you can easily imagine, quickly led to an even more spirited discussion about how gender of both author and reader might influence the way we think about the structure of writing.[2]

Effective listening skills are the basis for effective note taking—an essential and powerful study tool.

Successful Intelligence Connections Online

Listen to author Sarah Kravits describe how to use analytical, creative, and practical intelligence to improve your listening skills.

Go to the *Keys to Success* Companion Website at www.prenhall.com/carter to listen or download as a podcast.

GET ANALYTICAL!

Discover Yourself as a Listener

Complete the following as you focus on your personal listening habits:

- Analyze how present you are as a listener. Are you easily distracted, or can you focus well? Do you prefer to listen or do you tend to talk?

- When you are listening, what tends to distract you?

- What happens to your listening skills when you become confused?

- How do you react when you strongly disagree with something your instructor says—when you are convinced that you are "right" and your instructor is "wrong"?

- Thinking about your answers and about your listening challenges, list two strategies from the chapter that will help you improve your listening skills:

  1. ______________________________
  2. ______________________________

How Can You Make the Most of Class Notes?

Taking notes makes you an active class participant—even when you don't say a word—and provides you with study materials. What's on the line is nothing short of your academic success.

Class notes have two primary purposes: to serve as a record of what happened in class and to use for studying, alone and in combination with your text notes. Because it is virtually impossible to take notes on everything you hear, note taking encourages you to use your analytical intelligence to critically evaluate what is worth remembering.

Note-Taking Systems

The most common note-taking systems are outlines, the Cornell system, and think links. Choose the system that you find most comfortable and that works best with course content. Be willing to change systems in different sitations.

Take Notes in Outline Form

Outlines use a standard structure to show how ideas interrelate. *Formal outlines* indicate idea dominance and subordination with Roman numerals, uppercase and lowercase letters, and numbers. In contrast, *informal outlines* show the same associations but replace the formality with a system of consistent indenting and dashes (see Key 6.3). Many students find informal outlines easier for in-class note taking. Key 6.4 shows how the structure of an informal outline helps a student take notes on the topic of tropical rain forests. The Multiple Intelligence Strategies table in this chapter (see page 191) is designed to help harness different learning approaches for an earth science course. Specifically, the table will suggest different note-taking strategies you can use when you study the topic of tropical rain forests.

From time to time, an instructor may give you a guide, usually in outline form, to help you take notes in class. This outline, known as

KEY 6.3

Outlines show levels of importance as they link details to main ideas.

FORMAL OUTLINE	INFORMAL OUTLINE
TOPIC	TOPIC
I. First Main Idea	First Main Idea
A. Major supporting fact	—Major supporting fact
B. Major supporting fact	—Major supporting fact
1. First reason or example	—First reason or example
2. Second reason or example	—Second reason or example
a. First supporting fact	—First supporting fact
b. Second supporting fact	—Second supporting fact
II. Second Main Idea	Second Main Idea
A. Major supporting fact	—Major supporting fact
1. First reason or example	—First reason or example
2. Second reason or example	—Second reason or example
B. Major supporting fact	—Major supporting fact

KEY 6.4

An informal outline is excellent for taking class notes.

Tropical Rain Forests[3]

—What are tropical rain forests?

  —Areas in South America and Africa, along the equator

  —Average temperatures between 25° and 30° C (77°–86° F)

  —Average annual rainfalls range between 250 to 400 centimeters (100 to 160 inches)

  —Conditions combine to create the Earth's richest, most biodiverse ecosystem.

    —A biodiverse ecosystem has a great number of organisms co-existing within a defined area.

    —Examples of rain forest biodiversity

      —2½ acres in the Amazon rain forest has 283 species of trees

      —A 3-square-mile section of a Peruvian rain forest has more than 1,300 butterfly species and 600 bird species.

      —Compare this biodiversity to what is found in the entire U.S.

        —only 400 butterfly species and 700 bird species

—How are humans changing the rain forest?

  —Humans have already destroyed about 40% of all rain forests.

    —They are cutting down trees for lumber or clearing the land for ranching or agriculture.

  —Biologist Edwin O. Wilson estimates that this destruction may lead to the extinction of 27,000 species.

  —Rain forest removal is also linked to the increase in atmospheric carbon dioxide, which worsens the greenhouse effect.

    —The greenhouse effect refers to process in which gases such as carbon dioxide trap the sun's energy in the Earth's atmosphere as heat, resulting in global warming.

  —Recognition of the crisis is growing as are conservation efforts.

guided notes, may be on the board, on an overhead projector, or on a handout that you receive at the beginning of class. Because guided notes are usually general and sketchy, they require that you fill in the details.

Use the Cornell System

The *Cornell note-taking system*, also known as the *T-note system*, consists of three sections on ordinary notepaper:[4]

- Section 1, the largest section, is on the right. Record your notes here in whatever form you choose. Skip lines between topics so you can clearly see where a section begins and ends.
- Section 2, to the left of your notes, is the *cue column*. Leave it blank while you read or listen, and then fill it in later as you review. You might insert key words or comments that highlight ideas, clarify meaning, add examples, link ideas, or draw diagrams. Many students use this column to raise questions, which they answer when they study.
- Section 3, at the bottom of the page, is known as the *summary area*. Here you reduce your notes to critical points, a process that will help you learn the material. Use this section to provide an overview of what the notes say.

MULTIPLE INTELLIGENCE STRATEGIES

FOR NOTE TAKING

APPLY DIFFERENT INTELLIGENCES TO TAKING NOTES IN EARTH SCIENCE.

INTELLIGENCE	USE MI STRATEGIES *to become a better note taker*	APPLY MI NOTE-TAKING STRATEGIES *to the topic of tropical rain forests for an earth science course*
 Verbal-Linguistic	• Rewrite your class notes in an alternate note-taking style to see connections more clearly. • Combine class and text notes to get a complete picture.	• Rewrite and summarize your reading and lecture notes to understand the characteristics of tropical rain forests.*
 Logical-Mathematical	• When combining notes into a master set, integrate the material into a logical sequence. • Create tables that show relationships.	• Create a table comparing and contrasting the different species found in a typical rain forest.
 Bodily-Kinesthetic	• Think of your notes as a crafts project that enables you to see "knowledge layers." Use colored pens to texture your notes. • Study with your notes spread in sequence around you so that you can see knowledge building from left to right.	• Fill a tube with 160 inches of water (that's $13\frac{1}{3}$ feet!) to give you a physical sense of the annual rainfall in a rain forest. Or fill a bathtub with 10 inches of water and multiply by 16 to imagine rainfall totals. How would you react to living with so much rain? Take notes on your reaction.
Visual-Spatial 	• Take notes using colored markers or pens. • Rewrite lecture notes in think link format, focusing on the most important points.	• As part of your notes, create a chart that covers the types of vegetation that grow in a rain forest. Use a different colored marker for each plant species.
Interpersonal 	• Try to schedule a study group right after a lecture to discuss class notes. • Review class notes with a study buddy. Compare notes to see what the other missed.	• Interview someone you know who has visited a rain forest about what she saw, or interview a natural scientist at a museum about this environment. Use a different note-taking system for each person.
 Intrapersonal	• Schedule some quiet time soon after a lecture to review and think about your notes. • As you review your notes, decide whether you grasp the material or need help.	• Think about the conflict between economic modernization and the preservation of rain forests in underdeveloped areas. Include your thoughts in your notes.
Musical 	• To improve recall, recite concepts in your notes to rhythms. • Write a song that includes material from your class and text notes. Use the refrain to emphasize what is important.	• Use the Internet to find songs about the biodiversity of rain forests written by indigenous peoples who live in or near them. Then, use the song to remember key concepts. Take notes on what you find.
Naturalistic 	• As you create a master note set, notice similarities and differences in concepts by organizing material into natural groupings.	• If possible, visit a museum of natural history with exhibits of rain forests. Try to see common characteristics that make vegetation and species thrive in this environment. Take notes on your observations.

* For information on tropical rain forests, see Frederick Lutgens, Edward Tarbuck, and Dennis Tasa, *Foundations of Earth Science*, 5th ed., Upper Saddle River, NJ: Prentice Hall, 2008.

Create this note-taking structure before class begins. Picture an upside-down letter T as you follow these directions:

- Start with a sheet of 8½-by-11-inch lined paper. Label it with the date and lecture title.
- To create the cue column, draw a vertical line about 2½ inches from the left side of the paper. End the line about 2 inches from the bottom of the sheet.
- To create the summary area, start at the point where the vertical line ends (about 2 inches from the bottom of the page) and draw a horizontal line that spans the entire paper.

Key 6.5 shows how the Cornell system is used in a business course.

Create a Think Link

A *think link*, also known as a *mind map* or *word web*, is a visual form of note taking that encourages flexible thinking. When you draw a think link, you use shapes and lines to link ideas with supporting details and examples. The visual design makes the connections easy to see, and shapes and pictures extend the material beyond words.

To create a think link, start by circling or boxing your topic in the middle of the paper. Next, draw a line from the topic and write the name of one major idea at the end of the line. Circle that idea. Then, jot down specific facts related to the idea, linking them to the idea with lines. Continue the process, connecting thoughts to one another with circles, lines, and words. Key 6.6, a think link on the sociological concept of stratification, follows this structure, just one of many possible designs.

Other examples of think link designs include stair steps showing connected ideas that build toward a conclusion, and a tree with trunk and roots as central concepts and branches as examples. Key 6.1 on page 184 shows another type of think link.

A think link may be difficult to construct in class, especially if your instructor talks quickly. If this is the case, transform your notes into think link format later when you review.

Use Other Visual Strategies

Other strategies that help organize information are especially useful to visual learners, although they may be too involved to complete during class. Use them when taking text notes or combining class and text notes for review. These strategies include the following:

- *Time lines.* Use a time line to organize information into chronological order. Draw a vertical or horizontal line on the page and connect each item to the line, in order, noting the dates and basic event descriptions.
- *Tables.* Use the columns and rows of a table to organize information as you condense and summarize your class and text notes.
- *Hierarchy charts.* Charts showing an information hierarchy can help you visualize how pieces fit together. For example, you can use a hierarchy chart to show levels within a government bureaucracy or levels of scientific classification of animals and plants.

KEY 6.5 The Cornell system has space for notes, comments, and a summary.

October 3, 200x, p. 1

UNDERSTANDING EMPLOYEE MOTIVATION

Why do some workers have a better attitude toward their work than others?

Purpose of motivational theories
—To explain role of human relations in motivating employee performance
—Theories translate into how managers actually treat workers

Some managers view workers as lazy; others view them as motivated and productive.

2 specific theories
—Human resources model, developed by Douglas McGregor, shows that managers have radically different beliefs about motivation.
—Theory X holds that people are naturally irresponsible and uncooperative
—Theory Y holds that people are naturally responsible and self-motivated

Maslow's Hierarchy

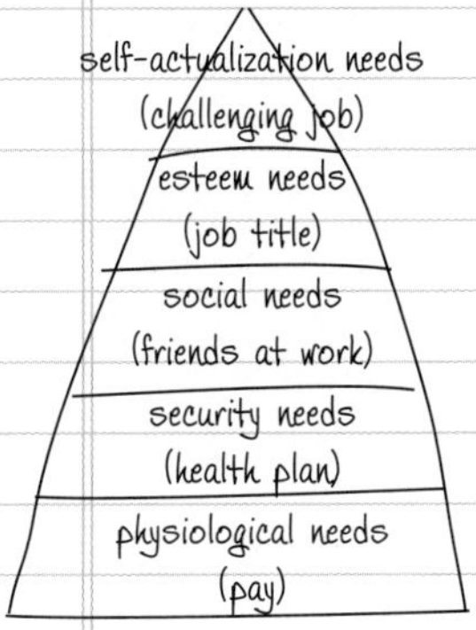

—Maslow's Hierarchy of Needs says that people have needs in 5 different areas, which they attempt to satisfy in their work.
—Physiological need: need for survival, including food and shelter
—Security need: need for stability and protection
—Social need: need for friendship and companionship
—Esteem need: need for status and recognition
—Self-actualization need: need for self-fulfillment
Needs at lower levels must be met before a person tries to satisfy needs at higher levels.
—Developed by psychologist Abraham Maslow

Two motivational theories try to explain worker motivation. The human resources model includes Theory X and Theory Y. Maslow's Hierarchy of Needs suggests that people have needs in 5 different areas: physiological, security, social, esteem, and self-actualization.

Note Taking Is a Three-Step Process

Taking good class notes requires practice—practice preparing, practice doing, and practice reviewing. Involved are a number of analytical and practical strategies.

Prepare

Showing up for class on time with pad and pen in hand is only the beginning.

KEY 6.6

Use a think link to connect ideas visually.

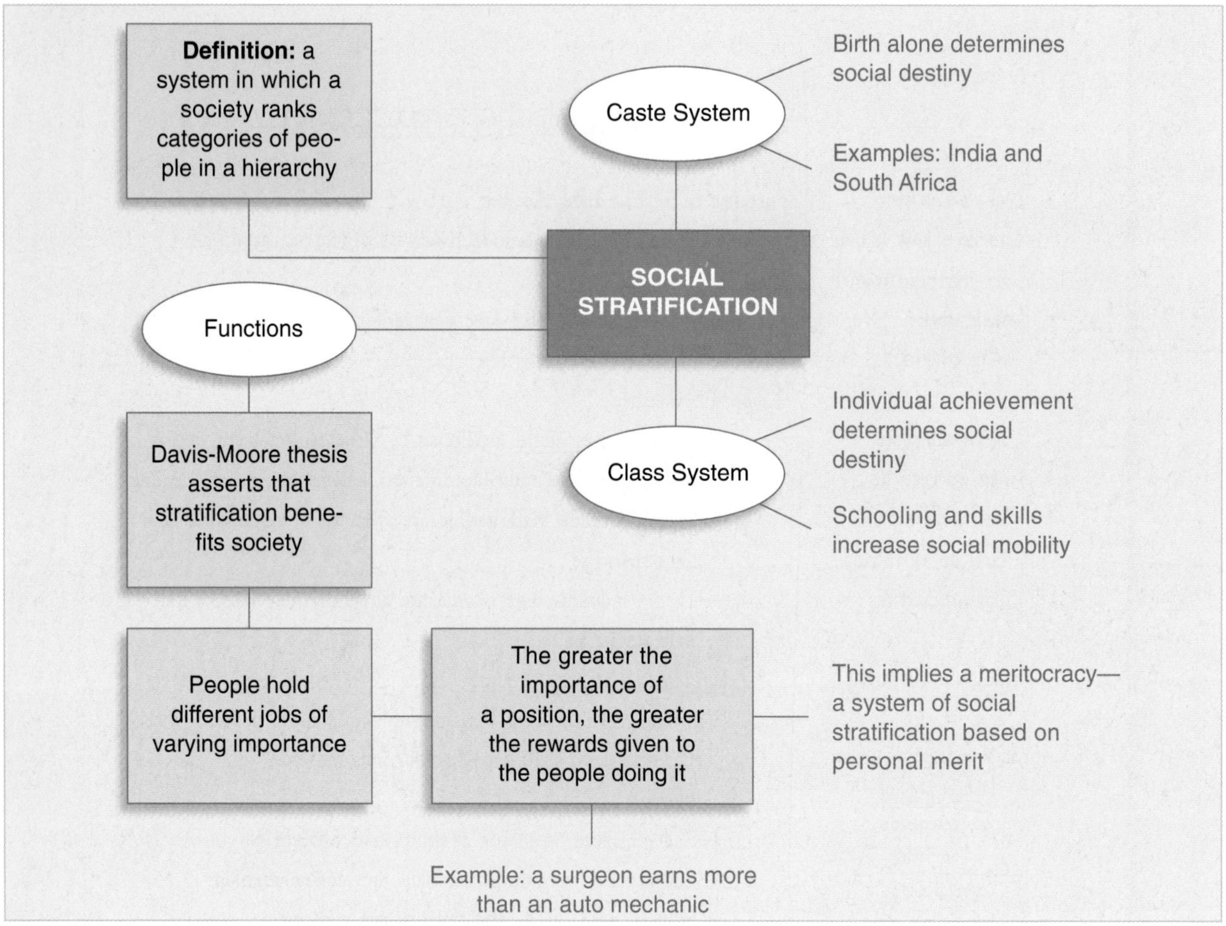
Definition: a system in which a society ranks categories of people in a hierarchy
Caste System
Birth alone determines social destiny
Examples: India and South Africa
SOCIAL STRATIFICATION
Functions
Davis-Moore thesis asserts that stratification benefits society
Class System
Individual achievement determines social destiny
Schooling and skills increase social mobility
People hold different jobs of varying importance
The greater the importance of a position, the greater the rewards given to the people doing it
This implies a meritocracy—a system of social stratification based on personal merit
Example: a surgeon earns more than an auto mechanic

Preview your reading material. *More than anything else you can do, reading assigned materials before class will give you the background to take effective notes.* Check your class syllabi daily to see when assignments are due, and then plan your reading time with these deadlines in mind. (The syllabus on page 14 shows when specific reading assignments are due.)

Review what you know. Taking 15 minutes before class to review your notes from the previous class and your reading assignment notes for that day will enable you to follow the lecture from the start. Without this preparation, you may find yourself flipping back in your notebook instead of listening to new information.

Gather your supplies. Use a separate notebook for each course, and start a new page for each class. If you use a three-ring binder, punch holes in handouts and insert them right after your notes for that day. If you use a laptop, open the file containing your class notes right away.

Location, location, location. Find a comfortable seat that is away from friends to minimize distractions. Be ready to write as soon as the instructor begins speaking.

Choose the best note-taking system. Use your emotional and social intelligence to select a system that will work best in each class. Take these factors into account when making your choices:

- *The instructor's style* (which will be clear after a few classes). In the same term, you may have one instructor who is organized and speaks slowly, another who jumps around and talks rapidly, and a third who digresses in response to questions. Be flexible enough to adapt your note taking to each situation.
- *The course material.* You may decide that an informal outline works best for a highly structured lecture and that a think link is right for a looser presentation. Try one note-taking system for several classes, then adjust if necessary.
- *Your learning style.* Choose strategies that make the most of your strengths and compensate for weaknesses. A visual-spatial learner might prefer think links or the Cornell system; a thinker type might be comfortable with outlines; an interpersonal learner might use the Cornell system and fill in the cue column in a study group. You might even find that one system is best in class and another in review sessions.

Gather support. In each class, set up a support system with one or two students so you can look at their notes after an absence.

Record Information Effectively During Class

The following practical suggestions will help you record what is important in a format that you can review later:

- Date and identify each page. When you take several pages of notes, add an identifying letter or number to the date to keep track of page order: 11/27A, 11/27B, for example, or 11/27—1 of 2, 11/27—2 of 2. Indicate the lecture topic at the top so you can gather all your notes on that topic.
- If your instructor jumps from topic to topic during a single class, it may help to start a new page for each new topic.
- Record whatever your instructor emphasizes by paying attention to verbal and nonverbal cues (see Key 6.7).
- Write down all key terms and definitions.
- Try to capture explanations of difficult concepts by noting relevant examples, applications, and links to other material.
- Write down every question your instructor raises, since these questions may be on a test.
- Be organized, but not fussy. Remember that you can always improve your notes later.
- Write quickly but legibly, using shorthand and short phrases instead of full sentences.

get practical!

Face a Note-Taking Challenge

In the spaces below, record how you will prepare to take notes in your most challenging course.

- Course name and date of class:

  ____

- List all the reading assignments you have to finish before your next class:

  ____

  ____

- Where will you sit in class to focus your attention and minimize distractions?

  ____

- Which note-taking system is best suited for the class and why?

  ____

  ____

- Write the phone numbers or e-mail addresses of two students whose notes you can look at if you miss a class:

  ____

  ____

- Leave blank spaces between points to make it easy see where one topic ends and another begins. (This suggestion does not apply if you are using a think link.)
- Draw pictures and diagrams to illustrate ideas.
- A consistent system will help you find information with minimal stresss. Use the same system to show importance—such as indenting, spacing, or underlining—on each page.
- If you have trouble understanding a concept, record as much as you can; then, leave space for an explanation, and flag the margin with a large question mark. After class, try to clarify your questions in the text or ask a classmate or your instructor for help.
- Consider that your class notes are part, but not all, of what you need to learn. As you will see later in this chapter, you will learn best when you combine your text and class notes into a comprehensive master set.

KEY 6.7
Instructors signal important material in a variety of ways.

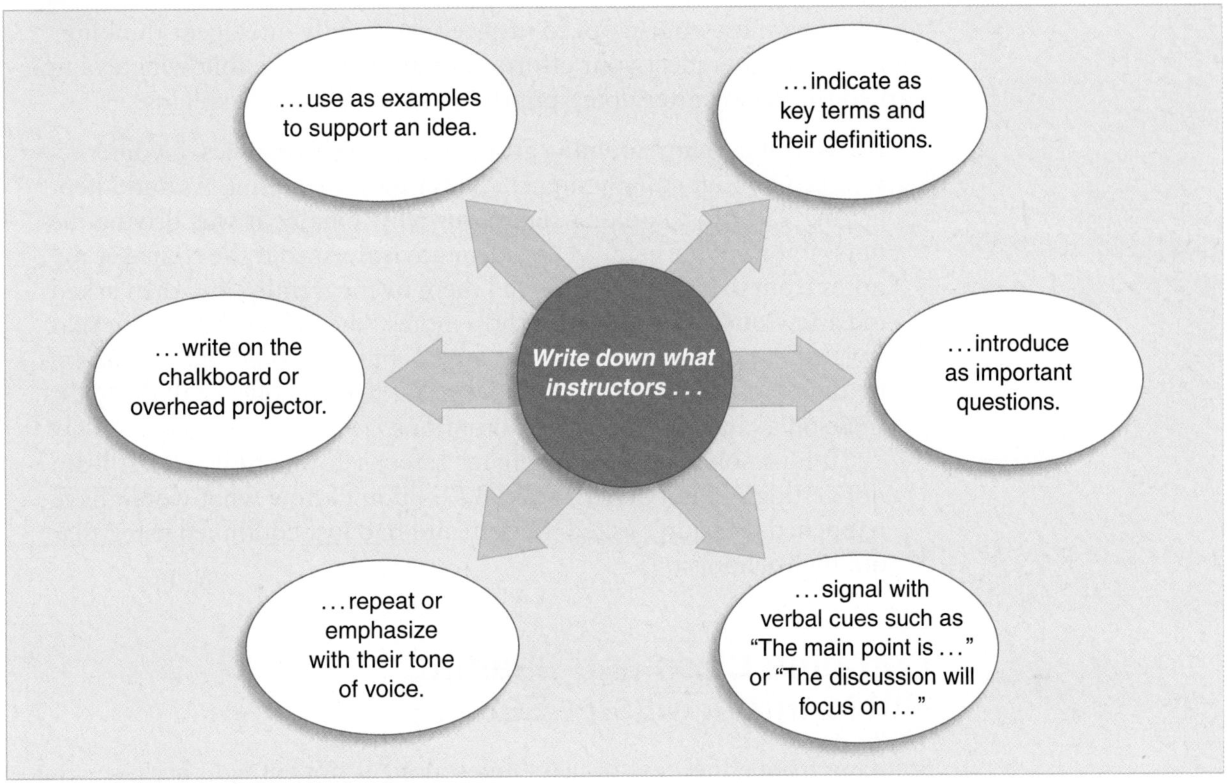
Write down what instructors . . .
. . . use as examples to support an idea.
. . . indicate as key terms and their definitions.
. . . write on the chalkboard or overhead projector.
. . . introduce as important questions.
. . . repeat or emphasize with their tone of voice.
. . . signal with verbal cues such as "The main point is . . ." or "The discussion will focus on . . ."

Take notes during class discussions. During discussion periods, one student may say something, then another, and finally the instructor may summarize or link the comments to make a point. Getting the most out of class discussions and recording critical points engages your ability to "read" others, which is the basis for social intelligence. Here are suggestions for recording what you need to know during these discussions:

- Listen carefully to everyone. Jot down relevant points and ignore points that seem tangential. If you're not sure, ask the instructor whether a student's statement is important.
- Listen for idea threads that weave through comments.
- Listen for ideas the instructor picks up on and for encouraging comments to students, such as "You make a great point," "I like your idea," and so on.
- Take notes when the instructor rephrases and clarifies a student's point.
- Try using a think link since discussions often take the form of brainstorming sessions. A think link will help you connect ideas that come at you from different perspectives.

Review and Revise

By their very nature, class notes require revision. They may be incomplete in some places, confusing in others, and illegible in still others. That is why it is critical that you review and revise your notes as soon as possible after class. This will enable you to fill in gaps while the material is fresh, to clarify sloppy handwriting, or to raise questions. Reviewing and revising your class notes prepares you for the vital step of combining class and text notes.

When you use your notes to inspire successfully intelligent thinking, your grades may reflect your efforts. The student in the following example learned this lesson after doing poorly on some tests. He explains:

> All four of us in my rooming group are taking economics. I would say we are all about equally smart. . . . Yet they are getting A's and I kept getting C's. I just couldn't figure out why. Finally, it was driving me nuts, so I went for help. My resident advisor asked if she could see my notes from that class. She looked them over carefully, and then asked me a few questions based on those notes. She helped me realize that I was great on "giving back the facts," but not so good at all at extending those facts to new situations. Yet here at college, all the questions on exams are about new situations. . . .
>
> It took someone here to help me refocus how I study. . . . I still am not getting A's, but at least solid B+'s. I don't know what would have happened if I hadn't asked for help and had just continued using that old high school style.[5]

Combine Class and Reading Notes into a Master Set

Studying from either text or class notes alone is not enough, because your instructor may present material in class that is not in your text or may gloss over topics that your text covers in depth. The process of combining class and text notes enables you to see patterns and relationships among ideas, find examples for difficult concepts, and much more.

Follow these steps to combine your class and text notes into a **master note set:**

MASTER NOTE SET

The complete, integrated note set that contains both class and text notes.

Step 1: Act quickly. Combine your class and reading notes into a logical, comprehensive presentation while the material is fresh in your mind.

Step 2: Focus on what's important by condensing to the essence. Now, reduce your combined notes so they contain only key terms and concepts. (You are likely to find repetition in your notes, which will make it easy to reduce the material.) Tightening and summarizing forces you to critically evaluate which ideas are most important and to rewrite your notes with only this material. As you begin to study, move back and forth between the full set and the reduced set. Key 6.8 shows a comprehensive outline and a reduced key term outline of the same material.

Step 3: Recite what you know. As you approach exam time, use the terms in your bare-bones notes as cues for reciting what you know about a topic. Many students assume that they know concepts simply because they understand what they read. What they are actually demonstrating is a passive understanding that doesn't necessarily mean that they can re-create the material on an exam or apply it to problems. Make the process more active by reciting out loud during study sessions, writing your responses on paper, making flash cards, or working with a partner.

KEY 6.8 Reducing a full set of notes into key term notes will help you master content.

MASTER SET OF CLASS AND TEXT NOTES

Different Views of Freedom and Equality in the American Democracy

I. U.S. democracy based on 5 core values: freedom and equality, order and stability, majority rule, protection of minority rights, and participation.
   A. U.S. would be a "perfect democracy" if it always upheld these values.
   B. U.S. is less than perfect; so it is called an "approaching democracy."

II. Freedom and Equality
   A. Historian Isaiah Berlin defines freedom as either positive or negative.
      1. Positive freedoms allow us to exercise rights under the Constitution, including right to vote.
      2. Negative freedoms safeguard us from government actions that restrict certain rights, such as the right to assemble. The 1st Amendment restricts government action by declaring that "Congress shall make no law . . ."
   B. The value of equality suggests that all people be treated equally, regardless of circumstance. Different views on what equality means and the implications for society.
      1. Equality of opportunity implies that everyone has the same chance to develop inborn talents.
         a. But life's circumstances—affected by factors like race and income—differ. This means that people start at different points and have different results. E.g., a poor, inner-city student will be less prepared for college than an affluent, suburban student.
         b. It is impossible to equalize opportunity for all Americans.
      2. Equality of result seeks to eliminate all forms of inequality, including economic differences, through wealth redistribution.
   C. Freedom and equality are in conflict, say text authors Berman and Murphy: "If your view of freedom is freedom from government intervention, then equality of any kind will be difficult to achieve. If government stays out of all citizen affairs, some people will become extremely wealthy, others will fall through the cracks, and economic inequality will multiply. On the other hand, if you wish to promote equality of result, then you will have to restrict some people's freedoms—the freedom to earn and retain an unlimited amount of money, for example."[6]

KEY TERM OUTLINE OF THE SAME MATERIAL

Different Views of Freedom and Equality in the American Democracy

I. America's 5 core values: freedom and equality, order and stability, majority rule, protection of minority rights, and participation
   a. "Perfect democracy"
   b. "Approaching democracy"

II. Value #1—Freedom and equality
   a. Positive Freedoms and Negative Freedoms
   b. Different views of equality: equality of opportunity versus equality of result
   c. Conflict between freedom and equality centers on differing views of government's role

Reviewing notes with a classmate improves your memory and comprehension of the material. These students look over notes together between classes.

Step 4: Use critical thinking. Now toss around ideas in the following ways as you reflect on your combined notes—both the comprehensive and reduced sets:

- Brainstorm examples from other sources that illustrate central ideas. Write down new ideas or questions that come up as you review.
- Think of ideas from your readings or from class that support or clarify your notes.
- Consider what in your class notes differed from your reading notes and why.
- Apply concepts to problems at the end of text chapters, to problems posed in class, or to real-world situations.

Step 5: Review and review again. To ensure learning and prepare for exams, review your key word summary and critical thinking questions until you know every topic.

Try to vary your review methods, focusing on active involvement. Recite the material to yourself, have a Q&A session with a study partner, take a practice test. Another helpful technique is to summarize your notes in writing from memory after you review them. This will tell you whether you'll be able to recall the information on a test. You may even want to summarize as you read, then summarize from memory, and compare the two summaries.

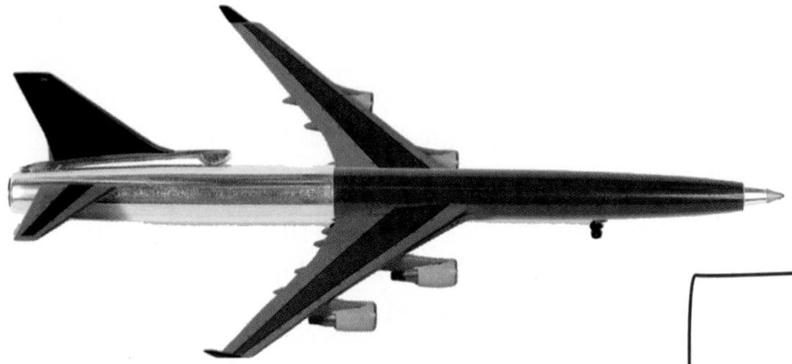

How Can You Take Notes Faster?

Personal **shorthand** is a practical intelligence strategy that enables you to write faster. Because you are the only intended reader, you can misspell and abbreviate words in ways that only you understand. A risk of using shorthand is that you might forget what your writing means. To avoid this problem, review your notes shortly after class and spell out words that could be misinterpreted.

SHORTHAND

A system of rapid handwriting that employs symbols, abbreviations, and shortened words to represent words and phrases.

Another risk is forgetting to remove shorthand from work you hand in. This can happen when you use the same system for class notes as you do when talking to friends online. For example, when students take notes in text message "language," they may be so accustomed to omitting capitalization and punctuation, using acronyms, and replacing long words with incorrect contractions that they may forget to correct their final work.

The following suggestions will help you master shorthand. Many will be familiar and, in fact, you may already use them to speed up your e-mail and text and instant messaging.

1. Use standard abbreviations in place of complete words:

w/	with	cf	compare, in comparison to
w/o	without	ff	following
→	means; resulting in	Q	question
←	as a result of	p.	page
↑	increasing	*	most importantly
↓	decreasing	<	less than
∴	therefore	>	more than
∵ or b/c	because	=	equals
≈	approximately	%	percent
+ or &	and	Δ	change
–	minus; negative	2	to; two; too
No. or #	number	vs	versus; against
i.e.	that is,	e.g.	for example
etc.	and so forth	c/o	care of
ng	no good	lb	pound

2. Shorten words by removing vowels from the middle of words:

prps = purpose
lwyr = lawyer
cmptr = computer

3. Substitute word beginnings for entire words:

assoc = associate; association
info = information
subj = subject

4. Form plurals by adding *s* to shortened words:

prblms = problems
envlps = envelopes
prntrs = printers

5. Make up your own symbols and use them consistently:

b/4 = before
4tn = fortune
2thake = toothache

6. Use standard or informal abbreviations for proper nouns such as places, people, companies, scientific substances, events, and so on:

DC = Washington, D.C.
H_2O = water
Moz. = Wolfgang Amadeus Mozart

7. If you know that a word or phrase will be repeated, write it once, and then establish an abbreviation for the rest of your notes. For example, the first time your political science instructor mentions the *Iraq Study Group*, the 2006 bipartisan commission that issued recommendations to the president on the Iraq War, write the name in full. After that, use the initials *ISG*.
8. Write only what is essential. Include only the information nuggets you want to remember, even if your instructor says much more. Do this by paring down your writing. Say, for example, your instructor had this to say on the subject of hate crimes:

   After the terrorist attacks on September 11, 2001, law enforcement officials noted a dramatic shift in the nature of hate crimes. For the first time, replacing crimes motivated by race as the leading type of hate crime were crimes that targeted religious and ethnic groups and particularly Muslims. [7]

   Your notes, which include some shorthand, might look something like this:

   —After 9/11 HCs ▲ & focus targeted religious and ethnic groups, esp. Muslims.
   —Reduction of HC based on race.

How Can You Improve Your Memory?

Your accounting instructor is giving a test tomorrow on key taxation concepts. You feel confident because you spent hours last week memorizing your notes. Unfortunately, as you start the test, you can't answer half the questions, even though you studied the material. This is not surprising, because most forgetting occurs within minutes after memorization.

If forgetting is so common, why do some people have better memories than others? Some may have an inborn talent for remembering. More often, though, they succeed because they take an active approach and master techniques to improve recall.

SHORT-TERM MEMORY
The brain's temporary information storehouse in which information remains for only a few seconds.

How Your Brain Remembers: Short-Term and Long-Term Memory

Memories are stored in three different "storage banks" in your brain. The first, called *sensory memory*, is an exact copy of what you see and hear and lasts for a second or less. Certain information is then selected from sensory memory and moved into **short-term memory,** a temporary information storehouse that maintains data for no more than 10 to 20 seconds. You are consciously aware of material in short-term memory. Unimportant information is quickly dumped. Important information is transferred to **long-term memory**—the mind's more permanent storehouse.

LONG-TERM MEMORY
The brain's permanent information storehouse from which information can be retrieved

Targeting long-term memory will solidify learning the most. "Short-term—or working—memory is useful when we want to remember a phone number until we can dial or an e-mail address until we can type it into the computer," says biologist James Zull. "We use short-term memory for these momentary challenges, all the time, every day, but it is limited in capacity, tenacity, and time."[8] Zull explains that short-term memory holds only small amounts of information for brief periods and is unstable—a distraction can easily bump out information. As you learn new material, your goal is to anchor information in long-term memory.

Memory Strategies Improve Recall

The following strategies will help improve your ability to remember what you learn.

Have Purpose, Intention, and Emotional Connection

Why can you remember the lyrics to dozens of popular songs but not the functions of the pancreas? Perhaps this is because you *want* to remember the lyrics or you have an emotional tie to them. To achieve the same results at school, try to create the purpose and will to remember. This is often linked to being emotionally involved with the material.

For example, as a student in a city-planning course, it may be easier for you to remember the complex rules surrounding housing subsidies if you think about families who benefit from these programs. If someone you know lives in a city housing project, the personal connection will probably make recall even easier.

Understand What You Memorize

If you are having trouble remembering something new, think about how the new idea fits into what you already know. A simple example: If you can't remember the meaning of the word *antebellum,* try to identify the word's root, prefix, or suffix. Knowing that the root *bellum* means "war" and the prefix *ante* means "before" will help you remember that *antebellum* means "before the war." If you take the additional step of searching the Internet for the term, you'll discover that the elegant plantation homes in the classic movie *Gone with the Wind* were built before the Civil War and are considered *antebellum architecture.*

This basic, practical principle applies to everything you study. Identify logical connections, and use these connections to aid learning. In a plant biology course, memorize plant families; in a history course, memorize events by linking them in a cause-and-effect chain.

Use Critical Thinking

Critical thinking encourages you to associate new information with what you already know. Imagine that you have to remember information about the signing of the Treaty of Versailles, the agreement that ended World War I. You might use critical thinking—combined with some quick Internet research—in the following ways:

- Recall everything that you know about the topic.
- Think about how this event is similar to other events in history.
- Consider what is different and unique about this treaty in comparison with other treaties.

- Explore the causes that led up to this event, and look at the event's effects.
- From the general idea of treaties that ended wars, explore other examples of such treaties.

Critical exploration of this kind will make it easier for you to remember specific facts and overarching concepts.

Recite, Rehearse, and Write

When you *recite* material, you repeat key concepts aloud, in your own words, to aid memorization. *Rehearsing* is similar to reciting but is done silently. *Writing* is reciting on paper. All three processes are practical tools that actively involve you in learning and remembering material. You will get the greatest benefit if you separate your learning into the following steps:

- As you read, focus on the points you want to remember. These are usually found in the topic sentences of paragraphs. Then recite, rehearse, or write down the ideas.
- Convert each main idea into a key word, phrase, or visual image—something that is easy to recall and that will set off a chain of memories that will bring you back to the original information. Write each key word or phrase on an index card.
- One by one, look at the key words on your cards and recite, rehearse, or write all the associated information you can recall. Check your recall against your original material.

These steps are part of the process for consolidating and summarizing your lecture and text notes as you study.

Reciting, rehearsing, and writing involve more than rereading material and parroting words out loud, in your head, or on paper. Because rereading does not necessarily require any involvement, you can reread without learning. However, you cannot help but think and learn as you convert text concepts into key points and rewrite important points as key words and phrases.

Limit and Organize the Items You Are Processing

This involves three key activities:

- *Separate main points from unimportant details.* Highlight only the key points in your texts, and write notes in the margins about central ideas (see Key 5.8 on page 170.)
- *Divide material into manageable sections.* Generally, when material is short and easy to understand, studying it from start to finish improves recall. Divide longer material into logical sections, master each section, put all the sections together, and then test your memory of all the material.
- *Use organizational tools.* Rely on an outline or another organizational tool to connect ideas. These tools will show logical connections and expose gaps in understanding.

Study During Short, Frequent Sessions

Research has shown that you can improve your chances of remembering material by learning it more than once. Spread your study sessions over time: A pattern of short sessions—say three 20-minute study sessions, followed by brief periods of rest—is more effective than continual studying with little or no rest. With this in mind, try studying during breaks in your schedule, and even consider using these time slots to study with classmates.

Sleep can actually aid memory because it reduces interference from new information. Because you can't always go to sleep immediately after studying for an exam, try postponing the study of other subjects until your exam is over. When studying for several tests at once, avoid studying two similar subjects back to back. Your memory is likely to be more accurate when you study history right after biology rather than chemistry after biology.

Practice the Middle

When you are trying to learn something, you usually study some material first, attack other material in the middle of the session, and approach still other topics at the end. The weak link is likely to be the material you study midway. It pays to give this material special attention in the form of extra practice.

Use Flash Cards

Flash cards are a great visual memory tool. They give you short, repeated review sessions that provide immediate feedback, and they are portable, which gives you the flexibility to use them wherever you go. Use the front of a 3-by-5-inch index card to write a word, idea, or phrase you want to learn. Use the back for a definition, explanation, and other key facts. Key 6.9 shows two flash cards used to study for a pychology exam.

Here are some suggestions for making the most of your flash cards:

- *Use the cards as a self-test.* As you go through them, divide them into two piles—the material you know and the material you are learning.

KEY 6.9

Flash cards help you memorize important facts.

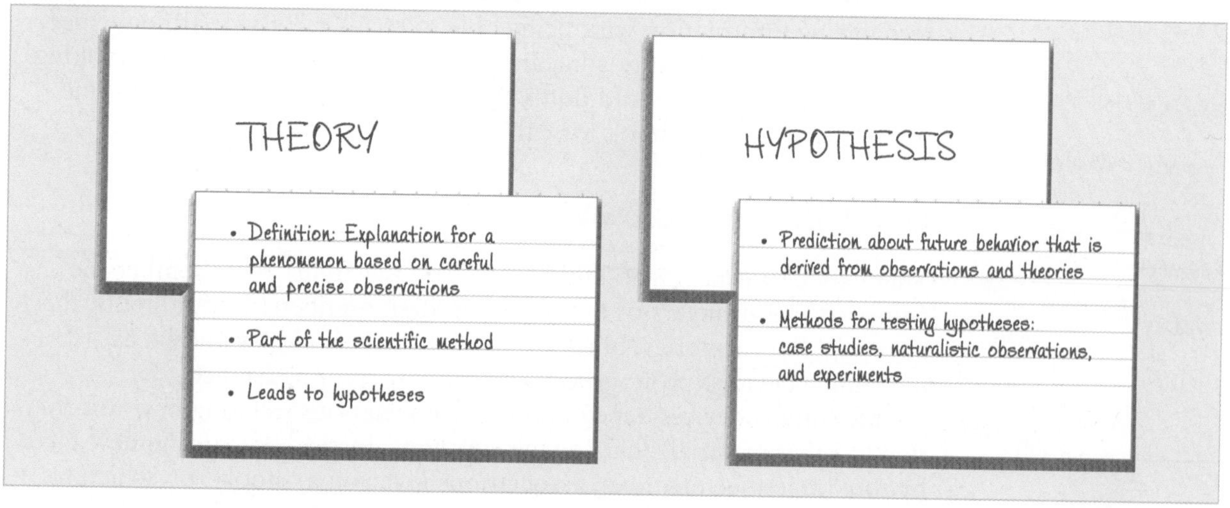
THEORY
• Definition: Explanation for a phenomenon based on careful and precise observations
• Part of the scientific method
• Leads to hypotheses
HYPOTHESIS
• Prediction about future behavior that is derived from observations and theories
• Methods for testing hypotheses: case studies, naturalistic observations, and experiments

- *Carry the cards with you and review them frequently.* You'll learn the most if you start using your flash cards early in the course, well ahead of exam time.
- *Shuffle the cards and learn the information in various orders.* This will help you avoid putting too much focus on some information and not enough on other.
- *Test yourself in both directions.* First, look at the terms and provide the definitions or explanations. Then turn the cards over and reverse the process.
- *Reduce the stack as you learn.* Eliminate cards when you are certain of your knowledge. Watching the pile get smaller is a reward that reinforces your motivation. As test time approaches, put all the cards together again for a final review.

Use a Tape Recorder and MP3 Player

Questions on tape can work like audio flash cards. One method is to record short-answer study questions, leaving 10 to 15 seconds between questions for you to answer out loud. Recording the correct answer after the pause will give you immediate feedback. For example, part of a recording for a writing class might say, "Three elements that require analysis before writing are . . . (10–15 second pause) . . . topic, audience, and purpose."

Pearson Education, the publisher of this and many of the other textbooks you will be using in college, developed VangoNotes to help you learn material through your MP3 player. Plug in your earphones to listen to chapter summaries and answer audio tests while walking between classes or shopping for food. Lindleigh Whetstone, a student at Tidewater Community College in Virginia, uses her iPod to learn Spanish when she is doing her laundry. "I get a lot more listening in than I did before," she says. She estimates that her listening/study time has grown from 30 minutes a week to about five hours a week.[9]

Use the Information

In the days after you learn something new, use your analytical intelligence to use what you learned. Think about other contexts in which the information applies and link it to new problems. Then test your knowledge to make sure the material is in long-term memory. "Don't confuse recognizing information with being able to recall it," says learning expert Adam Robinson. "Be sure you can recall the information without looking at your notes for clues. And don't move on until you have created some sort of sense-memory hook for calling it back up when you need it."[10]

MNEMONIC DEVICES
Memory techniques that use vivid associations to link new information with information you already know.

Use Mnemonic Devices

There are performers who build careers on the ability to remember the names of 100 strangers or repeat 30 ten-digit numbers. Undoubtedly, they have superior memories, but they also rely on techniques known as **mnemonic devices** (pronounced neh-*mahn*-ick) for assistance.

Mnemonic devices depend on vivid associations (relating new information to other material) that engage emotions. Instead of learning new facts by *rote* (repetitive practice), associations give you a "hook" on which to

hang these facts for later retrival. They are formed with the help of your creative intelligence.

There are different kinds of mnemonic devices, including visual images and associations and acronyms. Study how these devices work, then apply them to your own challenges. These devices take time and effort to create, and you'll need motivation to remember them. Because of this, it is smart to use mnemonic devices only when you really need them—for instance, to distinguish confusing concepts that consistently trip you up or to recall items in order.

Create Visual Images and Associations

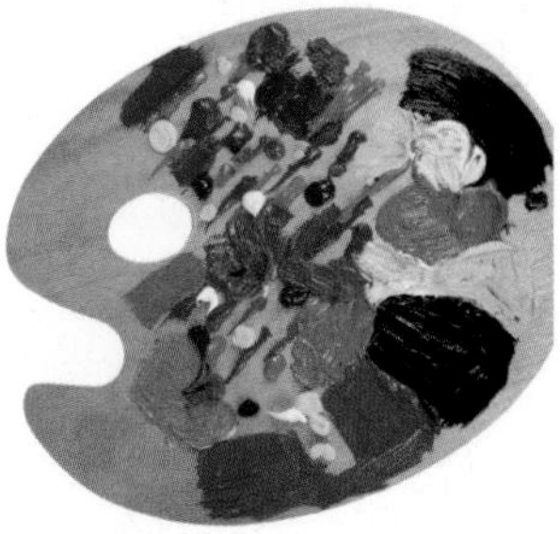

To remember that the Spanish artist Picasso painted *The Three Women*, you might imagine the women in a circle dancing to a Spanish song with a pig and a donkey (pig-asso). The most effective images involve bright colors, three dimensions, action scenes, inanimate objects with human traits, and humor. The more outlandish the image, the better.

Use Visual Images to Remember Items in a List

Using the *mental walk* strategy, imagine yourself storing new ideas in familiar locations. Say, for example, that for your biology course you have to remember the major endocrine glands, starting in the brain and working downward through the body. To do this, think of your route to the library. You pass the campus theater, the science center, the bookstore, the cafeteria, the athletic center, and the social science building before reaching your destination. At each spot along the way, you "place" the concept you want to learn. You then link the concept with a similar-sounding word that brings to mind a vivid image (see Key 6.10):

- At the campus theater, you imagine bumping into actor Brad Pitt, who is holding two cell phones and has a terrible cold (pituitary gland).
- At the science center, you visualize Mr. Universe with bulging thighs. When you are introduced, you learn that his name is Roy (thyroid gland).
- At the campus bookstore, you envision a second Mr. Universe with his thighs covered in mustard (thymus gland).
- In the cafeteria, you see an ad for Dean Al for president (adrenal gland).
- At the athletic center, you visualize a student throwing a ball into a pan and creatures applauding from the bleachers (pancreas).
- At the social science building, you imagine receiving a standing ovation (ovaries).
- And at the library, you visualize sitting at a table taking a test that is easy (testes).

Create Acronyms

An acronym is a word formed from the first letters of a series of words created in order to help you remember the series. In history class, you can remember the Allies during World War II—Britain, America, and Russia—with the acronym *BAR*. This is an example of a *word acronym,* because the first letters of the items you want to remember spell a word. Keep in mind that the word or words spelled don't necessarily have to be real words.

ACRONYM

A word formed from the first letters of a series of words, created to help you recall the series.

KEY 6.10

A mental walk mnemonic helps you remember items in a list.

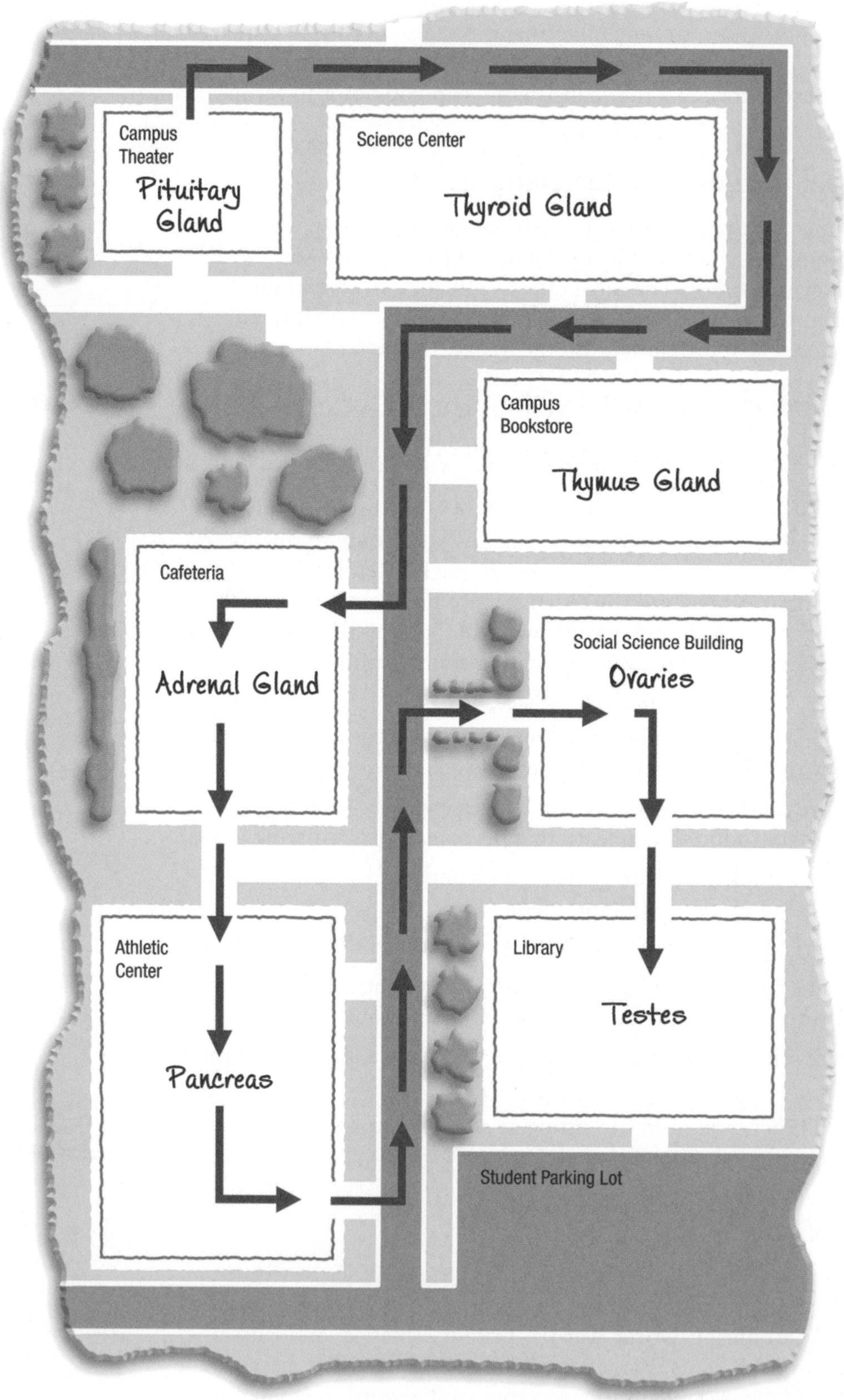

Other acronyms take the form of an entire sentence in which the first letter of each word in the sentence stands for the first letter of the memorized term. This is called a *list order acronym.* For example, music students use the phrase *Every Good Boy Does Fine* to remember the notes that correspond to the lines on the treble clef (E, G, B, D, and F).

You can create your own acronyms. For example, to remember the names of the first six U.S. presidents—Washington, Adams, Jefferson, Madison, Monroe, and Adams—you notice that the first letters of their last names read *W A J M M A.* To remember them, first you might insert an *e* after the *J* and create a short nonsense word: *wajemma.* Then, to make sure you don't forget the nonsense word, picture the six presidents sitting in a row and wearing pajamas.

Use Songs or Rhymes

Some of the classic mnemonic devices are rhyming poems that tend to stick in your mind. One you may have heard is the rule about the order of *i* and *e* in spelling.

> I before E, except after C, or when sounded like "A" as in "neighbor" and "weigh." Four exceptions if you please: either, neither, seizure, seize.

Use your creativity to make up your own poems or songs, linking familiar tunes or rhymes with information you want to remember. Thinking back to the "wajemma" example, imagine that you want to remember the presidents' first names as well. You might set these names—George, John, Thomas, James, James, and John—to the tune of "Happy Birthday." Or, to extend the history theme, you might use the first musical phrase of "The Star-Spangled Banner."

Haverford College physics professor Walter Smith hosts a Web site—www.physicssongs.org—dedicated to helping students enjoy physics and learn essential concepts by putting them to music. Here, for example, is "The Gauss's Law Song," written by Professor Smith and Marian McKenzie and sung to the tune of "East Side, West Side."

Inside, outside, count the lines to tell—

If the charge is inside, there will be net flux as well.

If the charge is outside, be careful and you'll see

The goings in and goings out are equal perfectly.

If you wish to know the field precise,

And the charge is symmetric,

you will find this law is nice—

Q upon a constant—eps'lon naught they say—

Equals closed surface integral of E dot n dA.

Professor Smith's students credit musical mnemonics for helping them retain complex equations. Some students, like Katie Baratz, have been inspired to write their own songs. For her final class project she paired lyrics entitled "In My Mind, I've Got Physics Equations" with the James Taylor tune "Carolina in My Mind."[12]

get creative!

Craft Your Own Mnemonic

Create a mnemonic to help you remember some facts.

- Identify a group of connected facts that you have to memorize—for example, for political science, the names of every presidential candidate after World War II; for literature, the names of all the characters in Shakespeare's *Romeo and Juliet*. Write your choice here:

- Now create your own mnemonic to remember the grouping using any of the devices in this chapter. Write the mnemonic here and on additional paper if necessary.

Improving your memory requires energy, time, and work. It also helps to master SQ3R, the textbook study technique that was introduced in chapter 5. By going through the steps in SQ3R and using the specific memory techniques described in this chapter, you will be able to learn more in less time—and remember what you learn long after exams are over. These techniques will be equally valuable when you start a career.

Successful Intelligence Wrap-Up

Achieving competence in listening, note taking, and memorizing requires more than just analytical ability. When you use all three components of successful intelligence to find your own way to listen and take in information, record information that you will need in the future, and remember what you learn, you set yourself up for future academic success. Here's how you have built skills in chapter 6:

Analytical

Within the material about listening, you examined the listening process and the challenges you face each step along the way, getting more specific in your analysis of your own listening skills with the *Get Analytical* exercise. You explored note-taking systems, considering what systems may work best for your particular classroom and study situations. Near the end of the chapter, you examined the nature of memory and the importance of memory challenges.

Creative

Investigating different note-taking systems may have inspired new ideas about how to approach note taking in your courses. With what you learned about note taking, you are prepared to create self-styled methods that suit your personal preferences, the material you are working with, and your instructor's style. After you explored how mnemonic devices work, completing the *Get Creative* exercise gave you experience in crafting your own original mnemonic device.

Practical

You compiled practical tools for listening actively in class, getting a sense of how to manage listening challenges. You explored how to use different note-taking systems in different situations, applying your knowledge to a specific note-taking challenge in the *Get Practical* exercise. You added practical techniques in personal shorthand and creating a master set of notes to your skills. You broadened your understanding of the ways in which experience solidifies memory.

Lagom

(lag-ohm)

In Swedish, the word *lagom* refers to the place between extremes, the spot that is neither too much nor too little, but just right. Many Swedish people aspire to this place in everything they do. They tend to seek stability yet remain open to what is new and different.

Think of the quest for *lagom* as you challenge yourself to improve your listening, note-taking, and memory skills. With *lagom* as your guide, you will appreciate that your goal is not perfection in any of these skills, but rather the ability to hear as much as you can, to take appropriate notes that will be the foundation for your studying, and to develop just the right number of memory strategies that will help you remember what is valuable. You can never hope to take in, record, and memorize every word that your instructor speaks—and that's okay. You are aiming for "just right."[13]

"Happiness does not come from doing easy work but from the afterglow of satisfaction that comes after the achievement of a difficult task that demanded our best."

THEODORE I. RUBIN, PSYCHIATRIST AND AUTHOR

PERSONAL TRIUMPH CASE STUDY

FROM HOMELESSNESS TO COLLEGE SUCCESS

VICTORIA GOUGH, STUDENT, GLENDALE COMMUNITY COLLEGE, GLENDALE, ARIZONA

Motivation. Perseverance. Drive. Determination. Words are inadequate to describe Victoria Gough's journey from homelessness to college success—a journey fueled by willpower, native intelligence, support from family, belief in herself, and practical learning methods. Read this account, then use separate paper or a computer file to answer the questions on page 214.

I grew up homeless in southern Illinois. I've lived in sheds, boxcars, and salvage yards—with my parents and without them. Sometimes I wouldn't eat for three days in a row. I attended school on and off starting in third grade, but never went back after eighth. I never set foot inside a high school. It may be hard to believe that people grow up this poor and isolated in the United States, but they do.

For a short while I lived with my dad. When he rejected us, my brothers and sister and I left. My mom told us we would have to go to a state home. When I refused, she convinced me to marry at 13, which I did. I had three children in five years. I was able to let my sister live with me. We got odd jobs cleaning houses for people and working at restaurants. We rented a trailer, which was the nicest place I'd ever lived. Meanwhile, I dreamed of going to school and longed to live in a house and go to a grocery store. I took a giant step toward that goal when I got my high school equivalency degree in 1993.

In 1994 I married again. My husband and I live near Glendale Community College, and he encouraged me to enroll. I entered the admissions office shaking like a leaf. The administrators helped me register for remedial classes to start with. In class I said as little as possible. I didn't know where to write my name on a paper or how to buy books at a bookstore. The first time I learned how to turn on a computer I cried.

My first instructor told me I should drop out before I couldn't get my money back. I went back to my admission counselor, who put me in a different class with a wonderful instructor. I ate up the material. When I started getting 100% correct on my papers, I thought maybe the teachers considered me a sympathy case. When I received a letter telling me I made the national honor roll, I thought they made a mistake. Slowly, I'm starting to realize how capable I really am. My long-term goal is to be involved in some type of research in the medical field.

I study from six to eight hours every day, because I have so much catching up to do. Recently, an instructor nominated me for the Outstanding Achievement award on our campus. She said she never had a student sit through as many classes as I do. If the instructor lets me, I sit through the class twice. The first time I listen, and the second time I take notes.

I see students on my campus who quit school, and I have friends who say, "This is too hard." I think they're giving up too easily. If I don't understand something in class, I'll raise my hand. Sometimes I'll hear students in the back of the class say, "Someone make her shut up." It hurts my feelings a little, but I feel sadder for them than for myself. They don't seem to realize what a treasure education is. If I keep going, I'll be able to get my associate's degree in general studies the same time my granddaughter graduates from high school. What a great celebration that will be!

My personal mission is to help my other family members to break free of their grim existence and to expose the marginalized in our society to the outside world. No one in my family has ever graduated from high school, and I'm the first to enroll in college. All my children graduated from high school and went on to college. My son has a Ph.D., is a professor of sociology and criminology, and has written a book. I get goose bumps thinking about how far I've come and all the possibilities ahead of me. Learning is one of the greatest joys of my life.

Elie Sanon, the student artist who created this drawing, emigrated from Haiti at 8 years old. Two years later his mother died, and like Victoria he had enormous adjustments to face, dealing with his loss as well as with a new country, a new language, and family financial pressures. He had shown artistic talent at an early age, and through encouragement from a mentor as well as his own determination, he was ultimately accepted to the prestigious Rhode Island School of Design where he is currently studying. For more of Elie's story, please visit www.prenhall.com/carter.

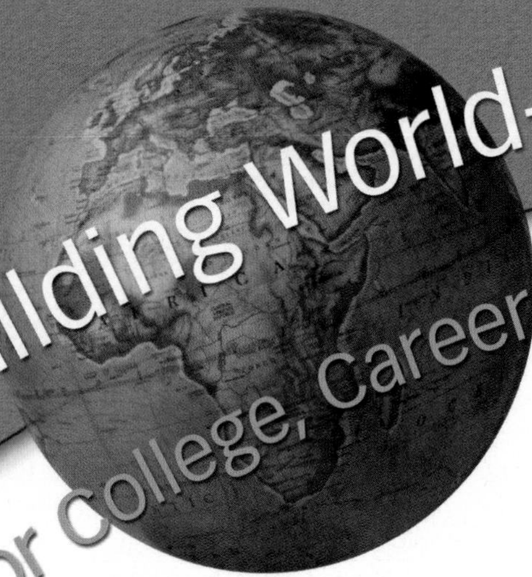

Building World-Class Skills for College, Career, and Life Success

SUCCESSFUL INTELLIGENCE

Think, Create, Apply

Learn from the experiences of others. Look back at Victoria Gough's Personal Triumph on page 213. Read her story, and then relate her experience to your own life by completing the following:

Think it through: ***Analyze your own motivation.*** How motivated are you to achieve your academic goals? What challenges have you overcome to get where you are today? From your memory of reaching important goals, what strategies will you use to make sure you complete your education? How does reading about Victoria affect your commitment to overcome obstacles in your life?

Think out of the box: ***Let others inspire ideas.*** Choose two people whom you respect. Put your listening skills to work: Spend a few minutes talking with each of them about the major obstacles they overcame to achieve success. Ask them for advice that will help ensure that you will stay in school and get a degree. From what you hear, begin brainstorming ideas about how to overcome obstacles that may stand in the way of graduation. Take notes throughout this listening process.

Make it happen: ***Put a practical plan together.*** Map out your action steps. Create a mnemonic device that will help you remember your plan. Envision your success as you put your plan into action.

TEAMWORK

Create Solutions Together

Create a note-taking team. In your most demanding course, form a study group with two classmates. Ask everyone to gather together a week's worth of class notes so that you can review and compare the different versions. Focus on the following:

- Legibility (Can everyone read what is written?)
- Completeness (Did you all record the same information? If not, why not?)
- Organizational effectiveness (Does everyone get an idea of how ideas flow?)
- Value of the notes as a study aid (Will this help everyone remember the material?)

What did you learn? Use your insights to improve your personal note-taking skills.

WRITING

Journal and Put Skills to Work

Record your thoughts on a separate piece of paper, in a journal, or on a computer file.

Journal entry: How people retain information. How do you react to the following statement?

> We retain 10% of what we read, 20% of what we hear, 30% of what we see, 50% of what we hear and see, 70% of what we say, and 90% of what we say and do.

How can you use this insight to improve your ability to retain information? What will you do differently as a result of this insight?

Real-life writing: Combining class and text notes. Create a master set of notes for one course that combines one week's classes and reading assignments. Your goal is to summarize and connect all the important information covered during the period.

PERSONAL PORTFOLIO

Prepare for Career Success

Learning more about career success. Put your listening and note-taking skills to work as you investigate what brings success in the workplace. Choose a career area that interests you, and then interview two people in that area—one from an academic setting (such as an instructor or an academic advisor) and one from the working world (a person who is doing a job that interests you). Choose a setting where you can listen well and take effective notes.

Ask your interview subjects what they feel is the recipe for success in their career. You might ask specifically about curriculum (what courses are required for this area, and what courses are beneficial but not required), other preparation such as extracurricular activities and internships, qualities such as leadership and commitment, day-to-day attitudes, and anything else you are wondering about. Ask them also about the role that listening, note-taking, and memory skills play in career success. For example, if you are interviewing an account manager at an advertising agency, he might tell you that the ability to listen well, take accurate notes, and recall critical concepts is essential at client meetings. Practicing and perfecting these skills while listening to your instructors will help you in your career.

When you complete your interviews, create a report that lays out the "recipe for success." Keep in mind the skills and attitudes you wish to develop as you choose next term's courses and activities.

Suggested Readings

Burley-Allen, Madelyn. *Listening: The Forgotten Skill: A Self-Teaching Guide*. New York: Wiley, 1995.

DePorter, Bobbi, and Mike Hernacki. *Quantum Notes: Whole-Brain Approaches to Note-Taking*. Chicago: Learning Forum, 2000.

Dunkel, Patricia A., Frank Pialorsi, and Joane Kozyrez. *Advanced Listening Comprehension: Developing Aural and Note-Taking Skills*, 3rd ed. Boston: Heinle & Heinle, 2004.

Higbee, Kenneth L. *Your Memory: How It Works and How to Improve It*. New York: Marlowe, 2001.

Lebauer, R. Susan. *Learn to Listen, Listen to Learn: Academic Listening and Note-Taking*. Upper Saddle River, NJ: Prentice Hall, 2000.

Levin, Leonard. *Easy Script Express: Unique Speed Writing Methods to Take Fast Notes and Dictation*. Chicago: Legend, 2000.

Lorayne, Harry. *Super Memory—Super Student: How to Raise Your Grades in 30 Days*. Boston: Little, Brown, 1990.

Lorayne, Harry. *The Memory Book: The Classic Guide to Improving Your Memory at Work, at School, and at Play*. New York: Ballantine Books, 1996.

Roberts, Billy. *Working Memory: Improving Your Memory for the Workplace*. London: Bridge Trade, 1999.

Roberts, Billy. *Educate Your Memory: Improvement Techniques for Students of All Ages*. London: Allison & Busby, 2000.

Zull, James. *The Art of Changing the Brain: Enriching the Practice of Teaching by Exploring the Biology of Learning*. Sterling, VA: Stylus, 2002.

Internet and Podcast Resources

Coping.org—Tools for Coping with Life's Stressors—Improving Listening Skills: **www.coping.org/dialogue/listen.htm**

Dyslexia at College—Taking Notes (tips on taking notes from books and at lectures): **www.dyslexia-college.com/notes.html**

ForgetKnot (a source for mnemonic devices): **http://members.tripod.com/~ForgetKnot**

Kishwaukee College Learning Skills Center (helpful advice on listening skills): **www.kish.cc.il.us/learning_skills_center/study_skills_help/good_listening.shtml**

Merriam-Webster's Word of the Day (free word of the day in audio form available on the Internet or as podcasts): **www.merriam-webster.com/cgi-bin/mwwod.pl**

Princeton Review Vocab Minute (free vocabulary-building podcasts using songs to help you remember): **RobinR@Review.com**

Prentice Hall Student Success Supersite: **www.prenhall.com/success**

Endnotes

[1]Ralph G. Nichols, "Do We Know How to Listen? Practical Helps in a Modern Age," *Speech Teacher*, March 1961, pp. 118–124.

[2]Richard J. Light, *Making the Most of College: Students Speak Their Minds*, Cambridge, MA: Harvard University Press, 2001, pp. 48–49. Copyright © 2001 by Richard J. Light. Reprinted by permission of the publisher.

[3]Teresa Audesirk, Gerald Audesirk, and Bruce E. Byers, *Life on Earth*, 2nd ed., Upper Saddle River, NJ: Prentice Hall, 2000, pp. 660–662.

[4]System developed by Cornell professor Walter Pauk. See Walter Pauk, *How to Study in College,* 7th ed., Boston: Houghton Mifflin, 2001, pp. 236–241.

[5]Light, *Making the Most of College*, p. 38.

[6]Based on Larry Berman and Bruce Allen Murphy, *Approaching Democracy: Portfolio Edition*, Upper Saddle River, NJ: Pearson/Prentice Hall, 2005, pp. 6–8.

[7]Information from Frank Schmalleger, *Criminal Justice Today*, 8th ed., Upper Saddle River, NJ: Prentice Hall, 2005, p. 71.

[8]James Zull, *The Art of Changing the Brain: Enriching Teaching by Exploring the Biology of Learning*, Sterling, VA: Stylus, 2002.

[9]Cited in Madlen Read, "Growing Number of Students Use MP3 Players as a Study Tool," *Napa Valley Register*, February 7, 2007 (www.napavalleyregister.com/articles/2007/02/07/business/local/doc45c9e13a31a47296818650.txt).

[10]Adam Robinson, *What Smart Students Know: Maximum Grades, Optimum Learning, Minimum Time*, New York: Three Rivers Press, 1993, p. 118.

[11]"The Gauss's Law Song," © 2001 Walter Fox Smith, Haverford College (www.haverford.edu/physics-astro/songs/Gauss).

[12]Christopher Conkey "It's All Relative: Songs to Make Physics Easier," *Wall Street Journal*, March 17, 2005, p. B1.

[13]Christopher J. Moore, *In Other Words: A Language Lover's Guide to the Most Intriguing Words Around the World,* New York: Walker, 2004, p. 45.

TEST TAKING

Showing What You Know

7

"Successfully intelligent people seek to perform in ways that not only are competent but distinguish them from ordinary performers. They realize that the gap between competence and excellence may be small but the greatest rewards, both internal and external, are for excellence."

ROBERT J. STERNBERG

When you successfully show what you know on tests, you achieve educational goals and develop confidence. Exams also help you gauge your progress so that, when needed, you can ramp up your efforts. Most importantly, smart test preparation results in real learning that you take from course to course and into your career and life. As you will see in this chapter, test taking is about preparation, persistence, and strategy—all of which tap into your analytical, creative, and practical abilities. It is also about conquering fears, focusing on details, and learning from mistakes.

In this chapter you explore answers to the following questions:

Chapter 7's Successful Intelligence Skills

Analytical

- Matching test-preparation strategies with personal needs
- Identifying the nature of test anxiety
- Analyzing how to answer objective and subjective test questions
- Identifying patterns that cause you to make test errors

Creative

- Constructing a new perspective of tests as helpful evaluative tools
- Developing a pretest to assess material mastery before an exam
- Creating an effective study schedule and regimen

Practical

- How to attack objective test questions
- How to write a test essay
- How to evaluate and learn from test mistakes

How Can Preparation Improve Test Performance?

You prepare for exams every day of the term. By attending class, staying on top of assignments, completing readings and projects, and participating in class discussions, you are actively learning and retaining what you need to know in order to do well on exams. This knowledge is the most important test-preparation tool you have.

The following additional measures will help you prepare as exams approach because they put your analytical, creative, and practical thinking skills into action.

Identify Test Type and Material Covered

Before you begin studying, be practical as you find out as much as you can about the test, including the following:

- *Topics that will be covered:* Will the test cover everything since the term began, or will it be more limited?

REAL QUESTIONS

How can I combat test anxiety?

Peter Changsak
Sheldon-Jackson College
Sitka, Alaska

I am a Yu'pik Eskimo from a village on the Yukon River. Before attending college, I worked for six years as a clerk at the Native Corporation, a gas station and general store. When the manager passed away, the business offered to make me a manager. Even though I knew how to do the work, I didn't feel I was ready, so I decided to go to school for more training.

I felt like I was a success at work, but I don't feel successful as a student. College life is different from what I am accustomed to. The hardest part has been taking tests. I study hard, but then when the test begins, my mind goes blank. Sometimes I feel like quitting, but I also think that I will have more choices if I stick with it. How can I conquer my test anxiety?

PRACTICAL ANSWERS

Tonjua Williams, M.Ed.
Associate Provost,
Health Programs
St. Petersburg College

Preparation and a positive attitude will help you cope with test pressure.

Many students experience test anxiety, especially when they are new to college. Often, anxiety is a result of feeling uncomfortable in unfamiliar waters. That's why the first test in a class can be nerve-racking. Preparation is the best way to deal with nerves:

- Attend class regularly.
- Pay attention and take good notes.
- Join a study group.
- Spend two hours studying outside of class for every hour you spend in class and start studying early.
- Communicate with your instructor to make sure you understand course expectations; use your syllabus as a guide.
- Before the exam, get plenty of rest and eat a light breakfast or snack.

To calm yourself right before the exam, try the following:

- Close your eyes, take a deep breath, then review the test.
- Start with questions you are comfortable answering.
- Look for clues that will help you answer more difficult questions.

After the exam review what you did right and wrong to pinpoint areas you need to work on.

Test anxiety, believe it or not, can encourage you to rise to the occasion. The stress of an upcoming test can help you work hard so you are fully prepared. It is important to think of exams as opportunities to show off your knowledge. Changing your attitude and looking forward to the chance to demonstrate what you know will help you do your best work.

- *Material you will be tested on:* Will the test cover only what you learned in class and in the text, or will it also include outside readings? Will you be given material to work with—for example, will you be asked to analyze a poem?
- *Types of questions:* Will the questions be objective (multiple-choice, true/false, sentence-completion), subjective (essay), or a combination?

- *How the test will be graded:* Will partial credit be given for short-answer questions? Do you need to show problem-solving steps to get full credit? Are certain sections worth more than others?

Your instructors may answer many of these questions. They may tell you the question format and the topics that will be covered. They may also drop hints about possible questions, either directly ("I might ask a question on . . .") or more subtly ("One of my favorite theories is . . . "). Use your social intelligence to pick up as many clues as you can.

As you begin thinking about the test, remember that *not all tests are created equal*—a quiz is not as important as a midterm or final, although accumulated grades on small quizzes add up and can make a difference in your final grade. Plan and prioritize your study time and energy according to the value of the quiz or test. Your syllabus will tell you when quizzes and tests are scheduled throughout the term (see page 14 for a sample syllabus).

Here are other practical strategies for predicting what may be on a test. To prepare effectively, combine these with the strategies you learned throughout *Keys to Success:*

Use SQ3R to identify what's important. Often, the questions you ask yourself as you read assigned materials will be part of the test. Textbook study questions are also good candidates.

Listen for clues at review sessions. Many instructors offer review sessions before midterms and finals in order to answer last-minute questions. Bring your questions to these sessions and listen to the questions others ask. They may cover material you thought you knew, but actually need to review or learn more about.

Make an appointment to see your instructor. Spending a few minutes talking about the test one-on-one may clarify misunderstandings and help you focus on what to study.

Talk to people who already took the course and look at comments on teacher evaluation Web sites. Try to get a sense of test difficulty, whether tests focus primarily on assigned readings or class notes, what materials are usually covered, and the types of questions that are asked. If you learn that the instructor emphasizes specific facts, for example, use flash cards to drill. If she emphasizes a global overview, focus on big-picture concepts. Use your social intelligence to make others want to share information about their experiences.

Examine old tests, if the instructor makes them available. You may find old tests in class, online, or on reserve in the library. Old tests will help you answer questions like these:

- Do tests focus on examples and details, general ideas and themes, or a combination?
- Are the questions straightforward, or confusing and sometimes tricky?
- Will you be asked to apply principles to new situations and problems?

After taking the first exam in a course, you will have a better idea of what to expect.

Create a Study Schedule and Checklist

Use the guidelines presented in the *Get Focused!* end-of-part section on page 106 to create a study plan and schedule. Make copies of the checklist on page 107 and complete it for every exam. It is an invaluable tool for organizing your pre-exam studying.

Studying for final exams, which usually take place the last week of the term, is a major commitment that requires careful time management. Your college may schedule study days (also called a "reading period") between the end of classes and the beginning of finals. Lasting from a day or two to several weeks, these days give you uninterrupted hours to prepare for exams and finish papers.

End-of-year studying often requires flexibility. For example, instead of working at the library during this period, some students at the University of Texas at Austin are often seen at Barton Springs, a spring-fed pool near campus. Anna Leeker and Jillian Adams chose this site to study biology because of the beautiful surroundings—and also because they had little choice. "We heard that the libraries are packed, and that students are waiting in line for tables," said Jillian. Both realize that they have to work to maintain their focus, no matter where they study.[1]

Prepare Through Careful Review

A thorough review, using analytical and practical strategies like the following, will give you the best shot at remembering material:

Use SQ3R. This reading method provides an excellent structure for reviewing your reading materials (see pages 157–166).

Actively review your combined class and text notes. One of the best ways to review for an exam is to combine and condense your text and class notes (see chapter 6). Work with this combined note set to prepare for exams as follows:

- *As exam time nears, go through your key terms and concepts outline and recite everything you know about a topic.* Reading your notes is not enough. Learning takes place only if you express content in your own words and apply it to problems.
- *Use critical thinking to become actively involved.* Think about examples and ideas from outside readings and experiences that illustrate concepts, and ideas and opinions that take another point of view. Use what you know to solve problems.
- *Continue to actively review until you demonstrate a solid knowledge of every topic.* Involve yourself with the material by taking a practice test, doing a Q&A with a study partner, and answering your SQ3R questions in writing one more time. Don't stop until you are sure you can apply concepts to new material.

Take a Pretest

Use end-of-chapter text questions to create your own pretest. If your course doesn't have an assigned text, develop questions from your notes and assigned outside readings. Old homework problems will also help target areas that need work. Choose questions that are likely to be covered, then answer them under test-like conditions—in a quiet place, with no books or notes (unless the exam is open book), and with a clock to tell you when to quit.

The same test-preparation skills you learn in college will help you do well on standardized tests for graduate school. Sharon Smith describes how students in her preparatory program used practice tests and other techniques to help boost their scores on the Medical College Admission Test (MCAT). They "started with un-timed practices in order to work on accuracy, and timed practices were incorporated as the term progressed. Everyone tried to finish the tests/passages in the allotted time, and, at the end of each practice session, go over answer choices to understand why they are correct or incorrect." During the spring term they were "given mock exams, and it was important to treat the mock MCAT as if it were the real exam. This gave the best assessment of performance on test day."[2]

get creative!

Write Your Own Test

Check your syllabi for the courses you are taking now, and find the test that is coming up first. Use the tips in this chapter to predict the material that will be covered on this test, the types of questions that will be asked (multiple-choice, essay, and so forth), and the nature of the questions (a broad overview of the material or specific details).

Then be creative. Your goal is to write questions that your instructor is likely to ask—interesting questions that tap what you have learned and make you think about the material in different ways. Go through the following steps:

1. Write the questions you come up with on a separate sheet of paper.
2. Use what you created as a pretest. Set up test-like conditions—a quiet, timed environment—and see how you do.
3. Evaluate your pretest answers against your notes and the text. How did you do?

   ____

   ____

4. Finally, after you take the actual exam, evaluate whether you think this exercise improved your performance. Would you use this technique again? Why or why not?

   ____

   ____

Prepare Physically

Most tests ask you to work at your best under pressure, so try to get a good night's sleep before the exam. Sleep improves your ability to remember what you studied before you went to bed.

Eating a light, well-balanced meal that is high in protein (eggs, milk, yogurt, meat, fish, nuts, or peanut butter) will keep you full longer than carbohydrates (breads, candy, or pastries). When time is short, don't skip breakfast—grab a quick meal such as a few tablespoons of peanut butter, a banana, or a high-protein granola bar.

Make the Most of Last-Minute Cramming

Cramming—studying intensively and around the clock right before an exam—often results in information going into your head and popping right back out when the exam is over. *If learning is your goal, cramming will not help you reach it.* The reality, however, is that you are likely to cram for tests, especially midterms and finals, from time to time in your college career. Use these hints to make the most of this study time:

- *Focus on crucial concepts.* Summarize the most important points and try to resist reviewing notes or texts page by page.
- *Create a last-minute study sheet to review right before the test.* Write down key facts, definitions, and formulas on a single sheet of paper or on flash cards. If you prefer visual notes, use think links to map out ideas and supporting examples.
- *Arrive early.* Review your study aids until you are asked to clear your desk.

After your exam, evaluate how cramming affected your performance. Did it help, or did it load your mind with disconnected details? Did it increase or decrease your anxiety when the test began? Then evaluate how cramming affected your recall. Within a few days, you will probably remember very little—a reality that will work against you in advanced courses that build on this knowledge and in careers that require it. Think ahead about how you can start studying earlier to prepare for your next exam.

TEST ANXIETY

A bad case of nerves that can make it hard to think or remember during an exam.

How Can You Work Through Test Anxiety?

Some students experience incapacitating stress, known as **test anxiety**, before and during exams, especially midterms and finals. Test anxiety can cause sweating, nausea, dizziness, headaches, and fatigue. It can reduce your ability to concentrate, make you feel overwhelmed, and cause you to "blank out" during the exam. As a result, test anxiety often results in lower grades that do not reflect what you really know. The following strategies, which tap your emotional intelligence, will help you control reactions that may get in the way of your performance.

Prepare and Have a Positive Attitude

Being on top of your work from the beginning of the term is the greatest stess reliever. Similarly, creating and following a detailed study plan will build knowledge and a sense of control, as will finding out what to expect on the exam. The following strategies will help you build a positive attitude:

- *See tests as opportunities to learn.* Instead of thinking of tests as contests that you either "win" or "lose," think of them as signposts along the way to mastering material.
- *Understand that tests measure performance, not personal value.* Grades don't reflect your ability to succeed or your self-worth. Whether you get an A or an F, you are the same person.
- *Believe that instructors are on your side.* Your instructors want you to do well, even when they give challenging tests—so contact them if you need help.
- *Seek study partners who challenge you.* Find study partners who inspire you to do your best. Try to avoid people who are also anxious because you may pick up their fears and negativity. (See chapter 1 for more on study groups.)

- *Get tutored.* Many schools offer tutoring help at no charge. Find out what's available and then sign up for sessions.
- *Practice relaxation.* When you feel test anxiety mounting, breathe deeply and slowly, close your eyes, and visualize positive mental images such as getting a good grade. Try to ease muscle tension—stretch your neck, tighten and then release your muscles.
- *Shut out negative vibrations.* If you arrive at the testing room early for a last-minute review, pick a seat far away from others who are nervously discussing the test.
- *Practice positive self-talk.* Tell yourself that you can do well and that it is normal to feel anxious, particularly before an important exam.
- *Remind yourself of your goals.* Connecting the test to your long-term goals will help you calm down as you focus on what's important.

Math exams are a special problem for many students. Dealing with the anxieties associated with these exams will be examined in the *Get Focused!* end-of-part section on pages 295–298 where you will find stress-management, studying, and exam-taking techniques.

Finally, a good attitude involves expecting different test-taking challenges from those you experienced in high school. College exams may ask you to critically analyze and apply material in ways that you never did before. For example, your history instructor may ask you to place a primary source in its historical context. Prepare for these challenges as you study by continually asking critical-thinking questions.

Test Anxiety and the Returning Student

Studying for a test with children underfoot is a reality for many students who are also parents. This student manages his 3-year-old while pursuing a degree from home.

If you're returning to school after years away, you may wonder how well you will handle exams. To deal with these feelings, focus on what you have learned through life experience, including the ability to handle work and family pressures. Without even knowing it, you may have developed the time-management, planning, organizational, and communication skills needed for college success.

In addition, your life experiences will give real meaning to abstract classroom ideas. For example, workplace relationships may help you understand social psychology concepts, and refinancing your home mortgage may help you grasp a key concept in economics—how the actions of the Federal Reserve Bank influence interest rate swings.

Parents who have to juggle child care with study time can find the challenge especially difficult before a test. Here are some suggestions that might help:

- *Find help.* Join a babysitting cooperative, switch off with a neighbor, post a sign for a part-time babysitter at the local high school.
- *Plan activities.* With younger children, have a supply of games, books, and videos. Give young artists a box of markers and unlimited paper. Then tell them to draw scenes of their family, their home, their friends—all in brilliant color.
- *Explain the time frame.* Tell school-aged children your study schedule and test date. Then promise them a reward for cooperating.

What General Strategies Can Help You Succeed on Tests?

Even though every test is different, there are general strategies that will help you handle almost all tests, including short-answer and essay exams.

Successful Intelligence Connections Online

Listen to author Sarah Kravits describe how to use analytical, creative, and practical intelligence to overcome the anxiety you feel before a big test.

Go to the *Keys to Success* Companion Website at www.prenhall.com/carter to listen or download as a podcast.

Choose the Right Seat

Your goal is to choose a seat that will put you in the right frame of mind and minimize distractions. Find a seat near a window, next to a wall, or in the front row so you can look into the distance. Know yourself: For many students, it's smart to avoid sitting near friends.

Write Down Key Facts

Before you even look at the test, write down key information, including formulas, rules, and definitions, that you don't want to forget. (Use the back of the question sheet so your instructor knows that you made these notes after the test began.)

Begin with an Overview

Although exam time is precious, spend a few minutes at the start gathering information about the questions—how many there are in each section, what types, and their point values. Use this information to schedule your time. For example, if a two-hour test is divided into two sections of equal value—an essay section with four questions and a short-answer section with 60 questions—you might spend an hour on the essays (15 minutes per question) and an hour on the short-answer section (one minute per question).

Take level of difficulty into account as you parcel out your time. For example, if you think you can get through the short-answer questions in 45 minutes and sense that the writing section will take longer, you can budget an hour and a quarter for the essays.

Read Test Directions

Reading test directions carefully can save you trouble. For example, although a history test of 100 true/false questions and one essay may look straightforward, the directions may tell you to answer 80 of the 100 questions or that the essay is optional. If the directions indicate that you are penalized for incorrect answers—meaning that you lose points instead of simply not gaining points—avoid guessing unless you're fairly certain.

When you read directions, you may learn that some questions or sections are weighted more heavily than others. For example, the short-answer questions may be worth 30 points, whereas the essays are worth 70. In this case, it's smart to spend more time on the essays.

Mark Up the Questions

QUALIFIERS

Words and phrases that can alter the meaning of a test question and that require careful attention.

Mark up instructions and key words to avoid careless errors. Circle **qualifiers**, such as *always, never, all, none, sometimes,* and *every*; verbs that communicate specific instructions; and concepts that are tricky or need special attention.

Take Special Care on Machine-Scored Tests

Use the right pencil (usually a #2) on machine-scored tests, and mark your answer in the correct space, filling it completely. (Use a ruler or your pencil as a straightedge to focus on the correct line for each question.) Periodically, check the answer number against the question number to make sure they match. If you mark the answer to question 4 in the space for question 5, not only will your response to question 4 be wrong, but also your responses to all subsequent questions will be off by a line. When you plan to return to a question and leave a space blank, put a small dot next to the number on the answer sheet. Neatness counts on these tests because the computer may misread stray pencil marks or partially erased answers.

Work from Easy to Hard

Begin with the easiest questions and answer them as quickly as you can without sacrificing accuracy. This will boost your confidence and leave more time for questions that require greater focus and effort. Mark tough questions as you reach them, and return to them after answering the questions you know.

Watch the Clock

Some students are so concerned about time that they rush through the test and have time left over. If this happens to you, spend the remaining time checking your work instead of leaving early. If, on the other hand, midway through the test you realize that you are falling behind, try to evaluate the best use of the remaining time. Being flexible will help you handle the crunch.

Take a Strategic Approach to Questions You Cannot Answer

Even if you are well prepared, you may be faced with questions you do not understand or cannot answer. What do you do in this situation?

- If your instructor is proctoring the exam, ask for clarification. Sometimes a simple rewording will make you realize that you really know the material.
- If this doesn't work, skip the question and come back to it later. Letting your subconscious mind work on the question sometimes makes a difference.
- Use what you do know about the topic to build logical connections that may lead you to the answer. Take a calculated risk by using your analytical intelligence.
- Try to remember where the material was covered in your notes and text. Creating this kind of visual picture may jog your memory about content as well.
- Start writing—even if you think you're going in the wrong direction and not answering the question that was asked. The act of writing about related material may help you recall the targeted information. You may want to do this kind of "freewriting" on a spare scrap of paper, think about what you've written, and then write your final answer on the test paper or booklet. Put yourself out there.
- If you think of an answer right before the bell, write on the paper that you only have minutes left, so you are answering in outline form. While most instructors will deduct points for this approach, they may also give partial credit because you showed that you know the material.

Master the Art of Intelligent Guessing

When you are unsure of an answer on an objective test, you can leave it blank or guess. As long as you are not penalized for incorrect answers, guessing may help you. When you use what you know to figure out what you don't know, you have a reasonable chance of guessing right.

When you check your work at the end of the test, decide whether you would make the same guesses again. Because your first instincts are usually best, chances are that you will leave your answers alone. However, you may notice something that changes your mind—a qualifier that affects meaning, for example—or you may recall information that you couldn't remember the first time around.

Be Prepared for Open-Book Exams

From time to time, you may encounter an *open-book* exam—an exam during which you have permission to access a particular set of materials, often including textbooks and readings. It's tempting to think that this type of exam will be a breeze—but don't be fooled. Put your preparation into high gear for any open-book exam, as many of them tend to be *harder* than a regular exam because of the fact that you can refer to your books.

The exam strategies you've been reading about—watch the clock, answer easy questions first, and so on—all apply to any open-book exam. Testtakingtips.com offers these additional specific tips:

- Be as familiar with the materials as you can, so you don't spend precious exam time wading through pages looking for a key fact.
- Know exactly what materials you are permitted to use, and bring everything on the list.
- If permitted, mark or flag important information in your materials for use as you proceed through the exam and/or write key points or formulas on a separate sheet.
- Don't rely too heavily on quoting your materials to support your key points. Prioritize your own voice.

Maintain Academic Integrity

Cheating as a strategy to pass a test or get a better grade robs you of the opportunity to learn, which, ultimately, is your loss. Cheating also jeopardizes your future if you are caught. You may be seriously reprimanded—or even expelled—if you violate your school's code of academic integrity. Remember too that cheating in school may damage your ability to get a job.

In recent years, cheating has become high-tech, with students using their cell phones, MP3 players, personal digital assistants (PDAs), graphing calculators, and Internet-connected laptops to share information through text messaging or to search the Internet. Because this type of cheating can be difficult to discover when exams are administered in large lecture halls, some instructors ban all electronic devices from the room.

How Can You Master Different Types of Test Questions?

Every type of test question has a different way of finding out how much you know about a subject. For **objective questions**, you choose or write a short answer, often making a selection from a limited number of choices. Multiple-choice, fill-in-the-blank, matching, and true/false questions fall into this category. **Subjective questions** demand the same information recall as objective questions, but they also require you to plan, organize, draft, and refine a response. All essay questions are subjective.

Key 7.1 shows samples of real test questions from Western civilization, geometry, Spanish, and biology college texts published by Pearson Education. Included are multiple-choice, true/false, fill-in-the-blank, matching, essay questions, and exercises. Problems and applications are also included for geometry. Analyzing the types, formats, and complexity of these questions will help you gauge what to expect when you take your exams.

As you review the questions on geometry in Key 7.1, look also at the Multiple Intelligence Strategies for Test Preparation on page 233. Harness the strategies that fit your learning strengths to prepare for geometry exams.

OBJECTIVE QUESTIONS
Short-answer questions that test your ability to recall, compare, and contrast information and to choose the right answer from a limited number of choices.

SUBJECTIVE QUESTIONS
Essay questions that require written responses that tap your personal knowledge and perspective.

KEY 7.1

Real test questions from real college texts.

From chapter 29, "The End of Imperialism," in *Western Civilization: A Social and Cultural History,* 2nd edition.[3]

- **MULTIPLE-CHOICE QUESTION**
  India's first leader after independence was:
  A. Gandhi B. Bose C. Nehru D. Sukharno *(answer: C)*
- **FILL-IN-THE-BLANK QUESTION**
  East Pakistan became the country of __________ in 1971.
  A. Burma B. East India C. Sukharno D. Bangladesh *(answer: D)*
- **TRUE/FALSE QUESTION**
  The United States initially supported Vietnamese independence. T F *(answer: false)*
- **ESSAY QUESTION**
  Answer one of the following:
  1. What led to Irish independence? What conflicts continued to exist after independence?
  2. How did Gandhi work to rid India of British control? What methods did he use?

From chapter 2, "Geometric Shapes and Measurement," in *College Geometry: A Problem-Solving Approach with Applications*, 2nd edition.[4]

- **EXERCISES/PROBLEMS**
  - All squares are kites, but not all kites are squares. What additional conditions must be satisfied for a kite to be a square? *(answer: Equiangular—all right angles)*
  - In the following figure, find one example of the following angles.
    a. supplementary b. complementary c. right d. adjacent e. acute f. obtuse

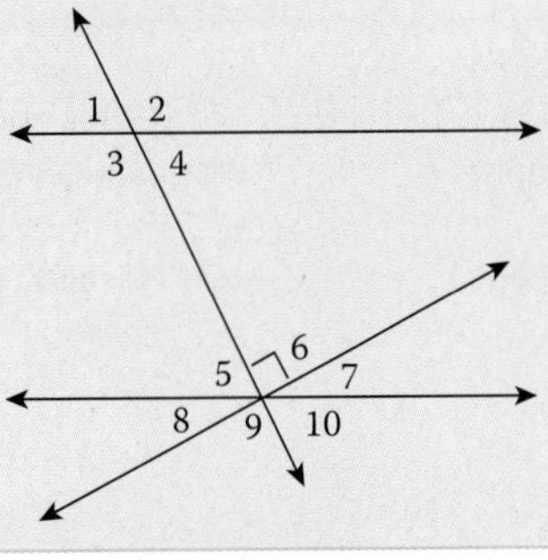

(Key 7.1 continues on next page)

(Geometry answers)

a. ∠1 and ∠2, ∠3 and ∠4, ∠1 and ∠3, ∠2 and ∠4, ∠6 and ∠9
b. ∠7 and ∠10, ∠5 and ∠8, ∠5 and ∠7, ∠8 and ∠10
c. ∠9 or ∠6
d. ∠1 and ∠2, ∠2 and ∠4, ∠4 and ∠3, ∠3 and ∠1, ∠5 and ∠6, ∠6 and ∠7, ∠7 and ∠10, ∠10 and ∠9, ∠9 and ∠8, ∠8 and ∠5
e. ∠1, ∠4, ∠7, ∠10, ∠8, ∠5
f. ∠2, ∠3

APPLICATIONS

- The bed of a gravel truck has the shape shown next where the lateral faces are rectangles. Describes the shape as completely as possible.

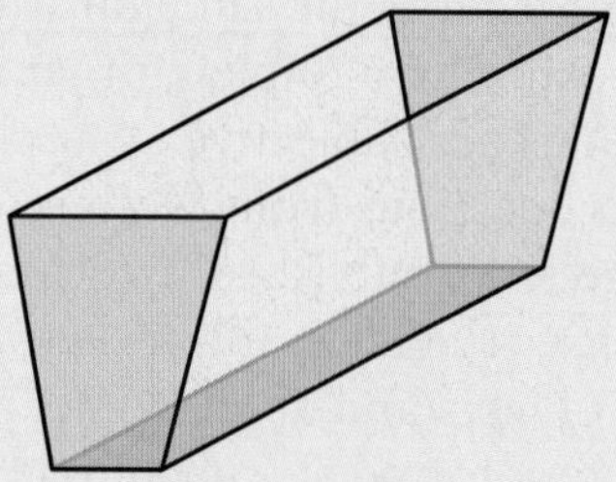

(answer: right trapezoidal prism)

TRUE/FALSE

- A circle is the set of all points in a plane that are the same distance from a fixed point. *T F*
- A parallelogram with four congruent sides is a rhombus. *T F*

(answers: T, T)

From *Mosaicos: Spanish as a World Language,* 3rd edition.[5]

MATCHING QUESTIONS

You are learning new words and your teacher asks you to think of an object similar to or related to the words he says. His words are listed below. Next to each word, write a related word from the list below.

el reloj	el cuaderno	el pupitre	una computadora
el televisor	la tiza	el lápiz	la mochila

1. el escritorio ____________
2. el bolígrafo ____________
3. la videocasetera ____________
4. la pizarra ____________
5. el libro ____________

(answers: 1. el pupitre; 2. el lápiz; 3. el televisor; 4. la tiza; 5. el cuaderno)

ESSAY QUESTION

Your mother always worries about you and wants to know what you are doing with your time in Granada. Write a short letter to her describing your experience in Spain. In your letter, you should address the following points:

1. What classes you take
2. When and where you study
3. How long you study every day
4. What you do with your time (mention three activities)
5. Where you go during your free time (mention two places)

From chapter 13, "DNA Structure and Replication," in *Biology: A Guide to the Natural World,* 2nd edition.[6]

MULTIPLE-CHOICE QUESTION

What units are bonded together to make a strand of DNA?

A. chromatids B. cells C. enzymes D. nucleotides E. proteins *(answer: D)*

TRUE/FALSE QUESTION

Errors never occur in DNA replication, because the DNA polymerases edit out mistakes. T F *(answer: false)*

FILL-IN-THE-BLANK QUESTION

In a normal DNA molecule, adenine always pairs with ________ and cytosine always pairs with ________.

(answers: thymine; guanine)

MATCHING QUESTIONS

Match the scientists and the approximate time frame (decades of their work) with their achievements.

Column 1	Column 2
____ 1. Modeled the molecular structure of DNA	____ A. George Beadle and Edward Tatum, 1930s and 1940s
____ 2. Generated X-ray crystallography images of DNA	____ B. James Watson and Francis Crick, 1950s
____ 3. Correlated the production of one enzyme with one gene	____ C. Rosalind Franklin and Maurice Wilkins, 1950s

(answers: 1–B; 2–C; 3–A)

MULTIPLE INTELLIGENCE STRATEGIES

FOR TEST PREPARATION

APPLY DIFFERENT INTELLIGENCES TO PREPARING FOR A GEOMETRY EXAM.

INTELLIGENCE	USE MI STRATEGIES *to improve test preparation*	APPLY MI TEST-PREP STRATEGIES *to study for a test on geometric shapes and measurement**
 Verbal-Linguistic	• Write test questions your instructor might ask. Answer the questions and then try rewriting them in a different format (essay, true/false, and so on). • Underline important words in review or practice questions.	• Underline important vocabulary words in the chapter. Then make a set of flash cards, with the word on one side and the definition on the other. Test yourself.
 Logical-Mathematical	• Logically connect what you are studying with what you know. Consider similarities, differences, and cause-and-effect relationships. • Draw charts that show relationships and analyze trends.	• Create a table that highlights the similarities and differences among polygons, circles, and three-dimensional shapes. Use columns to note qualities such as number of sides, number of angles, measurement of angles, formulas that apply consistently, and special features (for example, in a rectangle, all angles are right angles).
 Bodily-Kinesthetic	• Use text highlighting to take a hands-on approach to studying. • Create a sculpture, model, or skit to depict a tough concept that will be on the test.	• Use pencils, popsicle sticks, pipe cleaners, containers, or other materials to create the shapes on which you will be tested.
Visual-Spatial 	• Make charts, diagrams, or think links illustrating concepts. • Make drawings related to possible test topics.	• Draw illustrations that represent all of the postulates (statements assumed to be true) in the chapter.
Interpersonal 	• Form a study group to prepare for your test. • In your group, come up with possible test questions. Then use the questions to test each other's knowledge.	• With a study partner, work through the exercise set on polygons and circles. Try either working through problems together or having partners "teach" problems to each other.
 Intrapersonal	• Apply concepts to your own life; think about how you would manage. • Brainstorm test questions and then take the sample "test" you developed.	• Reread the "Geometry Around Us" material in your text to reinforce your understanding of how geometry functions in the real world. Write two additional ideas about how geometry relates to your world.
 Musical	• Recite text concepts to rhythms or write a song to depict them. • Explore relevant musical links to reading material.	• Write a song that helps you remember the types of triangles and their definitions.
Naturalistic 	• Try to notice similarities and differences in objects and concepts by organizing your study materials into relevant groupings.	• Create a table or visual organizer that arranges all of the types of two- and three-dimensional shapes into logical groupings.

* For information on geometric shapes and measurement, see Gary L. Musser, Lynn E. Trimpe, and Vikki R. Maurer, *College Geometry: A Problem-Solving Approach with Applications,* 2nd ed., Upper Saddle River, NJ: Pearson/Prentice Hall, 2008.

Note that some suggestions are repeated in the following sections, in order to reinforce the importance of these suggestions and their application to different types of test questions.

Multiple-Choice Questions

Multiple-choice questions are the most popular type of question on standardized tests. Examples of these questions are on page 235. The following analytical and practical strategies will help you answer them:

Read the directions carefully. Directions tell you precisely what to do. For example, whereas most test items ask for a single correct answer, some give you the option of marking several choices that are correct.

Read each question thoroughly and try to think of the answer before looking at the choices. Then read the choices and make your selection. When the answer you thought of matches one of the choices, it is most likely correct. Do not second-guess!

Underline key words and phrases. If the question is complicated, try to break it down into small sections that are easy to understand.

Make sure you read every word of every answer. Instructors have been known to include answers that are right, except for a single word. Focus especially on qualifying words such as *always, never, tend to, most, often,* and *frequently*. Look also for negatives in a question ("Which of the following is *not* . . . ").

Once you read every word, take the question on face value. Don't spend time "reading between the lines" to figure out what the instructor is *really* asking.

If you don't know the answer, eliminate answers that you know or suspect are wrong. If you can leave yourself with two possible answers, you will have a 50-50 chance of making the right choice. To narrow down, ask these questions about each of the choices:

- *Is the choice accurate on its own terms?* If there's an error in the choice—for example, a term that is incorrectly defined—the answer is wrong.
- *Is the choice relevant?* An answer may be accurate, but unrelated to the question.
- *Are there any qualifiers?* Absolute qualifiers like *always, never, all, none,* or *every* often signal an exception that makes a choice incorrect. For example, the statement "Normal children *always* begin talking before the age of 2" is untrue (most normal children begin talking before age 2, but some start later). Analysis has shown that choices containing conservative qualifiers like *often, most, rarely*, or *may sometimes be* are often correct.
- *Do the choices give clues?* Does a puzzling word remind you of a word you know? Do any parts of an unfamiliar word—its prefix, suffix, or root—ring a bell?

When questions are linked to a reading passage, read the questions first. This will help you focus on the information you need to answer the questions.

True/False Questions

Read true/false questions carefully to evaluate what they are asking. If you're stumped, guess (unless you're penalized for wrong answers). Some examples of true/false questions are on page 235.

Here are examples of the kinds of multiple-choice questions you might encounter in a psychology course[7] (the correct answer follows each question):

1. Arnold is at the company party and has had too much to drink. He releases all of his pent-up aggression by yelling at his boss, who promptly fires him. Arnold normally would not have yelled at his boss, but after drinking heavily he yelled because
   a. parties are places where employees are supposed to be able to "loosen up."
   b. alcohol is a stimulant.
   c. alcohol makes people less concerned with the negative consequences of their behavior.
   d. alcohol inhibits brain centers that control the perception of loudness.

   (answer: c)
2. Which of the following has not been shown to be a probable cause of or influence in the development of alcoholism in our society?
   a. Intelligence
   b. Culture
   c. Personality
   d. Genetic vulnerability

   (answer: a)
3. Geraldine is a heavy coffee drinker who has become addicted to caffeine. If she completely ceases her intake of caffeine over the next few days, she is likely to experience each of the following *except:*
   a. depression.
   b. lethargy.
   c. insomnia.
   d. headaches.

   (answer: c)

Look for qualifiers in true/false questions—such as *all*, *only*, and *always* (the absolutes that often make a statement false) and *generally*, *often*, *usually*, and *sometimes* (the conservatives that often make a statement true)—that can make a true statement false and vice versa. For example, "The grammar rule 'I before E except after C' is *always* true" is false, whereas "The grammar rule 'I before E except after C' is *usually* true" is true. The qualifier makes the difference.

Be sure to read *every* word of a true/false question to avoid jumping to an incorrect conclusion. Common problems in reading too quickly include missing negatives (*not, no*) that would change your response and deciding on an answer before reading the complete statement.

Here are some examples of the kinds of true/false questions you might encounter in an introduction to psychology course[8] (the correct answer follows each question):

Are the following questions true or false?

1. Alcohol use is clearly related to increases in hostility, aggression, violence, and abusive behavior. *(true)*
2. Marijuana is harmless. *(false)*
3. Simply expecting a drug to produce an effect is often enough to produce the effect. *(true)*
4. Alcohol is a stimulant. *(false)*

Matching Questions

Matching questions ask you to match the terms in one list with the terms in another list, according to the directions. For example, the directions may tell you to match a communicable disease with the microorganism that usually causes it. The following strategies will help you handle these questions.

Make sure you understand the directions. The directions tell you whether each answer can be used only once (common practice) or more than once.

Work from the column with the longest entries. The column on the left usually contains terms to be defined or questions to be answered, while the column on the right has longer definitions or answers. Reading the items on the right only once will save time as you work to match them with the shorter phrases on the left.

Start with the matches you know. On your first run-through, mark these matches with a penciled line. When you can use an answer only once, you may have to make changes if you reconsider a choice.

Finally, tackle the matches you're not sure of. On your next run-through, focus on the more difficult matches. If one or more phrases seem to have no correct answer and you can use answers only once, consider the possibility that one of your sure-thing answers is wrong.

Fill-in-the-Blank Questions

Fill-in-the-blank questions, also known as sentence-completion questions, ask you to supply one or more words or phrases to complete the sentence. Some examples are below. The following strategies will help.

Here are examples of fill-in-the-blank questions you might encounter in an introductory astronomy course[9] (correct answers follow questions):

1. A __________ is a collection of hundreds of billions of stars. *(galaxy)*
2. Rotation is the term used to describe the motion of a body around some __________. *(axis)*
3. The solar day is measured relative to the sun; the sidereal day is measured relative to the __________. *(stars)*
4. On December 21, known as the __________ __________, the sun is at its __________ __________.
(winter solstice; southernmost point)

Be logical. Insert your answer; then reread the sentence to be sure it is factually and grammatically correct. Consider thinking of the right answer *before* looking at the choices, then finding the choice that most closely matches.

Note the length and number of the blanks. These are clues but not absolute guideposts. If two blanks appear together, the instructor is probably looking for a two-word answer. If a blank is longer than usual, the correct response may require additional space. However, if you are certain of an answer that doesn't seem to fit the blanks, trust your knowledge.

If there is more than one blank and the blanks are widely separated, treat each one separately. Answer each as if it were a separate sentence-completion question.

Think outside the box. If you can think of more than one correct answer, consider putting them both down. Your instructor may be impressed by your assertiveness and creativity.

If you are uncertain, guess. Have faith that after hours of studying, your guess is not completely random.

Essay Questions

Essay questions ask you to express your knowledge and views in a less structured way than short-answer questions. With freedom of thought and expression comes the challenge to organize your ideas and write well under time pressure.

The following steps will help improve your responses to essay questions. The process is basically a less extensive version of a general writing process—you plan, draft, revise, and edit your response. The primary differences here are that you are writing under time pressure and that you are working from memory.

Essay questions require you to budget some planning time when you think through how you will spend the time allotted for the test. This student works through an essay question on a final exam.

1. Start by reading the questions. Decide which to tackle (if there's a choice). Use critical thinking to identify exactly what the question is asking.

2. Map out your time. Use the techniques you learned earlier in this chapter to schedule your time, remembering that things don't always go as planned. Try to remain flexible if an answer takes longer than expected.

3. Focus on action verbs. Verbs, like those in Key 7.2 on the next page, tell you what to do to answer the question. Underline them and use them to guide your writing.

4. Plan. Think carefully about what the question is asking and what you know about the topic. On a piece of scrap paper, create an informal outline or a think link to map your ideas and supporting evidence. Then develop a thesis statement that defines your content and point of view. If necessary—and if you have the time—reorganize your planning notes into an exact writing road map.

The biggest mistake students make in answering essay questions is to skip the planning stage and start writing without thinking through their answers. Not only does planning result in a better essay, it also reduces stress. Instead of scrambling for ideas as you write, you are carrying out an organized plan.

To answer question three in the box of sample essay questions below, one student created the planning outline shown in Key 7.3. Notice how abbreviations and shorthand help the student write quickly (see chapter 6 for shorthand notes strategies).

Here are some examples of essay questions you might encounter in an interpersonal communication course. In each case, notice the action verbs from Key 7.2.

1. Summarize the role of the self-concept as a key to interpersonal relationships and communication.
2. Explain how internal and external noise affects the ability to listen effectively.
3. Describe three ways that body language affects interpersonal communication.

KEY 7.2

Focus on action verbs on essay tests.

ANALYZE—Break into parts and discuss each part separately.	
COMPARE—Explain similarities and differences.	
CONTRAST—Distinguish between items being compared by focusing on differences.	
CRITICIZE—Evaluate the issue, focusing on its problems or deficiencies.	
DEFINE—State the essential quality or meaning.	
DESCRIBE—Paint a complete picture; provide the details of a story or the main characteristics of a situation.	
DIAGRAM—Present a drawing, chart, or other visual.	
DISCUSS—Examine completely, using evidence and often presenting both sides of an issue.	
ELABORATE ON—Start with information presented in the question, and then add new material.	
ENUMERATE/LIST/IDENTIFY—Specify items in the form of a list.	
EVALUATE—Give your opinion about the value or worth of something, usually by weighing positive and negative effects, and justify your conclusion.	
EXPLAIN—Make the meaning of something clear, often by discussing causes and consequences.	
ILLUSTRATE—Supply examples.	
INTERPRET—Explain your personal views and judgments.	
JUSTIFY—Discuss the reasons for your conclusions or for the question's premise.	
OUTLINE—Organize and present main and subordinate points.	
PROVE—Use evidence and logic to show that something is true.	
REFUTE—Use evidence and logic to show that something is not true or how you disagree with it.	
RELATE—Connect items mentioned in the question, showing, for example, how one item influenced the other.	
REVIEW—Provide an overview of ideas and establish their merits and features.	
STATE—Explain clearly, simply, and concisely.	
SUMMARIZE—Give the important ideas in brief, without comments.	
TRACE—Present a history of the way something developed, often by showing cause and effect.	

5. Draft. Your first draft on an exam is usually the one you hand in. If you plan effectively, you should have enough material to construct a suitable answer. Use the following guidelines as you draft your answer:

- Spend the bulk of your time developing your thesis and supporting evidence and logic. Most instructors do not expect fully developed introductions or conclusions.

GET ANALYTICAL!

Write to the Verb

Focusing on the action verbs in essay test instructions can mean the difference between giving instructors what they want and answering off the mark. Try this exercise.

- Start by choosing a topic you learned about in this text—for example, the concept of successful intelligence or different barriers to listening. Write your topic here:

  ____

  ____

- Put yourself in the role of instructor. Write an essay question on this topic, using one of the action verbs in Key 7.2 to frame the question. For example, "List the three aspects of successful intelligence," or "Analyze the classroom-based challenges associated with internal barriers to listening." Write your question here:

  ____

  ____

- Now choose three other action verbs from Key 7.2. Use each one to rewrite your original question:

  1. ____
  2. ____
  3. ____

- Finally, analyze how each new verb changes the focus of the essay:

  1. ____

     ____
  2. ____

     ____
  3. ____

     ____

- Start by stating your thesis, and then get right to the evidence that backs it up.
- Pay close attention to how you organize your ideas and how well you support them with evidence. Try to structure your essay so that each paragraph presents an idea that supports the thesis.

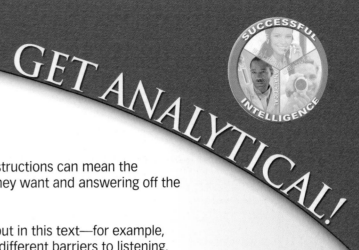

KEY 7.3

Create an informal outline during essay tests.

Roles of BL in IC
1. To contradict or reinforce words
   — e.g., friend says "I'm fine"
2. To add shades of meaning
   — saying the same sentence in 3 diff. ways
3. To make lasting 1st impression
   — impact of nv cues and voice tone greater than words
   — we assume things abt person based on posture, eye contact, etc.

- Use clear language and tight logic to link ideas to your thesis and to create transitions between paragraphs.
- Look back at your outline periodically to make sure you cover everything.
- Wrap it up with a short, to-the-point conclusion.

Pay attention to the test directions when drafting your answer. Your essay may need to be of a certain length, for example, or may need to take a certain form (for example, a particular format such as a business letter). Finally, write on only one side of the page so that the grader can easily read your response.

6. Revise. Take a few moments to evaluate your word choice, paragraph structure, and style. Although you may not have the time or opportunity to rewrite your entire answer, you can certainly improve it with minor deletions or additions in the margin. If you find a problem in your work—an idea without support, for example, or some unnecessary information—add the new material in the margins and cross out what you don't need. When adding material, you can indicate with an arrow where it fits or note that inserts can be found on separate pages. If you have more than one insert, label each to avoid confusion (Insert #1, Insert #2). Be neat as you make changes.

As you check over your essay, ask yourself these questions:

- Have I answered the question?
- Does my essay begin with a clear thesis statement, and does each paragraph start with a strong topic sentence that supports the thesis?

- Have I provided the support necessary in the form of examples, statistics, and relevant facts to prove my argument?
- Is my logic sound and convincing?
- Have I covered all the points in my original outline?
- Is my conclusion an effective wrap-up?
- Does every sentence effectively communicate my point?

7. Edit. Check for mistakes in grammar, spelling, punctuation, and usage. No matter your topic, correct language leaves a positive impression and reduces problems that may lower your grade.

Key 7.4 shows the student's completed response to the essay question on body language, including the word changes and inserts she made while revising the draft.

Neatness is crucial. No matter how good your ideas are, if your instructor can't read them your grade will suffer. If your handwriting is a problem, try printing or skipping every other line, and be sure to write on only one side of the page. Students with illegible handwriting might ask to take the test on a computer.

The purpose of a test is to see how much you know, not merely to get a grade. Embrace this attitude to learn from your mistakes.

How Can You Learn from Test Mistakes?

In life—and on exams—people learn most from their mistakes. With exam in hand, use the following strategies to reduce the likelihood of making the same errors again. (If your instructor posts grades but does not hand exams back, ask to see your paper.)

Try to identify patterns in your mistakes. Ask yourself global questions that may help you identify correctable patterns:

- *Can you identify your biggest problems?* Did you get nervous, misread the question, fail to study enough, study incorrectly, focus on memorizing material instead of on understanding and applying it?
- *Did your instructor's comments clarify what you failed to do?* Did your answer lack specificity? Did you fail to support your thesis with concrete examples? Was your analysis weak?
- *Were you surprised by the questions?* For example, did you expect them all to be from the lecture notes and text instead of from your notes, text, and supplemental readings?
- *Did you make careless errors?* Did you misread the question or directions, blacken the wrong box on the answer sheet, skip a question, write illegibly?

KEY 7.4

Response to an essay question with revision marks.

QUESTION: Describe three ways that body language affects interpersonal communication.

Body language plays an important role in interpersonal communication and helps shape the impression you make, [, especially when you meet someone for the first time] Two of the most important functions of body language are to contradict and reinforce verbal statements. When body language contradicts verbal language, the message ~~conveyed~~ delivered by the body is dominant. For example, if a friend tells you that she is feeling "fine," but her posture is slumped, [her eye contact minimal,] and her facial expression troubled, you have every reason to wonder whether she is telling the truth. If the same friend tells you that she is feeling fine and is smiling, walking with a bounce in her step, and has direct eye contact, her body language is ~~telling the truth.~~ [accurately reflecting and reinforcing her words.]

The nonverbal cues that make up body language also have the power to add shades of meaning. Consider this statement: "This is the best idea I've heard all day." If you were to say this three different ways—in a loud voice while standing up; quietly while sitting with arms and legs crossed and looking away; and while ~~maintening~~ maintaining eye contact and taking the receiver's hand—you might send three different messages.

Finally, the impact of nonverbal cues can be greatest when you meet someone for the first time. [Although first impressions emerge from a combination of nonverbal cues, tone of voice, and choice of words, nonverbal elements (cues and tone) usually come across first and strongest.] When you meet someone, you tend to make assumptions based on nonverbal behavior such as posture, eye contact, gestures, and speed and style of movement.

In summary, nonverbal communication plays a ~~crusial~~ crucial role in interpersonal relationships. It has the power to send an accurate message that may ~~destroy~~ belie the speaker's words, offer shades of meaning, and set the tone of a first meeting.

- *Did you make conceptual or factual errors?* Did you misunderstand a concept? Did you fail to master facts or concepts? Did you skip part of the text or miss classes in which ideas were covered?

Honest answers will help you change the way you study for the next exam.

Rework the questions you got wrong. Based on instructor feedback, try to rewrite an essay, recalculate a math problem from the original question, or

redo questions following a reading selection. If you discover a pattern of careless errors, redouble your efforts to be more careful, and save time to double-check your work from now on.

After reviewing your mistakes, fill in your knowledge gaps. If you made mistakes because you didn't understand important concepts, develop a plan to learn the material.

Talk to your instructor. Focus on specific mistakes on objective questions or a weak essay. The fact that you care enough to review your errors will leave a positive, lasting impression. If you are not sure why you were marked down on an essay, ask what you could have done better. If you feel that an essay was unfairly graded, ask for a rereading. When you use your social intelligence and approach your instructor in a nondefensive way, you are likely to receive help.

Rethink the way you studied. Make changes to avoid repeating your errors. Use the varied techniques in *Keys to Success* to study more effectively so that you can show yourself and your instructors what you are capable of

get practical!

Learn from Your Mistakes

Look at an exam on which your performance fell short. If possible, choose one that contains different types of objective and subjective questions. With the test and the answer sheet in hand, use your analytical thinking skills to answer the following questions and learn from your mistakes:

- Identify the types of questions on which you got the most correct answers (for example, matching, essay, multiple-choice):

  ____

- Identify the types of questions on which you made the greatest number of errors:

  ____

- Analyze your errors to identify patterns—for example, did you misread test instructions or ignore qualifiers that changed meaning? What did you find?

  ____

  ____

- Finally, list two practical steps you are prepared to take during your next exam to avoid the same problems:

  Action 1: ________________________________

  Action 2: ________________________________

doing. The earlier in the term you make positive adjustments the better, so make a special effort to analyze and learn from early test mistakes.

If you fail a test, don't throw it away. Use it to review troublesome material, especially if you will be tested on it again. You might also want to keep it as a reminder that you can improve if you have the will to succeed. When you compare a failure to later successes, you'll see how far you've come.

Successful Intelligence Wrap-Up

Tests ask you to show what you know to someone who will judge your performance. However, far more important than the information a test gives to an instructor is the information it gives to you, the test taker. Tests can be your road map to subject mastery, showing you what you have learned, what you are still learning, and what stumps you. Here's how you have built skills in chapter 7:

Analytical

You examined test-preparation techniques with an eye toward what works best for you. You investigated specific ways to maximize your chances of answering objective and subjective test questions correctly. In the *Get Analytical* exercise, you wrote a series of original essay questions, analyzing the effect that different action verbs had on what the questions were asking. You considered the potential positive effects from a careful analysis of test mistakes.

Creative

With the *Get Creative* exercise, you produced your own pretest that will help you assess if you have mastered crucial material. In reading about test anxiety, you encountered a different perspective of tests as opportunities to learn rather than contests that you win or lose. The scheduling and study techniques may have inspired you to create a personal study schedule and regimen that help you make the most of your time.

Practical

You gathered specific test-preparation techniques. You learned specific ways to calm test anxiety and to attack objective test questions. You expanded your knowledge of how to use planning tools, such as a key word outline, to help you write test essays. You deepened your understanding of how examining test mistakes helps you learn from experience. In the *Get Practical* exercise, you explored your mistakes on a particular test and identified steps you will take to avoid the same mistakes in the future.

hart ducha

(hahrt doo-cha)

In Polish, *hart ducha* literally means "strength of spirit" or "strength of will" to overcome life's challenges. In college, instructors challenge you on tests to demonstrate what you know and what you can do. Both before and during each test, your success depends on your *hart ducha*. With strength of will, you can commit to spending hours learning, reviewing, thinking about, and memorizing course material instead of cramming at the last minute. Think carefully about your approach because it determines far more than your exam grade. It determines what you will get out of your education.

There are no shortcuts to test success. Only old-fashioned hard work, driven by a powerful strength of will, will enable you to reach your academic potential.[10]

"The Five P's of Success: Prior preparation prevents poor performance."

JAMES A. BAKER III, FORMER SECRETARY OF STATE
AND WHITE HOUSE CHIEF OF STAFF

Building World-Class Skills for College, Career, and Life Success

SUCCESSFUL INTELLIGENCE

Think, Create, Apply

Prepare effectively for tests. Take a careful look at your performance on and preparation for a recent test.

Step 1. Think it through: ***Analyze how you did.*** Were you pleased or disappointed with your performance and grade? Why?

____

____

Thinking about your performance, look at the problems listed below. Circle those that you feel were a factor in this exam. Fill in the empty spaces with problems not listed.

- Incomplete preparation
- Fatigue
- Feeling rushed during the test
- Shaky understanding of concepts
- Poor guessing techniques
- Feeling confused about directions
- Test anxiety
- Poor essay organization or writing
- ______________________
- ______________________
- ______________________

Now for each problem you identified, think about why you made mistakes.

Step 2. Think out of the box: ***Be creative about test-preparation strategies.*** If you had absolutely no restrictions on time or access to materials, how would you have prepared for this test to improve your performance? Describe briefly what your plan would be and how it would minimize the problems you encountered.

____

____

Now think back to your actual test preparation. What techniques did you use and how much time did you spend?

____

____

How does what you would do under ideal circumstances differ from what you actually did?

____

____

Step 3. Make it happen: ***Improve preparation for the next exam.*** Think about the practical actions you will take the next time you face a similar test. Write your answers here.

Actions I took this time, but do not intend to take next time:

____

____

Actions I did not take this time, but intend to take next time:

____

____

TEAMWORK

Create Solutions Together

Test study group. Form a study group with two or three other students. When your instructor announces the next exam, ask each study group member to record everything he or she does to prepare for the exam, including things like these:

- Learning what to expect on the test (topics and material that will be covered, types of questions that will be asked)
- Examining old tests
- Creating and following a study schedule and checklist
- Using SQ3R to review material
- Taking a pretest
- Getting a good night's sleep
- Doing last-minute cramming
- Mastering general test-taking strategies
- Mastering strategies for handling specific types of test questions

After the exam, come together to compare preparation strategies. What important differences can you identify in the routines followed by group members? How did learning styles play a role in those differences? How do you suspect that different routines affected test performance and outcome? On a separate piece of paper or on a computer file, for your own reference, write down what you learned from the test-preparation habits of your study mates that may help you as you prepare for upcoming exams.

WRITING

Journal and Put Skills to Work

Record your thoughts on a separate piece of paper, in a journal, or on a computer file.

Journal entry: Test anxiety. Do you experience test anxiety? Describe how tests generally make you feel (you might include an example of a specific test situation and what happened). Identify your specific test-taking fears, and brainstorm ideas for how to overcome fears and self-defeating behaviors.

Real-life writing: Ask your instructor for feedback on a test. Nearly all students have been in the position of believing that the response they wrote on an essay exam was marked down unfairly. The next time this happens to you—when you have no idea why you lost points or disagree with the instructor's assessment of your work—draft a respectful e-mail to your instructor explaining your position and asking for a meeting to discuss the essay. (See e-mail etiquette guidelines in Quick Start to College.) Use clear logic to defend your work and refer back to what you learned in class and in the text. It is important to address specifically any comments or criticisms the instructor made on the test paper. Before sending the e-mail, analyze your argument: Did you make your case effectively, or was the instructor correct? When you have the meeting, the work you did on the e-mail will prepare you to defend your position.

PERSONAL PORTFOLIO

Prepare for Career Success

Complete the following in your electronic portfolio or on separate paper.

Compiling a résumé. What you have accomplished in various work and school situations will be important for you to emphasize on a résumé when you apply for jobs. Your roles at work, in school, at home, and in the community help you gain knowledge and experience.

To start, use two sheets of paper or a computer to brainstorm. On one electronic page or sheet of paper, list your education and skills information. On another, list job experience. For each job, record job title, the dates of employment, and the tasks you performed (if the job had no particular title, come up with one yourself). Be as detailed as possible—it's best to write down everything you remember. When you compile your résumé, you will make this material more concise. Keep this list and update it periodically as you gain experience and accomplishments.

Using the information you have gathered and Key 7.5 as your guide, draft a résumé. Remember that there are many ways to construct a résumé; consult other resources for different styles. You may want to reformat your résumé according to a style that your career counselor or instructor recommends. Also, if you already have a specific career focus, that career area may favor a particular style of résumé. Ask questions to be sure.

Keep this résumé draft in hard copy and on a computer hard drive or disk. When you need to submit a résumé with a job application, update the draft and print it out on high-quality paper.

KEY 7.5

Set yourself apart with an attractive, clear résumé.

Désirée Williams

237 Custer Street, San Francisco, CA 94101 • 650/555-5252 (w) or 415/555-7865 (h)
• fax: 707/555-2735 • e-mail: desiree@zzz.com

EDUCATION

2005 to present	San Francisco State University, San Francisco, CA Pursuing a B.A. in the Spanish BCLAD (Bilingual, Cross-Cultural Language Acquisition Development) Education and Multiple Subject Credential Program. Expected graduation: June 2008.

PROFESSIONAL EMPLOYMENT

10/06 to present	**Research Assistant, Knowledge Media Lab** Developing ways for teachers to exhibit their inquiry into their practice of teaching in an online, collaborative, multimedia environment.
5/05 to present	**Webmaster/Web Designer** Work in various capacities at QuakeNet, an Internet Service Provider and Web Commerce Specialist in San Mateo, CA. Designed several sites for the University of California, Berkeley, Graduate School of Education, as well as private clients such as A Body of Work and Yoga Forever.
9/05 to 6/06	**Literacy Coordinator** Coordinated, advised, and created literacy curriculum for an America Reads literacy project at Prescott School in West Oakland. Worked with non-reader 4th graders on writing and publishing, incorporating digital photography, Internet resources, and graphic design.
8/05	**Bilingual Educational Consultant** Consulted for Children's Television Workshop, field-testing bilingual materials. With a research team, designed bilingual educational materials for an ecotourism project run by an indigenous rain forest community in Ecuador.
1/05 to 6/06	**Technology Consultant** Worked with 24 Hours in Cyberspace, an online worldwide photojournalism event. Coordinated participation of schools, translated documents, and facilitated public relations.

SKILLS

Languages:	Fluent in Spanish. Proficient in Italian and Shona (majority language of Zimbabwe).
Computer:	Programming ability in HTML, Javascript, Pascal, and Lisp. Multimedia design expertise in Adobe Photoshop, Netobjects Fusion, Adobe Premiere, Macromedia Flash, and many other visual design programs.
Personal:	Perform professionally in Mary Schmary, a women's a cappella quartet. Have climbed Mt. Kilimanjaro.

Here are some general tips for writing a résumé.

- Always put your name and contact information at the top. Make it stand out.
- State an objective if it is appropriate—for instance, if your focus is specific or you are designing this résumé for a particular interview or career area.
- List your postsecondary education, starting from the latest and working backward. This may include summer school, night school, seminars, and accreditations.
- List jobs in reverse chronological order (most recent job first). Include all types of work experience (full-time, part-time, volunteer, internship, and so on).
- When you describe your work experience, use action verbs and focus on what you have accomplished, rather than on the description of assigned tasks.
- List references on a separate sheet. You may want to put "References upon request" at the bottom of your résumé.
- Use formatting (larger font sizes, different fonts, italics, bold, and so on) and indents selectively to help the important information stand out.
- Get several people to look at your résumé before you send it out. Other readers will have ideas that you haven't thought of and may find errors that you have missed.

Suggested Readings

Browning, William G. *Cliffs Memory Power for Exams*. Lincoln, NE: Cliffs Notes, 1990.

Frank, Steven. *Test Taking Secrets: Study Better, Test Smarter, and Get Great Grades*. Holbrook, MA: Adams Media, 1998.

Fry, Ron. "*Ace*" *Any Test*, 5th ed. Florence, KY: Thomson Delmar Learning, 2004.

Hamilton, Dawn. *Passing Exams: A Guide for Maximum Success and Minimum Stress*. New York: Continuum International, 2003.

Kesselman-Turkel, Judy, and Franklynn Peterson. *Test Taking Strategies*. Madison: University of Wisconsin Press, 2004.

Luckie, William R., and Wood Smethurst. *Study Power: Study Skills to Improve Your Learning and Your Grades*. Cambridge, MA: Brookline Books, 1997.

Meyers, Judith N. *Secrets of Taking Any Test: Learn the Techniques Successful Test-Takers Know*. New York: Learning Express, July 2000.

Internet and Podcast Resources

Palm Beach Community College (list of sites offering information on test-taking skills): **www.pbcc.edu/x6838.xml**

TestTakingTips.com (tips to improve your test-taking and study skills): **www.testtakingtips.com**

University of North Dakota—Study Strategies Homepage: **www.d.umn.edu/student/loon/acad/strat**

Prentice Hall Student Success SuperSite: **www.prenhall.com/success**

Endnotes

[1]From Ben Gose, "Notes from Academe: Living It Up on the Dead Days," *Chronicle of Higher Education,* June 7, 2002 (http://chronicle.com/weekly/v48/i39/39a04801.htm).

[2]From "Students Speak," MEDPREP: Medical/Dental Education Preparatory Program, Southern Illinois University School of Medicine (www.siumed.edu/medprep/studentsspeak.html).

[3]Western civilization test items from Margaret L. King, *Western Civilization: A Social and Cultural History*, 2nd ed., Upper Saddle River, NJ: Pearson Education, 2003. Questions from *Instructor's Manual and Test Item File* by Dolores Davison Peterson. Used with permission.

[4]Geometry exercises from Gary L. Musser, Lynn E. Trimpe, and Vikki R. Maurer, *College Geometry: A Problem-Solving Approach with Applications,* 2nd ed., Upper Saddle River, NJ: Pearson/Prentice Hall, 2008, pp. 99–101. Used with permission.

[5]Spanish test items from Matilde Olivella de Castells, Elizabeth Guzmán, Paloma Lupuerta, and Carmen García, *Mosaicos: Spanish as a World Language,* 3rd ed., Upper Saddle River, NJ: Prentice Hall, 2002. Questions from *Testing Program* by Mark Harpring. Used with permission.

[6]Biology test items from David Krogh, *Biology: A Guide to the Natural World,* 2nd ed., Upper Saddle River, NJ: Prentice Hall, 2002. Questions from *Test Item File* edited by Dan Wivagg. Used with permission.

[7]From Gary W. Piggrem and Charles G. Morris, *Test Item File* for *Understanding Psychology,* 3rd ed., 1996. Reprinted by permission of Pearson Education, Inc., Upper Saddle River, NJ.

[8]Ibid.

[9]From Eric Chaisson and Steve McMillan, *Astronomy Today,* 3rd ed., 1999. Reprinted by permission of Pearson Education, Inc., Upper Saddle River, NJ.

[10]Christopher J. Moore, *In Other Words: A Language Lover's Guide to the Most Intriguing Words Around the World,* New York: Walker, 2004, p. 45.

INDEX

Credits and Acknowledgments

Successful intelligence excerpts, chapter-opening quotes, and themes reprinted with permission of Simon & Schuster Adult Publishing Group from SUCCESSFUL INTELLIGENCE by Robert J. Sternberg. Copyright © 1996 by Robert J. Sternberg. Materials extracted and adapted from pp. 12, 19, 127–128, 251–269. Note: from pp. 251–269 material extracted are heading words only.

Excerpts on pages 139, 177, and 188 reprinted by permission of the publisher from MAKING THE MOST OF COLLEGE: STUDENTS SPEAK THEIR MINDS by Richard J. Light, pp. 23–24, 38, 48–49. Cambridge, MA: Harvard University Press, copyright © 2001 by Richard J. Light.

Photo Credits

All individual photos for Real Questions/Practical Answers and Personal Triumph Case Study features provided by photo subjects.

Photo objects throughout this text from Fotolia and Hemera Technology.

2, Wyatt McSpadden/*The New York Times;* **9,** Phil Marino/*The New York Times;* **23,** Tami Chappell/*The New York Times;* **34,** © Copyright 2000 PhotoDisc, Inc.; **45,** Ruth Fremson/*The New York Times*; **48,** C.J. Gunther/*The New York Times;* **66,** Marilynn Yee/*The New York Times;* **80,** Nicole Bengiveno/*The New York Times;* **85,** Steve Ruark/*The New York Times;* **93,** Laura Pedrick/*The New York Times;* **110,** Suzy Allman/*The New York Times;* **115,** Angel Franco/*The New York Times;* **127,** Michelle Agins/*The New York Times;* **144,** Tony Cenicola/*The New York Times;* **152,** Joyce Dopkeen/*The New York Times;* **165,** Sara Davis/*The New York Times;* **180,** Suzanne DeChillo/*The New York Times;* **185,** Michelle Agins/*The New York Times;* **200,** Jim Wilson/*The New York Times;* **218,** Josh Anderson/*The New York Times;* **227,** Laura Pedrick/*The New York Times;* **237,** Paul Boisvert/*The New York Times*, © Copyright 2000 PhotoDisc, Inc.

CMF 95
Math Fundamentals

Taken From:
Math Basics for the Health Care Professional, Third Edition
by Michele Benjamin Lesmeister

CMF 95
Math Fundamentals

Contents

Unit 1

Whole Number Review

Mathematics is a key skill of health care workers. As a health care worker, you know that accuracy is important. Being competent in whole number concepts and addition, subtraction, multiplication, and division will form the basis for successful computations on the job. These basic skills form the foundation for the other daily math functions you will use in the workplace.

> Approach math matter-of-factly; math is a job skill and a life skill.

The number line is a line labeled with the integers in increasing order from left to right. The number line extends in both directions:

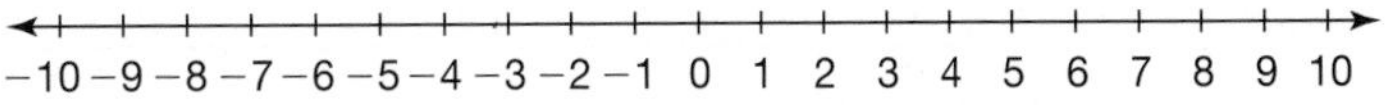

Remember that any integer on the right is always greater than the integer on the left.

Symbols and Number Statements

Symbols may be used to show the relationship among numbers.

Symbol	Meaning	Example
$=$	is equal to	$1 + 7 = 8$
$>$	is greater than	$19 > 6$
$<$	is less than	$5 < 12$
$\leq$	is equal to or less than	age ≤ 5
$\geq$	is equal to or greater than	weight $\geq$ 110 pounds

A number statement or simple equation shows the relationship between numbers, operations and/or symbols.

Practice 1: Use the symbols ($=$, $>$, and $<$, $\leq$, $\geq$) to complete the number statement.

1. 14 __$<$__ 34
2. -5 __$<$__ 0
3. 12 __$>$__ 7
4. 12 P.M. __$=$__ noon
5. Seven less than 4 __$\leq$__ the numbers $-5, -4, -3$
6. \$2.00 __$=$__ 2 hundred pennies
7. 235 __$>$__ 187
8. 2 nickels __$<$__ a quarter
9. 245 __$>$__ $78 + 34 + 3$
10. One dollar + 2 quarters __$>$__ \$1.35
11. The numbers 0, 1, 2, are __$\geq$__ the number 2
12. 3 __$<$__ $4 \div 2$

Practice 2: Write five number statements:

1. ____________________
2. ____________________
3. ____________________
4. ____________________
5. ____________________

Addition

Review

To add, line up the numbers in a vertical column and add to find the total. In addition problems, the total, or answer, is called the *sum*.

Practice Find the sum of each problem.

1. 1 + 4 + 5 + 9 =
2. 51 + 23 =
3. 297 + 90 + 102 + 3 =
4. 216 + 897 =
5. 1,773 + 233 + 57 =
6. 9 + 245 + 32 =
7. 11 + 357 + 86 + 34 =
8. 24,578 + 9,075 =
9. 443 + 2,087 + 134 =
10. 910 + 3 + 125 =

Applications Inventory is an important clerical function in the health care industry. Sometimes this work is done by supply technicians, clerks, nursing assistants, or other staff. Keeping accurate inventory reduces overstocking and helps avoid the problem of under stocking medical supplies.

1. Inventory is done monthly at the Golden Years Care Center. Find the sum for each category.

Category	**Sum**
a. Examination gloves: 31 + 88 + 47 + two boxes of 50	_____
b. Thermometer covers: 281 + 304 + 17 + 109	_____
c. Medicine cups: 313 + 245 + 106 + 500 + 12	_____
d. Boxes of disposable syringes (50 per box): 2 + 6 + 9 + 3	_____

2. Intake and output totals require addition skills. Unlike household measurements in cups, health care patient intake and output units are measured in cubic centimeters (cc). Intake includes oral ingestion of fluids and semi-liquid food, intravenous feedings, and tubal feedings.
   Find the intake totals.

Type of Intake	**Cubic Centimeters (cc)**	**Sum**
a. Oral	120, 210, 150, 240	_____
b. Intravenous	250, 500	_____
c. Blood	500	_____
d.	Total Intake	_____

The intake sums would be charted in the patient's medical record.

3. Measuring output is important because it helps the health care worker ensure a patient's health and hydration. Output is measured in cubic

centimeters. Output includes liquid bowel movements or diarrhea, urine, emesis (vomiting), and gastric drainage. Find the output totals.

	Type of Output	Cubic Centimeters (cc)	Sum
a.	Diarrhea	100, 200	_____
b.	Urine	330, 225, 105, 60	_____
c.	Gastric Drainage	40, 35	_____
d.	Blood/Emesis	110	_____
e.		Total Output	_____

4. Assuming that the patient is the same as in problems 2 and 3, has this patient had a greater intake or a greater output? _______

Subtraction

Review

To subtract, line up the numbers according to place value. Place value shows the ones, tens, hundreds, etc. columns. Start with the right side of the math problem and work your way toward the left side, subtracting each column.

> Fewer errors occur if the subtraction problem is set up vertically. Rewrite the problems.

Example

$89 - 31 =$ _____ $\qquad 475 - 34 =$ _____

$$\begin{array}{r} 89 \\ \underline{-31} \\ 58 \end{array} \qquad \begin{array}{r} 475 \\ \underline{-34} \\ 441 \end{array}$$

If a number cannot be subtracted from the number directly above it, then increase the value of the smaller number by borrowing 1 from the column to its immediate left.

> Keep track of borrowing by marking through the column borrowed from and reducing the numbers involved by 1.

Example

$$\begin{array}{r} 3\,{}^{7}\!\not{8}\,{}^{1}1 \\ \underline{-\ 65} \\ 316 \end{array}$$

Practice

1. 475 − 81 =
2. 176 − 37 =
3. 289 − 54 =
4. 4,547 − 2,289 =
5. 1,236 − 799 =
6. 1,575 − 896 =
7. 2,001 − 128 =
8. 10,300 − 497 =
9. 4,301 − 89 =
10. 4,547 − 2,289 =

Applications

Subtraction is used in inventory as well. Some applications are given below.

1. At the beginning of the month, a dental office started with 2,258 latex examination gloves. On the last working day of the month, 784 remained. How many gloves were used during the month?

2. Inventory of dental file labels is to be kept at 2,000. Paula's inventory indicates 579 on hand. How many labels does she need to order?

3. Labels come in boxes of 500. Use the answer from problem 2 to determine how many boxes of labels Paula should order to obtain the required 2,000 minimum inventory. Draw a sketch to help visualize this problem.

4. Patients see the dentist most during the summer months. Dr. Brown has a total of 13,576 patient files. If he sees 8,768 of these patients during the summer, how many remain to be contacted for an appointment?

Multiplication

Memorizing the multiplication tables is essential to sound mental math. If you have been calculator dependent or have forgotten some of the tables, practice memorizing the multiplication tables using the chart shown in Table 1.1.

Table 1.1 Multiplication Table

X	1	2	3	4	5	6	7	8	9	10	11	12
1												
2												
3												
4												
5												
6												
7												
8												
9												
10												
11												
12												

Review

To multiply, line up the numbers according to place value. By putting the largest number on top of the problem, you will avoid careless errors.

Avoid These Common Errors

Remember, you are multiplying, not adding.

Remember to move the numbers from the second and succeeding lines over one column to the left—use a zero (0) to indicate these movements.

$2 \times 14 = \underline{\quad\quad}$ $\rightarrow$

$$\begin{array}{r} 14 \\ \times\ 2 \\ \hline 28 \end{array}$$

$$\begin{array}{r} 178 \\ \times\ 23 \\ \hline 534 \\ 3560 \\ \hline 4{,}094 \end{array}$$

Move the second line of numbers one place to the left. Adding a zero keeps your numbers aligned.

Practice

1. 12×8
2. 82×13
3. $1{,}306 \times 18$
4. 70×9
5. $1{,}020 \times 98$
6. 189×27
7. 512×24
8. 927×35
9. $5{,}791 \times 16$
10. 803×17
11. 346×12
12. $9{,}004 \times 73$

Applications

1. Last month a nurse worked fourteen 10-hour shifts and two 12-hour shifts. At $21 per hour, what was the nurse's total hourly income before deductions?
2. Health-care facilities monitor all medications taken by their patients. Assume that the same dosage is given each time the medication is dispensed. What is the total daily dosage of each medication received?

Total medication received is as follows:

a. Patient Bao	50 milligrams	4 times a day	_____	milligrams
b. Patient Mary	25 milligrams	2 times a day	_____	milligrams
c. Patient Luke	125 micrograms	3 times a day	_____	micrograms
d. Patient Vang	375 micrograms	2 times a day	_____	micrograms

3. The radiology lab ordered 15 jackets for its staff. The jackets cost approximately $35 each. What is the estimated cost of this order?

Prime Factorization

Sometimes in a math class, students are asked to use factor trees to illustrate prime factors of a number. A factor is a number which divides exactly into another number. When two or more factors are multiplied, they form a product. A prime factor is a number that can only be the product of 1 and itself.

For example: 4 (factor) × 12 (factor) = 48 (product)

The prime factors of 48 are 2 and 3. (2 × 2 × 2 × 3 = 24)

48
^
4 12
^ ^
2 2 4 3
^
2 2

$2 \times 2 \times 2 \times 2 \times 3 = 48$
or $2^4 \bullet 3 = 48$
or $(2^4)(3) = 48$

Note that $16 \times 3 = 48$.

The prime factors are still the same:

$2 \times 2 \times 2 \times 2 \times 3$.

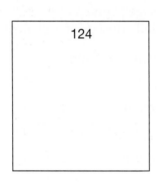

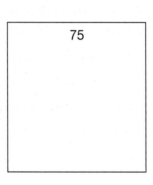

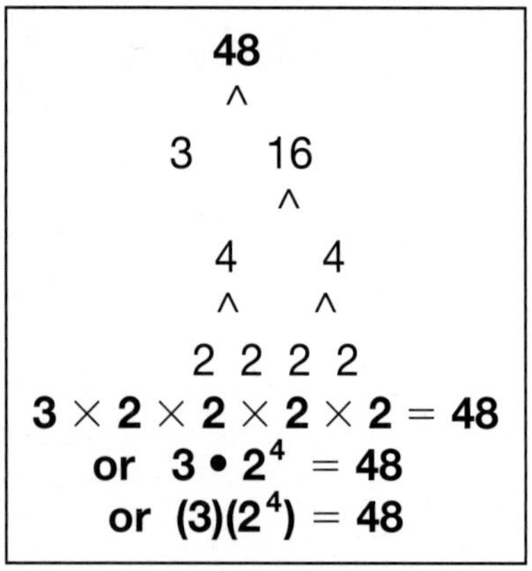

The prime factors are always the same for any number.

Practice Draw the factor trees for the following numbers and write the prime factors on the lines below.

124	75	92

1. ____________ 2. ____________ 3. ____________

Division

Review

To divide whole numbers determine (a) what number is being divided into smaller portions; and (b) the size of the portions.

Division can appear in three formats:

a. $27 \div 3 =$

b. Twenty-seven divided by three

c. $3\overline{)27}$

Setting up the problem correctly will help ensure the correct answer.

Example

81	$\div$	$3 =$ ______	means eighty-one divided by three
↑		↑	or how many 3s are in 81.
dividend		divisor	The answer is the quotient.

$$\begin{array}{r l}
 & 27 \leftarrow \text{quotient} \\
\text{divisor} \rightarrow & 3\overline{)81} \leftarrow \text{dividend} \\
 & \underline{6} \\
 & 21 \\
 & \underline{21} \\
 & 0
\end{array}$$

Practice the correct setup, but do not work the problems.

1. Divide 145 by 76
2. 1,209 ÷ 563
3. Forty-nine divided by seventeen is what number?
4. What is 8,794 ÷ 42?
5. A person works a total of 2,044 hours a year. How many days does the person work if he works 8 hours a day?

Follow the steps below to complete all of your whole number division problems:

Step 1: Underline the number of places that the divisor can go into, then write the number of times the divisor can go into the dividend on the quotient line. Place it directly above the underlined portion of the number. This keeps track of your process. Multiply the number by the divisor and place it below the underlined portion of the dividend. Then subtract the numbers.

Example

$$\begin{array}{r}
1 \\
34\overline{)\underline{54}92} \\
\underline{-34} \\
20
\end{array}$$

Step 2: Bring down the next number of the dividend. Use an arrow to keep alignment and track of which numbers you have worked with. Then repeat step 1.

$$\begin{array}{r}
161 \\
34\overline{)\underline{54}92} \\
\underline{-34\downarrow} \\
20
\end{array}
\qquad
\begin{array}{r}
161 \text{ R } 18 \\
34\overline{)\underline{54}92}\phantom{\text{ R } 18} \\
\underline{-34\downarrow}\phantom{2\text{ R } 18} \\
209\phantom{\text{ R } 18} \\
\underline{204\downarrow}\phantom{\text{ R } 18} \\
52\phantom{\text{ R } 18} \\
\underline{34}\phantom{\text{ R } 18} \\
18\phantom{\text{ R } 18}
\end{array}$$

Repeat steps 1 and 2 until all the numbers of the dividend have been used. The number remaining is called the remainder. Place it next to an *R* to the right of the quotient. In fractions, the remainder becomes a fraction; in whole numbers, it remains a whole number.

After bringing a number down from the dividend, a number must be placed in the quotient. Zeros may be used as place holders. Follow the division steps as shown above to solve the practice problems.

$$\begin{array}{r} 106\text{ R }41 \\ 75\overline{)7991} \\ -75\downarrow \\ \hline 49 \\ -0\downarrow \\ \hline 491 \\ -450 \\ \hline 41 \end{array}$$

Practice

1. $6\overline{)564}$
2. $3\overline{)5736}$
3. $4\overline{)12345}$
4. $956 \div 66 =$
5. $4\overline{)1244}$
6. $53\overline{)5088}$
7. $15\overline{)23648}$
8. $1{,}254 \div 29 =$
9. $2\overline{)46882}$
10. $18\overline{)12564}$
11. $7\overline{)87543}$
12. $74{,}943 \div 271 =$

Applications

1. Room rates vary by the services provided. At the local hospital, intensive care unit (ICU) rooms are $784 a day. Bob's overall room charge was $10,192. How many days was Bob in ICU?

2. Carbohydrates have 4 calories per gram. If a serving of soup has 248 calories of carbohydrates, how many grams of carbohydrates are in that serving?

3. A medical assistant subscribes to 14 magazines for the office. If the total subscription bill is $294, what is the average cost of each magazine subscription?

4. A pharmacy technician receives a shipment of 302 boxes of acetaminophen. This shipment needs to be returned to the supplier because the expiration date on the medicine did not allow sufficient time to sell the medicine. If each case holds 36 individual boxes, how many cases must the pharmacy technician use to pack the medicine?

5. A surgical technologist made $39,744 last year. He is paid twice a month. What is the gross or total amount of each of his paychecks?

6. A licensed practical nurse gives 1,800 milligrams of a penicillin-type drug over a 36-hour time period. If the dosage occurs every 6 hours, how many milligrams are in each dose if each dose is the same amount?

7. Each gram of fat contains 9 calories. How many grams of fat are in 81 calories of fat in a piece of steak?

Solving for the Unknown Number with Basic Mathematics

Sometimes number statements in math class ask for the unknown number. Looking for an unknown number is an aspect of algebra. Solving for these requires that one understand the relationship between the numbers.

For example, _____ + 12 = 75

To find the unknown number, you must subtract 12 from 75. The answer, or unknown number, is 63.

Practice 1: Use addition to solve for the unknown number.

1. 13 + _____ = 87
2. _____ + 12 + 2 = 145
3. 45 + _____ = 98
4. _____ = 98 + 17
5. _____ + 987 = 1,000

Practice 2: Use subtraction to solve for the unknown number.

1. 98 − 12 = _____
2. 237 − _____ = 67
3. _____ − 17 = 543
4. 45 − 19 = _____
5. 12 = _____ − 23

Practice 3: Use multiplication to solve for the unknown number.

1. 13 × 3 = _____
2. _____ × 11 = 99
3. _____ × 23 = 92
4. 125 × _____ = 500
5. _____ = 15 × 5

Practice 4: Use division to solve for the unknown number.

1. 396 ÷ 3 = _____
2. _____ ÷ 12 = 4
3. 51 ÷ _____ = 17
4. 125 = _____ ÷ 5
5. 108 ÷ 6 = _____

Rounding

Review

Whole numbers have place values. The number 3,195 has four specific place values:

3,	1	9	5
↑	↑	↑	↑
thousand	hundreds	tens	ones

(three thousand one hundred ninety-five)

By using the place values in a number, we can round the number to a particular and specific place unit. Rounding is valuable because it helps to estimate supplies, inventory, and countable items to the nearest unit.

> Rounding is used when an exact number is not necessary, as in taking inventory and ordering: Round up to make a full case of a product when you are placing an order. If a full case has 36 boxes and you need to order 32 boxes, you will order 1 case or 36 boxes, so you have rounded up to the nearest case.

Rounding is accomplished in three steps.

Example Round 7,872 to the nearest hundred.

Step 1: Locate the hundreds place and underline it.

7,872

Step 2: Circle the number to the right of the underlined number.

7,8⑦2

Step 3: If the circled number is 5 or greater, add 1 to the underlined number and change the number(s) to the right of the underlined number to zero(s).

7, 8 ⑦ 2
↓ ↓
7, 9 0 0

Rounding is used a great deal in health care. Rounding of whole numbers exists in inventory and packaging of supplies as well as in daily activities.

Practice

1. Round to the nearest 10:

   a. 3,918 3920 c. 6,952 6950 e. 15,932 15930

   b. 139 140 d. 1,925 1930 f. 99 100

2. Round to the nearest 100:

   a. 3,918 3900 c. 8,975 9,000 e. 35,292 35,300

   b. 3,784 3800 d. 17,854 17,900 f. 1,925 1900

3. Round to the nearest 1,000:

   a. 3,190 3000 c. 6,950 7000 e. 432,500 433000

   b. 87,987 88000 d. 12,932 13,000 f. 2,987 3,000

Additional rounding practice will be presented in Unit 3: Decimals.

Estimation

Estimation is a method of coming up with a math answer that is general, not specific. When we estimate, we rely on rounding to help us get to this general answer. For example, with money rounding is done to the nearest dollar. If an amount has 50 cents or more, *round* to the nearest dollar and drop the cent amount. If an amount is under 50 cents, *retain* the dollar amount and drop the cent amount.

Example Estimate Bob's expenses for his co-payment of his dental expenses for his two six-month checkups.

	Actual Expense	Estimated Expense
March	$65.85	$66
October	$59.10	$59

Add the estimated expenses of $66 + $59 = _____
The estimated annual total is $125.
So estimation is a skill that uses rounding to reach a general rather than a specific answer.

Practice

1. Find the sum using estimation to the nearest dollar:
   a. $56.90 + $12.45 + $124.78
   b. $127.46 + $13.98 + $21.20
   c. $23.45 + $32.29 + $56.65
   d. $2,900.87 + $12.89
2. Find the sum using estimation to the nearest hour:
   a. 1 hour 25 minutes + 2 hours 14 minutes + 5 hours 37 minutes
   b. 7 hours 8 minutes + 10 hours 34 minutes + 15 hours 45 minutes
   c. 3 hours 35 minutes + 22 hours 16 minutes + 9 hours 59 minutes
   d. 6 hours 39 minutes + 13 hours 18 minutes + 5 hours 2 minutes

Basics of Statistical Analysis

The basics of statistical analysis includes the topics of *mean* (average), *mode*, *median*, and *range*. Each of these topics deals with groups or subsets of numbers and their relationships to each other and the set as a whole.

Arithmetic Mean or Average

Review The arithmetic *mean* is also called the average. An average is a number that represents a group of the same unit of measure. It provides a general number that represents this group of numbers if all the numbers were the same units. Averages are useful in health occupations because they provide general trends and information. Averages are computed using addition and division skills.

To compute a mean or average, follow these two steps:

Step 1: Add the individual units of measure.

Step 2: Divide the sum of the units of measure by the number of individual units.

Example Mary Ann wanted to know the average score of her anatomy and physiology tests. Her scores were 92%, 79%, 100%, 89%, and 95%.

Step 1: $92 + 79 + 100 + 89 + 95 = 455$

Step 2: There were a total of 5 grades.

$$\begin{array}{r} 91 \\ 5\overline{)455} \\ \underline{45\downarrow} \\ 5 \\ \underline{5} \\ 0 \end{array}$$

Mary Ann's average score was 91%.

Practice

1. Deb needed to purchase new calendars for the examination rooms. Find the average if the calendars cost \$11, \$7, \$10, \$5, \$10, \$12, \$8, and \$9.

2. Certified nursing assistants work a varied number of hours every week at Village Nursing Home. The weekly hours are 32, 38, 40, 35, 40, 16, and 30. What is the average number of hours each assistant works?

3. The staff phone use during morning break is increasing. The director is considering adding additional phones and is researching the usage in minutes. Using the following data, compute the average length of each call: 7, 4, 3, 1, 2, 4, 5, 7, and 12.

4. A diabetic patient is counting calories. The patient adds up calories from portions of fruit: 90, 80, 60, 15, 40. What is the average caloric intake from each portion?

5. Beth was working hard to increase the fruit and vegetables in her diet. She kept a log of servings: Monday, 8; Tuesday, 7; Wednesday, 6; Thursday, 5; Friday, 8; Saturday, 6; Sunday, 9. What is the mean daily intake of fruits and vegetables for Beth?

Median

The *median* is the middle number in a list of numbers. To determine the median, follow these steps:

Step 1: Sort the list of numbers from smallest to largest.

Step 2: Cross off one number from each end of the line of numbers until one number is reached in the middle.

Example Find the median of this set of numbers: 23, 54, 76, 34, 12.

Step 1: Sort from smallest to largest — 12, 23, 34, 54, 76

Step 2: Cross a number off from each end until the middle number is reached. — ~~12~~, 23, 34, 54, ~~76~~ / ~~12~~, ~~23~~, 34, ~~54~~, ~~76~~

34 is the median

If there is an even set of numbers, the final two numbers are added and then divided by 2 to get the median. For example, consider the following set of numbers: 23, 54, 76, 34, 12, 36.

Step 1: Sort from smallest to largest — 12, 23, 34, 36, 54, 76

Step 2: Cross a number off from each end until the last pair is reached. — ~~12~~, 23, 34, 36, 54, ~~76~~ / ~~12~~, ~~23~~, 34, 36, ~~54~~, ~~76~~

Step 3: Add the two remaining numbers — $34 + 36 = 70$

Step 4: Divide the answer by 2 to get the median. — $70 \div 2 = 35$

35 is the median.

Note: The median may include a partial number such as $^1/_2$ or 0.5.

Practice

1. Bah's temperature fluctuated all day. Her temperature readings were 98, 99, 97, 101, and 100. What is her median temperature?

2. The young patients played a game. The scores for five games were 365, 251, 105, 280, and 198. What is the median of this set of scores?

3. The medical assistant was working on inventory. She wanted to figure out the median of the number of cases of protective sheeting that were used for the first six months of the year in the large medical practice.

Month	Number of cases
January	26
February	22
March	31
April	28
May	26
June	19

What is the median for this set of data?

4. Azeb is an excellent student. She is curious about the median of her test scores in biology class. Her scores are 99, 100, 98, 97, 100. Her median is ______________.

5. The students were measuring tardiness to class by incidence each week. Look at the data set: 7, 8, 10, 10, 15, 12, 8, 7. What is the mean of this data set?

Mode

The mode is the "most popular" value or the most frequently occurring item in a set of numbers to locate the mode in a series or listing of numbers, locate the number, which occurs the most.

For example, look at the calories of Bob's snack food intake for a two-day period:

Bob's caloric intake of snacks by day

Saturday: 120, 120, 50, 78, 134, 187

Sunday: 220, 125, 90, 85, 120, 120

What is the mode of the calorie intake of Bob's snack intake over this two-day period?

The answer is 120. It occurs four times.

Practice

1. Look at the pH values of the following data set: 8, 11, 23, 14, 8, 12. What is the mode for this data set?

2. Look at the prices of toothbrushes: $2.00; $4.00, $3.00; $3.00, $1.00; $3.00. What is the mode of these toothbrush prices?

3. The color combinations preferred by new dental offices include: paint sample #24, paint sample #154, paint sample #654, paint sample #24, paint sample #154, paint sample #24, and paint sample #63. What is the mode?

4. Designer eyeglass frames cost a lot. This season's top selling frame prices are from $330, $199, $230, $400, $497, and $330. What is the mode of these eyeglass frame prices?

5. The Healthville Residence is having a problem with absenteeism during the summer months.

The administrator wants to find out who is missing work the most. First add the days absent for each employee, and write the number in the "Total days absent" column. Compare the total days absent from work; what is the mode for the number of days absent for the summer months?

Employee	Days absent in June	Days absent in July	Days absent in August	Total days absent
Verna	3	2	2	________
Xuyen	4	4	3	________
Cam	3	2	1	________
Debbie	3	3	3	________
Ed	2	2	2	________
Vasily	1	3	4	________
Ted	3	2	2	________

Range

The range of a set of numbers is the largest value in the set minus the smallest value in the set. Note that the range is a single number, not many numbers. The range is the difference between the largest and the smallest numbers.

For example, the hospital delivered six babies today. The weight in pounds of these newborns was 6, 9, 10, 8, 7, 5.

Step 1: Locate the smallest number and the largest number 5 and 10

Step 2: Subtract the smallest number from the largest number. $10 - 5 = 5$

The range is 5.

Practice:

1. The age of patients in the hospital fluctuates. Look at the data and calculate the range of patients' ages: 68, 94, 23, 45, 98, 100, 69 18, 25, 75, 87.

2. The workforce at the Village care Center is diverse in age. Look at the data and calculate the range of workers' ages: 19, 21, 24, 23, 45, 34, 28, 25, 31, 56, 64, 71, 49, 52.

3. The breakfast meals served in the cafeteria vary in calories. Look at the data and calculate the range of calories in the meals: 120, 220, 280, 340, 440, 480.

4. The public health nurse has a rural route to drive each week. What is the range that the daily miles, 7, 14, 23, 24, 16, 12, record?

5. The bandages sold in a local drug store have a wide price range. Each bandage costs as follows: 50 cents, 35 cents, 78 cents, 89 cents, 99 cents, 12 cents, and 25 cents. What is the range in individual bandage costs?

Roman Numerals

In our daily lives, we use Arabic numerals 0 to 9 and combinations of these digits to do most of our mathematical activities. In the health care field, Roman numerals are sometimes used along with Arabic numerals. Roman numerals are often found in prescriptions and in medical records and charts. Roman numerals consist of lower- and uppercase letters that represent numbers. For medical applications, Roman numerals will be written in lowercase letters for the numbers 1 to 10. Use uppercase when smaller numbers are part of a number over 30 such as 60: LX not lx. Do not use commas in Roman numerals.

Roman Numerals

Roman numerals are formed by combining the numbers.

1 = i or I	6 = vi or VI	$^1/_2$ = ss
2 = ii or II	7 = vii or VII	50 = L
3 = iii or III	8 = viii or VIII	100 = C
4 = iv or IV	9 = ix or IX	500 = D
5 = v or V	10 = x or X	1,000 = M

Mnemonic Device Note the pattern: 50-100-500-1000

L = 50	Lovely
C = 100	Cats
D = 500	Don't
M = 1000	Meow!

This will help you to remember the order and value of each Roman numeral.

Use the following basic Roman numeral concepts to accurately read and write Roman numerals.

Concept 1

Add Roman numerals of the same or decreasing value when they are placed next to each other. Read these from left to right.

Examples

vii = 5 + 2 = 7 xxi = 10 + 10 + 1 = 21

Practice Write the numerals in Arabic or Roman numerals.

1. xiii
2. xv
3. xxxi
4. LV
5. MI
6. 17
7. 31
8. 120
9. $1\frac{1}{2}$
10. 11

Concept 2

Subtract a numeral of decreasing or lesser value from the numeral to its right.

Examples

iv = 5 − 1 = 4 XC = 100 − 10 = 90

IM = 1000 − 1 = 999 xix = 10 + 10 − 1 = 19

Practice Write the numerals in Arabic or Roman numerals:

1. ixss
2. XL
3. CD
4. LM
5. XCIX
6. 19
7. 39
8. $24\frac{1}{4}$
9. 240
10. 499

Concept 3

When converting long Roman numerals to Arabic numerals, it is helpful to separate the Roman numerals into groups and work from both ends.

Example

CDLXXIV → CD L XX IV

1. Start with the IV = 5 − 1 = 4	4
2. Next, X+ X = 20	20
3. C − D = 500 − 100 = 400	400
4. L = 50	+50
5. Then add the elements	474

Practice

1. CXIV
2. LVIII
3. DXIV
4. MDCIXss
5. LXXXIX
6. XLss
7. CDIV
8. MCML
9. DXCIIss
10. CMLXXIVss

This method of separating the elements and working from both ends also works well for converting from Arabic to Roman numerals.

Example Convert 637 to Roman numerals

600	DC
30	XXX
7	VII

Then rewrite the Roman numeral from the largest number on the left to the smallest numbers on the right. → DCXXXVII

Practice

1. $14\frac{1}{2}$
2. 33
3. 146
4. 329
5. 999
6. 789
7. 450
8. 76
9. 17
10. 1294

Mixed Practice Convert between Roman numerals and Arabic numerals:

1. DCCL
2. XXIVss
3. XVIII
4. 23

5. 19
6. 1,495
7. 607
8. CCLIVss
9. 66
10. MVII
11. CMVIII
12. MCDLIV
13. 362
14. 16
15. 999
16. XXXIXss
17. LXXVIII
18. $309\frac{1}{2}$
19. 2,515
20. What should you do to convert a number with decimal 0.5 in it to a Roman numeral?

Time in Allied Health

Universal (military) time is used in many health-care facilities. The Universal time system avoids the confusion over A.M. and P.M. Universal time is based on the 24-hour clock, which begins at 0001, which is one minute after midnight.

Colons are not used between these numbers. Compare the two clocks below:

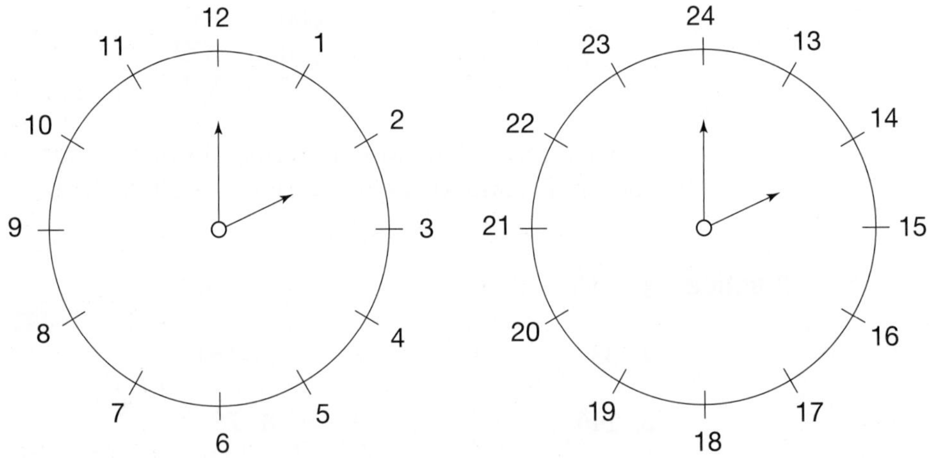

How to Convert to Universal Time:

The hours have four digits:	1 A.M. or 1:00 A.M. = 0100 10 A.M. or 10:00 A.M. = 1000
Add 1200 to any time after noon	2 P.M. or 2:00 P.M. = 1400 2 + 1200 = 1400 in Universal time 5:36 P.M. or 5:36 P.M. = 1736 in Universal time

Practice 1: Complete the chart.

Standard Time		Universal or Military Time
12:05 A.M.	*0005*	_____
3:15 P.M.	*1200*	_____
7:39 A.M.	*0315*	_____
7:39 P.M.	*(1515)*	_____
12:45 P.M.	*1245*	_____
8:17 A.M.		_____
5:57 P.M.		_____
1:23 A.M.		_____
9:25 P.M.		_____
11:03 P.M.		_____

handwritten right margin: 2400 0001 / 0100 / 0200 / 0300 / 0400 / 0500 / 0600 / 0700 / 0800 / 900 / 1000 / 1100 / 1200 / (100p) 1300

handwritten under 11:03 P.M.: 12 / 23

Practice 2: Complete the chart.

Universal or Military Time	Standard Time
1256	_____
0136	_____
0009	_____
1236	_____
0048	_____
2400	_____
1524	_____
2006	_____
0912	_____
1630	_____

WHOLE NUMBER SELF-TEST

1. Complete this number statement. 329 + _____ + 217 = 1,621

2. An activity director in a long-term care facility is purchasing recreational supplies. Find the sum of the purchases: 3 Bingo games at $13

each, 10 puzzles at $9 each, 24 jars of paint at $3 each, and 2 rolls of paper for $31 each.

3. Using the information from problem 2 above, determine the mean (average) cost of these supplies. Round to the nearest dollar.

4. A medical assistant student needs 250 hours of practical work experience to complete the college's course. If the student has completed 184 hours, how many hours remain to fulfill the requirement?

5. Three certified nursing assistants assist 16 rooms of patients on the Saturday morning shift. If each room has 3 patients, how many patients does each assistant care for if they are equally divided up among the staff?

6. Uniform jackets are required at Valley Pharmacy. Each pharmacy technician is asked to purchased two jackets at $21 per jacket and one name badge for $8. What is the cost of these items for each pharmacy technician?

7. The medical clerk is asked to inventory the digital thermometers. In the six examination rooms, the clerk finds the following number of digital thermometers: 2, 4, 5, 2, 1, and 3. The total inventory is 17.

8. The dental assistants in a new office are setting up their free patient sample display. They order the following:

	Quantity	Unit	Item	Per Unit Cost (in dollars)	Total Cost
a.	1,500	each	toothbrush	1	1500
b.	100	each	floss (smooth)	2	200
c.	75	each	floss (glide)	2	150
d.	1,000	per 100	information booklet	10	1100
e.	25	each	poster	15	375
f.				Subtotal	2325

9. After a mild heart attack, Mary spent 3 days in a coronary care unit. Her room bill was $2,898. What was her daily room rate?

$966.00

10. White blood cell (WBC) count can indicate illness or health. The WBC count of patient B is checked. Before surgery, the WBC count of patient B was 12,674; post-surgery, he had a count of 6,894. What is the difference in patient B's count before and after surgery?

5,780

11. The cook has a variety of meals to prepare for Villa Center's residents. She averages 16 vegetarian meals every day of the week. Round the number of weekly meals to the nearest 10.

17

12. The newest staff member at the hospital is a surgery technologist. Her pay is approximately $14 an hour. If she is scheduled to work 36 hours a week, what is her weekly pay before deductions?

504

13. Read the number: 956,123.
The place value of the underlined digit is Ten Thousands.

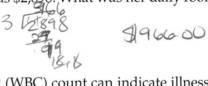

Unit 2

Fractions

Part-to-Whole Relationships

A fraction is a number that has two parts: a part and a whole. A minute is 1 part of 60 minutes in a whole hour. This relationship of part to whole can be shown in a fraction:

$$\frac{1}{60} \begin{array}{l} \leftarrow \text{numerator (the part)} \\ \leftarrow \text{denominator (the whole)} \end{array}$$

The 1 is called the *numerator*, and it represents the part of the whole. The 60 is the *denominator*, and it represents the whole or sum of the parts. Take another common part-to-whole relationship. Many people sleep an average of 8 hours a night. The relationship of sleeping hours to total hours in a day is 8 to 24, or $^{8}/_{24}$, or a reduced fraction of $^{1}/_{3}$.

Fractions are important to know because you will come across them many times in health care occupations. Fractions appear in medication dosages, measurements, sizes of instruments, work assignments, and time units. Practice writing out the numerator (part) to denominator (whole) relationships:

Example

$$\frac{1}{12} = \text{one part to twelve total parts}$$

1. $\frac{3}{4}$ = three parts to four Parts

2. $\frac{5}{6}$ = five parts to Six parts

3. $\frac{7}{8}$ = Seven parts to Eight Parts

4. $\frac{16}{21}$ = Sixteen parts to Twenty one parts

Proper or common fractions are fractions with a numerator less than the number of the denominator: $^{3}/_{7}$, $^{24}/_{47}$, $^{9}/_{11}$. The value of any proper or common fraction will be less than 1.

Mixed numbers are fractions that include both a whole number and a proper fraction: $3^{3}/_{4}$, $12^{9}/_{11}$, $101^{13}/_{22}$.

An *improper fraction* has a numerator equal to or larger than the denominator: $^{17}/_{12}$, $^{33}/_{11}$, $^{9}/_{9}$. Improper fractions are equal to 1 or larger. Improper fractions are used in the multiplication and division of fractions. Answers that appear as improper fractions need to be reduced so that the answer is a mixed number.

Equivalent Fractions

Understanding *equivalent fractions* is important in making measurement decisions. Equivalent fractions represent the same relationship of part to whole, but there are more pieces or parts involved. The fractions involved, however, are equal. The size of the pieces or parts is what varies.

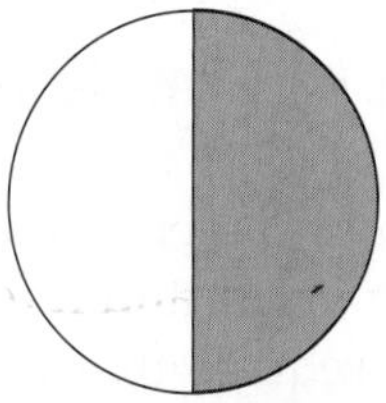

2 large pieces
$^{1}/_{2}$ is shaded

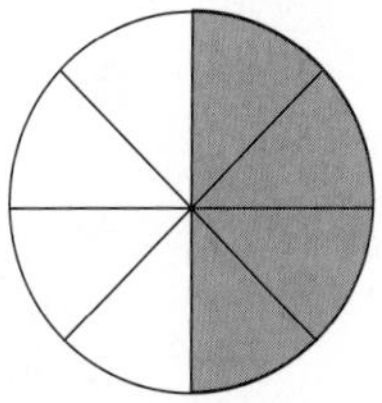

8 smaller pieces
$^{4}/_{8}$ are shaded

The shaded areas are the same size; the number of parts varies. Making fractions equal is easy using multiplication. Look at the fractions: $^{1}/_{6}$ and $^{?}/_{18}$. The denominators are 6 and 18. Ask: 6 times what = 18? The answer is 3, so multiply the numerator by 3, and you will have formed an equivalent fraction. Thus, $^{1}/_{6} = ^{3}/_{18}$.

The key to getting the correct answer is in remembering that the number the denominator is multiplied by must also be used to multiply the numerator. If this method is difficult for you, then divide the smaller denominator into the larger one; your answer will then be multiplied by the first numerator to get the second numerator.

$$\frac{1}{6} = \frac{?}{18} \quad 6\overline{)18}, \text{ then } 3 \times 1 = 3$$

Another way to work this problem is:

$$\frac{1(\times 3)}{6(\times 3)} = \frac{3}{18}$$

Thus, $\frac{1}{6} = \frac{3}{18}$.

Practice

1. $\frac{1}{2} = \frac{?}{12}$
2. $\frac{1}{4} = \frac{?}{16}$
3. $\frac{1}{5} = \frac{?}{40}$
4. $\frac{2}{14} = \frac{?}{28}$
5. $\frac{5}{9} = \frac{?}{27}$
6. $\frac{1}{13} = \frac{?}{39}$
7. $\frac{4}{8} = \frac{?}{72}$
8. $\frac{1}{5} = \frac{?}{100}$
9. $\frac{7}{9} = \frac{42}{?}$
10. $\frac{1}{3} = \frac{8}{?}$

The skill of making equivalent fractions will be used in adding, subtracting, and comparing fractions.

Reducing to Lowest or Simplest Terms

As in making fractions equivalent, reducing fractions to their lowest or simplest terms is another important fraction skill. Most tests and practical applications of fractions require that the answers be in the lowest terms. After each calculation of addition, subtraction, multiplication, or division, you will need to reduce the answer to its lowest terms. Two methods will help you get to the lowest terms:

Multiplication Method

To use the multiplication method, look at the numbers in the fraction. Find a number that divides into both the numerator and denominator evenly. Such numbers are called *factors* of the numbers. Write out the multiplication for the numerator and denominator. Cross out the two identical numbers in the multiplication problems. What is left will be the reduced fraction.

$$\frac{2}{16} = \frac{2 \times 1}{2 \times 8} \rightarrow \frac{\not{2} \times 1}{\not{2} \times 8}$$

So, $^2/_6 = {}^1/_8$. Depending on the multiple you choose, you may need to do this more than once.

$$\frac{8}{24} = \frac{\not{4} \times 2}{\not{4} \times 6} = \frac{2}{6} \rightarrow \frac{1}{3}$$

or

$$\frac{8}{24} = \frac{\not{8} \times 1}{\not{8} \times 3} = \frac{1}{3}$$

Sometimes students only partially reduce a fraction, so try to find the largest possible factor of the numbers when you are reducing.

Choose the largest possible multiple to avoid having to repeat the steps in reduction.

Division Method

Look at the numbers of the numerator and the denominator. Choose a number that divides into both the numerator and the denominator. Next, divide the numerator and denominator by that number. Check to ensure that the resulting fraction is in its lowest form.

$$\frac{2}{16} = \frac{2 \div 2}{16 \div 2} = \frac{1}{8}$$

$$\frac{8}{24} = \frac{8 \div 4}{24 \div 4} = \frac{2}{6}$$

This fraction is not reduced, so it must be reduced again.

$$\frac{2}{6} = \frac{2 \div 2}{6 \div 2} = \frac{1}{3}$$

This fraction is reduced to its lowest form.

How do you decide on the best method to use?

Choose your strongest skill—multiplication or division—and use it to reduce fractions.

You will make fewer errors if you select one method and use it consistently.

Practice

1. $\frac{2}{14}$
2. $\frac{3}{27}$
3. $\frac{4}{8}$
4. $\frac{13}{39}$
5. $\frac{25}{100}$
6. $\frac{64}{72}$

7. $\frac{24}{48}$

9. $\frac{15}{45}$

8. $\frac{63}{90}$

10. $\frac{5}{255}$

When working with a mixed number, set aside the whole number. Handle the fraction portion of the number and then place it beside the whole number.

$$14\frac{3}{9} \rightarrow 14 \text{ and } \frac{3}{9} \rightarrow \frac{3}{9} = \frac{1 \times 3}{3 \times 3} = \frac{1}{3} \rightarrow 14\frac{1}{3}$$

Set aside the whole number, reduce the fraction, then replace the whole number next to the reduced fraction.

Practice

1. $13\frac{2}{8}$
2. $7\frac{12}{16}$
3. $1\frac{33}{66}$
4. $2\frac{2}{20}$
5. $3\frac{3}{12}$
6. $5\frac{14}{64}$
7. $2\frac{11}{99}$
8. $10\frac{30}{80}$
9. $6\frac{45}{90}$
10. $4\frac{22}{30}$

Fractional parts or relationships are common in health care.

Example In a class of 30 people, 13 students are male and 17 are female. To write the relationship of the number of males to the total number of students, we place the part (13) over the whole (30) or total number of students.

$$\frac{13}{30}$$

Practice Write the fractional part that represents the relationships of the part to the whole. Then reduce all your answers to the lowest form.

1. 50 of the 125 patients see the physical therapist each week.
2. The dietitian uses 35 six-ounce glasses and 50 eight-ounce glasses at breakfast. Represent in fraction form the relationship of six-ounce glasses to eight-ounce glasses used at breakfast.
3. 30 out of 90 patients at the short-term care facility are women. What is the fractional part of women to total patients?
4. 14 female babies and 16 male babies were born on Saturday. Express the female babies to male babies as a fraction.
5. About 500 medicine cups are used daily at a long-term care facility. The nurse claims that approximately 4,000 medicine cups are used a week. What is the day-to-week use rate of medicine cups?

Improper Fractions

Working with improper fractions also requires reducing fractions. An improper fraction is a fraction that has a larger numerator than a denominator.

$$\frac{16}{8} = \frac{8 \times 2 = 2}{8 \times 1 = 1} \rightarrow 2$$

If the numerator and the denominator do not have a common number by which the numbers can be multiplied, simply divide the denominator into the numerator.

$$\frac{11}{8} \quad \begin{array}{r} 1\frac{3}{8} \\ 8\overline{)11} \\ \underline{8} \\ 3 \end{array}$$

The remainder 3 is a whole number. Place it on top of the divisor to form a fraction.

Improper fractions are either whole numbers or mixed numbers.

Improper fractions are used for dividing mixed numbers.

Practice

1. $\frac{15}{2}$
2. $\frac{18}{4}$
3. $\frac{39}{2}$

4. $\frac{27}{5}$

5. $\frac{66}{7}$

6. $\frac{7}{3}$

7. $\frac{19}{8}$

8. $\frac{16}{2}$

9. $\frac{100}{100}$

10. $\frac{23}{18}$

Adding Fractions with Like Denominators

Addition of fractions with the same denominator is straightforward. Follow the two steps below:

Step 1: Line up the fractions vertically, add the numerators, and place the answer over the common, or like, denominator.

Step 2: Reduce, if necessary. Check your work to ensure accuracy.

$$\begin{array}{r} \frac{3}{6} \\ +\frac{2}{6} \\ \hline \frac{5}{6} \end{array} \qquad \begin{array}{r} \frac{4}{8} \\ +\frac{5}{8} \\ \hline \frac{9}{8} \end{array} \quad \text{Reduce by } 9 \div 8 = 1\frac{1}{8}$$

When reducing the answer, you find that the result is a whole number with a 1 for its denominator. In this case, use the numerator, a whole number alone. Do not use the 1 since the answer is actually a whole number rather than a fraction.

Step 1: $\begin{array}{r} \frac{12}{15} \\ +\frac{18}{15} \\ \hline \frac{30}{15} \end{array}$ **Step 2:** $\frac{30 = \cancel{15} \times 2}{15 = \cancel{15} \times 1} \quad \frac{2}{1} = 2$

If a whole number exists with the fractions, simply add it separately and place the fraction next to the answer. The whole number will be affected only if the fraction answer is larger than 1—then the whole number resulting from the fraction addition is added to the whole number answer.

Example

$$\begin{array}{r} 14\frac{2}{8} \\ +7\frac{1}{8} \\ \hline 21\frac{3}{8} \end{array}$$

Add the fractions: $\frac{2}{8} + \frac{1}{8} = \frac{3}{8}$

Add the whole numbers: $14 + 7 = 21$

Write the answer. No reduction is necessary.

Example

$$\begin{array}{r} 10\frac{2}{4} \\ +4\frac{3}{4} \\ \hline 14\frac{5}{4} \end{array}$$

Add the fractions: $\frac{2}{4} + \frac{3}{4} = \frac{5}{4}$

Add $10 + 4 = 14$

$^5/_4$ must be reduced. It is an improper fraction.

Divide 5 by 4 $= 1^1/_4$. The whole number 1 is added to 14 ($14 + 1 = 15$) and the fraction $^1/_4$ is placed next to the whole so that the answer is $15\,^1/_4$.

Practice Add the following fractions. Reduce as necessary:

1. $\frac{1}{6} + \frac{5}{6}$
2. $\frac{2}{8} + \frac{4}{8}$
3. $\frac{9}{10} + \frac{11}{10}$
4. $\frac{1}{13} + \frac{4}{13}$
5. $\frac{3}{12} + \frac{4}{12}$
6. $\frac{2}{5} + \frac{3}{5}$
7. $\frac{3}{13} + \frac{4}{13}$
8. $13\frac{8}{12} + 2\frac{2}{12}$
9. $10\frac{1}{6} + 12\frac{4}{6}$

10. $11\frac{1}{4} + \frac{3}{4}$

11. $\frac{3}{5} + \frac{1}{5}$

12. $\frac{2}{7} + \frac{3}{7} + \frac{4}{7}$

13. $\frac{3}{8} + \frac{4}{8} + \frac{1}{8}$

14. $2\frac{1}{12} + 3\frac{5}{12} + 6\frac{4}{12}$

15. $101\frac{3}{4} + 33\frac{1}{4} + 5\frac{1}{4}$

Finding the Common Denominator

Adding and subtracting fractions requires that the denominator be of the same number, also referred to as a *common denominator*. The lowest common denominator is the smallest number or multiple that both of the denominators of the fractions can go into.

By using multiplication, find a smallest number or multiple that the numbers can go into.

Step 1:

$$\begin{array}{lcl} \frac{2}{3} & \frac{}{3 \times 2} & = \frac{?}{6} \\ +\frac{1}{6} & \begin{array}{l}\rightarrow \\ \rightarrow\end{array} & \frac{1}{6} \end{array}$$

In the above problem, 3 and 6 are the denominators. 3 × 2 = 6, so 6 is the common denominator.

Step 2: Once you have the common denominator in place, multiply the numerator by the same number with which you multiplied the denominator. The result will be equivalent fractions, so the number relationships remain the same.

$$\begin{array}{lcr} \frac{2}{3} & \frac{2 \times 2}{3 \times 2} & = \frac{4}{6} \\ +\frac{1}{6} & \begin{array}{l}\rightarrow \\ \rightarrow\end{array} & +\frac{1}{6} \\ \hline & & \frac{5}{6} \end{array}$$

Practice Find the common denominator in the following pairs of numbers. Set the problems up vertically and think about their multiples to find the common denominators.

> Fewer errors occur if the setup is vertical. You can see the numbers and their relationships easier.

1. $\frac{2}{4}$ and $\frac{1}{5}$
2. $\frac{3}{8}$ and $\frac{1}{16}$
3. $\frac{22}{44}$ and $\frac{1}{11}$
4. $\frac{1}{9}$ and $\frac{5}{45}$
5. $\frac{2}{5}$ and $\frac{3}{25}$
6. $\frac{3}{7}$ and $\frac{9}{49}$
7. $\frac{1}{200}$ and $\frac{5}{20}$
8. $\frac{4}{50}$ and $\frac{10}{150}$
9. $\frac{3}{9}$ and $\frac{4}{27}$
10. $\frac{1}{6}$ and $\frac{4}{18}$

Practice Add the following fractions with unlike denominators:

1. $\frac{3}{5} + \frac{1}{4}$
2. $\frac{1}{2} + \frac{4}{6}$
3. $\frac{4}{9} + \frac{2}{3}$
4. $\frac{7}{10} + \frac{3}{5}$
5. $\frac{11}{30} + \frac{2}{15}$
6. $\frac{5}{25} + \frac{1}{5}$
7. $\frac{4}{7} + \frac{1}{21}$
8. $\frac{2}{5} + \frac{1}{10} + \frac{3}{10}$
9. $\frac{3}{5} + \frac{1}{3} + \frac{2}{15}$
10. $\frac{2}{3} + \frac{1}{12} + \frac{2}{4}$

11. $\frac{1}{10} + \frac{1}{2} + \frac{4}{5}$

12. $12\frac{1}{6} + \frac{3}{4}$

13. $55\frac{1}{3} + 51\frac{5}{9}$

14. $5\frac{1}{2} + 2\frac{4}{5} + 5\frac{3}{10}$

15. $4\frac{3}{4} + 1\frac{1}{16} + 3\frac{2}{32}$

Sometimes one must consider a wider range of possible numbers for common denominators. For example, you may have a pair of fractions in which one of the denominators cannot be multiplied by a number to get the other denominator. In this case, it is often easiest to simply multiply the two denominators with each other. The result will be a common denominator.

Example

$$\frac{3}{13} \text{ and } \frac{1}{4}$$

What is the common denominator? If you multiply 13 × 4, your answer is 52. Use that number as the common denominator.

> To find the more difficult common denominators, multiply the denominators with each other.

$$\frac{3}{13} \rightarrow 13 \times 4 = 52$$

$$\frac{1}{4} \rightarrow 4 \times 13 = 52$$

Then multiply each numerator by the same number that you multiplied its denominator by. Do this for each fraction and the result will be a common denominator.

$$\frac{3}{13} \rightarrow \frac{3 \times 4 = 12}{13 \times 4 = 52}$$

$$\frac{1}{4} \rightarrow \frac{1 \times 13 = 13}{4 \times 13 = 52}$$

By finding the common denominator, you have also created equivalent fractions.

Practice Find the common denominator for each of the following sets of fractions:

1. $\frac{3}{4}$ and $\frac{2}{5}$

2. $\frac{7}{8}$ and $\frac{1}{3}$

3. $\frac{24}{32}$ and $\frac{1}{6}$

4. $\frac{1}{7}$ and $\frac{4}{8}$

5. $\frac{3}{5}$ and $\frac{7}{9}$

6. $\frac{2}{26}$ and $\frac{1}{3}$

7. $\frac{3}{9}$ and $\frac{1}{4}$

8. $\frac{2}{5}$ and $\frac{6}{9}$

9. $\frac{3}{10}$ and $\frac{2}{3}$

10. $\frac{1}{9}$ and $\frac{7}{8}$

Practice Add the following mixed fractions:

1. $3\frac{2}{3} + 6\frac{1}{4}$

2. $10\frac{1}{2} + 13\frac{5}{22}$

3. $9\frac{1}{6} + 4\frac{3}{9}$

4. $11\frac{7}{8} + 2\frac{1}{7}$

5. $\frac{1}{2} + 4\frac{1}{7} + 2\frac{1}{14}$

6. $12\frac{3}{5} + 22\frac{1}{30}$

7. $10\frac{4}{5} + 8\frac{1}{6}$

8. $3\frac{4}{9} + 1\frac{2}{3} + 5\frac{2}{9}$

9. $11\frac{2}{5} + 7\frac{1}{2}$

10. $7\frac{11}{16} + 3\frac{4}{8} + \frac{1}{2}$

11. $2\frac{2}{9} + 6\frac{1}{3} + 8\frac{2}{27}$

12. $6\frac{2}{3} + 8\frac{4}{5} + 3\frac{6}{10}$

13. $6\frac{1}{4} + 13\frac{2}{3} + 19\frac{1}{2}$

14. $6\frac{7}{16} + \frac{3}{24} + 2\frac{1}{48}$

15. $\frac{3}{5} + \frac{6}{30} + 12\frac{2}{3}$

16. $8\frac{9}{11} + 3\frac{1}{33} + \frac{2}{66}$

17. $3\frac{5}{16} + \frac{5}{8} + \frac{2}{4}$

18. $\frac{5}{6} + 3\frac{3}{9} + 7\frac{2}{3}$

19. $4\frac{5}{6} + \frac{2}{5} + \frac{4}{15}$

20. $55\frac{4}{17} + 101\frac{3}{51}$

Applications

1. The certified nurse assistants weigh patients each month. Mrs. Smith weighed 120 pounds last month. Over the last two months, she gained $1\frac{1}{2}$ and $\frac{1}{4}$ pounds. What is Mrs. Smith's current weight?

2. The lab technician uses a cleaning solution daily. The technician used $4\frac{1}{2}$ ounces, $1\frac{1}{3}$ ounces, and 5 ounces of the cleaning solutions. What is the total amount of solution used?

3. A new baby grew $\frac{3}{4}$ of an inch in June and $\frac{7}{16}$ of an inch in July. How many total inches did the baby grow during these two months?

4. A sick child drinks $\frac{1}{2}$ cup of juice and an hour later $\frac{3}{4}$ cup of water. At dinner, the child drinks $1\frac{1}{4}$ cups more of water. What is the child's total fluid intake?

5. The nurse gives a patient $1\frac{1}{2}$ grains of medication followed by $2\frac{1}{3}$ grains. What is the total dosage the nurse has dispensed to the patient?

Ordering Fractions

Comparing fractions in health-care fields appears when sizes of medical items or pieces of equipment are being computed. It is useful to be able to determine the size relationships of instruments and place them in order for a surgeon before a surgery. This is accomplished by using the common denominator method.

Know these symbols: <, =, >

3 is less than 4 is represented by $3 < 4$

7 is greater than 5 is represented by $7 > 5$

$\frac{2}{2}$ equals 1 is represented by $\frac{2}{2} = 1$

Example Which is larger $^1/_4$ or $^3/_8$?

Step 1: Convert the fractions to give each a common denominator.

$$\frac{1}{4} \quad \frac{1 \times 2}{4 \times 2} = \frac{2}{8}$$

$$\frac{3}{8} \rightarrow \quad \frac{3}{8}$$

Step 2: Order by the numerators now that the fractions have the same denominator. 3 is larger than 2, so $^3/_8 > {^2/_8}$ or $^1/_4$.

Practice Order the following fractions from largest to smallest.

1. $\frac{1}{4}, \frac{2}{9}, \frac{4}{12}$

2. $\frac{9}{22}, \frac{5}{11}, \frac{8}{11}$

3. $\frac{6}{25}, \frac{20}{50}, \frac{33}{100}$

4. $\frac{7}{8}, \frac{2}{16}, \frac{3}{4}, \frac{1}{2}$

Subtraction of Fractions

Subtraction of fractions follows the same basic principles as addition of fractions. The fractions must have common denominators before any subtraction can be done.

Example **Step 1:** Make a common denominator if necessary.

$$\frac{7}{8} - \frac{5}{8} = \_\_\_ \text{ (8 is the common denominator.)}$$

Step 2: Subtract the numerators and then reduce if necessary.

$$\frac{7}{8} - \frac{5}{8} = \frac{2}{8}, \text{ which is reduced to } \frac{1}{4}.$$

Practice

1. $\frac{3}{9} - \frac{2}{9}$
2. $\frac{5}{8} - \frac{2}{8}$
3. $\frac{3}{11} - \frac{1}{11}$
4. $\frac{22}{44} - \frac{11}{44}$
5. $10\frac{5}{12} - 8\frac{3}{12}$
6. $25\frac{3}{4} - 20\frac{1}{4}$
7. $101\frac{13}{24} - 56\frac{10}{24}$
8. $6\frac{6}{7} - \frac{3}{5}$
9. $\frac{15}{16} - \frac{7}{16}$
10. $20\frac{5}{6} - 12\frac{2}{6}$
11. $\frac{3}{4} - \frac{1}{2}$
12. $\frac{6}{8} - \frac{1}{4}$
13. $12\frac{1}{2} - \frac{3}{10}$
14. $20\frac{6}{14} - 2\frac{3}{7}$
15. $39\frac{11}{18} - 8\frac{3}{6}$
16. $25\frac{1}{3} - 20\frac{1}{8}$
17. $124\frac{11}{12} - \frac{5}{6}$
18. $18\frac{3}{4} - 12\frac{2}{3}$
19. $200\frac{9}{11} - 188\frac{2}{3}$
20. $500\frac{4}{5} - 150\frac{2}{9}$

Borrowing in Subtraction of Fractions

Two specific situations require that a number be borrowed in the subtraction of fractions: (1) subtraction of a fraction from a whole number, and (2) after a common denominator is established and the top fraction of the problem is less or smaller than the fraction that is being subtracted from it.

Recall that the borrowing in whole numbers is accomplished as shown below. Set the problem up vertically.

$$124 - 8 = \_\_\_\_$$

Step 1: Borrow 1 from the tens column. Add it to the ones column.

Step 2: Subtract.

$$\begin{array}{r} 1^{1}\not{2}^{1}4 \\ -8 \\ \hline 116 \end{array}$$

In fractions, the same borrowing concept is used; the format varies only slightly. The difference is that the borrowed number must be put into a fractional form.

> Any whole number over itself equals 1. So $^{101}/_{101} = 1$, $^{3}/_{3} = 1$, and $^{12}/_{12} = 1$.

Example

$$\begin{array}{r} 17\frac{3}{8} \\ -14\frac{4}{8} \\ \hline \end{array}$$

In the example above, the numerator 4 in the second fraction cannot be subtracted from the first fraction's numerator 3. Thus, borrowing is required in the first fraction.

$$\begin{array}{r} 1^{6}\not{7}\frac{3}{8} + \frac{8}{8} \\ -14\frac{4}{8} \\ \hline \end{array}$$

Step 1: Borrow 1 from the whole number. Convert the 1 into an improper fraction having the same common denominator as the first fraction. Then add the two fractions.

Step 2: Rewrite the problem so it incorporates the changes, then subtract the numerator only. Place it over the denominator. Reduce as necessary.

$$\begin{array}{r} 16\frac{11}{8} \\ -\ 14\frac{4}{8} \\ \hline 2\frac{7}{8} \end{array}$$

Borrowing in Subtraction Rules

1. Must have a common denominator.
2. To borrow from the whole number, make it a fractional part.
3. Add fractional parts.
4. Subtract; reduce if necessary.

Practice

1. $11 - \frac{5}{6}$
2. $9 - \frac{3}{5}$
3. $10 - \frac{2}{8}$
4. $13 - \frac{5}{9}$
5. $15 - \frac{7}{13}$
6. $30 - \frac{4}{11}$
7. $8\frac{2}{7} - 2\frac{3}{7}$
8. $14\frac{3}{12} - 10\frac{10}{12}$
9. $15\frac{1}{5} - 4\frac{4}{5}$
10. $9\frac{2}{4} - 5\frac{3}{4}$

Remember that when you are subtracting, the first rule is that you must have a common denominator. Once the common denominator is in place, borrow if necessary. Then subtract, placing the answer over the denominator; reduce as necessary.

Practice

1. $14\frac{2}{5} - 6\frac{3}{4}$
2. $34\frac{1}{4} - 10\frac{4}{5}$
3. $36\frac{1}{6} - 16\frac{3}{5}$
4. $13\frac{3}{4} - 7\frac{7}{8}$

5. $16\frac{3}{11} - 10\frac{1}{2}$

6. $19\frac{1}{2} - 15\frac{7}{12}$

7. $112\frac{1}{2} - \frac{11}{15}$

8. $18\frac{3}{7} - 2\frac{7}{14}$

9. $45\frac{3}{8} - 13\frac{3}{4}$

10. $125\frac{2}{12} - 28\frac{5}{6}$

11. $29\frac{1}{4} - 12\frac{5}{12}$

12. $12\frac{1}{6} - 1\frac{4}{5}$

13. $90\frac{4}{9} - 13\frac{3}{4}$

14. $28\frac{1}{7} - 4\frac{6}{7}$

15. $13\frac{2}{20} - 6\frac{6}{10}$

Additional Practice

1. $12\frac{1}{2} - 4\frac{7}{8}$

2. $14 - \frac{3}{7}$

3. $12\frac{1}{16} - 2\frac{5}{16}$

4. $20\frac{2}{3} - 10\frac{7}{9}$

5. $54\frac{1}{2} - 42\frac{3}{4}$

6. $22\frac{3}{5} - 17\frac{5}{6}$

7. $87 - 14\frac{2}{7}$

8. $225\frac{1}{4} - 34\frac{3}{8}$

9. $90\frac{1}{3} - 6\frac{3}{4}$

10. $45 - \frac{15}{16}$

Application

1. A patient is on a low sodium, low fat diet. Three months ago the patient weighed $210\frac{1}{4}$ pounds. Now the patient weighs $198\frac{3}{4}$ pounds. How many pounds did the patient lose?

2. The school nurse encourages all students to drink at least 4 pints of water daily. Most students drink at least $1\frac{1}{2}$ pints. How much additional water should the students consume?

3. The pharmacy technician helps with annual inventory. If there were 125 boxes of computer labels at the beginning of the inventory period, and $25\frac{3}{4}$ remain, how many boxes of labels were used throughout the year?

4. The dietitian had a 100 pound bag of unbleached flour at the beginning of the month. If she used $73\frac{1}{2}$ pounds, how much flour does she have left?

5. The recreation center is helping residents make placemats for the holidays. Each resident is given 45 inches of decorative edging per placemat. If each placemat uses $41\frac{1}{2}$ inches of decorative edging, how much edging is left over from each placemat?

Multiplication of Fractions

To facilitate multiplication and division of fractions, set up the problems horizontally.

One of the simplest computations in fractions is to multiply a common fraction. No common denominator is needed.

Example

Step 1: Set up the problem horizontally and multiply the fraction straight across.

$$\frac{7}{8} \times \frac{1}{4} \begin{matrix} \rightarrow \\ \rightarrow \end{matrix} = \frac{7}{32}$$

Step 2: Reduce to the lowest terms, if necessary. $\frac{7}{32}$ does not need to be reduced.

Practice

1. $\frac{3}{4} \times \frac{1}{12}$
2. $\frac{1}{2} \times \frac{4}{5}$
3. $\frac{7}{9} \times \frac{4}{5}$
4. $\frac{2}{3} \times \frac{4}{6}$
5. $\frac{1}{5} \times \frac{3}{7}$
6. $\frac{12}{48} \times \frac{1}{2}$
7. $\frac{6}{9} \times \frac{2}{3}$
8. $\frac{10}{100} \times \frac{2}{5}$
9. $\frac{1}{3} \times \frac{13}{22}$
10. $\frac{4}{5} \times \frac{1}{20}$

Review some number concepts in fractions that will help ensure accurate answers.

> Any number over itself equals 1: $^{4}/_{4}$, $^{8}/_{8}$, and $^{105}/_{105}$ all equal 1. Any numerator that has 1 as its denominator should be represented as a whole number:
>
> $$\frac{4}{1} = 4, \frac{6}{1} = 6, \frac{51}{1} = 51, \text{ and } \frac{102}{1} = 102$$

Multiplying a Fraction by a Whole Number

To multiply a fraction by a whole number, follow these steps:

Example

$$\frac{1}{6} \times 2 = \_\_\_\_$$

Step 1: Make the whole number into a fraction by placing a 1 as its denominator.

$$\frac{1}{6} \times \frac{2}{1}$$

Any whole number can become a fraction by placing a 1 as the denominator. 14 = $^{14}/_{1}$

Step 2: Multiply straight across and then reduce if necessary.

$$\frac{1}{6} \times \frac{2}{1} = \frac{2}{6} \to \frac{1}{3}$$

Reduce to $\frac{1}{3}$.

Practice

1. $\frac{1}{4} \times 6$
2. $3 \times \frac{2}{5}$
3. $\frac{7}{15} \times 35$
4. $24 \times \frac{2}{7}$
5. $7 \times \frac{8}{10}$
6. $16 \times \frac{1}{3}$
7. $\frac{5}{9} \times 21$
8. $\frac{5}{30} \times 200$
9. $\frac{1}{8} \times 32$
10. $\frac{11}{50} \times 20$

Reducing before You Multiply as a Timesaver

When multiplying, you can expedite the work by reducing before you multiply. This is useful because it relies on the multiples of the numbers to reduce the numbers you are multiplying. This saves time at the end of the problem because you won't have to spend so much time reducing the answer.

Look at the numbers involved in $^{2}/_{5} \times {}^{3}/_{4}$. If a numerator number can go into a denominator number evenly, then canceling is possible.

$$\frac{{}^{1}\cancel{2}}{5} \times \frac{3}{\cancel{4}_{2}}$$ The 2 goes into the 4 twice because $2 \times 2 = 4$

Then multiply the changed numerals straight across.

$$\frac{1 \times 3}{5 \times 2} = \frac{3}{10}$$

The answer is $^3/_{10}$. If the problem was done without canceling, the answer after multiplication would be $^6/_{20}$, which needs to be reduced to $^3/_{10}$. Reducing first saves time by allowing you to work with smaller numbers. For more complicated problems, it may be easier to cancel by writing out the number involved.

Example

Step 1: Write out the multiples of each number to find numbers that each can go into evenly.

$$\begin{matrix} (10 \times 1) & & (3 \times 1) \\ \dfrac{10}{15} & \times & \dfrac{3}{100} \\ (3 \times 5) & & (10 \times 10) \end{matrix}$$

Step 2: Then, begin by crossing out the matching numbers, working from top to bottom and crossing out like numbers. Cross out the matching numbers.

$$\begin{matrix} (\not{1}\not{0} \times 1) & & (\not{3} \times 1) \\ \dfrac{10}{15} & \times & \dfrac{3}{100} \\ (\not{3} \times 5) & & (\not{1}\not{0} \times 10) \end{matrix}$$

Step 3: Then multiply the remaining numbers straight across.

$$\begin{matrix} (\not{1}\not{0} \times 1) & & (\not{3} \times 1) & \rightarrow 1 \times 1 = 1 \\ \dfrac{10}{15} & \times & \dfrac{3}{100} & \\ (\not{3} \times 5) & & (\not{1}\not{0} \times 10) & \rightarrow 5 \times 10 = 50 \end{matrix} \Bigg\} \frac{1}{50}$$

When there are more than two fractions, reducing of fractions can occur anywhere within the fraction as long as the reducing is done by the top and bottom numbers. There can be multiple reductions of fractions as well.

For example:

$\frac{11}{16} \times \frac{3}{12} \times \frac{8}{66}$ → Set the problem up using the factors for each number.

$$\begin{matrix} (11 \times 1) & & (3 \times 1) & & (2 \times 4) \\ \dfrac{11}{16} & \times & \dfrac{3}{12} & \times & \dfrac{8}{66} \\ (2 \times 8) & & (4 \times 3) & & (6 \times 11) \end{matrix}$$

$$\begin{matrix} (\cancel{11} \times 1) & & (\cancel{3} \times 1) & & (\cancel{2} \times \cancel{4}) \\ \frac{11}{16} & \times & \frac{3}{12} & \times & \frac{8}{66} \\ (\cancel{2} \times 8) & & (\cancel{4} \times \cancel{3}) & & (6 \times \cancel{11}) \end{matrix} \quad \text{After reducing, multiply to get } \frac{1}{48}$$

Practice

1. $\frac{4}{5} \times \frac{15}{7}$
2. $\frac{12}{20} \times \frac{4}{24}$
3. $\frac{3}{7} \times \frac{21}{36}$
4. $\frac{5}{6} \times \frac{3}{30}$
5. $\frac{11}{15} \times \frac{3}{44}$
6. $\frac{3}{7} \times \frac{7}{11}$
7. $\frac{14}{20} \times \frac{10}{28}$
8. $\frac{1}{3} \times \frac{3}{6} \times \frac{2}{4}$
9. $\frac{11}{16} \times \frac{4}{12} \times \frac{22}{44}$
10. $\frac{9}{10} \times \frac{1}{3} \times \frac{8}{13}$
11. $\frac{8}{14} \times \frac{25}{48} \times \frac{7}{50}$
12. $\frac{5}{12} \times \frac{33}{34} \times \frac{17}{20} \times \frac{60}{66}$

Multiplication of Mixed Numbers

Mixed numbers are whole numbers with fractions. Multiplication involving mixed numbers requires that the mixed number be changed to an improper fraction.

Example Change $1^3/_4$ into an improper fraction.

Step 1: Multiply the whole number times the denominator, then add the numerator.

$$1\frac{3}{4} \rightarrow 1 \times 4 + 3 = 7$$

Step 2: Place the answer from step 1 over the denominator.

$$1\frac{3}{4} \rightarrow 1 \times 4 + 3 = 7 \rightarrow \frac{7}{4}$$

$$\frac{7}{4} \quad \text{So } 1\frac{3}{4} = \frac{7}{4}$$

This improper fraction is not further reduced or changed. It may now be multiplied by another fraction.

Practice Change these mixed numbers into improper fractions.

1. $8\frac{1}{4}$
2. $5\frac{2}{3}$
3. $17\frac{3}{5}$
4. $24\frac{4}{7}$
5. $2\frac{3}{12}$
6. $4\frac{3}{8}$
7. $3\frac{5}{9}$
8. $12\frac{1}{4}$
9. $4\frac{5}{12}$
10. $10\frac{1}{3}$

After converting mixed numbers to improper fractions, continue by following the same rules as for multiplying common fractions.

Example

$$\frac{1}{3} \times 5\frac{1}{4}$$

Step 1: Change the mixed number into an improper fraction.

$$5\frac{1}{4} \rightarrow 5 \times 4 = 20 + 1 = \frac{21}{4}$$

Step 2: Reduce, if possible.

$$\underset{(\cancel{3} \times 1)}{\frac{1}{3}} \times \overset{(\cancel{3} \times 7)}{\frac{21}{4}}$$

Step 3: Multiply straight across.

$$\frac{1 \times 7 = 7}{1 \times 4 = 4}$$

Step 4: Change the improper fraction to a mixed fraction.

$$\frac{7}{4} \rightarrow 7 \div 4 = 1\frac{3}{4}$$

Example

$$3\frac{1}{4} \times 5\frac{2}{5}$$

Step 1: Change to improper fractions.

$$3\frac{1}{4} \rightarrow 3 \times 4 = 12 + 1 = \frac{13}{4} \text{ and}$$

$$5\frac{2}{5} \rightarrow 5 \times 5 = 25 + 2 = \frac{27}{5}$$

Step 2: Reduce, if possible.

$$\frac{13}{4} \times \frac{27}{5} \text{ — not possible}$$

Step 3: Multiply straight across.

$$\frac{13}{4} \times \frac{27}{5} = \frac{351}{20}$$

Step 4: Reduce — Divide 351 by 20. Write it as a mixed fraction.

$$\begin{array}{r} 17\frac{11}{20} \\ 20\overline{)351} \\ \underline{20\downarrow} \\ 151 \\ \underline{140} \\ 11 \end{array}$$

Answer: $17\frac{11}{20}$

Practice

1. $2\frac{5}{12} \times \frac{1}{7}$
2. $4\frac{2}{3} \times \frac{4}{5}$
3. $\frac{3}{10} \times 1\frac{3}{4}$
4. $2\frac{1}{8} \times \frac{6}{11}$
5. $\frac{4}{9} \times 1\frac{2}{3}$
6. $3\frac{5}{7} \times 2\frac{5}{14}$
7. $17\frac{1}{4} \times 2\frac{1}{3}$
8. $1\frac{1}{4} \times 2\frac{1}{5}$
9. $2\frac{1}{5} \times 1\frac{3}{4}$
10. $3\frac{1}{6} \times 3\frac{1}{4}$

Applications

1. A bottle of medicine contains 30 doses. How many doses are in $2^1/_3$ bottles?

2. The nurse worked a total of $2^1/_4$ hours overtime. She is paid $32 an hour for overtime work. What are her overtime earnings?

3. One tablet contains 250 milligrams of pain medication. How many milligrams are in $3^1/_2$ tablets?

4. One cup holds 8 ounces of liquid. If a cup is $^2/_3$ full, how many ounces are in the cup?

5. The dietitian is working in a long-term care residence. Each day she prepares a high protein drink for 25 residents. If each drink measures $^{3}/_{4}$ cup, how many total cups of the drink will she prepare a day?

Division of Fractions

To divide fractions, two steps are required to compute the answer.

Example Solve: $\frac{1}{8} \div \frac{1}{4} =$ ______

Step 1: Change the sign to a × sign.

$$\frac{1}{8} \div \frac{1}{4} \rightarrow \frac{1}{8} \times \frac{1}{4}$$

Step 2: Invert the fraction to the right of the ÷ sign.

$$\frac{1}{8} \div \frac{1}{4} \rightarrow \frac{1}{8} \times \frac{4}{1}$$

This inversion causes the fraction to change from $^{1}/_{4}$ to $^{4}/_{1}$, which is called the reciprocal of $^{1}/_{4}$.

The reciprocal of any fraction is its inverse:

$$\frac{2}{3} \rightarrow \frac{3}{2} \quad \frac{12}{35} \rightarrow \frac{35}{12} \text{ and } \frac{9}{11} \rightarrow \frac{11}{9}$$

Step 3: Follow the steps of multiplication of fractions: Reduce if possible; then multiply straight across and reduce as necessary.

(4 × 1)

Reduce $\frac{1}{8} \times \frac{4}{1} = \frac{1}{2}$

(4 × 2)

Example Solve: $\frac{4}{9} \div \frac{1}{3} =$ ______

Step 1: Change the ÷ sign to an × sign.

$$\frac{4}{9} \times \frac{1}{3}$$

Step 2: Invert the fraction after the ÷ sign.

$$\frac{4}{9} \times \frac{3}{1}$$

Step 3: Multiply straight across.

$$\frac{4}{9} \times \frac{3}{1} = \frac{12}{9} \qquad \text{Reduce} \quad 9\overline{)12}\ \to 1\frac{3}{9},\ \ \underline{-9}$$

The answer is $1\frac{3}{9}$. Note $\frac{3}{9}$ reduces to $\frac{1}{3}$, so the answer is $1\frac{1}{3}$.

Practice

1. $\frac{3}{7} \div \frac{3}{5}$
2. $\frac{5}{35} \div \frac{11}{21}$
3. $\frac{3}{12} \div \frac{6}{7}$
4. $\frac{7}{9} \div \frac{4}{5}$
5. $\frac{8}{9} \div \frac{1}{9}$
6. $33 \div \frac{11}{12}$
7. $\frac{1}{3} \div 15$
8. $6 \div \frac{1}{3}$
9. $\frac{7}{28} \div 30$
10. $8\frac{6}{10} \div 1\frac{4}{5}$
11. $4\frac{3}{8} \div 1\frac{2}{16}$
12. $7\frac{1}{2} \div 3\frac{1}{5}$
13. $12\frac{4}{8} \div 4\frac{1}{2}$
14. $12\frac{4}{10} \div 3\frac{1}{3}$
15. $5\frac{1}{2} \div 1\frac{1}{8}$

16. $3\frac{5}{8} \div 2\frac{1}{2}$

17. $2\frac{3}{14} \div 9\frac{2}{7}$

18. $1\frac{7}{9} \div \frac{8}{11}$

19. $10\frac{6}{7} \div 7\frac{1}{2}$

20. $1\frac{9}{12} \div \frac{1}{12}$

Applications

1. A lab technician worked $45\frac{3}{4}$ hours in 5 days. He worked the same number of hours each day. How many hours a day did he work?

2. How many $\frac{1}{4}$ gram doses can be obtained from a $7\frac{1}{2}$ gram vial of medication?

3. The pharmacy technician's paycheck was for $1,123.85. If the technician worked $84\frac{1}{2}$ hours, what is the hourly rate of pay?

4. The nurse must give a patient 9 milligrams of a medication. If the tablets are 2 milligrams each, how many tablets are needed?

5. The pharmacy has 5 gram vials of medication. How many $\frac{1}{2}$ gram doses are available?

Fraction Formula

Follow these two setups:

To convert Celsius to Fahrenheit: $\left(°C \times \frac{9}{5}\right) + 32 = °F$

To convert Fahrenheit to Celsius: $(°F - 32) \times \frac{5}{9} = °C$

The decimal unit (Unit 3) will include the formula for handling temperature conversions using decimals.

Follow these steps to change a Fahrenheit temperature to a Celsius temperature:

Example 5°C = _____ °F

Step 1: Solve within the parentheses first, and then work left to right.

$$\left(°C \times \frac{9}{5}\right) + 32 = °F$$

$$°C \times \frac{9}{5} \rightarrow 5 \times \frac{9}{5} = \frac{45}{5} \quad 5\overline{)45} = 9$$

$$\begin{array}{r} 9 \\ 5\overline{)45} \\ \underline{45} \end{array}$$

Step 2: Add 32 to the step 1 answer to get the °C.

$$9 + 32 = 41\ °F$$

> Fractions are used to convert between Celsius and Fahrenheit temperatures. Fractions are more accurate than decimals because there is no change in the numbers as a result of the rounding of decimals.

Practice

1. 20°C = _____ °F
2. 35°C = _____ °F
3. 25°C = _____ °F
4. 60°C = _____ °F
5. 40°C = _____ °F
6. 45°C = _____ °F
7. 80°C = _____ °F
8. 15°C = _____ °F

Follow these steps to change a Fahrenheit temperature to a Celsius temperature:

Example

122°F = ______°C

Step 1: Solve within the parenthesis first. $(°F - 32) \times \frac{5}{9} = °C$

°F − 32 = ______ Subtract 32 from the Fahrenheit temperature.

$$\begin{array}{r} 122°F \\ \underline{-32} \\ 90 \end{array}$$

Step 2: Multiply step 1 answer by $^5/_9$ to get the °C.

$$90 \times \frac{5}{9} = \frac{450}{9}$$ Divide 450 by 9.

$$\begin{array}{r} 50 \\ 9\overline{)450} \\ \underline{45\downarrow} \\ 00 \end{array}$$

So, 122°F is 50°C.

Practice

1. 104°F = _____ °C
2. 32°F = _____ °C
3. 50°F = _____ °C
4. 113°F = _____ °C
5. 59°F = _____ °C
6. 131°F = _____ °C
7. 86°F = _____ °C
8. 122°F = _____ °C

Some temperatures will require working with decimals. Additional practice will be provided in Unit 3: Decimals.

Complex Fractions

Complex fractions are used to help nurses and pharmacy technicians compute exact dosages. Complex fractions may also more efficiently solve difficult problems. A complex fraction is a fraction within a fraction.

Example

$$\frac{\frac{1}{4}}{6} \nwarrow \quad \frac{\frac{3}{4}}{\frac{1}{100}} \nwarrow$$

These fraction lines should be viewed as a division sign.

Complex fractions are solved by using the rules of division. These examples become:

$$\frac{1}{4} \div 6 \rightarrow \frac{1}{4} \div \frac{6}{1} \rightarrow \frac{1}{4} \times \frac{1}{6} = \frac{1}{24}$$

$$\frac{3}{4} \div \frac{1}{100} \rightarrow \frac{3}{4} \div \frac{1}{100} \rightarrow \frac{3}{4} \times \frac{100}{1} = \frac{300}{4} \quad \text{Reduce to } \frac{75}{1} = 75$$

Whole numbers require placing a 1 as a denominator prior to any division or multiplication of their digits.

Practice Solve these complex fractions. Reduce to the lowest terms.

1. $\dfrac{\frac{3}{8}}{4}$

6. $\dfrac{\frac{3}{4}}{\frac{2}{3}}$

2. $\dfrac{\frac{1}{8}}{100}$

7. $\dfrac{\frac{1}{125}}{\frac{2}{200}}$

3. $\dfrac{\frac{1}{300}}{50}$

8. $\dfrac{\frac{1}{2}}{\frac{1}{4}}$

4. $\dfrac{40}{\frac{1}{25}}$

9. $\dfrac{\frac{1}{80}}{\frac{1}{75}}$

5. $\dfrac{\frac{1}{50}}{\frac{1}{60}}$

10. $\dfrac{\frac{1}{10}}{\frac{1}{100}}$

Dosage problems will also combine complex fractions with whole numbers and decimal numbers to compute the correct dosage. This work will be further covered in Unit 11: Dosage Calculations.

$$\dfrac{\frac{1}{300}}{\frac{1}{100}} \times 200$$

Example These types of problems appear more difficult than they actually are. Group the work into sections so that it is manageable, and you can track your progress.

Step 1: Solve the complex fraction first by dividing it.

$$\frac{1}{300} \div \frac{1}{100} \rightarrow \frac{1}{300} \times \frac{100}{1} = \frac{100}{300} \rightarrow \text{ Reduce to } \frac{1}{3}$$

Step 2: Next, rewrite the entire problem.

$\frac{1}{3} \times 200$ Then work this portion of the problem.

$\frac{1}{3} \times \frac{200}{1} = \frac{200}{3}$ Reduce by dividing 200 by 3.

The answer is $66\frac{2}{3}$. If the problem has a fraction it in, the answer may have a fraction in it. Do not convert this fraction to a decimal number.

Practice Solve these problems.

1. $\dfrac{\frac{5}{8}}{\frac{1}{4}} \times 2$

2. $\dfrac{\frac{1}{200}}{\frac{1}{100}} \times 80$

3. $\dfrac{\frac{15}{500}}{\frac{1}{100}} \times 4$

4. $\dfrac{\frac{1}{125}}{\frac{1}{500}} \times 25$

5. $\dfrac{\frac{1}{3}}{\frac{1}{2}} \times 1\frac{1}{2}$

6. $\dfrac{\frac{1}{100}}{\frac{2}{25}} \times 10\frac{1}{4}$

FRACTION SELF-TEST

Reduce all answers to lowest terms.

1. A day has 24 hours. Six hours is what fractional part of the 24 hours?

2. Write two equivalent fractions for $\frac{1}{6}$.

3. Reduce $\frac{122}{11}$

4. $8\frac{1}{6} + 3\frac{3}{4}$

5. $52 - 12\frac{1}{5}$

6. $14\frac{1}{2} \times 2\frac{1}{8}$

7. $5\frac{2}{6} \div 12$

8. 77° F = _____ ° C

9. Order from smallest to largest: $\frac{3}{8}, \frac{1}{3}, \frac{1}{4}, \frac{2}{12}$

10. Solve: $\frac{\frac{1}{4}}{\frac{1}{8}} \times 25$

11. The doctor orders grain $\frac{1}{8}$ of a medicine. The nurse has grain $\frac{1}{6}$ on hand in the medicine cabinet. Will the nurse give more or less of the dose on hand? _____

12. The physical therapist asks Mr. Smith to walk 20 minutes in one hour to improve his ambulation. What fractional part of an hour is Mr. Smith to exercise? _____

13. Among the fractions $\frac{1}{3}, \frac{1}{5}, \frac{5}{8}$, which one is equivalent to $\frac{15}{24}$? _____

14. On the dietitian's beverage tray, there are 16 filled six-ounce glasses. Four glasses contain prune juice and two glasses contain red wine. What fractional part of the glasses contains some beverage other than prune juice or red wine? Express the answer as a fraction. _____

15. Sally works in a nursery. Her job includes recording an accurate weight for each baby. One baby weighs $7\frac{1}{3}$ pounds, two babies weigh $6\frac{1}{2}$ pounds, and a fourth baby weighs $5\frac{7}{8}$ pounds. What is the current total weight of the babies? _____

Unit 3

Decimals

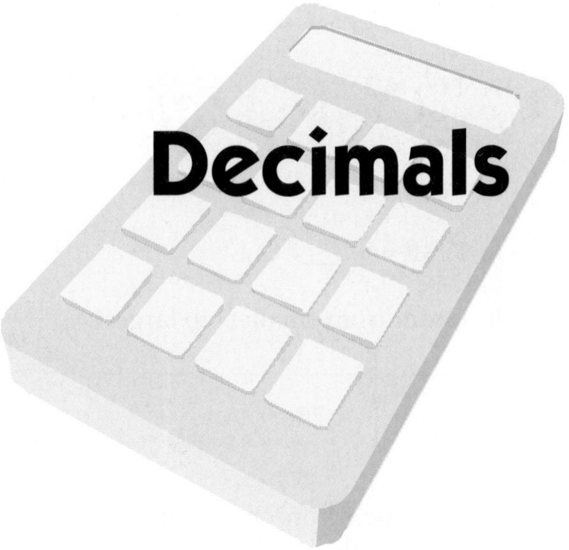

Decimals are used every day in health care settings. Understanding the application of decimals provides a strong foundation for measurement conversions, the metric system, medication dosages, and general charting work. Most medication orders are written using the metric system, which relies on decimals.

A decimal represents a part or fraction of a whole number. Decimal numbers are parts of 10s, 100s, 1000s, and so on. In other words, decimals are multiples of ten. The decimal point (•) represents the boundary between whole numbers and decimal numbers.

Decimal Place Values

whole numbers					decimal numbers				
thousands	hundreds	tens	ones	and	tenths	hundredths	thousandths	ten-thousandths	hundred-thousandths
	1	0	4	•	9	9			

Consider $104.99. We understand this number to be one hundred four dollars and ninety-nine cents. The decimal point is the *and* if we write the number in words.

Any number to the left of the decimal point is always a whole number and any number to the right of the decimal point is a decimal number. Without a whole number, a decimal number is always less than 1. So we understand that 0.89 and 0.123 are less than 1.

Health care workers include a zero to the left of the decimal point for any decimal that does not include a whole number. This signals the reader that the dose, measurement, or amount is less than 1. The zero also helps avoid errors caused by misreading a decimal number. This does not change the value of the number.

Examples

0.89 and 0.123

Decimal Place Values

whole numbers					decimal numbers				
thousands	hundreds	tens	ones	and	tenths	hundredths	thousandths	ten-thousandths	hundred-thousandths
		4	2	•	1	2	5		

Reading decimal numbers is simple if you follow these tips: To read decimal numbers, say the numbers from left to right as if they were whole numbers, then add the decimal place value.

42.125 → read as forty-two and one hundred twenty-five thousandths.

Identify decimal numbers by looking for the words that end in "th" or "ths."

Write the decimals in words using this method:

1. 0.7

2. 0.89

3. 0.05

4. 4.3

5. 150.075

6. 34.009

7. 125.023

8. 47.9

9. 18.08

10. 0.126

Write the following words in decimal numbers:

1. two tenths

2. thirteen thousandths

3. three hundred and two thousandths

4. sixteen hundredths

5. six and three hundredths

To double-check your work, the final or last number should be placed in the place value spot of the words used to describe it. If it is hundredths, then the second decimal place must have a number in it.

Example

fifty-six thousandths

0.056

↑ thousandths place

Rounding Decimals

Decimals are rounded in health care to create manageable numbers. We may have a difficult time visualizing a number such as 14.39757. However, we can easily understand the number 14.4 or 14.40. Rounding to a specific decimal place is accomplished in the same way that whole numbers are rounded. In general, health care workers round decimal numbers to the nearest tenth or the nearest hundredth.

Example Round 1.75 to the nearest tenth.

Step 1: Underline the place to which you are rounding

$1.\underline{7}5$

Step 2: Circle one number to the right of the underlined number. If the circled number is 5 or greater, add 1 to the underlined number, and drop all the numbers to the right of the changed number.

$1.\underline{7}\boxed{5} \rightarrow 1.8$

If the circled number is less than 5, do not change the underlined number, and drop all the numbers to the right of that number.

Sometimes a health care worker will round to the tenths place value and the whole number will be affected.

Example Round 4.97 to the nearest tenth.

Step 1: 4.9̲7

Step 2: 4.9[7] 4.9(Add 1 to 9) = 5.0 or 5

Practice Round to the nearest tenth:

1. 6.74
2. 249.86
3. 0.78
4. 3.612
5. 25.02
6. 704.95
7. 0.0943
8. 349.37
9. 9.89
10. 0.087

Round to the nearest hundredth:

1. 17.327
2. 0.975
3. 4.8166
4. 0.0650
5. 0.0074
6. $2,104.399
7. 32.651
8. 9.27194
9. 46.085
10. 4.719

When and which place value to round to is a frequently asked question. General guidelines for rounding will be provided in Unit 11: Dosage Calculations.

Comparing Decimals

Comparing decimals is valuable in health occupations because many different pieces of equipment are used that may be in metric measurements. Decimals are part of the metric system, thus understanding them is necessary to determine which instrument or measurement is larger or smaller. Comparing decimals is a skill that is also useful in sorting and ordering inventory items by size.

To compare decimals, you will rely on your eyes rather than any specific math computation.

Example Which is larger: 0.081 or 0.28?

Step 1: Line the decimals up like buttons on a shirt. This will help make the decimal numbers appear to have the same number of decimal places.

0.081
0.28

Step 2: Add zeros to fill in the empty place values so that the numbers have the same number of places or digits.

0.081
0.280

Step 3: Disregard the decimal point for a moment and read the numbers as they are written from left to right, including the added zero place values.

$0.081 \rightarrow$ eighty-one
$0.280 \rightarrow$ two hundred eighty

So, 0.28 is larger than 0.081.

Practice Which decimal number is smaller?

1. 0.9 or 0.89
2. 0.025 or 0.5
3. 2.12 or 2.012
4. 0.4 or 0.04
5. 0.0033 or 0.03

Which is larger?

1. 0.0785 or 0.0195
2. 0.345 or 0.35
3. 0.5 or 0.055
4. 100.75 or 100.07
5. 0.0679 or 0.675

Using the same method, arrange the sets of numbers from largest to smallest:

1. 0.75, 7.5, 0.7, 7.075, 0.07
2. 0.01, 1.01, 10.01, 1.001

3. 0.5, 5.15, 5.55, 5.05, 0.05
4. 0.04, 0.004, 0.4, 0.044

Addition of Decimals

To add decimals, first line up the decimal points, then add. This might mean that the problem presented in a horizontal pattern may need to be rewritten in a vertical pattern.

A whole number always has a decimal point to the right side of the final number: 56 = 56.

$$2.32 + 0.14 = ? \rightarrow \begin{array}{r} 2.32 \\ +0.14 \\ \hline 2.46 \end{array}$$

$$48 + 1.75 = \_\_\_\_ \rightarrow \begin{array}{r} 48.00 \\ +\ 1.75 \\ \hline 49.75 \end{array}$$

← Place a decimal point and fill the empty spaces with zeros.

Lining up the decimals is the first step in ensuring the correct answer for the addition of decimals.

$$2.46 + 0.005 + 1.3 = \_\_\_\_ \rightarrow \begin{array}{r} 2.460 \\ 0.005 \\ +\ 1.300 \\ \hline 3.765 \end{array}$$

Fill the empty spaces with zeros.

Step 1: Line up the decimals. The order of the numbers to be added is unimportant.

Step 2: Add the numbers and bring the decimal point straight down.

Practice

1. 0.9 + 36 + 1.25
2. 15.2 + 17.071 + 0.74
3. 0.11 + 86 + 0.125
4. 10.79 + 0.99 + 0.25
5. 0.0096 + 50.24 + 39
6. 0.849 + 1.6 + 56.3
7. 14.28 + 16.24 + 97
8. 0.75 + 23.87 + 124.07

9. $13.75 + 0.001 + 200.53$

10. $35.01 + 76.02 + 0.0998$

Applications

1. A 25-year-old patient receives the following medication dosages daily: 1.5 milligrams, 2.25 milligrams, and 0.75 milligrams. What is his total dosage?

2. A child weighs 15.9 kilograms. The child has gained 0.9 and 1.5 kilograms during the past two months. What is the child's current weight?

3. Patient Smith receives 4 tablets of medication dosages daily: One tablet is 225 milligrams, two tablets are 0.125 milligrams each, and one tablet is 0.75 milligrams. What is the patient's total daily dosage of medication in milligrams?

4. One tablet is labeled 124 milligrams and another is labeled 0.5 milligrams. What is the total dosage of these two tablets?

5. A child measured 122 centimeters in a semiannual checkup with the doctor. What would be the child's height at the next office visit if the child grew by 2.54 centimeter?

Subtraction of Decimals

To subtract decimals, two steps are followed:

$$95.5 - 0.76 = \underline{\qquad}$$

Step 1: Set the problem up vertically. Put the larger number or the number from which the second number is to be subtracted above, then line up the decimals.

$$\begin{array}{r} 95.50 \\ -\ 0.76 \\ \hline \end{array}$$

← Fill in the empty places with zeros.

Step 2: Subtract and then bring the decimal straight down.

$$\begin{array}{r} 9{}^{4}\cancel{5}.{}^{14}\cancel{5}{}^{1}0 \\ -\ 0.\ 7\ 6 \\ \hline 94.\ 7\ 4 \end{array}$$

Practice

1. 3.4 − 2.68 =
2. 69.4 − 5.04 =
3. 15 − 0.935 =
4. 0.48 − 0.3925 =
5. 3.7 − 0.1987 =
6. 12 − 1.932 =
7. 0.2 − 0.025 =
8. 14.47 − 0.3108 =
9. 87.56 − 0.124 =
10. 0.07 − 0.007 =

Applications

1. A patient started with a 1 liter bag of IV solution. When the doctor checked in on the patient, the bag contained 0.35 liters of solution. How much solution was infused into the patient?

2. A bottle of medicine contains 30 milliliters. After withdrawing 2.25 milliliters for an injection, how many milliliters of medicine remain in the bottle?

3. A patient is to receive 4.25 milligrams of a drug daily. The patient has already received 2.75 milligrams. What is his remaining dosage in milligrams?

4. Patient B is on a low fat diet. He weighed 89.9 kilograms last month. This month he weighs 88.45 kilograms. How many kilograms has he lost?

5. A patient had a temperature of 101.4°F. If after medication, the patient's temperature is 99.6°F, what is the decrease in temperature?

Multiplication of Decimals

To multiply decimals, use the same process as in whole number multiplication. Do not line up the decimals. The decimal places are counted, not aligned in decimal multiplication.

Example

$$4.75 \times .4$$

Step 1: Write the problem vertically.

$$\begin{array}{r} 4.75 \\ \times\ .4 \\ \hline \end{array}$$

Step 2: Multiply the numbers.

$$\begin{array}{r} 4.75 \\ \times\ .4 \\ \hline 1900 \end{array}$$

Step 3: Count the total number of decimal places in the two numbers multiplied together. Count these places from the right in to the left. Then begin at the right of the answer and count over the same number of places and place the decimal point.

4.75
 UU 2 places
0.4
 U 1 place
1.900
 UUU

Place the decimal point three places from the right. The extra zeros are dropped unless they serve a particular purpose, such as place holders for money in dollar figures.

17.750 → 17.75
205.12600 → 205.126
$12.00 → $12.00

Practice Set up multiplication problems vertically:

1. 4.2×3
2. 9.3×7
3. 21×1.6
4. 465×0.3
5. 9.17×14
6. 0.985×50
7. 6.74×0.12
8. 3.190×0.56
9. 0.278×1.7
10. 4.79×2.2
11. 0.08×0.03
12. 5.6×0.39
13. 5.175×29.2
14. $3,764 \times 13.75$
15. 9.708×0.17
16. 114.6×22.6
17. 190.8×0.04
18. 827.9×1.9
19. 574×12.095
20. 0.135×73.7
21. 53.9×24.9
22. 204.7×13.87
23. 0.347×28.95
24. 94.13×32.09

Applications

1. Village Center health care workers' earnings start at $10.52 an hour. If the employees work 40 hours per week, what is the minimum amount that each worker could earn in a week?

2. One mile has 1.6 kilometers. How many kilometers are in 35.5 miles?

3. Sheila earns $13.05 an hour. If she works 124 hours in August, what are her gross earnings for the month?

4. One kilogram equals 2.2 pounds. If patient A weighs 79.5 kilograms, what is his weight in pounds?

5. The recreation department is making placemats. The cost of materials for each placemat is $1.28. The activity director is estimating the cost of materials for 100 placemats. What is the estimated budget needed for this project?

Division of Decimals

To divide decimals, one needs to place the decimal point first, then divide the numbers. Once the decimal point is placed, it is not moved. Students have a tendency to want to move the decimal point once the division process is underway; the result is an error in decimal placement.

Follow the steps below to divide a number that has a decimal in the dividend:

Step 1: Move the decimal point straight up to the same place in the quotient. Place the decimal point and then divide the numbers.

$$6\overline{)2.58}$$

Step 2: Divide, adding a zero in front of all decimal numbers that do not include a whole number.

$$\begin{array}{r} 0.43 \\ 6\overline{)2.58} \\ \underline{2\,4} \\ 18 \\ \underline{18} \\ 0 \end{array}$$

Practice

1. $19\overline{)11.97}$
2. $5\overline{)67.75}$
3. $2\overline{)0.464}$
4. $21\overline{)9.03}$
5. $12\overline{)1.44}$
6. $4\overline{)68.4}$
7. $32\overline{)1676.8}$
8. $17\overline{)51.17}$
9. $25\overline{)75.50}$
10. $34\overline{)2603.72}$

Zeros as Placeholders in Decimal Division

Health care students may need some practice in dividing decimals that involve zeros in the quotient. This is one area where errors are commonly made. To avoid this situation, recall that after a number has been brought down from the dividend, the divisor must be applied to that number. Place the decimal point and then divide the number. If the divisor does not go into the dividend, then a zero must be placed in the quotient. Use a zero to hold a space.

Example

$$\begin{array}{r} 2.405 \\ 14\overline{)33.67} \\ \underline{28\downarrow\ \ \ } \\ 56\ \ \ \\ \underline{56\downarrow\ } \\ 07\ \ \\ \underline{0\downarrow} \\ 70 \\ \underline{70} \\ 0 \end{array}$$

Because 14 cannot go into 7, place a zero in the quotient.

Setup Tip

Remember in division problem setup

475 ÷ 4.5 = → $*4.5\overline{)475}$

*The last number in the problem divides into the first number.

To divide a decimal number by a decimal number, change the divisor to a whole number by moving the decimal point to the right. Then move the decimal point in the dividend the same number of places. Use zeros as placeholders if needed. Then place the decimal point and divide.

For example, $0.42\overline{)0.6216}$

Step 1: Move the decimal $0.42\overline{)0.6216}$ Rewrite → $42\overline{)62.16}$

Step 2: Divide $42\overline{)62.16}$

Practice

1. $530 \div 0.5$
2. $0.081 \div 9$
3. $66.56 \div 32$
4. $0.022 \div 11$
5. $3.297 \div 3$
6. $0.6250 \div 5$
7. $183.96 \div 6$
8. $6.030 \div 3$
9. $0.18891 \div 0.9$
10. $12.24 \div 4$

Additional Practice

1. $0.5\overline{)2.65}$
2. $0.04\overline{)6.48}$
3. $2.6\overline{)0.104}$
4. $0.55\overline{)141.35}$
5. $3.8\overline{)5.282}$
6. $0.7\overline{)78.75}$
7. $0.02\overline{)8.078}$
8. $0.3\overline{)4.608}$

Simplified Multiplication and Division of Decimals

Using the shortcuts of simplified multiplication and division can save time in working with decimals. In health-care fields, this shortcut is important to your work in metrics and in efficiently working longer problems.

This shortcut only works with multiples of ten: 10, 100, 1,000, etc. The process is straightforward. To multiply, move the decimal point to the right. To divide, move the decimal point to the left. The number of spaces depends on which multiple you are working with. Look at the number of zeros included in the multiple, then move the decimal in either direction depending on the operation: multiplication or division, the same number of spaces and the number of zeros.

Simplified Multiplication

To multiply by 10, locate the decimal point and move it to the right by one place.

To multiply by 100, locate the decimal point and move it to the right by two places.

To multiply by 1,000, locate the decimal point and move it to the right by three places.

Whole numbers have their decimal places to the far right of the last digit: 9 = 9., 75 = 75., 125 = 125.

Example

4.5 × 10 = 45

4.5 = 45

U

$$\begin{array}{r} 4.5 \\ \times\ 10 \\ \hline 45.0 \end{array}$$

(The Zero is dropped.)

Note that the answer is the same if the problem is worked the long way. Sometimes zeros must be added as placeholders.

In simplified multiplication locate the decimal point, count the zeros in the divisor and move the decimal point the same number of places to the right.

Example Zeros must fill the spaces if needed.

34.7 × 1000 = _____

34.7 0 0 =

UUU → 34,700

Practice

1. 13.5 × 10 1350
2. 4.56 × 100 45,600 456
3. 125.75 × 10 1257.5
4. 1,000 × 45.3 45300

5. 0.06×100 = 6

6. 0.234×10 2.34

7. $12.670 \times 1,000$ 12,670

8. 0.975×100 97.5

9. $0.476 \times 1,000$ 476

10. 87×10 870

11. 1.345×10 13.45

12. $98.345 \times 1,000$ 98,345

13. 1.009×10 10.09

14. 32.901×100 3290.1

15. $23.850 \times 1,000$ 23,850

Simplified Division

To divide by 10, locate the decimal point and move it to the left by one place.

To divide by 100, locate the decimal point and move it to the left by two places.

To divide by 1,000, locate the decimal point and move it to the left by three places.

In simplified division, locate the decimal point, count the zeros in the divisor and move the decimal point the same number of places to the left.

Example $9.5 \div 10 =$ _____ $0.75 \div 100 =$ _____
9.5   0 0 0.75 $\rightarrow$ 0.0075   Zeros must be used to fill
$\cup \rightarrow 0.95$ $\cup\cup$ in places if needed.

Practice   1. $12.9 \div 10$ 1.29

2. $45.56 \div 100$ 4556

3. $125 \div 10$ 125

4. $98,762 \div 1,000$ .098762

5. $0.25 \div 10$ .625

6. $176.5 \div 100$

7. 15.8 ÷ 100

8. 3,234 ÷ 10

9. 32.50 ÷ 100

10. 0.09 ÷ 10

11. 10,010 ÷ 1,000

12. 9,765 ÷ 1,000

13. 3.076 ÷ 100

14. 429.6 ÷ 1,000

15. 10.275 ÷ 100

Applications

1. A nursing student spends $379.50 for textbooks. If the student purchases six textbooks, what is the average cost of each book?

2. A patient's goal is to lose 24.6 pounds. The doctor wants the patient to lose these pounds slowly, over a twelve-month period. How many pounds should the patient attempt to lose each month?

3. Doctor Brown prescribed a medication dosage of 4.5 grams. How many 1.5 grams tablets need to be administered?

4. The dietitian serves a protein dish at three meals. If the total daily grams of protein are 225.9 grams, assuming that the grams are equally divided for the three meals a day, what is the average meal's grams of protein?

5. Bob made $131.20 in 5 hours. What is his hourly wage?

Changing Decimals to Fractions

It is important to be able to convert between number systems so that you are comfortable with comparing sizes of items or quantities of supplies. Changing decimals to fractions requires the use of decimal places and placing the numbers in fractions that represent the very same numbers.

Example Convert 0.457 to a fraction.

Step 1: To convert a decimal to a fraction, count the number of decimal places in the decimal number.

$0.\underline{4}\,\underline{5}\,\underline{7}$ Three decimal places means thousandths in decimal numbers.

Step 2: Write the number 457 as the numerator and 1,000 as the denominator.

$$\frac{457}{1{,}000}$$

Step 3: Reduce if necessary $\frac{457}{1{,}000}$ cannot be reduced. The answer is $\frac{457}{1{,}000}$.

Example Convert 2.75 to a fraction.

Step 1: Place 2 as the whole number. Your answer is going to be a mixed number because there is a whole number. Count the decimal places in $.\underline{7}\,\underline{5}$ = two places.

2 _____

Step 2: Write 75 as the numerator and 100 as the denominator.

$$2\frac{75}{100}$$

Step 3: Reduce the fraction to $2\,{}^{3}\!/_{4}$ because

$$\frac{75}{100} = \frac{\cancel{25} \times 3}{\cancel{25} \times 4} \rightarrow \frac{3}{4}$$

The answer is $2\frac{3}{4}$.

Practice Convert the decimals to fractions:

1. 0.04

2. 0.025

3. 6.25

4. 1.78

5. 225.05

6. 10.5

7. 7.75

8. 0.08

9. 9.3

10. 100.46

Changing Fractions to Decimals

To change fractions to decimals, divide the denominator into the numerator. Critical to the success of this division is the placement of the decimal point. Once it is placed, do not move it.

Example Change $^3/_4$ to a decimal. Divide the denominator into the numerator. Place a decimal point after 3 and also in the quotient. Then add a zero after 3 and divide. Add zeros as needed to continue the division process.

$$\begin{array}{r} .75 \\ 4\overline{)3.0} \\ \underline{28\downarrow} \\ 20 \\ \underline{20} \\ 0 \end{array}$$

Example Change $^1/_3$ into a decimal. Divide 3 into 1. Place the decimal point. Add zeros as needed to continue division. The division may not come out evenly but rather begin to repeat itself. After two places, make the remainder into a fraction by putting the remaining number over the divisor.

$$\begin{array}{r} .33\frac{1}{3} \\ 3\overline{)1.0} \\ \underline{9\downarrow} \\ 10 \\ \underline{9} \\ 1 \end{array}$$

When the decimal answer is a number like 0.50, drop the final zero so that the answer is 0.5.

Practice

1. $\frac{1}{2}$

2. $\frac{3}{5}$

3. $\frac{7}{8}$

4. $\frac{1}{6}$

5. $\frac{6}{25}$

6. $\frac{5}{12}$

7. $\frac{3}{15}$

8. $\frac{7}{10}$

9. $\frac{5}{6}$

10. $\frac{3}{18}$

Temperature Conversions with Decimals

The following temperature conversions include decimals. Round the decimal numbers in temperatures to the nearest tenth place. The temperature conversion used in Unit 2: Fractions, relied on fractions. The same fraction method can be converted into a decimal method. In deciding which method to use, select the method of fractions or decimals based on your strongest skill. Then consistently use that conversion formula.

Decimal Conversion Formula

To convert Celsius to Fahrenheit, $(°C \times 1.8) + 32 = °F$

To convert Fahrenheit to Celsius, $(°F - 32) \div 1.8 = °C$

Example To convert from Celsius to Fahrenheit

$$41°C = \_\_\_\_ °F$$

Step 1: Solve the parentheses first, and then work left to right. Multiply the Celsius temperature by 1.8. The number 1.8 is the decimal form of $^9/_5$.

$$\begin{array}{r} 41 \\ \times\ 1.8 \\ \hline 328 \\ 41 \\ \hline 73.8 \end{array}$$

Step 2: Add 32 to the step 1 answer.

$$\begin{array}{r} 73.8 \\ +\ 32 \\ \hline 105.8 \end{array}$$

The answer is 105.8°F.

To convert from Fahrenheit to Celsius

Step 1: Subtract the 32 from the Fahrenheit temperature.

$$\begin{array}{r} 107.6 \\ -\ 32 \\ \hline 75.6 \end{array}$$

Step 2: Divide the step 1 answer by 1.8.

$$\rightarrow 1.8\overline{)75.6} \rightarrow \quad \begin{array}{r} 42. \\ 18\overline{)756.} \\ \underline{72} \\ 36 \\ \underline{36} \\ 0 \end{array}$$

∪ ∪

The answer is 42°C.

Practice

1. 34°C = _____ °F
2. 46.6°F = _____ °C
3. 107°C = _____ °F
4. 101.5°F = _____ °C
5. 42°C = _____ °F
6. 40°F = _____ °C
7. 100.4°F = _____ °C

8. 69°C = _____ °F

9. 12°C = _____ °F

10. 105.8°F = _____ °C

Solving Mixed Fraction and Decimal Problems

Sometimes problems will include both fractions and decimals. The very same processes of solving the problems are still needed; however, the order of handling the parts of the problem may vary. Group the math computations inside the problem to best manage the separate operations.

> If the problem has a complex fraction multiplied by a decimal number, work the complex fraction first. Then complete the decimal multiplication.

Example

$$\frac{\frac{1}{2}}{\frac{1}{5}} \times 2.2 =$$

Step 1: $\frac{1}{2} \div \frac{1}{5} \rightarrow \frac{1}{2} \times \frac{5}{1} = \frac{5}{2}$

Reduce to $2\frac{1}{2}$. Make the $\frac{1}{2}$ into .5 so that the multiplication is easy. So by first working the complex fraction, the answer is 2.5.

Step 2: Multiply 2.5 × 2.2.

$$\begin{array}{r} 2.5 \\ \times\ 2.2 \\ \hline 50 \\ 50 \\ \hline 5.50 \end{array}$$

The answer to this mixed problem is 5.5.

> If the problem includes a decimal number, solve the decimals by first multiplying straight across, then complete the process by dividing that answer by the denominator. This allows for the division of decimals only once, and it saves time.

Example

$$\frac{0.25}{0.5} \times 1.5$$

Step 1: Multiply 0.25×1.5.

$$\begin{array}{r} 0.25 \\ \times\ 1.5 \\ \hline 125 \\ 25 \\ \hline 0.375 \end{array}$$

Step 2: Divide 0.375 by 0.5.

$0.5\overline{)0.375}$

$$\begin{array}{r} 0.75 \\ 0.5\overline{)0.375} \\ \underline{0.35} \\ 0025 \\ \underline{0025} \\ 0 \end{array}$$

The answer is 0.75.

Practice

1. $\dfrac{\frac{1}{200}}{\frac{1}{100}} \times 4.4$

2. $\dfrac{0.8}{0.64} \times 4.5$

3. $\dfrac{\frac{3}{4}}{\frac{1}{4}} \times 2.5$

4. $\dfrac{0.75}{0.15} \times 1.5$

5. $\dfrac{0.002}{0.125} \times 10.5$

6. $\dfrac{\frac{1}{12}}{\frac{1}{6}} \times 3.6$

7. $\dfrac{0.005}{0.01} \times 15.35$

8. $\dfrac{7\frac{1}{2}}{1\frac{1}{2}} \times 5.4$

DECIMAL SELF-TEST

1. Write in words: 0.045

2. What is the sum of 1.7, 19, 0.25, and 0.8?

3. $17 - 0.075$

4. 4.5×1.009

5. $18.04 \div 0.2$

6. Round to the nearest hundredth: 978.735

7. Order these decimals from largest to smallest: 0.81, 0.080, 0.018, 8.018.

8. 10.009×100

9. A child receives 0.5 milligrams of a drug 4 times a day. How many milligrams is the child's daily dose?

10. A patient receives 2.25 grams of a medication daily. Tablets come in 0.75 gram dosages. How many tablets does the patient take daily?

11. Convert this decimal to a fraction: 0.125

12. Convert this fraction to a decimal: $\frac{13}{50}$

13. Convert this fraction to a decimal: $3\frac{5}{8}$

14. Convert 103° Fahrenheit to °Celsius.

15. Solve:

$$\frac{0.136}{0.2} \times 2.5$$

Unit 4

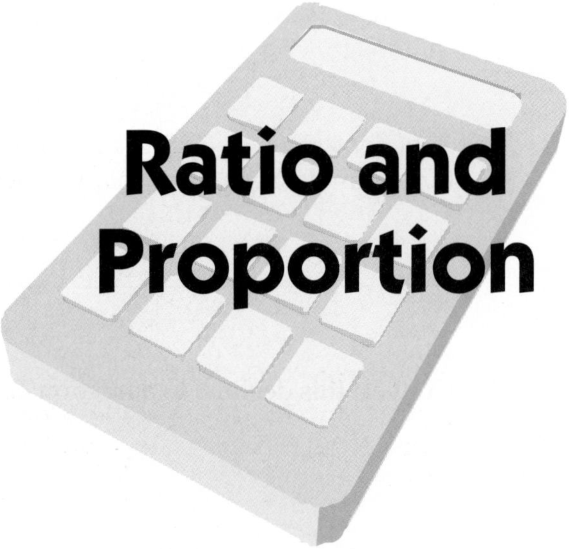

Ratio and Proportion

Ratio

A ratio is used to show a relationship between two numbers. These numbers are separated by a colon (:) as in 3 : 4. Ratios may be presented in three formats that provide the setup for solving proportions.

a. 3 : 4

b. $\frac{3}{4}$

c. 3 is to 4

The relationship can represent something as simple as the 1 : 3 ratio commonly used to mix frozen juices. We use 1 can of frozen juice concentrate to 3 cans of water. Ratios are fractions that represent a part-to-whole relationship. Ratios are always reduced to their lowest form. For example, 8 hours of sleep to 24 hours in a day

$$8 : 24 \rightarrow \frac{8}{24} \quad \frac{\not{8} \times 1}{\not{8} \times 3} = \frac{1}{3}, \quad \text{so the ratio is } 1 : 3.$$

Write the following relationships as ratios using a colon. Reduce to the lowest terms, if necessary.

1. 5 days out of 7 days

2. eight teeth out of thirty-two teeth

3. 3 students out of 15 students

4. 16 scalpels to 45 syringes

5. 7 inlays to 14 crowns

Simplifying ratios is an important skill. To simplify a ratio, divide the first number by the second.

For example, simplify the following ratio: $4\frac{1}{2} : 6$

$$4\frac{1}{2} \div 6 \rightarrow \frac{9}{2} \div \frac{6}{1} \rightarrow \frac{9}{2} \times \frac{1}{6} = \frac{9}{12} \rightarrow \frac{3 \times 3}{3 \times 4} = \frac{3}{4}$$ which becomes 3 : 4 as a simplified ratio.

The answer is 3 : 4.

For example, simplify the following ratio: $11\frac{1}{4}$

Convert the mixed number into an improper fraction, then reduce if necessary.

$$11\frac{1}{4} \rightarrow 11 \times 4 + 1 = 45 \rightarrow \frac{45}{4} = 45 : 4$$

The answer is 45 : 4.

Simplify the following ratios. Write each answer as a ratio.

1. $45 : 1\frac{2}{3}$ = ______________________

2. $\frac{120}{100} : 12$ = ______________________

3. $15 : \frac{3}{4}$ = ______________________

4. $\frac{1}{3} : 45$ = ______________________

5. $0.8 : \frac{2}{5}$ = ______________________

6. $\frac{1}{2} : \frac{1}{8}$ = ______________________

7. $4\frac{1}{3} : 7$ = ______________________

8. $0.875 : \frac{1}{4}$ = ______________________

9. $2\frac{1}{2}$ = ______________________

10. $\frac{2}{3}:0.33$ = ______________________

Proportion

Proportions can be applied to almost every health care profession in one way or another. In addition to on-the-job applications, proportions provide a simple and quick method for solving many everyday math problems such as measurement conversions, recipe conversions for increasing or decreasing the amounts of ingredients, and map mileage.

Proportions are *two or more equivalent ratios or fractions*. The terms of the first ratio/fraction have the same relationship of part to whole as the second ratio/fraction.

Example

$$\frac{3}{4} = \frac{15}{20} \text{ or } 3:4::15:20$$

:: means =

Test the two ratios/fractions to see whether they are equivalent by multiplying diagonally (cross multiply).

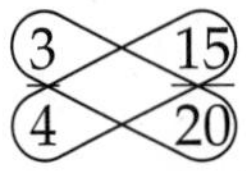

$4 \times 15 = 60$ and $3 \times 20 = 60$. This is a proportion.

If the two numbers that are diagonal result in the same answer when they are multiplied, you are working with a proportion.

Proportions are powerful tools in health care. You can rely on them for solving a majority of your math conversions and problems. Check to see if the following ratios are proportions:

Are these ratios proportions?

1. $5:2 = 4:1$ _____ Yes _____ No
2. $16:15 = 8:7$ _____ Yes _____ No
3. $40:30 = 4:3$ _____ Yes _____ No
4. $10:16 = 5:8$ _____ Yes _____ No
5. $100:1 = 50:2$ _____ Yes _____ No

Solving for *x*

The ratio and proportion method of solving for x is done in two steps.

Step 1: Set the problems up like fractions. If units of measure such as inches and feet are given, place inches across from inches and feet across from feet. Then cross multiply (diagonally) the two numbers. Set the ratios up like fractions using a vertical line.

$$\frac{3}{4} = \frac{?}{16} \quad 3 \times 16 = 48$$

Step 2: Divide the answer from step 1 by the remaining number.

$$\begin{array}{r} 12 \\ 4\overline{)48} \\ \underline{4\downarrow} \\ 8 \\ \underline{8} \end{array}$$

The quotient 12 is the answer to ? or x. This method is an easy way to find the answers for measurement conversions, dosage conversions, and math questions that provide part but not all of the information.

Practice Solve for x or ?

1. $20 : 40 = x : 15$
2. $x : 1 = 5 : 10$
3. $4 : 8 = 8 : x$
4. $7 : x = 21 : 24$
5. $3 : 9 = ? : 81$
6. $13 : 39 = 1 : ?$
7. $2 : 11 = ? : 77$
8. $x : 125 = 5 : 25$
9. $2 : 26 = 4 : ?$
10. $1 : x = 5 : 200$

Using ratios is often the simplest method of solving other health care math problems, such as dosage calculations and measurement problems.

Example Zoe weighs 35 pounds. The doctor ordered a drug that relies on milligrams of medication to kilograms of body weight. The pharmacy technician will need to convert pounds to kilograms. By using the ratio of 1 kilogram to 2.2 pounds, the answer is quickly computed.

$$\begin{array}{cc} \textit{known} & \textit{unknown} \\ \dfrac{1 \text{ kilogram}}{2.2 \text{ pounds}} & \dfrac{?}{35 \text{ pounds}} \end{array}$$

Step 1: Multiply the numbers diagonally.

$$1 \times 35 = 35$$

Step 2: Divide 35 by 2.2. The answer is 15.9 kilograms.

So 35 pounds equals 15.9 kilograms.

Example How many pounds are in 24 ounces?

Set the problem up by placing what you know on the left side of the equation and what you do not know on the right. If you set up all your problems with the known on the left and the unknown on the right, you will have less information for the brain to process because the pattern will be familiar to you.

$$\overset{\textit{known}}{\frac{1\text{ pound}}{16\text{ ounces}}} \quad \overset{\textit{unknown}}{\frac{?\text{ pounds}}{24\text{ ounces}}}$$

Step 1: $1 \times 24 = 24$

Step 2: $24 \div 16 = 1.5$

The answer is $1\frac{1}{2}$ pounds or 1.5 pounds.
An answer for a ratio may have a decimal or a fraction in it.

Example Bob is 176 centimeters (cm) tall. How tall is he in inches? Round the answer to the nearest tenth.

$$\overset{\textit{known}}{\frac{1\text{ inch}}{2.54\text{ cm}}} \quad \overset{\textit{unknown}}{\frac{?\text{ inches}}{176\text{ cm}}}$$

Step 1: $1 \times 176 = 176$

Step 2: $176 \div 2.54 = 69.29$

Rounded to the nearest tenth.
The answer is 69.3 inches.

```
        69.29
    ________
254)17600
    1524↓
    2360
    2286↓
      740
      508↓
     2320
     2286
       34
```

Some basic guidelines need to be followed for formatting answers in measurement conversions:

If the answer is in feet, yards, cups, pints, quarts, gallons, teaspoons, tablespoons, or pounds, use fractions if there is a remainder.

If the answer is in kilograms, milliliters, or money amounts, use decimals. The correct format ensures correct answers.

Approximate Equivalents

1 inch	= 2.54 centimeters	1 cup	= 8 ounces
1 foot	= 12 inches	1 pint	= 500 milliliters
1 yard	= 3 feet	1 quart	= 32 ounces
1 pound	= 16 ounces	1 quart	= 1,000 milliliters
1 kilogram	= 2.2 pounds		
1 tablespoon	= 3 teaspoons	1 fluid ounce	= 30 milliliters
1 quart	= 2 pints	1 teaspoon	= 5 milliliters
1 gallon	= 4 quarts	1 fluid ounce	= 2 tablespoons

Notice that the conversions are set up so that the unit (1) elements are all on the left and that these will be placed on the top of the known part of the ratio and proportion equation. This simplifies the learning process, expedites learning, and helps recall of these conversions.

Practice

Because inches are rounded to the nearest tenth, go to the hundredth place and then stop multiplying. At that point, you will have enough information to round to the nearest tenth.

Using this ratio and proportion setup, solve the following conversions.

known _______ = _______ *unknown*

Set up these conversions using ratios and proportions.

1. 23 feet = _____ yards → $\frac{1\text{ yd}}{3\text{ ft}} = \frac{?}{23\text{ ft}}$
2. 12 quarts = _____ gallons
3. 4 quarts = _____ pints
4. 4 pints = _____ cups
5. 3 tablespoons = _____ teaspoons
6. $2\frac{1}{2}$ quarts = _____ milliliters

7. $\frac{1}{2}$ cup = _____ ounces

8. 1 injection at $29.50 = 3 injections at _____

9. $3\frac{1}{2}$ pounds = _____ ounces

10. 3 medicine cups = _____ milliliters

(One medicine cup equals 1 fluid ounce)

11. 12.5 mL = _____ teaspoons

12. 5 fluid ounces = _____ tablespoons

13. _____ tablespoons = 15 teaspoons

14. 64 ounces = _____ cups

15. 750 milliliters = _____ pints

16. 48 inches = _____ feet

17. 5 pounds = _____ ounces

18. _____ quarts = 5,000 milliliters

29. _____ kilograms = 11 pounds

20. $3\frac{1}{2}$ cups = _____ ounces

More practice with conversions of measurements between systems and with multiple steps in conversions will be given in Unit 6: Combined Applications.

Word Problems Using Proportions

When solving word problems involving proportions, follow these two basic steps:

Step 1: Set the problem up so that the same type of elements are directly across from one another.

Example If 12 eggs cost $1.49, how much do 18 eggs cost?

$$\frac{\text{Eggs}}{\text{Cost}} = \frac{\text{Eggs}}{\text{Cost}} \begin{matrix}\rightarrow \\ \rightarrow\end{matrix} \frac{12 \text{ eggs}}{\$1.49} = \frac{18 \text{ eggs}}{\$?}$$

Step 2: Ensure that the story problem is understood, then place the known information on the left side of the proportion and the unknown on the right. By doing so, you will not switch the ratio relationships, but rather rely on the known part to whole relationships.

1. A caplet contains 325 milligrams of medication. How many caplets contain 975 milligrams of medication?

2. If a dose of 100 milligrams is contained in 4 cubic centimeters, how many cubic centimeters are in 40 milligrams?

3. If 35 grams of pure drug are contained in 150 milliliters, how many grams are contained in 75 milliliters?

4. Two tablets of ulcer medication contain 350 milligrams of medication. How many milligrams are in twelve tablets?

5. If 1 kilogram equals 2.2 pounds, how many kilograms are in 61.6 pounds?

Solving for *X* in More Complex Problems Using Proportion

Decimals and fractions may appear in your proportion problems. Although the numbers may be visually distracting, the *very* same principles apply.

Example

$$0.25 \text{ mg} : 0.8 \text{ mL} = 0.125 \text{ mg} : x \text{ mL}$$

Step 1: Place mg across from mg and mL across from mL. Place the known information on the left side of the equation and the unknown on the right.

$$\begin{array}{cc} \textit{known} & \textit{unknown} \\ \dfrac{0.25 \text{ mg}}{0.8 \text{ mL}} & \dfrac{0.125 \text{ mg}}{x \text{ mL}} \end{array}$$

Cross multiply $0.8 \times 0.125 \text{ mg} = 0.1$.

Step 2: $0.1 \div 0.25 = 0.4 \text{ mL}$

Example

$$\frac{1}{8} : \frac{1}{2} :: 1 : x$$

Step 1: Set up and cross multiply. Multiply $\frac{1}{2} \times 1 = \frac{1}{2}$.

$$\frac{1/8}{1/2} = \frac{1}{x}$$

Step 2: Divide $\frac{1}{2}$ by $\frac{1}{8}$.

$$\frac{1}{2} \div \frac{1}{8} \rightarrow \frac{1}{2} \times \frac{8}{1} = \frac{8}{2}, \quad \text{which is reduced to 4.}$$

Sometimes you will find that medical dosages have both fractions and decimals in the problems. Analyze the situation and convert the numbers into the same system. As a general rule, fractions are always more accurate for calculating than decimals because some decimal numbers have repeating digits, which create variable answers.

Example

$$\frac{1}{16} : 1.6 :: \frac{1}{8} x$$

Step 1: Convert 1.6 into a fraction. So $1.6 = 1\frac{6}{10}$. Then multiply $1\frac{6}{10} \times \frac{1}{8} = \frac{2}{10}$

$$\frac{1/16}{1\,^6/_{10}} = \frac{1/8}{x} \qquad 1\frac{6}{10} \times \frac{1}{8} = \frac{16}{10} \times \frac{1}{8} = \frac{16}{80} \text{ or } \frac{2}{10}$$

Step 2: Divide $\frac{2}{10}$ by $\frac{1}{16}$.

$$\frac{2}{10} \div \frac{1}{16} \rightarrow \frac{2}{10} \times \frac{16}{1} = \frac{32}{10} \quad \text{Reduced to } 3\frac{2}{10} \rightarrow 3\frac{1}{5}.$$

Practice Include a unit of measure in your answer. Round any partial unit to the nearest tenth.

> Tablets can be divided if they are scored; use $\frac{1}{2}$ not 0.5

1. $1.5 \text{ mg} : 2 \text{ caps} = 4.5 \text{ mg} : x \text{ caps}$
2. $8 \text{ mg} : 2.5 \text{ mL} = 4 \text{ mg} : x \text{ mL}$

3. $12.5 \text{ mg} : 5 \text{ mL} = 24 \text{ mg} : x \text{ mL}$

4. $0.3 \text{ mg} : 1 \text{ tab} = 6 \text{ mg} : x \text{ tabs}$

5. grains $\frac{1}{4} : 15 \text{ mg} =$ grains ? : 60 mg

6. $x \text{ mg} : \frac{1}{2} \text{ tab} = 6 \text{ mg} : 4 \text{ tabs}$

7. grains $\frac{1}{100} : 2 \text{ mL} =$ grains $\frac{1}{15c} : x \text{ mL}$

8. $600 \text{ mg} : 1 \text{ cap} = x \text{ mg} : 2 \text{ caps}$

9. $1000 \text{ units} : 1 \text{ mL} = 2400 \text{ units} : x \text{ mL}$

10. $1 \text{ tab} : 0.1 \text{ mg} = x \text{ tabs} : 0.15 \text{ mg}$

11. A drug comes in 100 milligram tablets. If the doctor orders 150 milligrams daily, how many tablets should the patient receive daily?

12. A medical chart states that the patient weighs 78.4 kilograms. What is the patient's weight in pounds? Round to the nearest tenth.

Nutritional Application of Proportions

Carbohydrates, fats, and protein provide fuel factors for our bodies. The factors are easily applied by using proportions to solve for the unknown.

Carbohydrates	→ 4 calories per 1 gram
Fats	→ 9 calories per 1 gram
Proteins	→ 4 calories per 1 gram

Example 400 carbohydrate calories = _____ grams

known	*unknown*
$\frac{1 \text{ gram}}{4 \text{ calories}}$	$\frac{? \text{ grams}}{400 \text{ calories}}$

Step 1: Multiply diagonally.

$$1 \times 400 = 400$$

Step 2: Divide answer from step 1 (400) by the remaining number in the equation (4).

$$\begin{array}{r} 100 \\ 4\overline{)400} \\ \underline{4} \\ 00 \end{array}$$

So 400 carbohydrate calories are available in 100 grams of carbohydrates.

Use proportion to solve the following problems:

1. 81 calories of fat = _____ grams
2. 120 calories of protein = _____ grams
3. 36 calories of carbohydrate = _____ grams
4. 145 calories of carbohydrate = _____ grams
5. _____ calories in 12 grams of protein
6. _____ calories in 99 grams of fat
7. _____ calories in 328 grams of carbohydrate
8. _____ calories in 2450 grams of protein

Proportion is also useful in solving measurement problems that have to do with amounts of sodium, calories, fat, and protein in food or an amount in a drug dosage. The proportion will use the information in a scenario to solve for the unknown quantities in a specific amount.

Example If one glass of milk contains 280 milligrams of calcium, how much calcium is in $1\frac{1}{2}$ glasses of milk?

$$\frac{1 \text{ glass}}{280 \text{ milligrams}} = \frac{1\frac{1}{2} \text{ glasses}}{? \text{ milligrams}}$$

$$280 \times 1\frac{1}{2} = 420 \text{ mg of calcium}$$

1. One-half cup of baked beans contains 430 milligrams of sodium. How many milligrams of sodium are there in $\frac{3}{4}$ cup of baked beans?

2. Baked beans contain 33 grams of carbohydrates in a $\frac{1}{2}$ cup serving. How many milligrams of carbohydrates are in three $\frac{1}{2}$ cup servings?

3. A $\frac{1}{2}$ cup serving of fruit cocktail contains 55 milligrams of potassium. How many milligrams of potassium are in 2 cups of fruit cocktail?

4. If $\frac{1}{2}$ cup of fruit cocktail contains 13 grams of sugar, then $1\frac{1}{4}$ cup of fruit cocktail contains how many grams of sugar?

5. Old-fashioned oatmeal contains 27 grams of carbohydrates per $\frac{1}{2}$ cup of dry oats. How many grams of carbohydrates are available in $2\frac{1}{4}$ cups of the dry oats?

Practice with Food Labels

Carefully read the label and then use the information from the label to solve each question.

Albert's Tomato Soup

Nutrition facts	Amount/serving %DV*		Amount/serving %DV*	
Serving size ½ cup (120 ml)	Total fat 0 g	0%	Total carbohydrates 20 g	7%
Condensed soup	Saturated fat 0 g	0%	Fiber 1 g	4%
Servings about 2.5	Cholesterol 0 mg	0%	Sugars 15 g	
Calories 90				
Fat calories 0	Sodium 710 mg	30%	Protein 2 g	
	Vitamin A 12% · Vitamin C 12% · Calcium 0% · Iron 0%			

*Percent daily values (%DV) are based on a 2,000 calorie diet.

1. If $\frac{1}{2}$ cup of soup equals 120 milliliters, then how many milliliters (mL) are in $3\frac{1}{2}$ cups of soup?

2. If a can has 2.5 servings, how many cans are needed to serve 10 people?

3. One serving contains 90 calories, how many calories are in $4\frac{1}{2}$ servings?

4. One gram of fiber constitutes 4% of a daily dietary value. How many grams of fiber would be present in 25% of the daily value?

5. How many grams of carbohydrates are present if the portion meets 15% of the daily value of carbohydrates? Round to the nearest tenth.

Use the information from the label to complete these proportions.

Big Al's Organic Sweet and Juicy Dried Plums

Nutrition facts Serving size 1½ oz (40 g in about 5 dried plums) Servings per container about 30		Amount per serving Calories 100 Calories from fat 0	
	%DV*		%DV*
Total fat 0 g	0%	Potassium 290 mg	8%
Saturated fat 0 g	0%	Total carbohydrates 24 g	8%
Cholesterol 0 mg	0%	Dietary fiber 3 g	11%
Sodium 5 mg	0%	Soluble fiber 1 g	
Vitamin A 10% (100% as beta carotene)		Insoluble fiber 1 g	
Vitamin C 0%		Sugars 12 g	
Calcium 2%		Protein 1 g	
Iron 2%		**Big Al's Organic Sweet and Juicy Dried Plums/Prunes**	

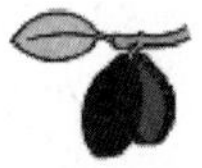

*Percent daily values (%DV) are based on a 2,000 calorie diet. Your daily values may be higher or lower depending on your calorie needs.

6. How many total grams (g) of weight are present in 34 prunes?

7. If 100 calories are consumed with 5 prunes, how many calories are consumed with 12 prunes?

8. If 5 prunes have 290 milligrams (mg) of potassium and that accounts for 8% of percent daily value, how many prunes are needed to equal 15% of the percent daily value? Round to the nearest whole number.

9. If 5 prunes equals 10% of the Vitamin A needed daily, what percent of the daily % of Vitamin A is present in 20 prunes?

10. If a serving size is $1\frac{1}{2}$ ounces (oz), how many ounces are five servings?

Use the information from the label to complete these proportions.

Jade's Soy Milk

Nutrition facts	Amount/serving %DV*	Amount/serving %DV*
Serving size 1 cup (240 ml)	Total fat 4 g 6%	Total Carbohydrates 4 g 1%
Servings about 8 per 1.89 L	Saturated fat 0.5 g 3%	Fiber 1 g 4%
Calories 80	Trans fat 0 g	Cholesterol 0 mg 0%
Fat calories 35	Polyunsaturated fat 2.5 g	Sugars 12 g
	Monounsaturated fat 1 g	Protein 7 g
	Sodium 85 mg 4%	Potassium 300 mg 8%
	Vitamin A 10% · Vitamin C 0% · Calcium 30% · Iron 6%	
	Vitamin D 10% · Folate 6% · Magnesium 10% · Selenium 8%	

*Percent daily values (%DV) are based on a 2,000 calorie diet.

11. If 1 cup of soup contains 4 grams (g) total fat, then how many grams of total fat are in $2\frac{3}{4}$ cups of Jade's Soy Milk?

12. If a cup of soy milk contains 85 milligrams of sodium, and an individual consumes $2\frac{2}{3}$ cups of soy milk per day, what is the sodium intake from soy milk? Round to the nearest whole number.

13. If one serving of Jade's Soy Milk provides 1% of the daily carbohydrates. How many milliliters make 5% of the daily carbohydrate intake?

14. One serving contains 80 calories, how many calories are in $3\frac{1}{4}$ servings?

15. If 1 cup of Jade's Soy Milk provides 1 gram of fiber and 4% of the recommended daily fiber intake, how many cups of this soy milk are needed to make 25% of the dietary fiber?

RATIO AND PROPORTION SELF-TEST

Show all your work.

1. Write a definition for proportion. Provide one health profession application or example.

2. $30 : 120 = ? : 12$

3. 1 glass contains 8 ounces. How many full glasses are in 78 ounces?

4. $\frac{1}{2} : 4 = \frac{1}{3} : x$

5. $x : 625 = 1 : 5$

6. If 10 milligrams are contained in 2 milliliters, how many milligrams are contained in 28 milliliters?

7. A tablet contains 30 milligrams of medication. How many tablets will be needed to provide Ms Smith with 240 milligrams of medication?

8. 100 micrograms of a drug are contained in 2 cubic centimeters. How many cubic centimeters are contained in 15 micrograms?

9. $\frac{1}{100}:6 = ?:8$

10. $0.04 : 0.5 = 0.12 : ?$

11. How many minutes are in 130 seconds? Your answer will have both minutes and seconds. Show your setup.

12. Four out of every six dental patients request fluoride treatment after their dental cleaning treatments. If 120 patients have dental cleanings this week, how many will choose to have fluoride treatments as well?

13. If the doctor's office uses 128 disposal thermometer covers each day, how many covers will be used in a five-day workweek?

14. Solve: $\frac{1}{125} : 3 :: \_\_\_\_ : 12$

15. If the doctor ordered six ounces of cranberry juice four times a day for four days, how many total ounces would be served the patient?

Unit 5

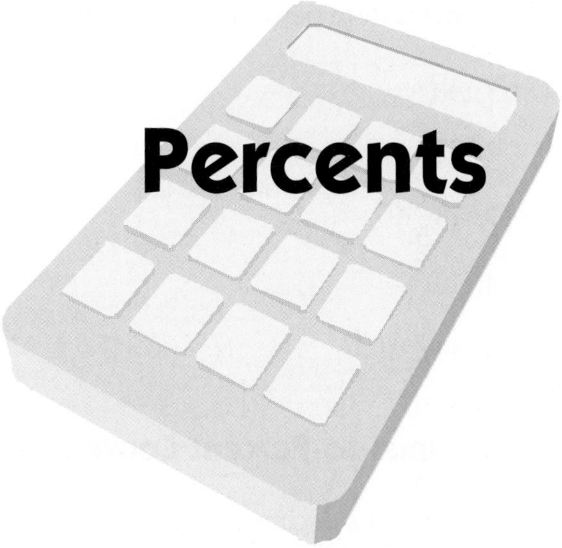

Percents

Percents are another example of a part-to-whole relationship in math. Percents are *parts of one hundred* and are represented by the % sign. Percents can be written as fractions: 35 parts of 100 or $^{35}/_{100}$.

Knowledge of percents in health care will help you understand the strength in percent of solutions for patient medications, interest on loans and taxes, and discounts and markups in pharmacies and retail stores. In general, percent applications are seen less frequently than fractions and decimals by general health care professionals.

Percent-to-Decimal Conversion

To convert a percent to a decimal, shift the decimal point two places to the *left*. The process of doing this quick division replaces having to divide the number by 100. This is the same method of simplified division as shown in Unit 3: Decimals.

> A whole number has its decimal to the far right of the final digit or number.
>
> 125% = 125.% 76% = 76.%

Example

75% → 7 5.% → 0.75
∪∪

If a percent has a fractional part, the decimal occurs between the whole number and the fractional part.

Example

$$33\frac{1}{3}\% \rightarrow 33.\frac{1}{3}\% \rightarrow 0.33\frac{1}{3}$$

Practice Convert from percents to decimals:

1. 45%
2. 57%
3. $78\frac{1}{5}\%$
4. 101%
5. $44\frac{1}{2}\%$

Decimal-to-Percent Conversion

To convert a decimal to a percent, shift the decimal point two places to the *right*. This is the simplified multiplication method as practiced in Unit 3: Decimals.

If a number has a decimal in it and you are converting from a decimal to a percent, use the existing decimal point as the starting point for the conversion. It is possible to have percents greater than 100.

> Begin counting from wherever the decimal is placed.
>
> $$0.023 \rightarrow 02.3\% \quad 2.56 \rightarrow 256\%$$
>
> Handle a mixed fraction by placing the decimal point between whole number and the fraction, then convert the fraction to a whole number by dividing the numerator by the denominator. Then move the decimal two places right and add a % sign.
>
> $$14\frac{3}{4} \rightarrow 14\,.\frac{3}{4} \rightarrow 14\,.\,7\,5 \rightarrow 1475\%$$
>
> ∪∪

Examples

$$0.25 \rightarrow 0.2\,5\% = 25\%$$

∪∪

$$13 \rightarrow 13. \rightarrow 13.0\,0 = 1300\%$$

∪∪

Practice Convert from decimals to percents:

1. 0.625
2. 55.75
3. 8.6

4. 12.5

5. 0.076

Mixed Practice
Convert

1. 76.89% to a decimal
2. 0.05% to a decimal
3. 86% to a decimal
4. 6.25 to a percent
5. 0.078 to a percent
6. $9\frac{3}{4}$ to a percent
7. $1.25\frac{1}{4}$ to a percent
8. $78\frac{1}{9}\%$ to a decimal
9. 1.5% to a decimal
10. $0.67\frac{1}{4}$ to a percent

Using Proportion to Solve Percent Problems

Proportions are also very useful in solving percent problems. To accomplish this, use the formula

$$\frac{\%}{100} = \frac{\text{is (the part)}}{\text{whole (the total)}}$$

To solve any percent problem, take the information from the problem and put it into the formula. There are three possible places that the information can go.

$$\frac{?}{100} = \frac{?}{?}$$

The 100 never changes because that indicates that every percent is part of 100. It is important to set up the problem correctly. The following questions ask for different information. Therefore, the setup of the problems will be different.

Problem	Setup
What is 25% of 75?	$\frac{25}{100} = \frac{?}{75}$
What % of 75 is 18.75?	$\frac{?}{100} = \frac{18.75}{75}$
18.75 is 25% of what?	$\frac{25}{100} = \frac{18.75}{?}$

Note that the ? is in a different place each time. When the problem is worked, each of the above answers will be different.

Practice Set up the problems, but do not solve.

1. What is 25% of 200?
2. 75 is what % of 125?
3. Find 8.5% of 224.
4. 40 percent of what number is 350?
5. 18 is what percent of 150?
6. What is $1\frac{1}{2}$% of 400?
7. 75 of 90 is what percent?
8. Out of 200, 140 is what percent?
9. 50% of what number is 75?
10. $8\frac{1}{3}$% of 144 is what?

To solve percent problems in health care, one needs to be aware that the problem may include whole numbers, fractions, and decimals. The skills used in percents draw on the foundation you have in these areas of math computation. It is important to remember and apply the fraction concepts learned when dealing with fractions in percents because a fraction is more accurate and exact than a decimal number that has a repeating final digit.

To solve percent problems, use the proportion method studied in Unit 4: Ratio and Proportion.

Example Fifteen is what percent of 300?

$$\frac{x\%}{100} = \frac{15}{300}$$

Step 1: Cross multiply the two numbers.

$$(100 \times 15 = 1500)$$

Step 2: Divide the step 1 answer by the remaining number—the number diagonal from the *x* or ?

$$1{,}500 \div 300 = 5$$

The answer is 5%. So we know that 15 is 5% of 300.

Practice

1. 15% of 120 is ______.
2. 33 is what % of 44?
3. 62 is what percent of 248?
4. 40% of 120 is what?
5. What is 35% of 16.8?
6. Find 9% of 3,090.
7. 45 is what percent of 200?
8. 74 is what percent of 74?
9. What is 44% of 40?
10. 121 is what % of 220?

More complex percents include fractions, and the most efficient way of handling these is as complex fractions. By setting up the problem in proportion format, the work is put into manageable steps. A common error is that students multiply the first two numbers and consider their work done; however, there is always a final division step that must be performed.

Example What is $8\frac{1}{3}$% of 150?

$$\frac{8\frac{1}{3}}{100} = \frac{x}{150}$$

Step 1: Multiply $8\frac{1}{3}$ and 150. Deal with the fraction; do not change it to a decimal because if you do, your answer will not be as exact. Convert the mixed fraction into an improper fraction. Multiply the whole number by the denominator and add the numerator. Place this number over the denominator. Then multiply this improper fraction by the number 150.

$$8\frac{1}{3} = \frac{25}{3} \times 150 = \frac{3{,}750}{3} = 1250$$

Step 2: Divide the step 1 answer of 1,250 by 100. Use simplified division. Simplified division moves the decimal 2 places to the left to divide by 100.

$$1{,}250 : 1{,}2\underset{\cup}{5}\,\underset{\cup}{0} = 12.5 \text{ or } 12\frac{1}{2} \quad 0.5 \text{ equals } \frac{1}{2}.$$

Practice

1. What is $33\frac{1}{3}\%$ of 125? Round to the nearest hundredth.

2. $1\frac{1}{2}\%$ of 400 is what?

3. $66\frac{2}{3}\%$ of 90 is what?

4. $35\frac{1}{4}\%$ is what part of 150? Round to the nearest hundredth.

5. $12\frac{1}{2}\%$ of 125 is what? Round to the nearest hundredth.

6. 50 is $83\frac{1}{3}\%$ of what number?

7. 160 is $12\frac{1}{2}\%$ of what number?

8. 45 is $15\frac{1}{3}\%$ of what number? Round to the nearest hundredth.

9. 200 is $37\frac{1}{2}\%$ of what number? Round to the nearest hundredth.

10. $87\frac{1}{2}\%$ of 120 is what?

Two other applications of percents are important for the health care student: the percent strength of a solution and the single trade discount.

Percent Strength of Solutions

The strength of solutions is an important application of percents. A solution is a liquid that has had medication, minerals, or other products dissolved in it. Percent strength refers to how much of a substance has been dissolved in a specific amount of liquid.

Key to percent strength is your knowledge of part-to-whole relationships: A percent is x parts to 100 total parts. Solution refers to a two-part substance: a solute that is the drug, mineral, or product and a solvent or liquid that can be a variety depending on the medical application. Solutes will occur either as a dry drug measured in grams or as a liquid measured in milliliters. The total volume of the liquid is always in milliliters.

Example A 15% drug solution has 15 parts of drug to 100 parts of solution. There are 15 grams of drug to 100 milliliters of solution. As a ratio, this would be shown in the reduced form as 3 : 20.

Sometimes the solution will be given as a ratio rather than a percent. To express the solution strength as a percent, set up the problem as a proportion with 100 ml of the total solution. Recall that percent is always part of 100.

Practice Percent strength: What is the ratio of pure drug to solution? Simplify, if necessary.

1. 4% solution ________________
2. 10% solution ________________
3. $1\frac{1}{2}$% solution ________________
4. 7.5% solution ________________
5. 5% solution ________________

Knowledge of proportion is useful in converting to smaller or larger amounts of solution. In health care, professionals may not always require 100 mL of a solution. It is important to maintain the correct ratio of pure drug to solution to ensure that the patient is getting the medication or solution the doctor intended. Note that the ratio of pure drug remains consistent no matter how much solution is to be prepared.

Example Percent strength 8% means that there are 8 g of drug to 100 mL of solution. If the doctor orders 25 mL of an 8% strength solution, then a proportion may be used to ensure that the ratio of pure drug to solution represents 8%.

$$\begin{array}{ccc} \textit{known} & & \textit{unknown} \\ \dfrac{8\text{ g of drugs}}{100\text{ mL solution}} & = & \dfrac{?\text{ g of drug}}{25\text{ mL solution}} \end{array}$$

Step 1: $8 \times 25 = 200$

Step 2: $200 \div 100 = 2$

So to make 25 mL of an 8% solution using this ratio of pure drug to solution, 2 g of pure drug to 25 mL of solution are required. This keeps the percent strength of the medication consistent with the doctor's order for an 8% strength solution. Note that the amount of mixed solution changes, not the percent strength itself.

Example Ten grams of drug in 25 mL of solution. What is the percent strength of this medication?

To convert this ratio into a percent, write it as a proportion. Then solve for *x* which will become the percent.

$$\begin{array}{ccc} \textit{known} & & \textit{unknown} \\ \dfrac{10\text{ g}}{25\text{ mL}} & = & \dfrac{x\text{ g}}{100\text{ mL}} \end{array}$$

Follow proportion steps to solve. Cross multiply $10 \times 100 = 1000$. Divide 1000 by $25 = 40$, so the answer is 40% strength.

Practice

1. The doctor has ordered a 5% saline solution to be prepared. How many grams of pure drug will be needed to make each of these amounts of solution at the 5% strength?
   a. 25 mL of solution
   b. 35 mL of solution
   c. 65 mL of solution
   d. 125 mL of solution

2. Nine milliliters of pure drug are in 100 mL of solution.
   a. What is the percent strength of the solution?
   b. How many milliliters of drug are in 75 mL of that solution?

3. Fifteen grams of pure drug are in 50 mL.
   a. What is the percent strength of the solution?
   b. How many grams of pure drug are in 200 mL of the solution?

Additional Practice with Solution Strength

1. A $12\frac{3}{4}$% strength solution has been prepared.
   a. How many grams of medication is in the $12\frac{3}{4}$% strength solution?
   b. How many milliliters of solution are in this $12\frac{3}{4}$% strength solution?
   c. Express this solution as a simplified ratio.
   d. How much pure drug is needed to create 35.5 mL of this solution? Round to the nearest tenth. Your answer will be in grams.
   e. How much pure drug is needed to create 80 mL of this solution? Your answer will be in grams.
   f. If you have 60 mL of solution, how many grams of pure drug will you have in order to keep the $12\frac{3}{4}$%? Round to the nearest tenth. Your answer will be in grams.

2. A 0.09% strength solution has been prepared.
   a. How many grams of medication is in the 0.09% strength solution?
   b. How many milliliters of solution are in this 0.09% strength solution?
   c. Express this solution as a simplified ratio.
   d. How much pure drug is needed to create 54 mL of this solution? Round to the nearest hundredth. Your answer will be in grams.
   e. How much pure drug is needed to create 24 mL of this solution? Round to the nearest hundredth. Your answer will be in grams.
   f. If you have 50 mL of solution, how many grams of pure drug will you have in order to keep the 0.09% solution. Round to the nearest hundredth. Your answer will be in grams.

3. A 78% strength solution has been prepared.
   a. How many grams of medication is in the 78% strength solution?
   b. How many milliliters of solution are in this 78% strength solution?
   c. Express this solution as a simplified ratio.
   d. How much pure drug is needed to create 65.5 mL of this solution? Round to the nearest tenth. Your answer will be in grams.
   e. How much pure drug is needed to create 90 mL of this solution? Round to the nearest tenth. Your answer will be in grams.
   f. If you have 450 mL of solution, how many grams of pure drug will you have in order to keep the 78%? Your answer will be in grams.

Single Trade Discount

Single trade discounts are useful to individuals who handle products or inventory that must be marked up. The single trade discount provides the net price of items when a single discount has been given. Some health care organizations that use certain name brands receive these discounts from manufacturers of the products they use or sell most often.

Example What is the net price of a surgical instrument listed at $189.90 with a trade discount of 40%?

Step 1: The percentage is first made into a decimal by moving the decimal point two places to the left. Then, multiply the list price by the trade discount.

> You may need to round your decimal number to the nearest cent.

$$\begin{array}{r} \$189.90 \\ \times \quad .40 \\ \hline 00000 \\ 75960 \\ \hline \$75.96 \end{array}$$

Step 2: Subtract the amount of the discount (the answer from step 1) from the list price to get the net price.

$$\begin{array}{r} \$189.90 \\ -75.96 \\ \hline \$113.94 \end{array}$$

The net price of this instrument is $113.94.

Practice Find the net price by using the single trade discount method. If necessary, round to the nearest penny. Show your work.

	List price	Trade discount	Amount of discount	Net price
1.	$475.50	15%	_____	_____
2.	$179.85	20%	_____	_____
3.	$125.55	12.5%	_____	_____
4.	$455.86	30%	_____	_____
5.	$352.90	25%	_____	_____
6.	$72.35	10%	_____	_____
7.	$250.40	45%	_____	_____
8.	$862.75	35%	_____	_____
9.	$158.00	40%	_____	_____
10.	$73.85	10%	_____	_____

PERCENT SELF-TEST

1. Write the definition of a percent. Provide one example.

2. Convert the following into percents:

a. $0.87\frac{1}{4}$

b. $\frac{5}{6}$

3. 75% of 325 is what number?

4. 8 is what % of 40?

5. 28 is 14% of what number?

6. What does $5\frac{1}{2}\%$ solution mean?

7. The doctor has ordered 25 mL of 9% saline solution. How much pure drug is needed to make this order?

8. The list price for a case of medicine is $129.50. Your pharmacy will receive a 12% trade discount.

a. What is the amount of the discount? ______

b. What is the net cost of a case of medicine? ______

9. What percent is 3 tablets of a prescription written for 36 tablets?

10. If a pharmacy gave a 15% discount on walkers, what would be the discount for a total bill of $326.00 for a six-month rental?

11. If a ratio of 3 : 25 is given for a solution, what percent strength is this solution?

12. What is $\frac{1}{2}$% of 500?

13. Express 8 : 125 as a percent.

14. What is $\frac{3}{4}$% of 20?

15. 35 is 0.05% of what?

Unit 6

Combined Applications

Health care workers rely on a variety of math systems to achieve their daily tasks. Knowledge of ways to convert efficiently between systems will benefit you on the job as your expertise grows and your circle of responsibility increases. It is important to have the ability to convert between fractions, decimals, ratios, and percents. Although these skills have been separately reviewed, they are brought together here to develop some strategies for doing these conversions in the most efficient way.

Conversions among Fractions, Decimals, Ratios, and Percent

Review the basics of conversion:

Conversion	Method/Formula
Fraction to decimal	Divide the denominator into the numerator.

$$\frac{3}{4} = \begin{array}{r} 0.75 \\ 4\overline{)3.0} \\ \underline{28\downarrow} \\ 20 \\ \underline{20} \\ 0 \end{array}$$

Decimal to fraction

Count the decimal places, place the number over 1 with zeros to match the same number of decimal places.

$$0.0\underline{2} \text{ (2 places)} \rightarrow \frac{2}{1\underline{0}\,\underline{0}} \text{ (2 zeros)}$$

Reduce to $\frac{1}{50}$.

Proper fraction to ratio, ratio to proper fraction

Ratios are shown with : instead of /. Fractions and ratios are interchangeable simply by changing the symbol.

$$\frac{1}{8} \rightarrow 1:8 \text{ and } 4:31 \rightarrow \frac{4}{31}$$

The first ratio number is always the numerator and the second ratio number is always the denominator. All fractions and ratios must be in lowest terms.

Mixed number to ratio, ratio to mixed number

If the fraction is a mixed number, the mixed number first must be made into an improper fraction before setting up the ratio.

$$1\frac{3}{4} \rightarrow 1 \times 4 + 3 = \frac{7}{4} \rightarrow 7:4$$

If the ratio is an improper fraction when the conversion is made, make it a mixed number.

$$\frac{11}{4} \rightarrow 11 \div 4 = 2\frac{3}{4}$$

Decimal to percent

Move the decimal point two places to the right. Add the percent sign.

$$0.25 \rightarrow 25\% \quad 1.456 \rightarrow 145.6\%$$

Percent to decimal

Move the decimal point two places to the left. Add zeros if needed as placeholders.

$$90\% \rightarrow 0.9 \text{ and } 5\% \rightarrow 0.05$$

$$57\frac{1}{2}\% \rightarrow 0.57\frac{1}{2} \text{ or } 0.575$$

Fraction to percent

Convert fraction to decimal, then to percent.

Decimal to ratio

Convert decimal to fraction, then change sign to ratio.

Convert the following numbers to the other number systems. Using the review sheet of conversion methods, try to compute only one math problem per line by carefully selecting the order of the conversions to be done. By carefully selecting the order of conversions, you will minimize extra work.

Example

Fraction	Decimal	Ratio	Percent
______	0.05	______	______

Figuring out the order takes a little practice. When 0.05 is changed to a percent first, no math calculation needs to be done: Simply move the decimal.

Fraction	Decimal	Ratio	Percent
______	0.05	______	5%

Next convert the decimal to a fraction. Count the number of decimal places and then place the 5 over a 1 with the same number of zeros as the decimal places. Reduce the fraction to lowest terms.

Fraction	Decimal	Ratio	Percent
$\frac{5}{100} \rightarrow \frac{1}{20}$	0.05	______	5%

Take the reduced fraction and write it in ratio form.

Fraction	Decimal	Ratio	Percent
$\frac{5}{100} \rightarrow \frac{1}{20}$	0.05	1 : 20	5%

Example

Fraction	Decimal	Ratio	Percent
$7\frac{3}{5}$	______	______	______

This mixed number must be made into an improper fraction before it can become a ratio.

$$\left(7 \times 5 + 3 = 38 \rightarrow \frac{38}{5}\right)$$

Change the signs from / to : to make the ratio.

Fraction	Decimal	Ratio	Percent
$7\frac{3}{5}$	______	38 : 5	______

Next change to a decimal. Handle the whole number 7 separately. Place it on the line as a whole number, then divide the denominator into the numerator.

$$3 \div 5 = 0.6$$

Add this to the whole number to make 7.6.

Fraction	Decimal	Ratio	Percent
$7\frac{3}{5}$	7.6	38 : 5	______

Finally, move the decimal point from the decimal number two places to the right. Add the percent sign.

Fraction	Decimal	Ratio	Percent
$7\frac{3}{5}$	7.6	38 : 5	760%

Suggested Order of Operations

If starting with percent, move from → decimal → fraction → ratio.

If starting with ratio, move from → fraction → decimal → percent.

If starting with fraction, move from → ratio → decimal → percent.

If starting with decimal, move from → percent → fraction → ratio.

Some conversions can be memorized easily:

$\frac{1}{2} \rightarrow 0.5 \rightarrow 50\%$

$\frac{1}{4} \rightarrow 0.25 \rightarrow 25\%$

$\frac{3}{4} \rightarrow 0.75 \rightarrow 75\%$

$\frac{1}{3} \rightarrow 0.33\frac{1}{3} \rightarrow 33\frac{1}{3}\%$

$\frac{2}{3} \rightarrow 0.66\frac{2}{3} \rightarrow 66\frac{2}{3}\%$

Provide the following measures. Reduce to lowest terms as necessary. Round to the nearest hundredth, if necessary.

	Fraction	Decimal	Ratio	Percent
1.	$\frac{3}{4}$	______	______	______
2.	______	______	1 : 20	______

	Fraction	Decimal	Ratio	Percent
3.	______	______	______	50%
4.	______	0.625	______	______
5.	______	______	1 : 250	______
6.	$\frac{7}{8}$	______	______	______
7.	______	0.06	______	______
8.	______	______	______	12.5%
9.	$\frac{1}{10}$	______	______	______
10.	______	______	______	$33\frac{1}{3}\%$
11.	______	1.36	______	______
12.	$12\frac{1}{2}$	______	______	______
13.	______	______	2 : 5	______
14.	______	$0.66\frac{2}{3}$	______	______
15.	______	______	16 : 25	______
16.	______	0.004	______	______
17.	$\frac{5}{6}$	______	______	______
18.	______	______	______	$7\frac{1}{4}\%$
19.	______	0.01	______	______
20.	______	______	7 : 3	______

Using Combined Applications in Measurement Conversion

In health care, a solid working knowledge of weights and measures is essential. Three systems of measure will be used in your work: household or standard measurement, metric measurement, covered in this unit, and apothecary measurement, covered in Unit 11: Dosage Calculations. Critical to your success in measurement conversion is your ability to remember a few key conversions and the proportion method for solving conversions. Metric-to-metric conversions use a different conversion method, which is also covered in Unit 11.

Household or standard measurements are used by all of us in our daily activities. Household measures tend to be less accurate than either metric or apothecary measures because of their nature and our methods of using them. So household measures are used in the less critical measurements in health care. Abbreviations of units of measure are used and some new abbreviations are introduced below:

Drop = gtt

Teaspoon = t (tsp)

Tablespoon = T (tbsp)

Practice Write the word for each abbreviation.

1. ft. = feet
2. yd. = yard
3. oz. = ounce.
4. T = Tablespoon
5. lb. = pound
6. t = teaspoon
7. qt. = quart
8. pt. = pint
9. gtt = Drop
10. gal. = Gallon.

Standard Units of Measure

The basics of standard measure conversion were covered in Unit 4: Ratio and Proportion. To refresh yourself on the application of proportion to measurement conversions, complete the review exercises.

Time

1 minute	= 60 seconds
1 day	= 24 hours
1 week	= 7 days
1 year	= 12 months

Weight

1 kilogram	= 2.2 pounds
1 pound	= 16 ounces

Linear Measure

1 foot	= 12 inches
1 yard	= 3 feet
1 meter	= 39.4 inches
1 inch	= 2.5 or 2.54 centimeters

Liquid Measure

1 tablespoon	= 3 teaspoons
1 cup	= 8 ounces
1 pint	= 2 cups
1 quart	= 2 pints
1 gallon	= 4 quarts

Approximate Equivalents

grain i	= 60 milligrams
1 teaspoon	= 5 milliliters
1 tablespoon	= 3 teaspoons
fluid dram 1	= 4 milliliters
fluid ounce 1	= fluid drams 8
fluid ounce 1	= 2 tablespoons
fluid ounce 1	= 30 milliliters
1 cup	= 250 milliliters
	= fluid ounces 8
1 pint	= 500 milliliters
	= 2 cups or fluid ounces 16
1 quart	= fluid ounces 32
	= 1 liter or 1000 milliliters
1 cubic centimeter	= 1 milliliter
1 kilogram	= 2.2 pounds
fluid ounce 1	= 2 tablespoons

Review Use the provided tables to assist you in proportion conversions.

1. 1250 milliliters = _____ pints
2. 15 kilograms = _____ pounds
3. 12.5 inches = _____ centimeters
4. _____ milliliters = 13 teaspoons
5. _____ ounces = 90 milliliters
6. 38.1 centimeters = _____ inches
7. _____ ounces = $1\frac{1}{2}$ pints
8. _____ quarts = 15 liters
9. _____ teaspoons = 12.5 milliliters
10. _____ cubic centimeters = 15 teaspoons

More Combined Applications

Sometimes measurement conversions require more than one conversion to get to the answer.

Example Two conversions are required to convert from ounces to teaspoons.

Step 1: Convert the ounces to milliliters:

$$\begin{array}{ccc} \textit{known} & & \textit{unknown} \\ \frac{1 \text{ ounce}}{20 \text{ mL}} & = & \frac{8 \text{ ounces}}{? \text{ mL}} \rightarrow 160 \text{ milliliters} \end{array}$$

Step 2: Convert milliliters to teaspoons.

$$\frac{1 \text{ teaspoon}}{5 \text{ mL}} = \frac{? \text{ teaspoons}}{160 \text{ mL}} \rightarrow 32 \text{ teaspoons}$$

These problems cannot be solved by making a straight conversion from what is known to what is unknown. A path must be developed so that you can establish how to get the answer. Think about what conversions most closely match the problem itself, then set up the problem.

Do not rush through the two-step conversions. These require some forethought about how to get from what is known to what is unknown.

Plastic medicine cups are used in the health care industry to measure liquid dosages. A medicine cup is typically marked off in milliliters. Often one medicine cup is 1 fluid ounce, which is 30 mL.

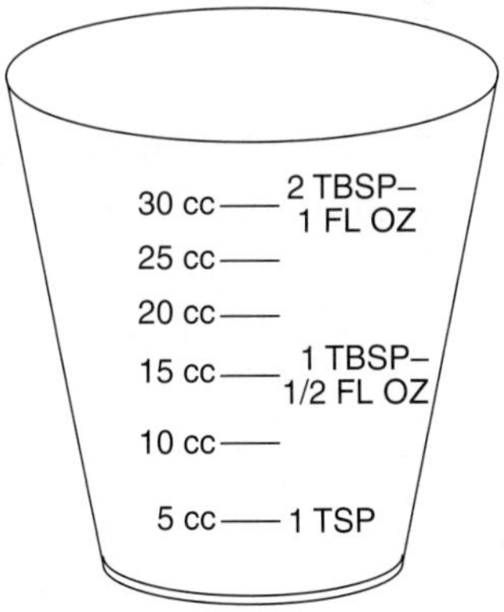

Practice

1. 1 medicine cup = _____ teaspoons
2. 3 teaspoons = _____ (drops)
3. $2\frac{1}{4}$ pints = _____ ounces
4. 1 cup = _____ teaspoons
5. 1 pint = _____ tablespoons
6. 15 tablespoons = _____ cubic centimeters
7. 68,000 grams = _____ pounds
8. 28 inches = _____ millimeters
9. _____ ounces = 24 teaspoons
10. $1\frac{1}{2}$ ounces = _____ teaspoons

Sometimes math problems require multiple setups. To solve these, group the work into the most logical format.

Example

$$\frac{25\%}{\frac{1}{4}}$$

Step 1: Look at the problem and decide what to do to make the units similar. Convert 25% into a fraction.

$$\rightarrow \frac{25}{100}$$

Step 2: Review the problem to see what operation should be completed.

$$\frac{\frac{25}{100}}{\frac{1}{4}}$$

This problem is a complex fraction. Divide the denominator of $^1/_4$ into the numerator of $^{25}/_{100}$.

$$\frac{25}{100} \div \frac{1}{4} \rightarrow \frac{25}{100} \times \frac{4}{1} = \frac{100}{100} = 1$$

Mixed Review Practice

1. $\dfrac{50\%}{\frac{1}{4}}$

2. $\dfrac{1{:}150}{1{:}300} \times 2$

3. $12\frac{1}{2}\% \times \dfrac{\frac{1}{2}}{\frac{3}{4}}$

4. $\dfrac{\frac{1}{2}\%}{4} \times 1000$

5. $5\% \times \dfrac{1{:}2}{3{:}4}$

Converting among Systems Worksheet

Provide the following measures. Reduce to lowest terms as necessary.

	Fraction	Decimal	Ratio	Percent
1.	$\frac{7}{8}$	______	______	______
2.	______	______	1 : 30	______
3.	______	______	______	75%
4.	$\frac{1}{17}$	______	______	______
5.	______	______	2 : 5	______
6.	$\frac{5}{6}$	______	______	______
7.	______	0.08	______	______
8.	______	______	______	10.25%

	Fraction	Decimal	Ratio	Percent
9.	$\frac{3}{5}$			
10.			1 : 200	
11.		1.625		
12.	$\frac{1}{8}$			
13.			11 : 50	
14.		0.15		
15.			3 : 25	
16.		0.008		
17.	$\frac{1}{6}$			
18.				$15\frac{1}{4}\%$
19.		0.04		
20.			9 : 10,000	

COMBINED APPLICATIONS SELF-TEST

Show all your work.

1. Convert $\frac{3}{75}$ to a decimal. 0.04
2. Convert $\frac{1}{2}\%$ to a ratio. 1 : 200
3. Convert 1.05 to a fraction. $1\frac{1}{20}$
4. Convert $4\frac{1}{8}$ to a ratio. $8 \times 4 + 1 = \frac{33}{8}$ 33 : 8
5. Convert $27\frac{1}{4}$ to a decimal. $4\overline{)1.0}$ = 27.25

6. Convert 12 : 200 to a percent.

$\frac{12}{200}$ $200\overline{)12}$

7. Convert 14.25% to a ratio.

8. $3\frac{1}{4}$ cups = _____ ounces

9. 12 fluid ounces = _____ tablespoons

10. $3\frac{1}{2}$ feet = _____ centimeters

11. 18 hours = _____ minutes

12. 1 gallon = _____ cups

13. If a teaspoon has approximately 60 drops, how many drops are in $2\frac{1}{3}$ tablespoons?

14. 12% × 0.67

15. $\dfrac{15\%}{\frac{1}{2}}$

Math for Health Care Professionals Post-Test

Whole Number Skills

1. Find the mean of the set of numbers: 16, 4, 25, 9, 10, 9, 3, 20 ___12___

2. 345 + ___276___ + 37 = 658

3. 1846 − 979 = ___867___

4. 324 × 87 = ___28,188___

5. $27\overline{)654}$ = ___24.22___

6. The heights of the members of Michele's family are 66 inches, 81 inches, 69 inches, 70 inches, and 64 inches. Find the range in height of the members of Michele's family. ___70 inches___

7. Convert from 8:15 P.M. standard time to universal time. ___0815___

Fraction Skills

8. Order the fractions from smallest to largest: $\frac{2}{3}, \frac{6}{7}, \frac{6}{21}, \frac{13}{21}$ $\frac{6}{21}$ $\frac{13}{21}$ $\frac{2}{3}$ $\frac{6}{7}$

9. $20\frac{3}{5} + 6 + 3\frac{5}{6} =$ ___$30\frac{13}{30}$___

10. $56\frac{1}{3} - 17\frac{11}{12} =$ ___$38\frac{5}{12}$___

11. $2\frac{4}{5} \times \frac{2}{7} \times 5 =$ 4

12. $4\frac{1}{6} \div \frac{3}{8} =$ $11\frac{1}{9}$

13. Solve: $\dfrac{\frac{1}{10}}{\frac{1}{200}} =$ 20.

Decimal Skills

14. Express as a fraction: 4.06 $4\frac{6}{10}$ $4\frac{3}{5}$

15. Express as a decimal: $12\frac{5}{8}$ 12.625

16. $10.6 + 6 + 2.09 =$ 18.69

17. $65.7 - 12.68 =$ 53.02

18. $0.9 \times 41.2 =$ 33.372

19. $248.06 \div 0.8 =$ 310.075

Ratio and Proportion Skills

20. A container holds 34 milliliters of medication. How many *full* 1.25 milliliter doses can be administered from this container? ________

21. Solve: $12 : 75 :: 2.5 : x$ Round to the nearest hundredth.

$x =$ 15.63

22. Solve: $8 : x :: 42 : 50$

$x =$ $9\frac{11}{21}$ Answer should be in mixed number.

23. Solve: $\frac{1}{2} : 8 :: x : 32$ $x =$ 2

24. Solve: $\frac{1}{50} : 10 :: \frac{10}{250} : x$ $x =$ 20

25. Simplify the ratio to the lowest terms: $9\frac{3}{8} : 5$ 15:5

Percent Skills

26. What is $3\frac{2}{3}\%$ of 125? Write the answer as a mixed number.

____

27. What percent is 22 of 144? 15.28% Round to the nearest hundredth.

28. 24% of 250 is what number? ________

29. The original price minus a $45 discount is the sale price of a new desk. The sale price is $350. What was the original price? ________

30. There are 8 grams of pure drug in 75 milliliters of solution. What is the percent strength of solution? Round to the nearest hundredth.

____

Combined Application

31. $5\frac{1}{4}$ feet = ________ inches

32. ________ quarts = $7\frac{1}{2}$ pints

33. 36 pounds = ________ kilograms

34. ________ teaspoons = 62 milliliters

35. Convert 0.7% to a fraction = ________

36. Convert $4\frac{1}{2}$ to a percent = ________

37. Convert 9 to a percent = ________

38. Write 0.002 as a fraction = ________

39. Write 0.03% as a decimal = ________

Pre-Algebra

40. 75 + (−8) = ________

41. −15 − 22 = ________

42. −72 ÷ 9 = ________

43. −124 × (−3) = ________

44. $21 + \sqrt{169}$ = ________

45. (100 − 40) ÷ 4 = ________

Drug Labels

46. Complete the table for this drug label. If the information is not provided, write *Not shown.*

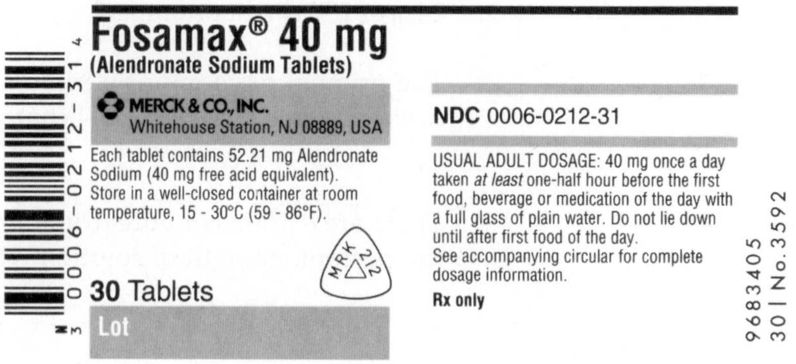

The labels for the products Prinivil, Fosamax, Singulair, Cozaar, Pepcid, Hyzaar, and Zocor are reproduced with the permission of Merck & Co., Inc., copyright owner.

Generic name __________

Trade name __________

Manufacturer __________

National Drug Code (NDC) number __________

Lot number (control number) __________

Drug form __________

Dosage strength __________

Usual adult dose __________

Total amount in vial, packet, box __________

Prescription warning __________

Expiration date __________

47. The medical assistant was asked to dispense 23 milliliters of a liquid medication. Shade the medicine cup to indicate this dosage.

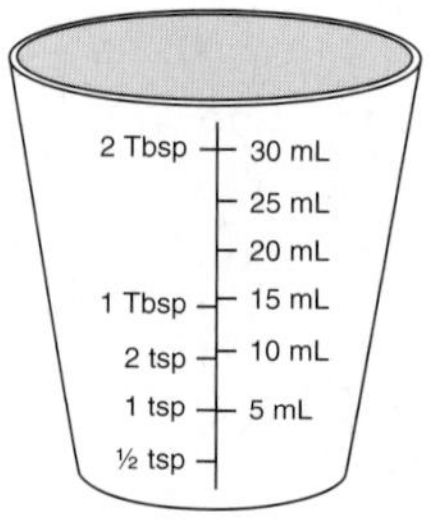

48. The physician has ordered an IM injection of 0.6 milliliters. Shade the syringe to indicate this volume of medication.

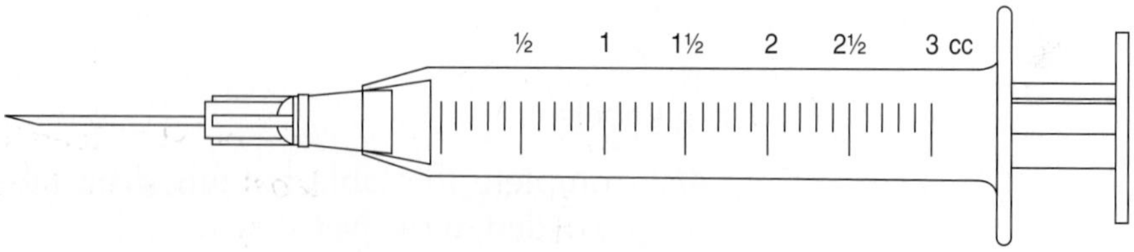

Metric Measurements

49. 9.43 micrograms = ________ milligrams

50. 193 grams = ________ kilogram. Round to the nearest tenth.

Apothecary Measurements

51. 12 fluid ounces = ________ milliliters

52. $4\frac{1}{4}$ teaspoons = ________ milliliters

53. $6\frac{1}{2}$ pints = ________ milliliters

54. 0.2 milligrams = grain ________

55. grain $\frac{1}{100}$ = ________ milligrams

56. 45 grams = grain ________

57. $4\frac{3}{4}$ teaspoons = ________milliliters

Oral Medications

58. Desired: Aspirin 0.5 grams every 4 hours
    Available: Aspirin 500 milligrams scored tablets
    Give: ________

59. The patient is ordered Vistaril 12 milligrams orally every 6 hours for nausea relief. You have on hand Vistaril oral suspension 5 milligrams per 2.5 milliliters.
    You adminster ________.

Dosage Calculations

60. Ordered: Zocor 50 milligrams
    Have: Zocor 12.5 milligrams per tablet
    Desired dose: ________

61. The doctor has ordered Zyloprim 0.5 gram orally twice a day. On hand is Zyloprim 100 milligrams scored tablets. The nurse should give ________.

62. The client receives an order for Augmentin 250 milligrams. The Augmentin is labeled 100 milligrams in 5 milliliters. The client will be given ________.

Parenteral Dosages

63. The physician orders megestrol acetate 600 milligrams per day. The megestrol acetate label reads, oral suspension 40 milligrams per milliliter. Give ________.

64. Give Dilaudid 0.5 milligrams IM from a vial that is labeled 5 milligrams per milliliter.
Give ________.

65. Ordered: Atropine sulfate 0.5 milligrams IM
Have: Atropine sulfate 0.25 milligrams per milliliter
Give ________

66. The doctor prescribes heparin 4000 units sub-Q four times a day. You have heparin 1500 units per milliliter. You give________.

67. Ordered: Quinidine 0.4 gram orally every 4 hours. Quinidine is supplied in 100 milligrams tablets. How many tablets will you give?________.

Calculating IV dosages

68. The patient with oliguria has an order for 125 milliliters of 0.9% NS over 2 hours. The drop factor is 15 drops per milliliter. How many drops per minute should be given?________

69. The nurse receives an order that reads: 1200 milliliters D_5W IV at 60 milliliter per hour. Infuse for ________.

70. The nurse will administer an IV solution at 125 milliliter per hour for 6 hours. What is the total volume infused? ________

Basic Dosages by Body Weight

Perform the calculations to determine whether the following is a therapeutic dosage for this child:

Ordered medication XZY 5 milligrams orally every 12 hours for a child weighing 14 pounds. You have medication XYZ 10 milligrams per milliliter. The recommended daily oral dosage for a child is 1.5 milligrams per kilogram per day in divided doses every 8 hours.

Medication XYZ
Oral Solution
10 mg/mL

71. This child's weight is 6.36 kilograms.

72. What is the recommended dosage for this child? 9.54 mg milligrams per day

Weight: 24 pounds 4 ounces
Ordered dose: 1.6 milligrams per kilogram per day
Recommended dosage from drug label: 3 milligrams every 8 hours

73. What is the daily dose? ________

74. What is the individual dose? ________

75. Does the dose ordered match the recommended dosage? ________

Answers for the Post-Test

1. 12
2. 276
3. 867
4. 28,188
5. 24.22, or 24 R 6, or $24\frac{2}{9}$
6. 17
7. 0815
8. $\frac{6}{21}, \frac{13}{21}, \frac{2}{3}, \frac{6}{7}$
9. $30\frac{13}{30}$
10. $38\frac{5}{12}$
11. 4
12. $11\frac{1}{9}$
13. 20
14. $4\frac{3}{50}$
15. 12.625
16. 18.69
17. 53.02
18. 37.08
19. 310.075
20. 27 doses
21. 21.29
22. $9\frac{11}{24}$
23. 2
24. 20
25. 15 : 8
26. $4\frac{7}{12}$
27. 15.28
28. 60
29. $395.00
30. 10.67
31. 63
32. 15
33. 16.4
34. 14
35. 70
36. 450%
37. 900%
38. $\frac{1}{500}$
39. $\frac{3}{10{,}000}$
40. 67
41. −37
42. −8
43. 372
44. 34
45. 15

46.

Generic name	Alendronate sodium
Trade name	Fosamax
Manufacturer	Merck & Co., Inc.
National Drug Code (NDC) number	0006-0212-31
Lot number (control number)	Not shown
Drug form	Tablet
Dosage strength	40 milligrams
Usual adult dose	40 milligrams Once a day taken at least one-half hour before the food, beverage, or medication of the day
Total amount in vial, packet, box	30 Tablets
Prescription warning	Rx only
Expiration date	Not shown

47. 23 milliliters

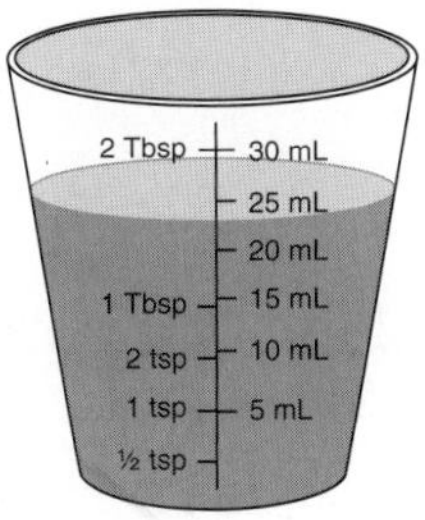

48. 0.6 milliliter

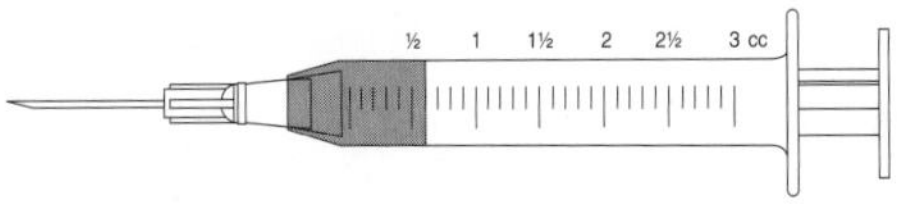

49. 0.00943 milligram

50. 0.2 kilogram

51. 360 milliliters

52. 21.25 milliliters

53. 3250 milliliters

54. grain $\frac{1}{300}$

55. 0.6 milligram

56. grain $7\frac{1}{2}$ or grain viiss

57. 23.75 milliliters

58. 1 tab

59. 6 milliliters

60. 4 tablets

61. 5 tablets

62. 12.5 milliliter

63. 15 milliliters

64. 0.1 milliliter

65. 2 milliliters

66. 2.67 milliliters

67. 4 tabs
68. 16 drops per minute
69. 20 hours
70. 750 milliliters
71. 6.36 kilograms
72. 9.54 milligrams per day
73. 18.37 milligrams per day
74. 6.12 milligrams
75. No, contact the physician for clarification.

Appendix of Practice Tests Units 1–6

Unit 1 Practice Exam Name ________________

Solve each problem below. Place your answer on the blank line.

1. $968 + 45 + 19 =$ ________
2. $529 + 3{,}456 =$ ________
3. The heights of the people in Michele's family are 68 inches, 65 inches, 73 inches, 74 inches, and 84 inches. Find the range of the people in Michele's family. ________
4. $709 +$ ________ $+ 49 = 1670$
5. $2{,}852 - 1{,}418 =$ ________
6. $2{,}003 -$ ________ $= 907$
7. ________ $- 95 = 896$
8. $1{,}455 - 509 =$ ________
9. Write 1322 in standard time. 3:22 pm
10. The dental office ordered 8 jackets for its staff. The jackets cost $37.00 each. What is the total cost for the 8 jackets? Write a number statement to solve this problem. Include the answer. ________
11. The heights of the members of Michele's family are 69 inches, 75 inches, 70 inches, 85 inches, and 73 inches. Find the median height of the members of Michele's family. ________
12. $14 \times 3 \times 12 =$ ________
13. $45 \times 138 =$ ________

14. Divide 932 by 8 = _______

15. 5,860 ÷ 14 = _______

16. $12\overline{)907}$ = _______

17. Heather's math tests had the following scores: 98, 75, 92, 98, 76, 87, 75, and 80. What is the mode of her scores? _______

18. Each gram of fat contains 9 calories. How many grams of fat are in 144 calories of fat in a piece of steak? _______

19. Bette was working hard to get a good grade. Her test scores were: 68%, 79%, 100%, 85%, and 88%. What is the mean or average of her grades? _______

20. Round 12,885 to the nearest ten. _______

21. Use one of the symbols (=, >, <, ≤, ≥) to complete the number statement: 285 + 17 _______ 51 × 6

22. Write the Roman numeral xixss as an Arabic numeral. _______

23. After a heart attack, Bob spent two days in the coronary care unit. His bill was $4,596.00. What was his daily room rate? Write a number statement that represents this problem. _______

24. Write a number statement using the symbol (>) _______

25. Find the prime factorization for 80. _______

Unit 2 Practice Exam Name ________________

Solve each problem. Put your answer on the blank line. Correct format is necessary.

1. Make into an equivalent fraction: $\frac{1}{4} = \frac{}{36}$ ________
2. Reduce to the lowest/simplest terms: $\frac{3}{129} =$ ________
3. Write as an improper fraction: $12\frac{3}{4} =$ ________
4. Write as a mixed number: $\frac{235}{9} =$ ________
5. $\frac{4}{5} + \frac{3}{8} =$ ________
6. $14\frac{3}{4} + \frac{5}{6} + 2\frac{7}{12} =$ ________
7. $22\frac{1}{5} + 1\frac{7}{9} =$ ________
8. $48\frac{2}{7} - 21\frac{5}{21} =$ ________
9. $676 - \frac{3}{11} =$ ________
10. $42\frac{5}{12} - 17\frac{5}{6} =$ ________
11. $\frac{3}{8} \times \frac{5}{7} =$ ________
12. $\frac{7}{12} \times 8 =$ ________
13. $7\frac{3}{4} \times 2\frac{1}{3} =$ ________
14. A bottle of medicine contains 12 doses of medication. How many full doses are in $4\frac{1}{4}$ bottles? ________
15. $\frac{3}{14} \div \frac{1}{5} =$ ________
16. $7\frac{1}{8} \div 10 =$ ________
17. How many full grain $\frac{3}{4}$ doses can be obtained from a grain $9\frac{1}{2}$ vial?
____
18. 35°C = ________°F

19. 68°F = _______ °C

20. $\frac{\frac{2}{5}}{\frac{1}{7}}$ = _______

21. $\frac{\frac{1}{200}}{\frac{1}{6}}$ = _______

22. Order the following the following fractions by writing them in order from smallest to largest—do not just put the number of the order on top of the fraction. $^1/_2$ $^3/_4$ $^4/_9$ $^{17}/_{36}$ _______

23. One cup holds 8 ounces. If a cup is $^2/_5$ full, how many ounces are in the cup? _______

24. The nurse gave the patient a tablet of grains $^1/_{20}$ of medicine followed by a second tablet of grains $^5/_{80}$. How many total grains of the medication did the patient receive? _______

25. The physical therapist suggested that Bob begin a series of stretches. He told Bob to work out for $^1/_3$ of an hour. How many minutes is $^1/_3$ of an hour? _______ minutes.

Unit 3 Practice Exam Name ________________

1. Write the words in decimal numbers: seven-hundredths. ________

2. Write the decimal number of 17.005 in words. ________

3. Round 25.075 to the nearest hundredth: ________

4. Which is larger: 10.07 or 10.7 = ________

5. $0.4 + 12 + 0.11 =$ ________

6. $36.05 + 1.7 + 0.009 =$ ________

7. One medication is labeled 48.5 milliliters and another is 0.5 milliliters. What is the total dosage in milliliters given of this medication? ________

8. $8.008 - 0.98 =$ ________

9. $0.9 - 0.007 =$ ________

10. Patient Smith was on a diet. He weighed 122.6 kilograms. After one month he weighed 112.8 kilograms. What was his total weight loss in one month? ________

11. $0.596 \times 2.3 =$ ________

12. $405 \times 3.02 =$ ________

13. $16\overline{)42.98}$ Round to the nearest tenth = ________

14. $1.9\overline{)28.09}$ Round to the nearest hundredth = ________

15. Change 2.85 to a fraction. Reduce if necessary. ________

16. Write $\frac{7}{8}$ as a decimal. ________

17. 98.5°F = ________ °C

18. 14°C = ________ °F

19. $\frac{12.50}{0.50} \times 4.5 =$ ________

20. Something was wrong with Tu. He felt sick, and he had a fever. At 3:00 P.M. his temperature was 101.8°F. By 5:00 P.M. it was 102.3°F. How many degrees had his temperature gone up by? ________

21. Valley Vista used a 45.6 ounce can of kidney beans in a chili casserole recipe. If each portion gets an equal amount of the beans and the recipe serves 9 people, how many ounces will each serving contain? Round to the nearest whole number. ________

22. I had an interview at the dental clinic for a dental assistant post. I had to stop to get gas. I put 7 gallons of gas in my car. Each gallon cost me $2.86. How much did I spend on gas? ________

23. The farm raises its own produce and meat. Will has a cow that produces milk. She gives 2.3 gallons of milk a day. How many gallons does she give in a month that has 30 days? ________

24. Bradley Benjamin heard that the nursing staff at Sky View earns $13.93 per hour. He is currently earning $12.46 per hour. How much more could he earn a week at Sky View than his current job if he calculated the rate for a 40 hour week? ________

25. Sally is trying to increase her dietary fiber intake. She eats 20.8 grams of fiber a day. If her goal is to eat 32 grams of dietary fiber, how many more grams of fiber does she need to eat? ________

Unit 4 Practice Exam Name ________________

Solve the ratio and proportion problems. Remember that ratios are reduced to their simplest form.

1. Write 8 days out of 15 as a ratio: ________

2. Is this an example of a proportion? Check the answer box.

   2 : 3 :: 20 : 15 ☐ Yes ☐ No

3. 5 : 30 = 12 : ? ? = ________

4. $\frac{1}{4} : 5 = ? : 70$? = ________

5. $82 : ? = \frac{1}{2} : 18$? = ________

6. $\frac{2}{4} = \frac{?}{98}$? = ________

7. $\frac{\frac{1}{2}}{\frac{1}{4}} = \frac{90}{?}$? = ________

8. $\frac{1}{12} : 28 = ? : 84$? = ________

9. If eggs cost $2.10 a dozen, how much do 16 eggs cost? ________

10. If Jerry makes $13.10 an hour, what is her pay for 15 hours? ________

11. A mouthwash cost $4.36 for 32 ounces. How much is paid per ounce? ________

12. Each calendar for the nursing home fund raiser costs $8.75. What is the cost for 25 calendars? ________

13. Simplify the following ratio $12\frac{1}{4} : 8$ ________

14. Simplify the following ratio $15 : \frac{1}{3}$ ________

15. Solve $^{1.7}/_{x} = {}^{8.2}/_{0.8}$ Round to the nearest tenth.________

16. A set of three surgical masks cost $1.39. How many complete sets of masks can you buy with a budget of ten dollars. Do not worry about tax or shipping ________

17. 17 teaspoons = ________ tablespoons

18. 1 inch = 2.5 centimeters so 17.8 inches = ________ centimeters. Round to the nearest tenth.

19. 1 kilogram = 2.2 pounds so 49 kilograms = ________ pounds

20. $\frac{5}{7\frac{2}{4}} = \frac{?}{12\frac{1}{2}}$? = ________

Thresa's Roasted Red Tomato Soup

Nutrition facts	Amount/serving	%DV*	Amount/serving	%DV*
Serving size ½ cup (120 milliliters)	Total fat 0 gram	0%	Total carbohydrates 20 grams	7%
	Saturated fat 0 gram	0%	Fiber 1 gram	4%
Condensed soup	Cholestrol 0 milligram	0%	Sugars 15 grams	
Servings about 2.5 Calories 90	Sodium 610 milligrams	30%	Protein 2 grams	
Fat calories 0	Vitamin A 10% · Vitamin C 10% · Calcium 0% · Iron %			

*Percent daily values (%DV) are based on a 2,000 calories diet.

21. If $^1/_2$ cup of soup equals 120 milliliters, then how many milliliters are in $3\,^1/_4$ cups of soup? ________

22. If a can has 2.5 servings, how many cans are needed to serve 12 people? ________

23. One serving contains 90 calories, how many calories are in $4\,^1/_2$ servings? ________

24. 1 gram of fiber constitutes 4% of a daily dietary value. How many grams of fiber would be present in 25% of the daily value? ________

25. How many grams of carbohydrates are present if the portion meets 30% of the daily value of carbohydrates? Round to the nearest tenth if necessary. ________

Unit 5 Practice Exam Name ________________

1. Convert $3\frac{1}{4}$ to a percent. ________
2. Convert 0.625 to a percent ________
3. Convert 453 to a percent ________
4. Convert $\frac{2}{5}$ to a percent ________
5. Convert $4\frac{1}{5}$ to a percent ________
6. Convert $\frac{\frac{2}{5}}{75}$ to a percent ________
7. Convert 45% to a decimal ________
8. Convert $5\frac{1}{4}\%$ to a decimal ________
9. Convert $\frac{3}{4}\%$ to a fraction ________
10. What is 12% of 233? ________
11. Find 56% of 250 ________
12. What is $22\frac{1}{2}\%$ of 400? ________
13. What percent of 80 is 14? ________
14. Find 32% of 360. ________
15. What is $12\frac{2}{3}\%$ of 120? ________
16. $15\frac{1}{4}\%$ of what number is 45.75? ________
17. What is 0.9% of 34? ________
18. Write the ratio of pure drug to solution: 16% ________
19. Write the ratio of pure drug to solution: 1.08% ________
20. Write the ratio of pure drug to solution: $2\frac{2}{5}\%$ ________

21. There are 3 grams of pure drug are in 45 milliliters of solution. What is the percent strength of solution? ________

22. There are 35 milliliters of pure drug in 100 milliliters of solution. How many milliliters of pure drug are needed to make 85 milliliters of this solution. ________

23. Take a 8% discount from a final sales price of $120.00. The final sales price would now be ________.

24. Write as a simplified ratio of the pure drug form: $6\frac{1}{4}\%$ solution ________

25. Write as a simplified ratio of the pure drug form: 9% solution________

Unit 6 Practice Exam Name ________________

1–15. Complete the table below:

Fraction	Decimal	Ratio	Percent
$\frac{1}{100}$	_______	_______	_______
_______	0.08	_______	_______
_______	_______	2 : 5	_______
_______	_______	_______	$5\frac{1}{4}\%$
_______	0.1	_______	_______

16. If 1 tablespoon is equivalent to 3 teaspoons, how many tablespoons are in 13 teaspoons? _______

17. One inch equals approximately 2.54 centimeters. If an infant is measured at 48 centimeters, how long is the infant in inches? Round to the nearest tenth. _______

18. One cup has 8 ounces. So $14\frac{1}{4}$ cups equals _______ ounces.

19. One teaspoon contains 5 milliliters. Nine and one-half teaspoons contains _______ milliliters.

20. If one pound contains 16 ounces, how many ounces are in 24 pounds? _______

21. If 1 kilogram equals 2.2 pounds, how many kilograms are in 70 pounds? _______

22. $3\frac{1}{4}$ feet = _______ inches

23. _______ quarts = 12 pints

24. 15 pounds = _______ kilograms

25. _______ teaspoons = 30 milliliters

Complete Answer Key for Student Work Text

Unit 1: Whole Number Review

Symbols and Number Statements Practice 1: p. 2

1. $<$
3. $>$
5. $\geq$
7. $>$
9. $>$
11. $\leq$

Practice 2: p. 2

Answers will vary

Addition Practice: p. 3

1. 19
3. 492
5. 2,063
7. 488
9. 2,664

Addition Applications: pp. 3–4

1. a. 266
   b. 711
   c. 1,176
   d. 20 boxes
3. a. 300
   b. 720
   c. 75
   d. 110
   e. 1,205

Subtraction Practice: p. 5

1. 394
3. 235
5. 437
7. 1,873
9. 4,212

Subtraction Applications: p. 5

1. 1,474
3. 3 boxes

Multiplication Practice: p. 7

1. 96
3. 23,508
5. 99,960
7. 12,288
9. 92,656
11. 4,152

Multiplication Applications: p. 7

1. $3,444.00
3. $525.00

Prime Factorization: p. 8

1. $2^2 \cdot 31$
3. $2^2 \cdot 23$

Division Setup Practice: p. 9

1. $76\overline{)145}$
3. $17\overline{)49}$
5. $8\overline{)2044}$

Division Practice: p. 10

1. 94
3. 3,086 R 1
5. 311
7. 1,576 R 8
9. 23,441
11. 12,506 R 1

Division Applications: pp. 10–11

1. 13 days
3. $21
5. $1,656.00
7. 9 grams

Solving for the Unknown Number with Basic Mathematics: p. 11

Practice 1: p .11

1. 74
3. 53
5. 13

Practice 2: p. 12

1. 86
3. 560
5. 35

Practice 3: p. 12

1. 39
3. 4
5. 75

Practice 4: p. 12

1. 132
3. 3
5. 18

Rounding Practice: p. 13

1. a. 3,920
   b. 140
   c. 6,950
   d. 1,930
   e. 15,930
   f. 100
3. a. 3,000
   b. 88,000
   c. 7,000
   d. 13,000
   e. 433,000
   f. 3,000

Estimation Practice: p. 14

1. a. $194
   b. $162
   c. $112
   d. $2,914

Basics of Statistical Analysis: p. 14

Mean/Average: p. 15

1. $9
3. 5
5. 7

Median: p. 16

1. 99
3. 26
5. 9

Mode: pp. 17–18

1. 8
3. #24
5. 6 & 7

Range: pp. 18–19

1. 82
3. 360
5. 87

Roman Numerals: Concept 1 Practice: p. 20

1. 13
3. 31
5. 1001
7. xxxi
9. iss

Concept 2 Practice: p. 20

1. $9\frac{1}{2}$
3. 400
5. 99
7. xxxix
9. CCXL

Concept 3 Practice: p. 21

1. 114
3. 514
5. 89
7. 404
9. $592\frac{1}{2}$

Practice: p. 21

1. xivss
3. CXLVI
5. IM
7. CDL
9. xvii

Mixed Practice: pp. 21–22

1. 750
3. 18
5. xix
7. DCVII
9. LXVI
11. 908
13. CCCLXII
15. IM
17. 78
19. MMDXV

Time in Allied Health: p. 22

Practice Convert to Universal Time: p. 23

1. 0005
3. 0739
5. 1245
7. 1757
9. 2125

Practice in Standard Time: p. 23

1. 12:56 P.M.
3. 12:09 A.M.
5. 12:48 A.M.
7. 3:24 P.M.
9. 9:12 P.M.

Whole Number Self-Test: pp. 23–25

1. 1,075
2. 263 dollars or $263.00
3. 7 dollars
4. 66
5. 16
6. 50
7. 17
8. a. $1,500
   b. $200
   c. $150
   d. $100
   e. $375
   f. $2,325.00
9. $966.00
10. 5,780
11. 110
12. $504
13. ten thousands
14. >
15. $19\frac{1}{2}$

Unit 2: Fractions

Part to Whole Relationships: p. 27

1. Three parts to four total parts
3. Seven parts to eight total parts

Equivalent Fractions Practice: p. 28

1. 6
3. 8
5. 15
7. 36
9. 54

Reducing Fractions Practice: pp. 29–30

1. $\frac{1}{7}$
3. $\frac{1}{2}$
5. $\frac{1}{4}$
7. $\frac{1}{2}$
9. $\frac{1}{3}$

Reducing Mixed Numbers Practice: p. 30

1. $13\frac{1}{4}$
3. $1\frac{1}{2}$
5. $3\frac{1}{4}$
7. $2\frac{1}{9}$
9. $6\frac{1}{2}$

Fractional Parts from Words Practice: p. 31

1. $\frac{2}{5}$
3. $\frac{1}{3}$
5. $\frac{1}{8}$

Improper Fractions to Mixed Numbers Practice: pp. 31–32

1. $7\frac{1}{2}$
3. $19\frac{1}{2}$
5. $9\frac{3}{7}$
7. $2\frac{3}{8}$
9. 1

Adding Like Denominators Practice: pp. 33–34

1. 1
3. 2
5. $\frac{7}{12}$
7. $\frac{7}{13}$
9. $22\frac{5}{6}$
11. $\frac{4}{5}$
13. 1
15. $140\frac{1}{4}$

Finding Common Denominator Practice: pp. 34–35

1. 20
3. 44
5. 25
7. 200
9. 27

Adding Unlike Fractions Practice: pp. 35–36

1. $\frac{17}{20}$
3. $1\frac{1}{9}$
5. $\frac{1}{2}$
7. $\frac{13}{21}$
9. $1\frac{1}{15}$
11. $1\frac{2}{5}$
13. $106\frac{8}{9}$
15. $8\frac{7}{8}$

Finding the Common Denominator Practice: pp. 36–37

1. 20
3. 192
5. 45
7. 36
9. 30

Adding Fractions Practice: pp. 37–38

1. $9\frac{11}{12}$
3. $13\frac{1}{2}$
5. $6\frac{5}{7}$
7. $18\frac{29}{30}$
9. $18\frac{9}{10}$
11. $16\frac{17}{27}$
13. $39\frac{5}{12}$
15. $13\frac{7}{15}$
17. $4\frac{7}{16}$
19. $5\frac{1}{2}$

Addition Applications: p. 38

1. $121\frac{3}{4}$
3. $1\frac{3}{16}$
5. $3\frac{5}{6}$

Ordering Fractions Practice: p. 39

1. $\frac{4}{12}, \frac{1}{4}, \frac{2}{9}$
3. $\frac{20}{50}, \frac{33}{100}, \frac{6}{25}$

Subtracting Like Fractions Practice: p. 40

1. $\frac{1}{9}$
3. $\frac{2}{11}$
5. $2\frac{1}{6}$
7. $45\frac{1}{8}$
9. $\frac{1}{2}$
11. $\frac{1}{4}$
13. $12\frac{1}{5}$
15. $31\frac{1}{9}$

17. $124\frac{1}{12}$

19. $12\frac{5}{33}$

Subtracting Mixed Numbers from Whole Numbers Practice: p. 42

1. $10\frac{1}{6}$

3. $9\frac{3}{4}$

5. $14\frac{6}{13}$

7. $5\frac{6}{7}$

9. $10\frac{2}{5}$

Subtracting Fractions Practice: pp. 42–43

1. $7\frac{13}{20}$

3. $19\frac{17}{30}$

5. $5\frac{17}{22}$

7. $111\frac{23}{30}$

9. $31\frac{5}{8}$

11. $16\frac{5}{6}$

13. $76\frac{25}{36}$

15. $6\frac{1}{2}$

Additional Practice in Subtraction with Borrowing: pp. 43–44

1. $8\frac{5}{8}$

3. $9\frac{3}{4}$

5. $11\frac{3}{4}$

7. $72\frac{5}{7}$

9. $83\frac{7}{12}$

Subtraction Application: p. 44

1. $11\frac{1}{2}$

3. $99\frac{1}{4}$

5. $3\frac{1}{2}$

Multiplication Practice: p. 45

1. $\frac{1}{16}$

3. $\frac{28}{45}$

5. $\frac{3}{35}$

7. $\frac{4}{9}$

9. $\frac{13}{66}$

Multiplication: Fractions and Whole Numbers Practice: p. 46

1. $1\frac{1}{2}$

3. $16\frac{1}{3}$

5. $5\frac{3}{5}$

7. $11\frac{2}{3}$

9. 4

Multiplication Practice: p. 48

1. $1\frac{5}{7}$

3. $\frac{1}{4}$
5. $\frac{1}{20}$
7. $\frac{1}{4}$
9. $\frac{11}{96}$
11. $\frac{1}{24}$

Making Improper Fractions Practice: p. 49

1. $\frac{33}{4}$
3. $\frac{88}{5}$
5. $\frac{27}{12}$
7. $\frac{32}{9}$
9. $\frac{53}{12}$

Multiplying Fractions: p. 51

1. $\frac{29}{84}$
3. $\frac{21}{40}$
5. $\frac{20}{27}$
7. $40\frac{1}{4}$
9. $3\frac{17}{20}$

Multiplication Application: pp. 51–52

1. 70 doses
3. 875 milligrams
5. $18\frac{3}{4}$ cups

Dividing Fractions Practice: pp. 53–54

1. $\frac{5}{7}$
3. $\frac{7}{24}$
5. 8
7. $\frac{1}{45}$
9. $\frac{1}{120}$
11. $3\frac{8}{9}$
13. $2\frac{7}{9}$
15. $4\frac{8}{9}$
17. $\frac{31}{130}$
19. $1\frac{47}{105}$

Division Applications: p. 54

1. $9\frac{3}{20}$
3. $13.30
5. 10

Celsius to Fahrenheit Temperature Conversions Practice: p. 55

1. 68
3. 77
5. 104
7. 176

Fahrenheit to Celsius Temperature Conversions Practice: p. 56

1. 40
3. 10
5. 15
7. 30

Complex Fractions Practice: p. 57

1. $\frac{3}{32}$

3. $\frac{1}{15{,}000}$

5. $1\frac{1}{5}$

7. $\frac{4}{5}$

9. $\frac{15}{16}$

Mixed Complex Fraction Problems Practice: p. 58

1. 5
3. 12
5. 1

Fraction Self-Test: pp. 58–59

1. $\frac{1}{4}$
2. Answers will vary: $\frac{2}{12}, \frac{3}{18}, \frac{4}{24}$, etc.
3. $11\frac{1}{11}$
4. $11\frac{11}{12}$
5. $39\frac{4}{5}$
6. $30\frac{13}{16}$
7. $\frac{4}{9}$
8. 25
9. $\frac{2}{12}, \frac{1}{4}, \frac{1}{3}, \frac{3}{8}$
10. 50
11. more
12. $\frac{1}{3}$
13. $\frac{5}{8}$
14. $\frac{3}{8}$
15. $26\frac{5}{24}$

Unit 3: Decimals

Decimals in Words: pp. 61–62

1. Seven tenths
3. Five hundredths
5. One hundred fifty and seventy-five thousands
7. One hundred nine and twenty-three thousands
9. Eighteen and eight hundredths

Words to Decimals: p. 62

1. 0.2
3. 300.002
5. 6.03

Rounding to the Nearest Tenth Practice: p. 63

1. 6.7
3. 0.8
5. 25.0 or 25
7. 0.1
9. 9.9

Rounding to the Nearest Hundredth Practice: p. 63

1. 17.33
3. 4.82
5. 0.01
7. 32.65
9. 46.09

Smaller Decimals Practice: p. 64

1. 0.89
3. 2.012
5. 0.0033

Larger Decimals Practice: p. 64

1. 0.0785
3. 0.5
5. 0.675

Ordering from Largest to Smallest Practice: pp. 64–65

1. 7.5, 7.075, 0.75, 0.7, 0.07
3. 5.55, 5.15, 5.05, 0.5, 0.05

Adding Decimals Practice: pp. 65–66

1. 38.15
3. 86.235
5. 89.2496
7. 127.52
9. 214.281

Addition Applications: p. 66

1. 4.5 milligrams
3. 226 milligrams
5. 124.54 centimeters

Subtracting Decimals Practice: p. 67

1. 0.72
3. 14.065
5. 3.5013
7. 0.175
9. 87.436

Subtraction Applications: pp. 67–68

1. 0.65 liters
3. 1.5 milligrams
5. 1.8°F

Multiplying Decimals Practice: p. 69

1. 12.6
3. 33.6
5. 128.38
7. 0.8088
9. 0.4726
11. 0.0024
13. 151.11
15. 1.65036
17. 7.632
19. 6,942.53
21. 1,342.11
23. 10.04565

Multiplication Applications: p. 70

1. $420.80
3. $1,618.20
5. $128.00

Dividing Decimals Practice: p. 71

1. 0.63
3. 0.232
5. 0.12
7. 52.4
9. 3.02

Dividing with Zeros as Placeholders Practice: p. 72

1. 1,060
3. 2.08
5. 1.099
7. 30.66
9. 0.2099

Additional Practice: p. 72

1. 5.3
3. 0.04
5. 1.39
7. 403.9

Simplified Multiplication Practice: pp. 73–74

1. 135
3. 1,257.5
5. 6
7. 12,670
9. 476
11. 13.45
13. 10.09
15. 23,850

Simplified Division Practice: pp. 74–75

1. 1.29
3. 12.5
5. 0.025
7. 0.158
9. 0.325
11. 10.01
13. 0.03076
15. 0.10275

Division Applications: p. 75

1. $63.25
3. 3 tablets
5. $26.24

Decimal to Fraction Conversion Practice: pp. 76–77

1. $\frac{1}{25}$
3. $6\frac{1}{4}$
5. $225\frac{1}{20}$
7. $7\frac{3}{4}$
9. $9\frac{3}{10}$

Fraction to Decimal Conversion Practice: p. 78

1. 0.5
3. 0.875
5. 0.24
7. 0.2
9. $0.83\frac{1}{3}$ or 0.083

Temperature Conversions with Decimals Practice: pp. 79–80

1. 93.2
3. 224.6
5. 107.6
7. 38
9. 53.6

Mixed Fraction and Decimal Problems Practice: p. 81

1. 2.2
3. 7.5
5. 0.168
7. 7.675

Decimal Self-Test: pp. 82–83

1. Forty-five thousandths
2. 21.75
3. 16.925
4. 4.5405
5. 90.2
6. 978.74
7. 8.018, 0.81, 0.08, 0.018
8. 1,000.9
9. 2 milligrams
10. 3 tablets
11. $\frac{1}{8}$
12. 0.26
13. 3.625
14. 39.4°C
15. 1.7

Unit 4: Ratio and Proportion

Ratios: pp. 84–85

1. 5 : 7
3. 1 : 5
5. 1 : 2

Simplifying Ratio: pp. 85–86

1. 27 : 1
3. 20 : 1
5. 2 : 1
7. 13 : 21
9. 5 : 2

Proportions: p. 86

1. No
3. Yes
5. No

Solving with Proportions Practice: p. 87

1. 7.5
3. 16
5. 27
7. 14
9. 52

Measurement Conversions Using Proportions Practice: pp. 89–90

1. $7\frac{2}{3}$
3. 8
5. 9
7. 4
9. 56
11. $2\frac{1}{2}$
13. 5
15. $1\frac{1}{2}$
17. 80
19. 5

Word Problems Using Proportions Practice: p. 91

1. 3 caplets
3. 17.5 grams
5. 28 kilograms

Solving for x in Complex Problems Practice: pp. 92–93

1. 6
3. 9.6
5. 1
7. $1\frac{1}{3}$
9. 2.4
11. 1.5

Nutrition Applications: p. 94

1. 9
3. 9
5. 48
7. 1312

pp. 94–95

1. 645
3. 220
5. 121.5

Practice with Food Labels: pp. 95–98

1. 840 milliliters
3. 405 calories
5. 42.9 grams
7. 240 calories
9. 40%
11. 11 grams
13. 1200 milliliters
15. $6\frac{1}{4}$ cups

Ratio and Proportion Self-Test: pp. 98–100

1. Answers vary.
2. 3
3. 9
4. $2\frac{2}{3}$
5. 125
6. 140 milligrams
7. 8 tablets
8. 0.3 cubic centimeters
9. $\frac{1}{75}$
10. 1.5
11. 2 minutes 10 seconds
12. 80 patients
13. 640

14. $\frac{4}{125}$

15. 96 ounces

Unit 5: Percents

Percent-to-Decimal Practice: p. 102

1. 0.45
3. $0.78\frac{1}{5}$ or 0.782
5. $0.44\frac{1}{2}$ or 0.445

Decimal-to-Percent Practice: pp. 102–103

1. 62.5%
3. 860%
5. 7.6%

Mixed Practice: p. 103

1. 0.7689
3. 0.86
5. 7.8%
7. $125\frac{1}{4}$% or 125.25%
9. 0.015

Set Up of Percents Practice: p. 104

1. $\frac{25}{100} = \frac{x}{200}$
3. $\frac{8.5}{100} = \frac{x}{224}$
5. $\frac{x}{100} = \frac{18}{150}$
7. $\frac{x}{100} = \frac{75}{90}$
9. $\frac{50}{100} = \frac{75}{x}$

Percents Practice: p. 105

1. 18
3. 25%
5. 5.88
7. 22.5%
9. 17.60

More Complex Percents Practice: p. 106

1. 41.67
3. 60
5. 15.63
7. 1280
9. 533.33

Percent Strength Practice: p. 107

1. 1 gram of pure drug to 25 milliliters of solution
3. 1.5 grams of pure drug to 100 milliliters of solution
5. 1 gram of pure drug to 20 milliliters of solution

Percent Equivalents in Solutions Practice: pp. 108–109

1. a. 1.25 grams
   b. 1.75 grams
   c. 3.25 grams
   d. 6.25 grams
3. a. 30%
   b. 60 grams

Additional Practice with Solution Strength: pp. 109–110

1. a. 12.75 grams
   b. 100 milliliters
   c. 51 : 400
   d. 4.5 grams
   e. 10.2 grams
   f. 7.7 grams
3. a. 78 grams
   b. 100 milliliters
   c. 39 : 50
   d. 51.1 grams
   e. 70.2 grams
   f. 351 grams

Single Trade Discounts Practice: p. 111

1. \$71.33 \$404.17
3. \$15.69 \$109.86
5. \$88.23 \$264.67
7. \$112.68 \$137.72
9. \$63.20 \$94.80

Percent Self-Test: pp. 111–113

1. Answers vary. A percent is a number which is part of a whole. 75% is 75 parts of 100.
2. a. $87\frac{1}{4}\%$ or 87.25%

   b. $83\frac{1}{3}\%$
3. 243.75
4. 20
5. 200
6. There are 5.5 grams of pure drug in 100 milliliters of solution.
7. 2.25 grams of pure drug
8. a. \$15.54

   b. \$113.96
9. 8.3% or $8\frac{1}{3}\%$
10. \$48.90
11. 12%
12. 2.5
13. 6.4%
14. 0.15
15. 70000

Unit 6: Combined Applications

Conversions: pp. 117–118

Fraction	Decimal	Ratio	Percent
1. $\frac{3}{4}$	0.75	3 : 4	75%
3. $\frac{1}{2}$	0.5	1 : 2	50%
5. $\frac{1}{250}$	0.004	1 : 250	0.4%
7. $\frac{3}{50}$	0.06	3 : 50	6%
9. $\frac{1}{10}$	0.1	1 : 10	10%
11. $1\frac{9}{25}$	1.36	34 : 25	136%
13. $\frac{2}{5}$	0.4	2 : 5	40%
15. $\frac{16}{25}$	0.64	16 : 25	64%
17. $\frac{5}{6}$	$0.83\frac{1}{3}$	5 : 6	$83\frac{1}{3}\%$
19. $\frac{1}{100}$	0.01	1 : 100	1%

Using Combined Application in Measurement Convertions Abbreviations: p. 119

1. Foot
3. Ounce
5. Pound
7. Quart
9. Drop

Standard Units of Measurement Conversion Review: p. 120

1. $2\frac{1}{2}$
3. 31.25 or 31.75
5. 3
7. 24
9. $2\frac{1}{2}$

More Combined Applications Practice: p. 121

1. 6
3. 36
5. 32
7. 149.6
9. 4

Mixed Review Practice: p. 122

1. 2
3. $\frac{1}{12}$
5. $\frac{1}{30}$

Converting among Systems: pp. 122–123

Fraction	Decimal	Ratio	Percent
1. $\frac{7}{8}$	0.875	7 : 8	$87\frac{1}{2}\%$
3. $\frac{3}{4}$	0.75	3 : 4	75%
5. $\frac{2}{5}$	0.40	2 : 5	40%
7. $\frac{2}{25}$	0.08	2 : 25	8%
9. $\frac{3}{5}$	0.6	3 : 5	60%
11. $1\frac{5}{8}$	1.625	13 : 8	162.5%
13. $\frac{11}{50}$	0.22	11 : 50	22%
15. $\frac{3}{25}$	0.12	3 : 25	12%
17. $\frac{1}{6}$	$0.16\frac{2}{3}$	1 : 6	$16\frac{2}{3}\%$
19. $\frac{1}{25}$	0.04	1 : 25	4%

Combined Application Self-Test: pp. 123–124

1. 0.04
2. 1 : 200
3. $1\frac{1}{20}$
4. 33 : 8
5. 27.25
6. 6%
7. 57 : 400
8. 26
9. 24
10. 105 or 106.68
11. 1,080
12. 16
13. 420
14. 0.0804
15. 0.3

Index

CAT 150
Anatomy, Physiology, and Terminology

Taken From:
Medical Terminology: A Living Language, Fourth Edition
by Bonnie F. Fremgen and Suzanne S. Frucht

A Commitment to Accuracy

As a student embarking on a career in health care you probably already know how critically important it is to be precise in your work. Patients and co-workers will be counting on you to avoid errors on a daily basis. Likewise, we owe it to you – the reader – to ensure accuracy in this book. We have gone to great lengths to verify that the information provided in *Medical Terminology: A Living Language* is complete and correct. To this end, here are the steps we have taken:

1. **Editorial Review**–We have assembled a large team of developmental consultants (listed on the preceding pages) to critique every word and every image in this book. No fewer than 12 content experts have read each chapter for accuracy. In addition, some members of our developmental team were specifically assigned to focus on the precision of each illustration that appears in the book.
2. **Medical Illustrations**–A team of medically-trained illustrators was hired to prepare each piece of art that graces the pages of this book. These illustrators have a higher level of scientific education than the artists for most textbooks, and they worked directly with the authors and members of our development team to make sure that their work was clear, correct, and consistent with what is described in the text
3. **Accurate Ancillaries**–Realizing that the teaching and learning ancillaries are often as vital to instruction as the book itself, we took extra steps to ensure accuracy and consistency within these components. Textbook co-author Suzanne Frucht served the dual role of editor/author of each of the ancillary components. She wrote or edited every test question, every PowerPoint slide, and every element of the student DVD-ROM and online courses. Her goal was to guarantee a tight mesh between the content in the book and the content in these additional resources. Finally, we assigned some members of our development team to specifically focus on critiquing every bit of content that comprises the instructional ancillary resources to confirm accuracy.

While our intent and actions have been directed at creating an error-free text, we have established a process for correcting any mistakes that may have slipped past our editors. Pearson takes this issue seriously and therefore welcomes any and all feedback that you can provide along the lines of helping us enhance the accuracy of this text. If you identify any errors that need to be corrected in a subsequent printing, please sending them to:

Pearson Health Editorial
Medical Terminology Corrections
One Lake Street
Upper Saddle River, NJ 07458

Thank you for helping Pearson to reach its goal of providing the most accurate medical terminology textbooks available.

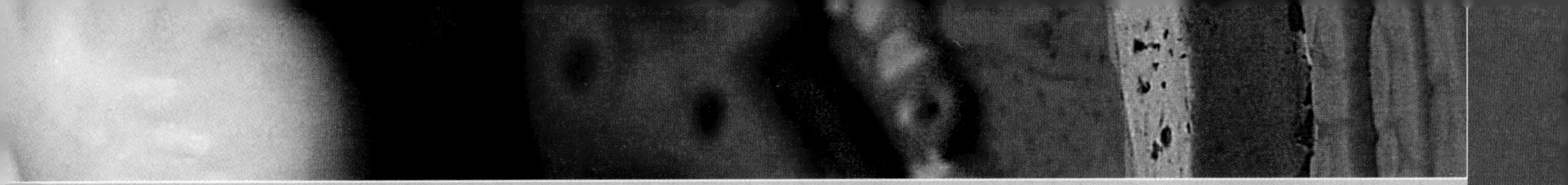

Contents

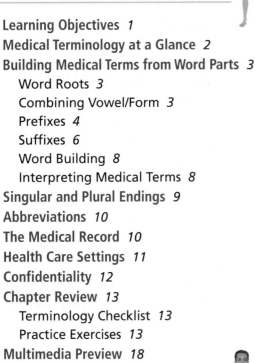

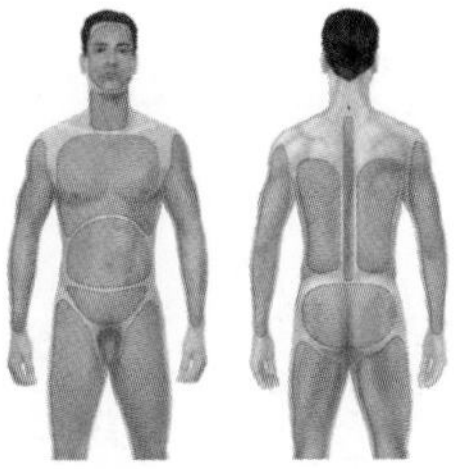

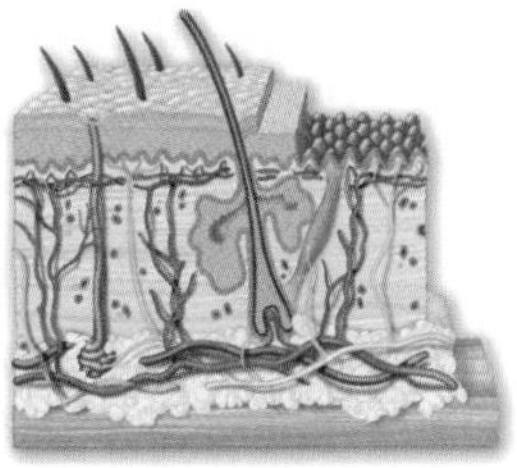

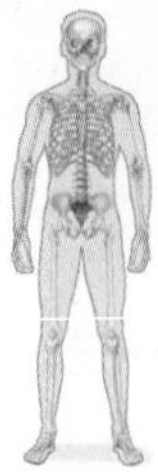

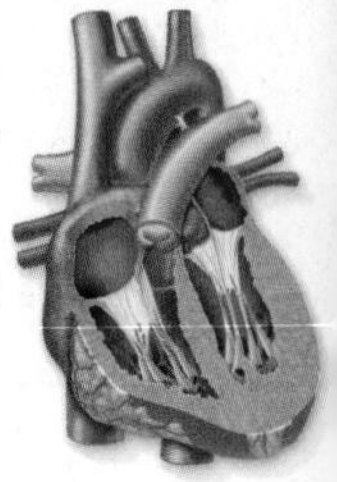

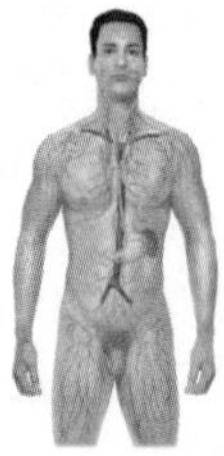

9 Urinary System 279

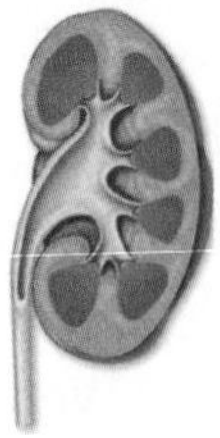

10 Reproductive System 311

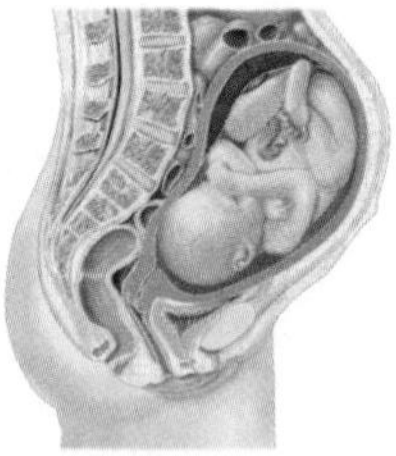

11 Endocrine System 355

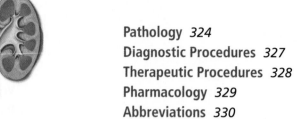

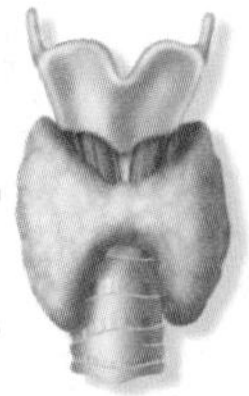

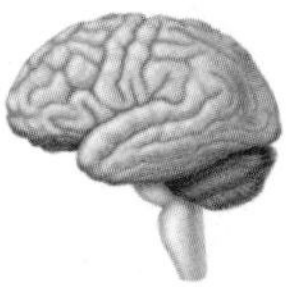

12 Nervous System 387

13 Special Senses: The Eye and Ear 423

SECTION I The Eye

SECTION II The Ear

Appendices 463

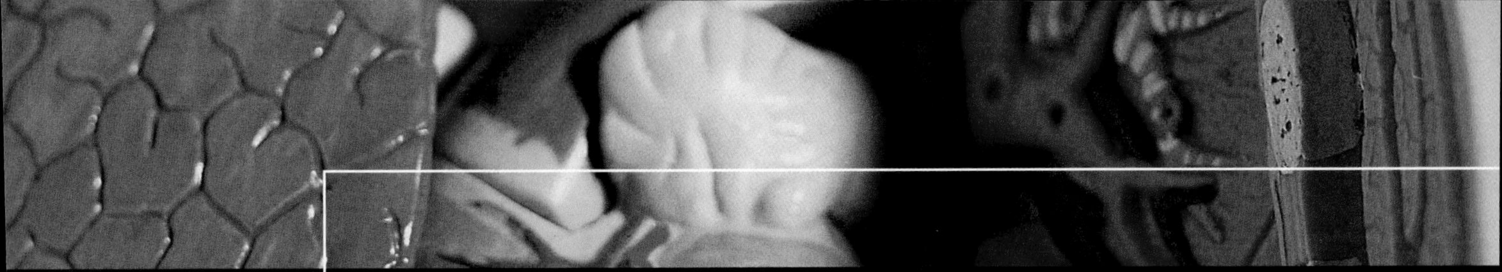

1 Introduction to Medical Terminology

Learning Objectives

Upon completion of this chapter, you will be able to:

- Discuss the four parts of medical terms.
- Recognize word roots and combining forms.
- Identify the most common prefixes and suffixes.
- Define word building and describe a strategy for translating medical terms.
- State the importance of correct spelling of medical terms.
- State the rules for determining singular and plural endings.
- Discuss the importance of using caution with abbreviations.
- Recognize the documents found in a medical record.
- Recognize the different healthcare settings.
- Understand the importance of confidentiality.

Medical Terminology at a Glance

Learning medical terminology can initially seem like studying a strange new language. However, once you understand some of the basic rules as to how medical terms are formed using word building, it will become much like piecing together a puzzle. The general guidelines for forming words; an understanding of word roots, combining forms, prefixes, and suffixes; pronunciation; and spelling are discussed in this chapter. Chapter 2 introduces you to terms used to describe the body as a whole. Chapters 3 through 13 each focus on a specific body system and present new combining forms, prefixes, and suffixes, as well as exercises to help you gain experience building new medical terms. Finally, Chapter 14 includes the terminology for several important areas of patient care. In addition, "Med Term Tips" are sprinkled throughout all of the chapters to assist in clarifying some of the material. New medical terms discussed in each section are listed separately at the beginning of the section, and each chapter contains numerous pathological, diagnostic, treatment, and surgical terms. You can use these lists as an additional study tool for previewing and reviewing terms.

Understanding medical terms requires you to be able to put words together or build words from their parts. It is impossible to memorize thousands of medical terms; however, once you understand the basics, you can distinguish the meaning of medical terms by analyzing their prefixes, suffixes, and word roots. Remember that there will always be some exceptions to every rule, and medical terminology is no different. We will attempt to point out these exceptions where they exist. Most medical terms, however, do follow the general rule that there is a **word root** or fundamental meaning for the word, a **prefix** and a **suffix** that modify the meaning of the word root, and sometimes a **combining vowel** to connect other word parts. You will be amazed at the seemingly difficult words you will be able to build and understand when you follow the simple steps in word building (see Figure 1.1 ■).

■ **Figure 1.1** Nurse completing a patient report. Healthcare workers use medical terminology in order to accurately and efficiently communicate patient information to each other.

Building Medical Terms from Word Parts

Four different word parts or elements can be used to construct medical terms:

1. The **word root** is the foundation of the word.	**cardi**ogram = record of the heart
2. A **prefix** is at the beginning of the word.	**peri**cardium = around the heart
3. A **suffix** is at the end of the word.	card**itis** = inflammation of the heart
4. The **combining vowel** is a vowel (usually o) that links the word root to another word root or a suffix.	cardi**o**my**o**pathy = disease of the heart muscle

The following sections on word roots, combining vowels and forms, prefixes, and suffixes will consider each of these word parts in more detail and present examples of some of those most commonly used.

Med Term Tip

Medical terms are built from word parts:

Word Building Part	Example (Meaning)
1. Word root	*cardi* (heart)
2. Prefix	*peri-* (around)
3. Suffix	*-itis* (inflammation)

When these components are put together, the word *pericarditis* is formed, meaning inflammation around the heart.

Word Roots

The word root is the foundation of a medical term and provides us with the general meaning of the word. The word root often indicates the body system or part of the body that is being discussed, such as *cardi* for heart. At other times the word root may be an action. For example, the word root *cis* means to cut (as in incision).

A term may have more than one word root. For example, **osteoarthritis** (oss tee oh ar THRY tis) combines the word root *oste* meaning bone and *arthr* meaning the joints. When the suffix *-itis*, meaning inflammation, is added, we have the entire word, meaning an inflammation involving bone at the joints.

Combining Vowel/Form

To make it possible to pronounce long medical terms with ease and to combine several word parts, a combining vowel is used. This is most often the vowel *o*. Combining vowels are utilized in two places: between a word root and a suffix or between two word roots.

To decide whether to use a combining vowel between a word root and suffix, first look at the suffix. If it begins with a vowel, do not use the combining vowel. If, however, the suffix begins with a consonant, then use a combining vowel. For example: To combine *arthr* with *-scope* will require a combining vowel: **arthroscope** (AR throh scope). But to combine *arthr* with *-itis* does not require a combining vowel: **arthritis** (ar THRY tis).

The combining vowel is typically kept between two word roots, even if the second word root begins with a vowel. For example, in forming the term **gastroenteritis** (gas troh en ter EYE tis) the combining vowel is kept between the two word roots *gastr* and *enter* (gastrenteritis is incorrect). As you can tell from pronouncing these two terms, the combining vowel makes the pronunciation easier.

When writing a word root by itself, its **combining form** is typically used. This consists of the word root and its combining vowel written in a word root/vowel form, for example, *cardi/o*. Since it is often simpler to pronounce word roots when they appear in their combining form, this format is used throughout this book.

Med Term Tip

Remember to break down every word into its components (prefix, word root/combining form, and suffix) when learning medical terminology. Do not try to memorize every medical term. Instead, figure out how the word is formed from its components. In a short time you will be able to do this automatically when seeing a new term.

Common Combining Forms

Some commonly used word roots in their combining form, their meaning, and examples of their use follow. Review the examples to observe when a combining vowel was kept and when it was dropped according to the rules presented on the preceding page.

Combining Form	Meaning	Example (Definition)
aden/o	gland	adenopathy (gland disease)
carcin/o	cancer	carcinoma (cancerous tumor)
cardi/o	heart	cardiac (pertaining to the heart)
chem/o	chemical	chemotherapy (treatment with chemicals)
cis/o	to cut	incision (process of cutting into)
dermat/o	skin	dermatology (study of the skin)
enter/o	small intestine	enteric (pertaining to the small intestine)
gastr/o	stomach	gastric (pertaining to the stomach)
gynec/o	female	gynecology (study of females)
hemat/o	blood	hematic (pertaining to the blood)
hydr/o	water	hydrocele (protrusion of water [in the scrotum])
immun/o	immune	immunology (study of immunity)
laryng/o	voice box	laryngeal (pertaining to the voice box)
morph/o	shape	morphology (study of shape)
nephr/o	kidney	nephromegaly (enlarged kidney)
neur/o	nerve	neural (pertaining to a nerve)
ophthalm/o	eye	ophthalmic (pertaining to the eye)
ot/o	ear	otic (pertaining to the ear)
path/o	disease	pathology (study of disease)
pulmon/o	lung	pulmonary (pertaining to the lungs)
rhin/o	nose	rhinoplasty (surgical repair of the nose)
ur/o	urine, urinary tract	urology (study of the urinary tract)

Prefixes

A new medical term is formed when a prefix is added to the front of the term. Prefixes frequently give information about the location of an organ, the number of parts, or the time (frequency). For example, the prefix *bi-* stands for two of something, such as **bilateral** (bye LAH ter al), which means having two sides. However, not every term will have a prefix.

Common Prefixes

Some of the more common prefixes, their meanings, and examples of their use follow. When written by themselves, prefixes are followed by a hyphen.

Prefix	Meaning	Example (Definition)
a-	without, away from	aphasia (without speech)
an-	without	anoxia (without oxygen)
ante-	before, in front of	antepartum (before birth)

anti-	against	antibiotic (against life)
auto-	self	autograft (a graft from one's own body)
brady-	slow	bradycardia (slow heartbeat)
dys-	painful, difficult	dyspnea (difficulty breathing)
endo-	within, inner	endoscope (instrument to view within)
epi-	upon, over	epigastric (upon or over the stomach)
eu-	normal, good	eupnea (normal breathing)
hetero-	different	heterograft (a graft from another person's body)
homo-	same	homozygous (having two identical genes)
hyper-	over, above	hypertrophy (overdevelopment)
hypo-	under, below	hypoglossal (under the tongue)
infra-	under, beneath, below	infraorbital (below, under the eye socket)
inter-	among, between	intervertebral (between the vertebrae)
intra-	within, inside	intravenous (inside, within a vein)
macro-	large	macrocephalic (having a large head)
micro-	small	microcephalic (having a small head)
neo-	new	neonate (newborn)
pan-	all	pancarditis (inflammation of all the heart)
para-	beside, beyond, near	paranasal (near or alongside the nose)
per-	through	percutaneous (through the skin)
peri-	around	pericardial (around the heart)
post-	after	postpartum (after birth)
pre-	before, in front of	prefrontal (in front of the frontal bone)
pseudo-	false	pseudocyesis (false pregnancy)
retro-	backward, behind	retrograde (movement in a backward direction)
sub-	below, under	subcutaneous (under, below the skin)
super-	above, excess	supernumerary (above the normal number)
supra-	above	suprapubic (above the pubic bone)
tachy-	rapid, fast	tachycardia (fast heartbeat)
trans-	through, across	transurethral (across the urethra)
ultra-	beyond, excess	ultrasound (high-frequency sound waves)

Med Term Tip

Be very careful with prefixes; many have similar spellings but very different meanings. For example:

anti- means "against"; *ante-* means "before"
inter- means "between"; *intra-* means "inside"
per- means "through"; *peri-* means "around"

Number Prefixes

Some common prefixes pertaining to the number of items or measurement, their meanings, and examples of their use follow.

Prefix	Meaning	Example (Definition)
bi-	two	bilateral (two sides)
hemi-	half	hemiplegia (paralysis of one side/half of the body)
mono-	one	monoplegia (paralysis of one extremity)
multi-	many	multigravida (woman pregnant more than once)
nulli-	none	nulligravida (woman with no pregnancies)
poly-	many	polyuria (large amounts of urine)

quad-	four	quadriplegia (paralysis of all four extremities)
semi-	partial, half	semiconscious (partially conscious)
tri-	three	triceps (muscle with three heads)
uni-	one	unilateral (one side)

Suffixes

A suffix is attached to the end of a word to add meaning, such as a condition, disease, or procedure. For example, the suffix *-itis,* which means inflammation, when added to *cardi-* forms the new word **carditis** (car DYE tis), which means inflammation of the heart. Every medical term *must* have a suffix. The majority of the time, the suffix is added to a word root, as in carditis above. However, terms can also be built from a suffix added directly to a prefix, without a word root. For example, the term **dystrophy** (DIS troh fee), which means abnormal development, is built from the prefix *dys-* (meaning abnormal) and the suffix *-trophy* (meaning development).

Med Term Tip

Remember, if a suffix begins with a vowel, the combining vowel is dropped: for example, *mastitis* rather than *mast**o**itis.*

Common Suffixes

Some common suffixes, their meanings, and examples of their use follow. When written by themselves, suffixes are preceded by a hyphen.

Suffix	Meaning	Example (Definition)
-algia	pain	gastralgia (stomach pain)
-cele	hernia, protrusion	cystocele (protrusion of the bladder)
-cise	cut	excise (to cut out)
-cyte	cell	erythrocyte (red cell)
-dynia	pain	cardiodynia (heart pain)
-ectasis	dilation	bronchiectasis (dilated bronchi)
-gen	that which produces	mutagen (that which produces mutations)
-genesis	produces, generates	osteogenesis (produces bone)
-genic	producing, produced by	carcinogenic (producing cancer)
-ia	state, condition	hemiplegia (condition of being half paralyzed)
-iasis	abnormal condition	lithiasis (abnormal condition of stones)
-ism	state of	hypothyroidism (state of low thyroid)
-itis	inflammation	cellulitis (inflammation of cells)
-logist	one who studies	cardiologist (one who studies the heart)
-logy	study of	cardiology (study of the heart)
-lysis	destruction	osteolysis (bone destruction)
-malacia	abnormal softening	chondromalacia (abnormal cartilage softening)
-megaly	enlargement, large	cardiomegaly (enlarged heart)
-oma	tumor, mass	carcinoma (cancerous tumor)
-osis	abnormal condition	cyanosis (abnormal condition of being blue)
-pathy	disease	myopathy (muscle disease)
-plasia	development, growth	dysplasia (abnormal development)
-plasm	formation, development	neoplasm (new formation)
-ptosis	drooping	proctoptosis (drooping rectum)

-rrhage	excessive, abnormal flow	hemorrhage (excessive bleeding)
-rrhea	discharge, flow	rhinorrhea (discharge from the nose)
-rrhexis	rupture	hysterorrhexis (ruptured uterus)
-sclerosis	hardening	arteriosclerosis (hardening of an artery)
-stenosis	narrowing	angiostenosis (narrowing of a vessel)
-therapy	treatment	chemotherapy (treatment with chemicals)
-trophy	nourishment, development	hypertrophy (excessive development)

Adjective Suffixes

The following suffixes are used to convert a word root into an adjective. These suffixes usually are translated as *pertaining to*.

Suffix	Meaning	Example (Definition)
-ac	pertaining to	cardiac (pertaining to the heart)
-al	pertaining to	duodenal (pertaining to the duodenum)
-an	pertaining to	ovarian (pertaining to the ovary)
-ar	pertaining to	ventricular (pertaining to a ventricle)
-ary	pertaining to	pulmonary (pertaining to the lungs)
-eal	pertaining to	esophageal (pertaining to the esophagus)
-iac	pertaining to	chondriac (pertaining to cartilage)
-ic	pertaining to	gastric (pertaining to the stomach)
-ical	pertaining to	neurological (pertaining to the study of the nerves)
-ile	pertaining to	penile (pertaining to the penis)
-ior	pertaining to	superior (pertaining to above)
-ory	pertaining to	auditory (pertaining to hearing)
-ose	pertaining to	adipose (pertaining to fat)
-ous	pertaining to	intravenous (pertaining to within a vein)
-tic	pertaining to	acoustic (pertaining to hearing)

Surgical Suffixes

The following suffixes indicate surgical procedures.

Suffix	Meaning	Example (Definition)
-centesis	puncture to withdraw fluid	arthrocentesis (puncture to withdraw fluid from a joint)
-ectomy	surgical removal	gastrectomy (surgically remove the stomach)
-ostomy	surgically create an opening	colostomy (surgically create an opening for the colon through the abdominal wall)
-otomy	cutting into	thoracotomy (cutting into the chest)
-pexy	surgical fixation	nephropexy (surgical fixation of a kidney)
-plasty	surgical repair	dermatoplasty (surgical repair of the skin)
-rrhaphy	suture	myorrhaphy (suture together muscle)

Med Term Tip

Surgical suffixes have very specific meanings:

-otomy means "to cut into"
-ostomy means "to create a new opening"
-ectomy means "to cut out" or "remove"

Procedural Suffixes

The following suffixes indicate procedural processes or instruments.

Suffix	Meaning	Example (Definition)
-gram	record or picture	electrocardiogram (record of heart's electricity)
-graph	instrument for recording	electrocardiograph (instrument for recording the heart's electrical activity)
-graphy	process of recording	electrocardiography (process of recording the heart's electrical activity)
-meter	instrument for measuring	audiometer (instrument to measure hearing)
-metry	process of measuring	audiometry (process of measuring hearing)
-scope	instrument for viewing	gastroscope (instrument to view stomach)
-scopy	process of visually examining	gastroscopy (process of visually examining the stomach)

Word Building

Word building consists of putting together several word elements to form a variety of terms. The combining form of a word may be added to another combining form along with a suffix to create a new descriptive term. For example, adding *hyster/o* (meaning uterus) to *salping/o* (meaning fallopian tubes) along with the suffix *-ectomy* (meaning surgical removal of) forms **hysterosalpingectomy** (hiss-ter-oh-sal-pin-JEK-toh-mee), the removal of both the uterus and the fallopian tubes. You will note that the combining vowel *o* is dropped when adding the suffix *-ectomy* since two vowels are not necessary.

Interpreting Medical Terms

The following strategy is a reliable method for puzzling out the meaning of an unfamiliar medical term.

Med Term Tip

To gain a quick understanding of a term, it may be helpful to you to read from the end of the word (or the suffix) back to the beginning (the prefix), and then pick up the word root. For example, *pericarditis* reads inflammation (*-itis*) surrounding (*peri-*) the heart (*cardi/o*).

Step	Example
1. Divide the term into its word parts.	gastr/o/enter/o/logy
2. Define each word part.	gastr = stomach o = combining vowel, no meaning enter = small intestine o = combining vowel, no meaning -logy = study
3. Combine the meaning of the word parts.	stomach, small intestine, study of

Pronunciation

You will hear different pronunciations for the same terms depending on where people were born or educated. As long as it is clear which term people are discussing, differing pronunciations are acceptable. Some people are difficult to understand over the telephone or on a transcription tape. If you have any doubt about a term being discussed, ask for the term to be spelled. For example, it is often difficult to hear the difference between the terms **abduction** and **adduction**. However, since the terms refer to opposite directions of movement, it is very important to double check if there is any question about which term was used.

Each new term in this book is introduced in boldface type, with the phonetic or "sounds like" pronunciation in parentheses immediately following. The part of the word that should receive the greatest emphasis during pronunciation appears in capital letters: for example, **pericarditis** (per ih car DYE tis). Toward the end of Chapters 2 through 14 is a Terminology Checklist. This is a list of all the key terms from the chapter. Each term is also pronounced on the CD-ROM packaged with this book. Listen to each word, then pronounce it silently to yourself or out loud. Check each term off the list as you master it. This list also serves as a review list for all the terms introduced in each chapter.

Spelling

Although you will hear differing pronunciations of the same term, there will be only one correct spelling. If you have any doubt about the spelling of a term or of its meaning, always look it up in a medical dictionary. If only one letter of the word is changed, it could make a critical difference for the patient. For example, imagine the problem that could arise if you note for insurance purposes that a portion of a patient's **ileum**, or small intestine, was removed when in reality he had surgery for removal of a piece of his **ilium**, or hip bone.

Med Term Tip

If you have any doubt about the meaning or spelling of a word, look it up in your medical dictionary. Even experienced medical personnel still need to look up a few words.

Some words have the same beginning sounds but are spelled differently. Examples include the following:

Sounds like *si*

psy	**psychiatry** (sigh-KIGH-ah-tree)
cy	**cytology** (sigh-TALL-oh-gee)

Sounds like *dis*

dys	**dyspepsia** (dis-PEP-see-ah)
dis	**dislocation** (dis-low-KAY-shun)

Singular and Plural Endings

Many medical terms originate from Greek and Latin words. The rules for forming the singular and plural forms of some words follow the rules of these languages rather than English. For example, the heart has a left atrium and a right atrium for a total of two *atria*, not two *atriums*. Other words, such as *virus* and *viruses*, are changed from singular to plural by following English rules. Each medical term needs to be considered individually when changing from the singular to the plural form. The following examples illustrate how to form plurals.

Words ending in	Singular	Plural
-a	vertebra	vertebrae
-ax	thorax	thoraces
-ex or -ix	appendix	appendices
-is	metastasis	metastases
-ma	sarcoma	sarcomata
-nx	phalanx	phalanges
-on	ganglion	ganglia
-us	nucleus	nuclei
-um	ovum	ova
-y	biopsy	biopsies

Abbreviations

Abbreviations are commonly used in the medical profession as a way of saving time. However, some abbreviations can be confusing, such as *SM* for simple mastectomy and *sm* for small. Use of the incorrect abbreviation can result in problems for a patient, as well as with insurance records and processing. If you have any concern that you will confuse someone by using an abbreviation, spell out the word instead. It is never acceptable to use one's own abbreviations. All types of healthcare facilities will have a list of approved abbreviations, and it is extremely important that you become familiar with this list and follow it closely. Throughout the book abbreviations are included, when possible, immediately following terms. In addition, a list of common abbreviations for each body system is given in each chapter. Finally, Appendix I provides a complete alphabetical listing of all the abbreviations used in this text.

The Medical Record

The **medical record** or chart documents the details of a patient's hospital stay. Each healthcare professional who has contact with the patient in any capacity completes the appropriate report of that contact and adds it to the medical chart. This results in a permanent physical record of the patient's day-to-day condition, when and what services he or she received, and the response to treatment. Each institution adopts a specific format for each document and its location within the chart. This is necessary because each healthcare professional must be able to locate quickly and efficiently the information he or she needs in order to provide proper care for the patient. The medical record is also a legal document. Therefore, it is essential that all chart components be completely filled out and signed. Each page must contain the proper patient identification information: the patient's name, age, gender, physician, admission date, and identification number.

While the patient is still in the hospital, a unit clerk is usually responsible for placing documents in the proper place. After discharge, the medical records department ensures that all documents are present, complete, signed, and in the correct order. If a person is readmitted, especially for the same diagnosis, parts of this previous chart can be pulled and added to the current chart for reference (see Figure 1.2 ■). Physicians' offices and other outpatient care providers such as clinics and therapists also maintain a medical record detailing each patient's visit to their facility.

A list of the most common elements of a hospital chart with a brief description of each follows.

■ **Figure 1.2** Health information professionals maintain accurate, orderly, and permanent patient records. Medical records are securely stored and available for future reference.

History and Physical—Written or dictated by the admitting physician; details the patient's history, results of the physician's examination, initial diagnoses, and physician's plan of treatment

Physician's Orders—Complete list of the care, medications, tests, and treatments the physician orders for the patient

Nurse's Notes—Record of the patient's care throughout the day; includes vital signs, treatment specifics, patient's response to treatment, and patient's condition

Physician's Progress Notes—Physician's daily record of the patient's condition, results of the physician's examinations, summary of test results, updated assessment and diagnoses, and further plans for the patient's care

Consultation Reports—Reports given by specialists whom the physician has asked to evaluate the patient

Ancillary Reports—Reports from various treatments and therapies the patient has received, such as rehabilitation, social services, or respiratory therapy

Diagnostic Reports—Results of diagnostic tests performed on the patient, principally from the clinical lab (for example, blood tests) and medical imaging (for example, X-rays and ultrasound)

Informed Consent—Document voluntarily signed by the patient or a responsible party that clearly describes the purpose, methods, procedures, benefits, and risks of a diagnostic or treatment procedure

Operative Report—Report from the surgeon detailing an operation; includes a pre- and postoperative diagnosis, specific details of the surgical procedure itself, and how the patient tolerated the procedure

Anesthesiologist's Report—Relates the details regarding the substances (such as medications and fluids) given to a patient, the patient's response to anesthesia, and vital signs during surgery

Pathologist's Report—Report given by a pathologist who studies tissue removed from the patient (for example, bone marrow, blood, or tissue biopsy)

Discharge Summary—Comprehensive outline of the patient's entire hospital stay; includes condition at time of admission, admitting diagnosis, test results, treatments and patient's response, final diagnosis, and follow-up plans

Healthcare Settings

The use of medical terminology is widespread. It provides healthcare professionals with a precise and efficient method of communicating very specific patient information to one another, regardless of whether they are in the same type of facility (see Figure 1.3 ■). Descriptions follow of the different types of settings where medical terminology is used.

Acute Care or General Hospitals—Provide services to diagnose (laboratory, diagnostic imaging) and treat (surgery, medications, therapy) diseases for a short period of time; in addition, they usually provide emergency and obstetrical care

Specialty Care Hospitals—Provide care for very specific types of diseases; for example, a psychiatric hospital

Nursing Homes or Long-Term Care Facilities—Provide long-term care for patients who need extra time to recover from an illness or injury before returning home, or for persons who can no longer care for themselves

Ambulatory Care, Surgical Centers, or Outpatient Clinics—Provide services that do not require overnight hospitalization; the services range from simple surgeries to diagnostic testing or therapy

Figure 1.3 A nurse and medical assistant review a patient's chart and plan his or her daily care.

Physicians' Offices—Provide diagnostic and treatment services in a private office setting

Health Maintenance Organization (HMO)—Provides a wide range of services by a group of primary-care physicians, specialists, and other healthcare professionals in a prepaid system

Home Health Care—Provides nursing, therapy, personal care, or housekeeping services in the patient's own home

Rehabilitation Centers—Provide intensive physical and occupational therapy; they include inpatient and outpatient treatment

Hospice—Provides supportive treatment to terminally ill patients and their families

Confidentiality

Anyone who works with medical terminology and is involved in the medical profession must have a firm understanding of confidentiality. Any information or record relating to a patient must be considered privileged. This means that you have a moral and legal responsibility to keep all information about the patient confidential. If you are asked to supply documentation relating to a patient, the proper authorization form must be signed by the patient. Give only the specific information that the patient has authorized. The Health Insurance Portability and Accountability Act of 1996 (HIPAA) set federal standards that provide patients with more protection of their medical records and health information, better access to their own records, and greater control over how their health information is used and to whom it is disclosed.

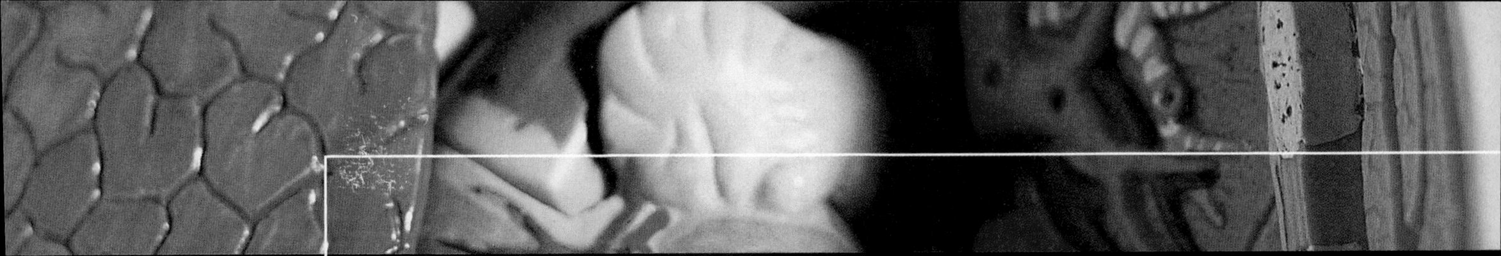

2 Body Organization

Learning Objectives

Upon completion of this chapter, you will be able to:

- Recognize the combining forms introduced in this chapter.
- Correctly spell and pronounce medical terms and anatomical structures relating to body structure.
- Discuss the organization of the body in terms of cells, tissues, organs, and systems.
- Describe the common features of cells.
- Define the four types of tissues.
- List the major organs found in the twelve organ systems.
- Describe the anatomical position.
- Define the body planes.
- Identify regions of the body.
- Define directional and positional terms.
- List the body cavities and their contents.
- Locate and describe the nine anatomical and four clinical divisions of the abdomen.
- Build body organization medical terms from word parts.
- Interpret abbreviations associated with body organization.

Body Organization at a Glance

Arrangement

The body is organized into levels. Each level is built from the one below it. In other words, the body as a whole is composed of systems, a system is composed of organs, an organ is composed of tissues, and tissues are composed of cells.

Levels

cells **tissues** **organs** **systems** **body**

Combining Forms

abdomin/o	abdomen	**muscul/o**	muscle
adip/o	fat	**neur/o**	nerve
anter/o	front	**organ/o**	organ
brachi/o	arm	**oste/o**	bone
caud/o	tail	**pelv/o**	pelvis
cephal/o	head	**peritone/o**	peritoneum
cervic/o	neck	**pleur/o**	pleura
chondr/o	cartilage	**poster/o**	back
crani/o	skull	**proxim/o**	near to
crur/o	leg	**pub/o**	genital region
cyt/o	cell	**somat/o**	body
dist/o	away from	**spin/o**	spine
dors/o	back of body	**super/o**	above
epitheli/o	epithelium	**system/o**	system
glute/o	buttock	**thorac/o**	chest
hist/o	tissue	**ventr/o**	belly
infer/o	below	**vertebr/o**	vertebra
later/o	side	**viscer/o**	internal organ
medi/o	middle		

Med Term Tip

The prefixes and suffixes introduced in Chapter 1 will be used over and over again in your medical terminology course, making it easier to recognize new terms more quickly. Beginning with this chapter new combining forms, prefixes, and suffixes will appear at the beginning of each chapter.

Body Organization Illustrated

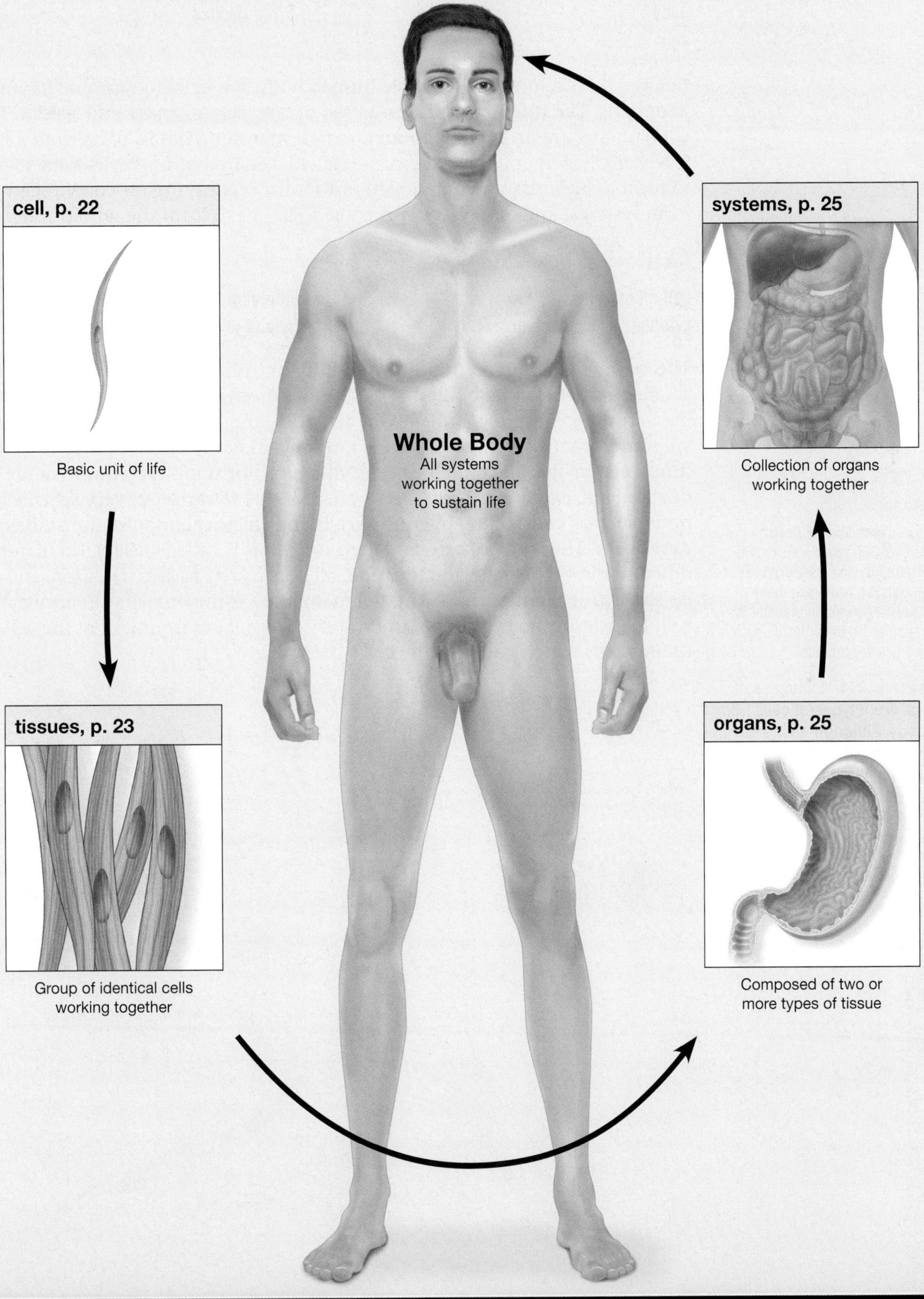

Levels of Body Organization

body **cell** **organs** **systems** **tissues**

Before taking a look at the whole human body, we need to examine its component parts. The human **body** is composed of **cells**, **tissues**, **organs**, and **systems**. These components are arranged in a hierarchical manner. That is, parts from a lower level come together to form the next higher level. In that way, cells come together to form tissues, tissues come together to form organs, organs come together to form systems, and all the systems come together to form the whole body.

Cells

cell membrane
cytology (sigh-TALL-oh-jee)
cytoplasm (SIGH-toh-plazm)
nucleus

The cell is the fundamental unit of all living things. In other words, it is the smallest structure of a body that has all the properties of being alive: responding to stimuli, engaging in metabolic activities, and reproducing itself. All the tissues and organs in the body are composed of cells. Individual cells perform functions for the body such as reproduction, hormone secretion, energy production, and excretion. Special cells are also able to carry out very specific functions, such as contraction by muscle cells and electrical impulse transmission by nerve cells. The study of cells and their functions is called **cytology**. No matter the difference in their shape and function, all cells have a **nucleus**, **cytoplasm**, and a **cell membrane** (see Figure 2.1). The cell membrane is the outermost boundary of a cell. It encloses the cytoplasm, the watery internal environment of the cell, and the nucleus which contains the cell's DNA.

Med Term Tip

Cells were first seen by Robert Hooke over 300 years ago. To him, the rectangular shapes looked like prison cells, so he named them cells. It was a common practice for early anatomists to name an organ solely on its appearance.

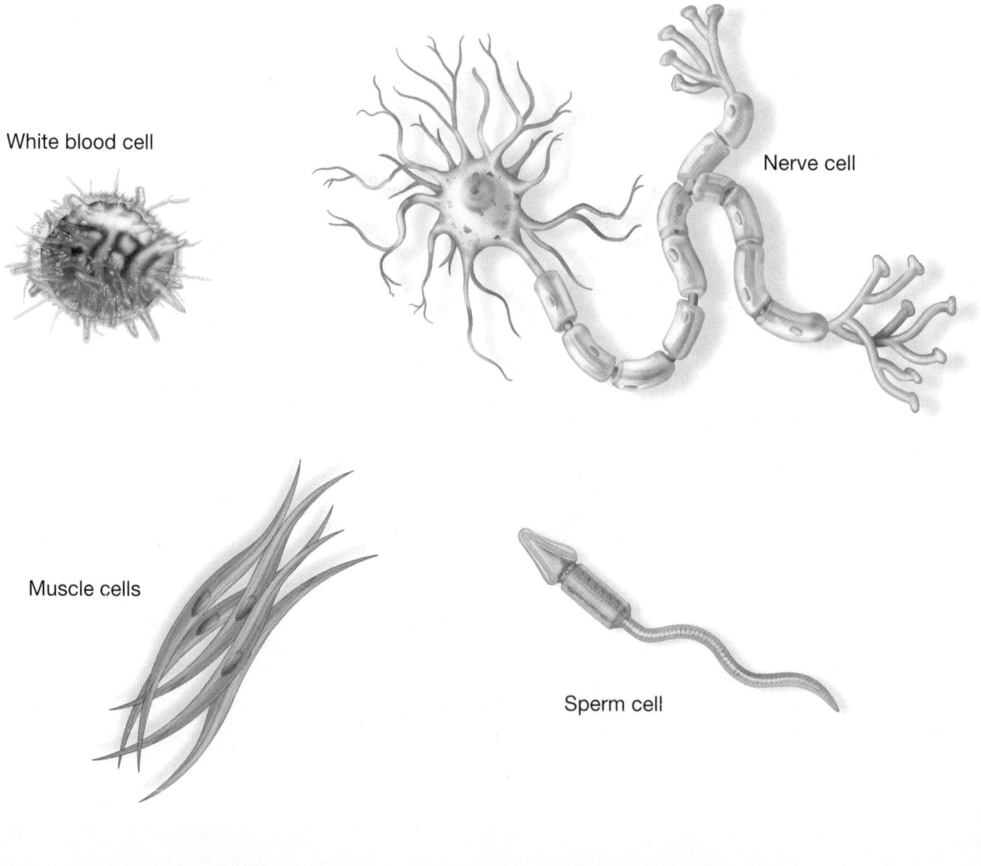

Figure 2.1 Examples of four different types of cells from the body. Although each cell has a cell membrane, nucleus, and cytoplasm, each has a unique shape depending on its location and function.

Tissues

connective tissue
epithelial tissue (ep-ih-THEE-lee-al)
histology (hiss-TALL-oh-jee)
muscle tissue
nervous tissue

Histology is the study of tissue. A tissue is formed when like cells are grouped together and function together to perform a specific activity. The body has four types of tissue: **muscle tissue**, **epithelial tissue**, **connective tissue**, and **nervous tissue**.

Muscle Tissue

cardiac muscle
muscle fibers
skeletal muscle
smooth muscle

Muscle tissue produces movement in the body through contraction, or shortening in length, and is composed of individual muscle cells called **muscle fibers** (see Figure 2.2 ■). Muscle tissue forms one of three basic types of muscles: **skeletal muscle**, **smooth muscle**, or **cardiac muscle**. Skeletal muscle is attached to bone. Smooth muscle is found in internal organs such as the intestine, uterus, and blood vessels. Cardiac muscle is found only in the heart.

Epithelial Tissue

epithelium (ep-ih-THEE-lee-um)

Epithelial tissue, or **epithelium**, is found throughout the body and is composed of close-packed cells that form the covering for and lining of body structures. For example, both the top layer of skin and the lining of the stomach are epithelial tissue (see Figure 2.2). In addition to forming a protective barrier, epithelial tissue may be specialized to absorb substances (such as nutrients from the intestine), secrete substances (such as sweat glands), or excrete wastes (such as the kidney tubules).

Med Term Tip

The term *epithelium* comes from the prefix *epi-* meaning "on top of" and the combining form *theli/o* meaning "nipple" (referring to any projection from the surface).

Connective Tissue

adipose (ADD-ih-pohs)
bone
cartilage (CAR-tih-lij)
tendons

Connective tissue is the supporting and protecting tissue in body structures. Because connective tissue performs many different functions depending on its location, it appears in many different forms so that each is able to perform the task required at that location. For example, **bone** provides structural support for the whole body. **Cartilage** is the shock absorber in joints. **Tendons** tightly connect skeletal muscles to bones. **Adipose** provides protective padding around body structures (see Figure 2.2).

Nervous Tissue

brain
nerves
neurons
spinal cord

Nervous tissue is composed of cells called **neurons** (see Figure 2.2). This tissue forms the **brain**, **spinal cord**, and a network of **nerves** throughout the entire body. This allows for the conduction of electrical impulses to send information between the brain and the rest of the body.

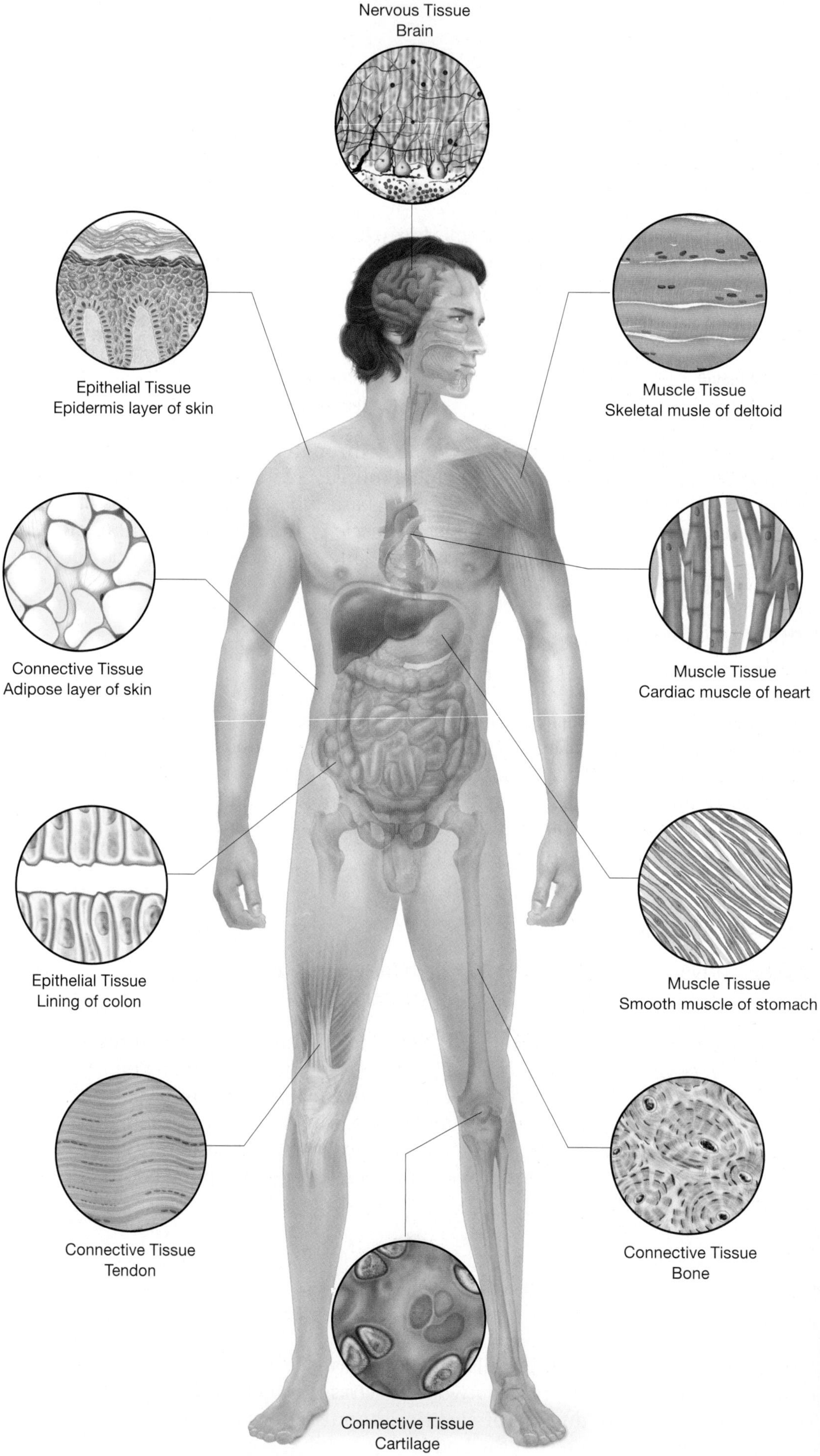

Figure 2.2 The appearance of different types of tissues—muscle, epithelial, nervous, connective—and their location within the body.

Organs and Systems

Organs are composed of several different types of tissue that work as a unit to perform special functions. For example, the stomach contains smooth muscle tissue, nervous tissue, and epithelial tissue that allow it to contract to mix food with digestive juices.

A system is composed of several organs working in a coordinated manner to perform a complex function or functions. To continue our example, the stomach plus the other digestive system organs—the oral cavity, esophagus, liver, pancreas, small intestine, and colon—work together to ingest, digest, and absorb our food.

Table 2.1 ■ presents the organ systems that will be studied in this textbook along with the major organs found in each system, the system functions, and the medical specialties that treat conditions of that system.

Table 2.1 Organ Systems of the Human Body

SYSTEM/MEDICAL SPECIALTY	STRUCTURES	FUNCTIONS
Integumentary (in-teg-you-MEN-tah-ree) **dermatology** (der-mah-TALL-oh-jee)	• skin • hair • nails • sweat glands • sebaceous glands 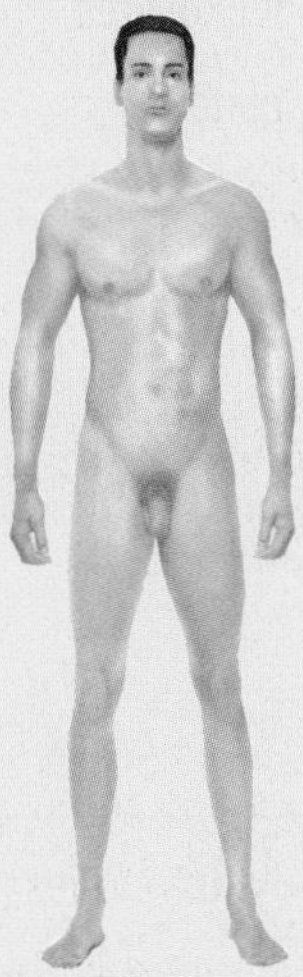	Forms protective two-way barrier and aids in temperature regulation.
Musculoskeletal (MS) (mus-qu-low-SKEL-et-all) **orthopedics** (or-thoh-PEE-diks) **orthopedic surgery** (or-the-PEE-dik)	• bones • joints • muscles 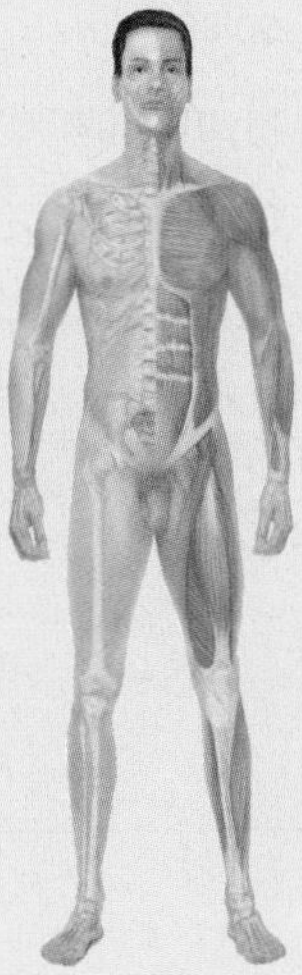	Skeleton supports and protects the body, forms blood cells, and stores minerals. Muscles produce movement.

Table 2.1 Organ Systems of the Human Body (continued)

SYSTEM/MEDICAL SPECIALTY	STRUCTURES	FUNCTIONS
Cardiovascular (CV) (car-dee-oh-VAS-kew-lar) **cardiology** (car-dee-ALL-oh-jee)	• heart • arteries • veins 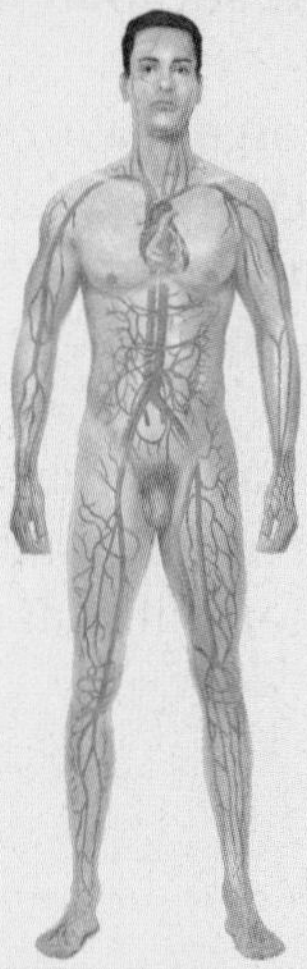	Pumps blood throughout the entire body to transport nutrients, oxygen, and wastes.
Blood (**Hematic** System) (he-MAT-tik) **hematology** (hee-mah-TALL-oh-jee)	• plasma • erythrocytes • leukocytes • platelets 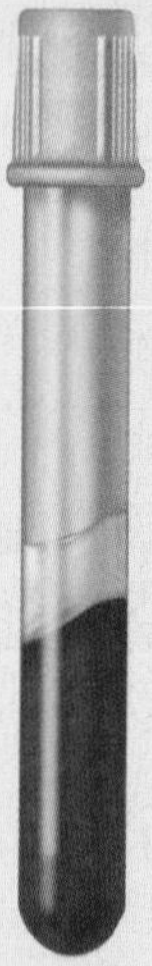	Transports oxygen, protects against pathogens, and controls bleeding.
Lymphatic (lim-FAT-ik) **immunology** (im-yoo-NALL-oh-jee)	• lymph nodes • lymphatic vessels • spleen • thymus gland • tonsils 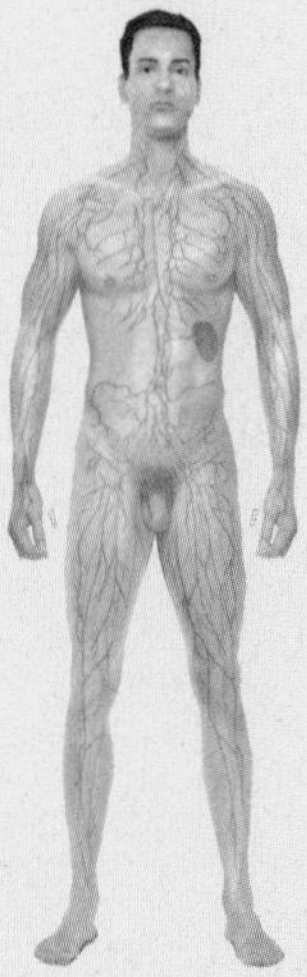	Protects the body from disease and invasion from pathogens.

Table 2.1 Organ Systems of the Human Body (continued)

SYSTEM/MEDICAL SPECIALTY	STRUCTURES	FUNCTIONS
Respiratory **otorhinolaryngology** (ENT) (oh-toh-rye-noh-lair-ing-GALL-oh-jee) **pulmonology** (pull-mon-ALL-oh-jee) **thoracic surgery** (tho-RASS-ik)	• nasal cavity • pharynx • larynx • trachea • bronchial tubes • lungs 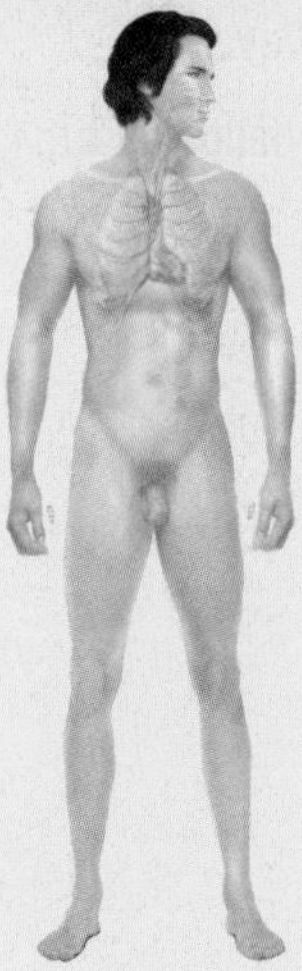	Obtains oxygen and removes carbon dioxide from the body.
Digestive or **Gastrointestinal** (GI) **gastroenterology** (gas-troh-en-ter-ALL-oh-jee) **proctology** (prok-TOL-oh-jee)	• oral cavity • pharynx • esophagus • stomach • small intestine • colon • liver • gallbladder • pancreas • salivary glands 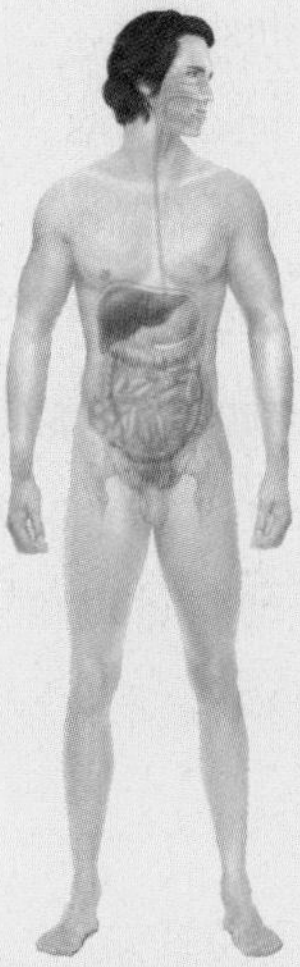	Ingests, digests, and absorbs nutrients for the body.
Urinary (YOO-rih-nair-ee) **nephrology** (neh-FROL-oh-jee) **urology** (yoo-RALL-oh-jee)	• kidneys • ureters • urinary bladder • urethra 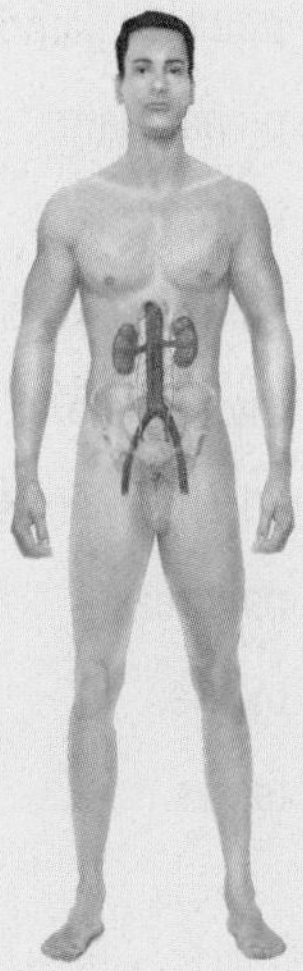	Filters waste products out of the blood and removes them from the body.

Table 2.1 Organ Systems of the Human Body (continued)

SYSTEM/MEDICAL SPECIALTY	STRUCTURES		FUNCTIONS
Female reproductive **gynecology** (GYN) (gigh-neh-KOL-oh-jee) **obstetrics** (OB) (ob-STET-riks)	• ovary • fallopian tubes • uterus • vagina • vulva • breasts	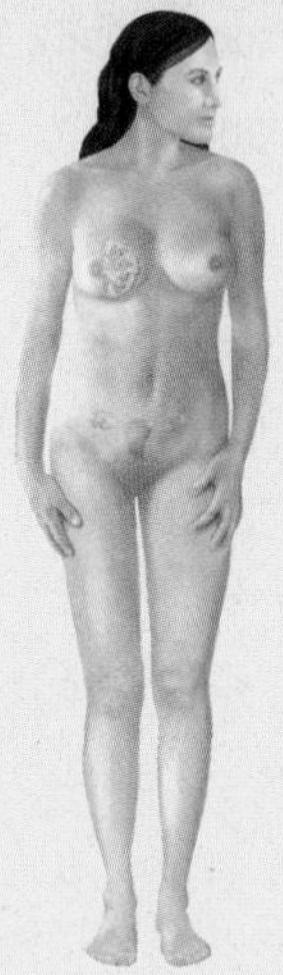	Produces eggs for reproduction and provides place for growing baby.
Male reproductive **urology** (yoo-RALL-oh-jee)	• testes • epididymis • vas deferens • penis • seminal vesicles • prostate gland • bulbourethral gland	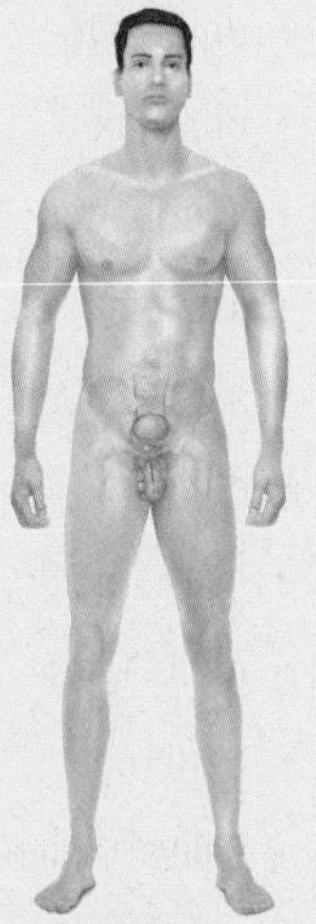	Produces sperm for reproduction.
Endocrine (EN-doh-krin) **endocrinology** (en-doh-krin-ALL-oh-jee)	• pituitary gland • pineal gland • thyroid gland • parathyroid glands • thymus gland • adrenal glands • pancreas • ovaries • testes	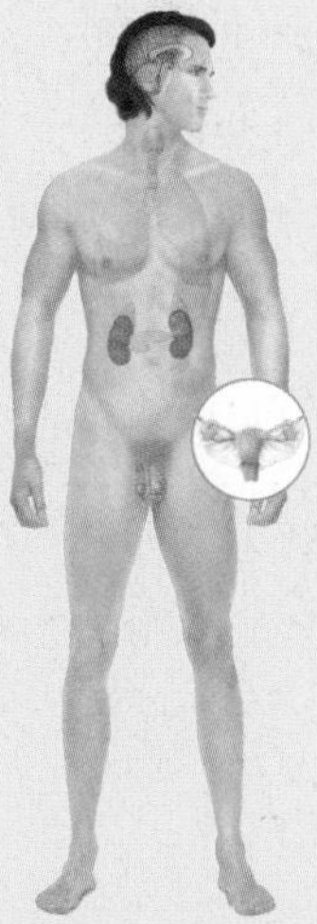	Regulates metabolic activities of the body.

Table 2.1 Organ Systems of the Human Body

SYSTEM/MEDICAL SPECIALTY	STRUCTURES	FUNCTIONS
Nervous **neurology** (noo-RAL-oh-jee) **neurosurgery** (noo-roh-SIR-jer-ee)	• brain • spinal cord • nerves 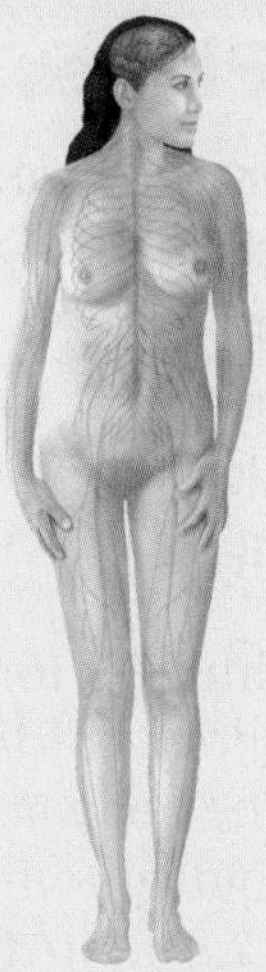	Receives sensory information and coordinates the body's response.
Special senses **ophthalmology** (off-thal-MALL-oh-jee)	• eye 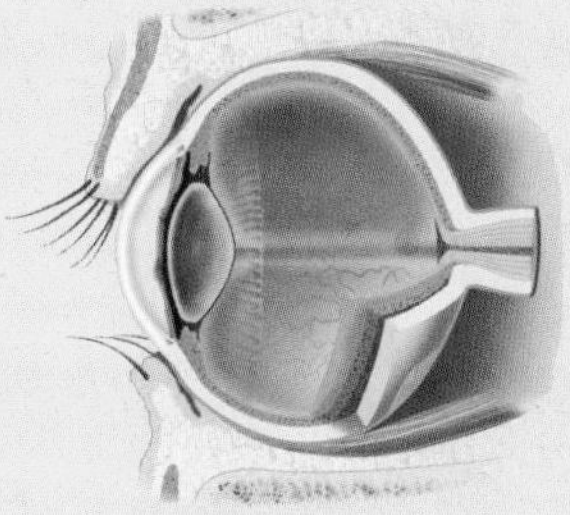	Vision
otorhinolaryngology (ENT) (oh-toh-rye-noh-lair-ing-GALL-oh-jee)	• ear 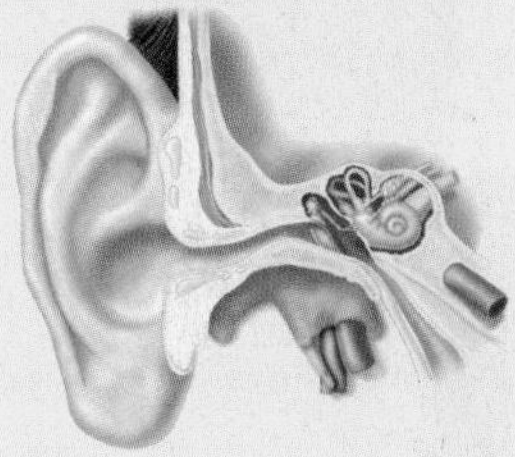	Hearing and balance

Body

anatomical position

As seen from the previous sections, the body is the sum of all the systems, organs, tissues, and cells found in it. It is important to learn the anatomical terminology that applies to the body as a whole in order to correctly identify specific locations and directions when dealing with patients. The **anatomical position** is used when describing the positions and relationships of structures in the human body. A body in the anatomical position is standing erect with the arms at the side of the body, the palms of the hands facing forward, and the eyes looking straight ahead. In addition, the legs are parallel with the feet, and the toes are pointing forward (see Figure 2.3 ■). For descriptive purposes the assumption is always that the person is in the anatomical position even if the body or parts of the body are in any other position.

Body Planes

coronal plane (kor-RONE-al)
coronal section
cross-section
frontal plane
frontal section
horizontal plane
longitudinal section
median plane
sagittal plane (SAJ-ih-tal)
sagittal section
transverse plane
transverse section

The terminology for body planes is used to assist medical personnel in describing the body and its parts. To understand body planes, imagine cuts slicing through the body at various angles. This imaginary slicing allows us to use more specific language when describing parts of the body. These body planes, illustrated in Figure 2.4 ■, include the following:

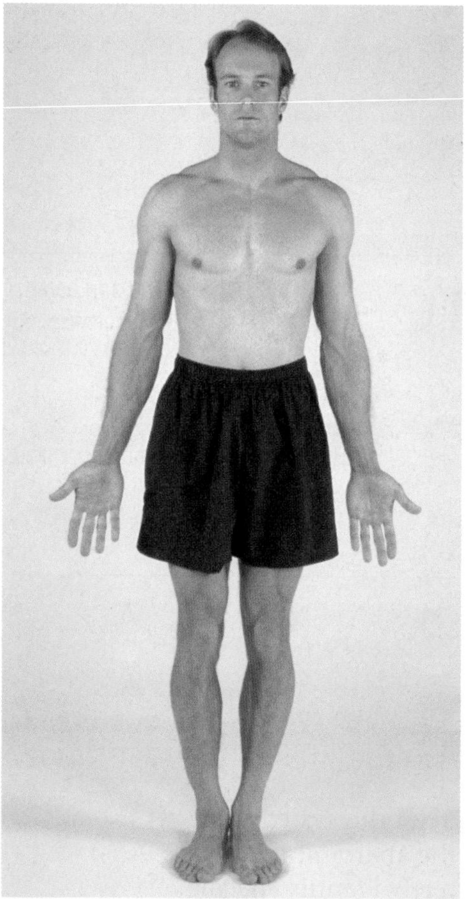

■ **Figure 2.3** The anatomical position: standing erect, gazing straight ahead, arms down at sides, palms facing forward, fingers extended, legs together, and toes pointing forward.

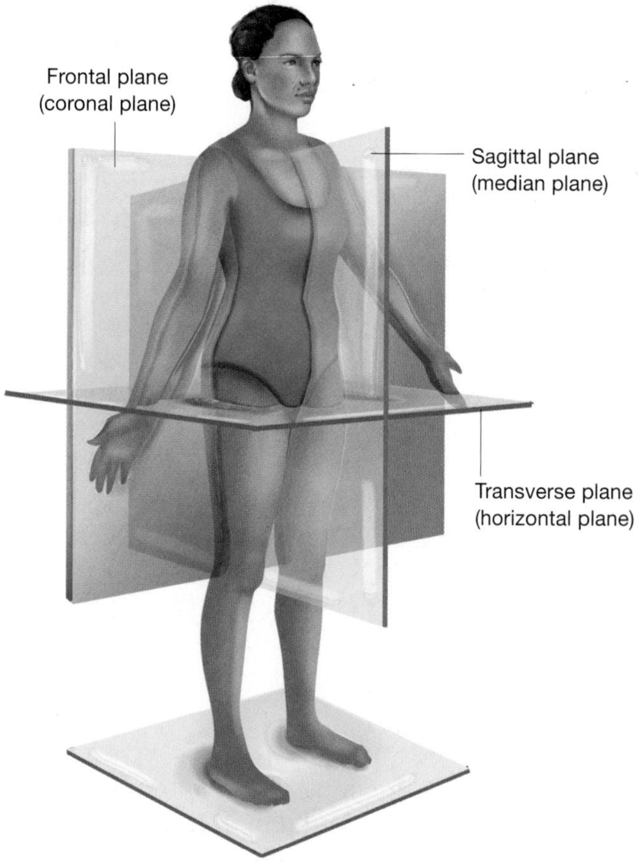

■ **Figure 2.4** The planes of the body. The sagittal plane is vertical from front to back, the frontal plane is vertical from left to right, and the transverse plane is horizontal.

1. **Sagittal plane:** This vertical plane, also called the **median plane**, runs lengthwise from front to back and divides the body or any of its parts into right and left portions. The right and left sides do not have to be equal. A cut along the sagittal plane yields a **sagittal section** view of the inside of the body.
2. **Frontal plane:** The frontal, or **coronal plane**, divides the body into front and back portions. In other words, this is a vertical lengthwise plane running from side to side. A cut along the frontal plane yields a **frontal** or **coronal section** view of the inside of the body.
3. **Transverse plane:** The transverse, or **horizontal plane**, is a crosswise plane that runs parallel to the ground. This imaginary cut would divide the body or its parts into upper and lower portions. A cut along the transverse plane yields a **transverse section** view of the inside of the body.

The terms **cross-section** and **longitudinal section** are frequently used to describe internal views of structures. A longitudinal section is a produced by a lengthwise slice along the long axis of a structure. A cross-section view is produced by a slice perpendicular to the long axis of the structure.

Body Regions

abdominal region (ab-DOM-ih-nal)
brachial region (BRAY-kee-all)
cephalic region (she-FAL-ik)
cervical region (SER-vih-kal)
~~**crural**~~ **region** (KREW-ral) Femoral.
dorsum (DOOR-sum)
gluteal region (GLOO-tee-all)
lower extremities
pelvic region (PELL-vik)
pubic region (PEW-bik)
thoracic region (tho-RASS-ik)
trunk
upper extremities
vertebral region (VER-tee-bral)

The body is divided into large regions that can easily be identified externally. The **cephalic region** is the entire head. The neck is the **cervical region** and connects the head to the **trunk** (the torso). The trunk is further subdivided into different anterior and posterior regions. The anterior side consists of the **thoracic** (the chest), **abdominal**, **pelvic**, and **pubic** (genital) **regions**. The posterior side consists of the **dorsum** (the back), **vertebral region**, and **gluteal** (buttock) **region**. The **upper extremities** (UE) and **lower extremities** (LE) are attached to the trunk. The upper extremities or **brachial regions** are the arms. The lower extremities or **crural regions** are the legs. See Figure 2.5 ■ to locate each region on the body.

Med Term Tip

As you learn medical terminology, it is important that you remember not to use common phrases and terms any longer. Many people commonly use the term *stomach* (an organ) when they actually mean *abdomen* (a body region).

Body Cavities

abdominal cavity
abdominopelvic cavity (ab-dom-ih-noh-PELL-vik)
cranial cavity (KRAY-nee-al)
diaphragm (DYE-ah-fram)
mediastinum (mee-dee-ass-TYE-num)
parietal layer (pah-RYE-eh-tal)
parietal peritoneum
parietal pleura
pelvic cavity
pericardial cavity (pair-ih-CAR-dee-al)
peritoneum (pair-ih-toh-NEE-um)
pleura (PLOO-rah)
pleural cavity (PLOO-ral)
spinal cavity
thoracic cavity
viscera (VISS-er-ah)
visceral layer (VISS-er-al)
visceral peritoneum
visceral pleura

The body is not a solid structure; it has many open spaces or cavities. The cavities are part of the normal body structure and are illustrated in Figure 2.6 ■. We

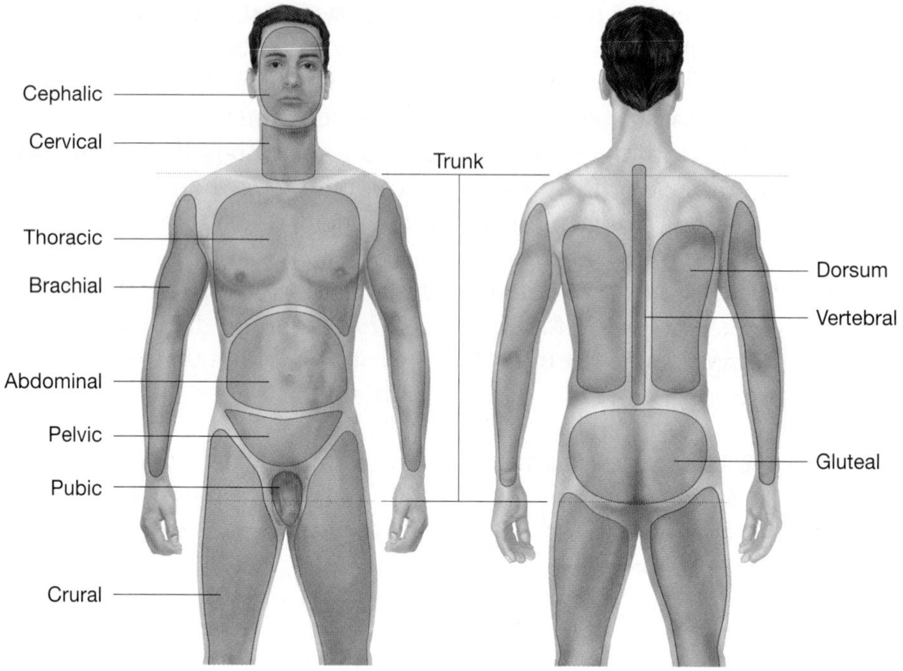

Figure 2.5 Anterior and posterior views of the body illustrating the location of various body regions.

can divide the body into four major cavities—two dorsal cavities and two ventral cavities.

The dorsal cavities include the **cranial cavity**, containing the brain, and the **spinal cavity**, containing the spinal cord.

The ventral cavities include the **thoracic cavity** and the **abdominopelvic cavity**. The thoracic cavity contains the two lungs and a central region between them called the **mediastinum**. The heart, aorta, esophagus, trachea, and thymus gland are located in the mediastinum. There is an actual physical wall between the thoracic cavity and the abdominopelvic cavity called the **diaphragm**. The diaphragm is a muscle used for breathing. The abdominopelvic cavity is generally subdivided into a superior **abdominal cavity** and an inferior **pelvic cavity**. The organs of the digestive, excretory, and reproductive systems are located in these cavities. The organs

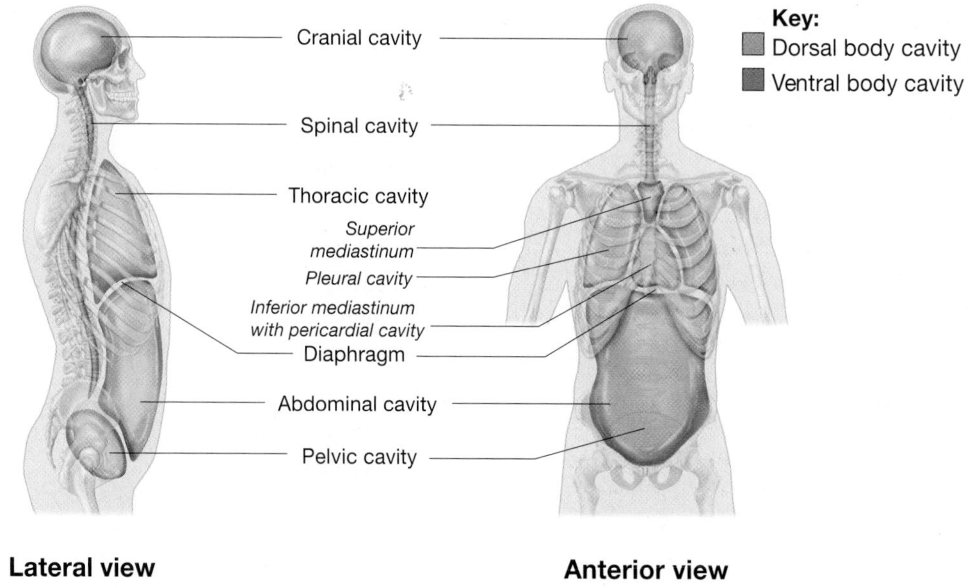

Figure 2.6 The dorsal (red) and ventral (blue) body cavities.

within the ventral cavities are referred to as a group as the internal organs or **viscera**. Table 2.2 ■ describes the body cavities and their major organs.

All of the cavities are lined by, and the viscera are encased in, a two-layer membrane called the **pleura** in the thoracic cavity and the **peritoneum** in the abdominopelvic cavity. The outer layer that lines the cavities is called the **parietal layer** (i.e., **parietal pleura** and **parietal peritoneum**), and the inner layer that encases the viscera is called the **visceral layer** (i.e., **visceral pleura** and **visceral peritoneum**).

Within the thoracic cavity, the pleura is subdivided, forming the **pleural cavity**, containing the lungs, and the **pericardial cavity**, containing the heart. The larger abdominopelvic cavity is usually subdivided into regions so different areas can be precisely referred to. Two different methods of subdividing this cavity are used: the anatomical divisions and the clinical divisions. Choose a method partly on personal preference and partly on which system best describes the patient's condition. See Table 2.3 ■ for a description of these methods for dividing the abdominopelvic cavity.

Med Term Tip

The kidneys are the only major abdominopelvic organ located outside the sac formed by the peritoneum. Because they are found behind this sac, their position is referred to as *retroperitoneal.*

Directional and Positional Terms

Directional terms assist medical personnel in discussing the position or location of a patient's complaint. Directional or positional terms also help to describe one process, organ, or system as it relates to another. Table 2.4 ■ presents commonly used terms for describing the position of the body or its parts. They are listed in pairs that have opposite meanings: for example, superior versus inferior, anterior versus posterior, medial versus lateral, proximal versus distal, superficial versus deep, and supine versus prone. Directional terms are illustrated in Figure 2.7 ■.

Med Term Tip

Remember when using location or direction terms, it is assumed that the patient is in the anatomical position unless otherwise noted.

Table 2.2 Body Cavities and Their Major Organs

CAVITY	MAJOR ORGANS
Dorsal cavities	
Cranial cavity	Brain
Spinal cavity	Spinal cord
Ventral cavities	
Thoracic cavity	Pleural cavity: lungs Pericardial cavity: heart Mediastinum: heart, esophagus, trachea, thymus gland, aorta
Abdominopelvic cavity	
Abdominal cavity	Stomach, spleen, liver, gallbladder, pancreas, and portions of the small intestines and colon
Pelvic cavity	Urinary bladder, ureters, urethra, and portions of the small intestines and colon *Female:* uterus, ovaries, fallopian tubes, vagina *Male:* prostate gland, seminal vesicles, portion of the vas deferens

Table 2.3 Methods of Subdividing the Abdominopelvic Cavity

Anatomical Divisions of the Abdomen

- **Right hypochondriac** (high-poh-KON-dree-ak): Right lateral region of upper row beneath the lower ribs.
- **Epigastric** (ep-ih-GAS-trik): Middle area of upper row above the stomach.
- **Left hypochondriac:** Left lateral region of the upper row beneath the lower ribs.
- **Right lumbar:** Right lateral region of the middle row at the waist.
- **Umbilical** (um-BILL-ih-kal): Central area over the navel.
- **Left lumbar:** Left lateral region of the middle row at the waist.
- **Right iliac** (ILL-ee-ak): Right lateral region of the lower row at the groin.
- **Hypogastric** (high-poh-GAS-trik): Middle region of the lower row beneath the navel.
- **Left iliac:** Left lateral region of the lower row at the groin.

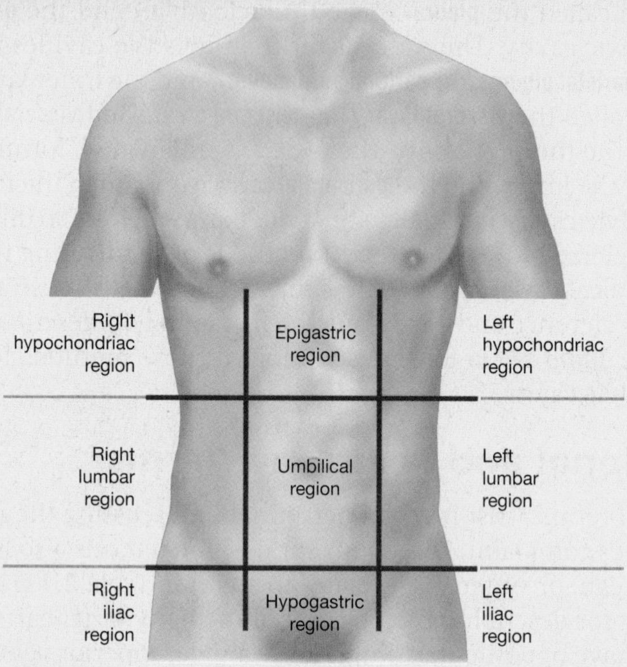

Med Term Tip

To visualize the nine anatomical divisions, imagine a tic-tac-toe diagram over this region.

Med Term Tip

The term *hypochondriac*, literally meaning "under the cartilage" (of the ribs), has come to refer to a person who believes he or she is sick when there is no obvious cause for illness. These patients commonly complain of aches and pains in the hypochondriac region.

Clinical Divisions of the Abdomen

- **Right upper quadrant (RUQ):** Contains majority of liver, gallbladder, small portion of pancreas, right kidney, small intestines, and colon.
- **Right lower quadrant (RLQ):** Contains small intestines and colon, right ovary and fallopian tube, appendix, and right ureter.
- **Left upper quadrant (LUQ):** Contains small portion of liver, spleen, stomach, majority of pancreas, left kidney, small intestines, and colon.
- **Left lower quadrant (LLQ):** Contains small intestines and colon, left ovary and fallopian tube, and left ureter.
- Midline organs: uterus, bladder, prostate gland.

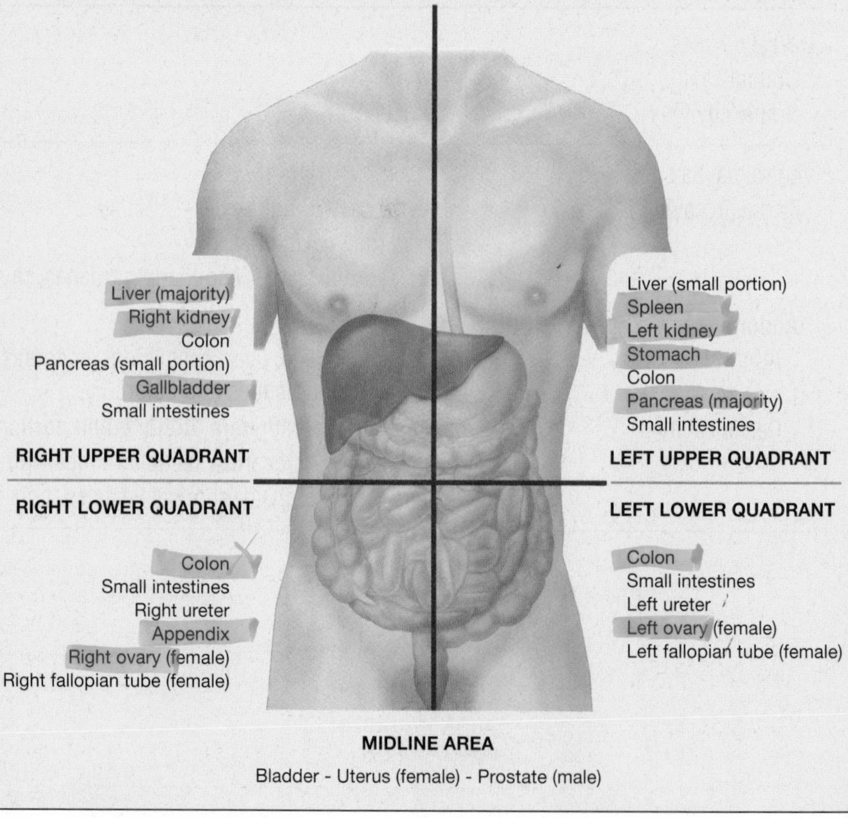

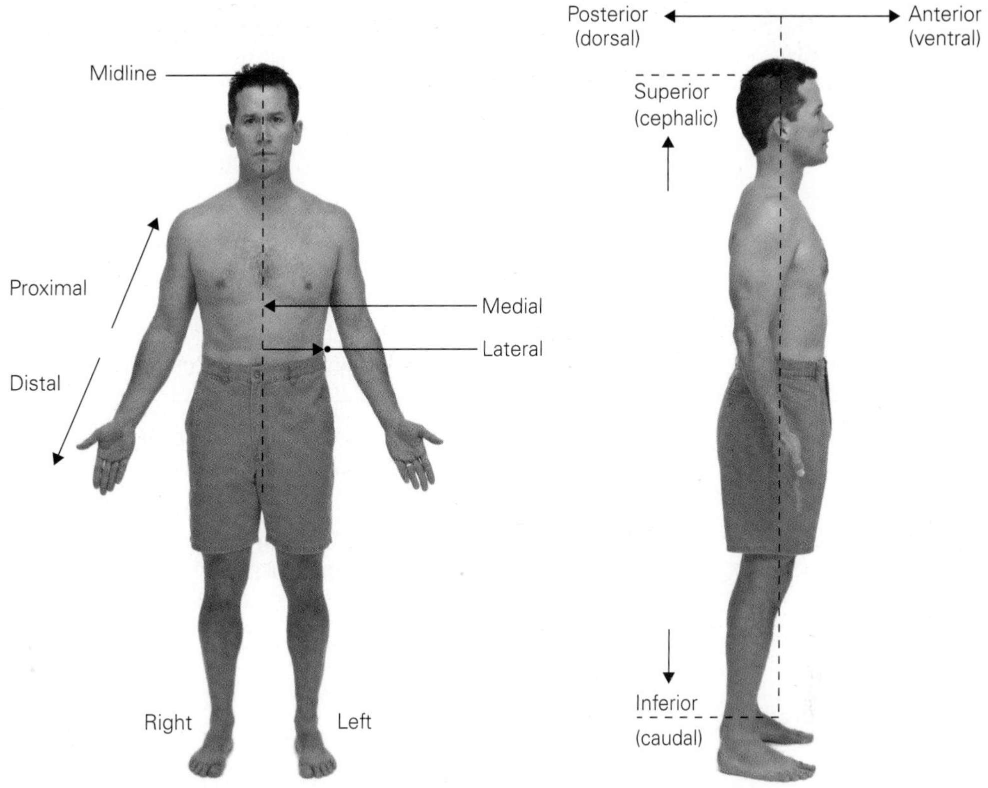

Figure 2.7 Anterior and lateral views of the body illustrating directional terms.

Table 2.4 Terms for Describing Body Position

superior (soo-PEE-ree-or) or **cephalic** (seh-FAL-ik)	More toward the head, or above another structure. (see Figure 2.7). *Example:* The adrenal glands are superior to the kidneys.
inferior (in-FEE-ree-or) or **caudal** (KAWD-al)	More toward the feet or tail, or below another structure. (see Figure 2.7). *Example:* The intestine is inferior to the heart.
anterior (an-TEE-ree-or) or **ventral** (VEN-tral)	More toward the front or belly-side of the body. (see Figure 2.7). *Example:* The navel is located on the anterior surface of the body.
posterior (poss-TEE-ree-or) or **dorsal** (DOR-sal)	More toward the back or spinal cord side of the body. (see Figure 2.7). *Example:* The posterior wall of the right kidney was excised.
medial (MEE-dee-al)	Refers to the middle or near the middle of the body or the structure. (see Figure 2.7). *Example:* The heart is medially located in the chest cavity.
lateral (lat) (LAT-er-al)	Refers to the side. (see Figure 2.7). *Example:* The ovaries are located lateral to the uterus.
proximal (PROK-sim-al)	Located nearer to the point of attachment to the body. (see Figure 2.7). *Example:* In the anatomical position, the elbow is proximal to the hand.
distal (DISS-tal)	Located farther away from the point of attachment to the body. (see Figure 2.7). *Example:* The hand is distal to the elbow.
apex (AY-peks)	Tip or summit of an organ. *Example:* We hear the heart beat by listening over the apex of the heart.

Table 2.4 Terms for Describing Body Position

base	Bottom or lower part of an organ. *Example:* On the X-ray, a fracture was noted at the base of the skull.
superficial	More toward the surface of the body. *Example:* The cut was superficial.
deep	Further away from the surface of the body. *Example:* An incision into an abdominal organ is a deep incision.
supine (soo-PINE)	The body lying horizontally and facing upward (see Figure 2.8A ■). *Example:* The patient is in the supine position for abdominal surgery.
prone (PROHN)	The body lying horizontally and facing downward (see Figure 2.8B ■). *Example:* The patient is placed in the prone position for spinal surgery.

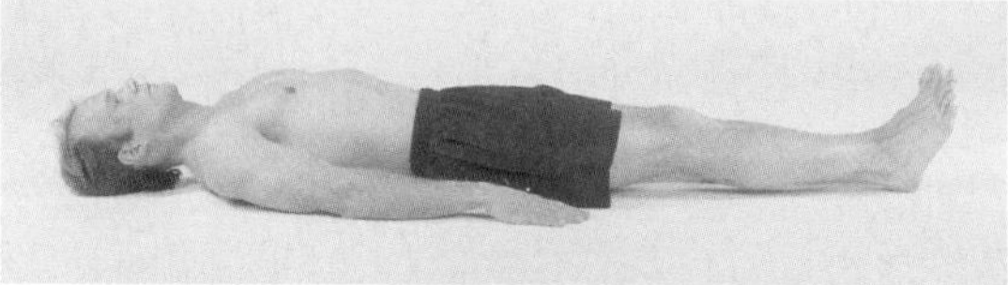

■ **Figure 2.8A** The supine position.

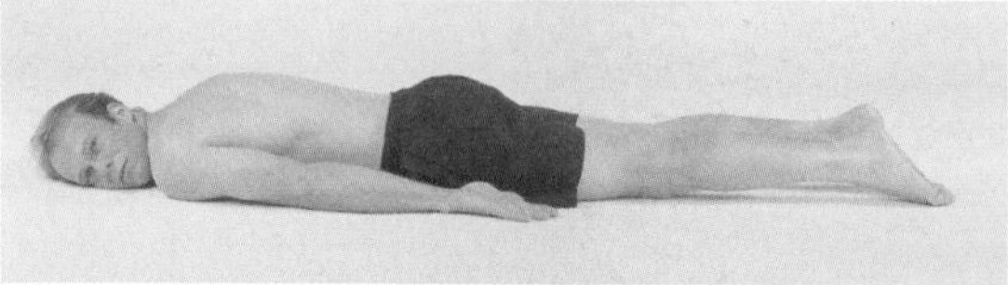

■ **Figure 2.8B** The prone position.

Word Building

When using medical terms to indicate different areas of the body or organs, it is usually necessary to turn the combining form into an adjective. For example, *gastr/o* becomes *gastric* or *ventr/o* becomes *ventral.* This is done by adding an adjective suffix to the combining form that translates as *pertaining to.* The following list contains examples of frequently used medical terms relating to body structure that are built directly from word parts. It is important to study this list because there are no rules about which of the several *pertaining to* suffixes to use.

COMBINING FORM	SUFFIX	MEDICAL TERM	DEFINITION
abdomin/o	-al	**abdominal** (ab-DOM-ih-nal)	pertaining to the abdomen
anter/o	-ior	**anterior** (an-TEE-ree-or)	pertaining to the front
brachi/o	-al	**brachial** (BRAY-kee-all)	pertaining to the arm
caud/o	-al	**caudal** (KAWD-al)	pertaining to the tail
cephal/o	-ic	**cephalic** (she-FAL-ik)	pertaining to the head
cervic/o	-al	**cervical** (SER-vih-kal)	pertaining to the neck
crani/o	-al	**cranial** (KRAY-nee-al)	pertaining to the skull
crur/o	-al	**crural** (KREW-ral)	pertaining to the leg
dist/o	-al	**distal** (DISS-tal)	pertaining to away
dors/o	-al	**dorsal** (DOR-sal)	pertaining to the back of body
epitheli/o	-al	**epithelial** (ep-ih-THEE-lee-al)	pertaining to the epithelium
glute/o	-al	**gluteal** (GLOO-tee-all)	pertaining to the buttocks
infer/o	-ior	**inferior** (in-FEE-ree-or)	pertaining to below

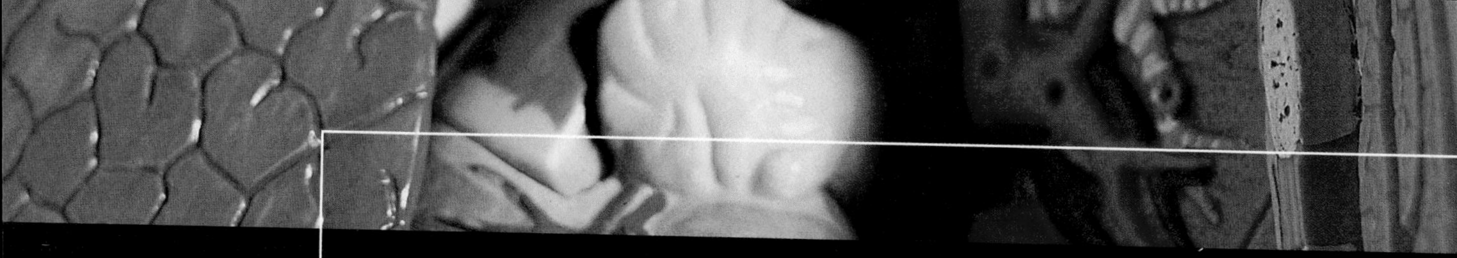

3 Integumentary System

Learning Objectives

Upon completion of this chapter, you will be able to:

- Identify and define the combining forms, prefixes, and suffixes introduced in this chapter.
- Correctly spell and pronounce medical terms and major anatomical structures relating to the integumentary system.
- List and describe the three layers of skin and their functions.
- List and describe the four purposes of the skin.
- List and describe the accessory organs of the skin.
- Build and define integumentary system medical terms from word parts.
- Identify and define integumentary system vocabulary terms.
- Identify and define selected integumentary system pathology terms.
- Identify and define selected integumentary system diagnostic procedures.
- Identify and define selected integumentary system therapeutic procedures.
- Identify and define selected medications relating to the integumentary system.
- Define selected abbreviations associated with the integumentary system.

Integumentary System at a Glance

Function

The skin provides a protective two-way barrier between our internal environment and the outside world. It also plays an important role in temperature regulation, houses sensory receptors to detect the environment around us and secretes important fluids.

Organs

skin **hair** **nails** **sebaceous glands** **sweat glands**

Combining Forms

albin/o	white
bi/o	life
cry/o	cold
cutane/o	skin
cyan/o	blue
derm/o	skin
dermat/o	skin
diaphor/o	profuse sweating
electr/o	electricity
erythr/o	red
hidr/o	sweat
ichthy/o	scaly, dry
kerat/o	hard, horny
leuk/o	white
lip/o	fat
melan/o	black
myc/o	fungus
necr/o	death
onych/o	nail
pil/o	hair
phot/o	light
py/o	pus
rhytid/o	wrinkle
scler/o	hard
seb/o	oil
trich/o	hair
ungu/o	nail
vesic/o	bladder
xer/o	dry

Suffixes

-derma	skin
-opsy	view of
-tome	instrument used to cut

Prefixes

allo-	other, different from usual
xeno-	strange, foreign

Integumentary System Illustrated

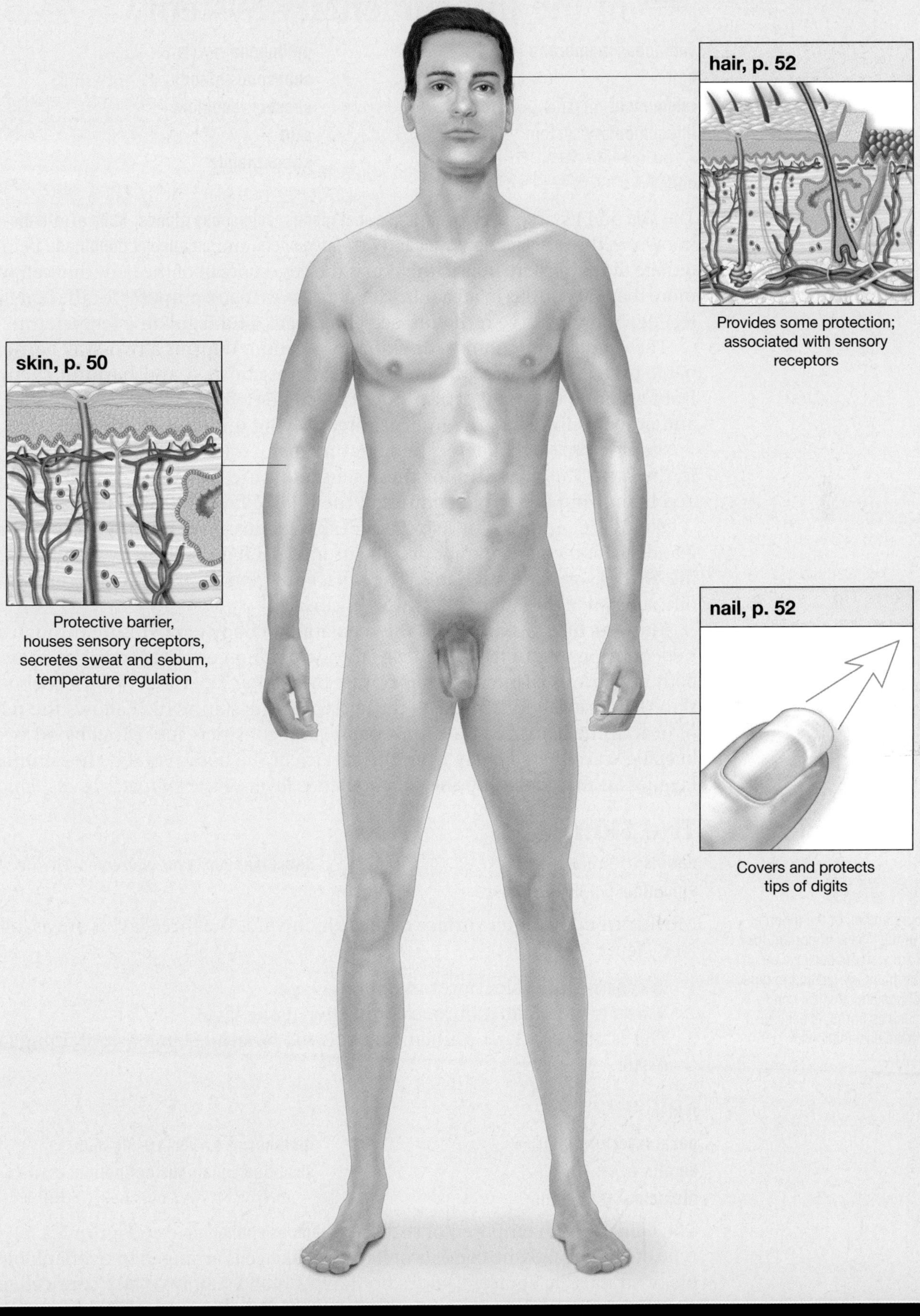

Anatomy and Physiology of the Integumentary System

cutaneous membrane (kew-TAY-nee-us)
hair
integument (in-TEG-you-mint)
integumentary system (in-teg-you-MEN-tah-ree)
nails
pathogens (PATH-oh-jenz)
sebaceous glands (see-BAY-shus)
sensory receptors
skin
sweat glands

The **skin** and its accessory organs—**sweat glands**, **sebaceous glands**, **hair**, and **nails**—are known as the **integumentary system**, with **integument** and **cutaneous membrane** being alternate terms for skin. In fact, the skin is the largest organ of the body and can weigh more than 20 pounds in an adult. The skin serves many purposes for the body: protecting, housing nerve receptors, secreting fluids, and regulating temperature.

The primary function of the skin is protection. It forms a two-way barrier capable of keeping **pathogens** (disease-causing organisms) and harmful chemicals from entering the body. It also stops critical body fluids from escaping the body and prevents injury to the internal organs lying underneath the skin.

Sensory receptors that detect temperature, pain, touch, and pressure are located in the skin. The messages for these sensations are conveyed to the spinal cord and brain from the nerve endings in the middle layer of the skin.

Fluids are produced in two types of skin glands: sweat and sebaceous. Sweat glands assist the body in maintaining its internal temperature by creating a cooling effect as sweat evaporates. The sebaceous glands, or oil glands, produce an oily substance that lubricates the skin surface.

Med Term Tip

Flushing of the skin, a normal response to an increase in environmental temperature or to a fever, is caused by an increased blood flow to the skin of the face and neck. However, in some people, it is also a response to embarrassment called blushing and is not easily controlled.

The structure of skin aids in the regulation of body temperature through a variety of means. As noted previously, the evaporation of sweat cools the body. The body also lowers its internal temperature by dilating superficial blood vessels in the skin. This brings more blood to the surface of the skin, which allows the release of heat. If the body needs to conserve heat, it constricts superficial blood vessels, keeping warm blood away from the surface of the body. Finally, the continuous layer of fat that makes up the subcutaneous layer of the skin acts as insulation.

The Skin

dermis (DER-mis)
epidermis (ep-ih-DER-mis)
subcutaneous layer (sub-kyoo-TAY-nee-us)

Med Term Tip

An understanding of the different layers of the skin is important for healthcare workers because much of the terminology relating to types of injections and medical conditions, such as burns, is described using these designations.

Moving from the outer surface of the skin inward, the three layers are as follows (see Figure 3.1 ■):

1. **Epidermis** is the thin, outer membrane layer.
2. **Dermis** is the middle, fibrous connective tissue layer.
3. The **subcutaneous layer** (Subcu, Subq) is the innermost layer, containing fatty tissue.

Epidermis

basal layer (BAY-sal)
keratin (KAIR-ah-tin)
melanin (MEL-ah-nin)
melanocytes (mel-AN-oh-sights)
stratified squamous epithelium (STRAT-ih-fyde SKWAY-mus ep-ih-THEE-lee-um)

The epidermis is composed of **stratified squamous epithelium** (see Figure 3.2 ■). This type of epithelial tissue consists of flat scale-like cells arranged in overlapping layers or strata. The epidermis does not have a blood supply or any connective tissue, so it is dependent for nourishment on the deeper layers of skin.

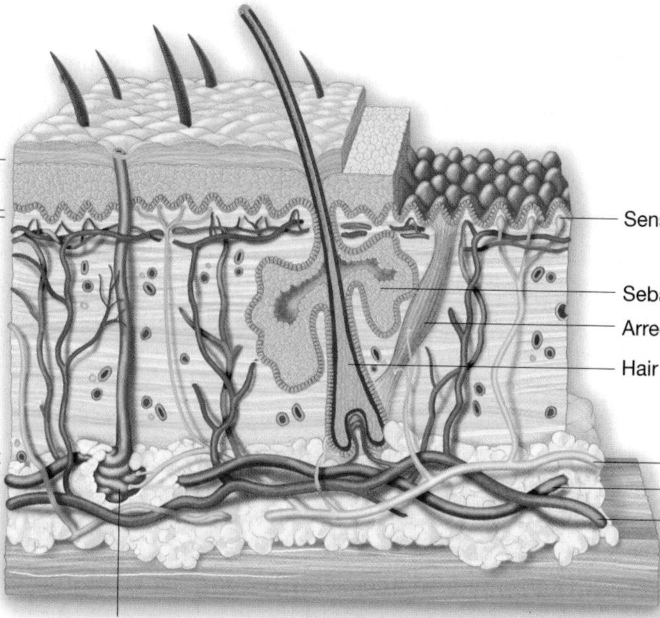

Figure 3.1 Skin structure, including the three layers of the skin and the accessory organs: sweat gland, sebaceous gland, and hair.

The deepest layer within the epidermis is called the **basal layer**. Cells in this layer continually grow and multiply. New cells that are forming push the old cells toward the outer layer of the epidermis. During this process the cells shrink, die, and become filled with a hard protein called **keratin**. These dead, overlapping, keratinized cells allow the skin to act as an effective barrier to infection and also make it waterproof.

The basal layer also contains special cells called **melanocytes**, which produce the black pigment **melanin**. Not only is this pigment responsible for the color of the skin, but it also protects against damage from the ultraviolet rays of the sun. This damage may be in the form of leatherlike skin and wrinkles, which are not hazardous, or it may be one of several forms of skin cancer. Dark-skinned people have more melanin and are generally less likely to get wrinkles or skin cancer.

Med Term Tip

We lose 30,000 to 50,000 old dead skin cells per minute and replace them with new younger cells. In fact, because of this process, our skin is replaced entirely about every seven years.

Med Term Tip

A suntan can be thought of as a protective response to the rays of the sun. However, when the melanin in the skin is not able to absorb all the rays of the sun, the skin burns and DNA may be permanently and dangerously damaged.

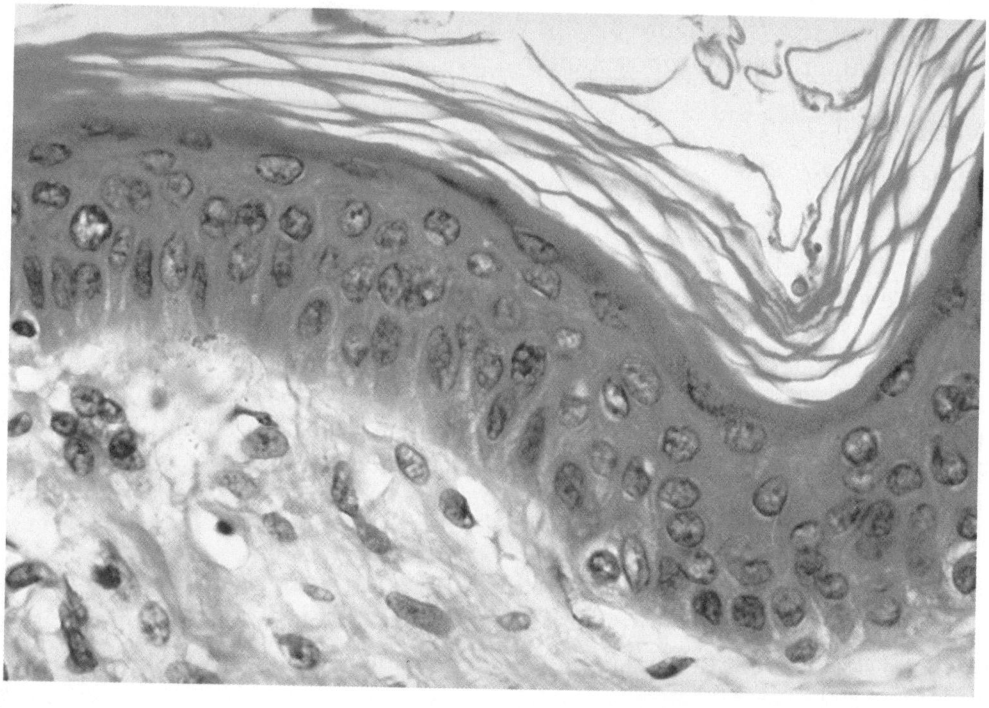

Figure 3.2 Photomicrograph of the epidermis layer of the skin.

Dermis

collagen fibers (KOL-ah-jen) **corium** (KOH-ree-um)

The dermis, also referred to as the **corium**, is the middle layer of skin, located between the epidermis and the subcutaneous layer. Its name means "true skin." Unlike the thinner epidermis, the dermis is living tissue with a very good blood supply. The dermis itself is composed of connective tissue and **collagen fibers**. Collagen fibers are made from a strong, fibrous protein present in connective tissue, forming a flexible "glue" that gives connective tissue its strength. The dermis houses hair follicles, sweat glands, sebaceous glands, blood vessels, lymph vessels, sensory receptors, nerve fibers, and muscle fibers.

Med Term Tip

Ridges formed in the dermis of our fingertips are what give each of us unique fingerprints. These do not change during a person's lifetime and so are a reliable means of identification. In fact, fingerprints are still visible on Egyptian mummies.

Subcutaneous Layer

hypodermis (high-poh-DER-mis) **lipocytes** (LIP-oh-sights)

The third and deepest layer of the skin is the subcutaneous layer, also called the **hypodermis**. This layer of tissue, composed of fat cells called **lipocytes**, protects the deeper tissues of the body and acts as insulation for heat and cold.

Accessory Organs

The accessory organs of the skin are the anatomical structures located within the dermis, including the hair, nails, sebaceous glands, and sweat glands.

Hair

arrector pili (ah-REK-tor pee-lie)
hair follicle (FALL-ikl)
hair root
hair shaft

The fibers that make up hair are composed of the protein keratin, the same hard protein material that fills the cells of the epidermis. The process of hair formation is much like the process of growth in the epidermal layer of the skin. The deeper cells in the **hair root** force older keratinized cells to move upward, forming the **hair shaft**. The hair shaft grows toward the skin surface within the **hair follicle**. Melanin gives hair its color. Sebaceous glands release oil directly into the hair follicle. Each hair has a small slip of smooth muscle attached to it called the **arrector pili** muscle (see Figure 3.3 ■). When this muscle contracts the hair shaft stands up and results in "goose bumps."

Med Term Tip

Our hair turns gray as part of the normal aging process when we no longer produce melanin.

Nails

cuticle (KEW-tikl)
free edge
lunula (LOO-nyoo-lah)
nail bed
nail body
nail root

Nails are a flat plate of keratin called the **nail body** that covers the ends of fingers and toes. The nail body is connected to the tissue underneath by the **nail bed**. Nails grow longer from the **nail root**, which is found at the base of the nail and is covered and protected by the soft tissue **cuticle**. The **free edge** is the exposed edge that is trimmed when nails become too long. The light-colored half-moon area at the base of the nail is the **lunula** (see Figure 3.4 ■).

Med Term Tip

Because of its rich blood supply and light color, the nail bed is an excellent place to check patients for low oxygen levels in their blood. Deoxygenated blood is a very dark purple-red and gives skin a bluish tinge called *cyanosis*.

Sebaceous Glands

sebum

Sebaceous glands, found in the dermis, secrete the oil **sebum**, which lubricates the hair and skin, thereby helping to prevent drying and cracking. These glands secrete

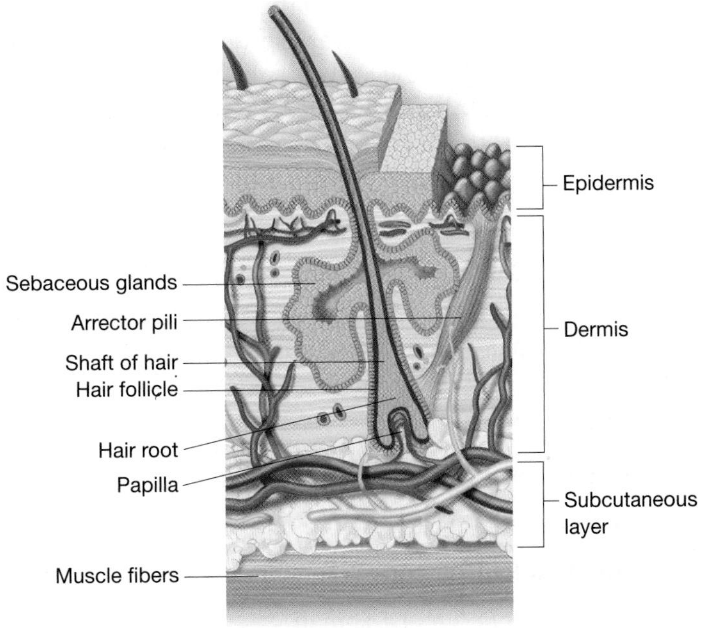

Figure 3.3 Structure of a hair and its associated sebaceous gland.

sebum directly into hair follicles, rather than a duct (see Figure 3.1). Secretion from the sebaceous glands increases during adolescence, playing a role in the development of acne. Sebum secretion begins to diminish as age increases. A loss of sebum in old age, along with sun exposure, can account for wrinkles and dry skin.

Sweat Glands

apocrine glands (APP-oh-krin)
perspiration
sudoriferous glands (sue-doh-RIF-er-us)
sweat duct
sweat pore

About two million sweat glands, also called **sudoriferous glands**, are found throughout the body. These highly coiled glands are located in the dermis. Sweat travels to the surface of the skin in a **sweat duct**. The surface opening of a sweat duct is called a **sweat pore** (see Figure 3.1).

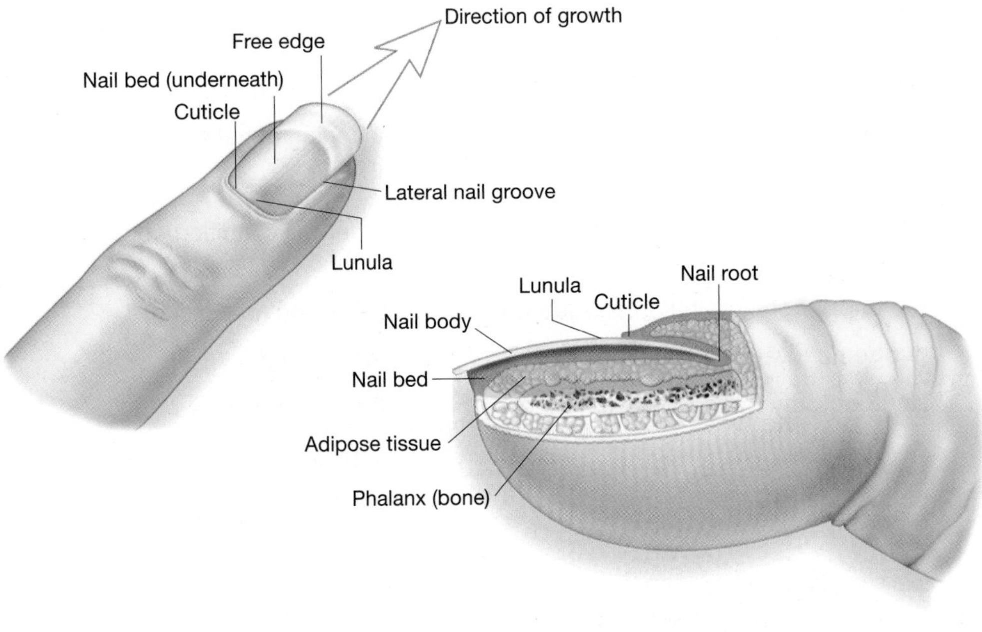

Figure 3.4 External and internal structures of nails.

Med Term Tip

Word Watch — be careful when using *hydro-* meaning "water" and *hidr/o* meaning "sweat."

Sweat glands function to cool the body as sweat evaporates. Sweat or **perspiration** contains a small amount of waste product but is normally colorless and odorless. However, there are sweat glands called **apocrine glands** in the pubic and underarm areas that secrete a thicker sweat, which can produce an odor when it comes into contact with bacteria on the skin. This is what we recognize as body odor.

Word Building

The following list contains examples of medical terms built directly from word parts. The definition for these terms can be determined by a straightforward translation of the word parts.

COMBINING FORM	COMBINED WITH	MEDICAL TERM	DEFINITION
cutane/o	sub- -ous	**subcutaneous** (sub-kyoo-TAY-neeus)	pertaining to under the skin
derm/o	epi- -al	**epidermal** (ep-ih-DER-mal)	pertaining to upon the skin
	hypo- -ic	**hypodermic** (high-poh-DER-mik)	pertaining to under the skin
	intra- -al	**intradermal** (in-trah-DER-mal)	pertaining to within the skin
dermat/o	-itis	**dermatitis** (der-mah-TYE-tis)	inflammation of the skin
	-logist	**dermatologist** (der-mah-TALL-oh-jist)	specialist in skin
	-osis	**dermatosis** (der-mah-TOH-sis)	abnormal condition of skin
	-pathy	**dermatopathy** (der-mah-TOP-ah-thee)	skin disease
	-plasty	**dermatoplasty** (DER-mah-toh-plas-tee)	surgical repair of the skin
hidr/o	an- -osis	**anhidrosis** (an-hi-DROH-sis)	abnormal condition of no sweat
	hyper- -osis	**hyperhidrosis** (high-per-hi-DROH-sis)	abnormal condition of excessive sweat
lip/o	-ectomy	**lipectomy** (lih-PECK-toh-mee)	removal of fat
	-oma	**lipoma** (lip-OH-mah)	fatty mass
melan/o	-oma	**melanoma** (mel-ah-NOH-mah)	black tumor
	-cyte	**melanocyte** (meh-LAN-oh-sight)	black cell
necr/o	-osis	**necrosis** (neh-KROH-sis)	abnormal condition of death
onych/o	-ectomy	**onychectomy** (on-ee-KECK-toh-mee)	removal of a nail
	-malacia	**onychomalacia** (on-ih-koh-mah-LAY-she-ah)	softening of nails
	myc/o -osis	**onychomycosis** (on-ih-koh-my-KOH-sis)	abnormal condition of nail fungus
	-phagia	**onychophagia** (on-ih-koh-FAY-jee-ah)	nail eating (nail biting)
py/o	-genic	**pyogenic** (pye-oh-JEN-ik)	pus forming
rhytid/o	-ectomy	**rhytidectomy** (rit-ih-DECK-toh-mee)	removal of wrinkles
	-plasty	**rhytidoplasty** (RIT-ih-doh-plas-tee)	surgical repair of wrinkles
seb/o	-rrhea	**seborrhea** (seb-or-EE-ah)	oily discharge

Word Building *(continued)*

COMBINING FORM	COMBINED WITH	MEDICAL TERM	DEFINITION
trich/o	myc/o -osis	**trichomycosis** (trik-oh-my-KOH-sis)	abnormal condition of hair fungus
ungu/o	-al	**ungual** (UNG-gwal)	pertaining to the nails
SUFFIX	**COMBINED WITH**	**MEDICAL TERM**	**MEANING**
-derma	erythr/o	**erythroderma** (eh-rith-roh-DER-mah)	red skin
	ichthy/o	**ichthyoderma** (ick-thee-oh-DER-mah)	scaly and dry skin
	leuk/o	**leukoderma** (loo-koh-DER-mah)	white skin
	py/o	**pyoderma** (pye-oh-DER-mah)	pus skin
	scler/o	**scleroderma** (sklair-ah-DER-mah)	hard skin
	xer/o	**xeroderma** (zee-roh-DER-mah)	dry skin

Vocabulary

TERM	DEFINITION
abrasion (ah-BRAY-zhun)	A scraping away of the skin surface by friction.
cicatrix (SICK-ah-trix)	A scar.
comedo (KOM-ee-do)	Collection of hardened sebum in hair follicle. Also called a *blackhead.*
contusion	Injury caused by a blow to the body; causes swelling, pain, and bruising. The skin is not broken.
cyanosis (sigh-ah-NOH-sis)	Bluish tint to the skin caused by deoxygenated blood.

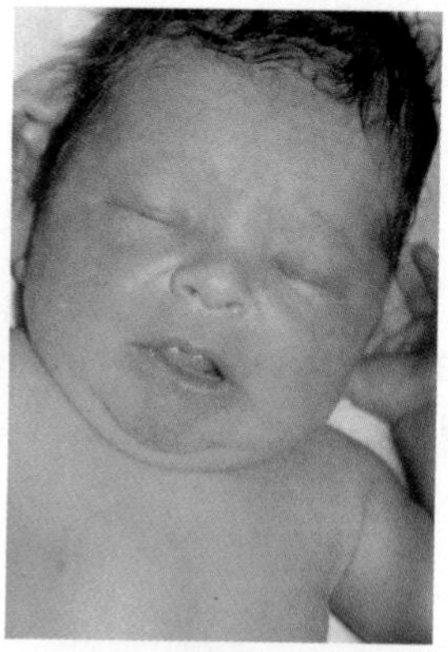

Figure 3.5 A cyanotic infant. Note the bluish tinge to the skin around the lips, chin, and nose. *(St. Bartholomew's Hospital, London/Photo Researchers, Inc.)*

TERM	DEFINITION
depigmentation (dee-pig-men-TAY-shun)	Loss of normal skin color or pigment.
dermatology (Derm, derm) (der-mah-TALL-oh-jee)	Branch of medicine involving diagnosis and treatment of conditions and diseases of the integumentary system. Physician is a *dermatologist.*
diaphoresis (dye-ah-for-REE-sis)	Profuse sweating.

Vocabulary *(continued)*

TERM	DEFINITION
ecchymosis (ek-ih-MOH-sis)	Skin discoloration caused by blood collecting under the skin following blunt trauma to the skin. A bruise (see Figure 3.6A ■).
erythema (er-ih-THEE-mah)	Redness or flushing of the skin.
eschar (ESH-shar)	A thick layer of dead tissue and tissue fluid that develops over a deep burn area.
hirsutism (HER-soot-izm)	Excessive hair growth over the body.
hyperemia (high-per-EE-mee-ah)	Redness of the skin due to increased blood flow.
hyperpigmentation (high-per-pig-men-TAY-shun)	Abnormal amount of pigmentation in the skin.
keloid (KEE-loyd)	Formation of a raised and thickened hypertrophic scar after an injury or surgery.

■ **Figure 3.7** Keloids, hypertrophic scarring on the back. *(Martin Rotker/Phototake NYC)*

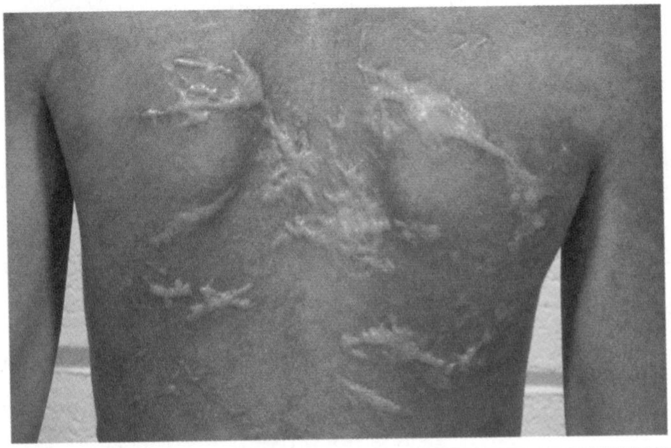

TERM	DEFINITION
keratosis (kair-ah-TOH-sis)	Term for any skin condition involving an overgrowth and thickening of the epidermis layer.
lesion (LEE-shun)	A general term for a wound, injury, or abnormality.
nevus (NEV-us)	Pigmented skin blemish, birthmark, or mole. Usually benign but may become cancerous.
pallor (PAL-or)	Abnormal paleness of the skin.
petechiae (peh-TEE-kee-eye)	Pinpoint purple or red spots from minute hemorrhages under the skin (see Figure 3.6B ■).

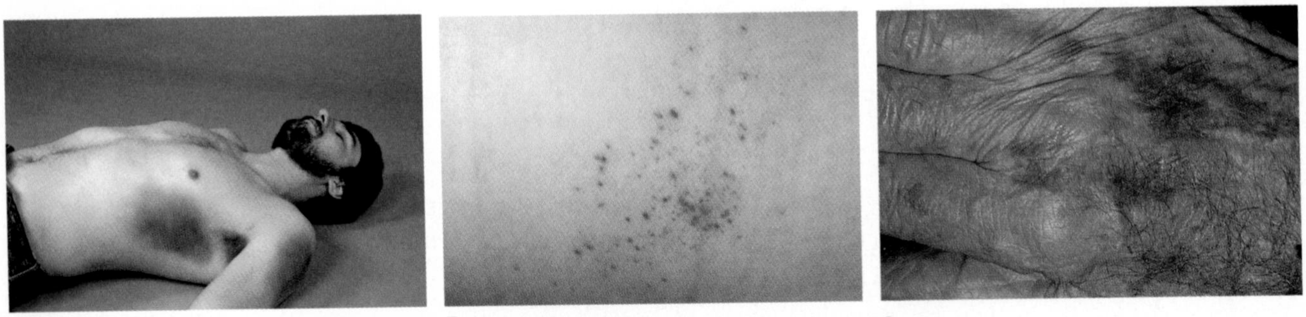

A. B. C.

■ **Figure 3.6** A) Male lying supine with large ecchymosis on lateral rib cage and shoulder. B) Petechiae, pinpoint skin hemorrhages. *(Custom Medical Stock Photo, Inc.)* C) Purpura, hemorrhaging into the skin due to fragile blood vessels. *(Caroll H. Weiss/Camera M.D. Studios)*

Vocabulary *(continued)*

TERM	DEFINITION
photosensitivity (foh-toh-sen-sih-TIH-vih-tee)	Condition in which the skin reacts abnormally when exposed to light, such as the ultraviolet (UV) rays of the sun.
plastic surgery	Surgical specialty involved in repair, reconstruction, or improvement of body structures such as the skin that are damaged, missing, or misshapen. Physician is a *plastic surgeon*.
pruritus (proo-RIGH-tus)	Severe itching.
purpura (PER-pew-rah)	Hemorrhages into the skin due to fragile blood vessels. Commonly seen in elderly people (see Figure 3.6C ■). **Med Term Tip** *Purpura* comes from the Latin word for "purple," which refers to the color of these pinpoint hemorrhages.
purulent (PYUR-yoo-lent)	Containing pus or an infection that is producing pus. Pus consists of dead bacteria, white blood cells, and tissue debris.
strawberry hemangioma (hee-man-jee-OH-ma) ■ **Figure 3.8** Strawberry hemangioma, a birthmark caused by a collection of blood vessels in the skin. *(H.C. Robinson/Science Photo Library/Photo Researchers, Inc.)*	Congenital collection of dilated blood vessels causing a red birthmark that fades a few months after birth. 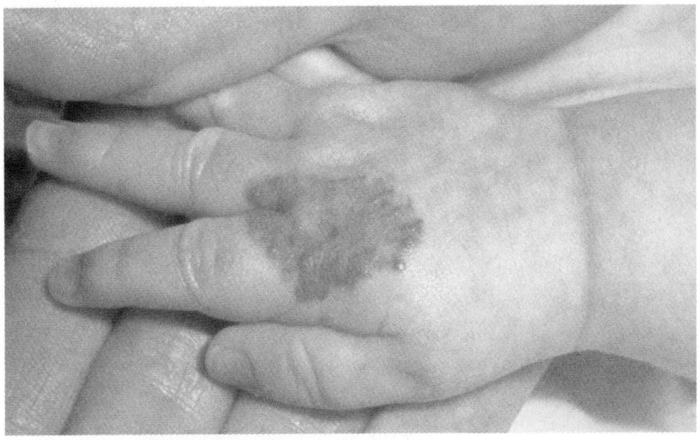
suppurative (SUP-pure-a-tiv)	Containing or producing pus.
urticaria (er-tih-KAY-ree-ah)	Also called *hives;* a skin eruption of pale reddish wheals with severe itching. Usually associated with food allergy, stress, or drug reactions.
verruca (ver-ROO-kah)	Commonly called *warts;* a benign growth caused by a virus. Has a rough surface that is removed by chemicals and/or laser therapy.

Pathology

Surface Lesions

cyst (SIST)

Fluid-filled sac under the skin (see Figures 3.9A & 3.9B ■).

A

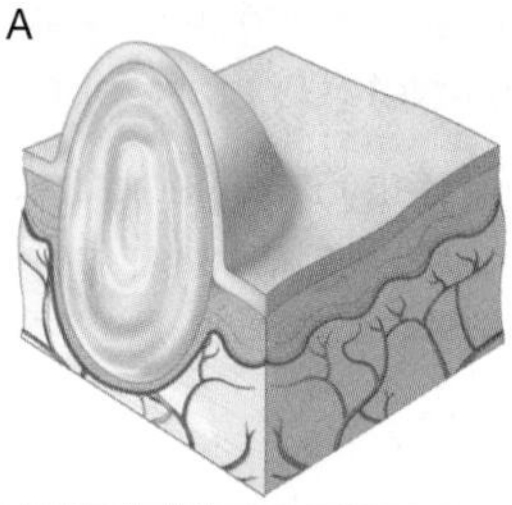

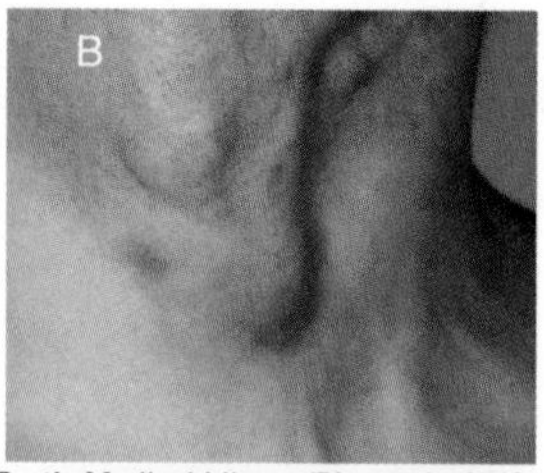

(Bart's Medical Library/Phototake NYC)

fissure (FISH-er)

Crack-like lesion or groove on the skin (see Figures 3.9C & 3.9D ■).

C

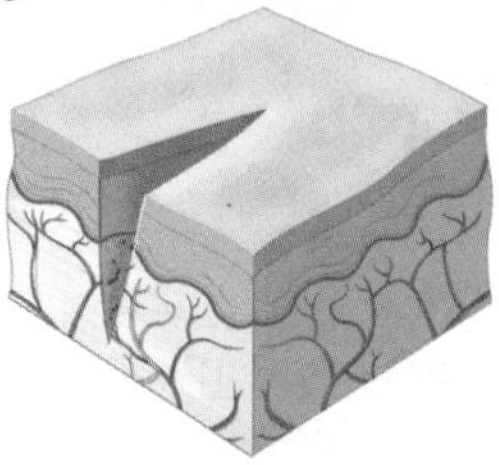

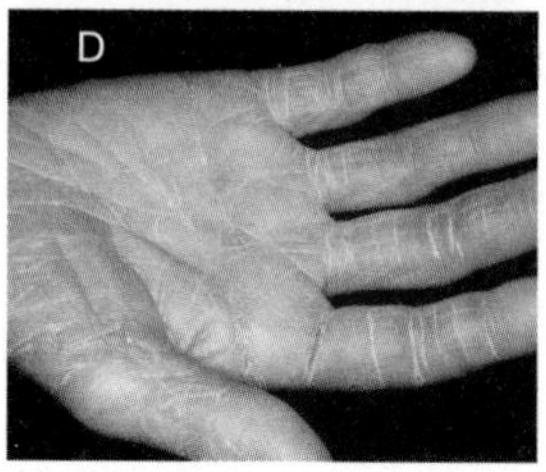

(Phototake NYC)

laceration

A torn or jagged wound; incorrectly used to describe a cut.

macule (MACK-yool)

Flat, discolored area that is flush with the skin surface. An example would be a freckle or a birthmark (see Figures 3.9E & 3.9F ■).

E

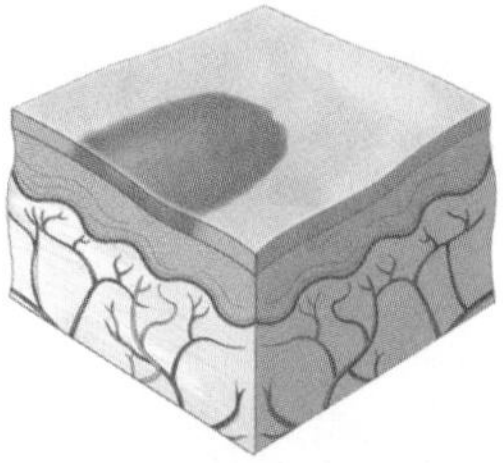

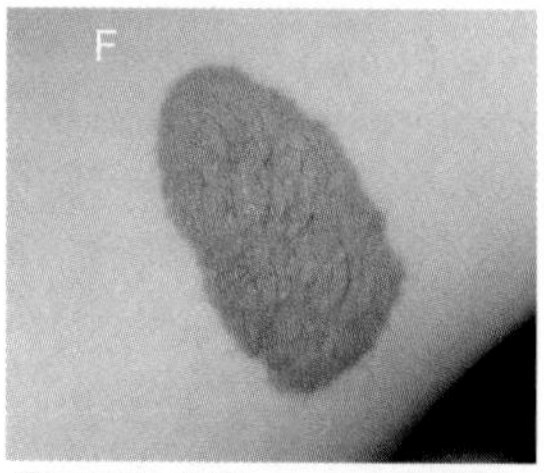

(Phototake NYC)

nodule (NOD-yool)

Firm, solid mass of cells in the skin larger than 0.5 cm in diameter (see Figures 3.9G & 3.9H ■).

G

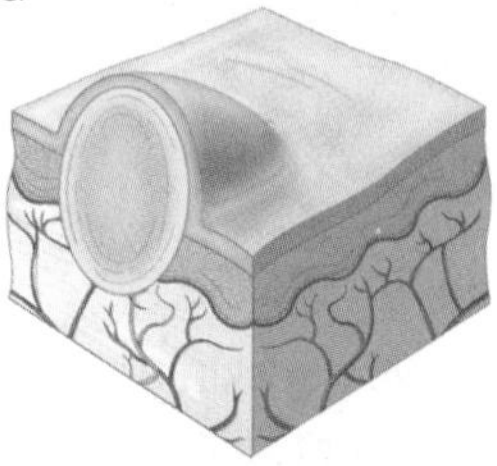

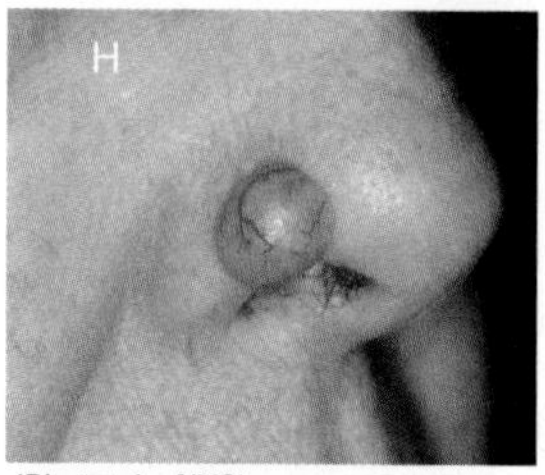

(Phototake NYC)

papule (PAP-yool)

Small, solid, circular raised spot on the surface of the skin less than 0.5 cm in diameter (see Figures 3.9I & 3.9J ■).

I

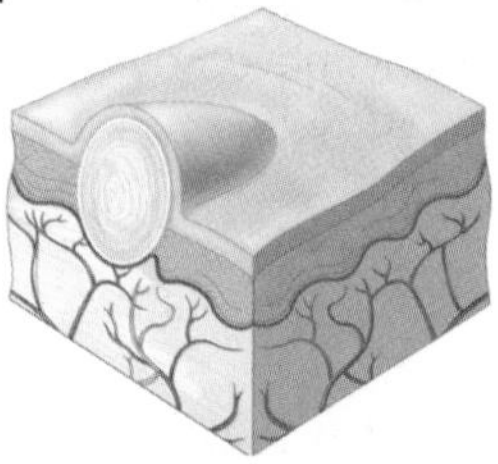

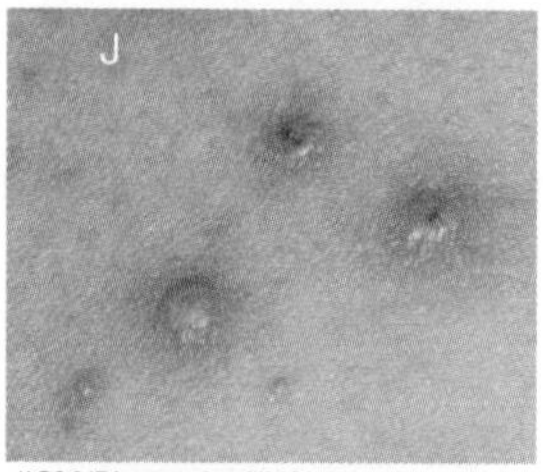

(ISM/Phototake NYC)

pustule (PUS-tyool)

Raised spot on the skin containing pus (see Figures 3.9E and 3.9K & 3.9L ■).

K

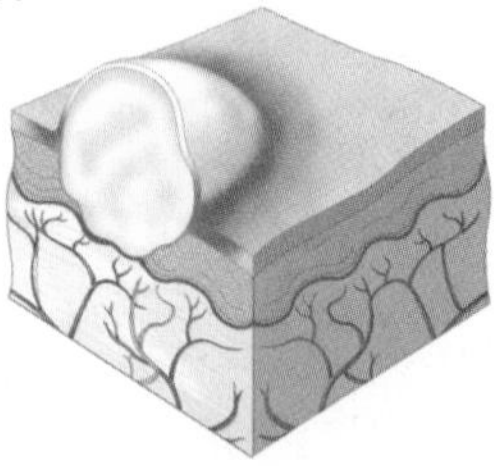

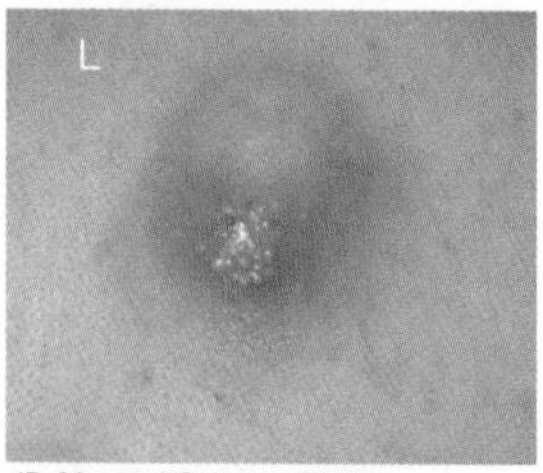

(P. Marazzi/Science Photo Library/Photo Researchers, Inc.)

Pathology *(continued)*

ulcer (ULL-ser)

Open sore or lesion in skin or mucous membrane (see Figures 3.9M & 3.9N ■).

M

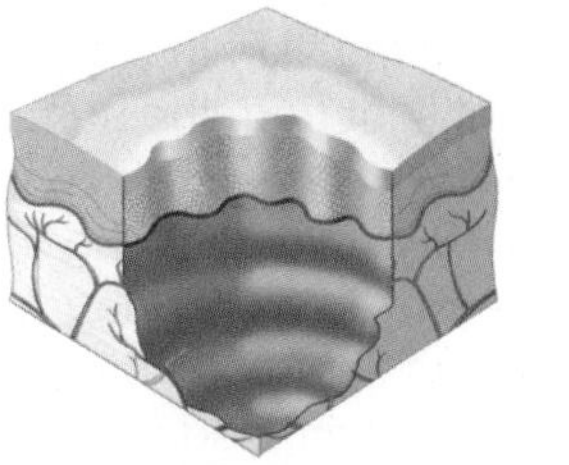

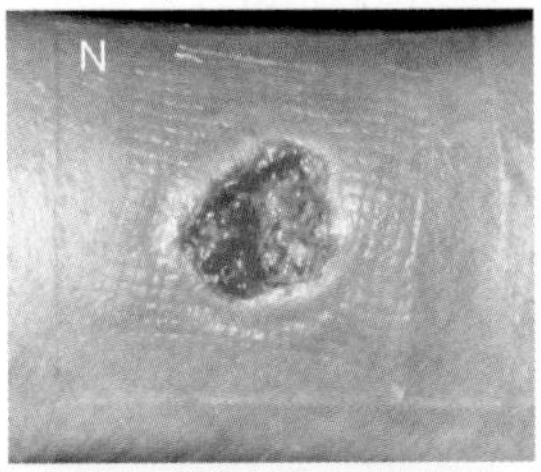

(Dr. P. Marazzi/Photo Researchers, Inc.)

vesicle (VESS-ikl)

A blister; small, fluid-filled raised spot on the skin (see Figures 3.9O & 3.9P ■).

O

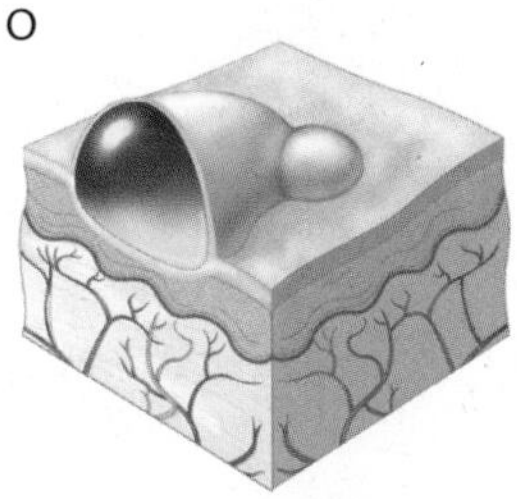

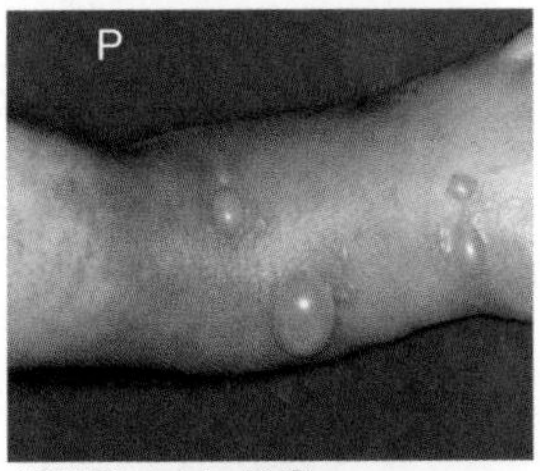

(ISM/Phototake NYC)

wheal (WEEL)

Small, round, swollen area on the skin; typically seen in allergic skin reactions such as *hives* and usually accompanied by urticaria (see Figures 3.9Q & 3.9R ■).

Q

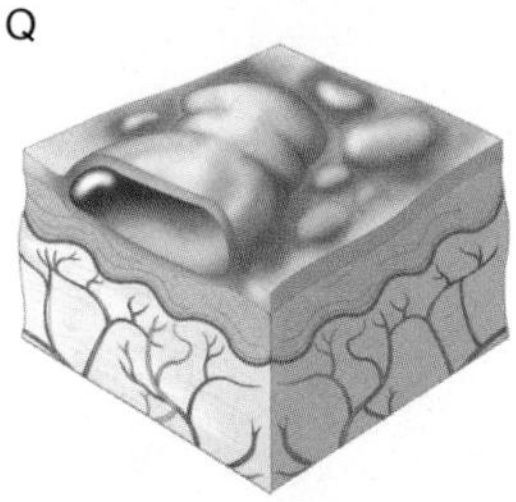

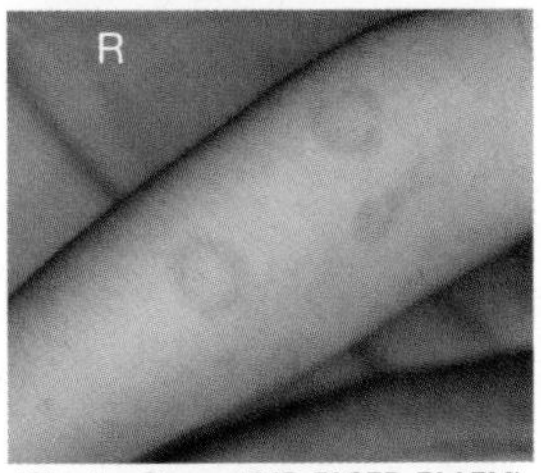

(Charles Stewart MD FACEP, FAAEM)

TERM	DEFINITION
■ ***Skin***	
abscess (AB-sess)	A collection of pus in the skin.
acne (ACK-nee)	Inflammatory disease of the sebaceous glands and hair follicles resulting in papules and pustules.
acne rosacea (ACK-nee roh-ZAY-she-ah)	Chronic form of acne seen in adults involving redness, tiny pimples, and broken blood vessels, primarily on the nose and cheeks.
acne vulgaris (ACK-nee vul-GAY-ris)	Common form of acne seen in teenagers. Characterized by comedo, papules, and pustules.
albinism (al-BIH-nizm)	A genetic condition in which the body is unable to make melanin. Characterized by white hair and skin and red pupils due to the lack of pigment. The person with albinism is called an *albino*.
basal cell carcinoma (BCC) (BAY-sal sell kar-sin-NOH-ma)	Cancerous tumor of the basal cell layer of the epidermis. A frequent type of skin cancer that rarely metastasizes or spreads. These cancers can arise on sun exposed skin.

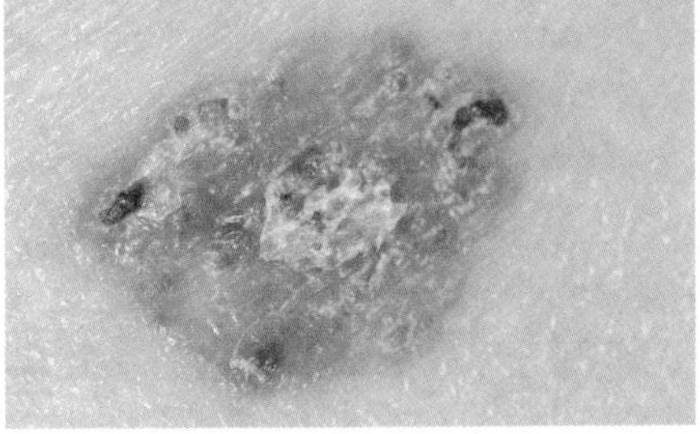

■ **Figure 3.10** Basal cell carcinoma. A frequent type of skin cancer that rarely metastasizes. *(ISM/Phototake NYC)*

Pathology *(continued)*

TERM	DEFINITION
burn	Damage to the skin that can result from exposure to open fire, electricity, ultraviolet light from the sun, or caustic chemicals. Seriousness depends on the amount of body surface involved and the depth of the burn. Depth of the burns is determined by the amount of damage to each layer skin and burns are categorized as 1st degree, 2nd degree, or 3rd degree. See Figure 3.11 for a description of the damage associated with each degree of burn. Extent of a burn is estimated using the Rule of Nines (see Figure 3.12).

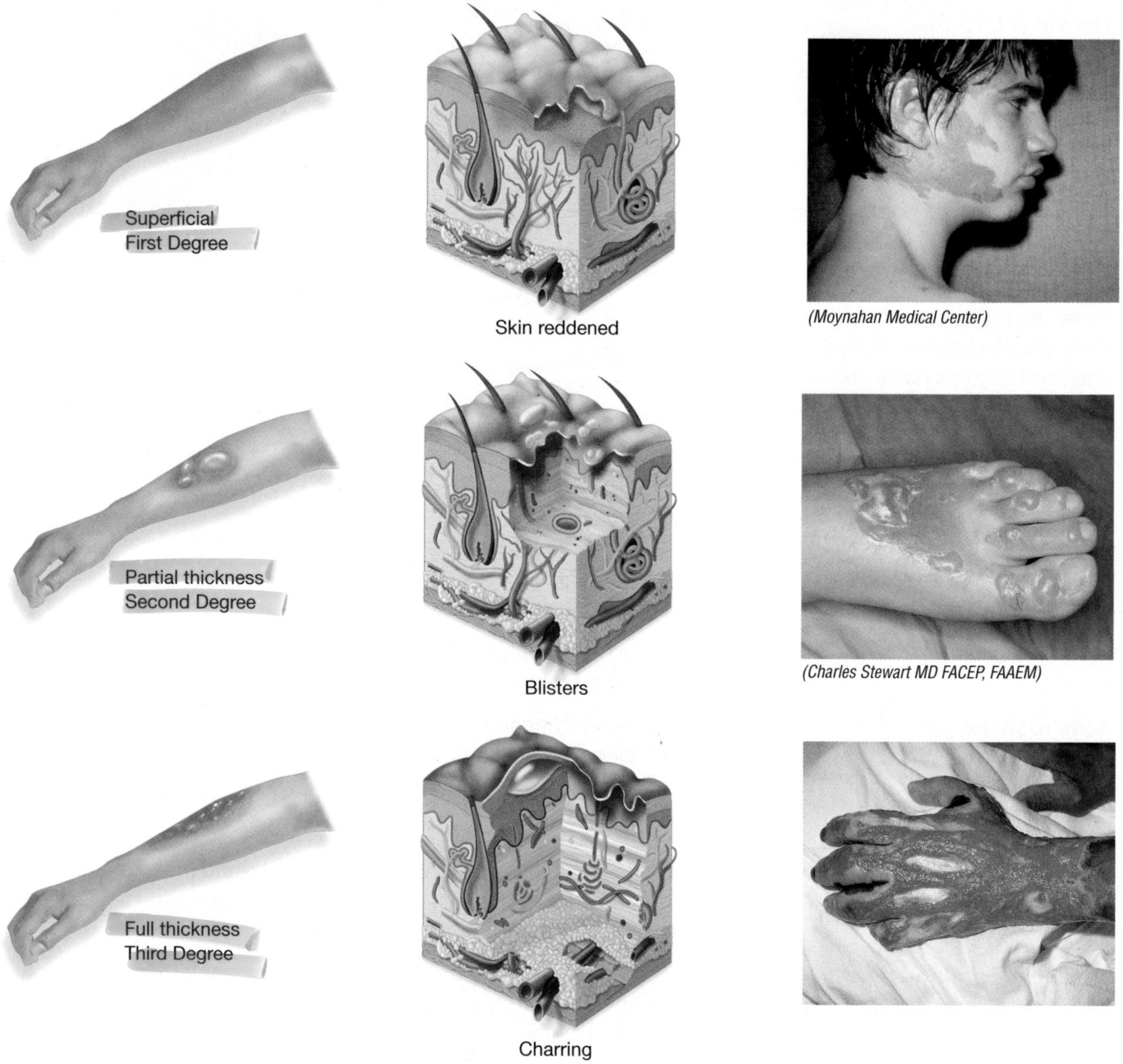

Figure 3.11 Comparison of the level of skin damage as a result of the three different degrees of burns.

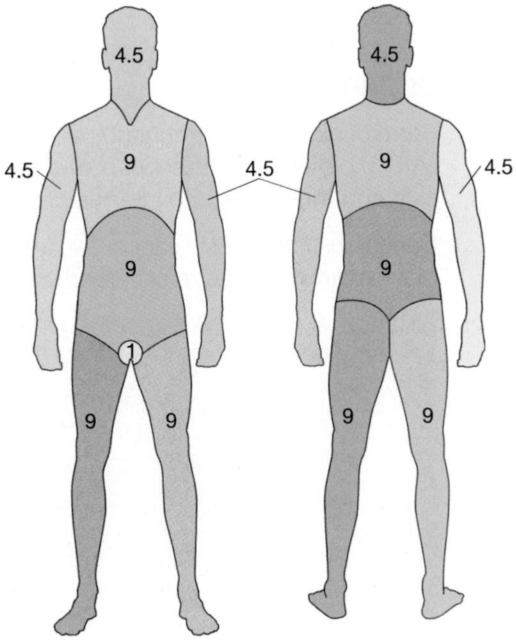

Figure 3.12 Rule of Nines. A method for determining percentage of body burned. Each differently colored section represents a percentage of the body surface. All sections added together will equal 100%.

Pathology *(continued)*

TERM	DEFINITION
cellulitis (sell-you-LYE-tis)	A diffuse, acute infection and inflammation of the connective tissue found in the skin.
decubitus ulcer (decub) (dee-KYOO-bih-tus)	Open sore caused by pressure over bony prominences cutting off the blood flow to the overlying skin. These can appear in bedridden patients who lie in one position too long and can be difficult to heal. Also called *bedsore* or *pressure sore.* **Med Term Tip** *Decubitus* comes from the Latin word *decumbo*, meaning "lying down," which leads to the use of the term for a bedsore or pressure sore.
dry gangrene (GANG-green)	Late stages of gangrene characterized by the affected area becoming dried, blackened, and shriveled; referred to as *mummified.*
eczema (EK-zeh-mah)	Superficial dermatitis of unknown cause accompanied by redness, vesicles, itching, and crusting.
gangrene (GANG-green)	Tissue necrosis usually due to deficient blood supply.
ichthyosis (ick-thee-OH-sis)	Condition in which the skin becomes dry, scaly, and keratinized.
impetigo (im-peh-TYE-goh)	A highly infections bacterial infection of the skin with pustules that rupture and become crusted over.

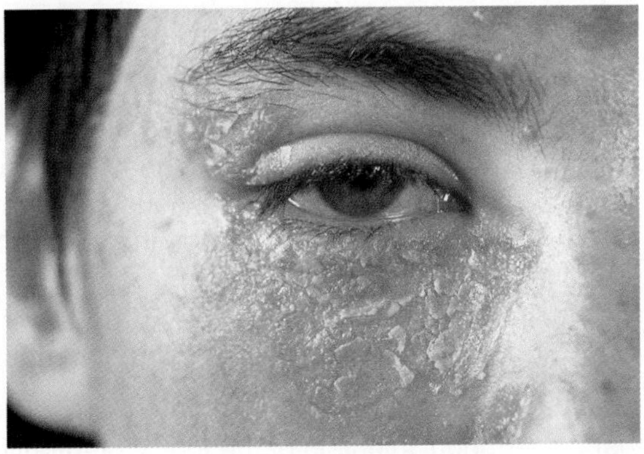

Figure 3.13 Impetigo, a highly contagious bacterial infection. Note the extensive crusting around the eye.
(Bart's Medical Library/Phototake NYC)

Pathology *(continued)*

TERM	DEFINITION
Kaposi's sarcoma (KAP-oh-seez sar-KOH-mah)	Form of skin cancer frequently seen in acquired immunodeficiency syndrome (AIDS) patients. Consists of brownish-purple papules that spread from the skin and metastasize to internal organs.
malignant melanoma (MM) (mah-LIG-nant mel-a-NOH-ma)	Dangerous form of skin cancer caused by an uncontrolled growth of melanocytes. May quickly metastasize or spread to internal organs.

Figure 3.14 Malignant melanoma. This tumor demonstrates the highly characteristic color of this tumor. *(ISM/Phototake NYC)*

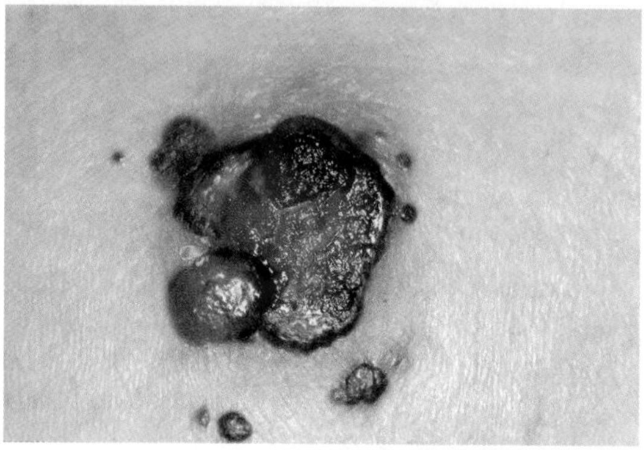

TERM	DEFINITION
pediculosis (peh-dik-you-LOH-sis)	Infestation with lice. The eggs laid by the lice are called nits and cling tightly to hair.
psoriasis (soh-RYE-ah-sis)	Chronic inflammatory condition consisting of papules forming "silvery scale" patches with circular borders.

Figure 3.15 Psoriasis. This photograph demonstrates the characteristic white skin patches of this condition.

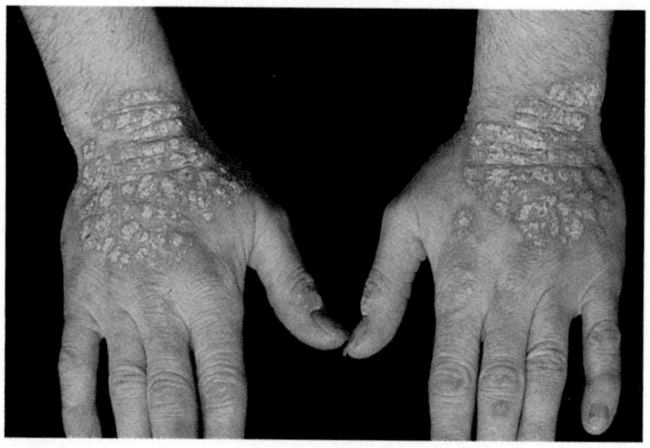

TERM	DEFINITION
rubella (roo-BELL-ah)	Contagious viral skin infection. Commonly called *German measles.*
scabies (SKAY-bees)	Contagious skin disease caused by an egg-laying mite that burrows through the skin and causes redness and intense itching; often seen in children.
sebaceous cyst (see-BAY-shus SIST)	Sac under the skin filled with sebum or oil from a sebaceous gland. This can grow to a large size and may need to be excised.
squamous cell carcinoma (SCC) (SKWAY-mus sell kar-sih-NOH-mah)	Cancer of the epidermis layer of skin that may invade deeper tissue and metastasize. Often begins as a sore that does not heal.
systemic lupus erythematosus (SLE) (sis-TEM-ik LOO-pus air-ih-them-ah-TOH-sis)	Chronic disease of the connective tissue that injures the skin, joints, kidneys, nervous system, and mucous membranes. May produce a characteristic red, scaly butterfly rash across the cheeks and nose.
tinea (TIN-ee-ah)	Fungal skin disease resulting in itching, scaling lesions.
tinea capitis (TIN-ee-ah CAP-it-is)	Fungal infection of the scalp. Commonly called *ringworm.*
tinea pedis (TIN-ee-ah PED-is)	Fungal infection of the foot. Commonly called *athlete's foot.*

Pathology *(continued)*

TERM	DEFINITION
varicella (VAIR-ih-chell-a)	Contagious viral skin infection. Commonly called *chicken pox.*
Figure 3.16 Varicella or chicken pox, a viral skin infection. In this photograph, the rash is beginning to form scabs.	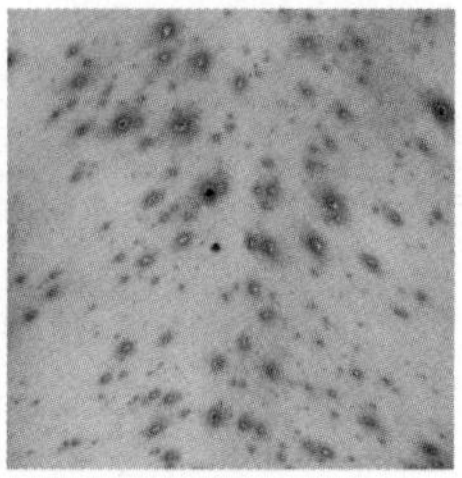
vitiligo (vit-ill-EYE-go)	Disappearance of pigment from the skin in patches, causing a milk-white appearance. Also called *leukoderma.*
wet gangrene (GANG-green)	An area of gangrene that becomes secondarily infected by pus-producing bacteria.
■ ***Hair***	
alopecia (al-oh-PEE-she-ah)	Absence or loss of hair, especially of the head. Commonly called *baldness.*
carbuncle (CAR-bung-kl)	Furuncle involving several hair follicles.
furuncle (FOO-rung-kl)	Bacterial infection of a hair follicle. Characterized by redness, pain, and swelling. Also called a *boil.*
■ ***Nails***	
onychia (oh-NICK-ee-ah)	Infected nail bed.
paronychia (pair-oh-NICK-ee-ah)	Infection of the skin fold around a nail.

Diagnostic Procedures

TERM	DEFINITION
■ ***Clinical Laboratory Tests***	
culture and sensitivity (C&S)	A laboratory test that grows a colony of bacteria removed from an infected area in order to identify the specific infecting bacteria and then determine its sensitivity to a variety of antibiotics.
■ ***Biopsy Procedures***	
biopsy (BX, bx) (BYE-op-see)	A piece of tissue is removed by syringe and needle, knife, punch, or brush to examine under a microscope. Used to aid in diagnosis. **Med Term Tip** Word Watch — be careful when using *bi-* meaning "two" and *bi/o* meaning "life."
exfoliative cytology (ex-FOH-lee-ah-tiv sigh-TALL-oh-jee)	Scraping cells from tissue and then examining them under a microscope.
frozen section (FS)	A thin piece of tissue is cut from a frozen specimen for rapid examination under a microscope.
fungal scrapings	Scrapings, taken with a curette or scraper, of tissue from lesions are placed on a growth medium and examined under a microscope to identify fungal growth.

Therapeutic Procedures

TERM	DEFINITION
Skin Grafting	
allograft (AL-oh-graft)	Skin graft from one person to another; donor is usually a cadaver.
autograft (AW-toh-graft) **Figure 3.17** A freshly applied autograft. Note that the donor skin has been perforated so that it can be stretched to cover a larger burned area. *(Courtesy of Dr. William Dominic, Community Regional Medical Center)*	Skin graft from a person's own body. 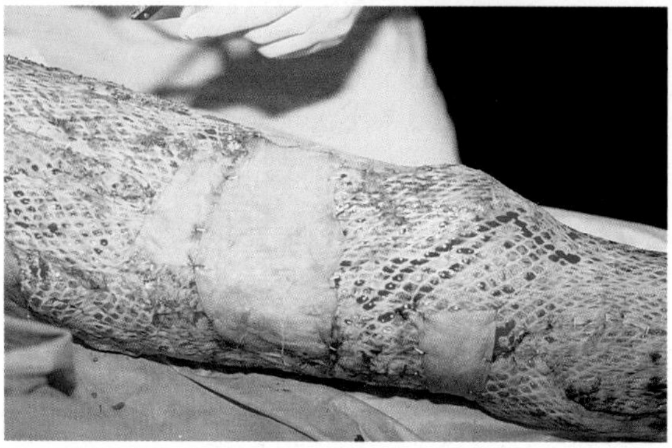
dermatome (DER-mah-tohm)	Instrument for cutting the skin or thin transplants of skin.
dermatoplasty (DER-mah-toh-plas-tee)	Skin grafting; transplantation of skin.
heterograft (HET-ur-oh-graft)	Skin graft from an animal of another species (usually a pig) to a human. Also called *xenograft.*
skin graft (SG)	The transfer of skin from a normal area to cover another site. Used to treat burn victims and after some surgical procedures. Also called *dermatoplasty.*
xenograft (ZEN-oh-graft)	Skin graft from an animal of another species (usually a pig) to a human. Also called *heterograft.*
Surgical Procedures	
cauterization (kaw-ter-ih-ZAY-shun)	Destruction of tissue by using caustic chemicals, electric currents, heat, or by freezing.
cryosurgery (cry-oh-SER-jer-ee)	The use of extreme cold to freeze and destroy tissue.
curettage (koo-REH-tahz)	Removal of superficial skin lesions with a curette (surgical instrument shaped like a spoon) or scraper.
debridement (de-BREED-mint)	Removal of foreign material and dead or damaged tissue from a wound.
electrocautery (ee-leck-troh-KAW-teh-ree)	To destroy tissue with an electric current.
incision and drainage (I&D)	Making an incision to create an opening for the drainage of material such as pus.
Plastic Surgery Procedures	
chemabrasion (kee-moh-BRAY-zhun)	Abrasion using chemicals. Also called a *chemical peel.*
dermabrasion (DERM-ah-bray-shun)	Abrasion or rubbing using wire brushes or sandpaper. Performed to remove acne scars, tattoos, and scar tissue.
laser therapy	Removal of skin lesions and birthmarks using a laser beam that emits intense heat and power at a close range. The laser converts frequencies of light into one small, powerful beam.
liposuction (LIP-oh-suck-shun)	Removal of fat beneath the skin by means of suction.
rhytidectomy (rit-ih-DECK-toh-mee)	Surgical removal of excess skin to eliminate wrinkles. Commonly referred to as a *face lift.*

Pharmacology

CLASSIFICATION	ACTION	GENERIC AND BRAND NAMES
anesthetics (an-es-THET-tics)	Applied to the skin to deaden pain.	lidocaine, Xylocaine; procaine, Novocain
antibiotics (an-tye-bye-AW-tics)	Kill bacteria causing skin infections.	bacitracin/neomycin/polymixinB, Neosporin ointment
antifungals (an-tye-FUNG-alls)	Kill fungi infecting the skin.	miconazole, Monistat; clotrimazole, Lotrimin
antiparasitics (an-tye-pair-ah-SIT-tics)	Kill mites or lice.	lindane, Kwell; permethrin, Nix
antipruritics (an-tye-proo-RIGH-tiks)	Reduce severe itching.	diphenhydramine, Benadryl; camphor/pramoxine/zinc, Caladryl
antiseptics (an-tye-SEP-tics)	Used to kill bacteria in skin cuts and wounds or at a surgical site.	isopropyl alcohol; hydrogen peroxide
anti-virals	Treats herpes simplex infection.	valacyclovir, Valtrex; famcyclovir, Famvir; acyclovir, Zovirax
corticosteroid cream	Specific type of powerful anti-inflammatory cream.	hydrocortisone, Cortaid; triamcinolone, Kenalog

Abbreviations

BCC	basal cell carcinoma
BX, bx	biopsy
C&S	culture and sensitivity
decub	decubitus ulcer
Derm, derm	dermatology
FS	frozen section
HSV	herpes simplex virus
I&D	incision and drainage
ID	intradermal
MM	malignant melanoma
SCC	squamous cell carcinoma
SG	skin graft
SLE	systemic lupus erythematosus
STSG	split-thickness skin graft
subcu, SC, sc, subq	subcutaneous
UV	ultraviolet

Med Term Tip

Word Watch—be careful when using the abbreviation *ID* meaning "intradermal" and *I&D* meaning "incision and drainage."

Chapter Review

Terminology Checklist

Below are all anatomy and physiology key terms, word building, vocabulary, pathology, diagnostic, therapeutic, and pharmacology terms presented in this chapter. Use this list as a study tool by placing a check in the box in front of each term as you master its meaning.

- ☐ abrasion
- ☐ abscess
- ☐ acne
- ☐ acne rosacea
- ☐ acne vulgaris
- ☐ albinism
- ☐ allograft
- ☐ alopecia
- ☐ anesthetics
- ☐ anhidrosis
- ☐ antibiotics
- ☐ antifungals
- ☐ antiparasitics
- ☐ antipruritics
- ☐ antiseptics
- ☐ anti-virals
- ☐ apocrine glands
- ☐ arrector pili
- ☐ autograft
- ☐ basal cell carcinoma
- ☐ basal layer
- ☐ biopsy
- ☐ burn
- ☐ carbuncle
- ☐ cauterization
- ☐ cellulitis
- ☐ chemabrasion
- ☐ cicatrix
- ☐ collagen fibers
- ☐ comedo
- ☐ contusion
- ☐ corium
- ☐ corticosteroid cream
- ☐ cryosurgery
- ☐ culture and sensitivity
- ☐ curettage
- ☐ cutaneous membrane
- ☐ cuticle
- ☐ cyanosis
- ☐ cyst
- ☐ debridement
- ☐ decubitus ulcer
- ☐ depigmentation
- ☐ dermabrasion
- ☐ dermatitis
- ☐ dermatologist
- ☐ dermatology
- ☐ dermatome
- ☐ dermatopathy
- ☐ dermatoplasty
- ☐ dermatosis
- ☐ dermis
- ☐ diaphoresis
- ☐ dry gangrene
- ☐ ecchymosis
- ☐ eczema
- ☐ electrocautery
- ☐ epidermal
- ☐ epidermis
- ☐ erythema
- ☐ erythroderma
- ☐ eschar
- ☐ exfoliative cytology
- ☐ fissure
- ☐ free edge
- ☐ frozen section
- ☐ fungal scrapings
- ☐ furuncle
- ☐ gangrene
- ☐ hair
- ☐ hair follicle
- ☐ hair root
- ☐ hair shaft
- ☐ heterograft
- ☐ hirsutism
- ☐ hyperemia
- ☐ hyperhidrosis
- ☐ hyperpigmentation
- ☐ hypodermic
- ☐ hypodermis
- ☐ ichthyoderma
- ☐ ichthyosis
- ☐ impetigo
- ☐ incision and drainage
- ☐ integument
- ☐ integumentary system
- ☐ intradermal
- ☐ Kaposi's sarcoma
- ☐ keloid
- ☐ keratin
- ☐ keratosis
- ☐ laceration
- ☐ laser therapy
- ☐ lesion
- ☐ leukoderma
- ☐ lipectomy
- ☐ lipocytes
- ☐ lipoma
- ☐ liposuction
- ☐ lunula
- ☐ macule
- ☐ malignant melanoma
- ☐ melanin
- ☐ melanocytes
- ☐ melanoma
- ☐ nail bed
- ☐ nail body
- ☐ nail root
- ☐ nails
- ☐ necrosis
- ☐ nevus
- ☐ nodule
- ☐ onychectomy
- ☐ onychia

Multimedia Preview

Additional interactive resources and activities for this chapter can be found on the Companion Website. For videos, games, and pronunciations, please access the accompanying DVD-ROM that comes with this book.

DVD-ROM Highlights

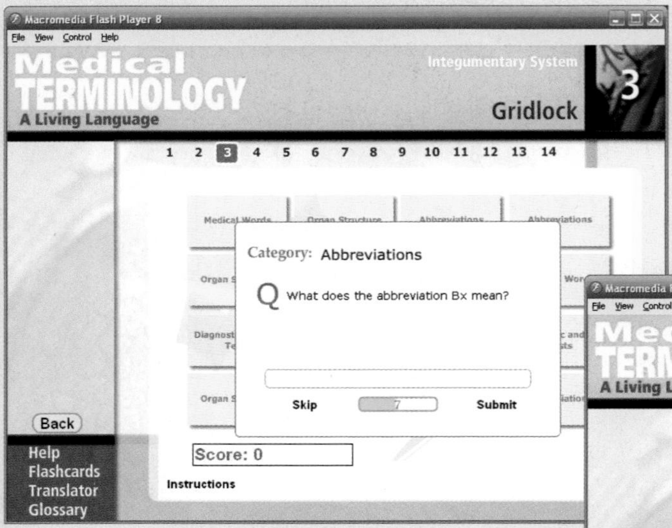

GRIDLOCK GAME

Are you a *Jeopardy!* champ? Prove your quiz show smarts by clicking here to answer the medical terminology questions hidden beneath the tiles. Get them all right to clear the grid.

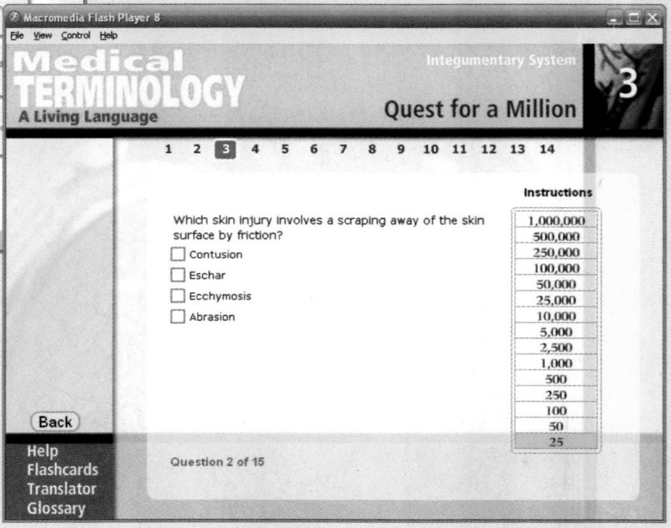

QUEST FOR A MILLION

Who wants to win a million points? If it's you, then click on this game to begin your challenge. If you correctly answer 15 questions in a row, then you're a winner. But be very careful, because one wrong response will take you back down to zero.

Website Highlights—www.prenhall.com/fremgen

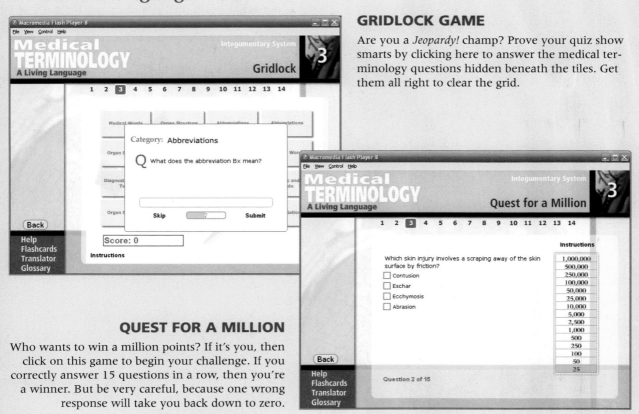

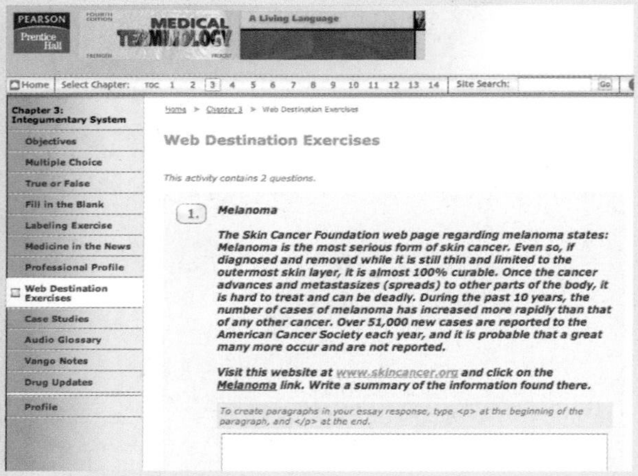

WEB DESTINATION EXERCISES

Surf the net to investigate key topics and then report your findings. This online activity challenges you to visit selected web links where you can explore important issues to reinforce your understanding.

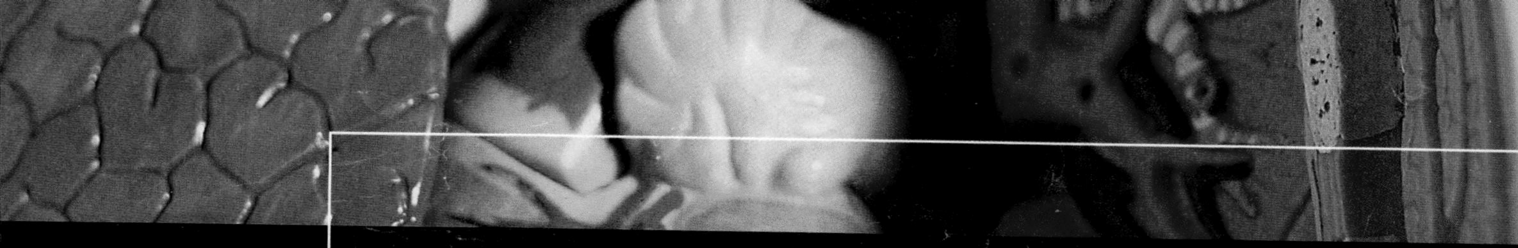

4 Musculoskeletal System

Learning Objectives

Upon completion of this chapter, you will be able to:

- Identify and define the combining forms, prefixes, and suffixes introduced in this chapter.
- Correctly spell and pronounce medical terms and major anatomical structures relating to the musculoskeletal system.
- Locate and describe the major organs of the musculoskeletal system and their functions.
- Correctly place bones in either the axial or the appendicular skeleton.
- List and describe the components of a long bone.
- Identify bony projections and depressions.
- Identify the parts of a synovial joint.
- Describe the characteristics of the three types of muscle tissue.
- Use movement terminology correctly.
- Build and define musculoskeletal system medical terms from word parts.
- Identify and define musculoskeletal system vocabulary terms.
- Identify and define selected musculoskeletal system pathology terms.
- Identify and define selected musculoskeletal system diagnostic procedures.
- Identify and define selected musculoskeletal system therapeutic procedures.
- Identify and define selected medications relating to the musculoskeletal system.
- Define selected abbreviations associated with the musculoskeletal system.

Section I: Skeletal System at a Glance

Function

The skeletal system consists of 206 bones that make up the internal framework of the [illegible], called the skeleton. The skeleton supports the body, protects internal organs, serves as a point [illegible]achment for skeletal muscles for body movement, produces blood cells, and stores minerals.

Organs

bones **joints**

Combining Forms

ankyl/o	stiff joint
arthr/o	joint
articul/o	joint
burs/o	sac
carp/o	wrist
cervic/o	neck
chondr/o	cartilage
clavicul/o	clavicle
coccyg/o	coccyx
cortic/o	outer portion
cost/o	rib
crani/o	skull
femor/o	femur
fibul/o	fibula
humer/o	humerus
ili/o	ilium
ischi/o	ischium
kyph/o	hump
lamin/o	lamina, part of vertebra
lord/o	bent backwards
lumb/o	loin
mandibul/o	mandible
maxill/o	maxilla
medull/o	inner portion
metacarp/o	metacarpals
metatars/o	metatarsals
myel/o	bone marrow, spinal cord
orth/o	straight
oste/o	bone
patell/o	patella
ped/o	child, foot
pelv/o	pelvis
phalang/o	phalanges
pod/o	foot
pub/o	pubis
radi/o	radius
sacr/o	sacrum
scapul/o	scapula
scoli/o	crooked, bent
spondyl/o	vertebrae
stern/o	sternum
synovi/o	synovial membrane
synov/o	synovial membrane
tars/o	ankle
thorac/o	chest
tibi/o	tibia
uln/o	ulna
vertebr/o	vertebra

Suffixes

-blast	immature, embryonic
-clasia	to surgically break
-desis	stabilize, fuse
-listhesis	slipping
-porosis	porous

Skeletal System Illustrated

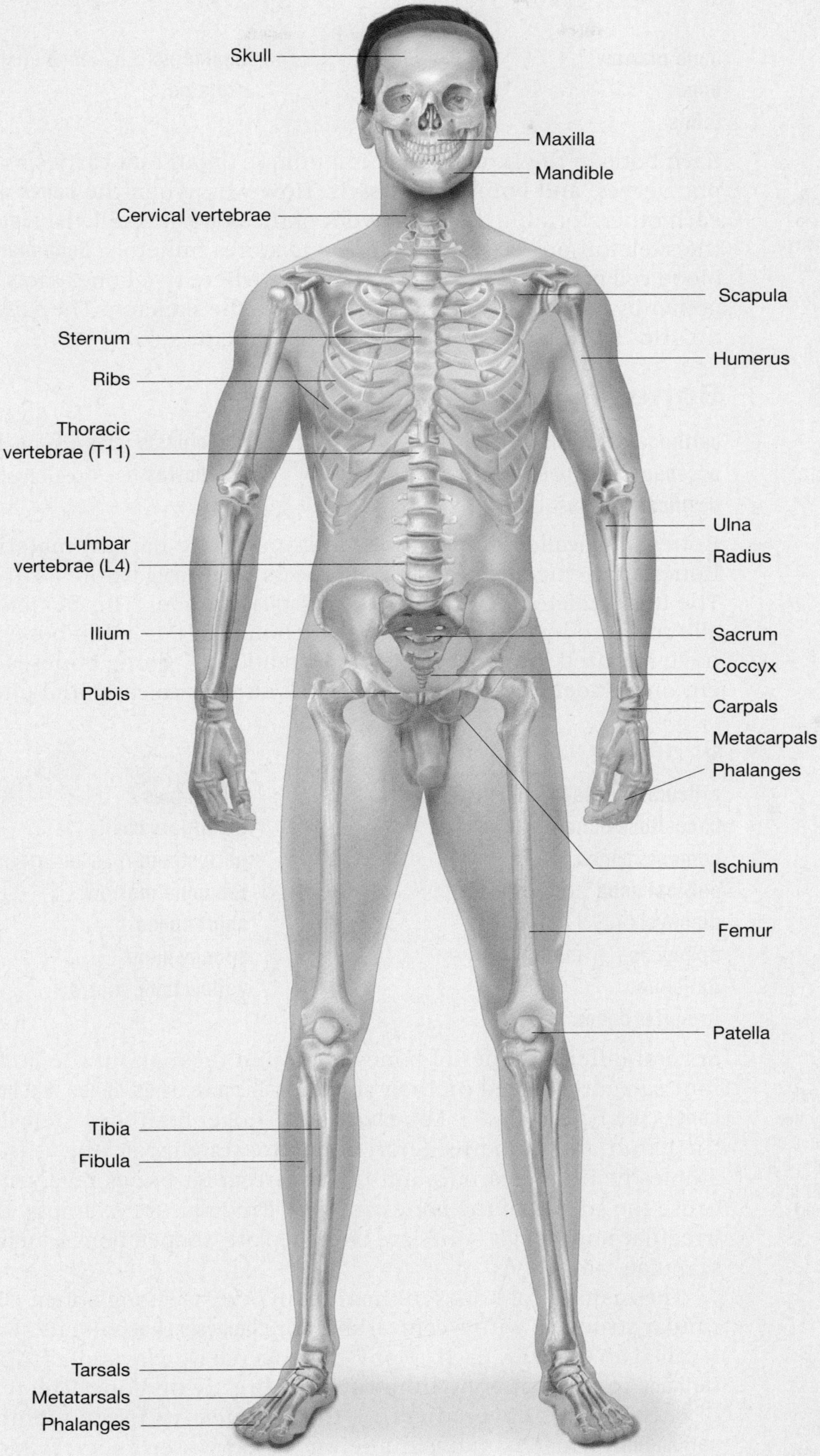

Anatomy and Physiology of the Skeletal System

bone marrow
bones
joints
ligaments (LIG-ah-ments)
skeleton

Med Term Tip

The term *skeleton*, from the Greek word *skeltos* meaning "dried up," was originally used in reference to a dried-up mummified body, but over time came to be used for bones.

Each bone in the human body is a unique organ that carries its own blood supply, nerves, and lymphatic vessels. However, when the **bones** are connected to each other, forming the framework of the body, it is called a **skeleton**. In addition, the skeleton protects vital organs and stores minerals. **Bone marrow** is the site of blood cell production. A **joint** is the place where two bones meet and are held together by **ligaments**. This gives flexibility to the skeleton. The skeleton, joints, and muscles work together to produce movement.

Bones

cartilage (CAR-tih-lij)
osseous tissue (OSS-ee-us)
ossification (oss-sih-fih-KAY-shun)
osteoblasts (OSS-tee-oh-blasts)
osteocytes (OSS-tee-oh-sights)

Bones, also called **osseous tissue**, are one of the hardest materials in the body. Bones are formed from a gradual process beginning before birth called **ossification**. The fetal skeleton is formed from a **cartilage** model. This flexible tissue is gradually replaced by **osteoblasts**, immature bone cells. In adult bones, the osteoblasts have matured into **osteocytes**. The formation of strong bones is greatly dependent on an adequate supply of minerals such as calcium and phosphorus.

Bone Structure

articular cartilage (ar-TIK-yoo-lar)
cancellous bone (CAN-sell-us)
compact bone
cortical bone (KOR-ti-kal)
diaphysis (dye-AFF-ih-sis)
epiphysis (eh-PIFF-ih-sis)
flat bones
irregular bones
long bones
medullary cavity (MED-you-lair-ee)
periosteum (pair-ee-AH-stee-um)
red bone marrow
short bones
spongy bone
yellow bone marrow

Med Term Tip

Do not confuse a long bone with a large bone. A long bone is not necessarily a large bone. The bones of your fingers are short in length, but since they are longer than they are wide, they are classified as long bones.

Several different types of bones are found throughout the body. They fall into four categories based on their shape: **long bones**, **short bones**, **flat bones**, and **irregular bones** (see Figure 4.1 ■). Long bones are longer than they are wide. Examples are the femur and humerus. Short bones are roughly as long as they are wide; examples being the carpals and tarsals. Irregular bones received their name because the shapes of the bones are very irregular; for example, the vertebrae are irregular bones. Flat bones are usually plate-shaped bones such as the sternum, scapulae, and pelvis.

The majority of bones in the human body are long bones. These bones have similar structure with a central shaft or **diaphysis** that widens at each end, which is called an **epiphysis**. Each epiphysis is covered by a layer of cartilage called **articular cartilage** to prevent bone from rubbing directly on bone. The remaining surface of each bone is covered with a thin connective tissue membrane called the **periosteum**, which contains numerous blood vessels, nerves, and lymphatic vessels. The dense and hard exterior surface bone is called **cortical** or **compact bone**.

Med Term Tip

The term *diaphysis* comes from the Greek term meaning "to grow between."

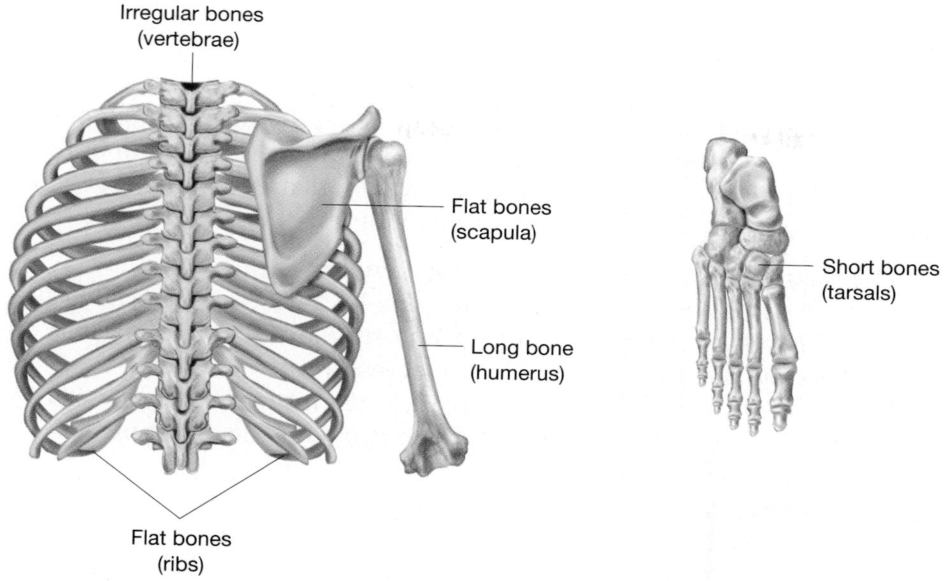

Figure 4.1 Classification of bones by shape.

Cancellous or **spongy bone** is found inside the bone. As its name indicates, spongy bone has spaces in it, giving it a spongelike appearance. These spaces contain **red bone marrow**. Red bone marrow manufactures most of the blood cells and is found in some parts of all bones.

The center of the diaphysis contains an open canal called the **medullary cavity**. This cavity contains **yellow bone marrow**, which is mainly fat cells. Figure 4.2 contains an illustration of the structure of long bones.

Bone Projections and Depressions

condyle (KON-dile)
epicondyle (ep-ih-KON-dile)
fissure (FISH-er)
foramen (for-AY-men)
fossa (FOSS-ah)
head
neck
process
sinus (SIGH-nus)
trochanter (tro-KAN-ter)
tubercle (TOO-ber-kl)
tuberosity (too-ber-OSS-ih-tee)

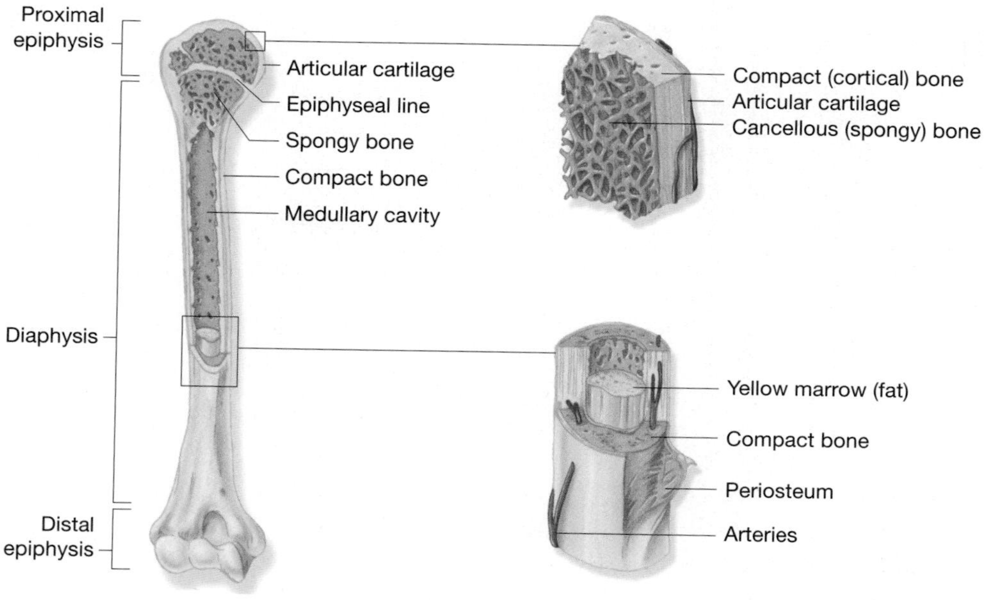

Figure 4.2 Components of a long bone. The entire long bone is on the left side accompanied by a blow-up of the proximal epiphysis and a section of the diaphysis.

Med Term Tip

The elbow, commonly referred to as the *funny bone,* is actually a projection of the ulna called the olecranon process.

Bones have many projections and depressions. Some are rounded and smooth in order to articulate with another bone in a joint. Others are rough to provide muscles with attachment points. The general term for any bony projection is a **process**. Then there are specific terms to describe the different shapes and locations of various processes. These terms are commonly used on operative reports and in physicians' records for clear identification of areas on the individual bones. Some of the common bony processes include the following:

1. The **head** is a large smooth ball-shaped end on a long bone. It may be separated from the body or shaft of the bone by a narrow area called the **neck**.
2. A **condyle** refers to a smooth rounded portion at the end of a bone.
3. The **epicondyle** is a projection located above or on a condyle.
4. The trochanter refers to a large rough process for the attachment of a muscle.
5. A **tubercle** is a small, rough process that provides the attachment for tendons and muscles.
6. The **tuberosity** is a large, rough process that provides the attachment of tendons and muscles.

See Figure 4.3 for an illustration of the processes found on the femur.

In addition, bones have hollow regions or depressions. The most common depressions are as follows:

1. A **sinus**, which is a hollow cavity within a bone.
2. A **foramen**, which is a smooth round opening for nerves and blood vessels.
3. A **fossa**, which consists of a shallow cavity or depression on the surface of a bone.
4. A **fissure**, which is a slit-type opening.

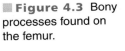

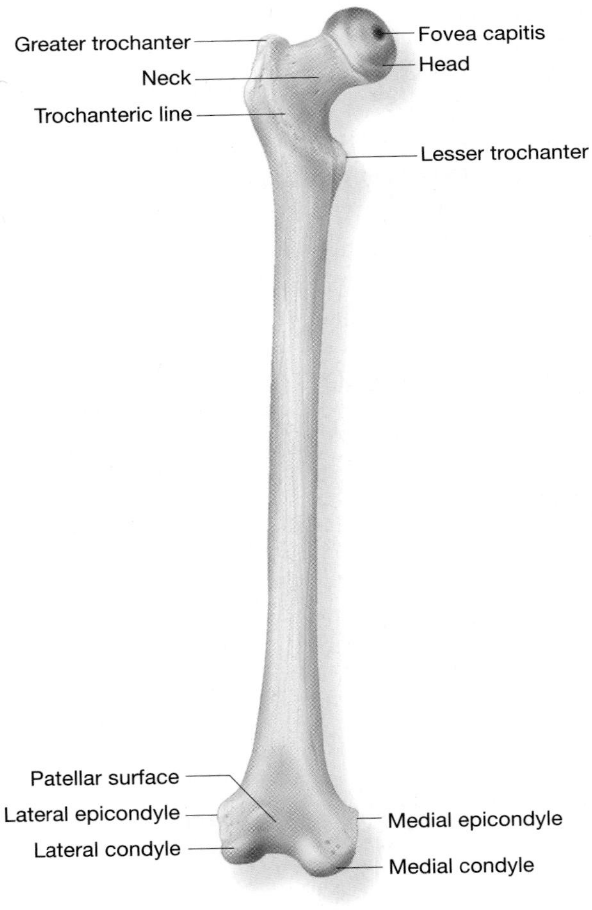

Figure 4.3 Bony processes found on the femur.

Skeleton

appendicular skeleton (app-en-DIK-yoo-lar) **axial skeleton** (AK-see-al)

The human skeleton has two divisions: the **axial skeleton** and the **appendicular skeleton**. Figures 4.4 and 4.8 illustrate the axial and appendicular skeletons.

Med Term Tip

Newborn infants have about 300 bones at birth that will fuse into 206 bones as an adult.

Axial Skeleton

cervical vertebrae
coccyx (COCK-six)
cranium (KRAY-nee-um)
ethmoid bone (ETH-moyd)
facial bones
frontal bone
hyoid bone (HIGH-oyd)
intervertebral disc (in-ter-VER-teh-bral)
lacrimal bone (LACK-rim-al)
lumbar vertebrae
mandible (MAN-dih-bl)
maxilla (mack-SIH-lah)
nasal bone
occipital bone (ock-SIP-eh-tal)
palatine bone (PAL-ah-tine)
parietal bone (pah-RYE-eh-tal)
rib cage
sacrum (SAY-crum)
sphenoid bone (SFEE-noyd)
sternum (STER-num)
temporal bone (TEM-por-al)
thoracic vertebrae
vertebral column (VER-teh-bral)
vomer bone (VOH-mer)
zygomatic bone (zeye-go-MAT-ik)

The axial skeleton includes the bones in the head, neck, spine, chest, and trunk of the body (see Figure 4.4 ■). These bones form the central axis for the whole body and protect many of the internal organs such as the brain, lungs, and heart.

The head or skull is divided into two parts consisting of the **cranium** and **facial bones**. These bones surround and protect the brain, eyes, ears, nasal cavity, and oral cavity from injury. The muscles for chewing and moving the head are attached to the cranial bones. The cranium encases the brain and consists of the **frontal**, **parietal**, **temporal**, **ethmoid**, **sphenoid**, and **occipital bones**. The facial bones surround the mouth, nose, and eyes and include the **mandible**, **maxilla**, **zygomatic**, **vomer**, **palatine**, **nasal**, and **lacrimal bones**. The cranial and facial bones are illustrated in Figure 4.5 ■ and described in Table 4.1 ■.

The **hyoid bone** is a single U-shaped bone suspended in the neck between the mandible and larynx. It is a point of attachment for swallowing and speech muscles.

The trunk of the body consists of the **vertebral column**, **sternum**, and **rib cage**. The vertebral or spinal column is divided into five sections: **cervical vertebrae**, **thoracic vertebrae**, **lumbar vertebrae**, **sacrum**, and **coccyx** (see Figure 4.6 ■ and Table 4.2 ■). Located between each pair of vertebrae, from the cervical through the lumbar regions, is an **intervertebral disc**. Each disc is composed of fibrocartilage to provide a cushion between the vertebrae. The rib cage has twelve pairs of ribs attached at the back to the vertebral column. Ten of the pairs are also attached to the sternum in the front (see Figure 4.7 ■). The lowest two pairs are called *floating ribs* and are attached only to the vertebral column. The rib cage serves to provide support for organs, such as the heart and lungs.

Med Term Tip

The term *coccyx* comes from the Greek word for the cuckoo because the shape of these small bones extending off the sacrum resembles this bird's bill.

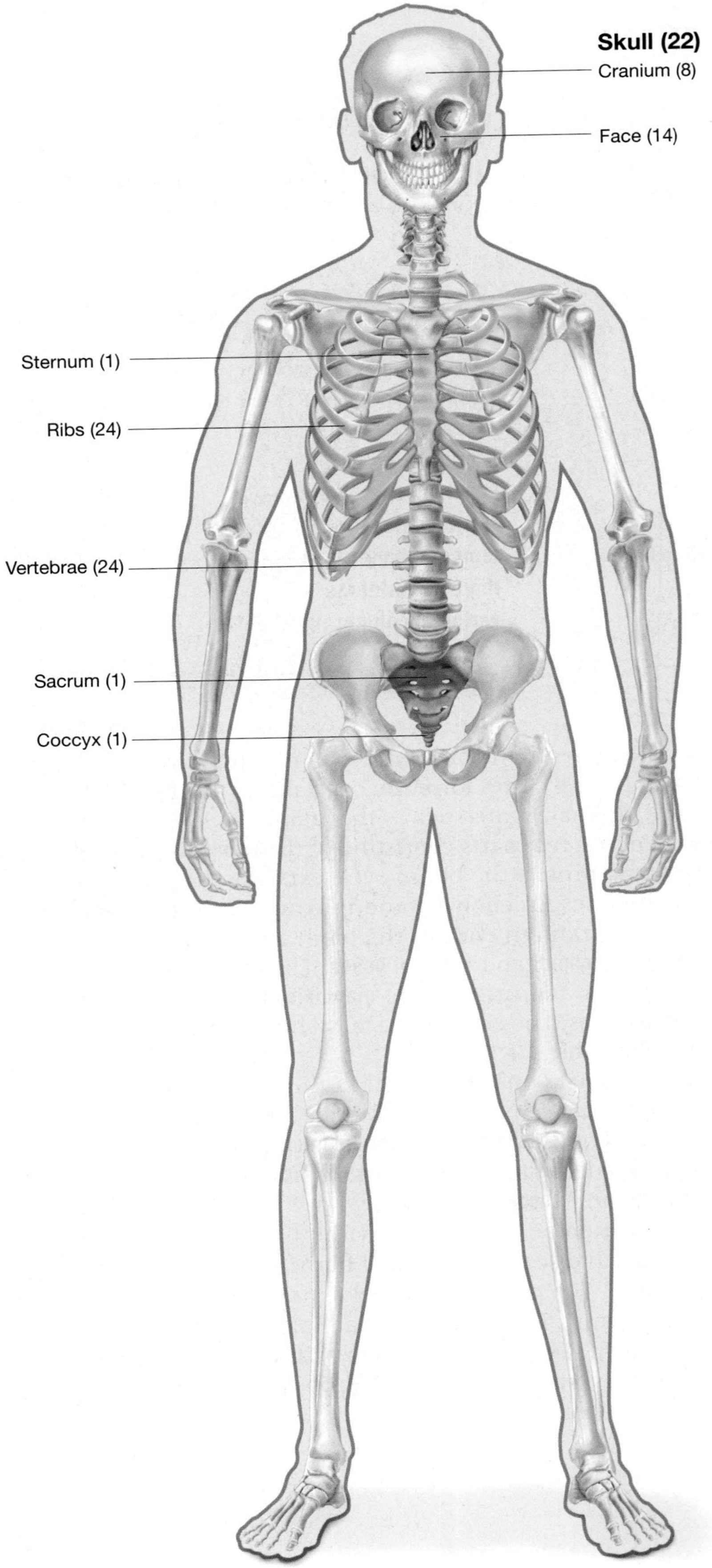

Figure 4.4 Bones of the axial skeleton.

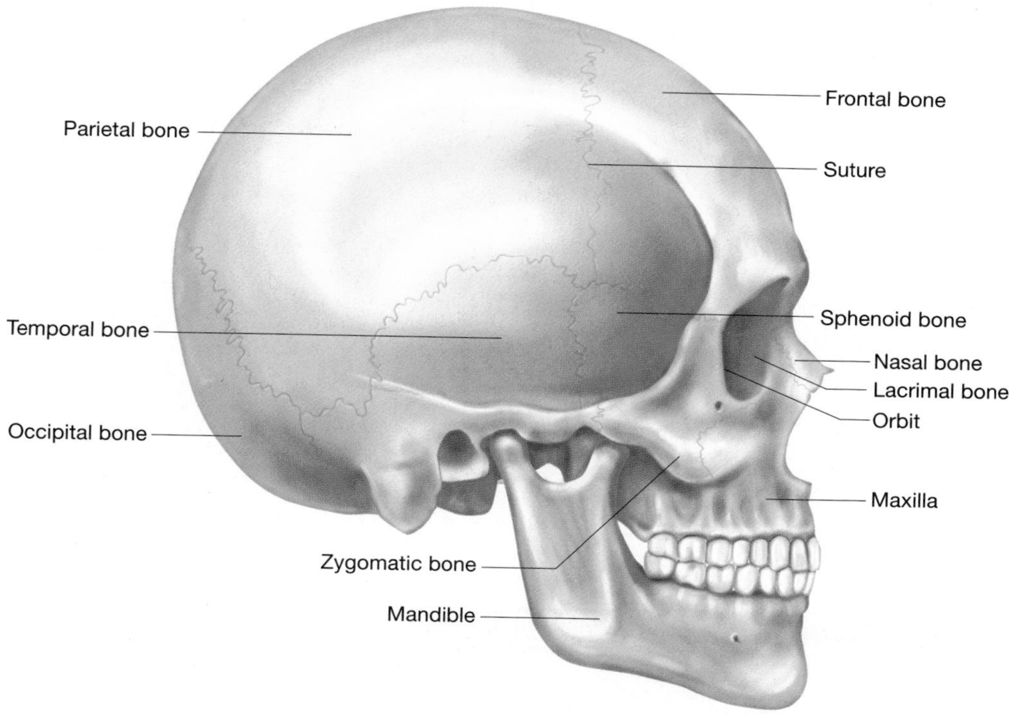

Figure 4.5 Bones of the skull.

Table 4.1 Bones of the Skull

NAME	NUMBER	DESCRIPTION
Cranial Bones		
Frontal bone	1	Forehead
Parietal bone	2	Upper sides of cranium and roof of skull
Occipital bone	1	Back and base of skull
Temporal bone	2	Sides and base of cranium
Sphenoid bone	1	Bat-shaped bone that forms part of the base of the skull, floor, and sides of eye orbit
Ethmoid bone	1	Forms part of eye orbit, nose, and floor of cranium
Facial Bones		
Lacrimal bone	2	Inner corner of each eye
Nasal bone	2	Form part of nasal septum and support bridge of nose
Maxilla	1	Upper jaw
Mandible	1	Lower jawbone; only movable bone of the skull
Zygomatic bone	2	Cheekbones
Vomer bone	1	Base of nasal septum
Palatine bone	1	Hard palate (PAH lat) of mouth and floor of the nose

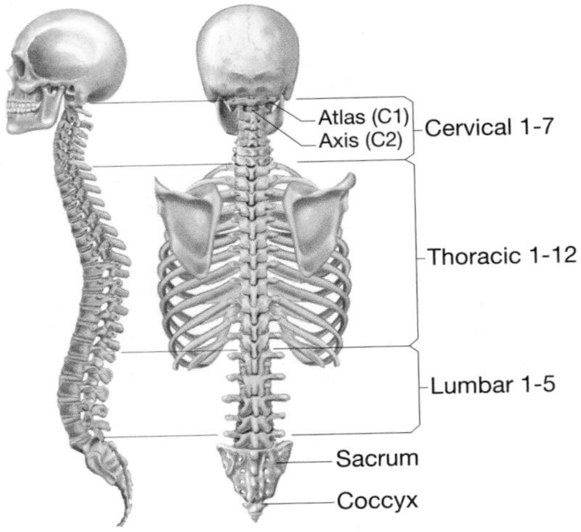

Figure 4.6 Divisions of the vertebral column.

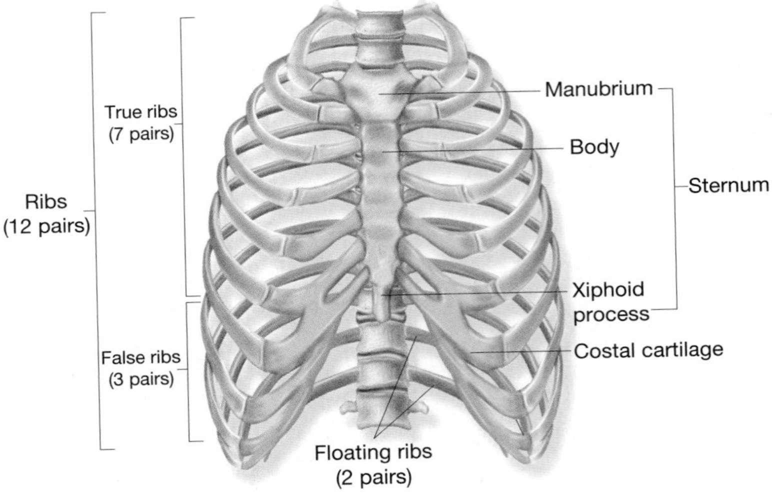

Figure 4.7 The structure of the rib cage.

Table 4.2 Bones of the Vertebral/Spinal Column

NAME	NUMBER	DESCRIPTION
Cervical vertebra	7	Vertebrae in the neck region
Thoracic vertebra	12	Vertebrae in the chest region with ribs attached
Lumbar vertebra	5	Vertebrae in the small of the back, about waist level
Sacrum	1	Five vertebrae that become fused into one triangular-shaped flat bone at the base of the vertebral column
Coccyx	1	Three to five very small vertebrae attached to the sacrum, often become fused

Appendicular Skeleton

carpals (CAR-pals)
clavicle (CLAV-ih-kl)
femur (FEE-mer)
fibula (FIB-yoo-lah)
humerus (HYOO-mer-us)
ilium (ILL-ee-um)
innominate bone (ih-NOM-ih-nayt)
ischium (ISS-kee-um)
lower extremities
metacarpals (met-ah-CAR-pals)
metatarsals (met-ah-TAHR-sals)
os coxae (OSS KOK-sigh)
patella (pah-TELL-ah)
pectoral girdle
pelvic girdle
phalanges (fah-LAN-jeez)
pubis (PYOO-bis)
radius (RAY-dee-us)
scapula (SKAP-yoo-lah)
tarsals (TAHR-sals)
tibia (TIB-ee-ah)
ulna (UHL-nah)
upper extremities

Med Term Tip

The term *girdle*, meaning something that encircles or confines, refers to the entire bony structure of the shoulder and the pelvis. If just one bone from these areas is being discussed, like the ilium of the pelvis, it would be named as such. If, however, the entire pelvis is being discussed, it would be called the pelvic girdle.

The appendicular skeleton consists of the **pectoral girdle, upper extremities, pelvic girdle,** and **lower extremities** (see Figure 4.8 ■). These are the bones for our appendages or limbs and along with the muscles attached to them, they are responsible for body movement.

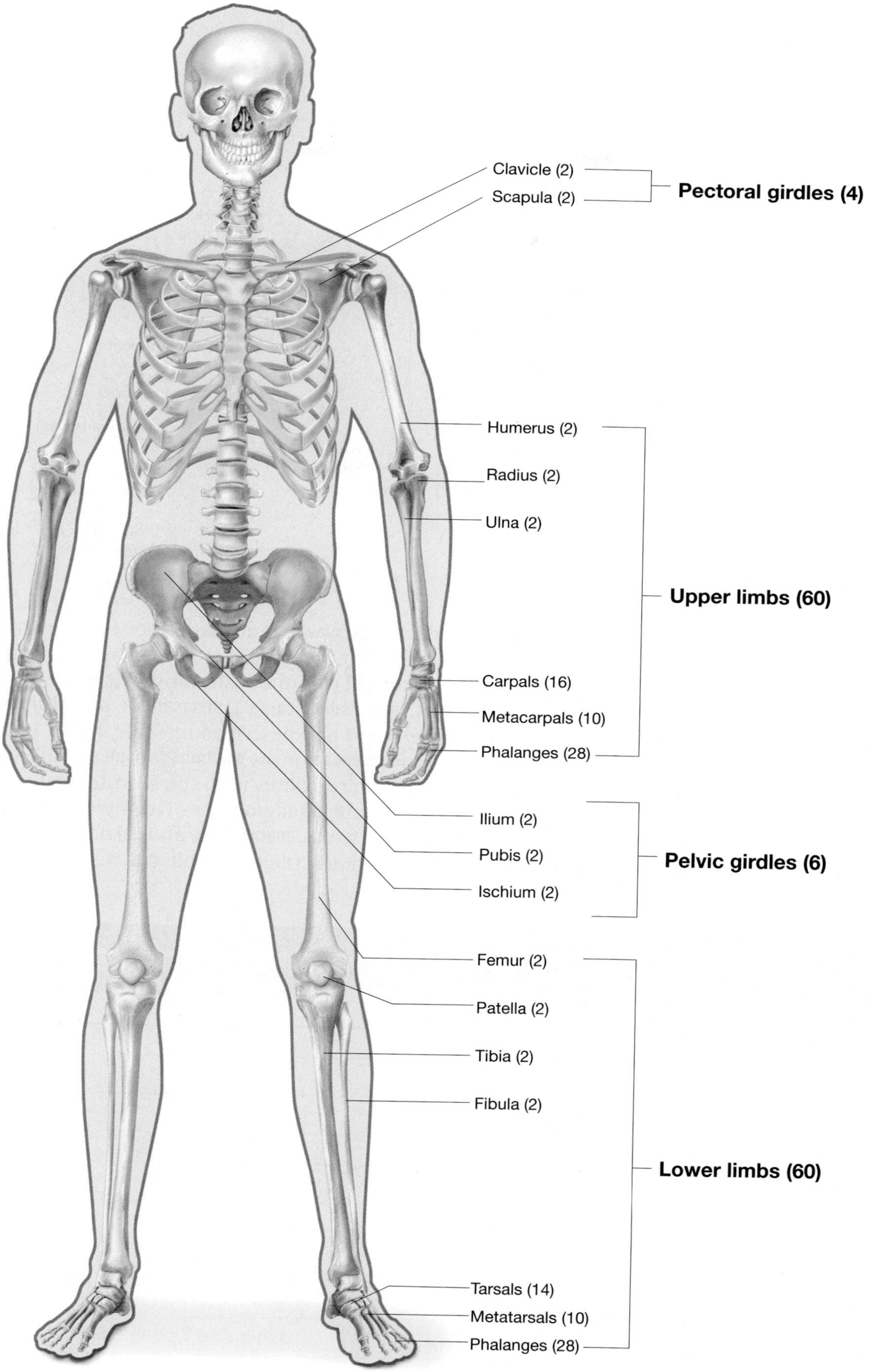

Figure 4.8 Bones of the appendicular skeleton.

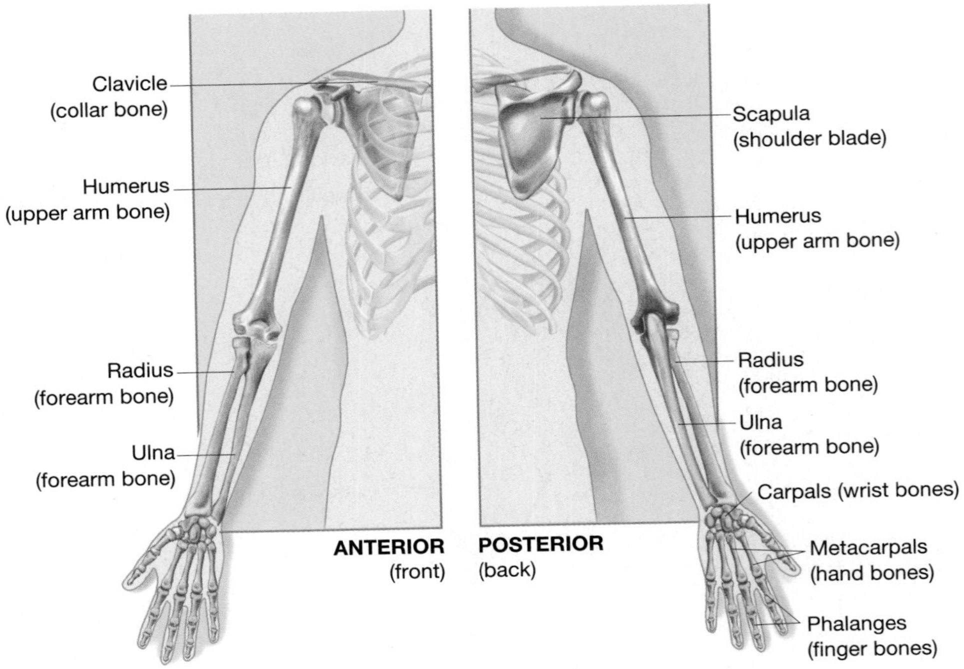

Figure 4.9 Anatomical and common names for the pectoral girdle and upper extremity.

The pectoral girdle consists of the **clavicle** and **scapula** bones. It functions to attach the upper extremity, or arm, to the axial skeleton by articulating with the sternum anteriorly and the vertebral column posteriorly. The bones of the upper extremity include the **humerus**, **ulna**, **radius**, **carpals**, **metacarpals**, and **phalanges**. These bones are illustrated in Figure 4.9 and described in Table 4.3.

The pelvic girdle is called the **os coxae** or the **innominate bone** or hipbone. It contains the **ilium**, **ischium**, and **pubis**. It articulates with the sacrum posteriorly to attach the lower extremity, or leg, to the axial skeleton. The lower extremity bones include the **femur**, **patella**, **tibia**, **fibula**, **tarsals**, **metatarsals**, and phalanges. These bones are illustrated in Figure 4.10 and described in Table 4.4.

Table 4.3 Bones of the Pectoral Girdle and Upper Extremity

NAME	NUMBER	DESCRIPTION
Pectoral Girdle		
Clavicle	2	Collar bone
Scapula	2	Shoulder blade
Upper Extremity		
Humerus	2	Upper arm bone
Radius	2	Forearm bone on thumb side of lower arm
Ulna	2	Forearm bone on little finger side of lower arm
Carpal	16	Bones of wrist
Metacarpals	10	Bones in palm of hand
Phalanges	28	Finger bones; three in each finger and two in each thumb

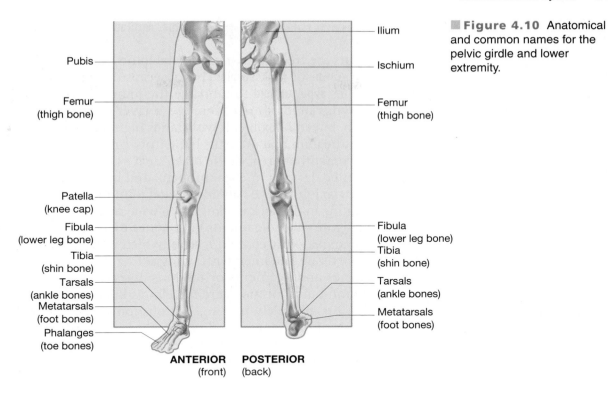

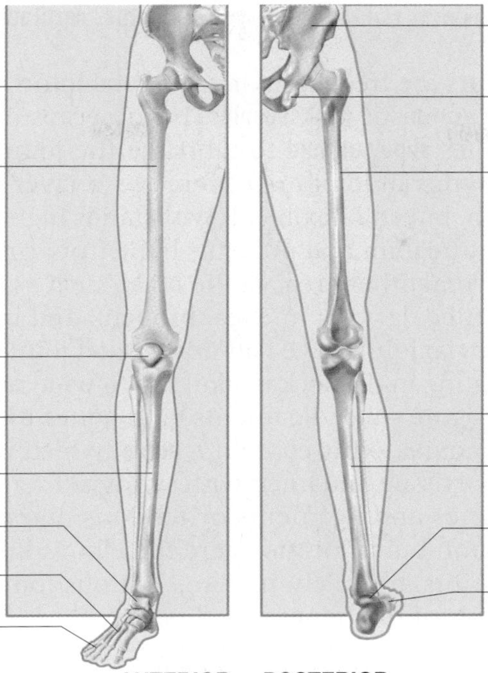

Figure 4.10 Anatomical and common names for the pelvic girdle and lower extremity.

Joints

articulation (ar-tik-yoo-LAY-shun)
bursa (BER-sah)
cartilaginous joints (car-tih-LAJ-ih-nus)
fibrous joints (FYE-bruss)
joint capsule
synovial fluid
synovial joint (sin-OH-vee-al)
synovial membrane

Joints are formed when two or more bones meet. This is also referred to as an **articulation**. There are three types of joints based on the amount of movement

Table 4.4 Bones of the Pelvic Girdle and Lower Extremity

NAME	NUMBER	DESCRIPTION
Pelvic Girdle/Os Coxae		
Ilium	2	Part of the hipbone
Ischium	2	Part of the hipbone
Pubis	2	Part of the hipbone
Lower Extremity		
Femur	2	Upper leg bone; thigh bone
Patella	2	Knee cap
Tibia	2	Shin bone; thicker lower leg bone
Fibula	2	Thinner, long bone in lateral side of lower leg
Tarsals	14	Ankle and heel bones
Metatarsals	10	Forefoot bones
Phalanges	28	Toe bones; three in each toe and two in each great toe

allowed between the bones: **synovial joints**, **cartilaginous joints**, and **fibrous joints** (see Figure 4.11 ■).

Most joints are freely moving synovial joints (see Figure 4.12 ■), which are enclosed by an elastic **joint capsule**. The joint capsule is lined with **synovial membrane**, which secretes **synovial fluid** to lubricate the joint. As noted earlier, the ends of bones in a synovial joint are covered by a layer of articular cartilage. Cartilage is very tough, but still flexible. It withstands high levels of stress to act as a shock absorber for the joint and prevents bone from rubbing against bone. Cartilage is found in several other areas of the body, such as the nasal septum, external ear, eustachian tube, larynx, trachea, bronchi, and intervertebral disks. One example of a synovial joint is the ball-and-socket joint found at the shoulder and hip. The ball rotating in the socket allows for a wide range of motion. Bands of strong connective tissue called ligaments bind bones together at the joint.

Med Term Tip

Bursitis is an inflammation of the bursa located between bony prominences such as at the shoulder. Housemaid's knee, a term thought to have originated from the damage to the knees that occurred when maids knelt to scrub floors, is a form of bursitis and carries the medical name *prepatellar bursitis*.

Some synovial joints contain a **bursa**, which is a saclike structure composed of connective tissue and lined with synovial membrane. Most commonly found between bones and ligaments or tendons, bursas function to reduce friction. Some common bursa locations are the elbow, knee, and shoulder joints.

Not all joints are freely moving. Fibrous joints allow almost no movement since the ends of the bones are joined by thick fibrous tissue, which may even fuse into solid bone. The sutures of the skull are an example of a fibrous joint. Cartilaginous joints allow for slight movement but hold bones firmly in place by a solid piece of cartilage. An example of this type of joint is the pubic symphysis, the point at which the left and right pubic bones meet in the front of the lower abdomen.

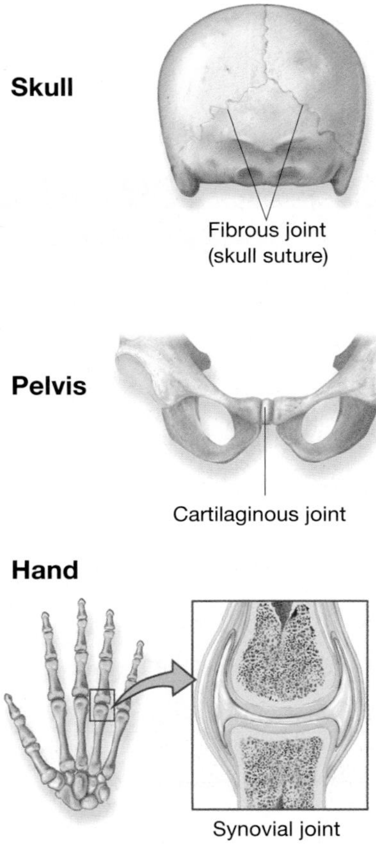

■ **Figure 4.11** Examples of three types of joints found in the body.

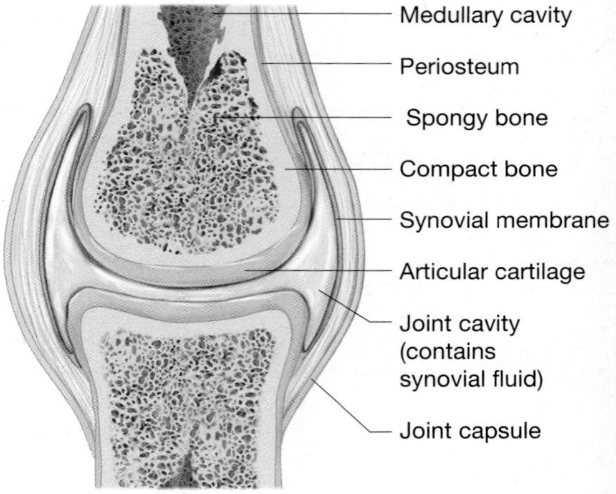

■ **Figure 4.12** Structure of a generalized synovial joint.

Word Building

The following list contains examples of medical terms built directly from word parts. The definition for these terms can be determined by a straightforward translation of the word parts.

COMBINING FORM	COMBINED WITH	MEDICAL TERM	DEFINITION
arthr/o	-algia	**arthralgia** (ar-THRAL-jee-ah)	joint pain
	-centesis	**arthrocentesis** (ar-thro-sen-TEE-sis)	puncture to withdraw fluid from a joint
	-clasia	**arthroclasia** (ar-throh-KLAY-see-ah)	surgically breaking a joint
	-desis	**arthrodesis** (ar-throh-DEE-sis)	fusion of a joint
	-gram	**arthrogram** (AR-throh-gram)	record of a joint
	-itis	**arthritis** (ar-THRY-tis)	joint inflammation
	-otomy	**arthrotomy** (ar-THROT-oh-mee)	incision into a joint
	-scope	**arthroscope** (AR-throw-skop)	instrument to view inside a joint
burs/o	-ectomy	**bursectomy** (ber-SEK-toh-mee)	removal of a bursa
	-itis	**bursitis** (ber-SIGH-tis)	inflammation of a bursa
chondr/o	-ectomy	**chondrectomy** (kon-DREK-toh-mee)	removal of cartilage
	-malacia	**chondromalacia** (kon-droh-mah-LAY-she-ah)	cartilage softening
	-oma	**chondroma** (kon-DROH-mah)	cartilage tumor
	-plasty	**chondroplasty** (KON-droh-plas-tee)	surgical repair of cartilage
cortic/o	-al	**cortical** (KOR-ti-kal)	pertaining to the outer portion
crani/o	intra- -al	**intracranial** (in-trah-KRAY-nee-al)	pertaining to inside the skull
	-otomy	**craniotomy** (kray-nee-OTT-oh-mee)	incision into the skull
medull/o	-ary	**medullary** (MED-you-lair-ee)	pertaining to the inner portion
myel/o	-oma	**myeloma** (my-ah-LOH-mah)	bone marrow tumor
oste/o	-algia	**ostealgia** (oss-tee-AL-jee-ah)	bone pain
	chondr/o -oma	**osteochondroma** (oss-tee-oh-kon-DROH-mah)	bone and cartilage tumor
	-clasia	**osteoclasia** (oss-tee-oh-KLAY-see-ah)	to surgically break a bone
	myel/o -itis	**osteomyelitis** (oss-tee-oh-mi-ell-EYE-tis)	inflammation of bone and bone marrow
	-otomy	**osteotomy** (oss-tee-OTT-ah-me)	incision into a bone
	-pathy	**osteopathy** (oss-tee-OPP-ah-thee)	bone disease
	-tome	**osteotome** (OSS-tee-oh-tohm)	instrument to cut bone
synov/o	-itis	**synovitis** (sih-no-VI-tis)	inflammation of synovial membrane
	-ectomy	**synovectomy** (sih-no-VEK-toh-mee)	removal of the synovial membrane
vertebr/o	inter- -al	**intervertebral** (in-ter-VER-teh-bral)	pertaining to between vertebrae

Building Adjective Forms of Bone Names

It is important to learn the names and combining forms of all the bones in medical terminology because they are so frequently used as adjectives to indicate location.

ADJECTIVE SUFFIX	COMBINED WITH	ADJECTIVE FORM	NOUN FORM
-ac	ili/o	**iliac** (ILL-ee-ack)	ilium
-al	carp/o	**carpal** (CAR-pal)	carpus
	cervic/o	**cervical** (CER-vih-kal)	neck
	cost/o	**costal** (COAST-all)	rib
	crani/o	**cranial** (KRAY-nee-all)	cranium
	femor/o	**femoral** (FEM-or-all)	femur
	humer/o	**humeral** (HYOO-mer-all)	humerus
	ischi/o	**ischial** (ISH-ee-all)	ischium
	metacarp/o	**metacarpal** (met-ah-CAR-pal)	metacarpus
	metatars/o	**metatarsal** (met-ah-TAHR-sal)	metatarsus
	radi/o	**radial** (RAY-dee-all)	radius
	sacr/o	**sacral** (SAY-kral)	sacrum
	stern/o	**sternal** (STER-nal)	sternum
	tars/o	**tarsal** (TAHR-sal)	tarsus
	tibi/o	**tibial** (TIB-ee-all)	tibia
-ar	clavicul/o	**clavicular** (cla-VIK-yoo-lar)	clavicle
	fibul/o	**fibular** (FIB-yoo-lar)	fibula
	lumb/o	**lumbar** (LUM-bar)	low back
	mandibul/o	**mandibular** (man-DIB-yoo-lar)	mandible
	patell/o	**patellar** (pa-TELL-ar)	patella
	scapul/o	**scapular** (SKAP-yoo-lar)	scapula
	uln/o	**ulnar** (UHL-nar)	ulna
-ary	maxill/o	**maxillary** (mack-sih-LAIR-ree)	maxilla
-eal	coccyg/o	**coccygeal** (cock-eh-JEE-all)	coccyx
	phalang/o	**phalangeal** (fay-lan-JEE-all)	phalanges
-ic	pelv/o	**pelvic** (PEL-vik)	pelvis
	pub/o	**pubic** (PYOO-bik)	pubis
	thorac/o	**thoracic** (tho-RASS-ik)	thorax

Vocabulary

TERM	DEFINITION
callus (KAL-us)	The mass of bone tissue that forms at a fracture site during its healing.
cast	Application of a solid material to immobilize an extremity or portion of the body as a result of a fracture, dislocation, or severe injury. It may be made of plaster of Paris or fiberglass.
chiropractic (ki-roh-PRAK-tik)	Healthcare profession concerned with diagnosis and treatment of malalignment conditions of the spine and musculoskeletal system with the intention of affecting the nervous system and improving health. Healthcare professional is a *chiropractor.*
crepitation (krep-ih-TAY-shun)	The noise produced by bones or cartilage rubbing together in conditions such as arthritis. Also called *crepitus.*
exostosis (eck-sos-TOH-sis)	A bone spur.
kyphosis (ki-FOH-sis)	Abnormal increase in the outward curvature of the thoracic spine. Also known as *hunchback* or *humpback*. See Figure 4.13 for an illustration of abnormal spine curvatures.

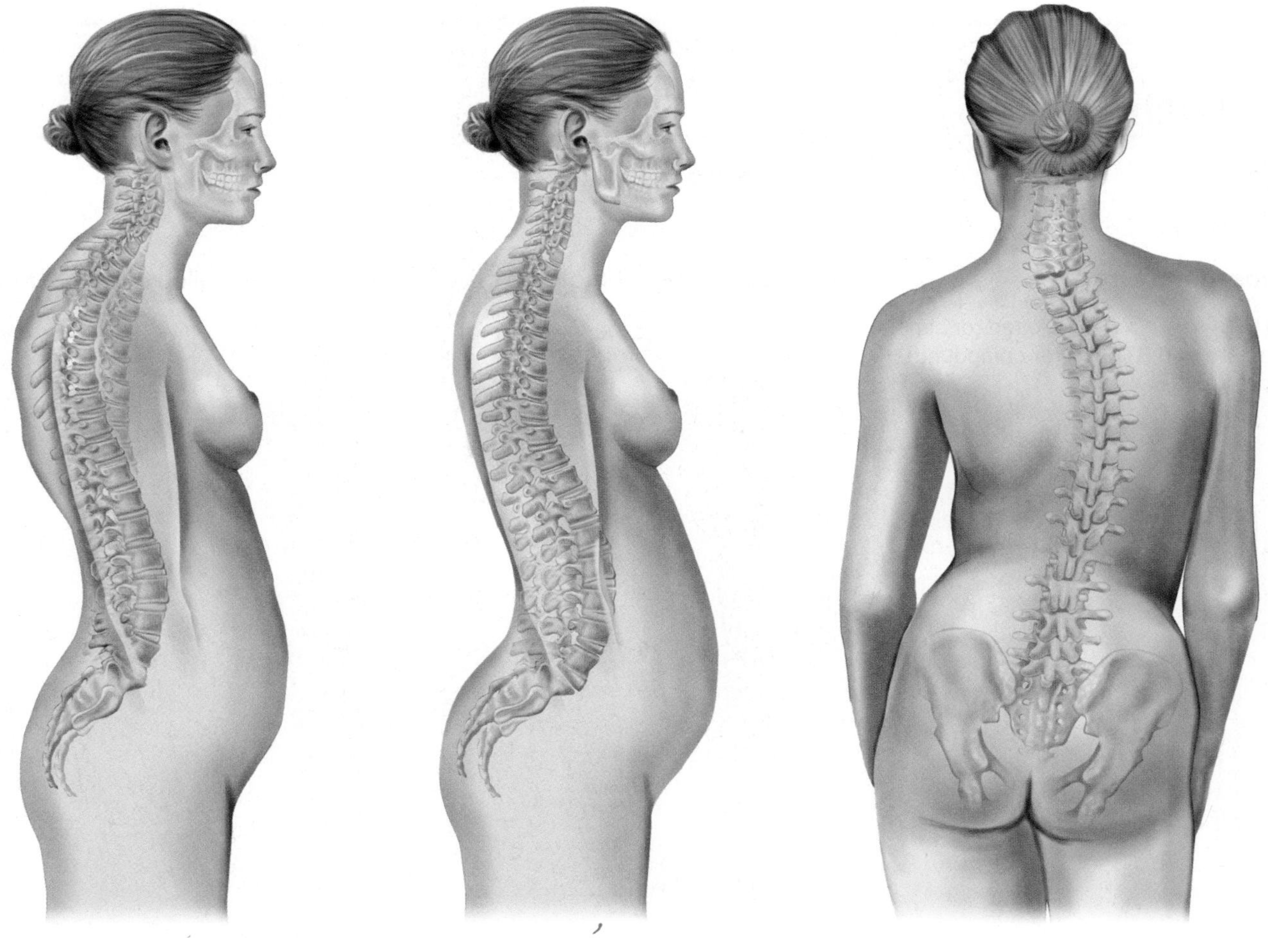

Kyphosis
(excessive posterior thoracic curvature - hunchback)

Lordosis
(excessive anterior lumbar curvature - swayback)

Scoliosis
(lateral curvature)

Figure 4.13 Abnormal spinal curvatures: kyphosis, lordosis, and scoliosis.

Vocabulary *(continued)*

TERM	DEFINITION
lordosis (lor-DOH-sis)	Abnormal increase in the forward curvature of the lumbar spine. Also known as *swayback*. See Figure 4.13 for an illustration of abnormal spine curvatures.
orthopedics (or-thoh-PEE-diks)	Branch of medicine specializing in the diagnosis and treatment of conditions of the musculoskeletal system. Also called *orthopedic surgery*. Physician is an *orthopedist* or *orthopedic surgeon*. Name derived from straightening (*orth/o*) deformities in children (*ped/o*).
orthotic (or-THOT-ik)	A brace or splint used to prevent or correct deformities. Person skilled in making and adjusting orthotics is an *orthotist.*
podiatry (po-DYE-ah-tree)	Healthcare profession specializing in diagnosis and treatment of disorders of the feet and lower legs. Healthcare professional is a *podiatrist.*
prosthesis (pross-THEE-sis)	Artificial device that is used as a substitute for a body part that is either congenitally missing or absent as a result of accident or disease. An example would be an artificial leg.
prosthetics (pross-THET-iks)	Healthcare profession specializing in making artificial body parts. Person skilled in making and adjusting prostheses is a *prosthetist.*

Pathology

TERM	DEFINITION
■ ***Fractures***	
closed fracture	Fracture in which there is no open skin wound. Also called a *simple fracture.*

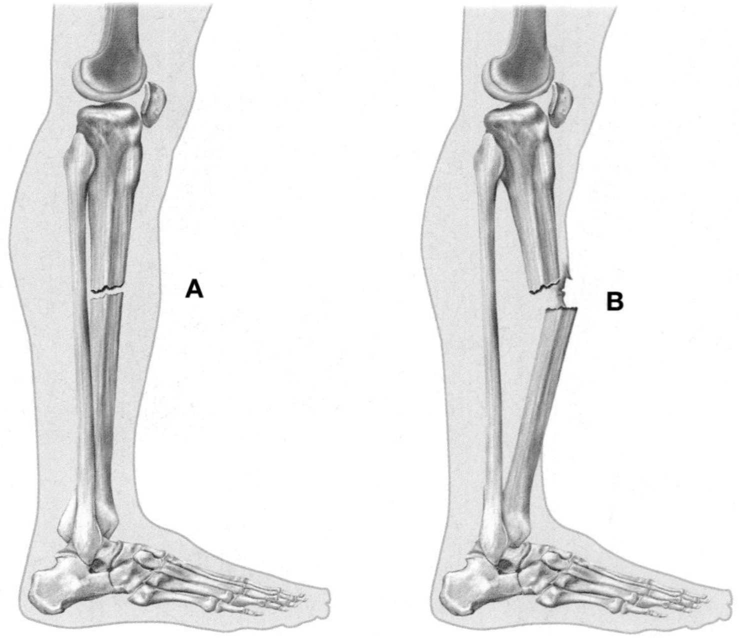

Figure 4.14 A) Closed (or simple) fracture and B) open (or compound) fracture.

Pathology *(continued)*

TERM	DEFINITION
Colles' (COL-eez) **fracture** **Figure 4.15** Colles' fracture. *(Charles Stewart MD FACEP, FAAEM)*	A common type of wrist fracture. 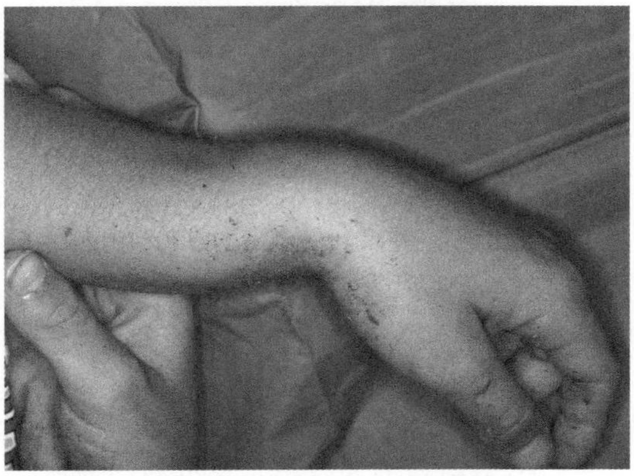
comminuted fracture (kom-ih-NYOOT-ed)	Fracture in which the bone is shattered, splintered, or crushed into many small pieces or fragments.
compound fracture	Fracture in which the skin has been broken through to the fracture. Also called an *open fracture* (see also Figure 4.14B).
compression fracture	Fracture involving loss of height of a vertebral body. It may be the result of trauma, but in older persons, especially women, it may be caused by conditions like osteoporosis.
fracture (FX, Fx)	A broken bone.
greenstick fracture	Fracture in which there is an incomplete break; one side of bone is broken and the other side is bent. This type of fracture is commonly found in children due to their softer and more pliable bone structure.
impacted fracture	Fracture in which bone fragments are pushed into each other.
oblique (oh-BLEEK) **fracture** **Figure 4.16** X-ray showing oblique fracture of the humerus. *(Charles Stewart MD FACEP, FAAEM)*	Fracture at an angle to the bone. 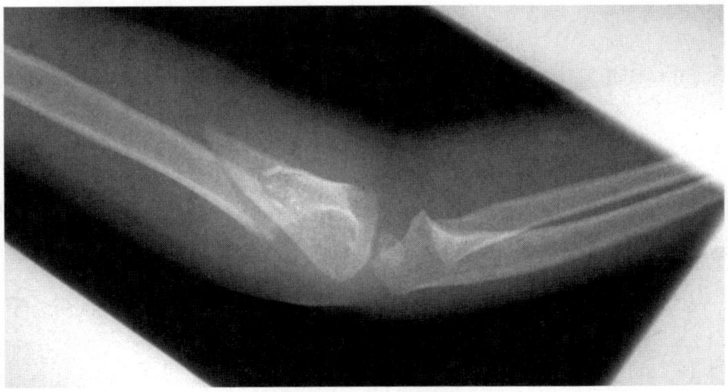
pathologic (path-a-LOJ-ik) **fracture**	Fracture caused by diseased or weakened bone.
spiral fracture	Fracture in which the fracture line spirals around the shaft of the bone. Can be caused by a twisting injury and is often slower to heal than other types of fractures.
stress fracture	A slight fracture caused by repetitive low-impact forces, like running, rather than a single forceful impact.

Pathology *(continued)*

TERM	DEFINITION
transverse fracture	Complete fracture that is straight across the bone at right angles to the long axis of the bone (see Figure 4.17 ■).
■ ***Bones***	
Ewing's sarcoma (YOO-wings sar-KOH-mah)	Malignant growth found in the shaft of long bones that spreads through the periosteum. Removal is treatment of choice, because this tumor will metastasize or spread to other organs.
osteogenic sarcoma (oss-tee-oh-GIN-ik sark-OH-mah)	The most common type of bone cancer. Usually begins in osteocytes found at the ends of long bones.
osteomalacia (oss-tee-oh-mah-LAY-she-ah)	Softening of the bones caused by a deficiency of calcium. It is thought that in children the cause is insufficient sunlight and vitamin D.
osteoporosis (oss-tee-oh-por-ROH-sis)	Decrease in bone mass that results in a thinning and weakening of the bone with resulting fractures. The bone becomes more porous, especially in the spine and pelvis.
Paget's (PAH-jets) **disease**	A fairly common metabolic disease of the bone from unknown causes. It usually attacks middle-aged and elderly people and is characterized by bone destruction and deformity. Named for Sir James Paget, a British surgeon.
rickets (RIK-ets)	Deficiency in calcium and vitamin D found in early childhood that results in bone deformities, especially bowed legs.
■ ***Spinal Column***	
ankylosing spondylitis (ang-kih-LOH-sing spon-dih-LYE-tis)	Inflammatory spinal condition that resembles rheumatoid arthritis. Results in gradual stiffening and fusion of the vertebrae. More common in men than women.
herniated nucleus pulposus (HNP) (HER-nee-ated NOO-klee-us pull-POH-sus)	Herniation or protrusion of an intervertebral disk; also called *herniated disk* or *ruptured disk.* May require surgery (see Figure 4.18 ■).
scoliosis (skoh-lee-OH-sis)	Abnormal lateral curvature of the spine. See Figure 4.13 for an illustration of abnormal spine curvatures.
spina bifida (SPY-nah BIF-ih-dah)	Congenital anomaly that occurs when a vertebra fails to fully form around the spinal cord.
spinal stenosis (ste-NOH-sis)	Narrowing of the spinal canal causing pressure on the cord and nerves.
spondylolisthesis (spon-dih-loh-liss-THEE-sis)	The forward sliding of a lumbar vertebra over the vertebra below it.
spondylosis (spon-dih-LOH-sis)	Specifically refers to ankylosing of the spine, but commonly used in reference to any degenerative condition of the vertebral column.
whiplash	Injury to the bones in the cervical spine as a result of a sudden movement forward and backward of the head and neck. Can occur as a result of a rear-end auto collision.
■ ***Joints***	
bunion (BUN-yun)	Inflammation of the bursa of the first metatarsophalangeal joint (base of the big toe).

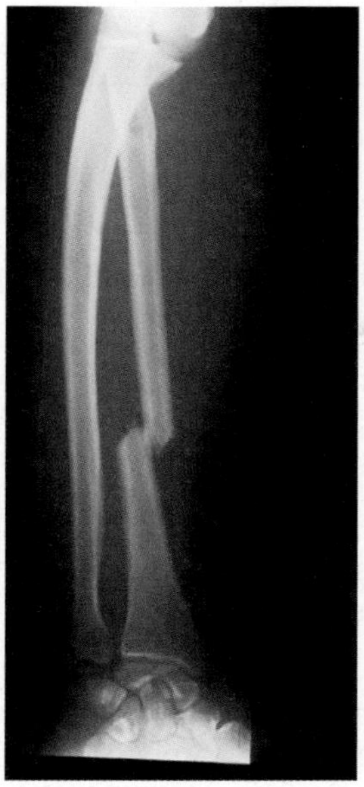

Figure 4.17 X-ray showing transverse fracture of radius. *(James Stevenson/Science Photo Library/ Photo Researchers, Inc.)*

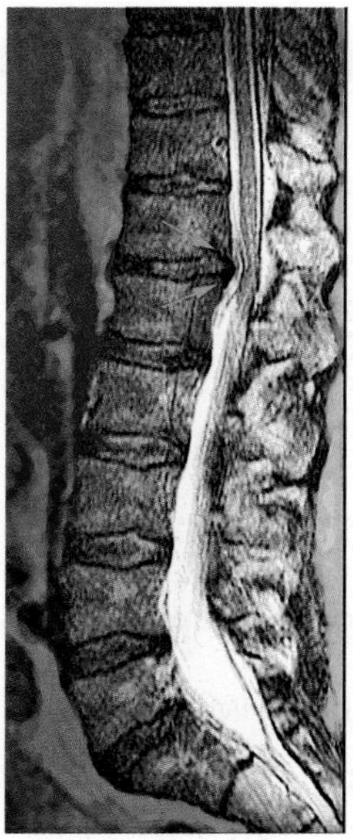

Figure 4.18 Color enhanced magnetic resonance imaging (MRI) image demonstrating a herniated nucleus pulposus putting pressure on the spinal cord (see arrows). *(ISM/Phototake NYC)*

Pathology *(continued)*

TERM	DEFINITION
dislocation	Occurs when the bones in a joint are displaced from their normal alignment and the ends of the bones are no longer in contact.
osteoarthritis (OA) (oss-tee-oh-ar-THRY-tis)	Arthritis resulting in degeneration of the bones and joints, especially those bearing weight. Results in bone rubbing against bone.
rheumatoid arthritis (RA) (ROO-mah-toyd ar-THRY-tis)	Chronic form of arthritis with inflammation of the joints, swelling, stiffness, pain, and changes in the cartilage that can result in crippling deformities; considered to be an autoimmune disease.
Figure 4.19 Patient with typical rheumatoid arthritis contractures.	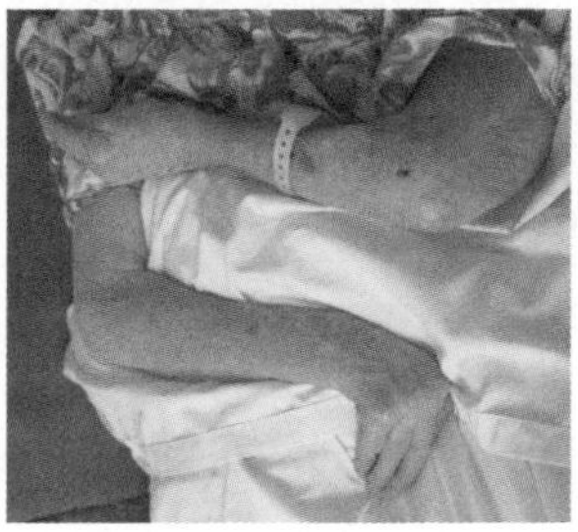
sprain	Damage to the ligaments surrounding a joint due to overstretching, but no dislocation of the joint or fracture of the bone.
subluxation (sub-LUCKS-a-shun)	An incomplete dislocation, the joint alignment is disrupted, but the ends of the bones remain in contact.
systemic lupus erythematosus (SLE) (sis-TEM-ik LOOP-us air-ih-them-ah-TOH-sis)	Chronic inflammatory autoimmune disease of connective tissue affects many systems that may include joint pain and arthritis. May be mistaken for rheumatoid arthritis.
talipes (TAL-ih-peez)	Congenital deformity causing misalignment of the ankle joint and foot. Also referred to as a *clubfoot*.

Diagnostic Procedures

TERM	DEFINITION
■ ***Diagnostic Imaging***	
arthrography (ar-THROG-rah-fee)	Visualization of a joint by radiographic study after injection of a contrast medium into the joint space.
bone scan	A nuclear medicine procedure in which the patient is given a radioactive dye and then scanning equipment is used to visualize bones. It is especially useful in identifying stress fractures, observing progress of treatment for osteomyelitis and locating cancer metastases to the bone.
dual-energy absorptiometry (DXA) (ab-sorp-she-AHM-eh-tree)	Measurement of bone density using low dose x-ray for the purpose of detecting osteoporosis.
myelography (my-eh-LOG-rah-fee)	Study of the spinal column after injecting opaque contrast material; particularly useful in identifying herniated nucleus pulposus pinching a spinal nerve.
radiography	A diagnostic imaging procedure using x-rays to study the internal structure of the body; especially useful for visualizing bones and joints.
■ ***Endoscopic Procedures***	
arthroscopy (ar-THROS-koh-pee)	Examination of the interior of a joint by entering the joint with an *arthroscope*. The arthroscope contains a small television camera that allows the physician to view the interior of the joint on a monitor during the procedure. Some joint conditions can be repaired during arthroscopy.

Therapeutic Procedures

TERM	DEFINITION
■ ***Surgical Procedures***	
amputation (am-pew-TAY-shun)	Partial or complete removal of a limb for a variety of reasons, including tumors, gangrene, intractable pain, crushing injury, or uncontrollable infection.
arthroscopic surgery (ar-throh-SKOP-ic)	Performing a surgical procedure while using an arthroscope to view the internal structure, such as a joint.
bone graft	Piece of bone taken from the patient used to take the place of a removed bone or a bony defect at another site.
bunionectomy (bun-yun-ECK-toh-mee)	Removal of the bursa at the joint of the great toe.
laminectomy (lam-ih-NEK-toh-mee)	Removal of the vertebral posterior arch to correct severe back problems and pain caused by compression of a spinal nerve.
percutaneous diskectomy (per-kyou-TAY-nee-us disk-EK-toh-mee)	A thin catheter tube is inserted into the intervertebral disk through the skin and the herniated or ruptured disk material is sucked out or a laser is used to vaporize it.
spinal fusion	Surgical immobilization of adjacent vertebrae. This may be done for several reasons, including correction for a herniated disk.
total hip arthroplasty (THA) (ar-thro-PLAS-tee)	Surgical reconstruction of a hip by implanting a prosthetic or artificial hip joint. Also called *total hip replacement (THR)* (see Figure 4.20 ■).

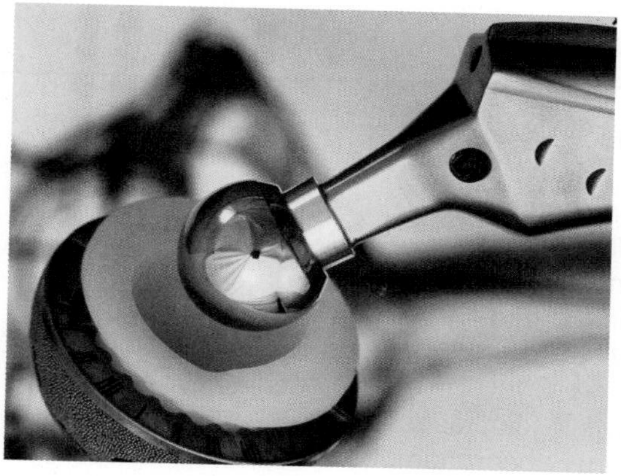

Figure 4.20 Prosthetic hip joint.
(Lawrence Livermore National Library/Science Photo Library/Photo Researchers, Inc.)

Therapeutic Procedures *(continued)*

TERM	DEFINITION
total knee arthroplasty (TKA) (ar-thro-PLAS-tee)	Surgical reconstruction of a knee joint by implanting a prosthetic knee joint. Also called *total knee replacement (TKR).*
Fracture Care	
fixation	A procedure to stabilize a fractured bone while it heals. *External fixation* includes casts, splints, and pins inserted through the skin. *Internal fixation* includes pins, plates, rods, screws, and wires that are applied during an *open reduction.*
reduction	Correcting a fracture by realigning the bone fragments. *Closed reduction* is doing this manipulation without entering the body. *Open reduction* is the process of making a surgical incision at the site of the fracture to do the reduction. This is necessary when bony fragments need to be removed or *internal fixation* such as plates or pins are required.
traction	Applying a pulling force on a fractured or dislocated limb or the vertebral column in order to restore normal alignment.

Pharmacology

CLASSIFICATION	ACTION	GENERIC AND BRAND NAMES
bone reabsorption inhibitors	Conditions that result in weak and fragile bones, such as osteoporosis and Paget's disease, are improved by medications that reduce the reabsorption of bones.	alendronate, Fosamax; ibandronate, Boniva
calcium supplements and Vitamin D therapy	Maintaining high blood levels of calcium in association with vitamin D helps maintain bone density; used to treat osteomalacia, osteoporosis, and rickets.	calcium carbonate, Oystercal, Tums; calcium citrate, Cal-Citrate, Citracal
corticosteroids	A hormone produced by the adrenal cortex that has very strong anti-inflammatory properties. It is particularly useful in treating rheumatoid arthritis.	prednisone; methylprednisolone, Medrol; dexamethasone, Decadron
nonsteroidal anti-inflammatory drugs (NSAIDs)	A large group of drugs that provide mild pain relief and anti-inflammatory benefits for conditions such as arthritis.	ibuprofen, Advil, Motrin; naproxen, Aleve, Naprosyn; salicylates, Aspirin

Abbreviations

AE	above elbow
AK	above knee
BDT	bone density testing
BE	below elbow
BK	below knee
BMD	bone mineral density
C1, C2, etc.	first cervical vertebra, second cervical vertebra, etc.
Ca	calcium
DJD	degenerative joint disease
DXA	dual-energy absorptiometry
FX, Fx	fracture
HNP	herniated nucleus pulposus
JRA	juvenile rheumatoid arthritis
L1, L2, etc.	first lumbar vertebra, second lumbar vertebra, etc.
LE	lower extremity
LLE	left lower extremity
LUE	left upper extremity
NSAID	nonsteroidal anti-inflammatory drug
OA	osteoarthritis
ORIF	open reduction–internal fixation
Orth, ortho	orthopedics
RA	rheumatoid arthritis
RLE	right lower extremity
RUE	right upper extremity
SLE	systemic lupus erythematosus
T1, T2, etc.	first thoracic vertebra, second thoracic vertebra, etc.
THA	total hip arthroplasty
THR	total hip replacement
TKA	total knee arthroplasty
TKR	total knee replacement
UE	upper extremity

Section II: Muscular System at a Glance

Function

Muscles are bundles, sheets, or rings of tissue that produce movement by contracting and pulling on the structures to which they are attached.

Organs

muscles

Combining Forms

fasci/o	fibrous band
fibr/o	fibers
kinesi/o	movement
muscul/o	muscle
my/o	muscle
myocardi/o	heart muscle
myos/o	muscle
plant/o	sole of foot
ten/o	tendon
tend/o	tendon
tendin/o	tendon

Suffixes

-asthenia	weakness
-kinesia	movement
-tonia	tone

Prefixes

ab-	away from
ad-	toward
circum-	around

Muscular System Illustrated

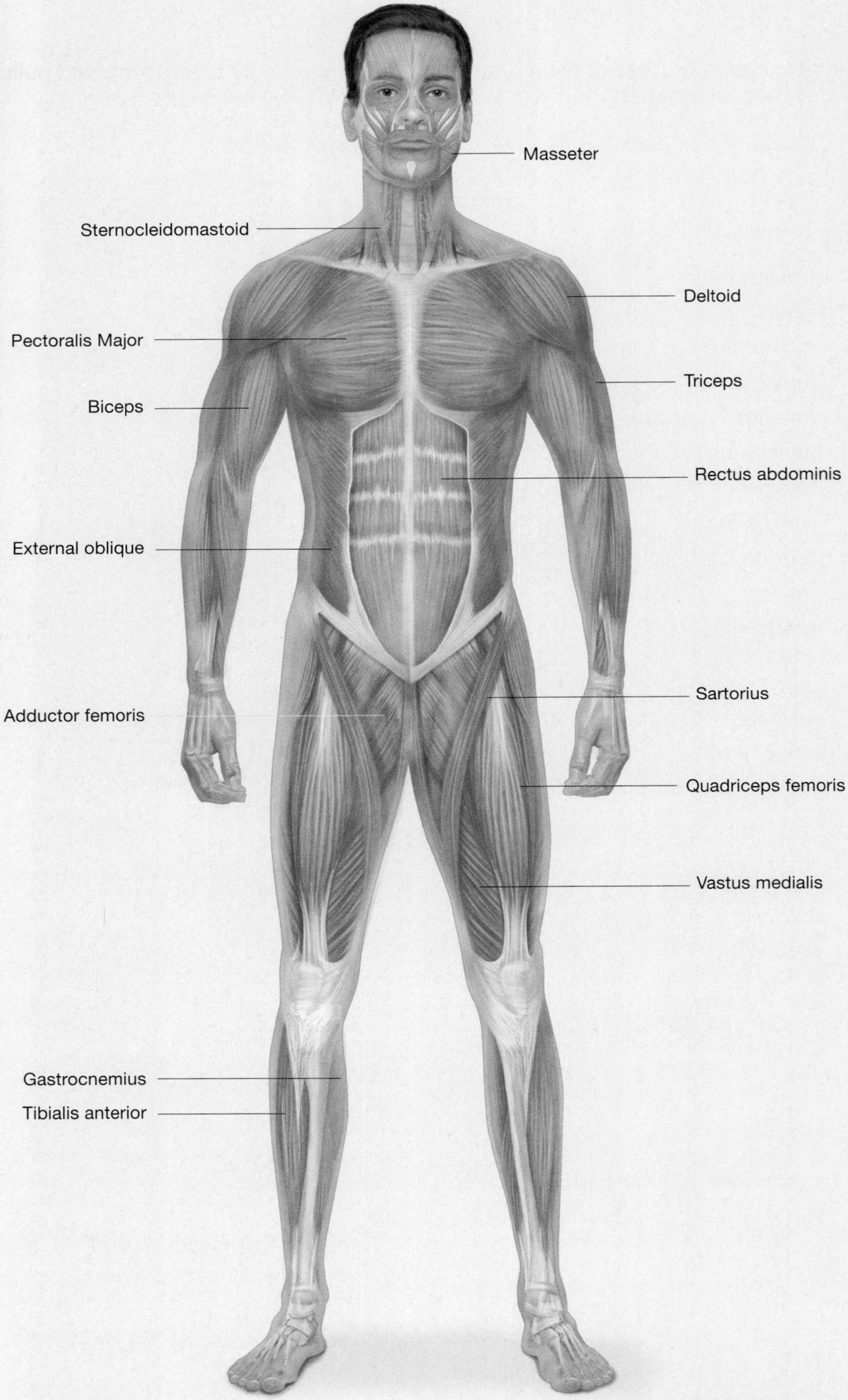

Anatomy and Physiology of the Muscular System

muscle tissue fibers
muscles

Muscles are bundles of parallel **muscle tissue fibers**. As these fibers contract (shorten in length) they produce movement of or within the body. The movement may take the form of bringing two bones closer together, pushing food through the digestive system, or pumping blood through blood vessels. In addition to producing movement, muscles also hold the body erect and generate heat.

Med Term Tip

The term *muscle* is the diminutive form of the Latin word *mus* or "little mouse." This is thought to describe how the skin ripples when a muscle contracts, like a little mouse running.

Types of Muscles

cardiac muscle
involuntary muscles
skeletal muscle
smooth muscle
voluntary muscles

The three types of muscle tissue are **skeletal muscle**, **smooth muscle**, and **cardiac muscle** (see Figure 4.21 ■). Muscle tissue may be either voluntary or involuntary. **Voluntary muscles** mean that a person consciously chooses which muscles to contract and how long and how hard to contract them. The skeletal muscles of the arm and leg are examples of this type of muscle. **Involuntary muscles** are under the control of the subconscious regions of the brain. The smooth muscles found in internal organs and cardiac muscles are examples of involuntary muscle tissue.

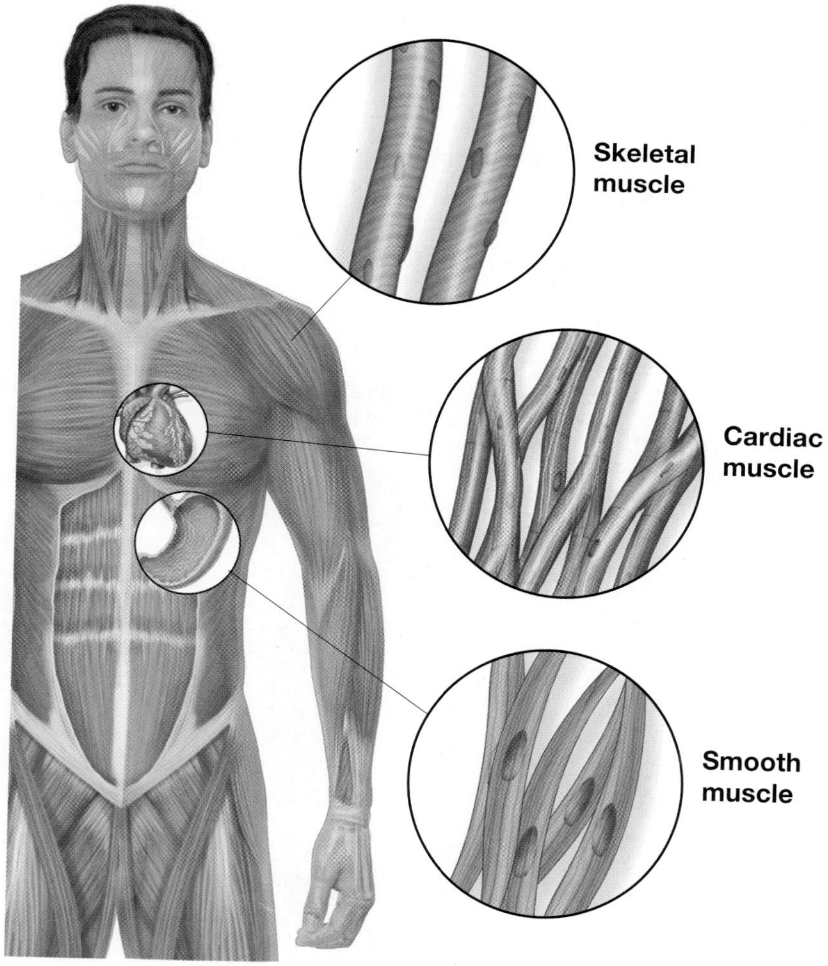

■ **Figure 4.21** The three types of muscles: skeletal, smooth, and cardiac.

Skeletal Muscle

fascia (FASH-ee-ah)
motor neurons
myoneural junction (MY-oh-NOO-rall)
striated muscle (stry-a-ted)
tendon (TEN-dun)

Skeletal muscles are directly or indirectly attached to bones and produce voluntary movement of the skeleton. It is also referred to as **striated muscle** because of its striped appearance under the microscope (see Figure 4.22 ■). Each muscle is wrapped in layers of fibrous connective tissue called **fascia**. The fascia tapers at each end of a skeletal muscle to form a very strong **tendon**. The tendon then inserts into the periosteum covering a bone to anchor the muscle to the bone. Skeletal muscles are stimulated by **motor neurons** of the nervous system. The point at which the motor nerve contacts a muscle fiber is called the **myoneural junction**.

Med Term Tip

The human body has more than 400 skeletal muscles, which account for almost 50% of the body weight.

Smooth Muscle

visceral muscle (vis-she-ral)

Smooth muscle tissue is found in association with internal organs. For this reason, it is also referred to as **visceral muscle**. The name smooth muscle refers to the muscle's microscopic appearance—it lacks the striations of skeletal muscle (see Figure 4.22). Smooth muscle is found in the walls of the hollow organs, such as the stomach, tube-shaped organs, such as the respiratory airways, and blood vessels. It is responsible for the involuntary muscle action associated with movement of the internal organs, such as churning food, constricting a blood vessel, and uterine contractions.

Cardiac Muscle

myocardium (my-oh-CAR-dee-um)

Cardiac muscle, or **myocardium**, makes up the wall of the heart (see Figure 4.22). With each involuntary contraction the heart squeezes to pump blood out of its chambers and through the blood vessels. This muscle will be more thoroughly described in Chapter 5, Cardiovascular System.

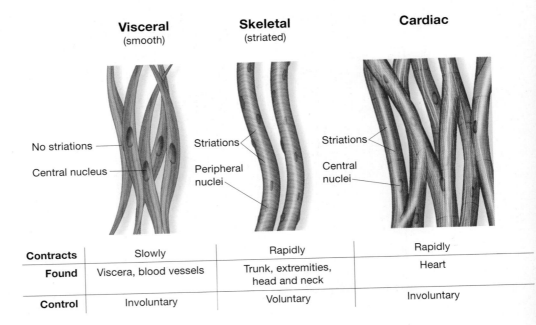

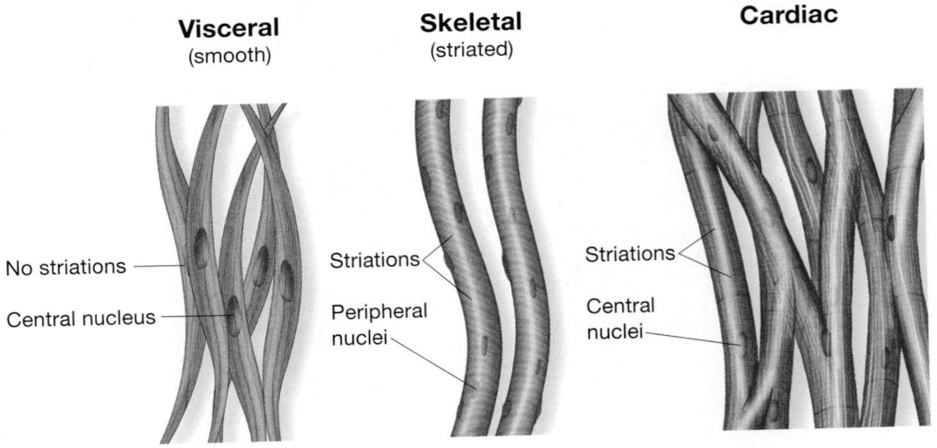

	Visceral	Skeletal	Cardiac
Contracts	Slowly	Rapidly	Rapidly
Found	Viscera, blood vessels	Trunk, extremities, head and neck	Heart
Control	Involuntary	Voluntary	Involuntary

■ **Figure 4.22** Characteristics of the three types of muscles.

Naming Skeletal Muscles

biceps (BYE-seps)
extensor carpi
external oblique
flexor carpi
gluteus maximus (GLOO-tee-us MACKS-ih-mus)
rectus abdominis (REK-tus ab-DOM-ih-nis)
sternocleidomastoid (STER-noh-KLY-doh-MASS-toid)

The name of a muscle often reflects its location, origin and insertion, size, action, fiber direction, or number of attachment points, as the following examples illustrate.

- **Location:** The term **rectus abdominis** means straight (rectus) abdominal muscle.
- **Origin and insertion:** The **sternocleidomastoid** is named for its two origins (stern/o for sternum and cleid/o for clavicle) and single insertion (mastoid process).
- **Size:** When gluteus, meaning rump area, is combined with maximus, meaning large, we have the term **gluteus maximus**.
- **Action:** The **flexor carpi** and **extensor carpi** muscles are named because they produce flexion and extension at the wrist.
- **Fiber direction:** The **external oblique** muscle is an abdominal muscle whose fibers run at an oblique angle.
- **Number of attachment points:** The term *bi*, meaning two, can form the medical term **biceps**, which refers to the muscle in the upper arm that has two heads or connecting points.

Skeletal Muscle Actions

action
antagonistic pairs
insertion
origin

Skeletal muscles are attached to two different bones and overlap a joint. When a muscle contracts, the two bones move, but not usually equally. The less movable of the two bones is considered to be the starting point of the muscle and is called the **origin**. The more movable bone is considered to be where the muscle ends and is called the **insertion**. The type of movement a muscle produces is called its **action**. Muscles are often arranged around joints in **antagonistic pairs**, meaning they produce opposite actions. For example, one muscle will bend a joint while its antagonist is responsible for straightening the joint. Some common terminology for muscle actions are described in Table 4.5 ■.

Table 4.5 Muscle Actions

ACTION	DESCRIPTION
Grouped by antagonistic pairs	
abduction (ab-DUCK-shun)	Movement away from midline of the body (see Figure 4.23 ▪)
adduction (ah-DUCK-shun)	Movement toward midline of the body (see Figure 4.23)
flexion (FLEK-shun)	Act of bending or being bent (see Figure 4.24 ▪)
extension (eks-TEN-shun)	Movement that brings limb into or toward a straight condition (see Figure 4.24)
dorsiflexion (dor-see-FLEK-shun)	Backward bending, as of hand or foot (see Figure 4.25A ▪)
plantar flexion (PLAN-tar-FLEK-shun)	Bending sole of foot; pointing toes downward (see Figure 4.25B ▪)

180°

Abduction
to 180°

Adduction
to 50°

0°

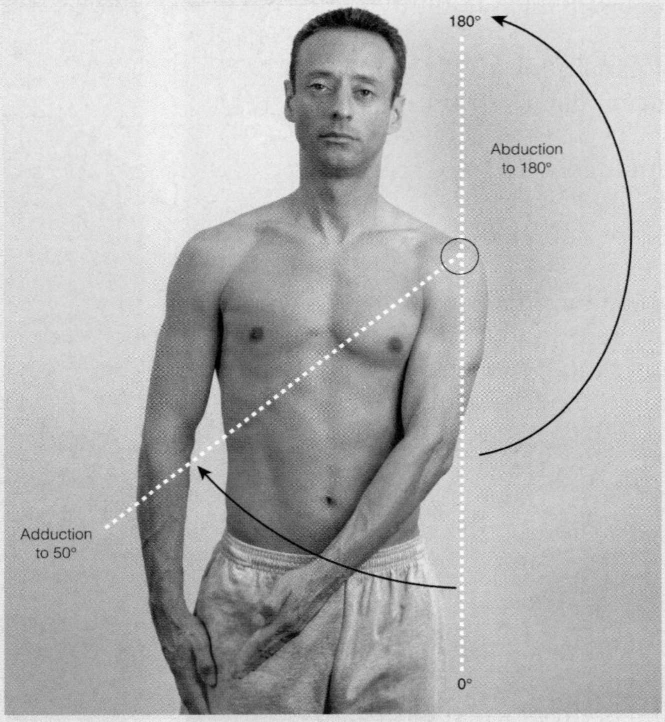

Figure 4.23 Abduction and adduction of the shoulder joint.

180°   160°

Flexion to 160°

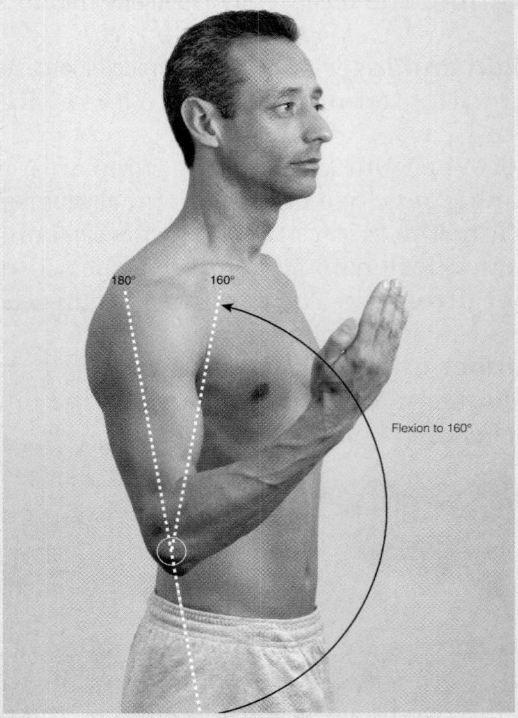

Figure 4.24 Flexion and extension of the elbow joint.

A   B

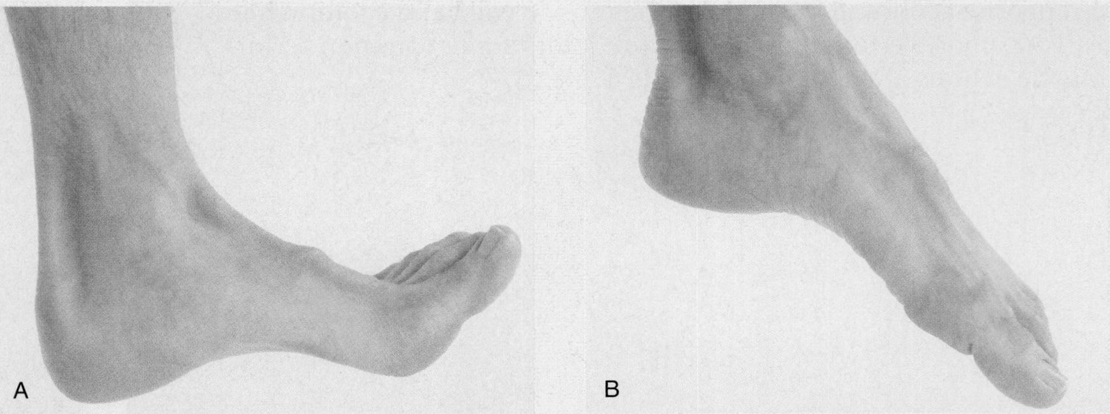

Figure 4.25 Dorsiflexion (a) and plantar flexion (b) of the ankle joint.

Table 4.5	Muscle Actions (continued)
ACTION	**DESCRIPTION**
eversion (ee-VER-zhun)	Turning outward (see Figure 4.26 ■)
inversion (in-VER-zhun)	Turning inward (see Figure 4.26)
pronation (proh-NAY-shun)	To turn downward or backward as with the hand or foot (see Figure 4.27 ■)
supination (soo-pin-NAY-shun)	Turning the palm or foot upward (see Figure 4.27)
elevation	To raise a body part, as in shrugging the shoulders
depression	A downward movement, as in dropping the shoulders
	The circular actions described below are an exception to the antagonistic pair arrangement
circumduction (sir-kum-DUCK-shun)	Movement in a circular direction from a central point. Imagine drawing a large circle in the air
opposition	Moving thumb away from palm; the ability to move the thumb into contact with the other fingers **Med Term Tip** Primates are the only animals with opposable thumbs.
rotation	Moving around a central axis

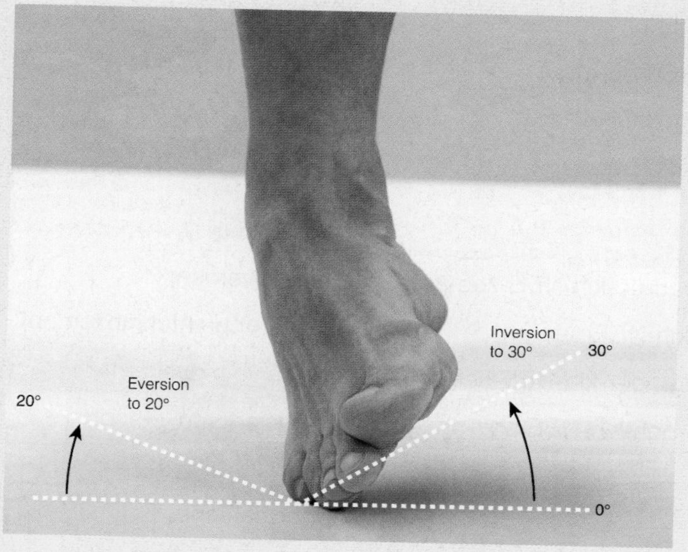

■ **Figure 4.26** Eversion and inversion of the foot.

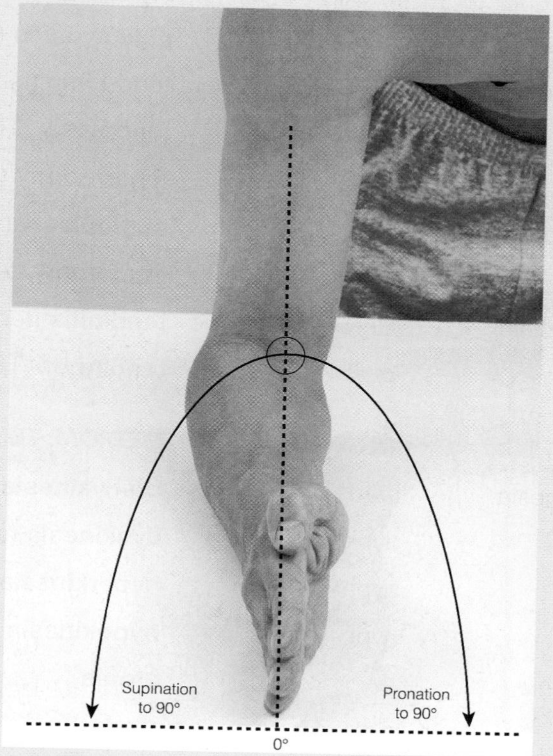

■ **Figure 4.27** Pronation and supination of the forearm.

Word Building

The following list contains examples of medical terms built directly from word parts. The definition for these terms can be determined by a straightforward translation of the word parts.

COMBINING FORM	COMBINED WITH PREFIX	MEDICAL TERM	DEFINITION
fasci/o	-al	**fascial** (FAS-ee-all)	pertaining to fascia
	-itis	**fasciitis** (fas-ee-EYE-tis)	inflammation of fascia
	-otomy	**fasciotomy** (fas-ee-OT-oh-mee)	incision into fascia
kinesi/o	-logy	**kinesiology** (kih-NEE-see-oh-loh-jee)	study of movement
muscul/o	-ar	**muscular** (MUSS-kew-lar)	pertaining to muscles
my/o	-algia	**myalgia** (my-AL-jee-ah)	muscle pain
	-asthenia	**myasthenia** (my-ass-THEE-nee-ah)	muscle weakness
	electr/o -gram	**electromyogram** (EMG) (ee-lek-troh-MY-oh-gram)	record of muscle electricity
	cardi/o -al	**myocardial** (my-oh-CAR-dee-al)	pertaining to heart muscle
	-pathy	**myopathy** (my-OPP-ah-thee)	muscle disease
	-plasty	**myoplasty** (MY-oh-plas-tee)	surgical repair of muscle
	-rrhaphy	**myorrhaphy** (MY-or-ah-fee)	suture a muscle
	-rrhexis	**myorrhexis** (my-oh-REK-sis)	muscle rupture
myos/o	poly- -itis	**polymyositis** (pol-ee-my-oh-SIGH-tis)	inflammation of many muscles
ten/o	-dynia	**tenodynia** (ten-oh-DIN-ee-ah)	tendon pain
	-plasty	**tenoplasty** (TEN-oh-plas-tee)	surgical repair of a tendon
	-rrhaphy	**tenorrhaphy** (tah-NOR-ah-fee)	suture a tendon
tend/o	-plasty	**tendoplasty** (TEN-doh-plas-tee)	surgical repair of tendon
	-otomy	**tendotomy** (tend-OT-oh-mee)	incision into tendon
tendin/o	-itis	**tendinitis** (ten-dih-NIGH-tis)	inflammation of tendon
	-ous	**tendinous** (TEN-din-us)	pertaining to tendons
SUFFIX	**COMBINED WITH PREFIX**	**MEDICAL TERM**	**DEFINITION**
-kinesia	brady-	**bradykinesia** (brad-ee-kih-NEE-see-ah)	slow movement
	dys-	**dyskinesia** (dis-kih-NEE-see-ah)	difficult or painful movement
	hyper-	**hyperkinesia** (high-per-kih-NEE-see-ah)	excessive movement
	hypo-	**hypokinesia** (HI-poh-kih-NEE-see-ah)	insufficient movement
-tonia	a-	**atonia**	lack of tone
	dys-	**dystonia**	abnormal tone
	hyper-	**hypertonia**	excessive tone
	hypo-	**hypotonia**	insufficient tone
	my/o	**myotonia**	muscle tone

Vocabulary

TERM	DEFINITION
adhesion	Scar tissue forming in the fascia surrounding a muscle, making it difficult to stretch the muscle.
atrophy (AT-rah-fee)	Poor muscle development as a result of muscle disease, nervous system disease, or lack of use; commonly referred to as *muscle wasting.*
contracture (kon-TRACK-chur)	Abnormal shortening of muscle fibers, tendons, or fascia making it difficult to stretch the muscle.
hypertrophy (high-PER-troh-fee)	Increase in muscle bulk as a result of using it, as in lifting weights
intermittent claudication (klaw-dih-KAY-shun)	Attacks of severe pain and lameness caused by ischemia of the muscles, typically the calf muscles; brought on by walking even very short distances.
spasm	Sudden, involuntary, strong muscle contraction.
torticollis (tore-tih-KOLL-iss)	Severe neck spasms pulling the head to one side. Commonly called *wryneck* or a *crick in the neck.*

Pathology

TERM	DEFINITION
■ ***Muscles***	
fibromyalgia (figh-broh-my-AL-jee-ah)	Condition with widespread aching and pain in the muscles and soft tissue.
lateral epicondylitis (ep-ih-kon-dih-LYE-tis)	Inflammation of the muscle attachment to the lateral epicondyle of the elbow. Often caused by strongly gripping. Commonly called *tennis elbow*.
muscular dystrophy (MD) (MUSS-kew-ler DIS-troh-fee)	Inherited disease causing a progressive muscle degeneration, weakness, and atrophy.
pseudohypertrophic muscular dystrophy (soo-doh-HIGH-per-troh-fic)	One type of inherited muscular dystrophy in which the muscle tissue is gradually replaced by fatty tissue, making the muscle look strong. Also called *Duchenne's muscular dystrophy*.
■ ***Tendons, Muscles, and/or Ligaments***	
carpal tunnel syndrome (CTS)	Repetitive motion disorder with pain caused by compression of the finger flexor tendons and median nerve as they pass through the carpal tunnel of the wrist.
ganglion cyst (GANG-lee-on)	Cyst that forms on tendon sheath, usually on hand, wrist, or ankle.
repetitive motion disorder	Group of chronic disorders involving the tendon, muscle, joint, and nerve damage, resulting from the tissue being subjected to pressure, vibration, or repetitive movements for prolonged periods.
rotator cuff injury	The rotator cuff consists of the joint capsule of the shoulder joint reinforced by the tendons from several shoulder muscles. The high degree of flexibility at the shoulder joint puts the rotator cuff at risk for strain and tearing.
strain	Damage to the muscle, tendons, or ligaments due to overuse or overstretching.

Diagnostic Procedures

TERM	DEFINITION
■ ***Clinical Laboratory Test***	
creatine phosphokinase (CPK) (KREE-ah-teen foss-foe-KYE-nase)	Muscle enzyme found in skeletal muscle and cardiac muscle. Blood levels become elevated in disorders such as heart attack, muscular dystrophy, and other skeletal muscle pathologies.
■ ***Additional Diagnostic Procedures***	
deep tendon reflexes (DTR)	Muscle contraction in response to a stretch caused by striking the muscle tendon with a reflex hammer. Test used to determine if muscles are responding properly.
electromyography (EMG) (ee-lek-troh-my-OG-rah-fee)	Study and record of the strength and quality of muscle contractions as a result of electrical stimulation.
muscle biopsy (BYE-op-see)	Removal of muscle tissue for pathological examination.

Treatment Procedures

TERM	DEFINITION
■ ***Surgical Procedures***	
carpal tunnel release	Surgical cutting of the ligament in the wrist to relieve nerve pressure caused by carpal tunnel syndrome, which can result from repetitive motion such as typing.
tenodesis (ten-oh-DEE-sis)	Surgical procedure to stabilize a joint by anchoring down the tendons of the muscles that move the joint.

Pharmacology

CLASSIFICATION	ACTION	GENERIC AND BRAND NAMES
skeletal muscle relaxants	Medication to relax skeletal muscles in order to reduce muscle spasms. Also called *antispasmodics*.	cyclobenzaprine, Flexeril; carisoprodol, Soma

Abbreviations

CTS	carpal tunnel syndrome	**EMG**	electromyogram
CPK	creatine phosphokinase	**IM**	intramuscular
DTR	deep tendon reflex	**MD**	muscular dystrophy

Chapter Review

Terminology Checklist

Below are all Anatomy and Physiology key terms, Word Building, Vocabulary, Pathology, Diagnostic, Therapeutic, and Pharmacology terms presented in this chapter. Use this list as a study tool by placing a check in the box in front of each term as you master its meaning.

- ☐ abduction
- ☐ action
- ☐ adduction
- ☐ adhesion
- ☐ amputation
- ☐ ankylosing spondylitis
- ☐ antagonistic pairs
- ☐ appendicular skeleton
- ☐ arthralgia
- ☐ arthritis
- ☐ arthrocentesis
- ☐ arthroclasia
- ☐ arthrodesis
- ☐ arthrogram
- ☐ arthrography
- ☐ arthroscope
- ☐ arthroscopic surgery
- ☐ arthroscopy
- ☐ arthrotomy
- ☐ articular cartilage
- ☐ articulation
- ☐ atonia
- ☐ atrophy
- ☐ axial skeleton
- ☐ biceps
- ☐ bone graft
- ☐ bone marrow
- ☐ bone reabsorption inhibitors
- ☐ bones
- ☐ bone scan
- ☐ bradykinesia
- ☐ bunion
- ☐ bunionectomy
- ☐ bursa
- ☐ bursectomy
- ☐ bursitis
- ☐ calcium supplements
- ☐ callus
- ☐ cancellous bone
- ☐ cardiac muscle
- ☐ carpal
- ☐ carpal tunnel release
- ☐ carpal tunnel syndrome
- ☐ cartilage
- ☐ cartilaginous joints
- ☐ cast
- ☐ cervical
- ☐ cervical vertebrae
- ☐ chiropractic
- ☐ chondrectomy
- ☐ chondroma
- ☐ chondromalacia
- ☐ chondroplasty
- ☐ circumduction
- ☐ clavicle
- ☐ clavicular
- ☐ closed fracture
- ☐ coccygeal
- ☐ coccyx
- ☐ Colles' fracture
- ☐ comminuted fracture
- ☐ compact bone
- ☐ compound fracture
- ☐ compression fracture
- ☐ condyle
- ☐ contracture
- ☐ cortical
- ☐ cortical bone
- ☐ corticosteroids
- ☐ costal
- ☐ cranial
- ☐ craniotomy
- ☐ cranium
- ☐ creatine phosphokinase
- ☐ crepitation
- ☐ deep tendon reflex
- ☐ diaphysis
- ☐ dislocation
- ☐ dorsiflexion
- ☐ dual-energy absorptiometry
- ☐ dyskinesia
- ☐ dystonia
- ☐ electromyogram
- ☐ electromyography
- ☐ elevation
- ☐ epicondyle
- ☐ epiphysis
- ☐ ethmoid bone
- ☐ eversion
- ☐ Ewing's sarcoma
- ☐ exostosis
- ☐ extension
- ☐ extensor carpi
- ☐ external oblique
- ☐ facial bones
- ☐ fascia
- ☐ fascial
- ☐ fasciitis
- ☐ fasciotomy
- ☐ femoral
- ☐ femur
- ☐ fibromyalgia
- ☐ fibrous joints
- ☐ fibula
- ☐ fibular
- ☐ fissure
- ☐ fixation
- ☐ flat bones
- ☐ flexion
- ☐ flexor carpi
- ☐ foramen
- ☐ fossa
- ☐ fracture
- ☐ frontal bone
- ☐ ganglion cyst
- ☐ gluteus maximus
- ☐ greenstick fracture

- ☐ head
- ☐ herniated nucleus pulposus
- ☐ humeral
- ☐ humerus
- ☐ hyoid bone
- ☐ hyperkinesia
- ☐ hypertonia
- ☐ hypertrophy
- ☐ hypokinesia
- ☐ hypotonia
- ☐ iliac
- ☐ ilium
- ☐ impacted fracture
- ☐ innominate bone
- ☐ insertion
- ☐ intermittent claudication
- ☐ intervertebral
- ☐ intervertebral disc
- ☐ intracranial
- ☐ inversion
- ☐ involuntary muscle
- ☐ irregular bones
- ☐ ischial
- ☐ ischium
- ☐ joint capsule
- ☐ joints
- ☐ kinesiology
- ☐ kyphosis
- ☐ lacrimal bone
- ☐ laminectomy
- ☐ lateral epicondylitis
- ☐ ligaments
- ☐ long bones
- ☐ lordosis
- ☐ lower extremities
- ☐ lumbar
- ☐ lumbar vertebrae
- ☐ mandible
- ☐ mandibular
- ☐ maxilla
- ☐ maxillary
- ☐ medullary
- ☐ medullary cavity
- ☐ metacarpal
- ☐ metatarsal
- ☐ motor neurons
- ☐ muscle biopsy
- ☐ muscles
- ☐ muscle tissue fibers
- ☐ muscular
- ☐ muscular dystrophy
- ☐ myalgia
- ☐ myasthenia
- ☐ myelography
- ☐ myeloma
- ☐ myocardial
- ☐ myocardium
- ☐ myoneural junction
- ☐ myopathy
- ☐ myoplasty
- ☐ myorrhaphy
- ☐ myorrhexis
- ☐ myotonia
- ☐ nasal bone
- ☐ neck
- ☐ nonsteroidal anti-inflammatory drugs
- ☐ oblique fracture
- ☐ occipital bone
- ☐ opposition
- ☐ origin
- ☐ orthopedics
- ☐ orthotic
- ☐ os coxae
- ☐ osseous tissue
- ☐ ossification
- ☐ ostealgia
- ☐ osteoarthritis
- ☐ osteoblasts
- ☐ osteochondroma
- ☐ osteoclasia
- ☐ osteocytes
- ☐ osteogenic sarcoma
- ☐ osteomalacia
- ☐ osteomyelitis
- ☐ osteopathy
- ☐ osteoporosis
- ☐ osteotome
- ☐ osteotomy
- ☐ Paget's disease
- ☐ palatine bone
- ☐ parietal bone
- ☐ patella
- ☐ patellar
- ☐ pathologic fracture
- ☐ pectoral girdle
- ☐ pelvic
- ☐ pelvic girdle
- ☐ percutaneous diskectomy
- ☐ periosteum
- ☐ phalangeal
- ☐ phalanges
- ☐ plantar flexion
- ☐ podiatry
- ☐ polymyositis
- ☐ process
- ☐ pronation
- ☐ prosthesis
- ☐ prosthetics
- ☐ pseudohypertrophic muscular dystrophy
- ☐ pubic
- ☐ pubis
- ☐ radial
- ☐ radiography
- ☐ radius
- ☐ rectus abdominis
- ☐ red bone marrow
- ☐ reduction
- ☐ repetitive motion disorder
- ☐ rheumatoid arthritis
- ☐ rib cage
- ☐ rickets
- ☐ rotation
- ☐ rotator cuff injury
- ☐ sacral
- ☐ sacrum
- ☐ scapula
- ☐ scapular
- ☐ scoliosis
- ☐ short bones
- ☐ sinus
- ☐ skeletal muscle
- ☐ skeletal muscle relaxants
- ☐ skeleton

Cardiovascular System at a Glance

Function

The cardiovascular system consists of the pump and vessels that distribute blood to all areas of the body. This system allows for the delivery of needed substances to the cells of the body as well as for the removal of wastes.

Organs

blood vessels
- **arteries**
- **capillaries**
- **veins**

heart

Combining Forms

angi/o	vessel
aort/o	aorta
arteri/o	artery
ather/o	fatty substance
atri/o	atrium
cardi/o	heart
coron/o	heart
hemangi/o	blood vessel
phleb/o	vein
sphygm/o	pulse
steth/o	chest
thromb/o	clot
valv/o	valve
valvul/o	valve
vascul/o	blood vessel
vas/o	vessel, duct
ven/o	vein
ventricul/o	ventricle

Suffixes

-manometer	instrument to measure pressure
-ole	small
-tension	pressure
-ule	small

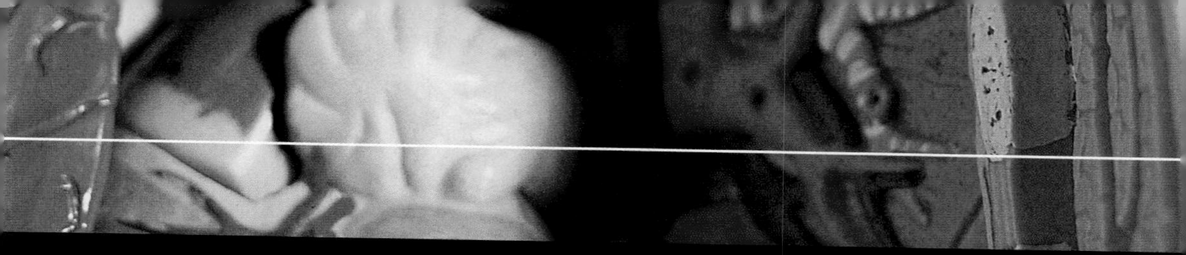

Cardiovascular System

Learning Objectives

Upon completion of this chapter, you will be able to:

- Identify and define the combining forms and suffixes introduced in this chapter.
- Correctly spell and pronounce medical terms and major anatomical structures relating to the cardiovascular system.
- Describe the major organs of the cardiovascular system and their functions.
- Describe the anatomy of the heart.
- Describe the flow of blood through the heart.
- Explain how the electrical conduction system controls the heartbeat.
- List and describe the characteristics of the three types of blood vessels.
- Define pulse and blood pressure.
- Build and define cardiovascular system medical terms from word parts.
- Identify and define cardiovascular system vocabulary terms.
- Identify and define selected cardiovascular system pathology terms.
- Identify and define selected cardiovascular system diagnostic procedures.
- Identify and define selected cardiovascular system therapeutic procedures.
- Identify and define selected medications relating to the cardiovascular system.
- Define selected abbreviations associated with the cardiovascular system.

Multimedia Preview

Additional interactive resources and activities for this chapter can be found on the Companion Website. For videos, games, and pronunciations, please access the accompanying DVD-ROM that comes with this book.

DVD-ROM Highlights

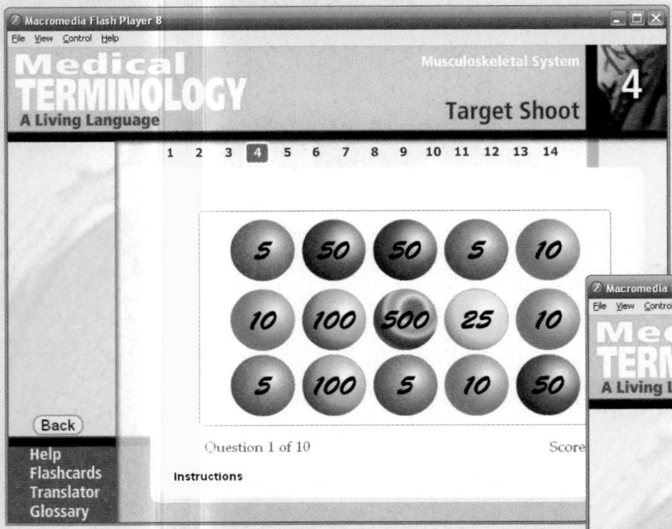

TARGET SHOOTING

Here's a game that requires a quick mind and an even faster finger! As colored balls flash on your screen, click on the highest point values to reveal a question. A correct answer earns the points. How high can you score?

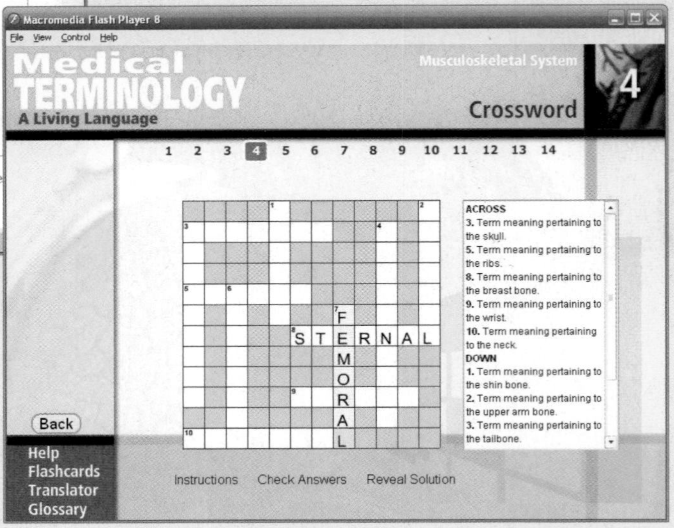

CROSSWORD PUZZLE

Here is where learning and fun intersect! Simply use the clues to complete the puzzle grid. Whether you're a crossword wizard or only a novice, this activity will reinforce your understanding of key terms and concepts.

Website Highlights—www.prenhall.com/fremgen

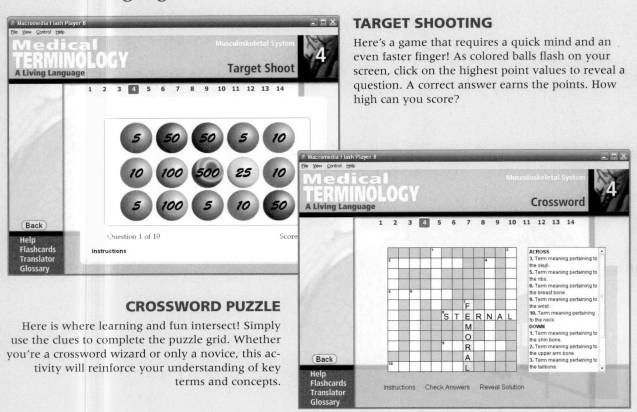

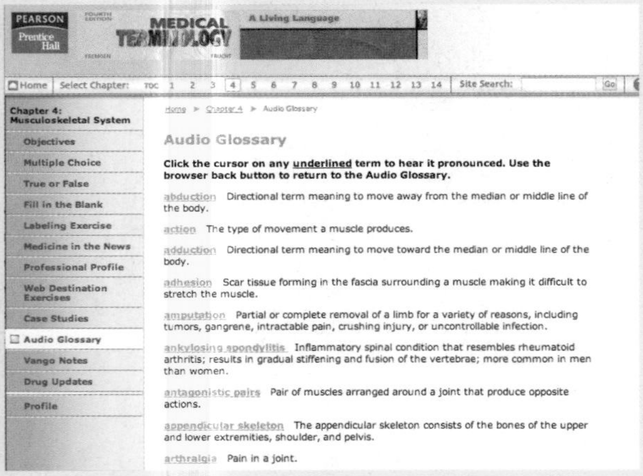

AUDIO GLOSSARY

Click here and take advantage of the free-access on-line study guide that accompanies your textbook. You'll find an audio glossary with definitions and audio pronunciations for every term in the book. By clicking on this URL you'll also access a variety of quizzes with instant feedback, links to download mp3 audio reviews, and current news articles.

Cardiovascular System Illustrated

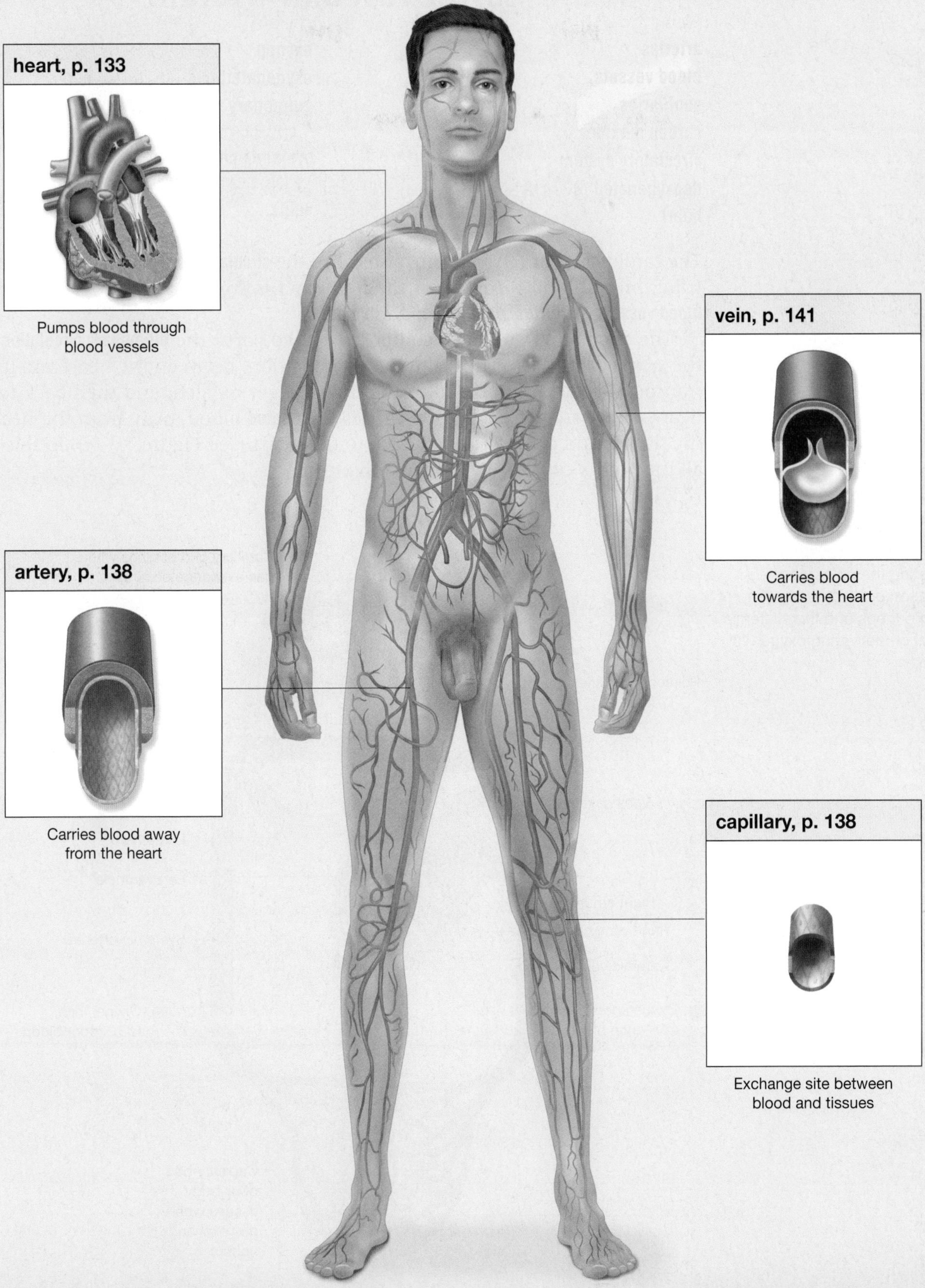

Anatomy and Physiology of the Cardiovascular System

arteries
blood vessels
capillaries
carbon dioxide
circulatory system
deoxygenated (dee-OK-sih-jen-ay-ted)
heart
oxygen
oxygenated (OK-sih-jen-ay-ted)
pulmonary circulation (PULL-mon-air-ee ser-kew-LAY-shun)
systemic circulation (sis-TEM-ik ser-kew-LAY-shun)
veins

The cardiovascular (CV) system, also called the **circulatory system,** maintains the distribution of blood throughout the body and is composed of the **heart** and the **blood vessels—arteries**, **capillaries**, and **veins.**

The circulatory system is composed of two parts: the **pulmonary circulation** and the **systemic circulation**. The pulmonary circulation, between the heart and lungs, transports **deoxygenated** blood to the lungs to get oxygen, and then back to the heart. The systemic circulation carries **oxygenated** blood away from the heart to the tissues and cells, and then back to the heart (see Figure 5.1 ■). In this way all the body's cells receive blood and oxygen.

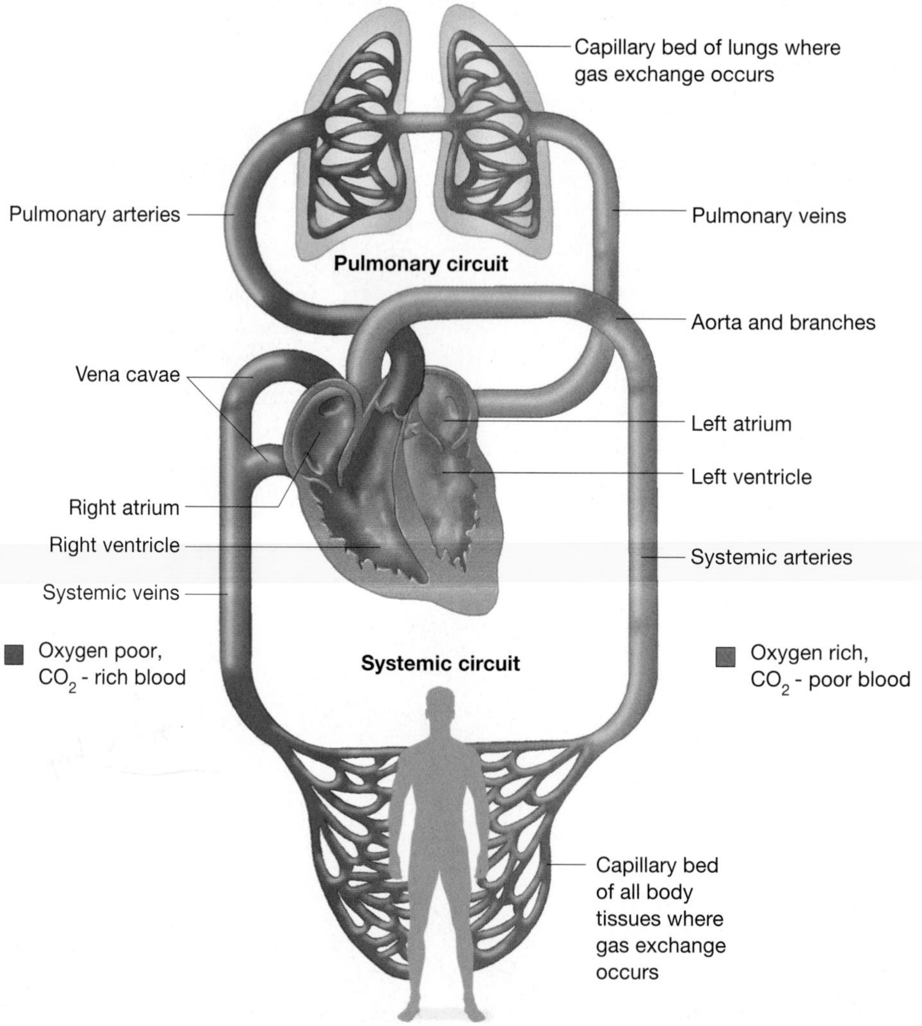

■ **Figure 5.1** A schematic of the circulatory system illustrating the pulmonary circulation picking up oxygen from the lungs and the systemic circulation delivering oxygen to the body.

In addition to distributing **oxygen** and other nutrients, such as glucose and amino acids, the cardiovascular system also collects the waste products from the body's cells. **Carbon dioxide** and other waste products produced by metabolic reaction are transported by the cardiovascular system to the lungs, liver, and kidneys where they are eliminated from the body.

Heart

apex (AY-peks)
cardiac muscle (CAR-dee-ak)

The heart is a muscular pump made up of **cardiac muscle** fibers that could be considered a muscle rather than an organ. It has four chambers, or cavities, and beats an average of 60 to 100 beats per minute (bpm) or about 100,000 times in one day. Each time the cardiac muscle contracts, blood is ejected from the heart and pushed throughout the body within the blood vessels.

The heart is located in the mediastinum in the center of the chest cavity, however, it is not exactly centered; more of the heart is on the left side of the mediastinum than the right. At about the size of a fist and shaped like an upside-down pear the heart lies directly behind the sternum. The tip of the heart at the lower edge is called the **apex** (see Figure 5.2 ■).

Med Term Tip

Your heart is approximately the size of your clenched fist and pumps 4,000 gallons of blood each day. It will beat at least three billion times during your lifetime.

Heart Layers

endocardium (en-doh-CAR-dee-um)
epicardium (ep-ih-CAR-dee-um)
myocardium (my-oh-CAR-dee-um)
parietal pericardium (pah-RYE-eh-tal pair-ih-CAR-dee-um)
pericardium (pair-ih-CAR-dee-um)
visceral pericardium (VISS-er-al pair-ih-CAR-dee-um)

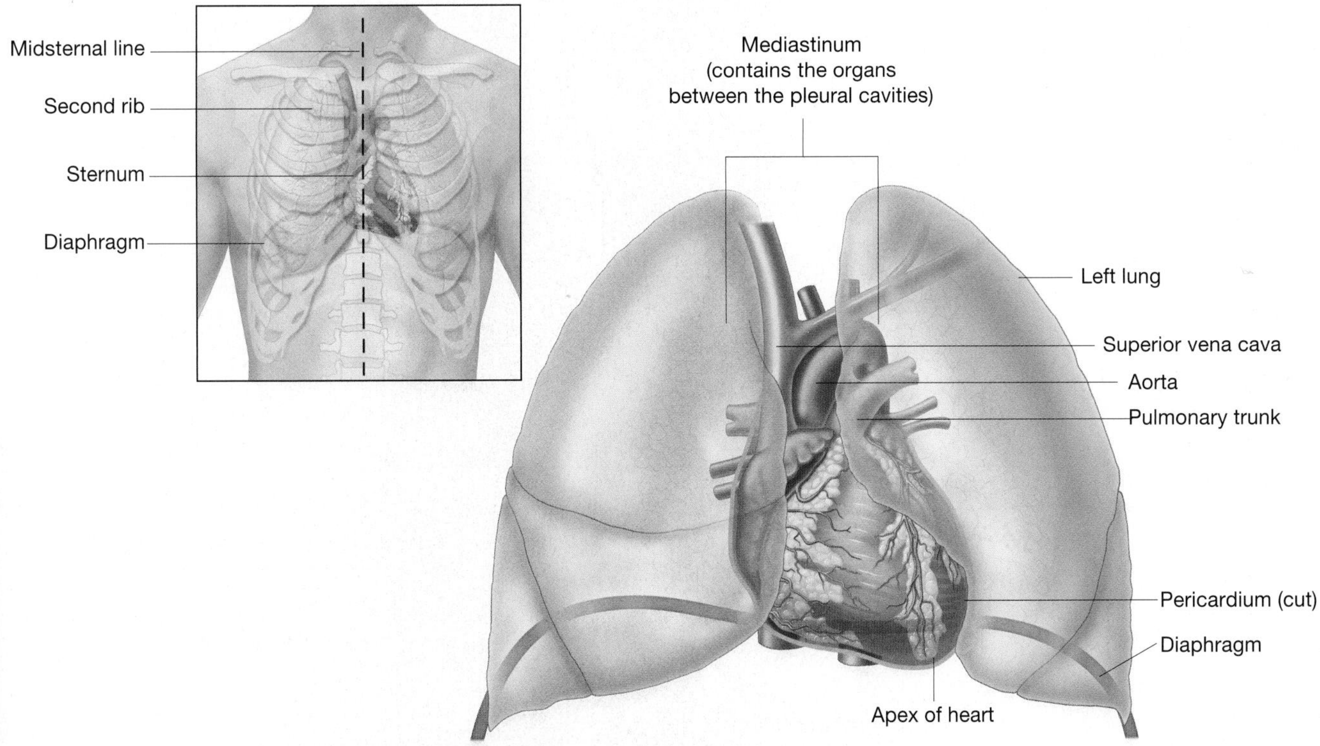

■ **Figure 5.2** Location of the heart within the mediastinum of the thoracic cavity.

Med Term Tip

These layers become important when studying the disease conditions affecting the heart. For instance, when the prefix *endo-* is added to *carditis,* forming *endocarditis*, we know that the inflammation is within the "inner layer of the heart." In discussing the muscular action of the heart the prefix *myo-*, meaning "muscle," is added to *cardium* to form the word *myocardium.* The diagnosis *myocardial infarction* (MI), or heart attack, means that the patient has an infarct or "dead tissue in the muscle of the heart." The prefix *peri-*, meaning "around," when added to the word *cardium* refers to the sac "surrounding the heart." Therefore, *pericarditis* is an "inflammation of the outer sac of the heart."

The wall of the heart is quite thick and composed of three layers (see Figures 5.3 ■ and 5.4 ■):

1. The **endocardium** is the inner layer of the heart lining the heart chambers. It is a very smooth, thin layer that serves to reduce friction as the blood passes through the heart chambers.
2. The **myocardium** is the thick muscular middle layer of the heart. Contraction of this muscle layer develops the pressure required to pump blood through the blood vessels.
3. The **epicardium** is the outer layer of the heart. The heart is enclosed within a double-layered pleural sac, called the **pericardium**. The epicardium is the **visceral pericardium**, or inner layer of the sac. The outer layer of the sac is the **parietal pericardium**. Fluid between the two layers of the sac reduces friction as the heart beats.

Heart Chambers

atria (AY-tree-ah)
interatrial septum (in-ter-AY-tree-al SEP-tum)
interventricular septum (in-ter-ven-TRIK-yoo-lar SEP-tum)
ventricles (VEN-trik-lz)

The heart is divided into four chambers or cavities (see Figures 5.3 and 5.4). There are two **atria**, or upper chambers, and two **ventricles**, or lower chambers. These chambers are divided into right and left sides by walls called the **interatrial septum** and the **interventricular septum**. The atria are the receiving chambers of the heart. Blood returning to the heart via veins first collects in the atria. The ventricles are the pumping chambers. They have a much thicker myocardium and their contraction ejects blood out of the heart and into the great arteries.

Med Term Tip

The term *ventricle* comes from the Latin term *venter,* which means "little belly." Although it originally referred to the abdomen and then the stomach, it came to stand for any hollow region inside an organ.

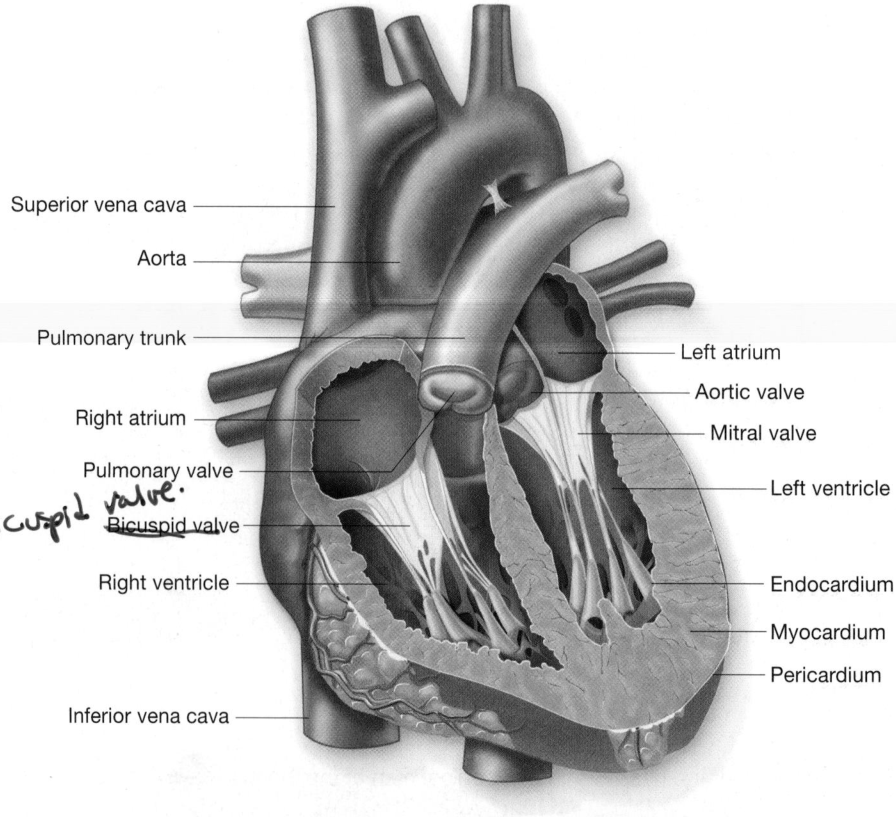

■ **Figure 5.3** Internal view of the heart illustrating the heart chambers, heart layers, heart valves, and major blood vessels associated with the heart.

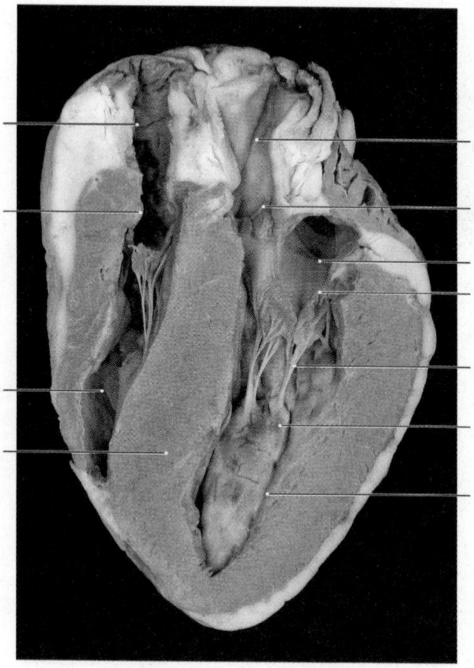

Figure 5.4 Internal view of heart specimen illustrating heart chambers, septum, and heart valves.

Heart Valves

aortic valve (ay-OR-tik)
atrioventricular valve (ay-tree-oh-ven-TRIK-yoo-lar)
bicuspid valve (bye-CUSS-pid)
cusps
mitral valve (MY-tral)
pulmonary valve (PULL-mon-air-ee)
semilunar valve (sem-ih-LOO-nar)
tricuspid valve (try-CUSS-pid)

Four valves act as restraining gates to control the direction of blood flow. They are situated at the entrances and exits to the ventricles (see Figures 5.4 and 5.5). Properly functioning valves allow blood to flow only in the forward direction by blocking it from returning to the previous chamber.

The four valves are as follows:

1. **Tricuspid valve:** an **atrioventricular valve** (AV), meaning that it controls the opening between the right atrium and the right ventricle. Once the blood enters the right ventricle, it cannot go back up into the atrium again. The prefix *tri-*, meaning three, indicates that this valve has three leaflets or **cusps**.
2. **Pulmonary valve:** a **semilunar valve**. The prefix *semi-*, meaning half, and the term **lunar**, meaning moon, indicate that this valve looks like a half moon. Located between the right ventricle and the pulmonary artery, this valve prevents blood that has been ejected into the pulmonary artery from returning to the right ventricle as it relaxes.
3. **Mitral valve:** also called the **bicuspid valve**, indicating that it has two cusps. Blood flows through this atrioventricular valve to the left ventricle and cannot go back up into the left atrium.
4. **Aortic valve:** a semilunar valve located between the left ventricle and the aorta. Blood leaves the left ventricle through this valve and cannot return to the left ventricle.

Med Term Tip

The heart makes two distinct sounds referred to as "lub-dupp." These sounds are produced by the forceful snapping shut of the heart valves. *Lub* is the closing of the atrioventricular valves. *Dupp* is the closing of the semilunar valves.

Blood Flow Through the Heart

aorta (ay-OR-tah)
diastole (dye-ASS-toe-lee)
inferior vena cava (VEE-nah KAY-vah)
pulmonary artery (PULL-mon-air-ee)
pulmonary veins
superior vena cava
systole (SIS-toe-lee)

Figure 5.5 Superior view of heart valves illustrating position, size, and shape of each valve.

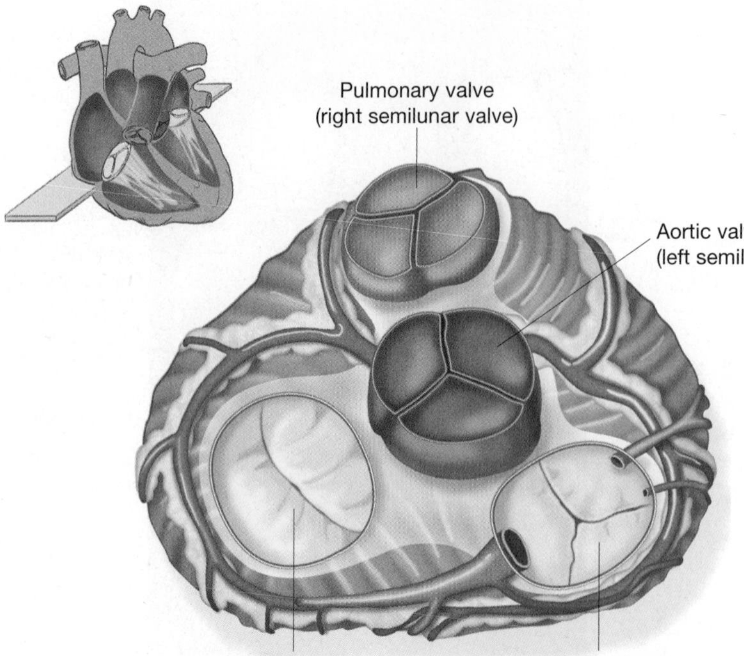

The flow of blood through the heart is very orderly (see Figure 5.6 ■). It progresses through the heart to the lungs, where it receives oxygen; then goes back to the heart; and then out to the body tissues and parts. The normal process of blood flow is as follows:

1. Deoxygenated blood from all the tissues in the body enters a relaxed right atrium via two large veins called the **superior vena cava** and **inferior vena cava**.
2. The right atrium contracts and blood flows through the tricuspid valve into the relaxed right ventricle.
3. The right ventricle then contracts and blood is pumped through the pulmonary valve into the **pulmonary artery**, which carries it to the lungs for oxygenation.
4. The left atrium receives blood returning to the heart after being oxygenated by the lungs. This blood enters the relaxed left atrium from the four **pulmonary veins**.
5. The left atrium contracts and blood flows through the mitral valve into the relaxed left ventricle.
6. When the left ventricle contracts, the blood is pumped through the aortic valve and into the **aorta**, the largest artery in the body. The aorta carries blood to all parts of the body.

It can be seen that the heart chambers alternate between relaxing in order to fill and contracting to push blood forward. The period of time a chamber is relaxed is **diastole**. The contraction phase is **systole**.

Conduction System of the Heart

atrioventricular bundle
atrioventricular node
autonomic nervous system (aw-toh-NOM-ik NER-vus SIS-tem)
bundle branches
bundle of His
pacemaker
Purkinje fibers (per-KIN-gee)
sinoatrial node (sigh-noh-AY-tree-al)

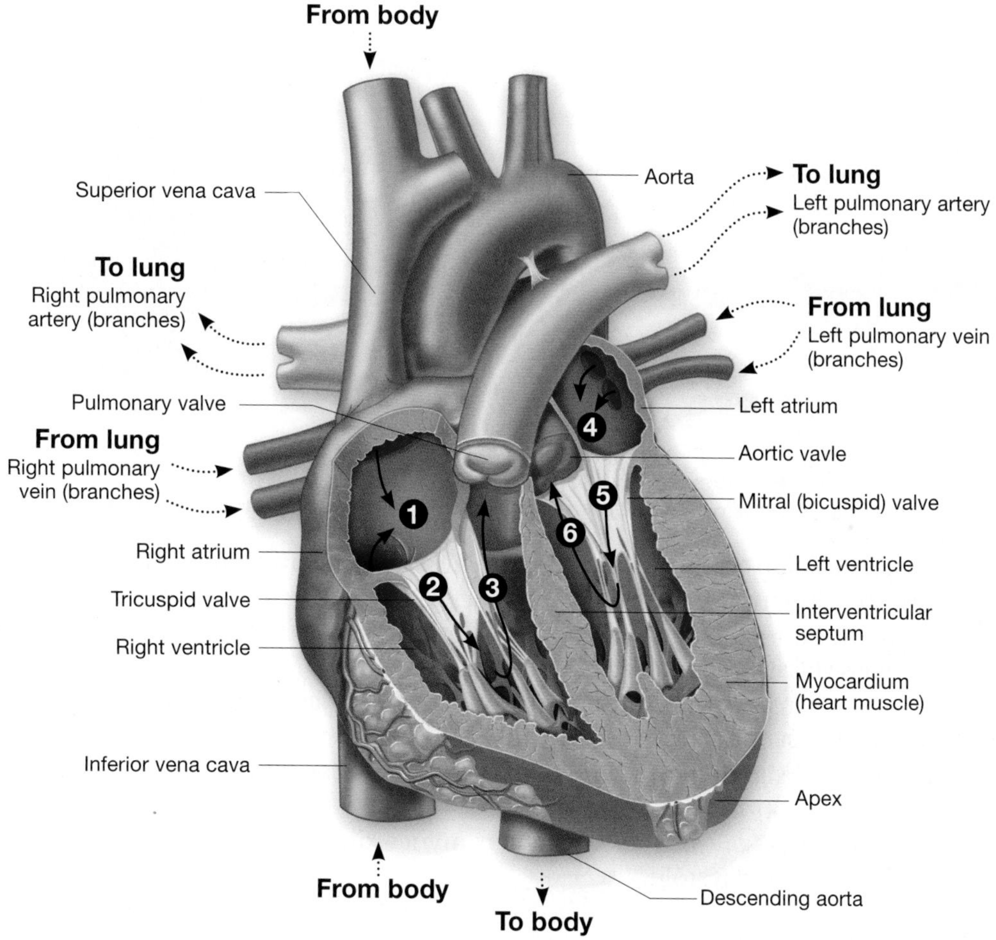

Figure 5.6 The path of blood flow through the chambers of the left and right side of the heart, including the veins delivering blood to the heart and arteries receiving blood ejected from the heart.

The heart rate is regulated by the **autonomic nervous system**; therefore, we have no voluntary control over the beating of our heart. Special tissue within the heart is responsible for conducting an electrical impulse stimulating the different chambers to contract in the correct order.

The path that the impulses travel is as follows (see Figure 5.7 ■):

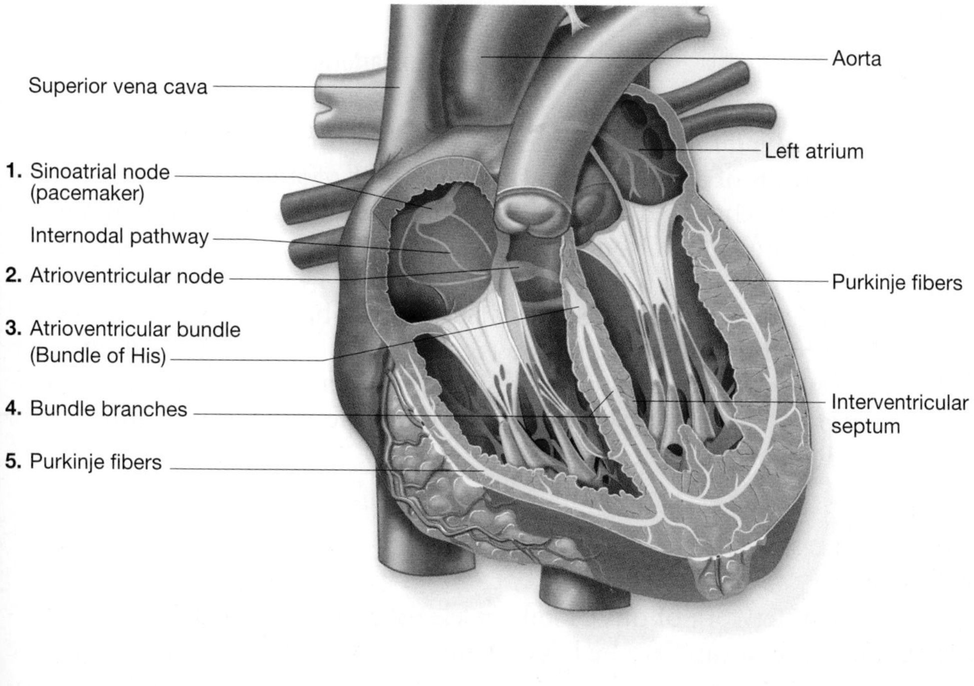

Figure 5.7 The conduction system of the heart; traces the path of the electrical impulse that stimulates the heart chambers to contract in the correct sequence.

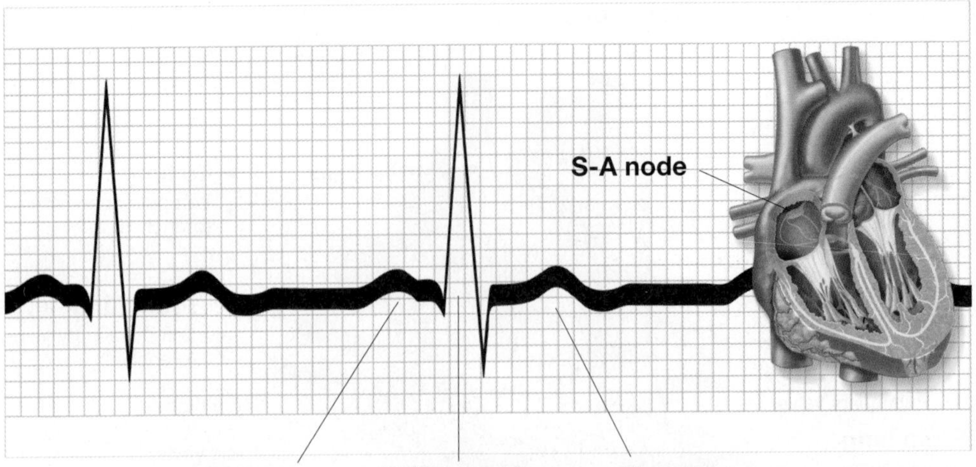

Figure 5.8 An electrocardiogram (EKG) wave, record of the electrical signal as it moves through the conduction system of the heart. This signal stimulates the chambers of the heart to contract and relax in the proper sequence.

1. The **sinoatrial (SA) node**, or **pacemaker**, is where the electrical impulses begin. From the sinoatrial node a wave of electricity travels through the atria, causing them to contract, or go into systole.
2. The **atrioventricular node** is stimulated.
3. This node transfers the stimulation wave to the **atrioventricular bundle** (formerly called **bundle of His**).
4. The electrical signal next travels down the **bundle branches** within the interventricular septum.
5. The **Purkinje fibers** out in the ventricular myocardium are stimulated, resulting in ventricular systole.

Med Term Tip

The electrocardiogram, referred to as an EKG or ECG, is a measurement of the electrical activity of the heart (see Figure 5.8). This can give the physician information about the health of the heart, especially the myocardium.

Blood Vessels

lumen (LOO-men)

There are three types of blood vessels: arteries, capillaries, and veins (see Figure 5.9). These are the pipes that circulate blood through out the body. The **lumen** is the channel within these vessels through which blood flows.

Arteries

arterioles (ar-TEE-ree-ohlz)

coronary arteries (KOR-ah-nair-ee AR-te-reez)

The arteries are the large, thick-walled vessels that carry the blood away from the heart. The walls of arteries contain a thick layer of smooth muscle that can contract or relax to change the size of the arterial lumen. The pulmonary artery carries deoxygenated blood from the right ventricle to the lungs. The largest artery, the aorta, begins from the left ventricle of the heart and carries oxygenated blood to all the body systems. The **coronary arteries** then branch from the aorta and provide blood to the myocardium (see Figure 5.10). As they travel through the body, the arteries branch into progressively smaller sized arteries. The smallest of the arteries, called **arterioles**, deliver blood to the capillaries. Figure 5.11 illustrates the major systemic arteries.

Med Term Tip

The term *coronary*, from the Latin word for crown, describes how the great vessels encircle the heart as they emerge from the top of the heart.

Capillaries

capillary bed

Capillaries are a network of tiny blood vessels referred to as a **capillary bed**. Arterial blood flows into a capillary bed, and venous blood flows back out (see Figure

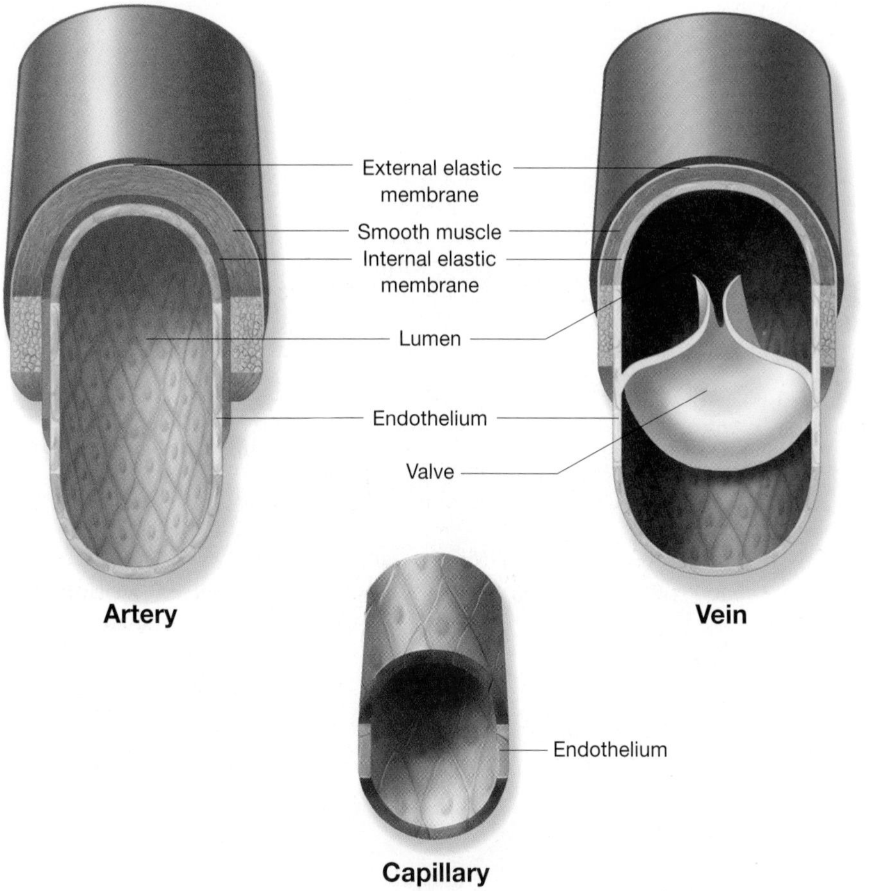

Figure 5.9 Comparative structure of arteries, capillaries, and veins.

5.9). Capillaries are very thin walled, allowing for the diffusion of the oxygen and nutrients from the blood into the body tissues. Likewise, carbon dioxide and waste products are able to diffuse out of the body tissues and into the bloodstream to be carried away. Since the capillaries are so small in diameter, the blood will not flow as quickly through them as it does through the arteries and veins. This means that the blood has time for an exchange of nutrients, oxygen, and waste material to take place. As blood exits a capillary bed, it returns to the heart through a vein.

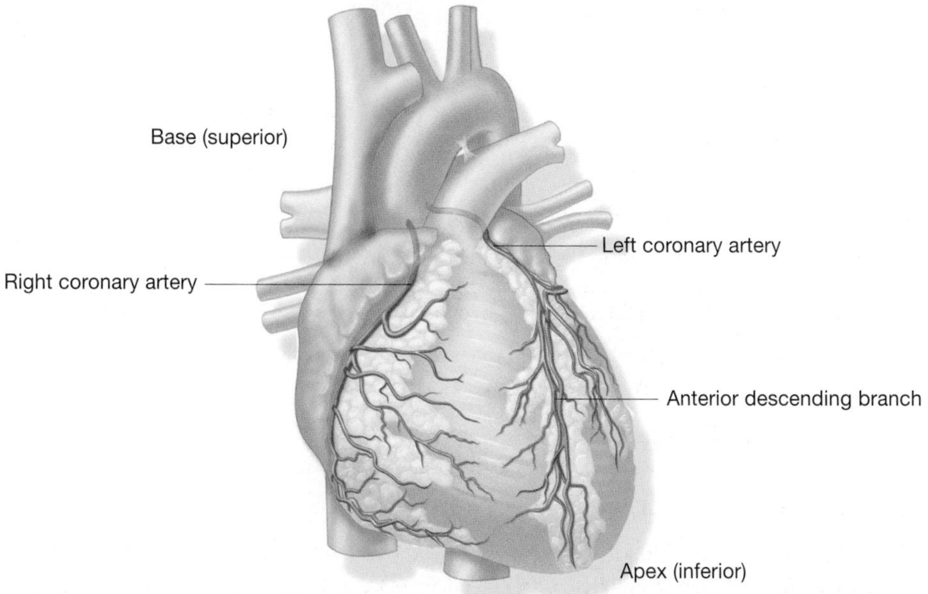

Figure 5.10 The coronary arteries.

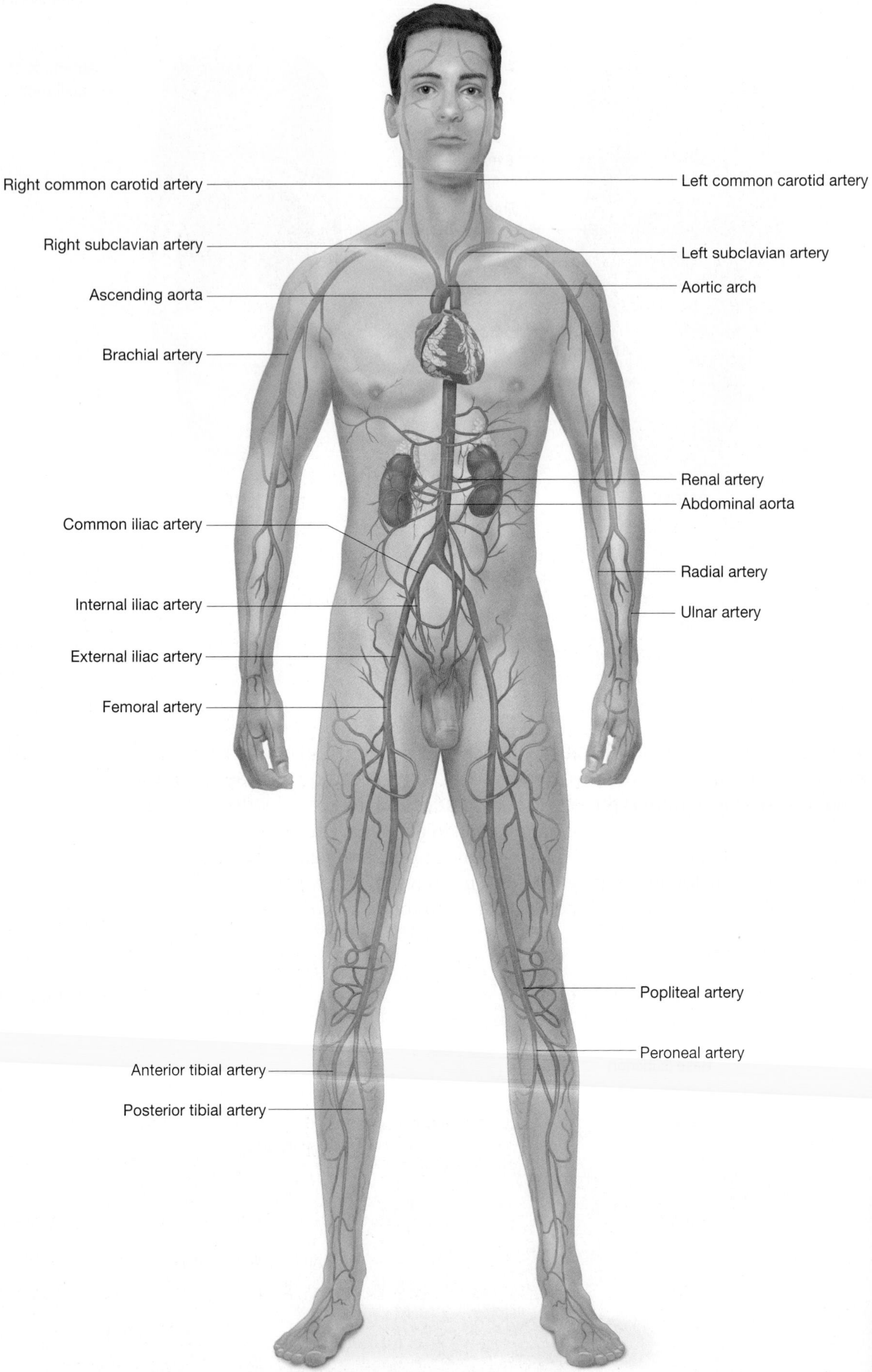

Right common carotid artery
Left common carotid artery
Right subclavian artery
Left subclavian artery
Ascending aorta
Aortic arch
Brachial artery
Renal artery
Abdominal aorta
Common iliac artery
Radial artery
Internal iliac artery
Ulnar artery
External iliac artery
Femoral artery
Popliteal artery
Peroneal artery
Anterior tibial artery
Posterior tibial artery

Figure 5.11 The major arteries of the body.

Veins

venules (VEN-yools)

The veins carry blood back to the heart. Blood leaving capillaries first enters small **venules**, which then merge into larger veins. Veins have much thinner walls than arteries, causing them to collapse easily. The veins also have valves that allow the blood to move only toward the heart. These valves prevent blood from backflowing; ensuring that blood always flows toward the heart (see Figure 5.9). The two large veins that enter the heart are the superior vena cava, which carries blood from the upper body, and the inferior vena cava, which carries blood from the lower body. Blood pressure in the veins is much lower than in the arteries. Muscular action against the veins and skeletal muscle contractions help in the movement of blood. Figure 5.12 ■ illustrates the major systemic veins.

Pulse and Blood Pressure

blood pressure (BP)
diastolic pressure (dye-ah-STOL-ik)
pulse
systolic pressure (sis-TOL-ik)

Blood pressure (BP) is a measurement of the force exerted by blood against the wall of a blood vessel. During ventricular systole, blood is under a lot of pressure from the ventricular contraction, giving the highest blood pressure reading—the **systolic pressure**. The **pulse** felt at the wrist or throat is the surge of blood caused by the heart contraction. This is why pulse rate is normally equal to heart rate. During ventricular diastole, blood is not being pushed by the heart at all and the blood pressure reading drops to its lowest point—the **diastolic pressure**. Therefore, to see the full range of what is occurring with blood pressure, both numbers are required. Blood pressure is also affected by several other characteristics of the blood and the blood vessels. These include the elasticity of the arteries, the diameter of the blood vessels, the viscosity of the blood, the volume of blood flowing through the vessels, and the amount of resistance to blood flow.

Med Term Tip

The instrument used to measure blood pressure is called a *sphygmomanometer.* The combining form *sphygm/o* means "pulse" and the suffix *-manometer* means "instrument to measure pressure." A blood pressure reading is reported as two numbers, for example, 120/80. The 120 is the systolic pressure and the 80 is the diastolic pressure. There is not one "normal" blood pressure number. The normal range for blood pressure in an adult is 90/60 to 140/90.

Word Building

The following list contains examples of medical terms built directly from word parts. The definition for these terms can be determined by a straightforward translation of the word parts.

COMBINING FORM	COMBINED WITH	MEDICAL TERM	DEFINITION
angi/o	-gram	**angiogram** (AN-jee-oh-gram)	record of a vessel
	-itis	**angiitis** (an-jee-EYE-tis)	inflammation of a vessel
	-plasty	**angioplasty** (AN-jee-oh-plas-tee)	surgical repair of a vessel
	-spasm	**angiospasm** (AN-jee-oh-spazm)	involuntary muscle contraction of a vessel
	-stenosis	**angiostenosis** (an-jee-oh-sten-OH-sis)	narrowing of a vessel
aort/o	-ic	**aortic** (ay-OR-tik)	pertaining to the aorta
arteri/o	-al	**arterial** (ar-TEE-ree-al)	pertaining to the artery
	-ole	**arteriole** (ar-TEE-ree-ohl)	small artery
	-rrhexis	**arteriorrhexis** (ar-tee-ree-oh-REK-sis)	ruptured artery
ather/o	-ectomy	**atherectomy** (ath-er-EK-toh-mee)	removal of fatty substance

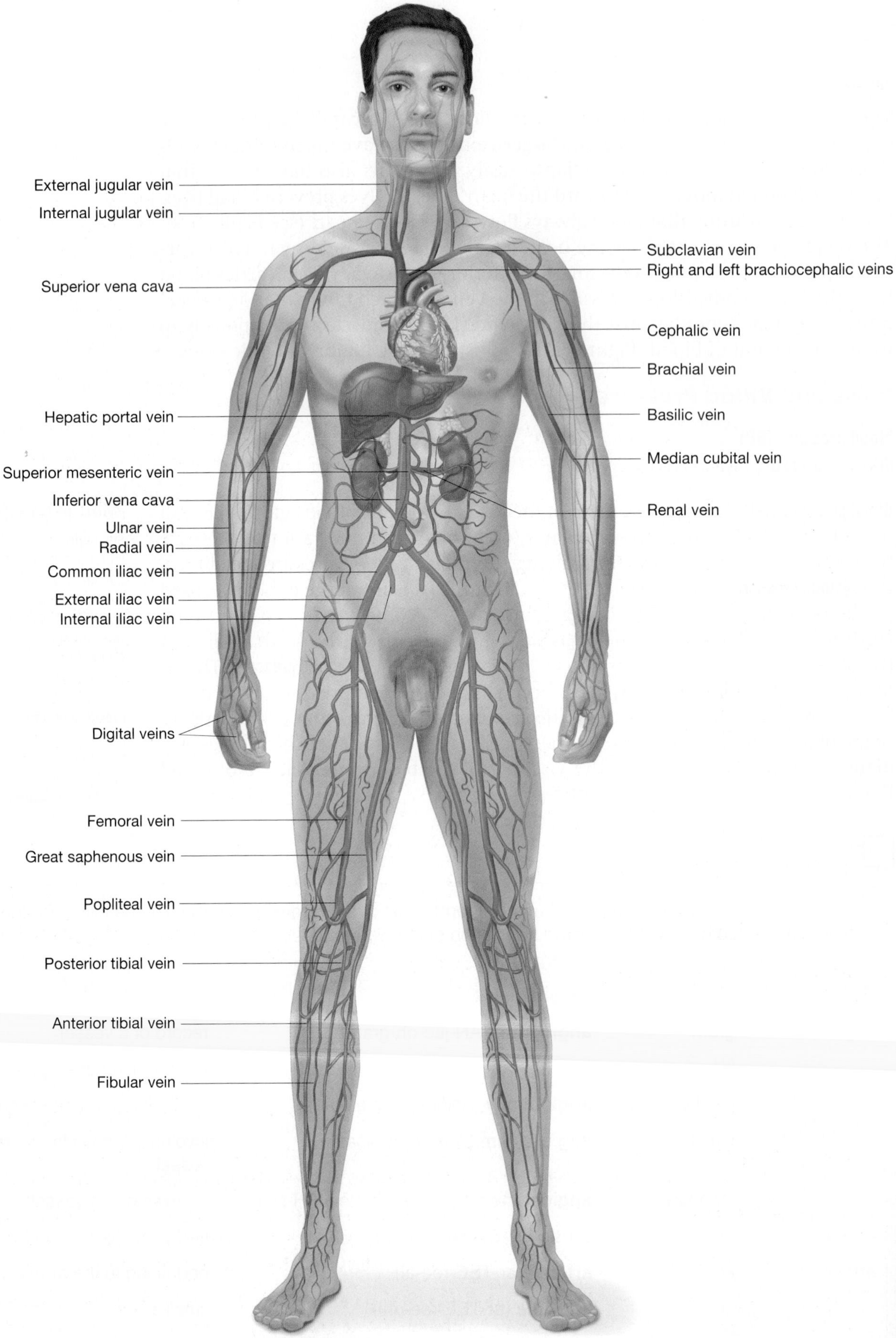
External jugular vein
Internal jugular vein
Superior vena cava
Hepatic portal vein
Superior mesenteric vein
Inferior vena cava
Ulnar vein
Radial vein
Common iliac vein
External iliac vein
Internal iliac vein
Digital veins
Femoral vein
Great saphenous vein
Popliteal vein
Posterior tibial vein
Anterior tibial vein
Fibular vein
Subclavian vein
Right and left brachiocephalic veins
Cephalic vein
Brachial vein
Basilic vein
Median cubital vein
Renal vein

Figure 5.12 The major veins of the body.

Word Building *(continued)*

COMBINING FORM	COMBINED WITH	MEDICAL TERM	DEFINITION
	-oma	**atheroma** (ath-er-OH-mah)	fatty substance tumor/growth
atri/o	-al	**atrial** (AY-tree-al)	pertaining to the atrium
	inter- -al	**interatrial** (in-ter-AY-tree-al)	pertaining to between the atria
cardi/o	-ac	**cardiac** (CAR-dee-ak)	pertaining to the heart
	brady- -ia	**bradycardia** (brad-ee-CAR-dee-ah)	state of slow heart
	electr/o -gram	**electrocardiogram** (ee-lek-tro-CAR-dee-oh-gram)	record of heart electricity
	-megaly	**cardiomegaly** (car-dee-oh-MEG-ah-lee)	enlarged heart
	my/o -al	**myocardial** (my-oh-CAR-dee-al)	pertaining to heart muscle
	-ologist	**cardiologist** (car-dee-ALL-oh-jist)	specialist in the heart
	-rrhexis	**cardiorrhexis** (card-dee-oh-REK-sis)	ruptured heart
	tachy- -ia	**tachycardia** (tak-ee-CAR-dee-ah)	state of fast heart
coron/o	-ary	**coronary** (KOR-ah-nair-ee)	pertaining to the heart
phleb/o	-itis	**phlebitis** (fleh-BYE-tis)	inflammation of a vein
valv/o	-plasty	**valvoplasty** (VAL-voh-plas-tee)	surgical repair of a valve
valvul/o	-itis	**valvulitis** (val-view-LYE-tis)	inflammation of a valve
	-ar	**valvular** (VAL-view-lar)	pertaining to a valve
vascul/o	-ar	**vascular** (VAS-kwee-lar)	pertaining to a blood vessel
ven/o	-ous	**venous** (VEE-nus)	pertaining to a vein
	-ule	**venule** (VEN-yool)	small vein
	-gram	**venogram** (VEN-oh-gram)	record of a vein
ventricul/o	-ar	**ventricular** (ven-TRIK-yoo-lar)	pertaining to a ventricle
	inter- -ar	**interventricular** (in-ter-ven-TRIK-yoo-lar)	pertaining to between the ventricles

Vocabulary

TERM	DEFINITION
auscultation (oss-kul-TAY-shun)	The process of listening to the sounds within the body by using a stethoscope.
cardiology (car-dee-ALL-oh-jee)	The branch of medicine involving diagnosis and treatment of conditions and diseases of the cardiovascular system. Physician is a *cardiologist.*
catheter (KATH-eh-ter)	A flexible tube inserted into the body for the purpose of moving fluids into or out of the body. In the cardiovascular system a catheter is used to place dye into blood vessels so they may be visualized on x-rays.
infarct (IN-farkt)	An area of tissue within an organ or part that undergoes necrosis (death) following the loss of its blood supply.
ischemia (is-KEYH-mee-ah)	The localized and temporary deficiency of blood supply due to an obstruction to the circulation.

Vocabulary *(continued)*

TERM	DEFINITION
murmur (MUR-mur)	An abnormal heart sound such as a soft blowing sound or harsh click. It may be quiet and heard only with a stethoscope, or so loud it can be heard several feet away. Also referred to as a *bruit.*
orthostatic hypotension (or-thoh-STAT-ik)	The sudden drop in blood pressure a person experiences when standing up suddenly.
palpitations (pal-pih-TAY-shunz)	Pounding, racing heartbeats.
plaque (plak)	A yellow, fatty deposit of lipids in an artery that are the hallmark of atherosclerosis.
regurgitation (re-ger-gih-TAY-shun)	To flow backwards. In the cardiovascular system this refers to the backflow of blood through a valve.
sphygmomanometer (sfig-moh-mah-NOM-eh-ter)	Instrument for measuring blood pressure. Also referred to as a *blood pressure cuff* (see Figure 5.13 ■).
stent	A stainless steel tube placed within a blood vessel or a duct to widen the lumen (see Figure 5.14 ■).
stethoscope (STETH-oh-scope)	Instrument for listening to body sounds (auscultation), such as the chest, heart, or intestines.

Pathology

TERM	DEFINITION
■ ***Heart***	
angina pectoris (an-JYE-nah PECK-tor-is)	Condition in which there is severe pain with a sensation of constriction around the heart. Caused by a deficiency of oxygen to the heart muscle.

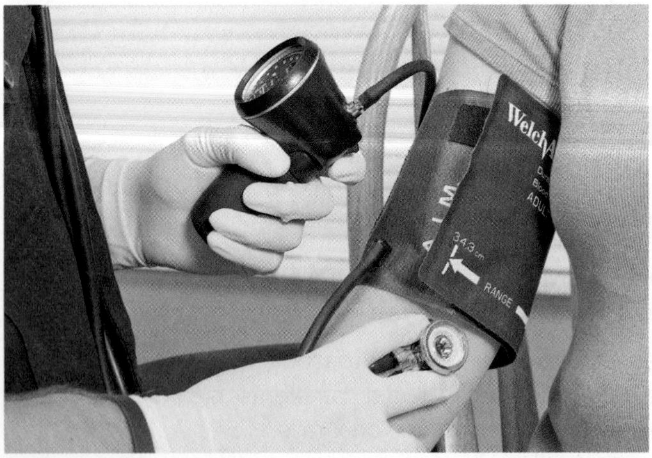

■ **Figure 5.13** Using a sphygmomanometer to measure blood pressure.

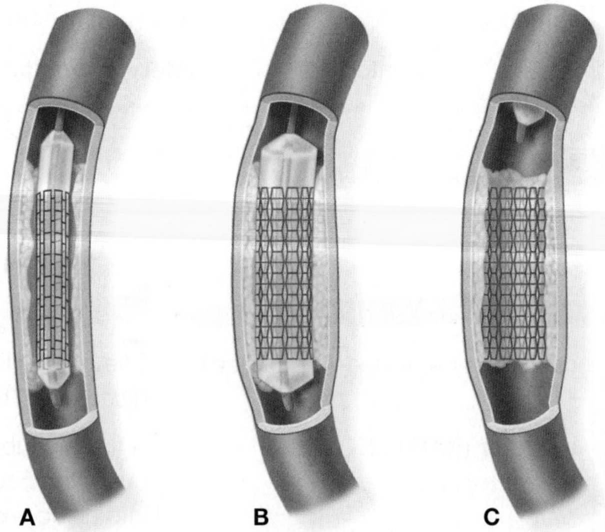

■ **Figure 5.14** The process of placing a stent in a blood vessel. A) A catheter is used to place a collapsed stent next to an atherosclerotic plaque; B) stent is expanded; C) catheter is removed, leaving the expanded stent behind.

Pathology *(continued)*

TERM	DEFINITION
arrhythmia (ah-RITH-mee-ah)	Irregularity in the heartbeat or action. Comes in many different forms; some are not serious, while others are life threatening.
bundle branch block (BBB)	Occurs when the electrical impulse is blocked from traveling down the bundle of His or bundle branches. Results in the ventricles beating at a different rate than the atria. Also called a *heart block.*
cardiac arrest	Complete stopping of heart activity.
cardiomyopathy (car-dee-oh-my-OP-ah-thee)	General term for a disease of the myocardium. Can be caused by alcohol abuse, parasites, viral infection, and congestive heart failure. One of the most common reasons a patient may require a heart transplant.
congenital septal defect (CSD)	A hole, present at birth, in the septum between two heart chambers; results in a mixture of oxygenated and deoxygenated blood. There can be an *atrial septal defect* (ASD) and a *ventricular septal defect* (VSD).
congestive heart failure (CHF) (kon-JESS-tiv)	Pathological condition of the heart in which there is a reduced outflow of blood from the left side of the heart because the left ventricle myocardium has become too weak to efficiently pump blood. Results in weakness, breathlessness, and edema.
coronary artery disease (CAD) (KOR-ah-nair-ee AR-ter-ee dis-EEZ)	Insufficient blood supply to the heart muscle due to an obstruction of one or more coronary arteries. May be caused by atherosclerosis and may cause angina pectoris and myocardial infarction.

Med Term Tip

All types of cardiovascular disease have been the number one killer of Americans since the 19th century. This disease kills more people annually than the next six causes of death combined.

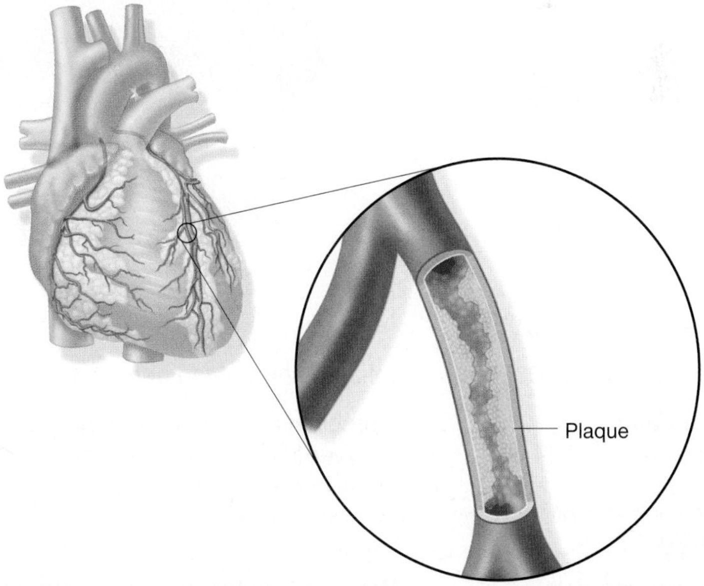

Figure 5.15 Formation of an atherosclerotic plaque within a coronary artery; may lead to coronary artery disease, angina pectoris, and myocardial infarction.

TERM	DEFINITION
endocarditis (en-doh-car-DYE-tis)	Inflammation of the lining membranes of the heart. May be due to bacteria or to an abnormal immunological response. In bacterial endocarditis, the mass of bacteria that forms is referred to as *vegetation.*
fibrillation (fih-brill-AY-shun)	An extremely serious arrhythmia characterized by an abnormal quivering or contraction of heart fibers. When this occurs in the ventricles, cardiac arrest and death can occur. Emergency equipment to defibrillate, or convert the heart to a normal beat, is necessary.

Pathology *(continued)*

TERM	DEFINITION
flutter	An arrhythmia in which the atria beat too rapidly, but in a regular pattern.
heart valve prolapse (PROH-laps)	Condition in which the cusps or flaps of the heart valve are too loose and fail to shut tightly, allowing blood to flow backward through the valve when the heart chamber contracts. Most commonly occurs in the mitral valve, but may affect any of the heart valves.
heart valve stenosis (steh-NOH-sis)	The cusps or flaps of the heart valve are too stiff. Therefore, they are unable to open fully, making it difficult for blood to flow through, or shut tightly, allowing blood to flow backward. This condition may affect any of the heart valves.
myocardial infarction (MI) (my-oh-CAR-dee-al in-FARC-shun)	Condition caused by the partial or complete occlusion or closing of one or more of the coronary arteries. Symptoms include a squeezing pain or heavy pressure in the middle of the chest (angina pectoris). A delay in treatment could result in death. Also referred to as a *heart attack*.

Figure 5.16 External and cross-sectional view of an infarct caused by a myocardial infarction.

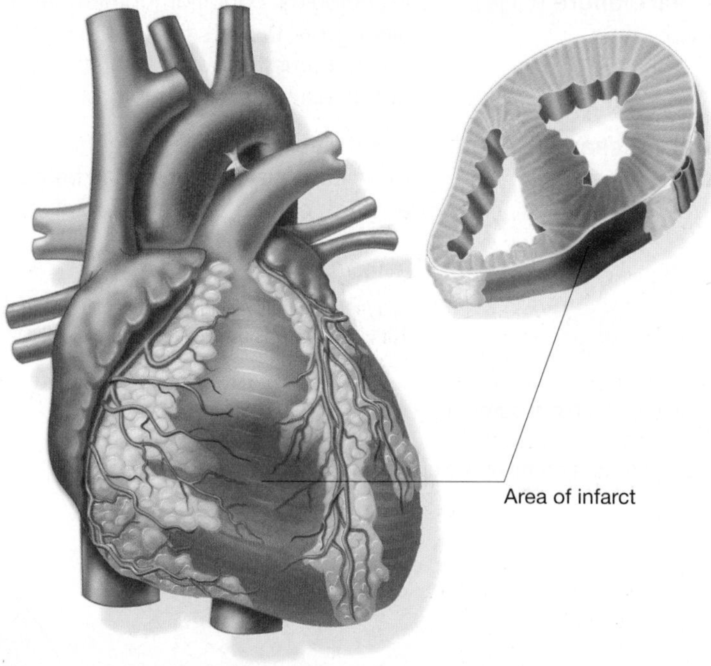

TERM	DEFINITION
myocarditis (my-oh-car-DYE-tis)	Inflammation of the muscle layer of the heart wall.
pericarditis (pair-ih-car-DYE-tis)	Inflammation of the pericardial sac around the heart.
tetralogy of Fallot (teh-TRALL-oh-jee of fal-LOH)	Combination of four congenital anomalies: pulmonary stenosis, an interventricular septal defect, improper placement of the aorta, and hypertrophy of the right ventricle. Needs immediate surgery to correct.
Blood Vessels	
aneurysm (AN-yoo-rizm)	Weakness in the wall of an artery resulting in localized widening of the artery. Although an aneurysm may develop in any artery, common sites include the aorta in the abdomen and the cerebral arteries in the brain (see Figure 5.17).
arteriosclerosis (ar-tee-ree-oh-skleh-ROH-sis)	Thickening, hardening, and loss of elasticity of the walls of the arteries. Most often due to atherosclerosis.

Pathology *(continued)*

TERM	DEFINITION
atherosclerosis (ath-er-oh-skleh-ROH-sis)	The most common form of arteriosclerosis. Caused by the formation of yellowish plaques of cholesterol on the inner walls of arteries (see Figure 5.18 ■).
coarctation of the aorta (CoA) (koh-ark-TAY-shun)	Severe congenital narrowing of the aorta.
embolus (EM-boh-lus)	The obstruction of a blood vessel by a blood clot that has broken off from a thrombus somewhere else in the body and traveled to the point of obstruction. If it occurs in a coronary artery, it may result in a myocardial infarction (see Figure 5.19 ■).
hemorrhoid (HIM-oh-royd)	Varicose veins in the anal region.

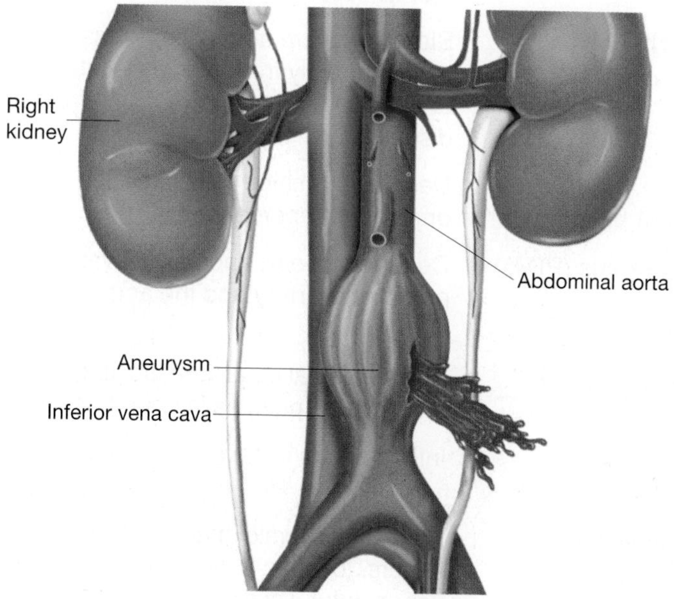

■ **Figure 5.17** Illustration of a large aneurysm in the abdominal aorta which has ruptured.

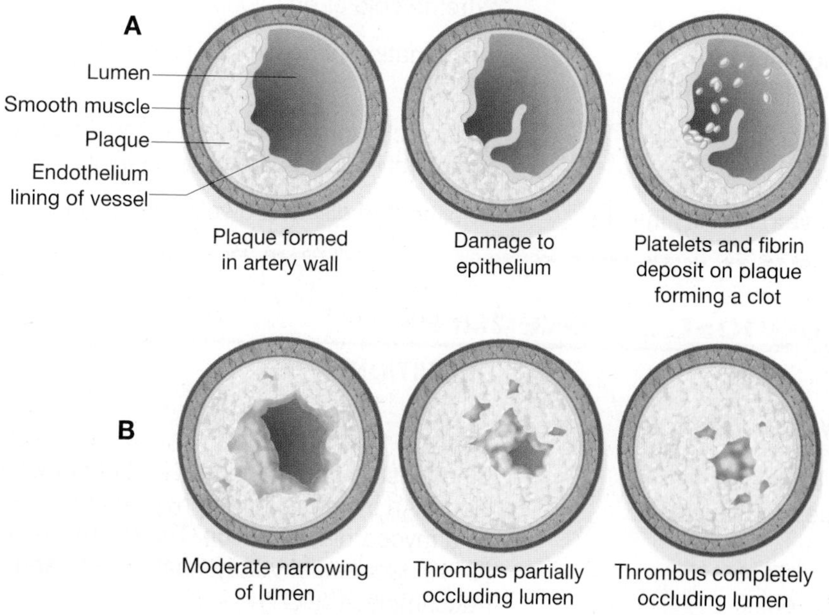

■ **Figure 5.18** Development of an atherosclerotic plaque that progressively narrows the lumen of an artery to the point that a thrombus fully occludes the lumen.

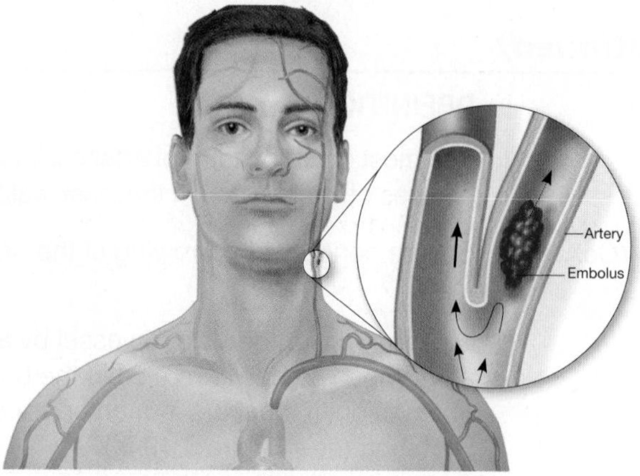

Figure 5.19 Illustration of an embolus floating in an artery. The embolus will eventually lodge in an artery that is smaller than it is, resulting in occlusion of that artery.

Pathology *(continued)*

TERM	DEFINITION
hypertension (HTN) (high-per-TEN-shun)	Blood pressure above the normal range. *Essential* or *primary hypertension* occurs directly from cardiovascular disease. *Secondary hypertension* refers to high blood pressure resulting from another disease such as kidney disease.
hypotension (high-poh-TEN-shun)	Decrease in blood pressure. Can occur in shock, infection, cancer, anemia, or as death approaches.
patent ductus arteriosus (PDA) (PAY-tent DUCK-tus ar-tee-ree-OH-sis)	Congenital heart anomaly in which the fetal connection between the pulmonary artery and the aorta fails to close at birth. This condition requires surgery.
peripheral vascular disease (PVD)	Any abnormal condition affecting blood vessels outside the heart. Symptoms may include pain, pallor, numbness, and loss of circulation and pulses.
polyarteritis (pol-ee-ar-ter-EYE-tis)	Inflammation of several arteries.
Raynaud's phenomenon (ray-NOZ)	Periodic ischemic attacks affecting the extremities of the body, especially the fingers, toes, ears, and nose. The affected extremities become cyanotic and very painful. These attacks are brought on by arterial constriction due to extreme cold or emotional stress.
thrombophlebitis (throm-boh-fleh-BYE-tis)	Inflammation of a vein resulting in the formation of blood clots within the vein.
thrombus (THROM-bus)	A blood clot forming within a blood vessel (see Figure 5.18). May partially or completely occlude the blood vessel.
varicose veins (VAIR-ih-kohs)	Swollen and distended veins, usually in the legs.

Diagnostic Procedures

TERM	DEFINITION
■ ***Clinical Laboratory Tests***	
cardiac enzymes (CAR-dee-ak EN-zyms)	Blood test to determine the level of enzymes specific to heart muscles in the blood. An increase in the enzymes may indicate heart muscle damage such as a myocardial infarction. These enzymes include creatine phosphokinase (CPK), lactate dehydrogenase (LDH), and glutamic oxaloacetic transaminase (GOT).
serum lipoprotein level (SEE-rum lip-oh-PROH-teen)	Blood test to measure the amount of cholesterol and triglycerides in the blood. An indicator of atherosclerosis risk.

Diagnostic Procedures *(continued)*

TERM	DEFINITION
■ ***Diagnostic Imaging***	
angiography (an-jee-OG-rah-fee)	X-rays taken after the injection of an opaque material into a blood vessel. Can be performed on the aorta as an aortic angiogram, on the heart as an angiocardiogram, and on the brain as a cerebral angiogram.
cardiac scan	Patient is given radioactive thallium intravenously and then scanning equipment is used to visualize the heart. It is especially useful in determining myocardial damage.
Doppler ultrasonography (DOP-ler ul-trah-son-OG-rah-fee)	Measurement of sound-wave echoes as they bounce off tissues and organs to produce an image. In this system, used to measure velocity of blood moving through blood vessels to look for blood clots or deep vein thromboses.
echocardiography (ek-oh-car-dee-OG-rah-fee)	Noninvasive diagnostic method using ultrasound to visualize internal cardiac structures. Cardiac valve activity can be evaluated using this method.
venography (vee-NOG-rah-fee)	X-ray of the veins by tracing the venous pulse. May be used to identify a thrombus. Also called *phlebography.*
■ ***Cardiac Function Tests***	
cardiac catheterization (CAR-dee-ak cath-eh-ter-ih-ZAY-shun)	Passage of a thin tube catheter through a blood vessel leading to the heart. Done to detect abnormalities, to collect cardiac blood samples, and to determine the blood pressure within the heart.
electrocardiography (ECG, EKG) (ee-lek-troh-car-dee-OG-rah-fee)	Process of recording the electrical activity of the heart. Useful in the diagnosis of abnormal cardiac rhythm and heart muscle (myocardium) damage.
Holter monitor	Portable ECG monitor worn by a patient for a period of a few hours to a few days to assess the heart and pulse activity as the person goes through the activities of daily living. Used to assess a patient who experiences chest pain and unusual heart activity during exercise and normal activities.
stress testing	Method for evaluating cardiovascular fitness. The patient is placed on a treadmill or a bicycle and then subjected to steadily increasing levels of work. An EKG and oxygen levels are taken while the patient exercises. The test is stopped if abnormalities occur on the EKG. Also called an *exercise test* or a *treadmill test*

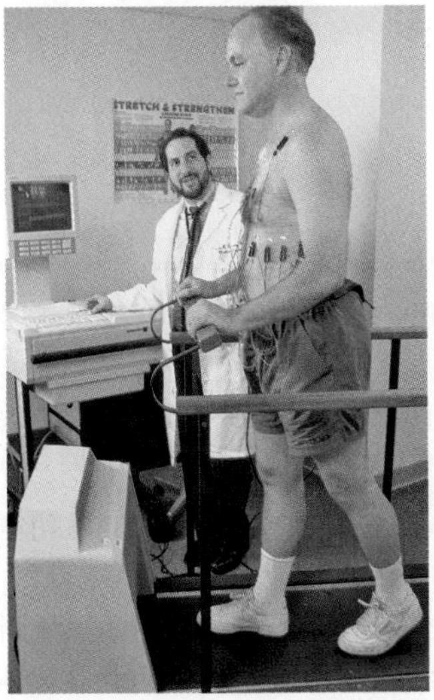

Figure 5.20 Man undergoing a stress test on a treadmill while physician monitors his condition. *(Jonathan Nourok/PhotoEdit Inc.)*

Therapeutic Procedures

TERM	DEFINITION
Medical Procedures	
cardiopulmonary resuscitation (CPR) (car-dee-oh-PULL-mon-air-ee ree-suss-ih-TAY-shun)	Procedure to restore cardiac output and oxygenated air to the lungs for a person in cardiac arrest. A combination of chest compressions (to push blood out of the heart) and artificial respiration (to blow air into the lungs) performed by one or two CPR-trained rescuers.
defibrillation (dee-fib-rih-LAY-shun)	A procedure that converts serious irregular heartbeats, such as fibrillation, by giving electric shocks to the heart using an instrument called a defibrillator. Also called *cardioversion.*
Figure 5.21 An emergency medical technician positions defibrillator paddles on the chest of a supine male patient.	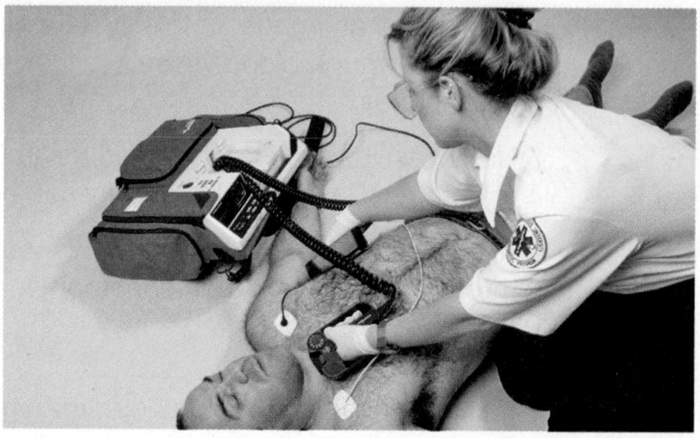
extracorporeal circulation (ECC) (EX-tra-core-poor-EE-al)	During open-heart surgery, the routing of blood to a heart-lung machine so it can be oxygenated and pumped to the rest of the body.
implantable cardioverter-defibrillator (CAR-dee-oh-ver-ter de-FIB-rih-lay-tor)	A device implanted in the heart that delivers an electrical shock to restore a normal heart rhythm. Particularly useful for persons who experience ventricular fibrillation.
pacemaker implantation	Electrical device that substitutes for the natural pacemaker of the heart. It controls the beating of the heart by a series of rhythmic electrical impulses. An external pacemaker has the electrodes on the outside of the body. An internal pacemaker has the electrodes surgically implanted within the chest wall (see Figure 5.22 ■).
thrombolytic therapy (throm-boh-LIT-ik THAIR-ah-pee)	Process in which drugs, such as streptokinase (SK) or tissue-type plasminogen activator (tPA), are injected into a blood vessel to dissolve clots and restore blood flow.
Surgical Procedures	
aneurysmectomy (an-yoo-riz-MEK-toh-mee)	The surgical removal of the sac of an aneurysm.
arterial anastomosis (ar-TEE-ree-all ah-nas-toe-MOE-sis)	The surgical joining together of two arteries. Performed if an artery is severed or if a damaged section of an artery is removed.
coronary artery bypass graft (CABG) (KOR-ah-nair-ee)	Open-heart surgery in which a blood vessel from another location in the body (often a leg vein) is grafted to route blood around a blocked coronary artery.
embolectomy (em-boh-LEK-toh-mee)	The removal of an embolus or clot from a blood vessel.
endarterectomy (end-ar-teh-REK-toh-mee)	Removal of the diseased or damaged inner lining of an artery. Usually performed to remove atherosclerotic plaques.

Therapeutic Procedures *(continued)*

TERM	DEFINITION
heart transplantation	Replacement of a diseased or malfunctioning heart with a donor's heart.
intracoronary artery stent (in-trah-KOR-ah-nair-ee AR-ter-ee)	Placing of a stent within a coronary artery to treat coronary ischemia due to atherosclerosis (see Figure 5.14).
ligation and stripping (lye-GAY-shun)	Surgical treatment for varicose veins. The damaged vein is tied off (ligation) and removed (stripping).
percutaneous transluminal coronary angioplasty (PTCA) (per-kyoo-TAY-nee-us trans-LOO-mih-nal KOR-ah-nair-ee AN-jee-oh-plas-tee)	The method for treating localized coronary artery narrowing. A balloon catheter is inserted through the skin into the coronary artery and inflated to dilate the narrow blood vessel (see Figure 5.23 ■).
valve replacement	Removal of a diseased heart valve and replacement with an artificial valve.

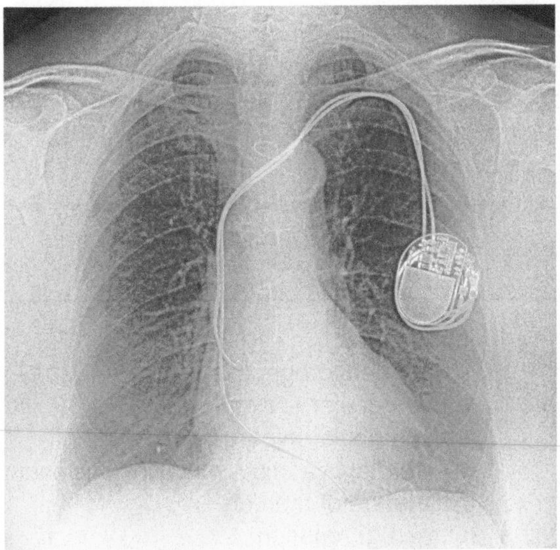

■ **Figure 5.22** Color enhanced X-ray showing a pacemaker implanted in the left side of the chest and the electrode wires running to the heart muscle. *(UHB Trust/Getty Images Inc.—Stone Allstock)*

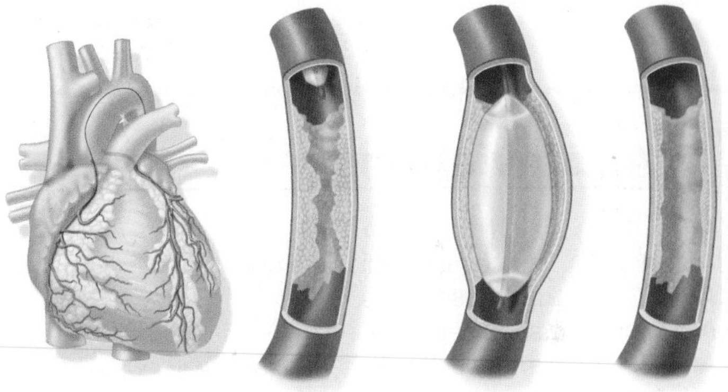

■ **Figure 5.23** Balloon angioplasty: A) deflated balloon catheter is approaching an atherosclerotic plaque; B) plaque is compressed by inflated balloon; C) plaque remains compressed after balloon catheter is removed.

Pharmacology

CLASSIFICATION	ACTION	GENERIC AND BRAND NAMES
ACE inhibitor drugs	Produce vasodilation and decrease blood pressure.	benazepril, Lotensin; catopril, Capoten
antiarrhythmic (an-tye-a-RHYTH-mik)	Reduces or prevents cardiac arrhythmias.	flecainide, Tambocor; ibutilide, Corvert
anticoagulant (an-tye-koh-AG-you-lant)	Prevent blood clot formation.	warfarin sodium, Coumadin, Warfarin
antilipidemic (an-tye-lip-ih-DEM-ik)	Reduces amount of cholesterol and lipids in the bloodstream; treats hyperlipidemia.	atorvastatin, Lipitor; simvastatin, Zocor

Pharmacology *(continued)*

CLASSIFICATION	ACTION	GENERIC AND BRAND NAMES
beta-blocker drugs	Treats hypertension and angina pectoris by lowering the heart rate.	metoprolol, Lopressor; propranolol, Inderal
calcium channel blocker drugs	Treats hypertension, angina pectoris, and congestive heart failure by causing the heart to beat less forcefully and less often.	diltiazem, Cardizem; nifedipine, Procardia
cardiotonic (card-ee-oh-TAHN-ik)	Increases the force of cardiac muscle contraction; treats congestive heart failure.	digoxin, Lanoxin
diuretic (dye-you-RET-ik)	Increases urine production by the kidneys, which works to reduce plasma and therefore blood volume, resulting in lower blood pressure.	furosemide, Lasix
thrombolytic (throm-boh-LIT-ik)	Dissolves existing blood clots.	clopidogrel, Plavix; alteplase, Activase
vasoconstrictor (vaz-oh-kon-STRICK-tor)	Contracts smooth muscle in walls of blood vessels; raises blood pressure.	metaraminol, Aramine
vasodilator (vaz-oh-DYE-late-or)	Relaxes the smooth muscle in the walls of arteries, thereby increasing diameter of the blood vessel. Used for two main purposes: increasing circulation to an ischemic area; reducing blood pressure.	nitroglycerine, Nitro-Dur; isoxsuprine, Vasodilan

Abbreviations

AF	atrial fibrillation
AMI	acute myocardial infarction
AS	arteriosclerosis
ASD	atrial septal defect
ASHD	arteriosclerotic heart disease
AV, A-V	atrioventricular
BBB	bundle branch block (L for left; R for right)
BP	blood pressure
bpm	beats per minute
CABG	coronary artery bypass graft
CAD	coronary artery disease
cath	catheterization
CC	cardiac catheterization, chief complaint
CCU	coronary care unit
CHF	congestive heart failure
CoA	coarctation of the aorta
CP	chest pain
CPK	creatine phosphokinase
CPR	cardiopulmonary resuscitation
CSD	congenital septal defect
CV	cardiovascular
DVT	deep vein thrombosis
ECC	extracorporeal circulation
ECG, EKG	electrocardiogram
ECHO	echocardiogram
GOT	glutamic oxaloacetic transaminase
HTN	hypertension
ICU	intensive care unit
IV	intravenous
LDH	lactate dehydrogenase
LVAD	left ventricular assist device
LVH	left ventricular hypertrophy
MI	myocardial infarction, mitral insufficiency
mm Hg	millimeters of mercury
MR	mitral regurgitation
MS	mitral stenosis

Med Term Tip

Word alert – be careful using the abbreviation *MS* which can mean either "mitral stenosis" or "multiple sclerosis."

MVP	mitral valve prolapse
P	pulse
PAC	premature atrial contraction
PDA	patent ductus arteriosus
PTCA	percutaneous transluminal coronary angioplasty
PVC	premature ventricular contraction
S1	first heart sound
S2	second heart sound
SA, S-A	sinoatrial
SGOT	serum glutamic oxaloacetic transaminase
SK	streptokinase
tPA	tissue-type plasminogen activator
Vfib	ventricular fibrillation
VSD	ventricular septal defect
VT	ventricular tachycardia

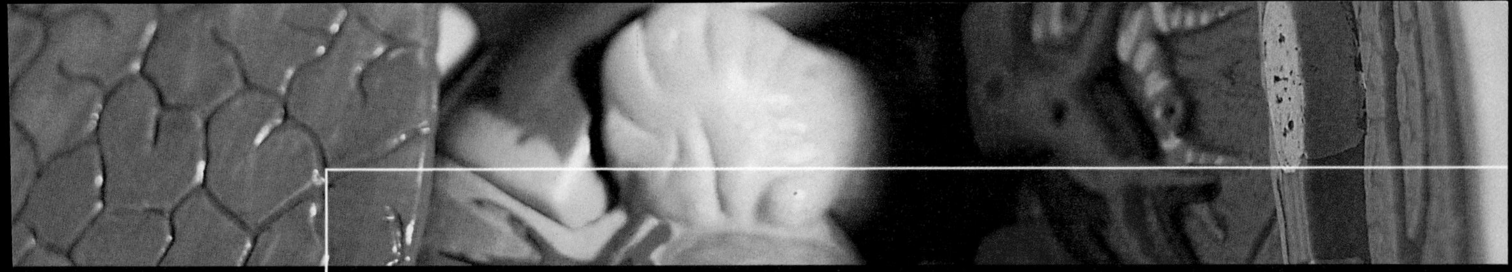

6 Blood and the Lymphatic and Immune Systems

Learning Objectives

Upon completion of this chapter, you will be able to:

- Recognize the combining forms and suffixes introduced in this chapter.
- Gain the ability to pronounce medical terms and major anatomical structures.
- List the major components, structures, and organs of the blood and lymphatic and immune systems and their functions.
- Describe the blood typing systems.
- Discuss immunity, the immune response, and standard precautions.
- Build blood and lymphatic and immune system medical terms from word parts.
- Define vocabulary, pathology, diagnostic, and therapeutic medical terms relating to the blood and lymphatic and immune system.
- Recognize types of medication associated with blood and the lymphatic and immune systems.
- Interpret abbreviations associated with blood and the lymphatic and immune systems.

Section I: Blood at a Glance

Function

Blood transports to all areas of the body gases, nutrients, and wastes either attached to red blood cells or dissolved in the plasma. White blood cells fight infection and disease, and platelets initiate the blood clotting process.

Components

formed elements

- **erythrocytes**
- **platelets**
- **leukocytes**

plasma

Combining Forms

agglutin/o	clumping
bas/o	base
chrom/o	color
coagul/o	clotting
eosin/o	rosy red
erythr/o	red
fibrin/o	fibers, fibrous
granul/o	granules
hem/o	blood
hemat/o	blood
leuk/o	white
morph/o	shape
neutr/o	neutral
phag/o	eat, swallow
sanguin/o	blood
thromb/o	clot

Suffixes

-apheresis	removal, carry away
-cytosis	more than the normal number of cells
-emia	blood condition
-globin	protein
-penia	abnormal decrease, too few
-phil	attracted to
-poiesis	formation
-stasis	standing still

Blood Illustrated

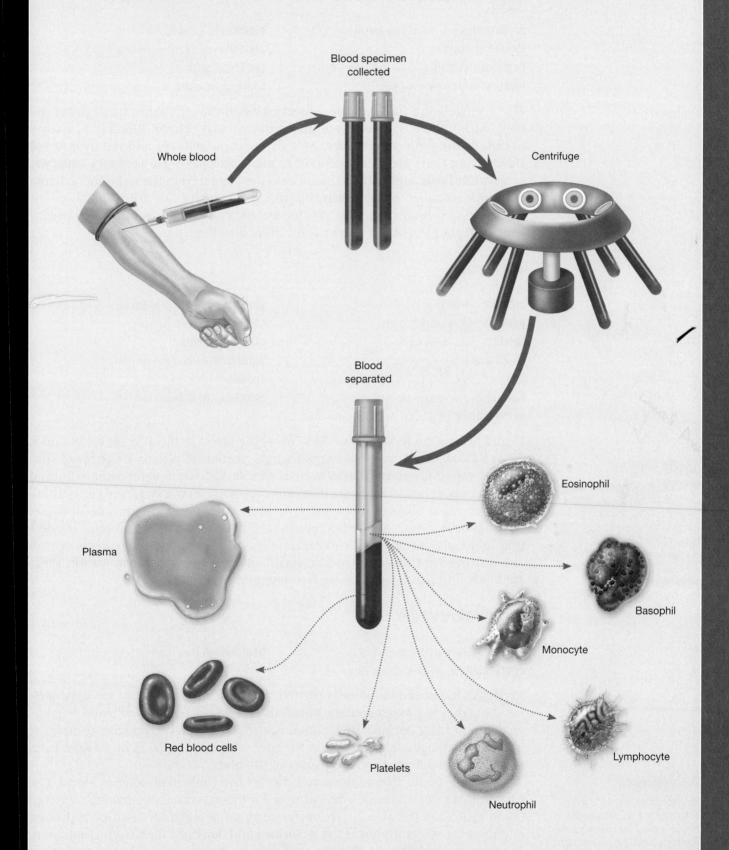

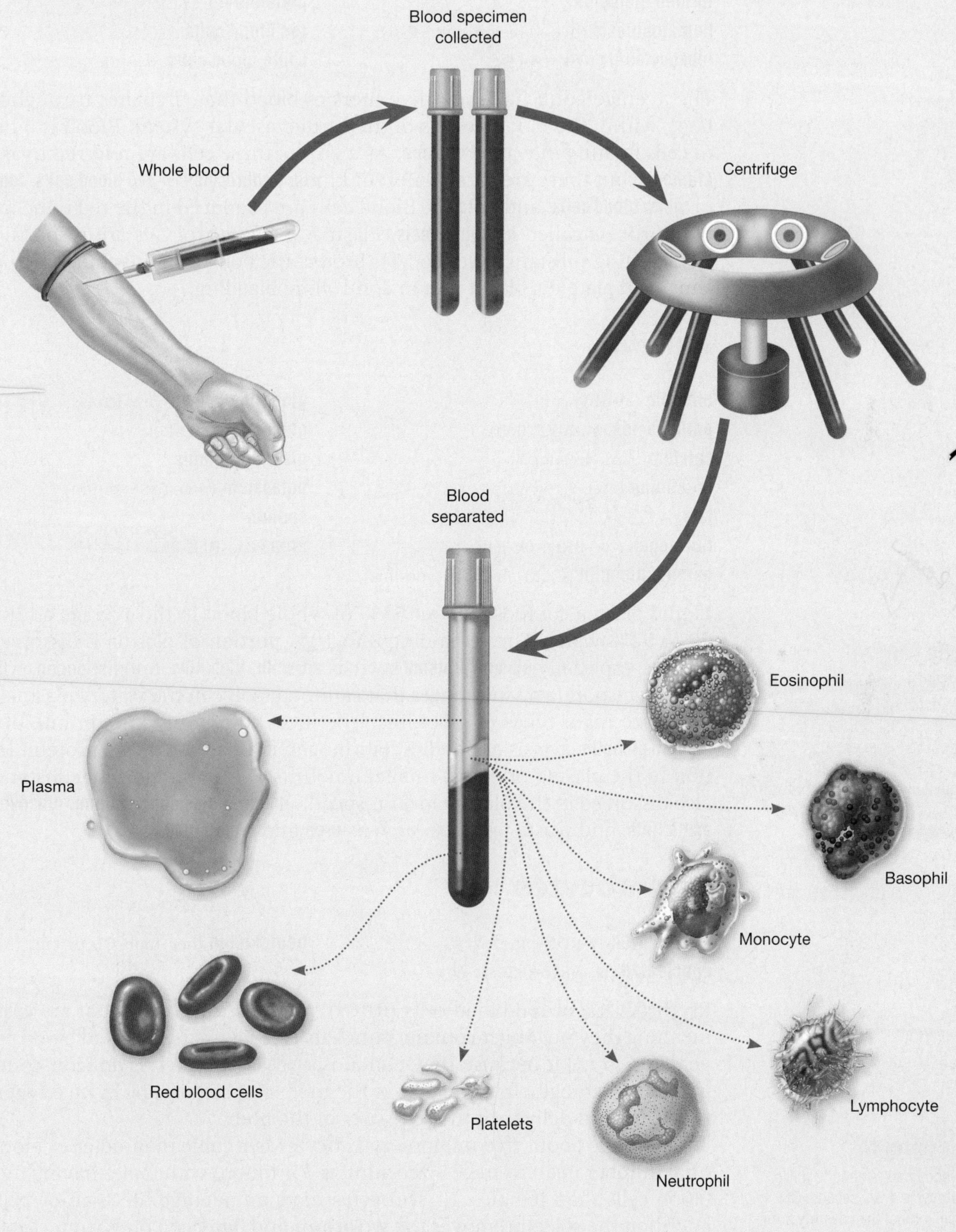

Anatomy and Physiology of Blood

erythrocytes (eh-RITH-roh-sights)   **plasma** (PLAZ-mah)
formed elements   **platelets** (PLAYT lets)
hematopoiesis (hee-mah-toh-poy-EE-sis)   **red blood cells**
leukocytes (LOO-koh-sights)   **white blood cells**

The average adult has about five liters of blood that circulates throughout the body within the blood vessels of the cardiovascular system. Blood is a mixture of cells floating in watery **plasma**. As a group, these cells are referred to as **formed elements**, but there are three different kinds: **erythrocytes** or **red blood cells**, **leukocytes** or **white blood cells**, and **platelets**. Blood cells are produced in the red bone marrow by a process called **hematopoiesis**. Plasma and erythrocytes are responsible for transporting substances, leukocytes protect the body from invading microorganisms, and platelets play a role in controlling bleeding.

Plasma

albumin (al-BEW-min)   **globulins** (GLOB-yew-lenz)
amino acids (ah-MEE-noh)   **glucose** (GLOO-kohs)
calcium (KAL-see-um)   **plasma proteins**
creatinine (kree-AT-in-in)   **potassium** (poh-TASS-ee-um)
fats   **sodium**
fibrinogen (fye-BRIN-oh-jen)   **urea** (yoo-REE-ah)
gamma globulin (GAM-ah GLOB-yoo-lin)

Liquid plasma composes about 55% of whole blood in the average adult and is 90 to 92% water. The remaining 8 to 10% portion of plasma is dissolved substances, especially **plasma proteins** such as **albumin**, **globulins**, and **fibrinogen**. Albumin helps transport fatty substances that cannot dissolve in the watery plasma. There are three main types of globulins. The most commonly known one of these, **gamma globulin**, acts as antibodies. Fibrinogen is a blood-clotting protein. In addition to the plasma proteins, smaller amounts of other important substances are also dissolved in the plasma for transport: **calcium**, **potassium**, **sodium**, **glucose**, **amino acids**, **fats**, and waste products such as **urea** and **creatinine**.

Erythrocytes

bilirubin (bil-ly-ROO-bin)   **hemoglobin** (hee-moh-GLOH-bin)
enucleated (ee-NEW-klee-ate-ed)

Erythrocytes, or red blood cells (RBCs), are biconcave disks that are **enucleated**, meaning they no longer contain a nucleus (see Figure 6.1 ■). Red blood cells appear red in color because they contain **hemoglobin**, which is an iron-containing pigment. Hemoglobin is the part of the red blood cell that picks up oxygen from the lungs and delivers it to the tissues of the body.

There are about five million erythrocytes per cubic millimeter of blood. The total number in an average-sized adult is 35 trillion, with males having more red blood cells than females. Erythrocytes have an average life span of 120 days, and then the spleen removes the worn-out and damaged ones from circulation. Much of the red blood cell, such as the iron, can be reused, but one portion, **bilirubin**, is a waste product disposed of by the liver.

Med Term Tip

Word watch—plasma and *serum* are not interchangeable words. Serum is plasma, but with fibrinogen removed or inactivated. This way it can be handled and tested without it clotting. The term *serum* is also sometimes used to mean antiserum or antitoxin.

Question #4 Review

Med Term Tip

Your body makes about 2 million erythrocytes every second. Of course, it must then destroy 2 million every second to maintain a relatively constant 30 trillion red blood cells.

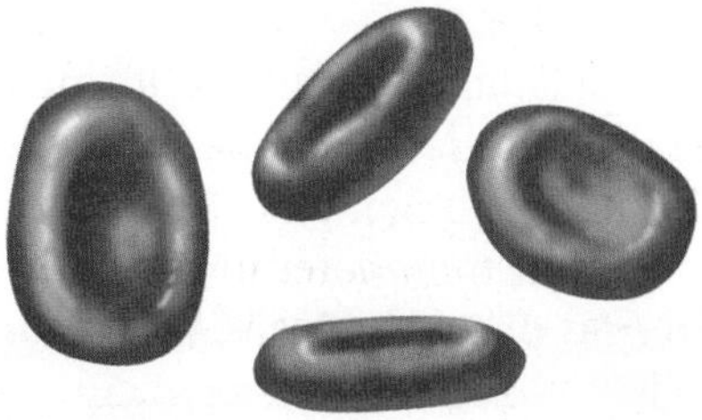

Figure 6.1 The biconcave disk shape of erythrocytes (red blood cells).

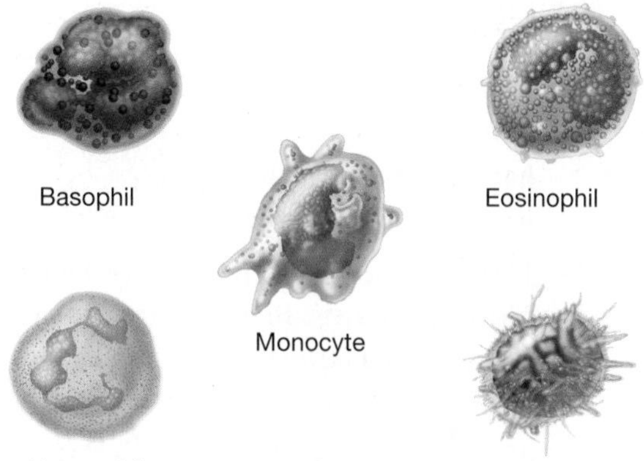

Figure 6.2 The five different types of leukocytes (white blood cells).

Leukocytes

agranulocytes (ah-GRAN-yew-loh-sights)
granulocytes (GRAN-yew-loh-sights)
pathogens (PATH-oh-ginz)

Leukocytes, also referred to as white blood cells (WBCs), provide protection against the invasion of **pathogens** such as bacteria, viruses, and other foreign material. In general, white blood cells have a spherical shape with a large nucleus, and there are about 8,000 per cubic millimeter of blood (see Figure 6.2 ■). There are five different types of white blood cells, each with its own strategy for protecting the body. The five can be subdivided into two categories: **granulocytes** (with granules in the cytoplasm) and **agranulocytes** (without granules in the cytoplasm). The name and function of each type is presented in Table 6.1 ■.

Med Term Tip

A ***phagocyte*** is a cell that has the ability to ingest (eat) and digest bacteria and other foreign particles. This process, ***phagocytosis***, is critical for the control of bacteria within the body.

Table 6.1 Leukocyte Classification

LEUKOCYTE	FUNCTION
Granulocytes	
Basophils (basos) (BAY-soh-fillz)	Release histamine and heparin to damaged tissues
Eosinophils (eosins) (ee-oh-SIN-oh-fillz)	Destroy parasites and increase during allergic reactions
Neutrophils (NOO-troh-fillz)	Important for phagocytosis; most numerous of the leukocytes
Agranulocytes	
Monocytes (monos) (MON-oh-sights)	Important for phagocytosis
Lymphocytes (lymphs) (LIM-foh-sights)	Plays several different roles in immune response

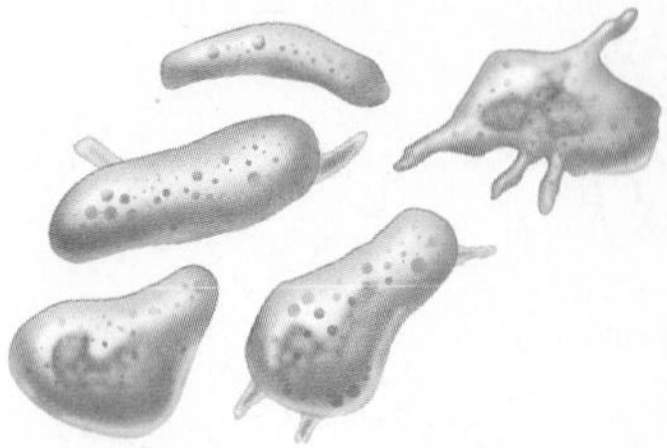

■ **Figure 6.3** Platelet structure.

Platelets

agglutinate (ah-GLOO-tih-nayt)
fibrin (FYE-brin)
hemostasis (hee-moh-STAY-sis)
prothrombin (proh-THROM-bin)
thrombin (THROM-bin)
thrombocyte (THROM-boh-sight)
thromboplastin (throm-boh-PLAS-tin)

Platelet, the modern term for **thrombocyte**, refers to the smallest of all the formed blood elements. Platelets are not whole cells, but rather are formed when the cytoplasm of a large precursor cell shatters into small plate-like fragments (see Figure 6.3 ■). There are between 200,000 and 300,000 per cubic millimeter in the body.

Platelets play a critical part in the blood-clotting process or **hemostasis**. They **agglutinate** or clump together into small clusters when a blood vessel is cut or damaged. Platelets also release a substance called **thromboplastin**, which, in the presence of calcium, reacts with **prothrombin**, a clotting protein in the blood, to form **thrombin**. Then thrombin, in turn, works to convert fibrinogen to **fibrin**, which eventually becomes the meshlike blood clot.

Blood Typing

ABO system
blood typing
Rh factor

Each person's blood is different due to the presence of antigens or markers on the surface of erythrocytes. Before a person receives a blood transfusion, it is important to do **blood typing.** This laboratory test determines if the donated blood is compatible with the recipient's blood. There are many different subgroups of blood markers, but the two most important ones are the **ABO system** and **Rh factor.**

ABO System

type A
type AB
type B
type O
universal donor
universal recipient

In the ABO blood system there are two possible red blood cell markers, A and B. A marker is one method by which cells identify themselves. A person with an A marker is said to have **type A** blood. Type A blood produces anti-B antibodies that will attack type B blood. The presence of a B marker gives **type B** blood and anti-A antibodies (that will attack type A blood). If both markers are present, the blood is **type AB** and does not contain any antibodies. Therefore, type AB blood will not attack any other blood type. The absence of either an A or a B marker results in **type O** blood, which contains both anti-A and anti-B antibodies. Type O blood will attack all other blood types, A, B, and AB. For further information on antibodies, refer to the lymphatic section later in this chapter.

Because type O blood does not have either marker A or B, it will not react with anti-A or anti-B antibodies. For this reason, a person with type O blood is referred to as a **universal donor.** In extreme cases, type O blood may be given to a person with any of the other blood types. Similarly, type AB blood is the **universal recipient**. A person with type AB blood has no antibodies against the other blood types and, therefore, in extreme cases, can receive any type of blood.

Rh Factor

Rh-negative
Rh-positive

Rh factor is not as difficult to understand as the ABO system. A person with the Rh factor on his or her red blood cells is said to be **Rh-positive** (Rh+). Since this person has the factor, he or she will not make anti-Rh antibodies. A person without the Rh factor is **Rh-negative** (Rh–) and will produce anti-Rh antibodies. Therefore, an Rh+ person may receive both an Rh+ and an Rh– transfusion, but an Rh– person can receive only Rh– blood.

Word Building

The following list contains examples of medical terms built directly from word parts. Their definitions can be determined by a straightforward translation of the word parts.

COMBINING FORM	COMBINED WITH	MEDICAL TERM	DEFINITION
fibrin/o	-gen	**fibrinogen** (fye-BRIN-oh-jen)	fiber producing
	-lysis	**fibrinolysis** (fye-brin-oh-LYE-sis)	destruction of fibers
	-ous	**fibrinous** (fye-brin-us)	pertaining to fibers
hem/o	-globin	**hemoglobin** (hee-moh-GLOH-bin)	blood protein
	-lysis	**hemolysis** (hee-MALL-ih-sis)	blood destruction
	-lytic	**hemolytic** (hee-moh-LIH-tik)	blood destruction
	-rrhage	**hemorrhage** (HEM-er-rij)	rapid flow of blood
hemat/o	-ologist	**hematologist** (hee-mah-TALL-oh-jist)	blood specialist
	-ic	**hematic** (hee-MAT-ik)	pertaining to blood
sanguin/o	-ous	**sanguinous** (SANG-gwih-nus)	pertaining to blood
SUFFIX	**COMBINED WITH**	**MEDICAL TERM**	**DEFINITION**
-cyte	erythr/o	**erythrocyte** (eh-RITH-roh-sight)	red cell
	leuk/o	**leukocyte** (LOO-koh-sight)	white cell
	thromb/o	**thrombocyte** (THROM-boh-sight)	clotting cell
	granul/o	**granulocyte** (GRAN-yew-loh-sight)	granular cell
	a- granul/o	**agranulocyte** (ah-GRAN-yew-loh-sight)	nongranular cell
-cytosis	erythr/o	**erythrocytosis** (ee-RITH-row-sigh-toe-sis)	too many red cells
	leuk/o	**leukocytosis** (LOO-koh-sigh-toh-sis)	too many white cells
	thromb/o	**thrombocytosis** (throm-boh-sigh-TOH-sis)	too many clotting cells
-penia	erythr/o	**erythropenia** (ee-RITH-row-pen-ee-ah)	too few red (cells)
	leuk/o	**leukopenia** (LOO-koh-pen-ee-ah)	too few white (cells)
	thromb/o	**thrombopenia** (THROM-boh-pen-ee-ah)	too few clotting (cells)
	pan- cyt/o	**pancytopenia** (pan-sigh-toe-PEN-ee-ah)	too few of all cells
-poiesis	erythr/o	**erythropoiesis** (eh-rith-roh-poy-EE-sis)	red (cell) producing
	hemat/o	**hematopoiesis** (hee-mah-toh-poy-EE-sis)	blood producing
	leuk/o	**leukopoiesis** (loo-koh-poy-EE-sis)	white (cell) producing
	thromb/o	**thrombopoiesis** (throm-boh-poy-EE-sis)	clotting (cell) producing

Vocabulary

TERM	DEFINITION
blood clot	The hard collection of fibrin, blood cells, and tissue debris that is the end result of hemostasis or the blood-clotting process.

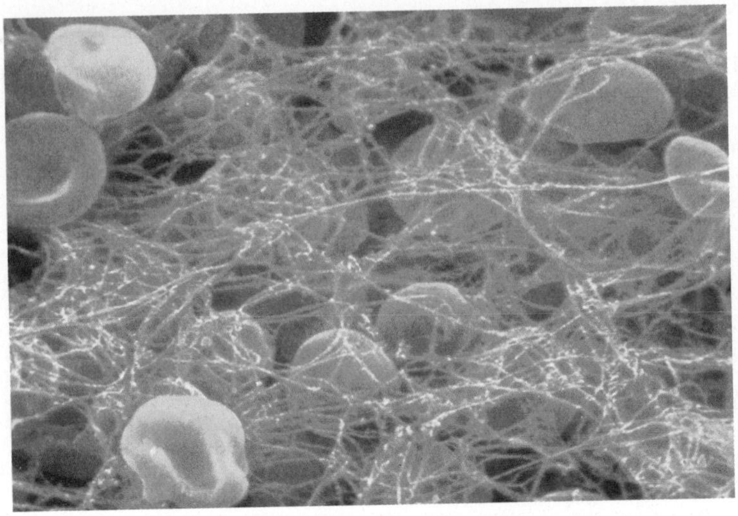

Figure 6.4 Electronmicrograph showing a blood clot. It is composed of fibrin, red blood cells, and tissue debris.

TERM	DEFINITION
coagulate (koh-ag-YOO-late)	To convert from a liquid to a gel or solid, as in blood coagulation.
dyscrasia (dis-CRAZ-ee-ah)	A general term indicating the presence of a disease affecting blood.
hematology (hee-mah-TALL-oh-jee)	The branch of medicine that specializes in treating diseases and conditions of the blood. Physician is a *hematologist*.
hematoma (hee-mah-TOH-mah)	The collection of blood under the skin as the result of blood escaping into the tissue from damaged blood vessels. Commonly referred to as a *bruise*. **Med Term Tip** Word watch—the term *hematoma* is confusing. Its simple translation is "blood tumor." However, it is used to refer to blood that has leaked out of a blood vessel and pooled in the tissues.
hemostasis (hee-moh-STAY-sis)	To stop bleeding or the stagnation of blood flow through the tissues.
packed cells	A transfusion of only the formed elements and without plasma.
whole blood	Refers to the mixture of both plasma and formed elements.

Pathology

TERM	DEFINITION
■ ***Blood***	
hemophilia (hee-moh-FILL-ee-ah)	Hereditary blood disease in which blood-clotting time is prolonged due to a lack of one vital clotting factor. It is transmitted by a sex-linked trait from females to males, appearing almost exclusively in males.
hyperlipidemia (HYE-per-lip-id-ee-mee-ah)	Condition of having too high a level of lipids such as cholesterol in the bloodstream. A risk factor for developing atherosclerosis and coronary artery disease.

Pathology *(continued)*

TERM	DEFINITION
septicemia (sep-tih-SEE-mee-ah)	Having bacteria or their toxins in the bloodstream. *Sepsis* is a term that means putrefaction. Commonly referred to as *blood poisoning*.
■ ***Erythrocytes***	
anemia (an-NEE-mee-ah)	A large group of conditions characterized by a reduction in the number of red blood cells or the amount of hemoglobin in the blood; results in less oxygen reaching the tissues.
aplastic anemia (a-PLAS-tik an-NEE-mee-ah)	Severe form of anemia that develops as a consequence of loss of functioning red bone marrow. Results in a decrease in the number of all the formed elements. Treatment may eventually require a bone marrow transplant.
hemolytic anemia (hee-moh-LIT-ik an-NEE-mee-ah)	An anemia that develops as the result of the excessive loss of erythrocytes.
hemolytic reaction (hee-moh-LIT-ik)	The destruction of a patient's erythrocytes that occurs when receiving a transfusion of an incompatible blood type. Also called a *transfusion reaction*.
hypochromic anemia (hi-poe-CHROME-ik an-NEE-mee-ah)	Anemia resulting from having insufficient hemoglobin in the erythrocytes. Named because the hemoglobin molecule is responsible for the dark red color of the erythrocytes.
iron-deficiency anemia	Anemia that results from having insufficient iron to manufacture hemoglobin.
pernicious anemia (PA) (per-NISH-us an-NEE-mee-ah)	Anemia associated with insufficient absorption of vitamin B_{12} by the digestive system. Vitamin B_{12} is necessary for erythrocyte production.
polycythemia vera (pol-ee-sigh-THEE-mee-ah VAIR-rah)	Production of too many red blood cells by the bone marrow. Blood becomes too thick to easily flow through the blood vessels.
sickle cell anemia	A genetic disorder in which erythrocytes take on an abnormal curved or "sickle" shape. These cells are fragile and are easily damaged, leading to a hemolytic anemia.

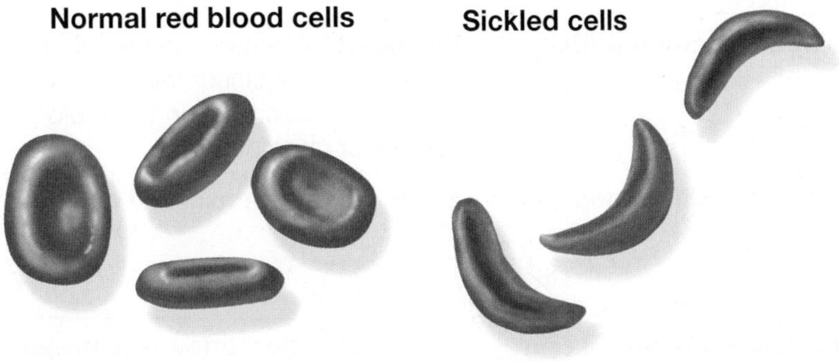

■ **Figure 6.5** Comparison of normal-shaped erythrocytes and the abnormal sickle shape noted in patients with sickle cell anemia.

TERM	DEFINITION
thalassemia (thal-ah-SEE-mee-ah)	A genetic disorder in which the body is unable to make functioning hemoglobin, resulting in anemia.
■ ***Leukocytes***	
leukemia (loo-KEE-mee-ah)	Cancer of the white blood cell-forming red bone marrow resulting in a large number of abnormal and immature white blood cells circulating in the blood.

Diagnostic Procedures

TERM	DEFINITION
■ ***Clinical Laboratory Tests***	
blood culture and sensitivity (C&S)	Sample of blood is incubated in the laboratory to check for bacterial growth. If bacteria are present, they are identified and tested to determine which antibiotics they are sensitive to.
complete blood count (CBC)	Combination of blood tests including: red blood cell count (RBC), white blood cell count (WBC), hemoglobin (Hgb), hematocrit (Hct), white blood cell differential, and platelet count.
erythrocyte sedimentation rate (ESR, sed rate) (eh-RITH-roh-sight sed-ih-men-TAY-shun)	Blood test to determine the rate at which mature red blood cells settle out of the blood after the addition of an anticoagulant. This is an indicator of the presence of an inflammatory disease.
hematocrit (HCT, Hct, crit) (hee-MAT-oh-krit)	Blood test to measure the volume of red blood cells (erythrocytes) within the total volume of blood.
hemoglobin (Hgb, hb) (hee-moh-GLOH-bin)	A blood test to measure the amount of hemoglobin present in a given volume of blood.
platelet count (PLAYT-let)	Blood test to determine the number of platelets in a given volume of blood.
prothrombin time (Pro time, PT) (proh-THROM-bin)	A measure of the blood's coagulation abilities by measuring how long it takes for a clot to form after prothrombin has been activated.
red blood cell count (RBC)	Blood test to determine the number of erythrocytes in a volume of blood. A decrease in red blood cells may indicate anemia; an increase may indicate polycythemia.
red blood cell morphology	Examination of a specimen of blood for abnormalities in the shape (morphology) of the erythrocytes. Used to determine diseases like sickle cell anemia.
sequential multiple analyzer computer (SMAC)	Machine for doing multiple blood chemistry tests automatically.
white blood cell count (WBC)	Blood test to measure the number of leukocytes in a volume of blood. An increase may indicate the presence of infection or a disease such as leukemia. A decrease in white blood cells may be caused by radiation therapy or chemotherapy.
white blood cell differential (diff) (diff-er-EN-shal)	Blood test to determine the number of each variety of leukocytes.
■ ***Medical Procedures***	
bone marrow aspiration (as-pih-RAY-shun)	Sample of bone marrow is removed by aspiration with a needle and examined for diseases such as leukemia or aplastic anemia.

Diagnostic Procedures *(continued)*

TERM	DEFINITION
phlebotomy (fleh-BOT-oh-me)	Incision into a vein in order to remove blood for a diagnostic test. Also called *venipuncture.*

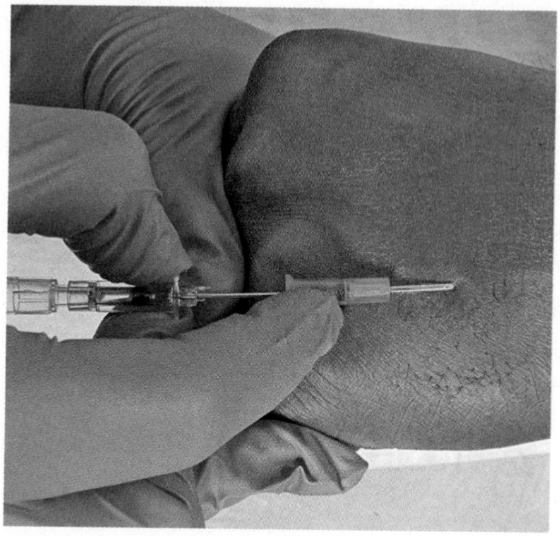

Figure 6.6 Phlebotomist using a needle to withdraw blood.

Therapeutic Procedures

TERM	DEFINITION
Medical Procedures	
autologous transfusion (aw-TALL-oh-gus trans-FYOO-zhun)	Procedure for collecting and storing a patient's own blood several weeks prior to the actual need. It can then be used to replace blood lost during a surgical procedure.
blood transfusion (trans-FYOO-zhun)	Artificial transfer of blood into the bloodstream.

Med Term Tip

Before a patient receives a blood transfusion, the laboratory performs a ***type and crossmatch.*** This test first double checks the blood type of both the donor's and recipient's blood. Then a crossmatch is performed. This process mixes together small samples of both bloods and observes the mixture for adverse reactions.

TERM	DEFINITION
bone marrow transplant (BMT)	Patient receives red bone marrow from a donor after the patient's own bone marrow has been destroyed by radiation or chemotherapy.
homologous transfusion (hoh-MALL-oh-gus trans-FYOO-zhun)	Replacement of blood by transfusion of blood received from another person.
plasmapheresis (plaz-mah-fah-REE-sis)	Method of removing plasma from the body without depleting the formed elements. Whole blood is removed and the cells and plasma are separated. The cells are returned to the patient along with a donor plasma transfusion.

Pharmacology

CLASSIFICATION	ACTION	GENERIC AND BRAND NAMES
anticoagulant (an-tih-koh-AG-yoo-lant)	Substance that prevents blood clot formation. Commonly referred to as *blood thinners*.	heparin, HepLock; warfarin, coumadin
antihemorrhagic (an-tih-hem-er-RAJ-ik)	Substance that prevents or stops hemorrhaging; a *hemostatic agent*.	aminocaproic acid, Amicar; vitamin K
antiplatelet agents (an-tih-PLATE-let)	Substance that interferes with the action of platelets. Prolongs bleeding time. Used to prevent heart attacks and strokes.	clopidogrel, Plavix; ticlopidine, Ticlid
hematinic (hee-mah-TIN-ik)	Substance that increases the number of erythrocytes or the amount of hemoglobin in the blood.	epoetin alfa, Procrit; darbepoetin alfa, Aranesp
thrombolytic (throm-boh-LIT-ik)	Term meaning able to dissolve existing blood clots.	alteplase, Activase; streptokinase, Streptase

Abbreviations

ALL	acute lymphocytic leukemia	**lymphs**	lymphocytes
AML	acute myelogenous leukemia	**monos**	monocytes
basos	basophils	**PA**	pernicious anemia
BMT	bone marrow transplant	**PCV**	packed cell volume
CBC	complete blood count	**PMN, polys**	polymorphonuclear neutrophil
CLL	chronic lymphocytic leukemia	**PT, pro-time**	prothrombin time
CML	chronic myelogenous leukemia	**RBC**	red blood cell
diff	differential	**Rh+**	Rh-positive
eosins, eos	eosinophils	**Rh–**	Rh-negative
ESR, SR, sed rate	erythrocyte sedimentation rate	**segs**	segmented neutrophils
HCT, Hct, crit	hematocrit	**SMAC**	sequential multiple analyzer computer
Hgb, Hb, HGB	hemoglobin	**WBC**	white blood cell

Section II: The Lymphatic and Immune Systems at a Glance

Function

The lymphatic system consists of a network of lymph vessels that pick up excess tissue fluid, cleanse it, and return it to the circulatory system. It also picks up fats that have been absorbed by the digestive system. The immune system fights disease and infections.

Organs

lymph nodes
lymphatic vessels
spleen
thymus gland
tonsils

Combining Forms

adenoid/o	adenoids
immun/o	protection
lymph/o	lymph
lymphaden/o	lymph node
lymphangi/o	lymph vessel
path/o	disease
splen/o	spleen
thym/o	thymus
tonsill/o	tonsils
tox/o	poison

Suffixes Relating

-globulin	protein

The Lymphatic and Immune Systems Illustrated

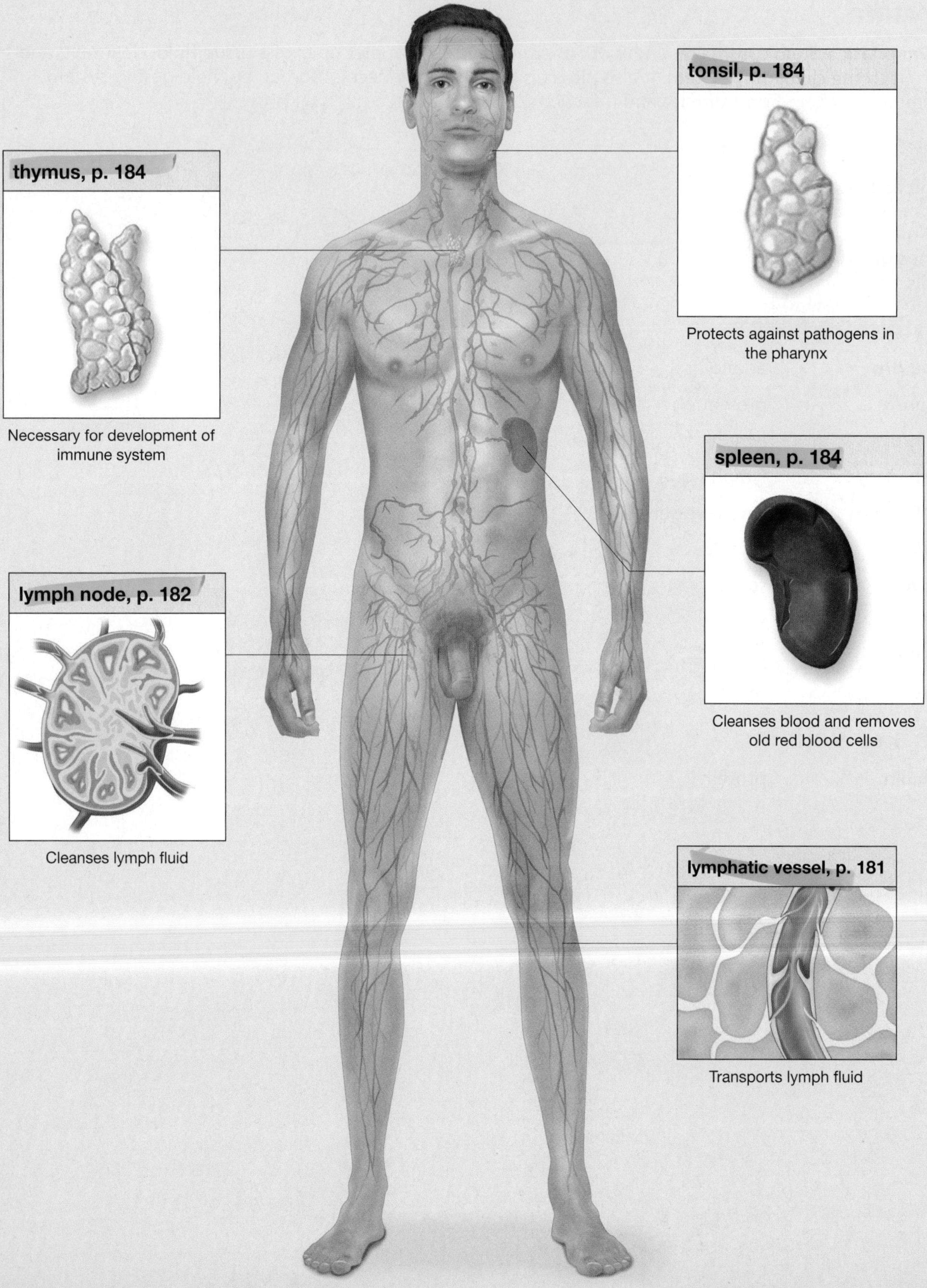

Anatomy and Physiology of the Lymphatic and Immune Systems

lacteals (lack-TEE-als)
lymph (LIMF)
lymph nodes
lymphatic vessels (lim-FAT-ik)
spleen
thymus gland (THIGH-mus)
tonsils (TON-sulls)

The lymphatic system consists of a network of **lymphatic vessels**, **lymph nodes**, the **spleen**, the **thymus gland**, and the **tonsils**. These organs perform several quite diverse functions for the body. First, they collect excess tissue fluid throughout the body and return it to the circulatory system. The fluid, once it is inside a lymphatic vessel, is referred to as **lymph**. Lymph vessels around the small intestines, called **lacteals**, are able to pick up absorbed fats for transport. Additionally, the lymphatic system works with the immune system to form the groups of cells, tissues, organs, and molecules that serve as the body's primary defense against the invasion of pathogens. These systems work together defending the body against foreign invaders and substances, as well as removing our own cells that have become diseased.

Lymphatic Vessels

lymphatic capillaries (CAP-ih-lair-eez)
lymphatic ducts
right lymphatic duct
thoracic duct
valves

The lymphatic vessels form an extensive network of vessels throughout the entire body. However, unlike the circulatory system, these vessels are not in a closed loop. Instead, they serve as one-way pipes conducting lymph from the tissues toward the thoracic cavity (see Figure 6.7 ■). These vessels begin as very

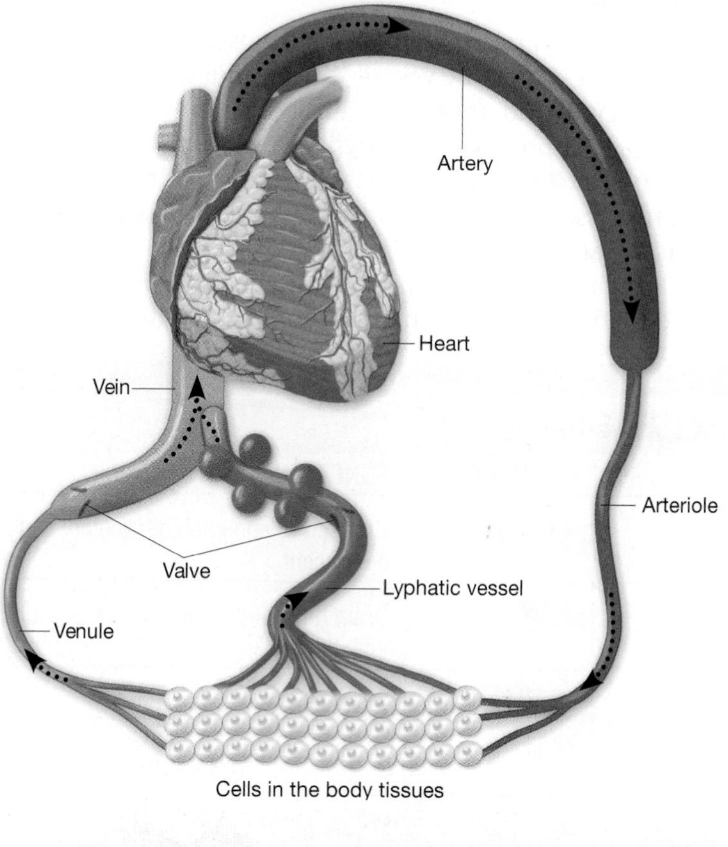

■ **Figure 6.7** Lymphatic vessels (green) pick up excess tissue fluid, purify it in lymph nodes, and return it to the circulatory system.

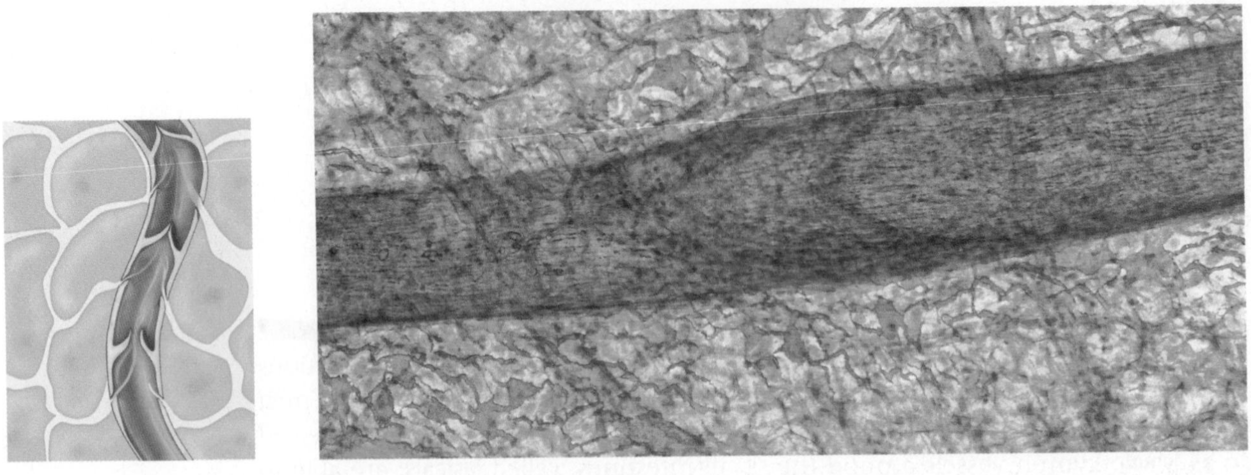

■ **Figure 6.8** A) Lymphatic vessel with valves within tissue cells; B) Photomicrograph of lymphatic vessel with valve clearly visible. *(Michael Abbey/Photo Researchers, Inc.)*

small **lymphatic capillaries** in the tissues. Excessive tissue fluid enters these capillaries to begin the trip back to the circulatory system. The capillaries merge into larger lymphatic vessels. This is a very low pressure system, so these vessels have **valves** along their length to ensure that lymph can only move forward toward the thoracic cavity (see Figure 6.8 ■). These vessels finally drain into one of two large **lymphatic ducts**, the **right lymphatic duct** or the **thoracic duct**. The smaller right lymphatic duct drains the right arm and the right side of the neck and chest. This duct empties lymph into the right subclavian vein. The larger thoracic duct drains lymph from the rest of the body and empties into the left subclavian vein (see Figure 6.9 ■).

Med Term Tip

The term *capillary* is also used to describe the minute blood vessels within the circulatory system. This is one of several general medical terms, such as valves, cilia, and hair that are used in several systems.

Lymph Nodes

lymph glands

Lymph nodes are small organs composed of lymphatic tissue located along the route of the lymphatic vessels. These nodes, also referred to as **lymph glands**, house lymphocytes and antibodies and therefore work to remove pathogens and cell debris as lymph passes through them on its way back to the thoracic cavity (see Figure 6.10 ■). Lymph nodes also serve to trap and destroy cells from cancerous tumors. Although found throughout the body, lymph nodes are particularly concentrated in several regions. For example, lymph nodes concentrated in the neck region drain lymph from the head. See Table 6.2 ■ and Figure 6.9 for a description of some of the most important sites for lymph nodes.

Med Term Tip

In surgical procedures to remove a malignancy from an organ, such as a breast, the adjacent lymph nodes are also tested for cancer. If cancerous cells are found in the tested lymph nodes, the disease is said to have spread or ***metastasized***. Tumor cells may then spread to other parts of the body by means of the lymphatic system.

Table 6.2 Sites for Lymph Nodes

NAME	LOCATION	FUNCTION
Axillary (AK-sih-lair-ee)	Armpits	Drain arms and shoulder region; cancer cells from breasts may be present
Cervical (SER-vih-kal)	Neck	Drain head and neck; may be enlarged during upper respiratory infections
Inguinal (ING-gwih-nal)	Groin	Drain legs and lower pelvis
Mediastinal (mee-dee-ass-TYE-nal)	Chest	Drain chest cavity

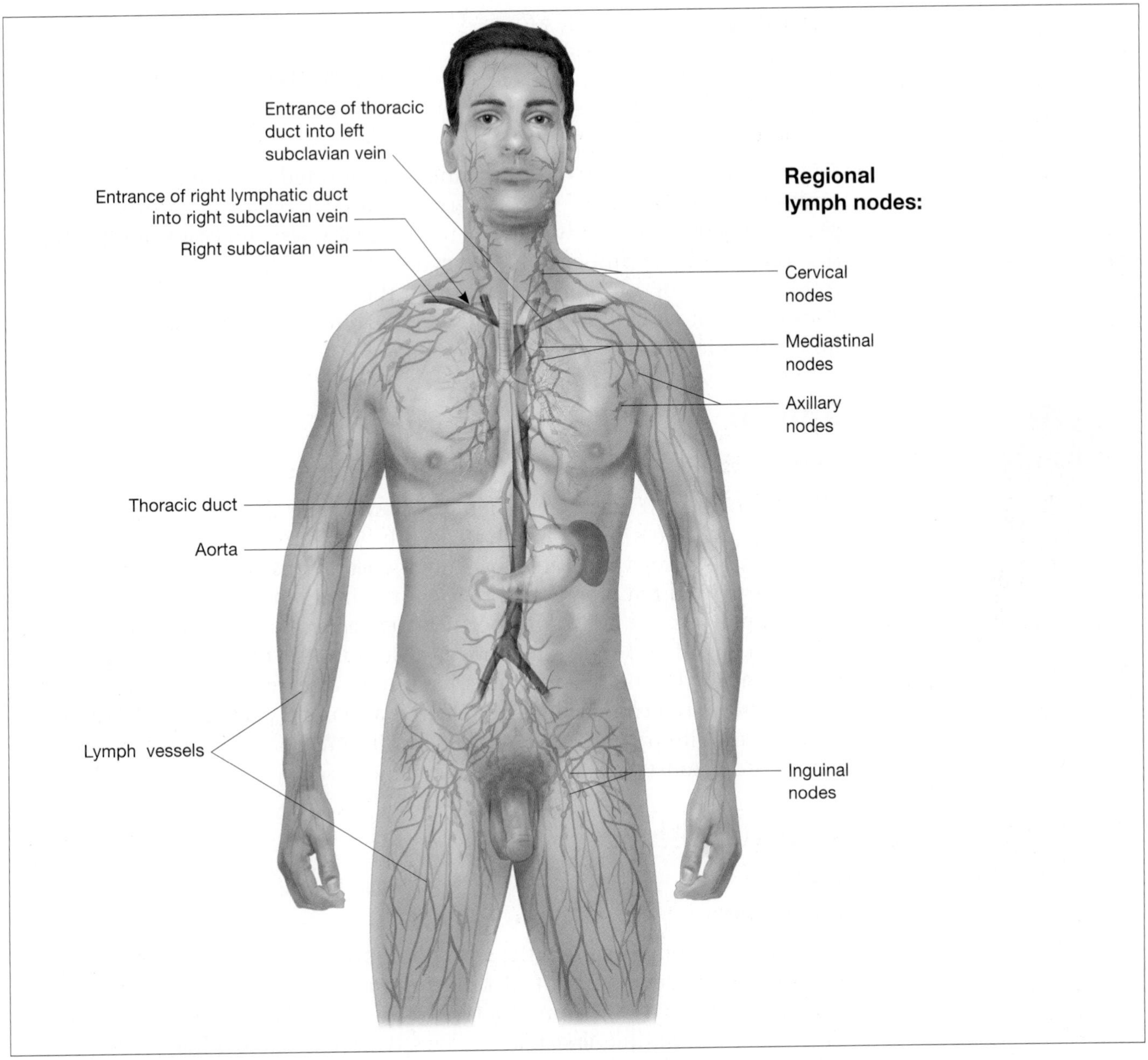

Figure 6.9 Location of lymph vessels, lymphatic ducts, and areas of lymph node concentrations.

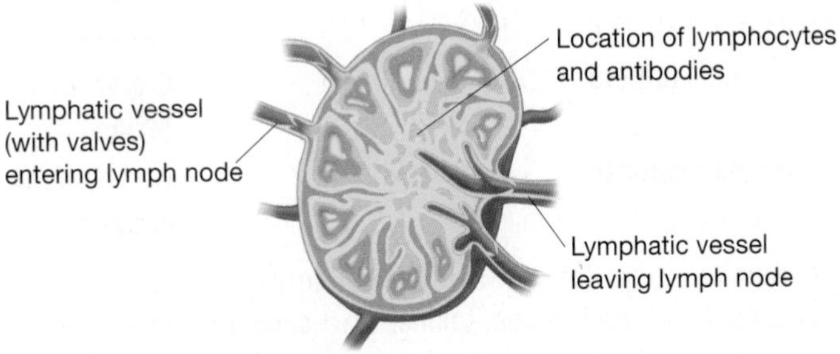

Figure 6.10 Structure of a lymph node.

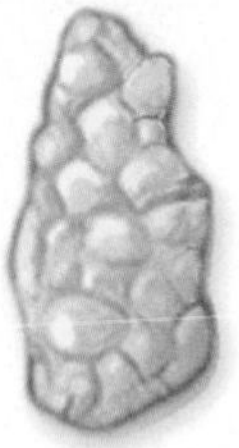

■ **Figure 6.11** The shape of a tonsil.

Tonsils

adenoids (ADD-eh-noydz)
lingual tonsils (LING-gwal)
palatine tonsils (PAL-ah-tyne)
pharyngeal tonsils (fair-IN-jee-al)
pharynx (FAIR-inks)

The tonsils are collections of lymphatic tissue located on each side of the throat or **pharynx** (see Figure 6.11 ■). There are three sets of tonsils: **palatine tonsils**; **pharyngeal tonsils**, commonly referred to as the **adenoids**; and **lingual tonsils**. All tonsils contain a large number of leukocytes and act as filters to protect the body from the invasion of pathogens through the digestive or respiratory systems. Tonsils are not vital organs and can safely be removed if they become a continuous site of infection.

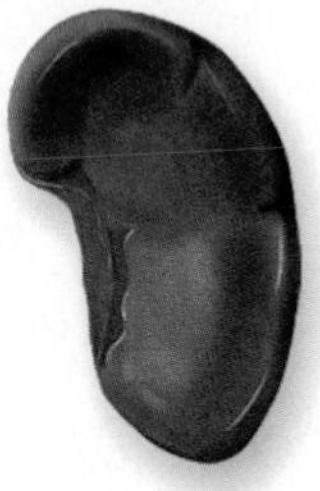

■ **Figure 6.12** The shape of the spleen.

Spleen

blood sinuses
macrophages (MACK-roh-fayj-ez)

The spleen, located in the upper left quadrant of the abdomen, consists of lymphatic tissue that is highly infiltrated with blood vessels (see Figure 6.12 ■). These vessels spread out into slow-moving **blood sinuses.** The spleen filters out and destroys old red blood cells, recycles the iron, and also stores some of the blood supply for the body. Phagocytic **macrophages** line the blood sinuses in the spleen to engulf and remove pathogens. Because the blood is moving through the organ slowly, the macrophages have time to carefully identify pathogens and worn-out red blood cells. The spleen is also not a vital organ and can be removed due to injury or disease. However, without the spleen, a person's susceptibility to a bloodstream infection may be increased.

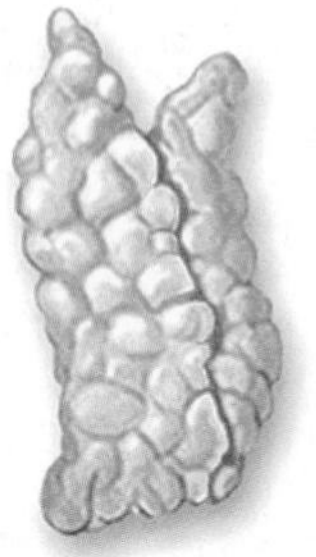

■ **Figure 6.13** The shape of the thymus gland.

Thymus Gland

T cells
T lymphocytes
thymosin (thigh-MOH-sin)

The thymus gland, located in the upper portion of the mediastinum, is essential for the proper development of the immune system (see Figure 6.13 ■). It assists the body with the immune function and the development of antibodies. This organ's hormone, **thymosin**, changes lymphocytes to **T lymphocytes** (simply called **T cells**), which play an important role in the immune response. The thymus is active in the unborn child and throughout childhood until adolescence, when it begins to shrink in size.

Immunity

acquired immunity
active acquired immunity
bacteria (bak-TEE-ree-ah)
cancerous tumors
fungi (FUN-jee)
immune response
immunity (im-YOO-nih-tee)
immunizations (im-yoo-nih-ZAY-shuns)
natural immunity
passive acquired immunity
protozoans (proh-toh-ZOH-anz)
toxins
vaccinations (vak-sih-NAY-shuns)
viruses

Immunity is the body's ability to defend itself against pathogens, such as **bacteria**, **viruses**, **fungi**, **protozoans**, **toxins**, and **cancerous tumors**. Immunity comes in two forms: **natural immunity** and **acquired immunity**. Natural immunity, also called *innate immunity*, is not specific to a particular disease and does not require prior exposure to the pathogenic agent. A good example of natural immunity is the macrophage. These leukocytes are present throughout all the tissues of the body, but are concentrated in areas of high exposure to invading bacteria, like the lungs and digestive system. They are very active phagocytic cells, ingesting and digesting any pathogen they encounter (see Figure 6.14 ■).

Acquired immunity is the body's response to a specific pathogen and may be established either passively or actively. **Passive acquired immunity** results when a person receives protective substances produced by another human or animal. This may take the form of maternal antibodies crossing the placenta to a baby or an antitoxin or gamma globulin injection. **Active acquired immunity** develops following direct exposure to the pathogenic agent. The agent stimulates the body's **immune response**, a series of different mechanisms all geared to neutralize the agent. For example, a person typically can catch chickenpox only once because once the body has successfully fought the virus, it will be able to more quickly recognize and kill it in the future. **Immunizations** or **vaccinations** are special types of active acquired immunity. Instead of actually being exposed to the infectious agent and having the disease, a person is exposed to a modified or weakened pathogen that is still capable of stimulating the immune response but not actually causing the disease.

Immune Response

antibody (AN-tih-bod-ee)
antibody-mediated immunity
antigen–antibody complex
antigens (AN-tih-jens)
B cells
B lymphocytes
cell-mediated immunity
cellular immunity
cytotoxic (sigh-toh-TOK-sik)
humoral immunity (HYOO-mor-al)
natural killer (NK) **cells**

Disease-causing agents are recognized as being foreign because they display proteins that are different from a person's own natural proteins. Those foreign proteins, called **antigens**, stimulate the immune response. The immune response consists of two distinct and different processes: **humoral immunity** (also called **antibody-mediated immunity**) and **cellular immunity** (also called **cell-mediated immunity**).

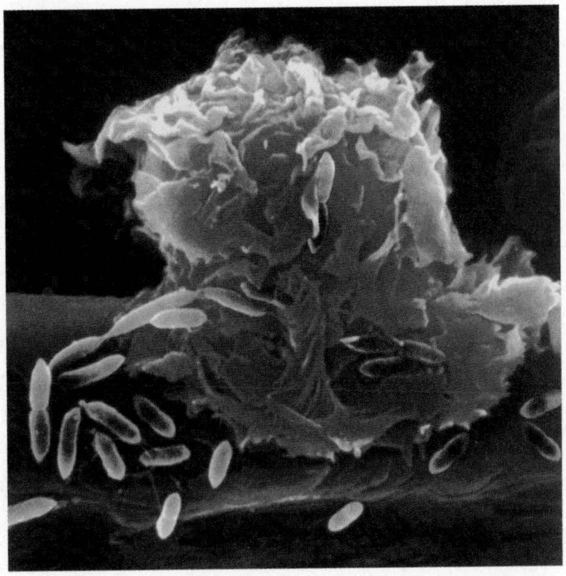

■ **Figure 6.14** Color enhanced photomicrograph showing a macrophage (purple) attacking *Escherichia coli* (yellow), a type of bacteria. *(Dennis Kunkel/Phototake NYC)*

Med Term Tip

The term *humoral* comes from the Latin word for "liquid." It is the old-fashioned term to refer to the fluids of the body.

Humoral immunity refers to the production of **B lymphocytes**, also called **B cells**, which respond to antigens by producing a protective protein, an **antibody**. Antibodies combine with the antigen to form an **antigen–antibody complex**. This complex either targets the foreign substance for phagocytosis or prevents the infectious agent from damaging healthy cells.

Cellular immunity involves the production of T cells and **natural killer** (NK) **cells**. These defense cells are **cytotoxic**, meaning that they physically attack and destroy pathogenic cells.

Standard Precautions

cross infection
nosocomial infection (no-so-KOH-mee-all)
Occupational Safety and Health Administration (OSHA)
reinfection
self-inoculation

Hospital and other healthcare settings contain a large number of infective pathogens. Patients and healthcare workers are exposed to each other's pathogens and sometimes become infected. An infection acquired in this manner, as a result of hospital exposure, is referred to as a **nosocomial infection**. Nosocomial infections can spread in several ways. **Cross infection** occurs when a person, either a patient or healthcare worker, acquires a pathogen from another patient or healthcare worker. **Reinfection** takes place when a patient becomes infected again with the same pathogen that originally brought him or her to the hospital. **Self-inoculation** occurs when a person becomes infected in a different part of the body by a pathogen from another part of his or her own body—such as intestinal bacteria spreading to the urethra.

With the appearance of the human immunodeficiency virus (HIV) and the hepatitis B virus (HBV) in the mid-1980s, the fight against spreading infections took on even greater significance. In 1987 the **Occupational Safety and Health Administration** (OSHA) issued mandatory guidelines to ensure that all employees at risk of exposure to body fluids are provided with personal protective equipment. These guidelines state that all human blood, tissue, and body fluids must be treated as if they were infected with HIV, HBV, or other bloodborne pathogens. These guidelines were expanded in 1992 and 1996 to encourage the fight against not just bloodborne pathogens, but all nosocomial infections spread by contact with blood, mucous membranes, nonintact skin, and all body fluids (including amniotic fluid, vaginal secretions, pleural fluid, cerebrospinal fluid, peritoneal fluid, pericardial fluid, and semen). These guidelines are commonly referred to as the Standard Precautions:

Med Term Tip

The simple act of thoroughly washing your hands is the most effective method of preventing the spread of infectious diseases.

1. Wash hands before putting on and after removing gloves and before and after working with each patient or patient equipment.
2. Wear gloves when in contact with any body fluid, mucous membrane, or nonintact skin or if you have chapped hands, a rash, or open sores.
3. Wear a nonpermeable gown or apron during procedures that are likely to expose you to any body fluid, mucous membrane, or nonintact skin.
4. Wear a mask and protective equipment or a face shield when patients are coughing often or if body fluid droplets or splashes are likely.
5. Wear a facemask and eyewear that seal close to the face during procedures that cause body tissues to be vaporized.
6. Remove for proper cleaning any shared equipment—such as a thermometer, stethoscope, or blood pressure cuff—that has come into contact with body fluids, mucous membrane, or nonintact skin.

Word Building

The following list contains examples of medical terms built directly from word parts. The definition for these terms can be determined by a straightforward translation of the word parts.

COMBINING FORM	COMBINED WITH	MEDICAL TERM	DEFINITION
adenoid/o	-ectomy	**adenoidectomy** (add-eh-noyd-EK-toh-mee)	removal of the adenoids
	-itis	**adenoiditis** (add-eh-noyd-EYE-tis)	inflammation of the adenoids
immun/o	-logist	**immunologist** (im-yoo-NALL-oh-jist)	immunity specialist
lymph/o	aden/o –ectomy	**lymphadenectomy** (lim-fad-eh-NEK-toh-mee)	removal of lymph gland
	aden/o –pathy	**lymphadenopathy** (lim-fad-eh-NOP-ah-thee)	lymph gland disease
	angi/o –gram	**lymphangiogram** (lim-FAN-jee-oh-gram)	record of lymph vessels
	angi/o -oma	**lymphangioma** (lim-fan-jee-OH-mah)	lymph vessel tumor
	-oma	**lymphoma** (lim-FOH-mah)	lymph tumor
	-tic	**lymphatic** (lim-FAT-ik)	pertaining to lymph
path/o	-genic	**pathogenic** (path-oh-JEN-ik)	disease producing
	-logy	**pathology** (path-OL-oh-gee)	study of disease
splen/o	-ectomy	**splenectomy** (splee-NEK-toh-mee)	removal of spleen
	-megaly	**splenomegaly** (splee-noh-MEG-ah-lee)	enlarged spleen
thym/o	-ectomy	**thymectomy** (thigh-MEK-toh-mee)	removal of the thymus
	-oma	**thymoma** (thigh-MOH-mah)	thymus tumor
tonsill/o	-ar	**tonsillar** (ton-sih-lar)	pertaining to tonsils
	-ectomy	**tonsillectomy** (ton-sih-LEK-toh-mee)	removal of the tonsils
	-itis	**tonsillitis** (ton-sil-EYE-tis)	inflammation of the tonsils

Vocabulary

TERM	DEFINITION
allergen (AL-er-jin)	An antigen that causes an allergic reaction.
allergist (AL-er-jist)	A physician who specializes in testing for and treating allergies.
allergy (AL-er-jee)	Hypersensitivity to a common substance in the environment or to a medication.
autoimmune disease	A disease resulting from the body's immune system attacking its own cells as if they were pathogens. Examples include systemic lupus erythematosus, rheumatoid arthritis, and multiple sclerosis.
hives	Appearance of wheals as part of an allergic reaction.

Vocabulary *(continued)*

TERM	DEFINITION
human immunodeficiency virus (HIV) (im-yoo-noh-dee-FIH-shen-see)	Virus that causes AIDS; also known as a **retrovirus.**
Figure 6.15 Color enhanced scanning electron micrograph of HIV virus (red) infecting T-helper cells (green). *(NIBSC/Science Photo Library/Photo Researchers, Inc.)*	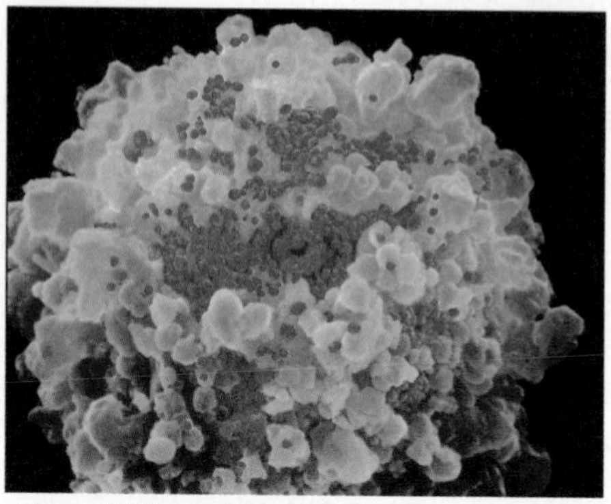
immunocompromised (im-you-noh-KOM-pro-mized)	Having an immune system that is unable to respond properly to pathogens. Also called *immunodeficiency disorder.*
immunoglobulins (im-yoo-noh-GLOB-yoo-linz)	Antibodies secreted by the B cells. All antibodies are immunoglobulins and assist in protecting the body and its surfaces from the invasion of bacteria. For example, the immunoglobulin IgA in colostrum, the first milk from the mother, helps to protect the newborn from infection.
immunology (im-yoo-NALL-oh-jee)	A branch of medicine concerned with diagnosis and treatment of infectious diseases and other disorders of the immune system. Physician is an *immunologist.*
inflammation (in-flah-MA-shun)	The tissues' response to injury from pathogens or physical agents. Characterized by redness, pain, swelling, and feeling hot to touch. **Med Term Tip** Word watch—the terms *inflammation* and *inflammatory* are spelled with two "m"s, while *inflame* and *inflamed* each have only one "m." These may be the most commonly misspelled terms by medical terminology students.
Figure 6.16 Inflammation as illustrated by cellulitis of the arm. Note that the area is red and swollen. It is also painful and hot to touch.	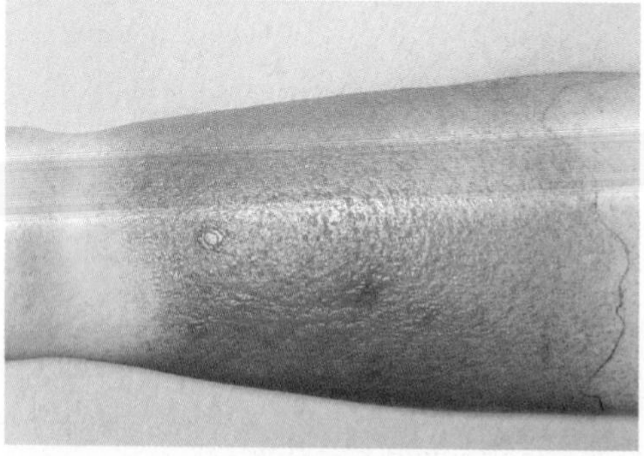
lymphedema (limf-eh-DEE-mah)	Edema appearing in the extremities due to an obstruction of the lymph flow through the lymphatic vessels.
opportunistic infections	Infectious diseases associated with patients who have compromised immune systems and therefore a lowered resistance to infections and parasites. May be the result of HIV infection.
urticaria (er-tih-KAY-ree-ah)	Severe itching associated with hives, usually linked to food allergy, stress, or drug reactions.

Pathology

TERM	DEFINITION
■ ***Allergic Reactions***	
anaphylactic shock (an-ah-fih-LAK-tik)	Life-threatening condition resulting from a severe allergic reaction. Examples of instances that may trigger this reaction include bee stings, medications, or the ingestion of foods. Circulatory and respiratory problems occur, including respiratory distress, hypotension, edema, tachycardia, and convulsions. Also called **anaphylaxis**.
■ ***Lymphatic System***	
elephantiasis (el-eh-fan-TYE-ah-sis)	Inflammation, obstruction, and destruction of the lymph vessels resulting in enlarged tissues due to edema.
Hodgkin's disease (HD) (HOJ-kins dih-ZEEZ)	Also called *Hodgkin's lymphoma.* Cancer of the lymphatic cells found in concentration in the lymph nodes. Named after Thomas Hodgkin, a British physician, who first described it.
Figure 6.17 Late-stage Hodgkin's disease with tumor eroding skin above cancerous lymph node.	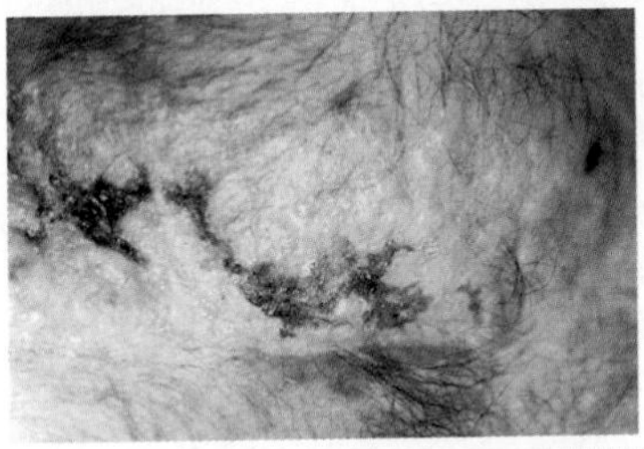
lymphadenitis (lim-fad-en-EYE-tis)	Inflammation of the lymph nodes. Referred to as *swollen glands.*
mononucleosis (mono) (mon-oh-nook-lee-OH-sis)	Acute infectious disease with a large number of abnormal lymphocytes. Caused by the Epstein–Barr virus. Abnormal liver function may occur.
non-Hodgkin's lymphoma (NHL)	Cancer of the lymphatic tissues other than Hodgkin's lymphoma.
■ ***Immune System***	
acquired immunodeficiency syndrome (AIDS) (ac-quired im-you-noh-dee-FIH-shen-see SIN-drohm)	Disease involving a defect in the cell-mediated immunity system. A syndrome of opportunistic infections occurring in the final stages of infection with the human immunodeficiency virus (HIV). This virus attacks T4 lymphocytes and destroys them, reducing the person's ability to fight infection.
AIDS-related complex (ARC)	Early stage of AIDS. There is a positive test for the virus, but only mild symptoms of weight loss, fatigue, skin rash, and anorexia.
graft vs. host disease (GVHD)	Serious complication of bone marrow transplant (graft). Immune cells from the donor bone marrow attack the recipient's (host's) tissues.
Kaposi's sarcoma (KS) (KAP-oh-seez sar-KOH-mah)	Form of skin cancer frequently seen in patients with AIDS. It consists of brownish-purple papules that spread from the skin and metastasize to internal organs. Named for Moritz Kaposi, an Austrian dermatologist.
***Pneumocystis carinii* pneumonia** (PCD) (noo-moh-SIS-tis kah-RYE-nee-eye new-MOH-nee-ah)	Pneumonia common in patients with AIDS that is caused by infection with an opportunistic parasite.
sarcoidosis (sar-koyd-OH-sis)	Disease of unknown cause that forms fibrous lesions commonly appearing in the lymph nodes, liver, skin, lungs, spleen, eyes, and small bones of the hands and feet.
severe combined immunodeficiency syndrome (SCIDS)	Disease seen in children born with a nonfunctioning immune system. Often these children are forced to live in sealed sterile rooms.

Diagnostic Procedures

TERM	DEFINITION
Clinical Laboratory Tests	
enzyme-linked immunosorbent assay (ELISA) (EN-zym LINK'T im-yoo-noh-sor-bent ASS-say)	A blood test for an antibody to the AIDS virus. A positive test means that the person has been exposed to the virus. There may be a false-positive reading, and then the Western blot test would be used to verify the results.
Western blot	Test used as a backup to the ELISA blood test to detect the presence of the antibody to HIV (AIDS virus) in the blood.
Diagnostic Imaging	
lymphangiography (lim-FAN-jee-oh-graf-ee)	X-ray taken of the lymph vessels after the injection of dye into the foot. The lymph flow through the chest is traced.
Additional Diagnostic Procedures	
Monospot	Test for infectious mononucleosis.
scratch test	Form of allergy testing in which the body is exposed to an allergen through a light scratch in the skin.

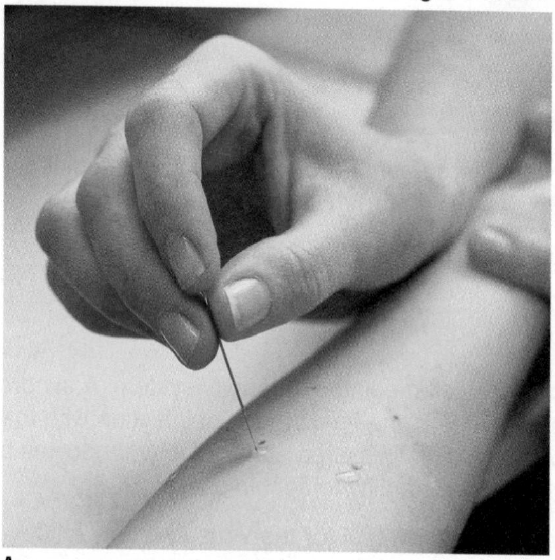

A.

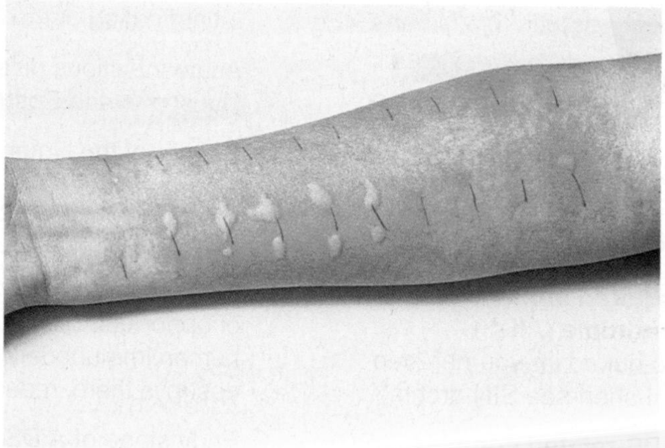

B.

Figure 6.18 A) Scratch test; patient is exposed to allergens through light scratch in the skin. B) Positive scratch test results. Inflammation indicates person is allergic to that substance. *(James King-Holmes/Science Photo Library/Photo Researchers, Inc.)*

Therapeutic Procedures

TERM	DEFINITION
Medical Procedures	
immunotherapy (IM-yoo-noh-thair-ah-pee)	Giving a patient an injection of immunoglobulins or antibodies in order to treat a disease. The antibodies may be produced by another person or animal, for example, antivenom for snake bites. More recent developments include treatments to boost the activity of the immune system, especially to treat cancer and AIDS.
vaccination (vak-sih-NAY-shun)	Exposure to a weakened pathogen that stimulates the immune response and antibody production in order to confer protection against the full-blown disease. Also called *immunization.*
Surgical Procedures	
lymphadenectomy (lim-fad-eh-NEK-toh-mee)	Removal of a lymph node. This is usually done to test for malignancy.

Pharmacology

CLASSIFICATION	ACTION	GENERIC AND BRAND NAMES
antihistamine (an-tih-HIST-ah-meen)	Blocks the effects of histamine released by the body during an allergic reaction.	cetirizine, Zyrtec; diphenhydramine, Benadryl
corticosteroids (core-tih-koh-STARE-royds)	A hormone produced by the adrenal cortex that has very strong anti-inflammatory properties. Particularly useful in treating autoimmune diseases.	prednisone; methylprednisolone, Solu-Medrol
immunosuppressants (im-yoo-noh-sue-PRESS-antz)	Blocks certain actions of the immune system. Required to prevent rejection of a transplanted organ.	mycophenolate mofetil, CellCept; cyclosporine, Neoral
protease inhibitor drugs (PROH-tee-ace)	Inhibits protease, an enzyme viruses need to reproduce.	indinavir, Crixivan; saquinavir, Fortovase
reverse transcriptase inhibitor drugs (trans-KRIP-tays)	Inhibits reverse transcriptase, an enzyme needed by viruses to reproduce.	lamivudine, Epivir; zidovudine, Retrovir

Abbreviations

AIDS	acquired immunodeficiency syndrome	**KS**	Kaposi's sarcoma
ARC	AIDS-related complex	**mono**	mononucleosis
ELISA	enzyme-linked immunosorbent assay	**NHL**	non-Hodgkin's lymphoma
GVHD	graft vs. host disease	**NK**	natural killer cells
HD	Hodgkin's disease	**PCP**	*Pneumocystis carinii* pneumonia
HIV	human immunodeficiency virus	**SCIDS**	severe combined immunodeficiency syndrome
Ig	immunoglobulins (IgA, IgD, IgE, IgG, IgM)		

Chapter Review

Terminology Checklist

Below are all Anatomy and Physiology key terms, Word Building, Vocabulary, Pathology, Diagnostic, Therapeutic, and Pharmacology terms presented in this chapter. Use this list as a study tool by placing a check in the box in front of each term as you master its meaning.

- ☐ ABO system
- ☐ acquired immunity
- ☐ acquired immunodeficiency syndrome
- ☐ active acquired immunity
- ☐ adenoidectomy
- ☐ adenoiditis
- ☐ adenoids
- ☐ agglutinate
- ☐ agranulocytes
- ☐ AIDS-related complex
- ☐ albumin
- ☐ allergen
- ☐ allergist
- ☐ allergy
- ☐ amino acids
- ☐ anaphylactic shock
- ☐ anaphylaxis
- ☐ anemia
- ☐ antibody
- ☐ antibody-mediated immunity
- ☐ anticoagulant
- ☐ antigen
- ☐ antigen–antibody complex
- ☐ antihemorrhagic
- ☐ antihistamine
- ☐ antiplatelet agent
- ☐ aplastic anemia
- ☐ autoimmune disease
- ☐ autologous transfusion
- ☐ axillary
- ☐ bacteria
- ☐ basophils
- ☐ B cells
- ☐ bilirubin
- ☐ blood clot
- ☐ blood culture and sensitivity
- ☐ blood sinuses
- ☐ blood transfusion
- ☐ blood typing
- ☐ B lymphocytes
- ☐ bone marrow aspiration
- ☐ bone marrow transplant
- ☐ calcium
- ☐ cancerous tumors
- ☐ cell-mediated immunity
- ☐ cellular immunity
- ☐ cervical
- ☐ coagulate
- ☐ complete blood count
- ☐ corticosteroids
- ☐ creatinine
- ☐ cross infection
- ☐ cytotoxic
- ☐ dyscrasia
- ☐ elephantiasis
- ☐ enucleated
- ☐ enzyme-linked immunosorbent assay (ELISA)
- ☐ eosinophils
- ☐ erythrocytes
- ☐ erythrocyte sedimentation rate
- ☐ erythrocytosis
- ☐ erythropenia
- ☐ erythropoiesis
- ☐ fats
- ☐ fibrin
- ☐ fibrinogen
- ☐ fibrinolysis
- ☐ fibrinous
- ☐ formed elements
- ☐ fungi
- ☐ gamma globulin
- ☐ globulins
- ☐ glucose
- ☐ graft vs. host disease
- ☐ granulocyte
- ☐ hematic
- ☐ hematinic
- ☐ hematocrit
- ☐ hematologist
- ☐ hematology
- ☐ hematoma
- ☐ hematopoiesis
- ☐ hemoglobin
- ☐ hemolysis
- ☐ hemolytic
- ☐ hemolytic anemia
- ☐ hemolytic reaction
- ☐ hemophilia
- ☐ hemorrhage
- ☐ hemostasis
- ☐ hives
- ☐ Hodgkin's disease
- ☐ homologous transfusion
- ☐ human immunodeficiency virus
- ☐ humoral immunity
- ☐ hyperlipidemia
- ☐ hypochromic anemia
- ☐ immune response
- ☐ immunity
- ☐ immunization
- ☐ immunocompromised
- ☐ immunoglobulins
- ☐ immunologist
- ☐ immunology
- ☐ immunosuppressants
- ☐ immunotherapy
- ☐ inflammation
- ☐ inguinal
- ☐ iron-deficiency anemia
- ☐ Kaposi's sarcoma
- ☐ lacteals
- ☐ leukemia

Multimedia Preview

Additional interactive resources and activities for this chapter can be found on the Companion Website. For videos, games, and pronunciations, please access the accompanying DVD-ROM that comes with this book.

DVD-ROM Highlights

PROFESSIONAL PROFILE: MEDICAL/CLINICAL LABORATORY TECHNICIAN (MLT/CLT)

Get a glimpse of what medical/clinical laboratory technicians do on the job each day by watching a video profile of this exciting career field. Each chapter presents a brief segment featuring a different health profession that you may chose to explore.

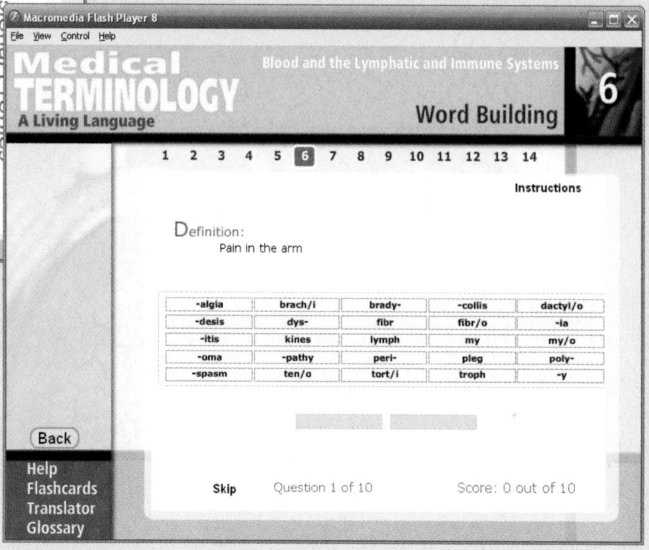

WORD BUILDING

Are you ready to master the technique of constructing terms using word parts? Put it all together by clicking and dragging the right prefixes, suffixes, roots, and combining forms together to match the definitions provided.

Website Highlights—www.prenhall.com/fremgen

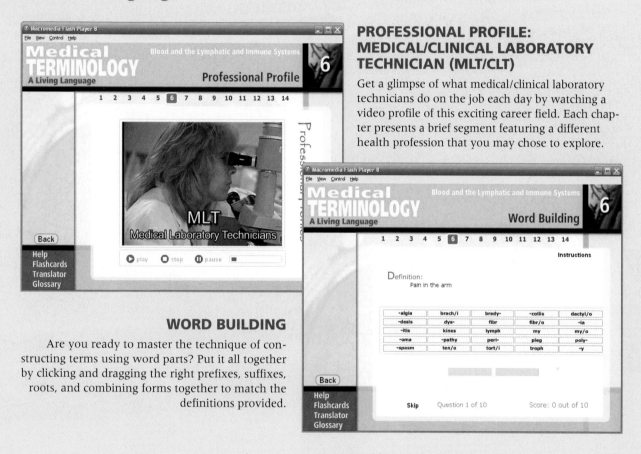

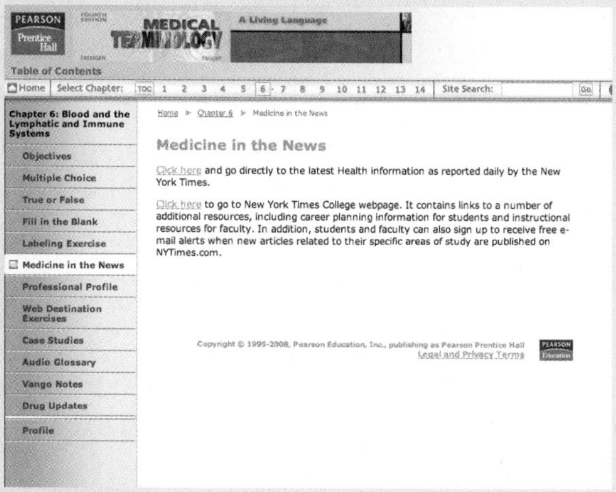

MEDICINE IN THE NEWS

Click here and take advantage of the free-access on-line study guide that accompanies your textbook. You'll be able to stay current with a link to medical news articles updated daily by *The New York Times*. By clicking on this URL you'll also access a variety of quizzes with instant feedback, links to download mp3 audio reviews, and an audio glossary.

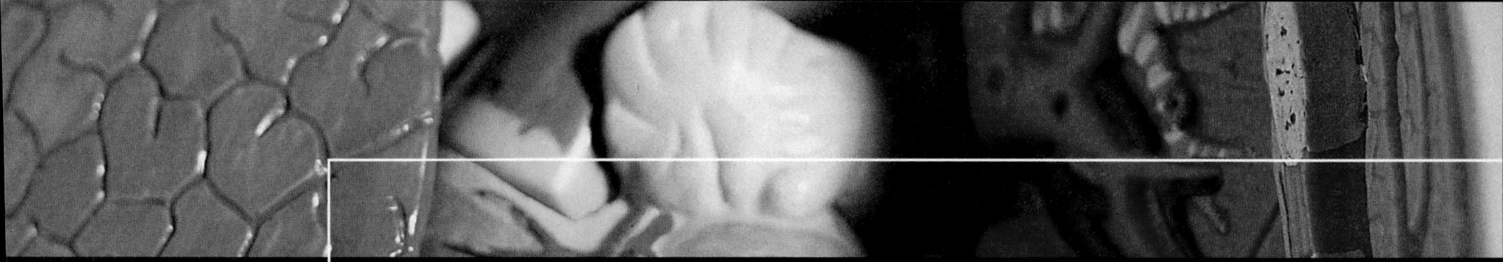

7 Respiratory System

Learning Objectives

Upon completion of this chapter, you will be able to:

- Identify and define the combining forms and suffixes introduced in this chapter.
- Correctly spell and pronounce medical terms and major anatomical structures relating to the respiratory system.
- Locate and describe the major organs of the respiratory system and their functions.
- List and describe the lung volumes and capacities.
- Describe the process of respiration.
- Build and define respiratory system medical terms from word parts.
- Identify and define respiratory system vocabulary terms.
- Identify and define selected respiratory system pathology terms.
- Identify and define selected respiratory system diagnostic procedures.
- Identify and define selected respiratory system therapeutic procedures.
- Identify and define selected medications relating to the respiratory system.
- Define selected abbreviations associated with the respiratory system.

Respiratory System at a Glance

Function

The organs of the respiratory system are responsible for bringing fresh air into the lungs, exchanging oxygen for carbon dioxide between the air sacs of the lungs and the blood stream, and exhaling the stale air.

Organs

nasal cavity
pharynx
larynx
trachea
bronchial tubes
lungs

Combining Forms

alveol/o	alveolus; air sac
anthrac/o	coal
atel/o	incomplete
bronch/o	bronchus
bronchi/o	bronchus
bronchiol/o	bronchiole
coni/o	dust
diaphragmat/o	diaphragm
epiglott/o	epiglottis
laryng/o	larynx
lob/o	lobe
nas/o	nose
orth/o	straight, upright
ox/o, ox/i	oxygen
pharyng/o	pharynx
pleur/o	pleura
pneum/o	lung, air
pneumon/o	lung, air
pulmon/o	lung
rhin/o	nose
sinus/o	sinus, cavity
spir/o	breathing
trache/o	trachea, windpipe

Suffixes

-capnia	carbon dioxide
-ectasis	dilated, expansion
-osmia	smell
-phonia	voice
-pnea	breathing
-ptysis	spitting
-thorax	chest

Respiratory System Illustrated

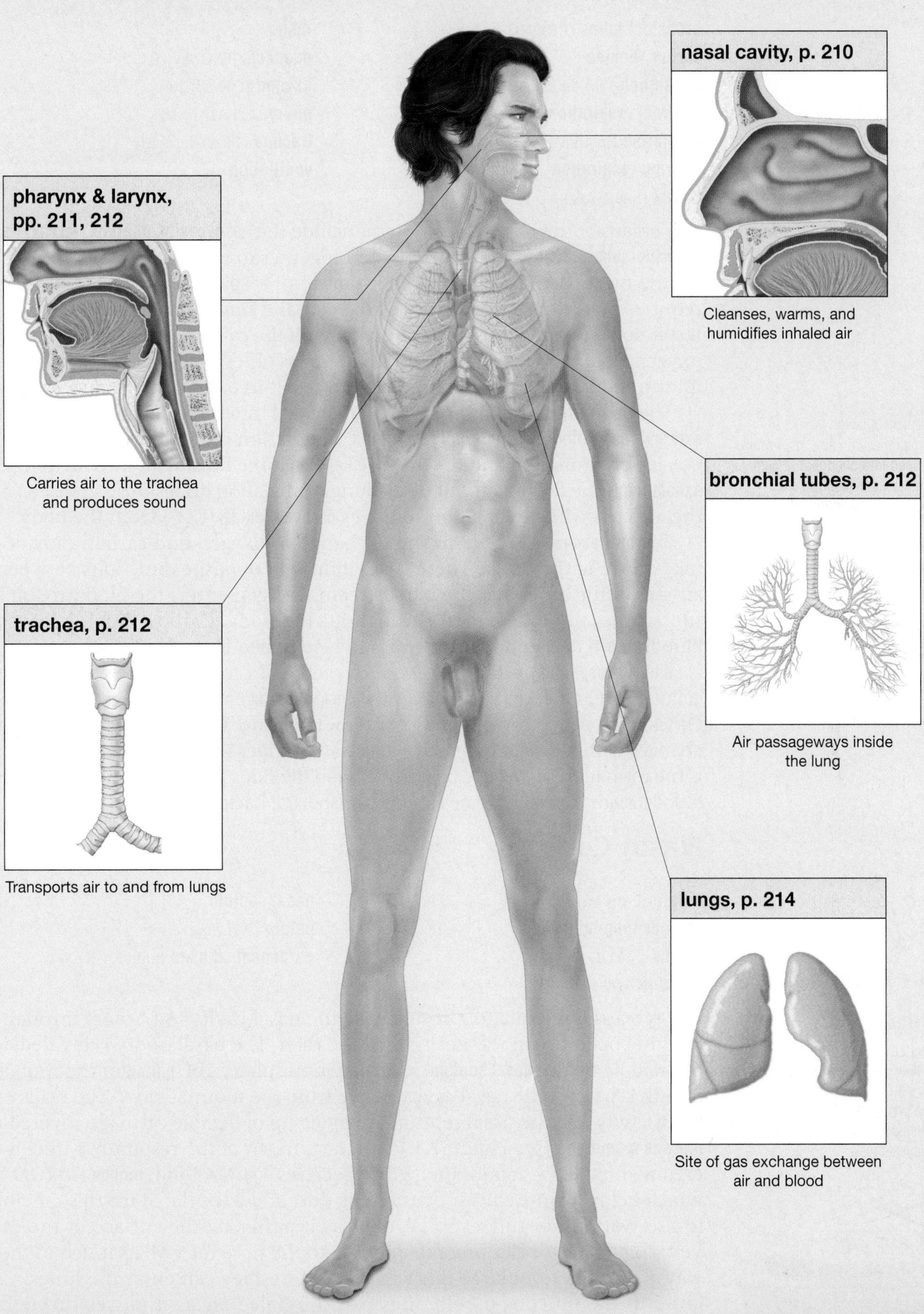

Anatomy and Physiology of the Respiratory System

bronchial tubes (BRONG-key-all)
carbon dioxide
exhalation (eks-hah-LAY-shun)
external respiration
inhalation (in-hah-LAY-shun)
internal respiration
larynx (LAIR-inks)
lungs
nasal cavity (NAY-zl)
oxygen (OK-sih-jen)
pharynx (FAIR-inks)
trachea (TRAY-kee-ah)
ventilation

The organs of the respiratory system include the **nasal cavity, pharynx, larynx, trachea, bronchial tubes,** and **lungs**—that function together to perform the mechanical and, for the most part, unconscious mechanism of respiration. The cells of the body require the continuous delivery of oxygen and removal of carbon dioxide. The respiratory system works in conjunction with the cardiovascular system to deliver oxygen to all the cells of the body. The process of respiration must be continuous; interruption for even a few minutes can result in brain damage and/or death.

Med Term Tip

The terms inhalation and *inspiration*, can be used interchangeably. Similarly, the terms exhalation and *expiration* are interchangeable.

The process of respiration can be subdivided into three distinct parts: **ventilation**, **external respiration**, and **internal respiration**. Ventilation is the flow of air between the outside environment and the lungs. **Inhalation** is the flow of air into the lungs, and **exhalation** is the flow of air out of the lungs. Inhalation brings fresh **oxygen** (O_2) into the air sacs, while exhalation removes **carbon dioxide** (CO_2) from the body.

External respiration refers to the exchange of oxygen and carbon dioxide that takes place in the lungs. These gases diffuse in opposite directions between the air sacs of the lungs and the bloodstream. Oxygen enters the bloodstream from the air sacs to be delivered throughout the body. Carbon dioxide leaves the bloodstream and enters the air sacs to be exhaled from the body.

Internal respiration is the process of oxygen and carbon dioxide exchange at the cellular level when oxygen leaves the bloodstream and is delivered to the tissues. Oxygen is needed for the body cells' metabolism, all the physical and chemical changes within the body that are necessary for life. The by-product of metabolism is the formation of a waste product, carbon dioxide. The carbon dioxide enters the bloodstream from the tissues and is transported back to the lungs for disposal.

Nasal Cavity

cilia (SIL-ee-ah)
mucous membrane
mucus (MYOO-kus)
nares (NAIR-eez)
nasal septum
palate (PAL-at)
paranasal sinuses (pair-ah-NAY-zl)

Med Term Tip

Word watch — The term *cilia* means hair, and there are other body systems that have cilia or cilia-like processes. For example, when discussing the eye, *cilia* means eyelashes.

Med Term Tip

Anyone who has experienced a nosebleed, or *epistaxis*, is aware of the plentiful supply of blood vessels in the nose.

The process of ventilation begins with the nasal cavity. Air enters through two external openings in the nose called the **nares**. The nasal cavity is divided down the middle by the **nasal septum**, a cartilaginous plate. The **palate** in the roof of the mouth separates the nasal cavity above from the mouth below. The walls of the nasal cavity and the nasal septum are made up of flexible cartilage covered with **mucous membrane** (see Figure 7.1 ■). In fact, much of the respiratory tract is covered with mucous membrane, which secretes a sticky fluid, **mucus** (MYOO kus), which helps cleanse the air by trapping dust and bacteria. Since this membrane is also wet, it moisturizes inhaled air as it passes by the surface of the cavity. Very small hairs or **cilia** line the opening to the nose (as well as much of the airways), and filter out large dirt particles before they can enter the lungs. Capillaries in the mucous membranes warm inhaled air as it passes through the airways. In addition, several **paranasal sinuses** or air-filled cavities are located within

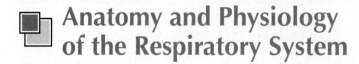

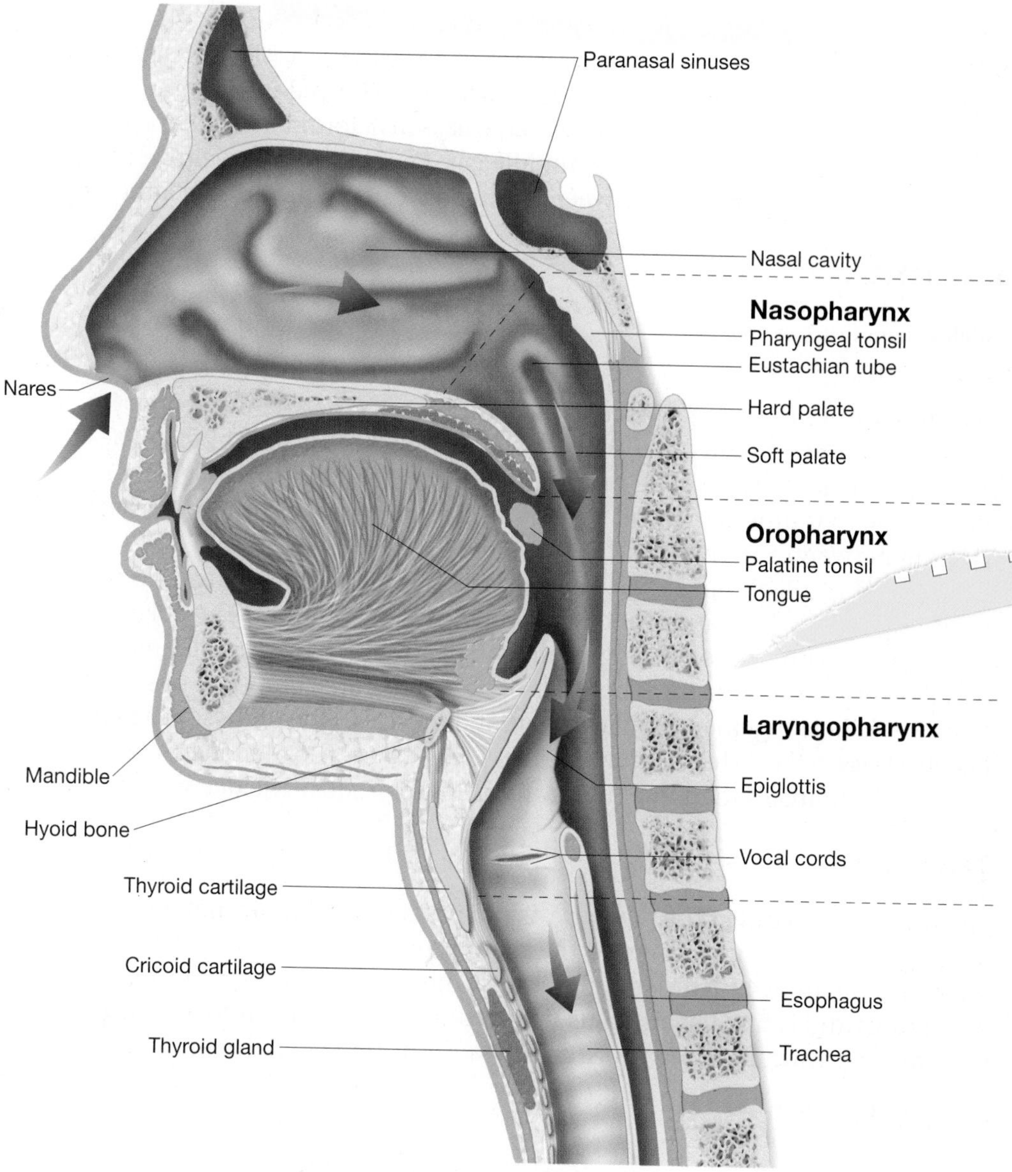

Figure 7.1 Sagittal section of upper respiratory system illustrating the internal anatomy of the nasal cavity, pharynx, larynx, and trachea.

the facial bones. The sinuses act as an echo chamber during sound production and give resonance to the voice.

Pharynx

adenoids (ADD-eh-noydz)
auditory tube
eustachian tube (yoo-STAY-she-en)
laryngopharynx (lair-ring-goh-FAIR-inks)
lingual tonsils (LING-gwal)
nasopharynx (nay-zoh-FAIR-inks)
oropharynx (or-oh-FAIR-inks)
palatine tonsils (PAL-ah-tine)
pharyngeal tonsils (fair-IN-jee-al)

Air next enters the pharynx, also called the *throat,* which is used by both the respiratory and digestive systems. At the end of the pharynx, air enters the trachea while food and liquids are shunted into the esophagus.

The pharynx is roughly a 5-inch-long tube consisting of three parts: the upper **nasopharynx**, middle **oropharynx**, and lower **laryngopharynx** (see Figure 7.1). Three pairs of tonsils, collections of lymphatic tissue, are located in the pharynx. Tonsils are strategically placed to help keep pathogens from entering the body through either the air breathed or food and liquid swallowed. The nasopharynx, behind the nose, contains the **adenoids** or **pharyngeal tonsils**. The oropharynx, behind the mouth, contains the **palatine tonsils** and the **lingual tonsils**. Tonsils are considered a part of the lymphatic system and were discussed in Chapter 6.

The opening of the **eustachian** or **auditory tube** is also found in the nasopharynx. The other end of this tube is in the middle ear. Each time you swallow, this tube opens to equalize air pressure between the middle ear and the outside atmosphere.

Med Term Tip

In the early 1970s it was common practice to remove the tonsils and adenoids in children suffering from repeated infections. However, it is now understood how important these organs are to remove pathogens from the air we breathe and the food we eat. Antibiotic treatment has also reduced the severity of infections.

Larynx

epiglottis (ep-ih-GLOT-iss)
glottis (GLOT-iss)
thyroid cartilage (THIGH-royd CAR-tih-lij)
vocal cords

The larynx or *voice box* is a muscular structure located between the pharynx and the trachea and contains the **vocal cords** (see Figures 7.1 and 7.2 ■). The vocal cords are not actually cordlike in structure, but rather they are folds of membranous tissue that produce sound by vibrating as air passes through the **glottis**, the opening between the two vocal cords.

A flap of cartilaginous tissue, the **epiglottis**, sits above the glottis and provides protection against food and liquid being inhaled into the lungs. The epiglottis covers the larynx and trachea during swallowing and shunts food and liquid from the pharynx into the esophagus. The walls of the larynx are composed of several cartilage plates held together with ligaments and muscles. One of these cartilages, the **thyroid cartilage**, forms what is known as the *Adam's apple*. The thyroid cartilage is generally larger in males than in females and helps to produce the deeper male voice.

Med Term Tip

Stuttering may actually result from faulty neuromuscular control of the larynx. Some stutterers can sing or whisper without difficulty. Both singing and whispering involve movements of the larynx that differ from those required for regular speech.

Med Term Tip

The term *Adam's apple* is thought to come from a fable that when Adam realized he had sinned in the Garden of Eden, he was unable to swallow the apple in his throat.

Trachea

The trachea, also called the *windpipe*, is the passageway for air that extends from the pharynx and larynx down to the main bronchi (see Figure 7.3 ■). Measuring approximately 4 inches in length, it is composed of smooth muscle and cartilage rings and is lined by mucous membrane and cilia. Therefore, it also assists in cleansing, warming, and moisturizing air as it travels to the lungs.

Bronchial Tubes

alveoli (al-VEE-oh-lye)
bronchioles (BRONG-key-ohlz)
bronchus (BRONG-kus)
pulmonary capillaries
respiratory membrane

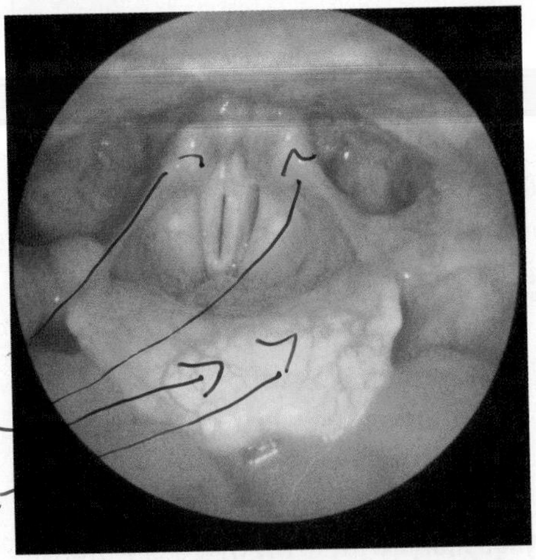

■ **Figure 7.2** The vocal cords within the larynx, superior view from the pharynx. *(CNRI/Phototake NYC)*

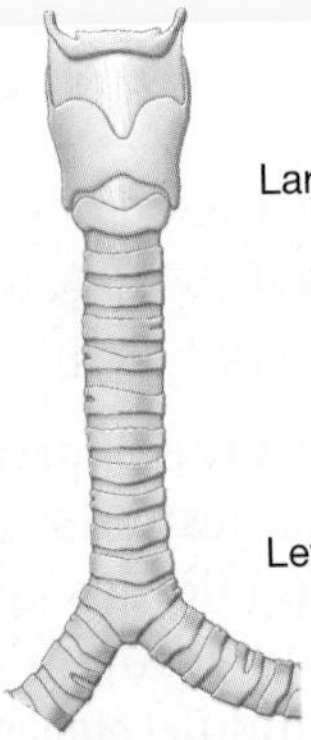

■ **Figure 7.3** Structure of the trachea which extends from the larynx above to the primary bronchi below.

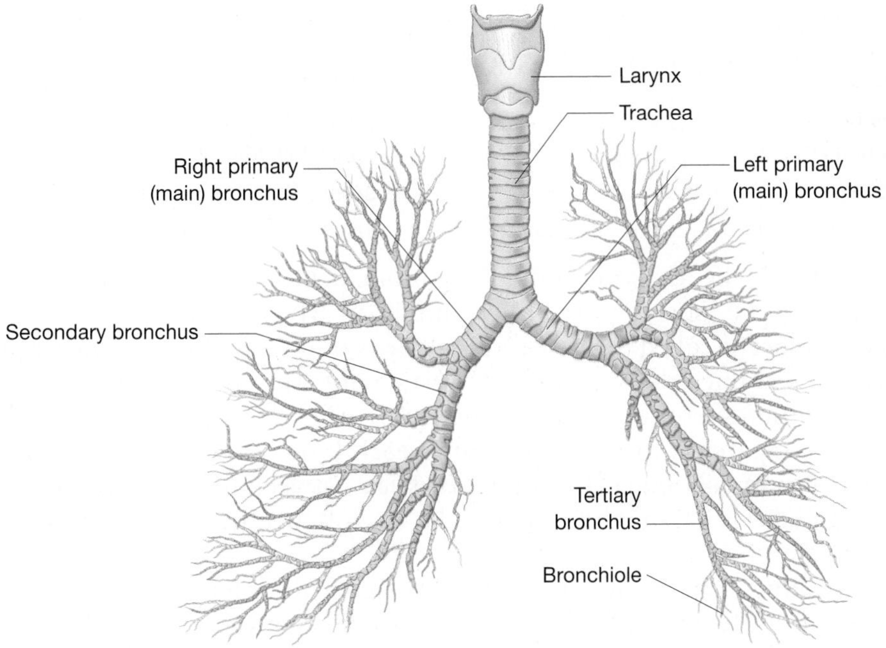

Figure 7.4 The bronchial tree, each primary (main) bronchus enters a lung and then branches into smaller and smaller secondary bronchi, tertiary bronchi, and bronchioles.

The distal end of the trachea divides to form the left and right primary (main) bronchi. Each **bronchus** enters one of the lungs and branches repeatedly to form secondary and tertiary bronchi. Each branch becomes narrower until the narrowest branches, the **bronchioles**, are formed (see Figure 7.4 ■). Each bronchiole terminates in a small group of air sacs, called **alveoli**. Each lung has approximately 150 million alveoli. The walls of alveoli are elastic, giving them the ability to expand to hold air and then recoil to their original size. A network of **pulmonary capillaries** from the pulmonary blood vessels tightly encases each alveolus (see Figure 7.5 ■). In fact, the walls of the alveoli and capillaries are so tightly associated with each other they are referred to as a single unit, the **respiratory membrane**. The exchange of oxygen and carbon dioxide between the air within the alveolus and the blood inside the capillaries takes place across the respiratory membrane.

Med Term Tip

The respiratory system can be thought of as an upside-down tree and its branches. The trunk of the tree consists of the pharynx, larynx, and trachea. The trachea then divides into two branches, the bronchi. Each bronchus divides into smaller and smaller branches. In fact, this branching system of tubes is referred to as the *bronchial tree*.

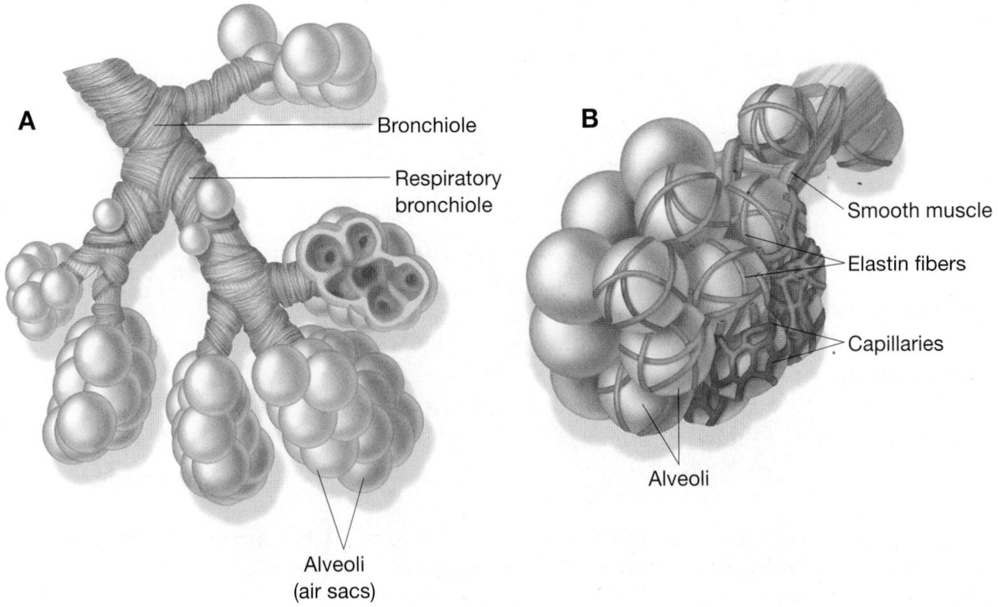

Figure 7.5 A) Each bronchiole terminates in an alveolar sac, a group of alveoli. B) Alveoli encased by network capillaries, forming the respiratory membrane.

Lungs

apex
base
hilum (HYE-lum)
lobes
mediastinum (mee-dee-ass-TYE-num)
parietal pleura (pah-RYE-eh-tal)
pleura (PLOO-rah)
pleural cavity
serous fluid (SEER-us)
visceral pleura (VISS-er-al)

Med Term Tip

Some of the abnormal lung sounds heard with a stethoscope, such as crackling and rubbing, are made when the parietal and/or visceral pleura become inflamed and rub against one another.

Each lung is the total collection of the bronchi, bronchioles, and alveoli. They are spongy to the touch because they contain air. The lungs are protected by a double membrane called the **pleura**. The pleura's outer membrane is the **parietal pleura**, which also lines the wall of the chest cavity. The inner membrane or **visceral pleura** adheres to the surface of the lungs. The pleural membrane is folded in such a way that it forms a sac around each lung referred to as the **pleural cavity.** There is normally slippery, watery **serous fluid** between the two layers of the pleura that reduces friction when the two layers rub together as the lungs repeatedly expand and contract.

The lungs contain divisions or **lobes**. There are three lobes in the larger right lung and two in the left lung. The pointed superior portion of each lung is the **apex**, while the broader lower area is the **base.** Entry of structures like the bronchi, pulmonary blood vessels, and nerves into each lung occurs along its medial border in an area called the **hilum**. The lungs within the thoracic cavity are protected from puncture and damage by the ribs. The area between the right and left lung is called the **mediastinum** and contains the heart, aorta, esophagus, thymus gland, and trachea. See Figure 7.6 for an illustration of the lungs within the chest cavity.

Lung Volumes and Capacities

pulmonary function test
respiratory therapist

For some types of medical conditions, like emphysema, it is important to measure the volume of air flowing in and out of the lungs to determine lung capac-

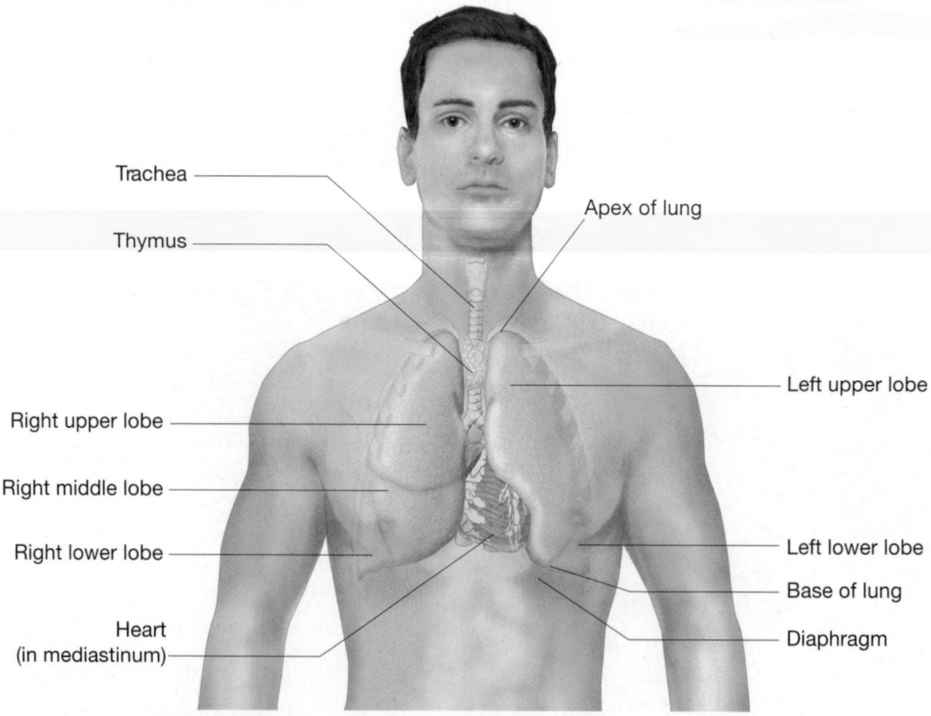

Figure 7.6 Position of the lungs within the thoracic cavity, anterior view illustrating regions of the lungs and their relationship to other thoracic organs.

ity. Lung volumes are measured by **respiratory therapists** to aid in determining the functioning level of the respiratory system. Collectively, these measurements are called **pulmonary function tests**. Table 7.1 ■ lists and defines the four lung volumes and four lung capacities.

Respiratory Muscles

diaphragm

intercostal muscles (in-ter-COS-tal)

Air moves in and out of the lungs due to the difference between the atmospheric pressure and the pressure within the chest cavity. This difference in pressure is produced by the **diaphragm**, which is the muscle separating the abdomen from the thoracic cavity. To do this, the diaphragm contracts and moves downward. This increase in thoracic cavity volume causes a decrease in pressure, or negative thoracic pressure, within the chest cavity. Air then flows into the lungs, inhalation, to equalize the pressure. The **intercostal muscles** between the ribs assist in inhalation by raising the rib cage to further enlarge the thoracic cavity. See Figure 7.7 ■ for an illustration of the role of the diaphragm in inhalation. Similarly, when the diaphragm and intercostal muscles relax, the thoracic cavity becomes smaller. This produces an increase in pressure within the cavity, or positive thoracic pressure, and air flows out of the lungs, resulting in exhalation. Therefore, a quiet, unforced exhalation is a passive process since it does not require any muscle contraction. When a forceful inhalation or exhalation is required, additional chest and neck muscles become active to create larger changes in thoracic pressure.

Med Term Tip

Diaphragmatic breathing is taught to singers and public speakers. You can practice this type of breathing by allowing your abdomen to expand during inhalation and contract during exhalation while your shoulders remain motionless.

Respiratory Rate

vital signs

Respiratory rate (measured in breaths per minute) is one of our **vital signs** (VS), along with heart rate, temperature, and blood pressure. Normally, respiratory rate

Table 7.1 Lung Volumes and Capacities

TERM	DEFINITION
Tidal volume (TV)	The amount of air that enters the lungs in a single inhalation or leaves the lungs in a single exhalation of quiet breathing. In an adult this is normally 500 mL.*
Inspiratory reserve volume (IRV)	The air that can be forcibly inhaled after a normal respiration has taken place. Also called *complemental air*, generally measures around 3,000 mL.*
Expiratory reserve volume (ERV)	The amount of air that can be forcibly exhaled after a normal quiet respiration. This is also called *supplemental air*, approximately 1,000 mL.*
Residual volume (RV)	The air remaining in the lungs after a forced exhalation; about 1,500 mL* in the adult.
Inspiratory capacity (IC)	The volume of air inhaled after a normal exhale.
Functional residual capacity (FRC)	The air that remains in the lungs after a normal exhalation has taken place.
Vital capacity (VC)	The total volume of air that can be exhaled after a maximum inhalation. This amount will be equal to the sum of TV, IRV, and ERV.
Total lung capacity (TLC)	The volume of air in the lungs after a maximal inhalation.

*There is a normal range for measurements of the volume of air exchanged. The numbers given are for the average measurement.

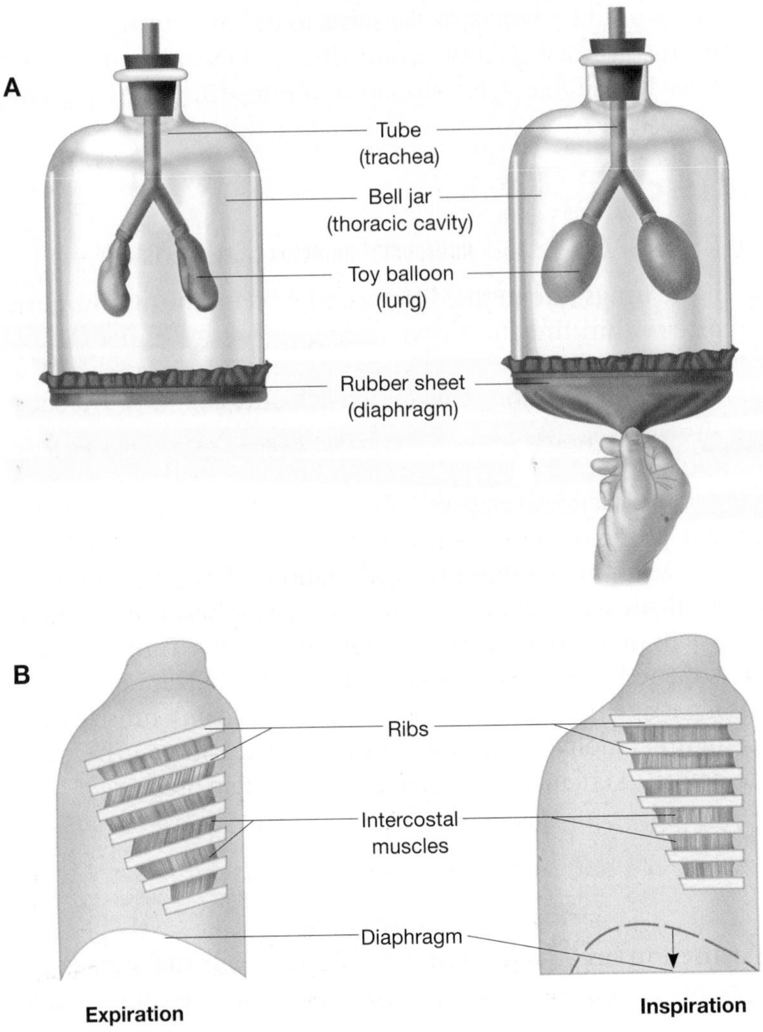

Figure 7.7 A) Bell jar apparatus demonstrating how downward movement of the diaphragm results in air flowing into the lungs. B) Action of the intercostal muscles lift the ribs to assist the diaphragm in enlarging the volume of the thoracic cavity.

Med Term Tip

When divers wish to hold their breath longer, they first hyperventilate (breath faster and deeper) in order to get rid of as much CO_2 as possible. This will hold off the urge to breathe longer, allowing a diver to stay submerged longer.

is regulated by the level of CO_2 in the blood. When the CO_2 level is high, we breathe more rapidly to expel the excess. Then, when CO_2 levels drop, our respiratory rate will also drop.

When the respiratory rate falls outside the range of normal, it may indicate an illness or medical condition. For example, when a patient is running an elevated temperature and has shortness of breath (SOB) due to pneumonia, the respiratory rate may increase dramatically. Or a brain injury or some medications, such as those for pain, can cause a decrease in the respiratory rate. See Table 7.2 ■ for normal respiratory rate ranges for different age groups.

Table 7.2 Respiratory Rates for Different Age Groups

AGE	RESPIRATIONS PER MINUTE
Newborn	30–60
1-year-old	18–30
16-year-old	16–20
Adult	12–20

Word Building

The following list contains examples of medical terms built directly from word parts. The definition for these terms can be determined by a straightforward translation of the word parts.

COMBINING FORM	COMBINED WITH	MEDICAL TERM	DEFINITION
bronch/o	-gram	**bronchogram** (BRONG-koh-gram)	record of the bronchus
	-itis	**bronchitis** (brong-KIGH-tis)	inflammation of a bronchus
	-plasty	**bronchoplasty** (BRONG-koh-plas-tee)	surgical repair of a bronchus
	-genic	**bronchogenic** (brong-koh-JEN-ik)	produced by the bronchus
	-scope	**bronchoscope** (BRONG-koh-scope)	instrument to view inside of bronchus
	-spasm	**bronchospasm** (BRONG-koh-spazm)	involuntary muscle spasm of bronchus
	-ial	**bronchial** (BRONG-ee-all)	pertaining to a bronchus
bronchi/o	-ectasis	**bronchiectasis** (brong-key-EK-tah-sis)	dilated bronchus
diaphragmat/o	-ic	**diaphragmatic** (dye-ah-frag-MAT-ik)	pertaining to the diaphragm
laryng/o	-ectomy	**laryngectomy** (lair-in-JEK-toh-mee)	removal of the voice box
	-itis	**laryngitis** (lair-in-JYE-tis)	inflammation of the voice box
	-plasty	**laryngoplasty** (lair-RING-goh-plas-tee)	surgical repair of the voice box
	-scope	**laryngoscope** (lair-RING-go-scope)	instrument to view voice box
	-eal	**laryngeal** (lair-in-GEE-all)	pertaining to the voice box
	-plegia	**laryngoplegia** (lair-RING-goh-plee-gee-ah)	paralysis of the voice box
lob/o	-ectomy	**lobectomy** (loh-BEK-toh-mee)	removal of a (lung) lobe
ox/i	-meter	**oximeter** (ox-IM-eh-ter)	instrument to measure oxygen
ox/o	an- -ia	**anoxia** (ah-NOK-see-ah)	condition of no oxygen
	hypo- -emia	**hypoxemia** (high-pox-EE-mee-ah)	insufficient oxygen in the blood
	hypo- -ia	**hypoxia** (high-POX-ee-ah)	insufficient oxygen condition
pleur/o	-centesis	**pleurocentesis** (ploor-oh-sen-TEE-sis)	puncture of the pleura to withdraw fluid
	-ectomy	**pleurectomy** (ploor-EK-toh-mee)	removal of the pleura
	-dynia	**pleurodynia** (ploor-oh-DIN-ee-ah)	pleural pain
pharyng/o	-itis	**pharyngitis** (fair-in-JYE-tis)	throat inflammation (*i.e., sore throat*)
	-eal	**pharyngeal** (fair-in-GEE-all)	pertaining to the throat
	nas/o -itis	**nasopharyngitis** (nay-zoh-fair-in-JYE-tis)	nose and throat inflammation (*i.e., common cold*)
pulmon/o	-logist	**pulmonologist** (pul-mon-ALL-oh-jist)	lung specialist
	-ary	**pulmonary** (PULL-mon-air-ee)	pertaining to the lung
rhin/o	-itis	**rhinitis** (rye-NYE-tis)	inflammation of the nose
	myc/o -osis	**rhinomycosis** (rye-noh-my-KOH-sis)	abnormal condition of nose fungus
	-plasty	**rhinoplasty** (RYE-noh-plas-tee)	surgical repair of the nose

Word Building (continued)

COMBINING FORM	COMBINED WITH	MEDICAL TERM	DEFINITION
	-rrhagia	**rhinorrhagia** (rye-noh-RAH-jee-ah)	rapid flow (of blood) from the nose
	-rrhea	**rhinorrhea** (rye-noh-REE-ah)	nose discharge (*i.e., runny nose*)
sinus/o	pan- -itis	**pansinusitis** (pan-sigh-nus-EYE-tis)	inflammation of all the sinuses
thorac/o	-algia	**thoracalgia** (thor-ah-KAL-jee-ah)	chest pain
	-ic	**thoracic** (tho-RASS-ik)	pertaining to the chest
	-otomy	**thoracotomy** (thor-ah-KOT-oh-mee)	incision into the chest
trache/o	endo- -al	**endotracheal** (en-doh-TRAY-kee-al)	pertaining to inside the trachea
	-otomy	**tracheotomy** (tray-kee-OTT-oh-mee)	incision into the trachea
	-stenosis	**tracheostenosis** (tray-kee-oh-steh-NOH-sis)	narrowing of the trachea

SUFFIX	COMBINED WITH	MEDICAL TERM	DEFINITION
-phonia	a-	**aphonia** (a-FOH-nee-ah)	no voice
	dys-	**dysphonia** (dis-FOH-nee-ah)	abnormal voice
-capnia	a-	**acapnia** (a-CAP-nee-ah)	lack of carbon dioxide
	hyper-	**hypercapnia** (high-per-CAP-nee-ah)	excessive carbon dioxide
-osmia	an-	**anosmia** (ah-NOZ-mee-ah)	lack of (sense of) smell
-pnea	a-	**apnea** (AP-nee-ah)	not breathing
	brady-	**bradypnea** (bray-DIP-nee-ah)	slow breathing
	dys-	**dyspnea** (DISP-nee-ah)	difficult, labored breathing
	eu-	**eupnea** (yoop-NEE-ah)	normal breathing
	hyper-	**hyperpnea** (high-per-NEE-ah)	excessive (deep) breathing
	hypo-	**hypopnea** (high-POP-nee-ah)	insufficient (shallow) breathing
	ortho-	**orthopnea** (or-THOP-nee-ah)	(sitting) straight breathing
	tachy-	**tachypnea** (tak-ip-NEE-ah)	rapid breathing
-thorax	hem/o	**hemothorax** (hee-moh-THOH-raks)	blood in the chest
	py/o	**pyothorax** (pye-oh-THOH-raks)	pus in the chest
	pneum/o	**pneumothorax** (new-moh-THOH-raks)	air in the chest

Vocabulary

TERM	DEFINITION
asphyxia (as-FIK-see-ah)	Lack of oxygen that can lead to unconsciousness and death if not corrected immediately; also called *asphyxiation* or *suffocation*. Some common causes include drowning, foreign body in the respiratory tract, poisoning, and electric shock.

Vocabulary *(continued)*

TERM	DEFINITION
aspiration (as-peer-RAY-shun)	Refers to withdrawing fluid from a body cavity using suction. For example, using a long needle and syringe to withdraw fluid from the pleural cavity or using a vacuum pump to remove phlegm from a patient's airways. In addition, it also refers to inhaling food, liquid, or a foreign object into the airways. Often leads to the development of pneumonia.
Cheyne–Stokes respiration (CHAIN STOHKS res-pir-AY-shun)	Abnormal breathing pattern in which there are long periods (10 to 60 seconds) of apnea followed by deeper, more rapid breathing. Named for John Cheyne, a Scottish physician, and Sir William Stokes, an Irish surgeon.
clubbing	The abnormal widening and thickening of the ends of the fingers and toes associated with chronic oxygen deficiency. Seen in patients with chronic respiratory conditions or circulatory problems.
cyanosis (sigh-ah-NO-sis)	Refers to the bluish tint of skin that is receiving an insufficient amount of oxygen or circulation.
epistaxis (ep-ih-STAKS-is)	Nosebleed.
hemoptysis (hee-MOP-tih-sis)	To cough up blood or blood-stained sputum.
hyperventilation (HYE-per-vent-ill-a-shun)	To breathe both too fast (tachypnea) and too deep (hyperpnea).
hypoventilation (HYE-poh-vent-ill-a-shun)	To breathe both too slow (bradypnea) and too shallow (hypopnea).
internal medicine	Branch of medicine involving the diagnosis and treatment of diseases and conditions of internal organs such as the respiratory system. The physician is an *internist*.
nasal cannula (CAN-you-lah)	Two-pronged plastic device for delivering oxygen into the nose; one prong is inserted into each naris.
orthopnea (or-THOP-nee-ah)	A term to describe dyspnea that is worsened by lying flat. In other words, the patient is able to breath easier when sitting straight up.
otorhinolaryngology (ENT) (oh-toh-rye-noh-lair-in-GOL-oh-jee)	Branch of medicine involving the diagnosis and treatment of conditions and diseases of the ear, nose, and throat region. The physician is an *otorhinolaryngologist*. This medical specialty may also be referred to *otolaryngology*.
patent (PAY-tent)	Open or unblocked, such as a patent airway.
percussion (per-KUH-shun)	Use of the fingertips to tap on a surface to determine the condition beneath the surface. Determined in part by the feel of the surface as it is tapped and the sound generated.
phlegm (FLEM)	Thick mucus secreted by the membranes that line the respiratory tract. When phlegm is coughed through the mouth, it is called *sputum*. Phlegm is examined for color, odor, and consistency.
pleural rub (PLOO-ral)	Grating sound made when the two layers of the pleura rub together during respiration. It is caused when one of the surfaces becomes thicker as a result of inflammation or other disease conditions. This rub can be felt through the fingertips when they are placed on the chest wall or heard through the stethoscope.

Vocabulary *(continued)*

TERM	DEFINITION
pulmonology (pull-mon-ALL-oh-jee)	Branch of medicine involved in diagnosis and treatment of diseases and disorders of the respiratory system. Physician is a *pulmonologist*.
rales (RALZ)	Abnormal crackling sound made during inspiration. Usually indicates the presence of fluid or mucus in the airways.
respiratory therapy	Allied health specialty that assists patients with respiratory and cardiopulmonary disorders. Duties of a *respiratory therapist* include conducting pulmonary function tests, monitoring oxygen and carbon dioxide levels in the blood, administering breathing treatments, and ventilator management.
rhonchi (RONG-kigh)	Somewhat musical sound during expiration, often found in asthma or infection. Caused by spasms of the bronchial tubes. Also called *wheezing*.
shortness of breath (SOB)	Term used to indicate that a patient is having some difficulty breathing; also called *dyspnea*. The causes can range from mild SOB after exercise to SOB associated with heart disease.
sputum (SPEW-tum)	Mucus or phlegm that is coughed up from the lining of the respiratory tract. **Med Term Tip** The term *sputum*, from the Latin word meaning "to spit," now refers to the material coughed up and spit out from the respiratory system.
stridor (STRIGH-dor)	Harsh, high-pitched, noisy breathing sound made when there is an obstruction of the bronchus or larynx. Found in conditions such as croup in children.
thoracic surgery (tho-RASS-ik)	Branch of medicine involving diagnosis and treatment of conditions and diseases of the respiratory system by surgical means. Physician is a *thoracic surgeon*.

Pathology

TERM	DEFINITION
■ ***Upper Respiratory System***	
croup (KROOP)	Acute respiratory condition found in infants and children that is characterized by a barking type of cough or stridor.
diphtheria (dif-THEAR-ee-ah)	Bacterial upper respiratory infection characterized by the formation of a thick membranous film across the throat and a high mortality rate. Rare now due to the DPT (diphtheria, pertussis, tetanus) vaccine.
pertussis (per-TUH-is)	Commonly called *whooping cough*, due to the whoop sound made when coughing. An infectious bacterial disease of the upper respiratory system that children receive immunization against as part of their DPT shots.
■ ***Bronchial Tubes***	
asthma (AZ-mah)	Disease caused by various conditions, like allergens, and resulting in constriction of the bronchial airways, dyspnea, coughing, and wheezing. Can cause violent spasms of the bronchi (bronchospasms) but is generally not a life-threatening condition. Medication can be very effective. **Med Term Tip** The term *asthma*, from the Greek word meaning "panting," describes the breathing pattern of a person having an asthma attack.

Pathology *(continued)*

TERM	DEFINITION
bronchiectasis (brong-key-EK-tah-sis)	The abnormal enlargement of bronchi; may be the result of a lung infection. This condition can be irreversible and result in destruction of the bronchial walls. Major symptoms include coughing up a large amount of purulent sputum, rales, and hemoptysis.
bronchogenic carcinoma (brong-koh-JEN-ik car-sin-OH-mah)	Malignant tumor originating in the bronchi. Usually associated with a history of cigarette smoking.

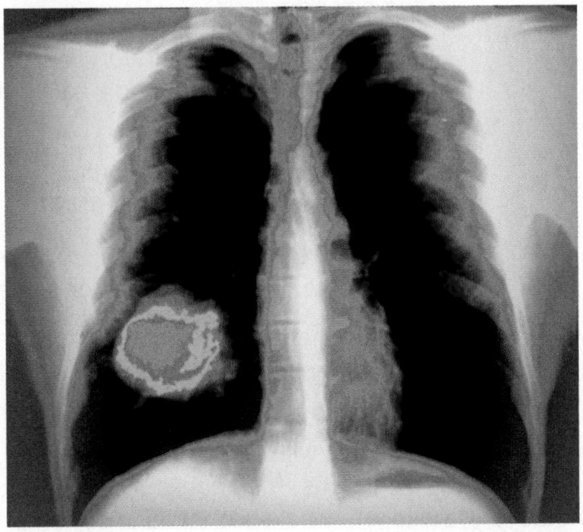

Figure 7.8 Color enchanced X-ray of large malignant tumor in right lower lung. *(ISM/Phototake NYC)*

■ *Lungs*

TERM	DEFINITION
adult respiratory distress syndrome (ARDS)	Acute respiratory failure in adults characterized by tachypnea, dyspnea, cyanosis, tachycardia, and hypoxemia. May follow trauma, pneumonia, or septic infections. Also called *acute respiratory distress syndrome.*
anthracosis (an-thra-KOH-sis)	A type of pneumoconiosis that develops from the collection of coal dust in the lung. Also called *black lung* or *miner's lung.*
asbestosis (az-bes-TOH-sis)	A type of pneumoconiosis that develops from collection of asbestos fibers in the lungs. May lead to the development of lung cancer.
atelectasis (at-eh-LEK-tah-sis)	Condition in which the alveoli in a portion of the lung collapse, preventing the respiratory exchange of oxygen and carbon dioxide. Can be caused by a variety of conditions, including pressure on the lung from a tumor or other object. Term also used to describe the failure of a newborn's lungs to expand.
chronic obstructive pulmonary disease (COPD) (PULL-mon-air-ee)	Progressive, chronic, and usually irreversible group of conditions, like emphysema, in which the lungs have a diminished capacity for inspiration (inhalation) and expiration (exhalation). The person may have dypsnea upon exertion and a cough.
cystic fibrosis (CF) (SIS-tik fye-BROH-sis)	Hereditary condition causing the exocrine glands to malfunction. The patient produces very thick mucus that causes severe congestion within the lungs and digestive system. Through more advanced treatment, many children are now living into adulthood with this disease.
emphysema (em-fih-SEE-mah)	Pulmonary condition characterized by the destruction of the walls of the alveoli, resulting in fewer overexpanded air sacs. Can occur as a result of long-term heavy smoking. Air pollution also worsens this disease. The patient may not be able to breathe except in a sitting or standing position.

Pathology *(continued)*

TERM	DEFINITION
histoplasmosis (his-toh-plaz-MOH-sis)	Pulmonary infection caused by the fungus *Histoplasma capsulatum*, found in dust and in the droppings of pigeons and chickens.
infant respiratory distress syndrome (IRDS)	A lung condition most commonly found in premature infants that is characterized by tachypnea and respiratory grunting. The condition is caused by a lack of surfactant necessary to keep the lungs inflated. Also called *hyaline membrane disease* (HMD) and *respiratory distress syndrome of the newborn.*
influenza (in-floo-EN-za)	Viral infection of the respiratory system characterized by chills, fever, body aches, and fatigue. Commonly called the *flu.*
Legionnaire's disease (lee-jen-AYRZ)	Severe, often fatal bacterial infection characterized by pneumonia and liver and kidney damage. Named after people who came down with it at an American Legion convention in 1976.
***Mycoplasma* pneumonia** (MY-koh-plaz-em)	A less severe but longer lasting form of pneumonia caused by the *Mycoplasma pneumoniae* bacteria. Also called *walking pneumonia.*
pneumoconiosis (noo-moh-koh-nee-OH-sis)	Condition that is the result of inhaling environmental particles that become toxic. Can be the result of inhaling coal dust (anthracosis) or asbestos (asbestosis).
***Pneumocystis carinii* pneumonia** (PCP) (noo-moh-SIS-tis kah-RYE-nee-eye new-MOH-nee-ah)	Pneumonia with a nonproductive cough, very little fever, and dyspnea caused by the fungus *Pneumocystis carinii.* An opportunistic infection often seen in those with weakened immune systems, such as AIDS patients.
pneumonia (new-MOH-nee-ah)	Inflammatory condition of the lung that can be caused by bacterial and viral infections, diseases, and chemicals. Results in the filling of the alveoli and air spaces with fluid.
pulmonary edema (PULL-mon-air-ee eh-DEE-mah)	Condition in which lung tissue retains an excessive amount of fluid, especially in the alveoli. Results in dyspnea.
pulmonary embolism (PULL-mon-air-ee EM-boh-lizm)	Blood clot or air bubble in the pulmonary artery or one of its branches. May cause an infarct in the lung tissue.
pulmonary fibrosis (fi-BROH-sis)	Formation of fibrous scar tissue in the lungs that leads to decreased ability to expand the lungs. May be caused by infections, pneumoconiosis, autoimmune diseases, and toxin exposure.
severe acute respiratory syndrome (SARS)	Acute viral respiratory infection that begins like the flu but quickly progresses to severe dyspnea; high fatality rate. First appeared in China in 2003.
silicosis (sil-ih-KOH-sis)	A type of pneumoconiosis that develops from the inhalation of silica (quartz) dust found in quarrying, glass works, sandblasting, and ceramics.
sleep apnea (AP-nee-ah)	Condition in which breathing stops repeatedly during sleep long enough to cause a drop in oxygen levels in the blood.
sudden infant death syndrome (SIDS)	Unexpected and unexplained death of an apparently well infant under one year of age. The child suddenly stops breathing for unknown reasons.
tuberculosis (TB) (too-ber-kyoo-LOH-sis)	Infectious disease caused by the bacteria *Mycobacterium tuberculosis.* Most commonly affects the respiratory system and causes inflammation and calcification in the lungs. Tuberculosis incidence is on the increase and is seen in many patients with weakened immune systems. Multidrug resistant tuberculosis is a particularly dangerous form of the disease because some bacteria have developed a resistance to the standard drug therapy.

Pathology (continued)

TERM	DEFINITION
Pleural Cavity	
empyema (em-pye-EE-mah)	Pus within the pleural space usually associated with a bacterial infection. Also called *pyothorax.*
pleural effusion (PLOO-ral eh-FYOO-zhun)	Abnormal accumulation of fluid in the pleural cavity preventing the lungs from fully expanding. Physicians can detect the presence of fluid by tapping the chest (percussion) or listening with a stethoscope (auscultation).
pleurisy (PLOOR-ih-see)	Inflammation of the pleura characterized by sharp chest pain with each breath. Also called *pleuritis.*
pneumothorax (new-moh-THOH-raks)	Collection of air or gas in the pleural cavity, which may result in collapse of the lung.

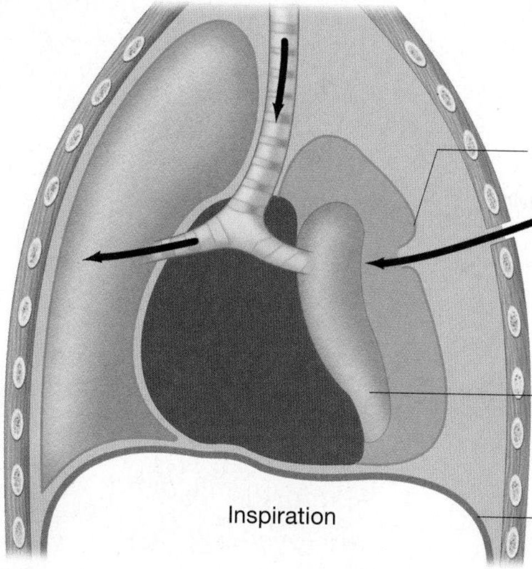

Figure 7.9 Pneumothorax. Figure illustrates how puncture of thoracic wall and tearing of pleural membrane allows air into lung and results in a collapsed lung.

Diagnostic Procedures

TERM	DEFINITION
Clinical Laboratory Tests	
arterial blood gases (ABGs) (ar-TEE-ree-al)	Testing for the gases present in the blood. Generally used to assist in determining the levels of oxygen (O_2) and carbon dioxide (CO_2) in the blood.
sputum culture and sensitivity (C&S) (SPEW-tum)	Testing sputum by placing it on a culture medium and observing any bacterial growth. The specimen is then tested to determine antibiotic effectiveness.
sputum cytology (SPEW-tum sigh-TALL-oh-jee)	Examining sputum for malignant cells.
Diagnostic Imaging	
bronchography (brong-KOG-rah-fee)	X-ray of the lung after a radiopaque substance has been inserted into the trachea or bronchial tube. Resulting x-ray is called a *bronchogram.*
chest x-ray (CXR)	Taking a radiographic picture of the lungs and heart from the back and sides.

Diagnostic Procedures *(continued)*

TERM	DEFINITION
pulmonary angiography (PULL-mon-air-ee an-jee-OG-rah-fee)	Injecting dye into a blood vessel for the purpose of taking an x-ray of the arteries and veins of the lungs.
ventilation-perfusion scan (per-FUSE-shun)	A nuclear medicine diagnostic test that is especially useful in identifying pulmonary emboli. Radioactive air is inhaled for the ventilation portion to determine if air is filling the entire lung. Radioactive intravenous injection shows whether blood is flowing to all parts of the lung.
■ ***Endoscopic Procedures***	
bronchoscopy (Bronch) (brong-KOSS-koh-pee)	Visual examination of the inside of the bronchi; uses an instrument called a *bronchoscope*.

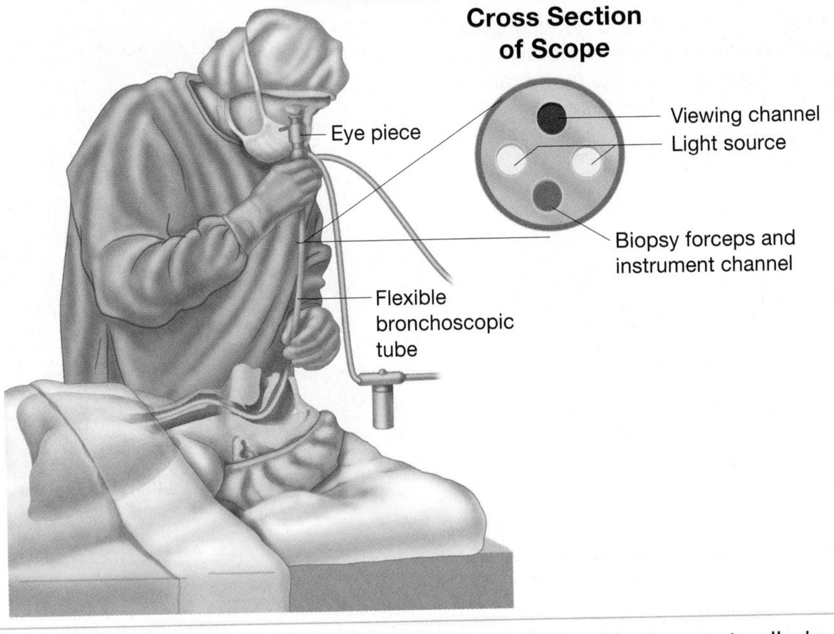

Figure 7.10 Bronchoscopy. Figure illustrates physician using a bronchoscope to inspect the patient's bronchial tubes. Advances in technology include using a videoscope which projects the internal view of the bronchus onto a video screen.

TERM	DEFINITION
laryngoscopy (lair-in-GOSS-koh-pee)	Examination of the interior of the larynx with a lighted instrument called a *laryngoscope*.
■ ***Pulmonary Function Tests***	
oximetry (ox-IM-eh-tree)	Measures the oxygen level in the blood using a device, an *oximeter*, placed on the patient's fingertip or ear lobe.
pulmonary function test (PFT) (PULL-mon-air-ee)	A group of diagnostic tests that give information regarding air flow in and out of the lungs, lung volumes, and gas exchange between the lungs and bloodstream.
spirometry (spy-ROM-eh-tree)	Procedure to measure lung capacity using a **spirometer**.
■ ***Additional Diagnostic Procedures***	
polysomnography (polly-som-NOG-rah-fee)	Monitoring a patient while sleeping to identify sleep apnea. Also called *sleep apnea study*.
sweat test	A test for cystic fibrosis. Patients with this disease have an abnormally large amount of salt in their sweat.
tuberculin skin tests (TB test) (too-BER-kyoo-lin)	Applying the tuberculin purified protein derivative (PPD) under the surface of the skin to determine if the patient has been exposed to tuberculosis. Also called a *Tine* or *Mantoux test*.

Therapeutic Procedures

TERM	DEFINITION
Respiratory Therapy	
aerosol therapy (AIR-oh-sol)	Medication suspended in a mist that is intended to be inhaled. Delivered by a *nebulizer*, which delivers the mist for a period of time while the patient breathes, or a *metered dose inhaler* (MDI), which delivers a single puff of mist.
endotracheal intubation (en-doh-TRAY-kee-al in-too-BAY-shun)	Placing a tube through the mouth, through the glottis, and into the trachea to create a patent airway.

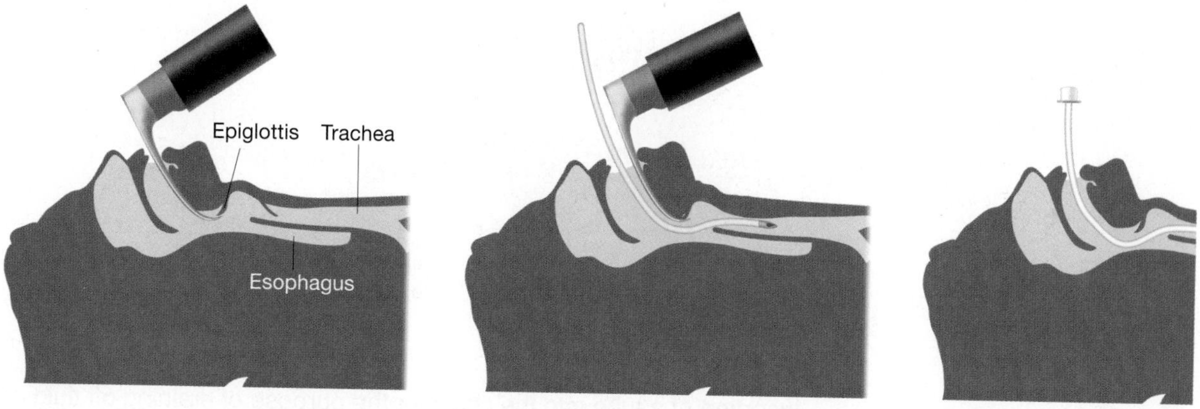

Figure 7.11 Endotracheal intubation. First, a lighted scope is used to identify the trachea from the esophagus. Next, the tube is placed through the pharynx and into the trachea. Finally, the scope is removed, leaving the tube in place.

TERM	DEFINITION
intermittent positive pressure breathing (IPPB)	Method for assisting patients in breathing using a mask that is connected to a machine that produces an increased positive thoracic pressure.
postural drainage	Drainage of secretions from the bronchi by placing the patient in a position that uses gravity to promote drainage. Used for the treatment of cystic fibrosis and bronchiectasis.
supplemental oxygen therapy	Providing a patient with additional concentration of oxygen to improve oxygen levels in the bloodstream. Oxygen may be provided by a mask or nasal cannula.
ventilator (VENT-ih-later)	A machine that provides artificial ventilation for a patient unable to breathe on his or her own. Also called a *respirator*.

Figure 7.12 Patient with tracheostomy tube in place receiving oxygen through mask placed over the tracheostomy opening and attached to a ventilator. *(Ansell Horn/Phototake NYC)*

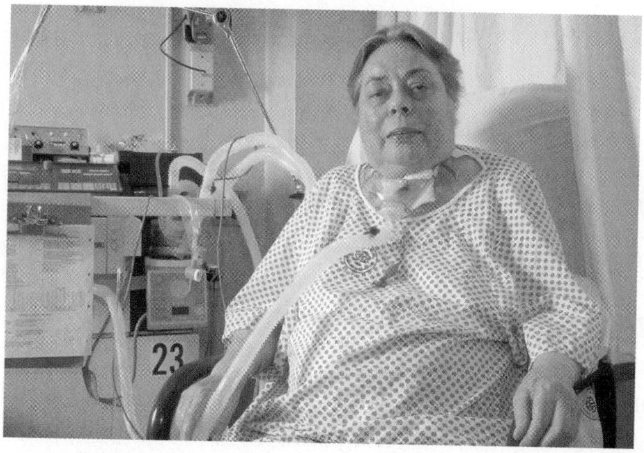

Therapeutic Procedures *(continued)*

TERM	DEFINITION
Surgical Procedures	
thoracentesis (thor-ah-sen-TEE-sis)	Surgical puncture of the chest wall for the removal of fluids. Also called *thoracocentesis*.

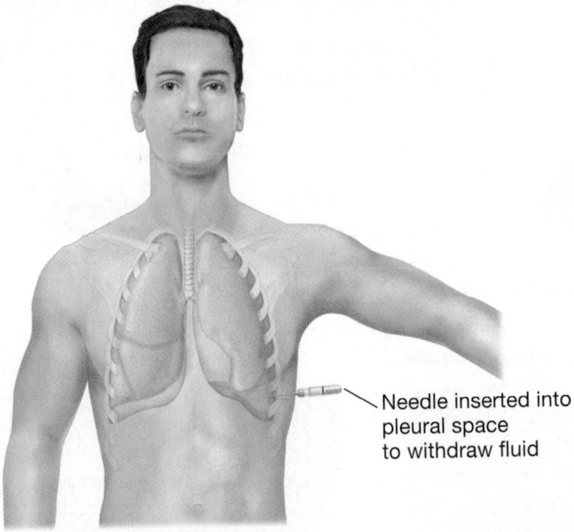

Figure 7.13 Thoracentesis. The needle is inserted between the ribs to withdraw fluid from the pleural sac at the base of the left lung.

TERM	DEFINITION
thoracostomy (thor-ah-KOS-toh-mee)	Insertion of a tube into the chest for the purpose of draining off fluid or air. Also called *chest tube*.
tracheostomy (tray-kee-OSS-toh-mee)	A surgical procedure often performed in an emergency that creates an opening directly into the trachea to allow the patient to breathe easier; also called *tracheotomy*.

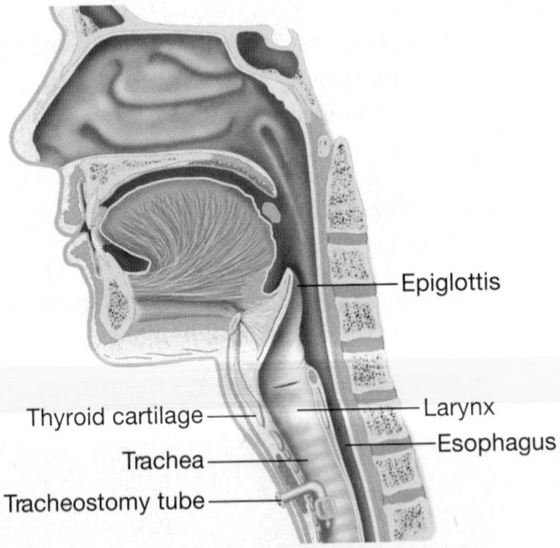

Figure 7.14 A tracheostomy tube in place, inserted through an opening in the front of the neck and anchored within the trachea.

TERM	DEFINITION
Additional Procedures	
cardiopulmonary resuscitation (CPR) (car-dee-oh-PULL-mon-air-ee ree-suss-ih-TAY-shun)	Emergency treatment provided by persons trained in CPR and given to patients when their respirations and heart stop. CPR provides oxygen to the brain, heart, and other vital organs until medical treatment can restore a normal heart and pulmonary function.
Heimlich maneuver (HYME-lik)	Technique for removing a foreign body from the trachea or pharynx by exerting diaphragmatic pressure. Named for Harry Heimlich, a U.S. thoracic surgeon.

Pharmacology

CLASSIFICATION	ACTION	GENERIC AND BRAND NAMES
antibiotic (an-tih-bye-AW-tic)	Kills bacteria causing respiratory infections.	ampicillin; amoxicillin, Amoxil; ciprofloxacin, Cipro
antihistamine (an-tih-HIST-ah-meen)	Blocks the effects of histamine that has been released by the body during an allergy attack.	fexofenadine, Allegra; loratadine, Claritan; diphenhydramine, Benadryl
antitussive (an-tih-TUSS-ive)	Relieves urge to cough.	hydrocodon, Hycodan; dextromethorphan, Vicks Formula 44
bronchodilator (BRONG-koh-dye-late-or)	Relaxes muscle spasms in bronchial tubes. Used to treat asthma.	albuterol, Proventil, Ventolin; salmetrol, Serevent; theophyllin, Theo-Dur
corticosteroids (core-tih-koh-STAIR-ryods)	Reduces inflammation and swelling in the respiratory tract.	fluticasone, Flonase; mometasone, Nasonex; triamcinolone, Azmacort
decongestant (dee-kon-JES-tant)	Reduces stuffiness and congestion throughout the respiratory system.	oxymetazoline, Afrin, Dristan, Sinex; pseudoephedrine, Drixoral, Sudafed
expectorant (ek-SPEK-toh-rant)	Improves the ability to cough up mucus from the respiratory tract.	guaifenesin, Robitussin, Mucinex
mucolytic (myoo-koh-LIT-ik)	Liquefies mucus so it is easier to cough and clear it from the respiratory tract.	N-acetyl-cysteine, Mucomyst

Abbreviations

ABGs	arterial blood gases
ARDS	adult (or acute) respiratory distress syndrome
Bronch	bronchoscopy
CO_2	carbon dioxide
COPD	chronic obstructive pulmonary disease
CPR	cardiopulmonary resuscitation
C&S	culture and sensitivity
CTA	clear to auscultation
CXR	chest x-ray
DOE	dyspnea on exertion
DPT	diphtheria, pertussis, tetanus injection
ENT	ear, nose, and throat
ERV	expiratory reserve volume
FRC	functional residual capacity
HMD	hyaline membrane disease
IC	inspiratory capacity
IPPB	intermittent positive pressure breathing
IRDS	infant respiratory distress syndrome
IRV	inspiratory reserve volume
LLL	left lower lobe
LUL	left upper lobe
MDI	metered dose inhaler
O_2	oxygen
PCP	*Pneumocystis carinii* pneumonia
PFT	pulmonary function test
PPD	purified protein derivative
R	respiration
RA	room air
RDS	respiratory distress syndrome
RLL	right lower lobe
RML	right middle lobe
RRT	registered respiratory therapist
RV	reserve volume
RUL	right upper lobe
SARS	severe acute respiratory syndrome
SIDS	sudden infant death syndrome
SOB	shortness of breath
TB	tuberculosis
TLC	total lung capacity
TPR	temperature, pulse, and respiration
TV	tidal volume
URI	upper respiratory infection
VC	vital capacity

Chapter Review

Terminology Checklist

Below are all Anatomy and Physiology key terms, Word Building, Vocabulary, Pathology, Diagnostic, Therapeutic, and Pharmacology terms presented in this chapter. Use this list as a study tool by placing a check in the box in front of each term as you master its meaning.

- ☐ acapnia
- ☐ adenoids
- ☐ adult respiratory distress syndrome
- ☐ aerosol therapy
- ☐ alveoli
- ☐ anosmia
- ☐ anoxia
- ☐ anthracosis
- ☐ antibiotic
- ☐ antihistamine
- ☐ antitussive
- ☐ apex
- ☐ aphonia
- ☐ apnea
- ☐ arterial blood gases
- ☐ asbestosis
- ☐ asphyxia
- ☐ aspiration
- ☐ asthma
- ☐ atelectasis
- ☐ auditory tube
- ☐ base
- ☐ bradypnea
- ☐ bronchial
- ☐ bronchial tube
- ☐ bronchiectasis
- ☐ bronchioles
- ☐ bronchitis
- ☐ bronchodilator
- ☐ bronchogenic
- ☐ bronchogenic carcinoma
- ☐ bronchogram
- ☐ bronchography
- ☐ bronchoplasty
- ☐ bronchoscope
- ☐ bronchoscopy
- ☐ bronchospasm
- ☐ bronchus
- ☐ carbon dioxide
- ☐ cardiopulmonary resuscitation
- ☐ chest x-ray
- ☐ Cheyne–Stokes respiration
- ☐ chronic obstructive pulmonary disease
- ☐ cilia
- ☐ clubbing
- ☐ corticosteroids
- ☐ croup
- ☐ cyanosis
- ☐ cystic fibrosis
- ☐ decongestant
- ☐ diaphragm
- ☐ diaphragmatic
- ☐ diphtheria
- ☐ dysphonia
- ☐ dyspnea
- ☐ emphysema
- ☐ empyema
- ☐ endotracheal
- ☐ endotracheal intubation
- ☐ epiglottis
- ☐ epistaxis
- ☐ eupnea
- ☐ eustachian tube
- ☐ exhalation
- ☐ expectorant
- ☐ expiratory reserve volume
- ☐ external respiration
- ☐ functional residual capacity
- ☐ glottis
- ☐ Heimlich maneuver
- ☐ hemoptysis
- ☐ hemothorax
- ☐ hilum
- ☐ histoplasmosis
- ☐ hypercapnia
- ☐ hyperpnea
- ☐ hyperventilation
- ☐ hypopnea
- ☐ hypoventilation
- ☐ hypoxemia
- ☐ hypoxia
- ☐ infant respiratory distress syndrome
- ☐ influenza
- ☐ inhalation
- ☐ inspiratory capacity
- ☐ inspiratory reserve volume
- ☐ intercostal muscles
- ☐ intermittent positive pressure breathing
- ☐ internal medicine
- ☐ internal respiration
- ☐ laryngeal
- ☐ laryngectomy
- ☐ laryngitis
- ☐ laryngopharynx
- ☐ laryngoplasty
- ☐ laryngoplegia
- ☐ laryngoscope
- ☐ laryngoscopy
- ☐ larynx
- ☐ Legionnaire's disease
- ☐ lingual tonsils
- ☐ lobectomy
- ☐ lobes
- ☐ lungs
- ☐ mediastinum
- ☐ mucolytic
- ☐ mucous membrane
- ☐ mucus
- ☐ *Mycoplasma* pneumonia
- ☐ nares
- ☐ nasal cannula
- ☐ nasal cavity

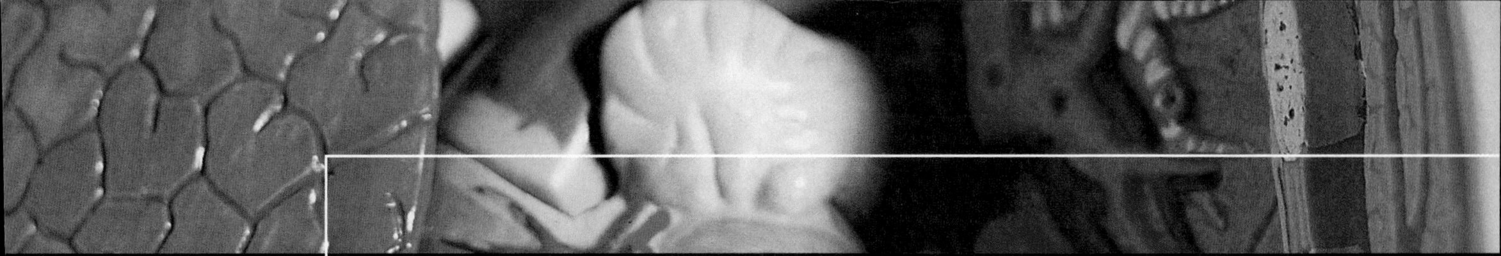

8 Digestive System

Learning Objectives

Upon completion of this chapter, you will be able to:

- Identify and define the combining forms and suffixes introduced in this chapter.
- Correctly spell and pronounce medical terms and major anatomical structures relating to the digestive system.
- Locate and describe the major organs of the digestive system and their functions.
- Describe the function of the accessory organs of the digestive system.
- Identify the shape and function of each type of tooth.
- Build and define digestive system medical terms from word parts.
- Identify and define digestive system vocabulary terms.
- Identify and define selected digestive system pathology terms.
- Identify and define selected digestive system diagnostic procedures.
- Identify and define selected digestive system therapeutic procedures.
- Identify and define selected medications relating to the digestive system.
- Define selected abbreviations associated with the digestive system.

Digestive System at a Glance

Function

The digestive system begins breaking down food through mechanical and chemical digestion. After being digested, nutrient molecules are absorbed into the body and enter the blood stream. Any food not digested or absorbed is eliminated as solid waste.

Organs

colon
esophagus
gallbladder (GB)
liver
oral cavity
pancreas
pharynx
salivary glands
small intestine
stomach

Combining Forms

an/o	anus	**gloss/o**	tongue
append/o	appendix	**hepat/o**	liver
appendic/o	appendix	**ile/o**	ileum
bar/o	weight	**jejun/o**	jejunum
bucc/o	cheek	**labi/o**	lip
cec/o	cecum	**lapar/o**	abdomen
chol/e	bile, gall	**lingu/o**	tongue
cholangi/o	bile duct	**lith/o**	stone
cholecyst/o	gallbladder	**odont/o**	tooth
choledoch/o	common bile duct	**or/o**	mouth
col/o	colon	**palat/o**	palate
colon/o	colon	**pancreat/o**	pancreas
dent/o	tooth	**pharyng/o**	throat, pharynx
duoden/o	duodenum	**proct/o**	anus and rectum
enter/o	small intestine	**pylor/o**	pylorus
esophag/o	esophagus	**rect/o**	rectum
gastr/o	stomach	**sialaden/o**	salivary gland
gingiv/o	gums	**sigmoid/o**	sigmoid colon

Suffixes

-emesis	vomit	**-phagia**	eat, swallow
-lithiasis	condition of stones	**-prandial**	pertaining to a meal
-orexia	appetite	**-tripsy**	surgical crushing
-pepsia	digestion		

Digestive System Illustrated

salivary glands, p. 250

Produces saliva

oral cavity, p. 244

Ingests, chews, and swallows food

esophagus, p. 247

Transports food to the stomach

stomach, p. 248

Secretes acid and mixes food to start digestion

pancreas, p. 251

Secretes digestive enzymes and buffers

liver & gallbladder, pp. 250, 251

Produces and stores bile

small intestine, p. 248

Digests and absorbs nutrients

colon, p. 249

Reabsorbs water and stores feces

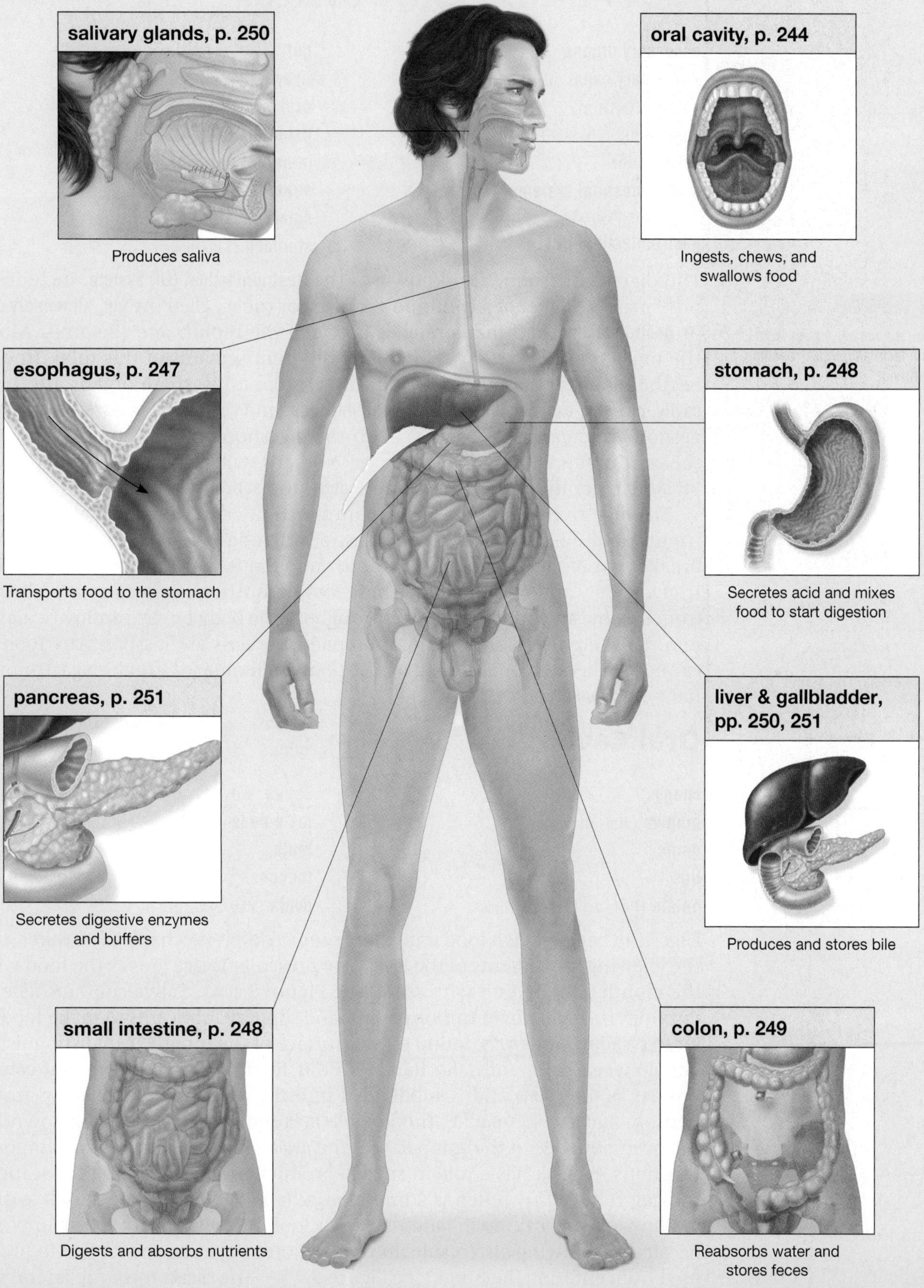

Anatomy and Physiology of the Digestive System

accessory organs
alimentary canal (al-ih-MEN-tar-ree)
colon (COH-lon)
esophagus (eh-SOFF-ah-gus)
gallbladder
gastrointestinal system (gas-troh-in-TESS-tih-nal)
gastrointestinal tract
gut
liver
oral cavity
pancreas (PAN-kree-ass)
pharynx (FAIR-inks)
salivary glands (SAL-ih-vair-ee)
small intestine
stomach (STUM-ak)

Med Term Tip

The term *alimentary* comes from the Latin term *alimentum* meaning "nourishment."

The digestive system, also known as the **gastrointestinal (GI) system,** includes approximately 30 feet of a continuous muscular tube, called the **gut, alimentary canal,** or **gastrointestinal tract** that stretches between the mouth and the anus. Most of the organs in this system are actually different sections of this tube. In order, beginning at the mouth and continuing to the anus, these organs are the **oral cavity, pharynx, esophagus, stomach, small intestine,** and **colon.** The **accessory organs** of digestion are organs that participate in the digestion process, but are not part of the continuous alimentary canal. These organs, which are connected to the gut by a duct, are the **liver, pancreas, gallbladder,** and **salivary glands.**

The digestive system has three main functions: digesting food, absorbing nutrients, and eliminating waste. Digestion includes the physical and chemical breakdown of large food particles into simple nutrient molecules like glucose, triglycerides, and amino acids. These simple nutrient molecules are absorbed from the intestines and circulated throughout the body by the cardiovascular system. They are used for growth and repair of organs and tissues. Any food that cannot be digested or absorbed by the body is eliminated from the gastrointestinal system as a solid waste.

Oral Cavity

cheeks
gingiva (JIN-jih-veh)
gums
lips
palate (PAL-at)
saliva (suh-LYE-vah)
taste buds
teeth
tongue
uvula (YU-vyu-lah)

Digestion begins when food enters the mouth and is mechanically broken up by the chewing movements of the **teeth.** The muscular **tongue** moves the food within the mouth and mixes it with **saliva** (see Figure 8.1 ■). Saliva contains digestive enzymes to break down carbohydrates and slippery lubricants to make food easier to swallow. **Taste buds,** found on the surface of the tongue, can distinguish the bitter, sweet, sour, and salty flavors in our food. The roof of the oral cavity is known as the **palate** and is subdivided into the hard palate, the bony anterior portion, and the soft palate, the flexible posterior portion. Hanging down from the posterior edge of the soft palate is the **uvula.** The uvula serves two important functions. First, it has a role in speech production. Second, it is the location of the gag reflex. This reflex is stimulated when food enters the throat without swallowing (for example, laughing with food in your mouth). It is important because swallowing also results in the epiglottis covering the larynx to prevent food from entering the lungs (see Figure 8.2 ■). The **cheeks** form the lateral walls of this cavity and the **lips** are the anterior opening. The entire oral cavity is lined

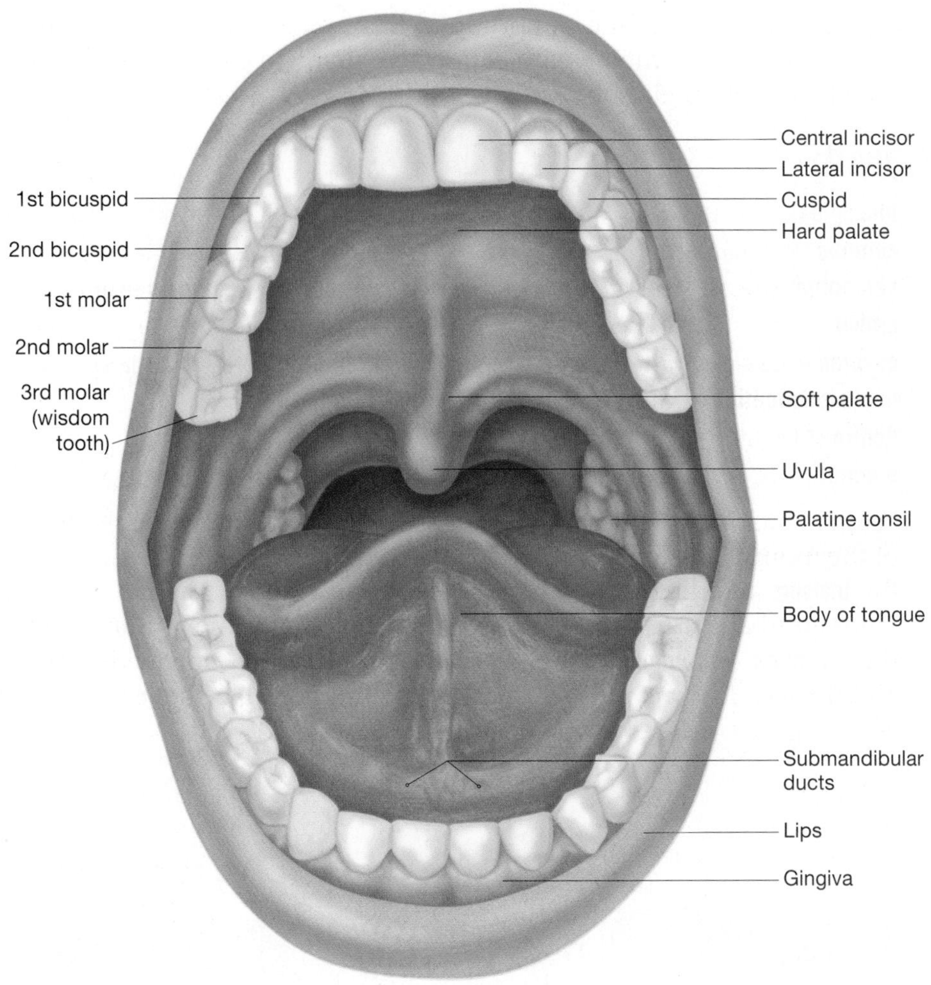

Figure 8.1 Anatomy of structures of the oral cavity.

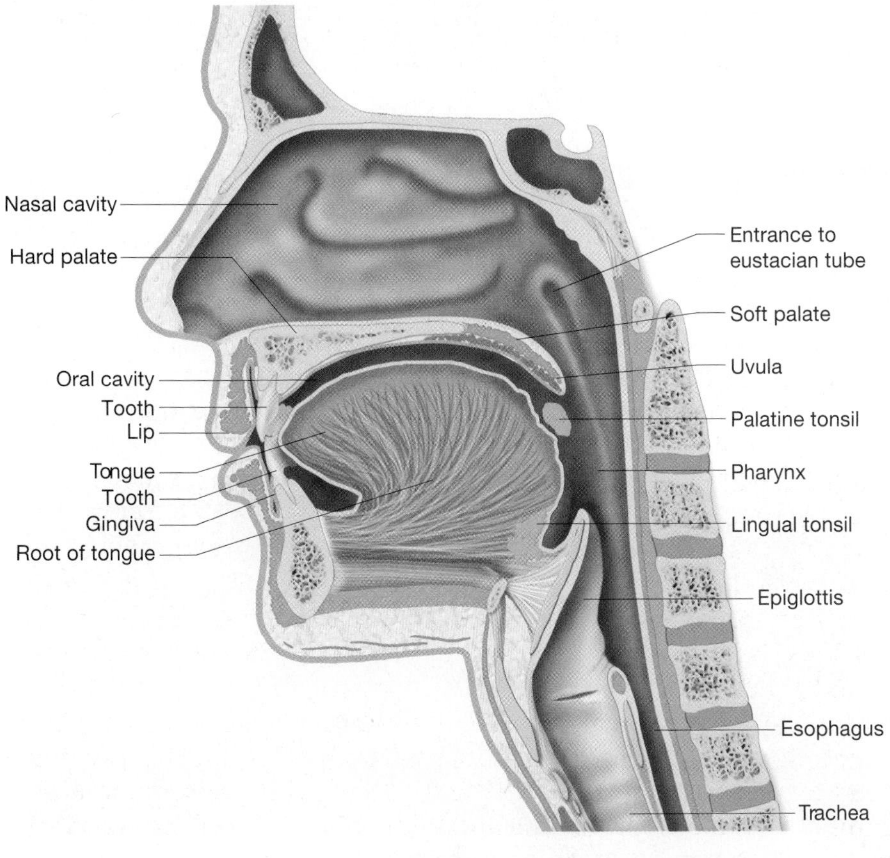

Figure 8.2 Sagittal view of the head and neck, illustrating structures of the oral cavity, and pharynx, and esophagus.

with mucous membrane. A portion of this mucous membrane forms the **gums**, or **gingiva**, which combine with connective tissue to cover the jaw bone and seal off the teeth in their bony sockets.

Teeth

bicuspids (bye-CUSS-pids)
canines (KAY-nines)
cementum (see-MEN-tum)
crown
cuspids (CUSS-pids)
deciduous teeth (dee-SID-yoo-us)
dentin (DEN-tin)
enamel
incisors (in-SIGH-zors)
molars (MOH-lars)
periodontal ligaments (pair-ee-on-DON-tal)
permanent teeth
premolars (pree-MOH-lars)
pulp cavity
root
root canal

Med Term Tip

There are three different molars, simply referred to as the first, second, or third molars. However, the third molar has a more common name, the wisdom tooth. Not every person ever forms all four wisdom teeth. Unfortunately, most people do not have enough room in their jaws for the third molars to properly erupt through the gum, a condition requiring surgical removal of the third molar referred to as an *impacted wisdom tooth.*

Teeth are an important part of the first stage of digestion. The teeth in the front of the mouth bite, tear, or cut food into small pieces. These cutting teeth include the **incisors** and the **cuspids** or **canines** (see Figure 8.3 ■). The remaining posterior teeth grind and crush food into even finer pieces. These grinding teeth include the **bicuspids**, or **premolars**, and the **molars**. A tooth can be subdivided into the **crown** and the **root**. The crown is that part of the tooth visible above the gum line; the

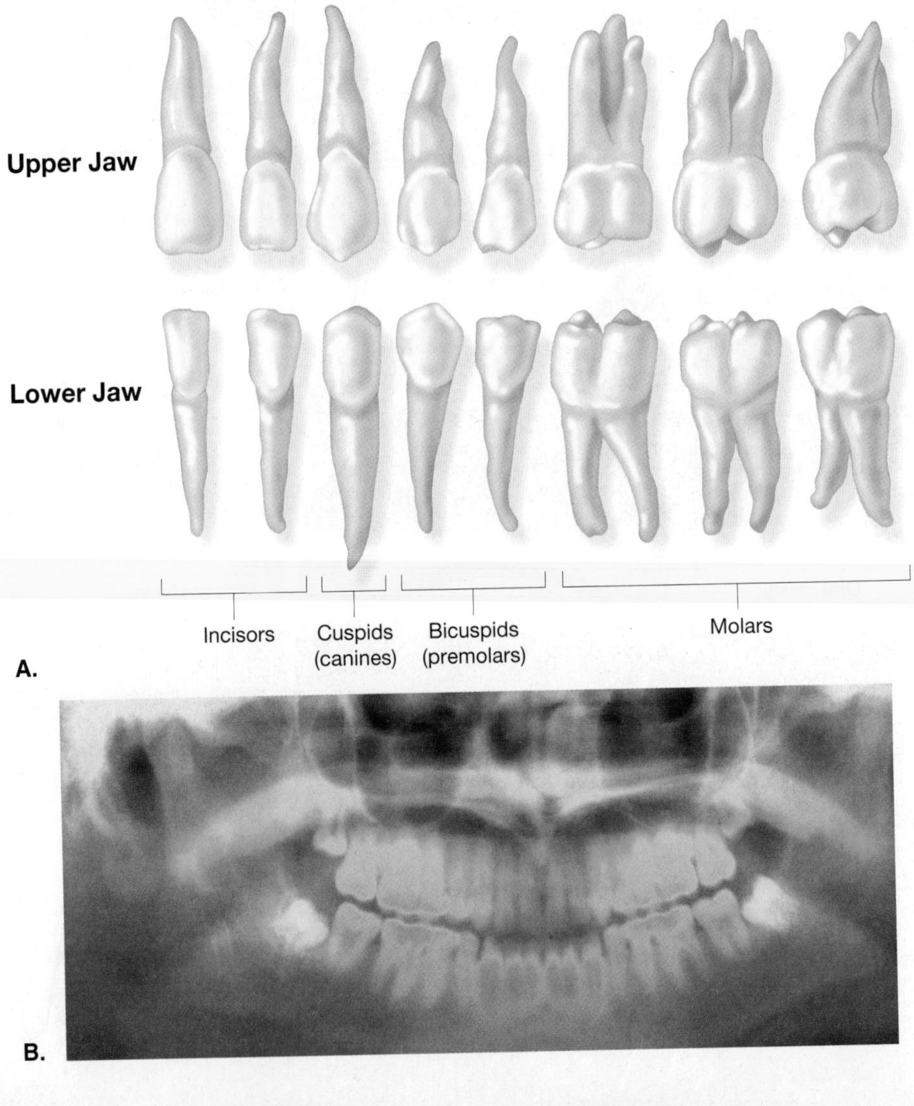

■ **Figure 8.3** A) The name and shape of the adult teeth. These teeth represent those found in the right side of the mouth. Those of the left side would be a mirror image. The incisors and cuspids are cutting teeth. The bicuspids and molars are grinding teeth. B) Color enhanced x-ray of all teeth. Note the four wisdom teeth (3rd molars) that have not erupted. *(Science Photo Library/Photo Researchers, Inc.)*

root is below the gum line. The root is anchored in the bony socket of the jaw by **cementum** and tiny **periodontal ligaments**. The crown of the tooth is covered by a layer of **enamel**, the hardest substance in the body. Under the enamel layer is **dentin**, the substance that makes up the main bulk of the tooth. The hollow interior of a tooth is called the **pulp cavity** in the crown and the **root canal** in the root. These cavities contain soft tissue made up of blood vessels, nerves, and lymph vessels (see Figure 8.4 ■).

Humans have two sets of teeth. The first set, often referred to as baby teeth, are **deciduous teeth.** There are 20 teeth in this set that erupt through the gums between the ages of 6 and 28 months. At approximately 6 years of age, these teeth begin to fall out and are replaced by the 32 **permanent teeth**. This replacement process continues until about 18 to 20 years of age.

Med Term Tip

The combining form *dent/o* means teeth. Hence we have terms such as dentist and dentistry. The combining form *odont/o* also means teeth and when combined with *orth/o*, which means straight, we have the speciality of *orthodontics*, or straightening teeth.

Pharynx

epiglottis (ep-ih-GLOT-iss)
laryngopharynx
oropharynx

When food is swallowed, it enters the **oropharynx** and then the **laryngopharynx** (see Figure 8.2). Remember from your study of the respiratory system in Chapter 7 that air is also traveling through these portions of the pharynx. The **epiglottis** is a cartilaginous flap that folds down to cover the larynx and trachea so that food is prevented from entering the respiratory tract and instead continues into the esophagus.

Esophagus

peristalsis (pair-ih-STALL-sis)

The esophagus is a muscular tube of about 10 inches long in adults. Food entering the esophagus is carried through the thoracic cavity and diaphragm and into the abdominal cavity where it enters the stomach (see Figure 8.5 ■). Food is

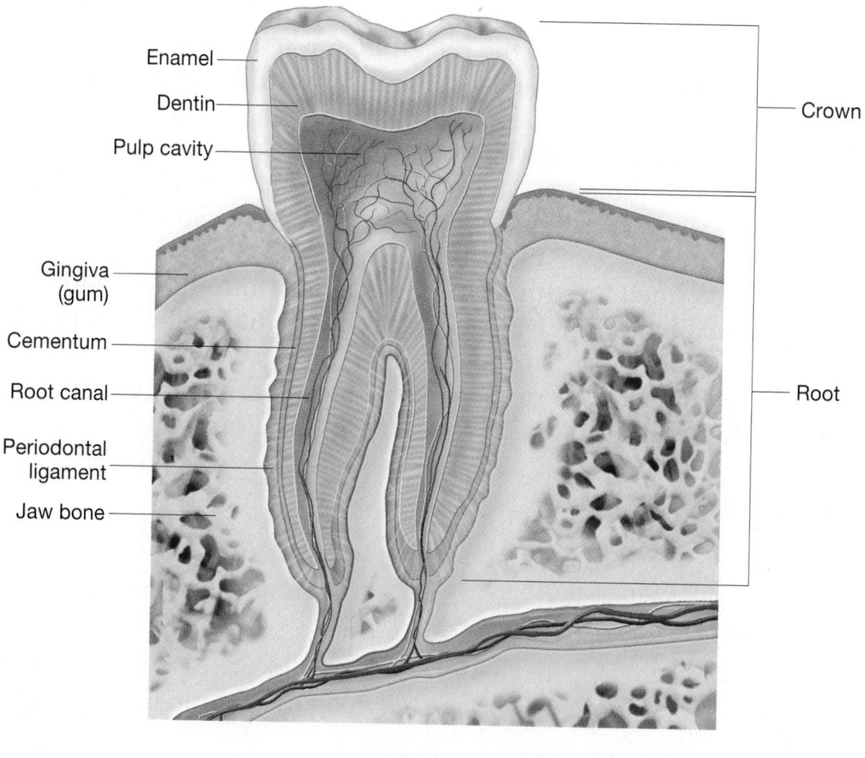

■ **Figure 8.4** An adult tooth, longitudinal view showing internal structures of the crown and root.

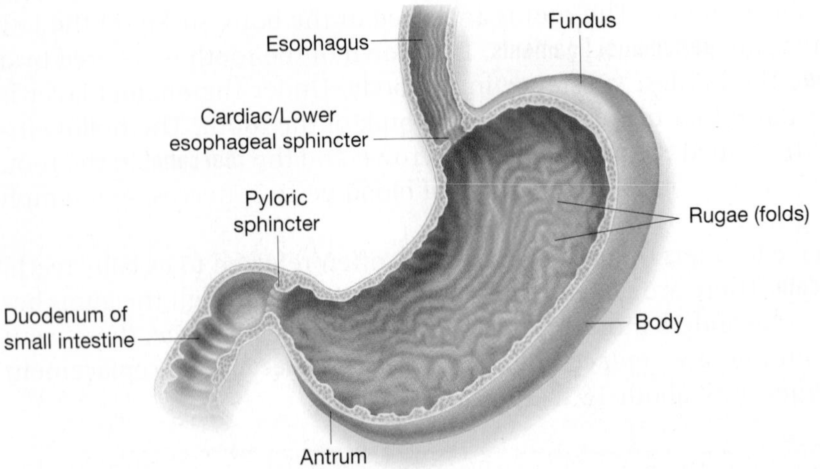

Figure 8.5 The stomach, longitudinal view showing regions and internal structures.

Med Term Tip

It takes about 10 seconds for swallowed food to reach the stomach.

propelled along the esophagus by wavelike muscular contractions called **peristalsis.** In fact, peristalsis works to push food through the entire gastrointestinal tract.

Stomach

antrum (AN-trum)
body
cardiac sphincter
chyme (KIGHM)
fundus (FUN-dus)
hydrochloric acid
lower esophageal sphincter (eh-soff-ah-JEE-al SFINGK-ter)
pyloric sphincter (pigh-LOR-ik SFINGK-ter)
rugae (ROO-gay)
sphincters (SFINGK-ters)

The stomach, a J-shaped muscular organ that acts as a bag or sac to collect and churn food with digestive juices, is composed of three parts: the **fundus** or upper region, the **body** or main portion, and the **antrum** or lower region (see Figure 8.5). The folds in the lining of the stomach are called **rugae**. When the stomach fills with food, the rugae stretch out and disappear. **Hydrochloric acid** (HCl) is secreted by glands in the mucous membrane lining of the stomach. Food mixes with hydrochloric acid and other gastric juices to form a liquid mixture called **chyme**, which then passes through the remaining portion of the digestive system.

Entry into and exit from the stomach is controlled by muscular valves called **sphincters**. These valves open and close to ensure that food can only move forward down the gut tube. The **cardiac sphincter**, named for its proximity to the heart, is located between the esophagus and the fundus. Also called the **lower esophageal sphincter** (LES), it keeps food from flowing backward into the esophagus.

Med Term Tip

It is easier to remember the function of the pyloric sphincter when you note that *pylor/o* means "gatekeeper." This gatekeeper controls the forward movement of food. Sphincters are rings of muscle that can be opened and closed to control entry and exit from hollow organs like the stomach, colon, and bladder.

The antrum tapers off into the **pyloric sphincter**, which regulates the passage of food into the small intestine. Only a small amount of the chyme is allowed to enter the small intestine with each opening of the sphincter for two important reasons. First, the small intestine is much narrower than the stomach and cannot hold as much as the stomach can. Second, the chyme is highly acidic and must be thoroughly neutralized as it leaves the stomach.

Small Intestine

duodenum (doo-oh-DEE-num / doo-OD-eh-num)
ileocecal valve (ill-ee-oh-SEE-kal)
ileum (ILL-ee-um)
jejunum (jee-JOO-num)

The small intestine, or small bowel, is the major site of digestion and absorption of nutrients from food. It is located between the pyloric sphincter and the colon (see Figure 8.6 ■). Because the small intestine is concerned with absorption of food products, an abnormality in this organ can cause malnutrition. The small intestine, with an average length of 20 feet, is the longest portion of the alimentary canal and has three sections: the **duodenum**, the **jejunum**, and the **ileum**.

- The duodenum, which extends from the pyloric sphincter to the jejunum, is about 10 to 12 inches long. Digestion is completed in the duodenum after the liquid chyme from the stomach is mixed with digestive juices from the pancreas and gallbladder.
- The jejunum, or middle portion, extends from the duodenum to the ileum and is about 8 feet long.
- The ileum is the last portion of the small intestine and extends from the jejunum to the colon. At 12 feet in length, it is the longest portion of the small intestine. The ileum connects to the colon with a sphincter called the **ileocecal valve**.

Colon

anal sphincter (AY-nal SFINGK-ter)
anus (AY-nus)
ascending colon
cecum (SEE-kum)
defecation
descending colon
feces (FEE-seez)
rectum (REK-tum)
sigmoid colon (SIG-moyd)
transverse colon
vermiform appendix (VER-mih-form ah-PEN-diks)

Fluid that remains after the complete digestion and absorption of nutrients in the small intestine enters the colon or large intestine (see Figure 8.7 ■). Most of this fluid is water that is reabsorbed into the body. The material that remains after absorption is solid waste called **feces** (or stool). This is the product evacuated in bowel movements (BM).

The colon is approximately 5 feet long and extends from the ileocecal valve of the small intestine to the **anus**. The **cecum** is a pouch or saclike area in the first two to three inches at the beginning of the colon. The **vermiform appendix** is a small worm-shaped outgrowth at the end of the cecum. The remaining colon consists of the **ascending colon**, **transverse colon**, **descending colon**, and **sigmoid colon**. The ascend-

Med Term Tip

Word watch—Be careful not to confuse the word root *ile/o* meaning "ileum," a portion of the small intestines, and *ili/o* meaning "ilium," a pelvic bone.

Med Term Tip

We can survive without a portion of the small intestine. For example, in cases of cancer, much of the small intestine and/or colon may have to be removed. The surgeon then creates an opening between the remaining intestine and the abdominal wall. The combining form for the section of intestine connected to the abdominal wall and the suffix *-ostomy* are used to describe this procedure. For example, if a person has a *jejunostomy*, the jejunum is connected to the abdominal wall and the ileum (and remainder of the gut tube) has been removed.

Med Term Tip

The term *colon* refers to the large intestine. However, you should be aware that many people use it incorrectly as a general term referring to the entire intestinal system, both small and large intestines.

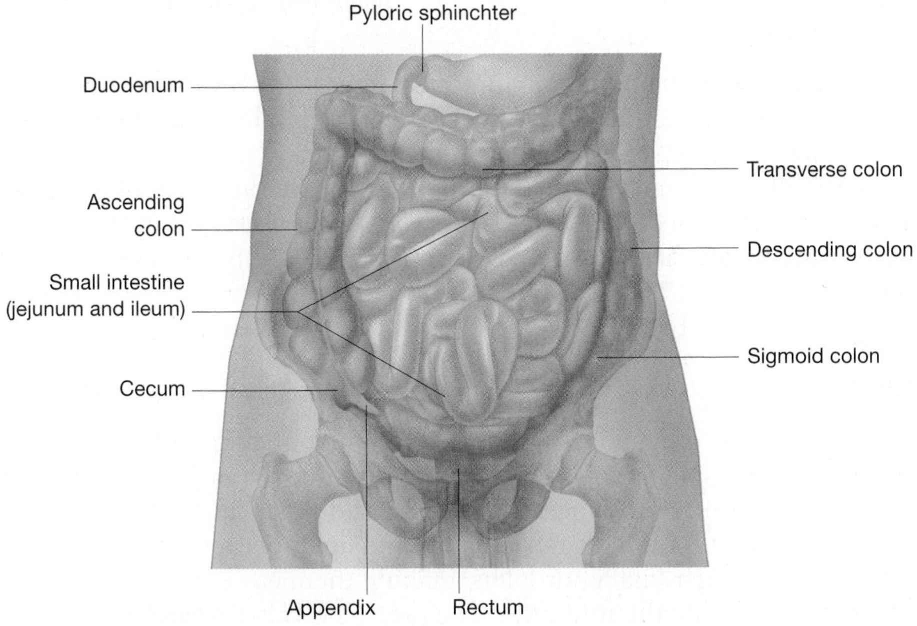

■ **Figure 8.6** The small intestine. Anterior view of the abdominopelvic cavity illustrating how the three sections of small intestine—duodenum, jejunum, ileum—begin at the pyloric sphincter and end at the colon, but are not arranged in a orderly fashion.

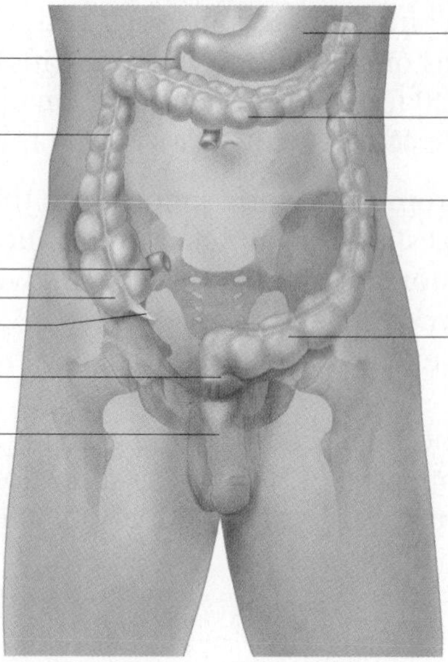

Figure 8.7 The regions of the colon beginning with the cecum and ending at the anus.

ing colon on the right side extends from the cecum to the lower border of the liver. The transverse colon begins where the ascending colon leaves off and moves horizontally across the upper abdomen toward the spleen. The descending colon then travels down the left side of the body to where the sigmoid colon begins. The sigmoid colon curves in an S-shape back to the midline of the body and ends at the **rectum**. The rectum, where feces is stored, leads into the anus, which contains the **anal sphincter**. This sphincter consists of rings of voluntary and involuntary muscles to control the evacuation of feces or **defecation**.

Med Term Tip

In anatomy the term *accessory* generally means that the structure is auxiliary to a more important structure. This is not true for these organs. Digestion would not be possible without the digestive juices produced by these organs.

Accessory Organs of the Digestive System

As described earlier, the accessory organs of the digestive system are the salivary glands, the liver, the pancreas, and the gallbladder. In general, these organs function by producing much of the digestive fluids and enzymes necessary for the chemical breakdown of food. Each is attached to the gut tube by a duct.

Salivary Glands

amylase (AM-ill-ace)
bolus
parotid glands (pah-ROT-id)
sublingual glands (sub-LING-gwal)
submandibular glands (sub-man-DIB-yoo-lar)

Salivary glands in the oral cavity produce saliva. This very watery and slick fluid allows food to be swallowed with less danger of choking. Saliva mixed with food in the mouth forms a **bolus**, chewed food that is ready to swallow. Saliva also contains the digestive enzyme **amylase** that begins the digestion of carbohydrates. There are three pairs of salivary glands. The **parotid glands** are in front of the ears, and the **submandibular glands** and **sublingual glands** are in the floor of the mouth (see Figure 8.8 ■).

Med Term Tip

The liver weighs about 4 pounds and has so many important functions that people cannot live without it. It has become a major transplant organ. The liver is also able to regenerate itself. You can lose more than half of your liver, and it will regrow.

Liver

bile (BYE-al)
emulsification (ee-mull-sih-fih-KAY-shun)

The liver, a large organ located in the right upper quadrant of the abdomen, has several functions, including processing the nutrients absorbed by the intestines, detoxifying harmful substances in the body, and producing **bile** (see Figure 8.9 ■). Bile is important for the digestion of fats and lipids because it breaks up large fat globules into much smaller droplets, making them easier to digest in the watery environment inside the intestines. The process is called **emulsification**.

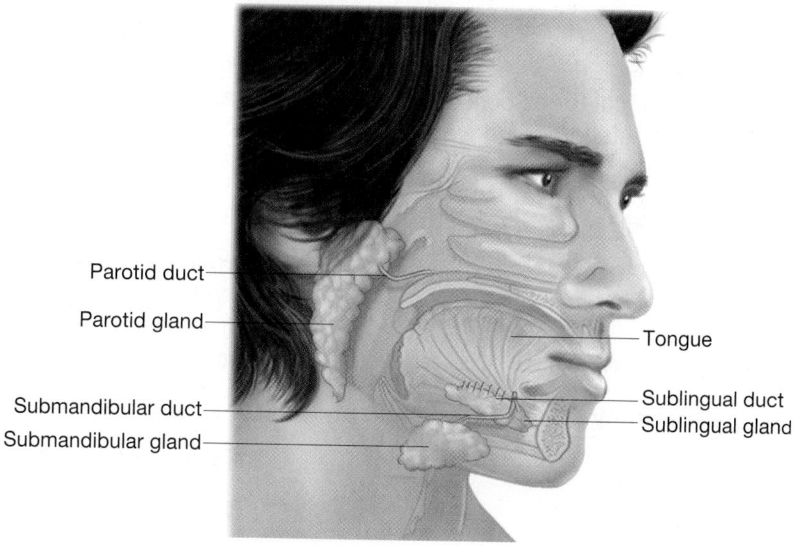

Figure 8.8 The salivary glands, parotid, sublingual, and submandibular. This images shows the position of each gland and its duct emptying into the oral cavity.

Gallbladder

common bile duct
cystic duct (SIS-tik)
hepatic duct (hep-PAT-tik)

Bile produced by the liver is stored in the gallbladder (GB). As the liver produces bile, it travels down the **hepatic duct** and up the **cystic duct** into the gallbladder (see Figure 8.9). In response to the presence of fat in the chyme, the muscular wall of the gallbladder contracts and sends bile back down the cystic duct and into the **common bile duct** (CBD), which carries bile to the duodenum where it is able to emulsify the fat in chyme.

Pancreas

buffers
pancreatic duct (pan-kree-AT-ik)
pancreatic enzymes (pan-kree-AT-ik EN-zimes)

The pancreas, connected to the duodenum by the **pancreatic duct,** produces two important secretions for digestion—**buffers** and **pancreatic enzymes** (see Figure 8.9). Buffers neutralize acidic chyme that has just left the stomach, and pancreatic enzymes chemically digest carbohydrates, fats, and proteins. The pancreas is also an endocrine gland that produces the hormones insulin and glucagon, which play a role in regulating the level of glucose in the blood and are discussed in further detail in Chapter 11.

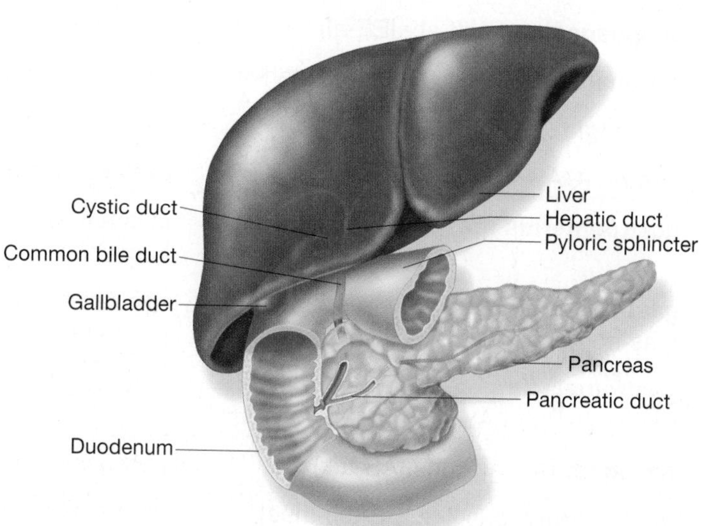

Figure 8.9 The accessory organs of the digestive system: the liver, gallbladder, and pancreas. Image shows the relationship of these three organs and their ducts to the duodenum.

Word Building

The following list contains examples of medical terms built directly from word parts. The definitions for these terms can be determined by a straightforward translation of the word parts.

COMBINING FORM	COMBINED WITH	MEDICAL TERM	DEFINITION
an/o	-al	**anal**	pertaining to the anus

Med Term Tip

Word watch—Be careful when using the combining form *an/o* meaning "anus" and the prefix *an* meaning "none."

COMBINING FORM	COMBINED WITH	MEDICAL TERM	DEFINITION
append/o	-ectomy	**appendectomy** (ap-en-DEK-toh-mee)	removal of the appendix
appendic/o	-itis	**appendicitis** (ah-pen-dih-SIGH-tis)	inflammation of the appendix
bucc/o	-al	**buccal** (BYOO-kal)	pertaining to cheeks
	labi/o -al	**buccolabial** (BYOO-koh-labe-ee-all)	pertaining to cheeks and lips
cholecyst/o	-ectomy	**cholecystectomy** (koh-lee-sis-TEK-toh-mee)	removal of the gallbladder
	-gram	**cholecystogram** (koh-lee-SIS-toh-gram)	record of the gallbladder
	-ic	**cholecystic** (koh-lee-SIS-tik)	pertaining to the gallbladder
	-algia	**cholecystalgia** (koh-lee-sis-TAL-jee-ah)	gallbladder pain
col/o	-ectomy	**colectomy** (koh-LEK-toh-mee)	removal of the colon
	-ostomy	**colostomy** (koh-LOSS-toh-mee)	create an opening in the colon
	rect/o -al	**colorectal** (kohl-oh-REK-tall)	pertaining to the colon and rectum
colon/o	-scope	**colonoscope** (koh-LON-oh-scope)	instrument to view colon
	-ic	**colonic** (koh-LON-ik)	pertaining to the colon
dent/o	-al	**dental** (DENT-al)	pertaining to teeth
	-algia	**dentalgia** (dent-AL-gee-ah)	tooth pain
duoden/o	-al	**duodenal** (duo-DEN-all / do-ODD-in-all)	pertaining to the duodenum
enter/o	-ic	**enteric** (en-TARE-ik)	pertaining to the small intestine
	-itis	**enteritis** (en-ter-EYE-tis)	small intestine inflammation
esophag/o	-eal	**esophageal** (eh-soff-ah-JEE-al)	pertaining to the esophagus
	-ectasis	**esophagectasis** (eh-soff-ah-JEK-tah-sis)	dilated esophagus
gastr/o	-algia	**gastralgia** (gas-TRAL-jee-ah)	stomach pain
	-ic	**gastric** (GAS-trik)	pertaining to the stomach
	enter/o -itis	**gastroenteritis** (gas-troh-en-ter-EYE-tis)	inflammation of stomach and small intestine
	enter/o -ologist	**gastroenterologist** (gas-troh-en-ter-ALL-oh-jist)	specialist in the stomach and small intestine
	-malacia	**gastromalacia** (gas-troh-mah-LAY-she-ah)	softening of the stomach
	nas/o -ic	**nasogastric** (nay-zoh-GAS-trik)	pertaining to the nose and stomach
	-ostomy	**gastrostomy** (gas-TROSS-toh-mee)	create an opening in the stomach

Word Building *(continued)*

COMBINING FORM	COMBINED WITH	MEDICAL TERM	DEFINITION
	-scope	**gastroscope** (GAS-troh-scope)	instrument to view inside the stomach
	-itis	**gastritis** (gas-TRY-tis)	stomach inflammation
	-ectomy	**gastrectomy** (gas-TREK-toh-mee)	removal of the stomach
gingiv/o	-al	**gingival** (JIN-jih-vul)	pertaining to the gums
	-itis	**gingivitis** (jin-jih-VIGH-tis)	inflammation of the gums
gloss/o	-al	**glossal** (GLOSS-all)	pertaining to the tongue
	hypo- -al	**hypoglossal** (high-poe-GLOSS-all)	pertaining to under the tongue
hepat/o	-itis	**hepatitis** (hep-ah-TYE-tis)	inflammation of the liver
	-oma	**hepatoma** (hep-ah-TOH-mah)	liver tumor
	-ic	**hepatic** (hep-AT-ik)	pertaining to the liver
ile/o	-al	**ileal** (ILL-ee-all)	pertaining to the ileum
	-ostomy	**ileostomy** (ill-ee-OSS-toh-mee)	create an opening in the ileum
jejun/o	-al	**jejunal** (jih-JUNE-all)	pertaining to the jejunum
lapar/o	-otomy	**laparotomy** (lap-ah-ROT-oh-mee)	incision into the abdomen
	-scope	**laparoscope** (LAP-ah-roh-scope)	instrument to view inside the abdomen
lingu/o	sub- -al	**sublingual** (sub-LING-gwal)	pertaining to under the tongue
odont/o	orth/o -ic	**orthodontic** (or-thoh-DON-tik)	pertaining to straight teeth
	peri- -ic	**periodontic** (pair-ee-oh-DON-tik)	pertaining to around the teeth
or/o	-al	**oral** (OR-ral)	pertaining to the mouth
palat/o	-plasty	**palatoplasty** (pa-LOT-toh-plas-tee)	surgical repair of the palate
pancreat/o	-itis	**pancreatitis** (pan-kree-ah-TYE-tis)	inflammation of the pancreas
	-ic	**pancreatic** (pan-kree-AT-ik)	pertaining to the pancreas
pharyng/o	-eal	**pharyngeal** (fair-in-JEE-all)	pertaining to the throat
	-plegia	**pharyngoplegia** (fair-in-goh-PLEE-jee-ah)	paralysis of the throat
	-plasty	**pharyngoplasty** (fair-ING-oh-plas-tee)	surgical repair of the throat
proct/o	-ptosis	**proctoptosis** (prok-top-TOH-sis)	drooping rectum and anus
	-logist	**proctologist** (prok-TOL-oh-jist)	specialist in the rectum and anus
	-pexy	**proctopexy** (PROK-toh-pek-see)	surgical fixation of the rectum and anus
pylor/o	-ic	**pyloric** (pie-LORE-ik)	pertaining to the pylorus
rect/o	-al	**rectal** (RECK-tall)	pertaining to the rectum
sialaden/o	-itis	**sialadenitis** (sigh-al-add-eh-NIGH-tis)	inflammation of a salivary gland
sigmoid/o	-scope	**sigmoidoscope** (sig-MOYD-oh-scope)	instrument to view inside the sigmoid colon
	-al	**sigmoidal** (sig-MOYD-all)	pertaining to the sigmoid colon

Word Building *(continued)*

SUFFIX	COMBINED WITH	MEDICAL TERM	DEFINITION
-emesis	hemat/o	**hematemesis** (hee-mah-TEM-eh-sis)	vomiting blood
	hyper-	**hyperemesis** (high-per-EM-eh-sis)	excessive vomiting
-orexia	an-	**anorexia** (an-oh-REK-see-ah)	absence of an appetite
	dys-	**dysorexia** (dis-oh-REKS-ee-ah)	abnormal appetite
-pepsia	brady-	**bradypepsia** (brad-ee-PEP-see-ah)	slow digestion
	dys-	**dyspepsia** (dis-PEP-see-ah)	difficult digestion
-phagia	a-	**aphagia** (ah-FAY-jee-ah)	unable to swallow/eat
	dys-	**dysphagia** (dis-FAY-jee-ah)	difficulty swallowing/eating
	poly-	**polyphagia** (pall-ee-FAY-jee-ah)	many (excessive) eating
-prandial	post-	**postprandial** (post-PRAN-dee-all)	after a meal

Vocabulary

TERM	DEFINITION
anorexia (an-oh-REK-see-ah)	A general term meaning loss of appetite that may accompany other conditions. Also used to refer to *anorexia nervosa*, which is a personality disorder involving refusal to eat.
ascites (ah-SIGH-teez)	Collection or accumulation of fluid in the peritoneal cavity.
bowel incontinence (in-CON-tih-nence)	Inability to control defecation.
bridge	Dental appliance that is attached to adjacent teeth for support to replace missing teeth.
cachexia (ka-KEK-see-ah)	Loss of weight and generalized wasting that occurs during a chronic disease.
constipation (kon-stih-PAY-shun)	Experiencing difficulty in defecation or infrequent defecation.
crown	Artificial covering for the tooth created to replace the original crown.
dental caries (KAIR-eez)	Gradual decay and disintegration of teeth caused by bacteria; may lead to abscessed teeth. Commonly called a *tooth cavity*.
dentistry	Branch of healthcare involved with the prevention, diagnosis, and treatment of conditions involving the teeth, jaw, and mouth. Dentistry is practiced by a *dentist* or *oral surgeon*.
denture (DEN-chur)	Partial or complete set of artificial teeth that are set in plastic materials. Acts as a substitute for the natural teeth and related structures.
diarrhea (dye-ah-REE-ah)	Passing of frequent, watery bowel movements. Usually accompanies gastrointestinal (GI) disorders.

Vocabulary *(continued)*

TERM	DEFINITION
emesis (EM-eh-sis)	Vomiting.
gastroenterology (gas-troh-en-ter-ALL-oh-jee)	Branch of medicine involved in diagnosis and treatment of diseases and disorders of the digestive system. Physician is a *gastroenterologist.*
hematochezia (he-mat-oh-KEY-zee-ah)	Passing bright red blood in the stools.
implant (IM-plant)	Prosthetic device placed in the jaw to which a tooth or denture may be anchored.
internal medicine	Branch of medicine involving the diagnosis and treatment of diseases and conditions of internal organs such as the digestive system. The physician is an *internist.*
jaundice (JAWN-diss)	Yellow cast to the skin, mucous membranes, and the whites of the eyes caused by the deposit of bile pigment from too much bilirubin in the blood. Bilirubin is a waste product produced when worn-out red blood cells are broken down. May be a symptom of a disorder such as gallstones blocking the common bile duct or carcinoma of the liver.
melena (me-LEE-nah)	Passage of dark tarry stools. Color is the result of digestive enzymes working on blood in the gastrointestinal tract.
nausea (NAW-see-ah)	The urge to vomit. **Med Term Tip** The term *nausea* comes from the Greek word for "seasickness."
obesity	Body weight that is above a healthy level. A person whose overweight interferes with normal activity and body function has *morbid obesity.*
orthodontics (or-thoh-DON-tiks)	Branch of dentistry concerned with correction of problems with tooth alignment. A specialist is an *orthodontist.*
periodontics (pair-ee-oh-DON-tiks)	Branch of dentistry concerned with treating conditions involving the gums and tissues surrounding the teeth. A specialist is a *periodontist.*
polyp (POLL-ip)	Small tumor with a pedicle or stem attachment. Commonly found on mucous membranes such as those lining the colon or nasal cavity. Colon polyps may be precancerous.
proctology (prok-TOL-oh-jee)	Branch of medicine involved in diagnosis and treatment of diseases and disorders of the anus and rectum. Physician is a *proctologist.*
pyrosis (pie-ROW-sis)	Pain and burning sensation usually caused by stomach acid splashing up into the esophagus. Commonly called *heartburn.*
regurgitation (ree-gur-jih-TAY-shun)	Return of fluids and solids from the stomach into the mouth.

Pathology

TERM	DEFINITION
■ ***Oral Cavity***	
aphthous ulcers (AF-thus)	Painful ulcers in the mouth of unknown cause. Commonly called *canker sores*.
cleft lip (CLEFT)	Congenital anomaly in which the upper lip and jaw bone fail to fuse in the midline leaving an open gap. Often seen along with a cleft palate. Corrected with surgery.
cleft palate (CLEFT-PAL-at)	Congenital anomaly in which the roof of the mouth has a split or fissure. Corrected with surgery.
herpes labialis (HER-peez lay-bee-AL-iz)	Infection of the lip by the herpes simplex virus type 1 (HSV-1). Also called *fever blisters* or *cold sores*.
periodontal disease (pair-ee-oh-DON-tal dih-ZEEZ)	Disease of the supporting structures of the teeth, including the gums and bones; the most common cause of tooth loss.
■ ***Esophagus***	
esophageal varices (eh-soff-ah-JEE-al VAIR-ih-seez)	Enlarged and swollen varicose veins in the lower end of the esophagus. If these rupture, serious hemorrhage results; often related to liver disease.
gastroesophageal reflux disease (GERD) (gas-troh-ee-sof-ah-GEE-all REE-fluks)	Acid from the stomach flows backward up into the esophagus causing inflammation and pain.
■ ***Stomach***	
gastric carcinoma (GAS-trik car-si-NOH-mah)	Cancerous tumor in the stomach.
hiatal hernia (high-AY-tal HER-nee-ah)	Protrusion of the stomach through the diaphragm (also called a *diaphragmatocele*) and extending into the thoracic cavity; gastroesophageal reflux disease is a common symptom.

Figure 8.10 A hiatal hernia or diaphragmatocele. A portion of the stomach protrudes through the diaphragm into the thoracic cavity.

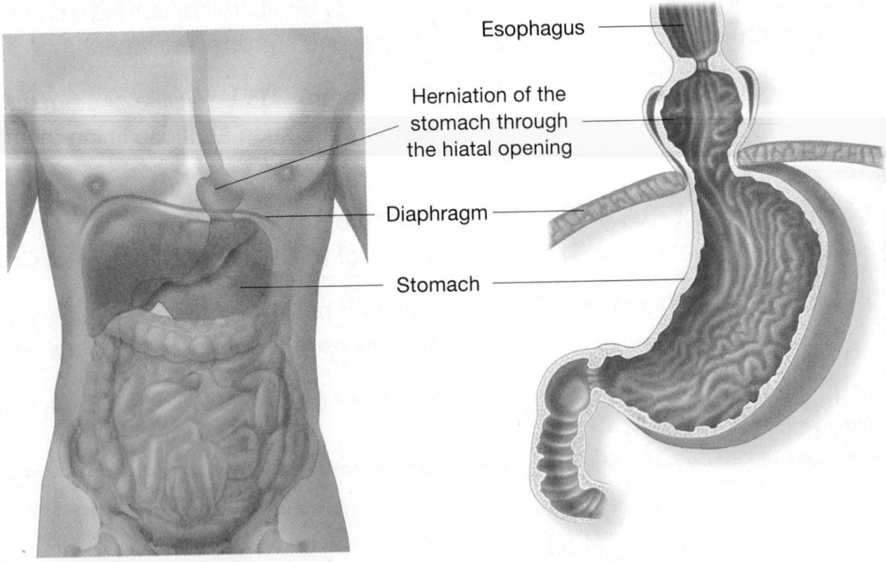

Pathology *(continued)*

TERM	DEFINITION
peptic ulcer disease (PUD) (PEP-tik ULL-sir)	Ulcer occurring in the lower portion of the esophagus, stomach, and/or duodenum; thought to be caused by the acid of gastric juices. Initial damage to the protective lining of the stomach may be caused by a *Helicobacter pylori* (*H. pylori*) bacterial infection. If the ulcer extends all the way through the wall of the stomach, it is called a *perforated ulcer* which requires immediate surgery to repair.

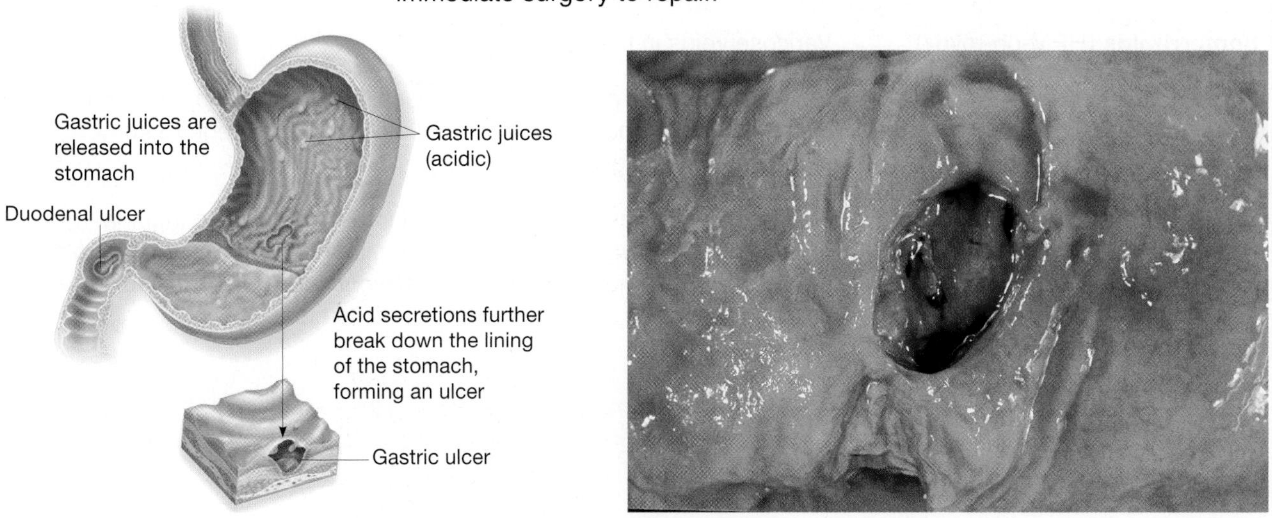

A. B.

Figure 8.11 A) Figure illustrating the location and appearance of a peptic ulcer in both the stomach and the duodenum. B) Photomicrograph illustrating a gastric ulcer. *(Dr. E. Walker/Science Photo Library/Photo Researchers, Inc.)*

■ *Small Intestine and Colon*

TERM	DEFINITION
anal fistula (FIH-styoo-lah)	Abnormal tubelike passage from the surface around the anal opening directly into the rectum.
colorectal carcinoma (kohl-oh-REK-tall car-ci-NOH-mah)	Cancerous tumor along the length of the colon and rectum.
Crohn's disease (KROHNZ dih-ZEEZ)	Form of chronic inflammatory bowel disease affecting primarily the ileum and/or colon. Also called *regional ileitis*. This autoimmune condition affects all the layers of the bowel wall and results in scarring and thickening of the gut wall.
diverticulitis (dye-ver-tik-yoo-LYE-tis)	Inflammation of a *diverticulum* (an outpouching off the gut), especially in the colon. Inflammation often results when food becomes trapped within the pouch.

Figure 8.12 Diverticulosis. Figure illustrates external and internal appearance of diverticula.

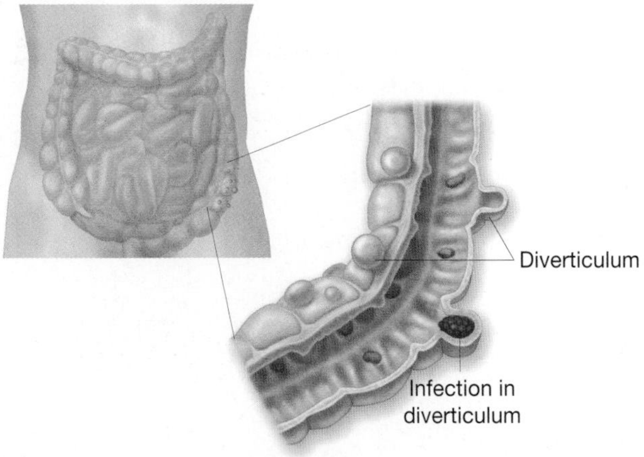

Pathology (continued)

TERM	DEFINITION
diverticulosis (dye-ver-tik-yoo-LOW-sis)	Condition of having diverticula (outpouches off the gut). May lead to *diverticulitis* if one becomes inflamed.
dysentery (dis-in-TARE-ee)	Disease characterized by diarrhea, often with mucus and blood, severe abdominal pain, fever, and dehydration. Caused by ingesting food or water contaminated by chemicals, bacteria, protozoans, or parasites.
hemorrhoids (HEM-oh-roydz)	Varicose veins in the rectum.
ileus (ILL-ee-us)	Severe abdominal pain, inability to pass stools, vomiting, and abdominal distension as a result of an intestinal blockage. May require surgery to reverse the blockage.
inguinal hernia (ING-gwih-nal HER-nee-ah)	Hernia or protrusion of a loop of small intestines into the inguinal (groin) region through a weak spot in the abdominal muscle wall that develops into a hole. May become *incarcerated* or *strangulated* if the muscle tightens down around the loop of intestines and cuts off its blood flow.

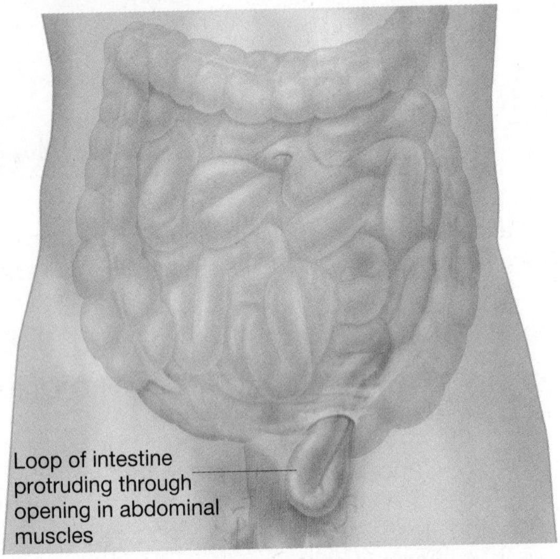

Figure 8.13 An inguinal hernia. A portion of the small intestine is protruding through the abdominal muscles into the groin region.

TERM	DEFINITION
intussusception (in-tuh-suh-SEP-shun)	Result of the intestine slipping or telescoping into another section of intestine just below it. More common in children.

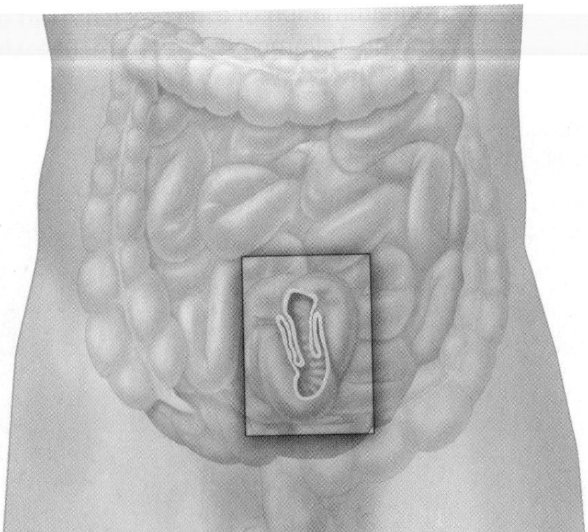

Figure 8.14 Intussusception. A short length of small intestine has telescoped into itself.

Pathology *(continued)*

TERM	DEFINITION
irritable bowel syndrome (IBS)	Disturbance in the functions of the intestine from unknown causes. Symptoms generally include abdominal discomfort and an alteration in bowel activity. Also called *spastic colon* or *functional bowel syndrome*.
polyposis (pall-ee-POH-sis)	Small tumors that contain a pedicle or stemlike attachment in the mucous membranes of the large intestine (colon); may be precancerous.

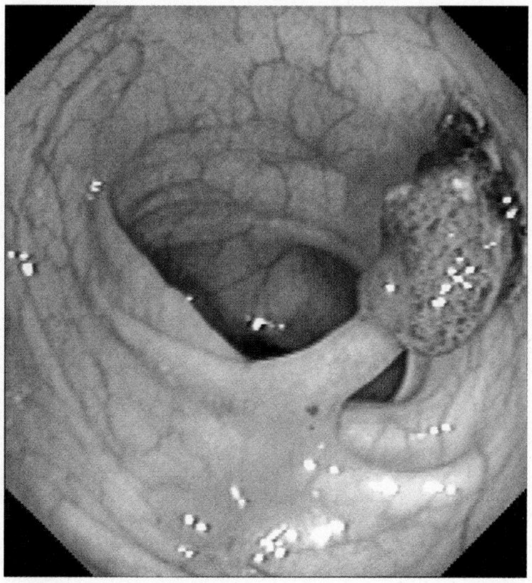

Figure 8.15 Photograph showing a polyp in the colon. Note the mushroom-like shape, an enlarged top growing at the end of a stem. *(ISM/Phototake NYC)*

TERM	DEFINITION
ulcerative colitis (ULL-sir-ah-tiv koh-LYE-tis)	Chronic inflammatory condition that produces numerous ulcers to form on the mucous membrane lining of the colon; the cause is unknown. Also known as *inflammatory bowel disease* (IBD).
volvulus (VOL-vyoo-lus)	Condition in which the bowel twists upon itself and causes an obstruction. Painful and requires immediate surgery.

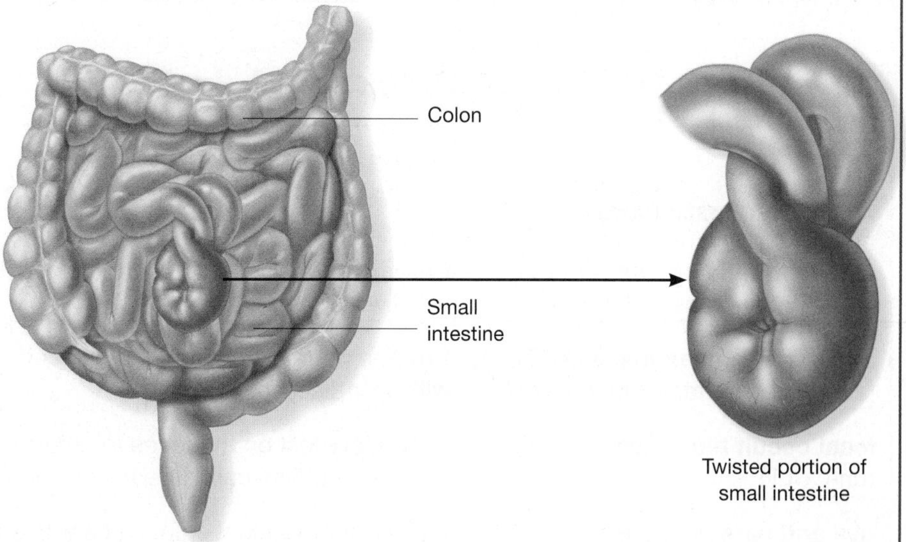

Figure 8.16 Volvulus. A length of small intestine has twisted around itself, cutting off blood circulation to the twisted loop.

Pathology *(continued)*

TERM	DEFINITION
■ ***Accessory Organs***	
cholecystitis (koh-lee-sis-TYE-tis)	Inflammation of the gallbladder; most commonly caused by gallstones in the gallbladder or common bile duct that block the flow of bile.
cholelithiasis (koh-lee-lih-THIGH-ah-sis)	Presence of gallstones; may or may not cause symptoms such as *cholecystalgia.*

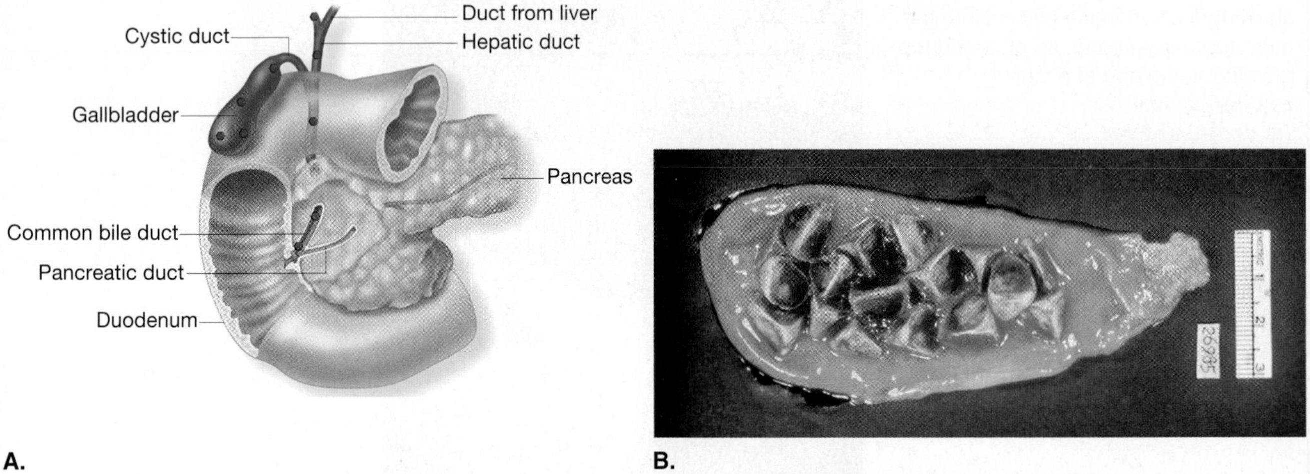

Figure 8.17 A) Cholelithiasis, red circles indicate common sites for gallstones including the gallbladder, cystic duct, hepatic duct, and common bile duct. B) Photograph of a gallbladder specimen with multiple gallstones. *(Martin Rotker/Phototake NYC)*

TERM	DEFINITION
cirrhosis (sih-ROH-sis)	Chronic disease of the liver associated with failure of the liver to function properly.
hepatitis (hep-ah-TYE-tis)	Inflammation of the liver, usually due to a viral infection. Different viruses are transmitted by different routes, such as sexual contact or from exposure to blood or fecally contaminated water or food.

Diagnostic Procedures

TERM	DEFINITION
■ ***Clinical Laboratory Tests***	
alanine transaminase (ALT) (AL-ah-neen trans-AM-in-nase)	Enzyme normally present in the blood. Blood levels are increased in persons with liver disease.
aspartate transaminase (AST) (ass-PAR-tate trans-AM-in-nase)	Enzyme normally present in the blood. Blood levels are increased in persons with liver disease.
fecal occult blood test (FOBT) (uh-CULT)	Laboratory test on the feces to determine if microscopic amounts of blood are present. Also called *hemoccult* or *stool guaiac.*
ova and parasites (O&P) (OH-vah and PAR-ah-sights)	Laboratory examination of feces with a microscope for the presence of parasites or their eggs.
serum bilirubin (SEE-rum BILLY-rubin)	Blood test to determine the amount of the waste product bilirubin in the bloodstream. Elevated levels indicate liver disease.

Diagnostic Procedures *(continued)*

TERM	DEFINITION
stool culture	Laboratory test of feces to determine if any pathogenic bacteria are present.
■ ***Diagnostic Imaging***	
bite-wing x-ray	X-ray taken with a part of the film holder held between the teeth and parallel to the teeth.
intravenous cholecystography (in-trah-VEE-nus koh-lee-sis-TOG-rah-fee)	Dye is administered intravenously to the patient, which allows for x-ray visualization of the gallbladder and bile ducts.
lower gastrointestinal series (lower GI series)	X-ray image of the colon and rectum is taken after the administration of barium (a radiopaque dye) by enema. Also called a *barium enema (BE)*.

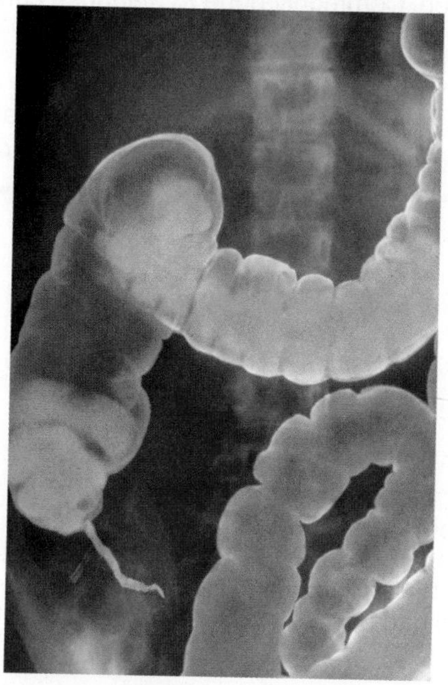

Figure 8.18 Color enhanced x-ray of the colon taken during a barium enema. *(CNRI/Science Photo Library/Photo Researchers, Inc.)*

TERM	DEFINITION
percutaneous transhepatic cholangiography (PTC) (per-kyoo-TAY-nee-us trans-heh-PAT-ik koh-lan-jee-OG-rah-fee)	Procedure in which contrast medium is injected directly into the liver to visualize the bile ducts. Used to detect obstructions.
upper gastrointestinal (UGI) **series**	Administering of a barium contrast material orally and then taking an x-ray to visualize the esophagus, stomach, and duodenum. Also called a *barium swallow*.
■ ***Endoscopic Procedures***	
colonoscopy (koh-lon-OSS-koh-pee)	Flexible fiberscope called a *colonoscope* is passed through the anus, rectum, and colon; used to examine the upper portion of the colon. Polyps and small growths can be removed during this procedure (see Figure 8.15).
endoscopic retrograde cholangiopancreatography (ERCP) (en-doh-SKOP-ik RET-roh-grayd koh-lan-jee-oh-pan-kree-ah-TOG-rah-fee)	Procedure using an endoscope to visually examine the hepatic duct, common bile duct, and pancreatic duct. Retrograde means to go in the backwards direction. In this case the endoscope is inserted through the anus and worked backwards to the area where the pancreatic and common bile ducts empty into the duodenum.

Diagnostic Procedures *(continued)*

TERM	DEFINITION
esophagogastroduodenoscopy (EGD) (eh-soff-ah-go-gas-troh-duo-den-OS-koh-pee)	Use of a flexible fiberoptic endoscope to visually examine the esophagus, stomach, and beginning of the duodenum.
gastroscopy (gas-TROS-koh-pee)	Procedure in which a flexible *gastroscope* is passed through the mouth and down the esophagus in order to visualize inside the stomach. Used to diagnose peptic ulcers and gastric carcinoma.
laparoscopy (lap-ar-OSS-koh-pee)	*Laparoscope* is passed into the abdominal wall through a small incision. The abdominal cavity is then visually examined for tumors and other conditions with this lighted instrument. Also called *peritoneoscopy*.
sigmoidoscopy (sig-moid-OS-koh-pee)	Procedure using a flexible *sigmoidoscope* to visually examine the sigmoid colon. Commonly done to diagnose cancer and polyps.
■ ***Additional Diagnostic Procedures***	
paracentesis (pair-ah-sin-TEE-sis)	Insertion of a needle into the abdominal cavity to withdraw fluid. Tests to diagnose diseases may be conducted on the fluid.

Therapeutic Procedures

TERM	DEFINITION
■ ***Dental Procedures***	
extraction	Removing or "pulling" of teeth.
root canal	Dental treatment involving the pulp cavity of the root of a tooth. Procedure is used to save a tooth that is badly infected or abscessed.
■ ***Medical Procedures***	
gavage	Using a nasogastric (NG) tube to place liquid nourishment directly into the stomach.
lavage	Using a nasogastric (NG) tube to wash out the stomach. For example, after ingestion of dangerous substances.
nasogastric intubation (NG tube) (NAY-zo-gas-trik in-two-BAY-shun)	Flexible catheter is inserted into the nose and down the esophagus to the stomach. May be used for feeding or to suction out stomach fluids.
total parenteral nutrition (TPN) (pair-in-TARE-all)	Providing 100% of a patient's nutrition intravenously. Used when a patient is unable to eat.
■ ***Surgical Procedures***	
anastomosis (ah-nas-toh-MOH-sis)	To surgically create a connection between two organs or vessels. For example, joining together two cut ends of the intestines after a section is removed.

Therapeutic Procedures *(continued)*

TERM	DEFINITION
bariatric surgery (bear-ee-AT-rik)	A group of surgical procedures such as stomach stapling and restrictive banding to reduce the size of the stomach. A treatment for morbid (extreme) obesity.
choledocholithotripsy (koh-led-oh-koh-LITH-oh-trip-see)	Crushing of a gallstone in the common bile duct.
colostomy (koh-LOSS-toh-mee)	Surgical creation of an opening of some portion of the colon through the abdominal wall to the outside surface. Fecal material (stool) drains into a bag worn on the abdomen.

Figure 8.19 A) The colon illustrating various ostomy sites. B) Colostomy in the descending colon, illustrating functioning stoma and nonfunctioning distal sigmoid colon and rectum.

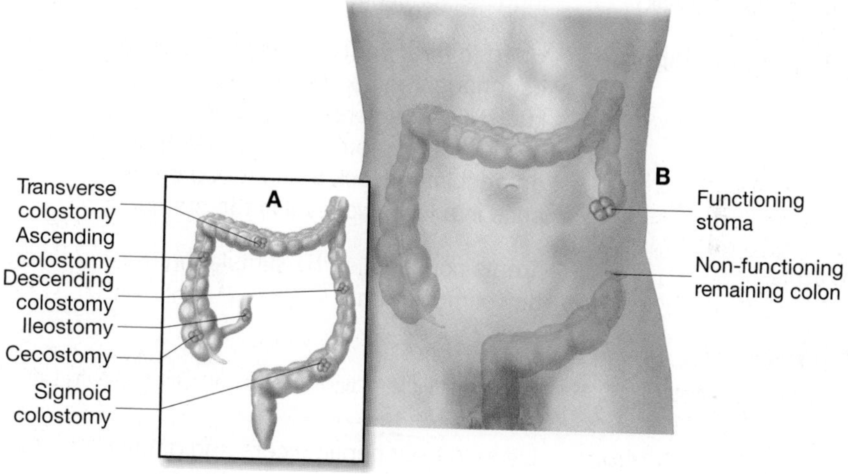

TERM	DEFINITION
diverticulectomy (dye-ver-tik-yoo-LEK-toh-mee)	Surgical removal of a diverticulum.
exploratory laparotomy (ek-SPLOR-ah-tor-ee lap-ah-ROT-oh-mee)	Abdominal operation for the purpose of examining the abdominal organs and tissues for signs of disease or other abnormalities.
fistulectomy (fis-tyoo-LEK-toh-mee)	Removal of a fistula.
gastric stapling	Procedure that closes off a large section of the stomach with rows of staples. Results in a much smaller stomach to assist very obese patients to lose weight.
hemorrhoidectomy (hem-oh-royd-EK-toh-mee)	Surgical removal of hemorrhoids from the anorectal area.
hernioplasty (her-nee-oh-PLAS-tee)	Surgical repair of a hernia. Also called *herniorrhaphy*.
laparoscopic cholecystectomy (lap-ar-oh-SKOP-ik koh-lee-sis-TEK-toh-mee)	Surgical removal of the gallbladder through a very small abdominal incision with the assistance of a laparoscope.
liver transplant	Transplant of a liver from a donor.

Pharmacology

CLASSIFICATION	ACTION	GENERIC AND BRAND NAMES
anorexiant (an-oh-REKS-ee-ant)	Treats obesity by suppressing appetite.	phendimetrazine, Adipost, Obezine; phentermine, Zantryl, Adipex
antacid	Used to neutralize stomach acids.	calcium carbonate, Tums; aluminum hydroxide and magnesium hydroxide, Maalox, Mylanta
antidiarrheal	Used to control diarrhea.	loperamide, Imodium; diphenoxylate, Lomotil; kaolin/pectin, Kaopectate
antiemetic (an-tye-ee-MEH-tik)	Treats nausea, vomiting, and motion sickness.	prochlorperazine, Compazine; promethazine, Phenergan
emetic (ee-MEH-tik)	Induces vomiting.	Ipecac syrup
H_2-receptor antagonist	Used to treat peptic ulcers and gastroesophageal reflux disease. When stimulated, H_2-receptors increase the production of stomach acid. Using an antagonist to block these receptors results in a low acid level in the stomach.	ranitidine, Zantac; cimetidine, Tagamet; famotidine, Pepcid
laxative	Treats constipation by stimulating a bowel movement.	senosides, Senokot; psyllium, Metamucil
Med Term Tip The term *laxative* that refers to a medication to stimulate a bowel movement comes from the Latin term meaning "to relax."		
proton pump inhibitors	Used to treat peptic ulcers and gastroesophageal reflux disease. Blocks the stomach's ability to secrete acid.	esomeprazole, Nexium; omeprazole, Prilosec

Abbreviations

ac	before meals
ALT	alanine transaminase
AST	aspartate transaminase
Ba	barium
BE	barium enema
BM	bowel movement
BS	bowel sounds
CBD	common bile duct
EGD	esophagogastroduodenoscopy
ERCP	endoscopic retrograde cholangiopancreatography
FOBT	fecal occult blood test
GB	gallbladder
GERD	gastroesophageal reflux disease
GI	gastrointestinal
HAV	hepatitis A virus
HBV	hepatitis B virus
HCI	hydrochloric acid
HCV	hepatitis C virus
HDV	hepatitis D virus
HEV	hepatitis E virus
HSV-1	herpes simplex virus type 1
IBD	inflammatory bowel disease
IBS	irritable bowel syndrome
IVC	intravenous cholangiography
NG	nasogastric (tube)
NPO	nothing by mouth
n&v	nausea and vomiting
O&P	ova and parasites
pc	after meals
PO	by mouth
pp	postprandial
PTC	percutaneous transhepatic cholangiography
PUD	peptic ulcer disease
TPN	total parenteral nutrition
UGI	upper gastrointestinal series

Urinary System Illustrated

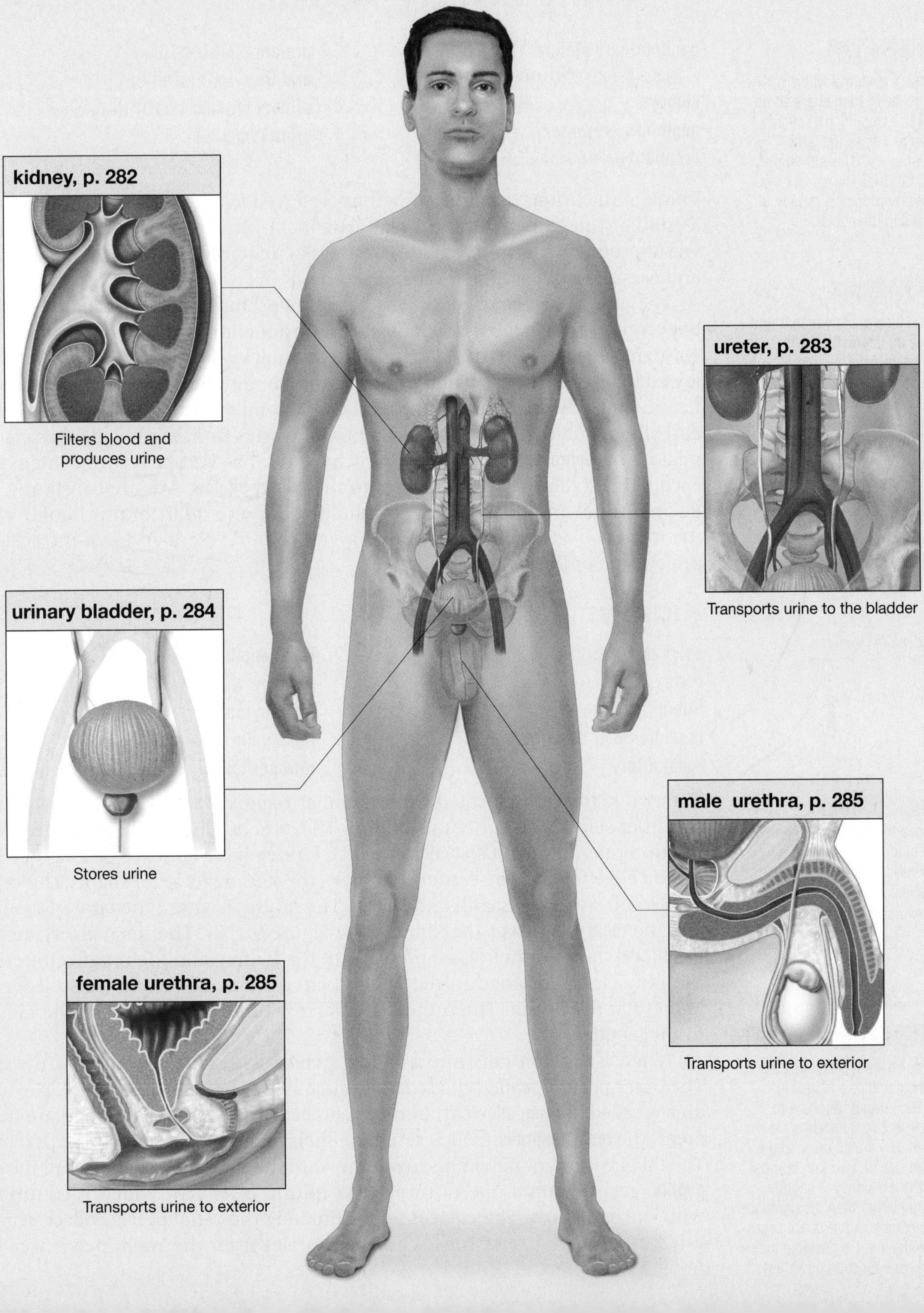

Anatomy and Physiology of the Urinary System

Med Term Tip

The urinary system and the male reproductive system share some of the same organs, particularly the urethra. Hence the term *genitourinary* (GU) is sometimes used to describe the urinary system. The reproductive system is discussed in Chapter 10.

Med Term Tip

From the time of early man, there has been an interest in urine. Drawings on cave walls and hieroglyphics in Egyptian pyramids reveal interest in urine as a means of determining the physical state of the body. Some of the first doctors, called *pisse prophets*, believed that examining the urine would help treat a patient. Now urologists treat disorders of the urinary tract in both men and women plus disorders of the male reproductive tract.

genitourinary system (jen-ih-toh-YOO-rih-nair-ee)
kidneys
nephrons (NEF-ronz)
uremia (yoo-REE-mee-ah)
ureters (yoo-REE-ters)
urethra (yoo-REE-thrah)
urinary bladder (YOO-rih-nair-ee)
urine (YOO-rin)

Think of the urinary system, sometimes referred to as the **genitourinary** (GU) **system**, as similar to a water filtration plant. Its main function is to filter and remove waste products from the blood. These waste materials result in the production and excretion of **urine** from the body.

The urinary system is one of the hardest working systems of the body. All the body's metabolic processes result in the production of waste products. These waste products are a natural part of life but quickly become toxic if they are allowed to build up in the blood, resulting in a condition called **uremia**. Waste products in the body are removed through a very complicated system of blood vessels and kidney tubules. The actual filtration of wastes from the blood takes place in millions of **nephrons**, which make up each of your two **kidneys**. As urine drains from each kidney, the **ureters** transport it to the **urinary bladder**. We are constantly producing urine, and our bladders can hold about one quart of this liquid. When the urinary bladder empties, urine moves from the bladder down the **urethra** to the outside of the body.

Kidneys

calyx (KAY-liks)
cortex (KOR-teks)
hilum (HIGH-lum)
medulla (meh-DULL-ah)
renal artery
renal papilla (pah-PILL-ah)
renal pelvis
renal pyramids
renal vein
retroperitoneal (ret-roh-pair-ih-toh-NEE-al)

Med Term Tip

At any one time, about 20 percent of your blood is being filtered by your kidneys. In this way, all your blood is cleansed every few minutes.

The two kidneys are located in the lumbar region of the back above the waist on either side of the vertebral column. They are not inside the peritoneal sac, a location referred to as **retroperitoneal**. Each kidney has a concave or indented area on the edge toward the center that gives the kidney its bean shape. The center of this concave area is called the **hilum**. The hilum is where the **renal artery** enters and the **renal vein** leaves the kidney (see Figure 9.1 ■). The renal artery delivers the blood that is full of waste products to the kidney and the renal vein returns the now cleansed blood to the general circulation. The ureters also leave the kidneys at the hilum. The ureters are narrow tubes that lead from the kidneys to the bladder.

Med Term Tip

The kidney bean is so named because it resembles a kidney in shape. Each organ weighs 4 to 6 ounces, is 2 to 3 inches wide and approximately 1 inch thick, and is about the size of your fist. In most people the left kidney is slightly higher and larger than the right kidney. Functioning kidneys are necessary for life, but it is possible to live with only one functioning kidney.

When a surgeon cuts into a kidney, several structures or areas are visible. The outer portion, called the **cortex**, is much like a shell for the kidney. The inner area is called the **medulla**. Within the medulla are a dozen or so triangular-shaped areas, the **renal pyramids**, which resemble their namesake, the Egyptian pyramids. The tip of each pyramid points inward toward the hilum. At its tip, called the **renal papilla**, each pyramid opens into a **calyx** (plural is *calyces*), which is continuous with the **renal pelvis**. The calyces and ultimately the renal pelvis collect urine as it is formed. The ureter for each kidney arises from the renal pelvis (see Figure 9.2 ■).

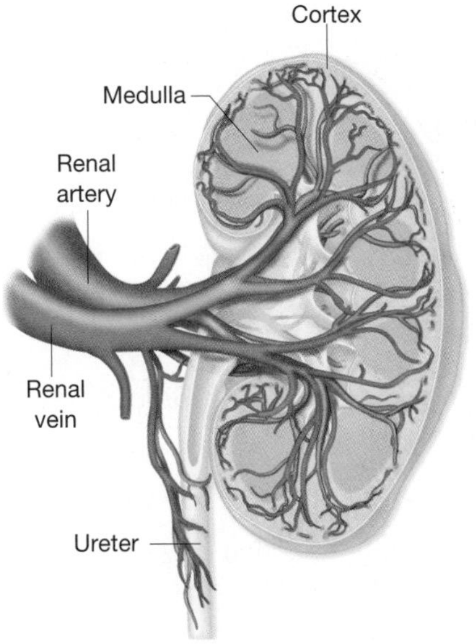

Figure 9.1 Kidney structure. Longitudinal section showing the renal artery entering and the renal vein and ureter exiting at the hilum of the kidney.

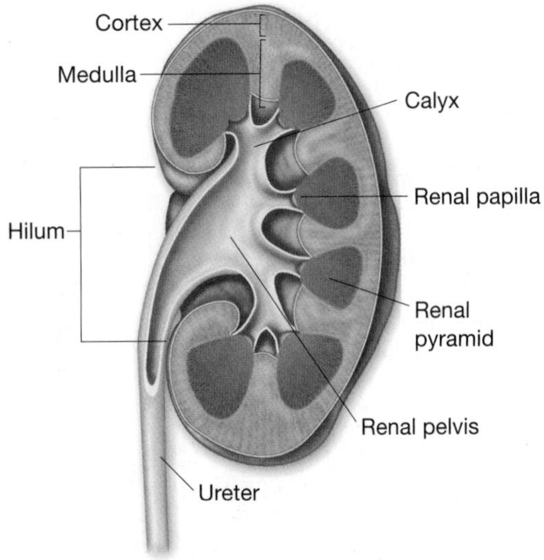

Figure 9.2 Longitudinal section of a kidney illustrating the internal structures.

Nephrons

afferent arteriole (AFF-er-ent)
Bowman's capsule
collecting tubule
distal convoluted tubule (DISS-tall con-voh-LOOT-ed)
efferent arteriole (EF-er-ent)
glomerular capsule (glom-AIR-yoo-lar)
glomerulus (glom-AIR-yoo-lus)
loop of Henle
proximal convoluted tubule (PROK-sim-al con-voh-LOOT-ed)
renal corpuscle (KOR-pus-ehl)
renal tubule

The functional or working unit of the kidney is the nephron. There are more than one million of these microscopic structures in each human kidney.

Each nephron consists of the **renal corpuscle** and the **renal tubule** (see Figure 9.3 ■). The renal corpuscle is the blood-filtering portion of the nephron. It has a double-walled cuplike structure called the **glomerular** or **Bowman's capsule** (also called the *glomerular capsule*) that encases a ball of capillaries called the **glomerulus.** An **afferent arteriole** carries blood to the glomerulus, and an **efferent arteriole** carries blood away from the glomerulus.

Water and substances that were removed from the bloodstream in the renal corpuscle flow into the renal tubules to finish the urine production process. This continuous tubule is divided into four sections: the **proximal convoluted tubule**, followed by the narrow **loop of Henle** (also called the *nephron loop*), then the **distal convoluted tubule**, and finally the **collecting tubule.**

Med Term Tip

Afferent, meaning moving toward, and *efferent*, meaning moving away from, are terms used when discussing moving either toward or away from the central point in many systems. For example, there are afferent and efferent nerves in the nervous system.

Ureters

As urine drains out of the renal pelvis it enters the ureter, which carries it down to the urinary bladder (see Figure 9.4 ■). Ureters are very narrow tubes measuring less than 1/4 inch wide and 10 to 12 inches long that extend from the renal pelvis to the urinary bladder. Mucous membrane lines the ureters just as it lines most passages that open to the external environment.

Med Term Tip

The terms *ureter* and *urethra* are frequently confused. Remember that there are two ureters carrying urine from the kidneys into the bladder. There is only one urethra, and it carries urine from the bladder to the outside of the body.

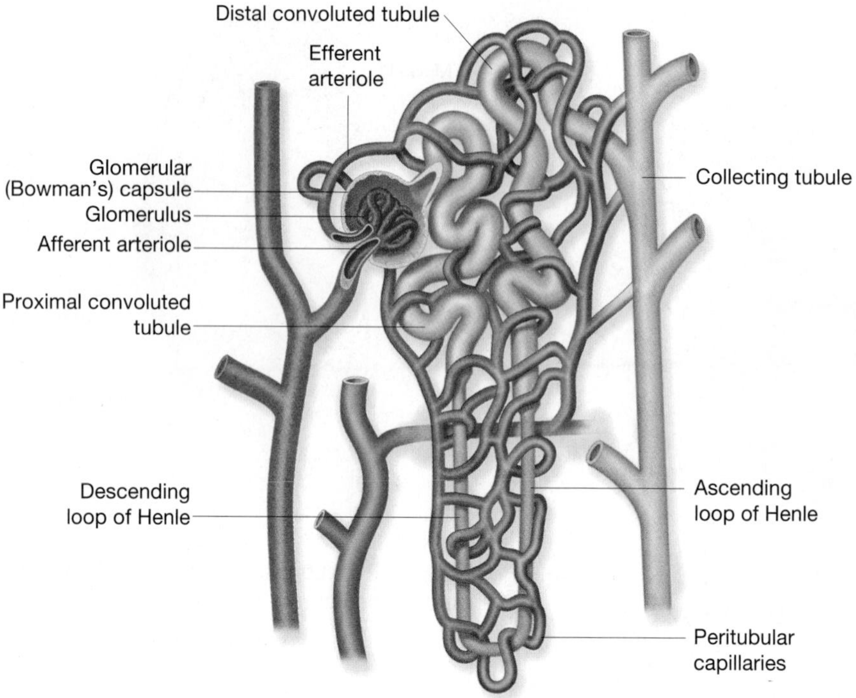

■ **Figure 9.3** The structure of a nephron, illustrating the nephron structure in relation to the circulatory system.

Urinary Bladder

external sphincter (SFINGK-ter)
internal sphincter
rugae (ROO-gay)
urination

The urinary bladder is an elastic muscular sac that lies in the base of the pelvis just behind the pubic symphysis (see Figure 9.5 ■). It is composed of three layers of smooth muscle tissue lined with mucous membrane containing **rugae** or folds that allow it to stretch. The bladder receives the urine directly from the ureters, stores it, and excretes it by **urination** through the urethra.

Generally, an adult bladder will hold 250 mL of urine. This amount then creates an urge to void or empty the bladder. Involuntary muscle action causes the bladder to contract and the **internal sphincter** to relax. The internal sphincter protects us from having our bladder empty at the wrong time. Voluntary action controls the **external sphincter**, which opens on demand to allow the intentional emptying of the bladder. The act of controlling the emptying of urine is developed sometime after a child is 2 years of age.

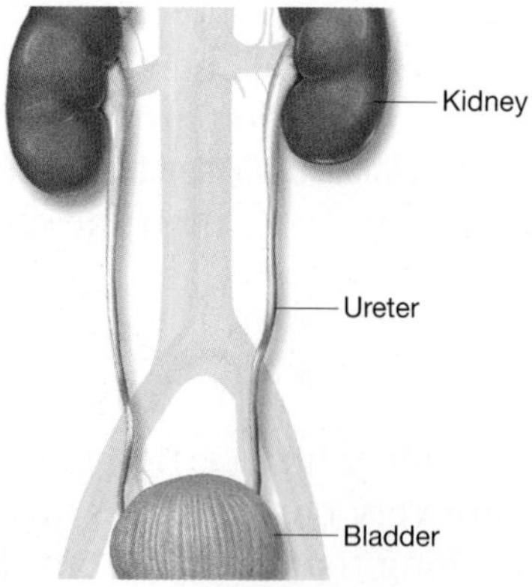

■ **Figure 9.4** The ureters extend from the kidneys to the urinary bladder.

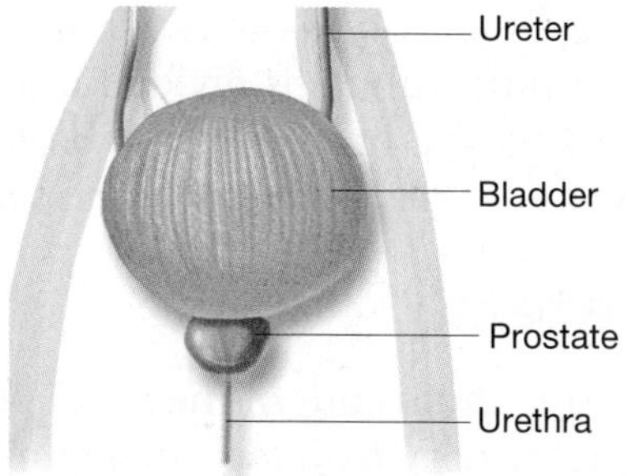

■ **Figure 9.5** The structure of the urinary bladder in a male. (Note the prostate gland.)

Urethra

urinary meatus (mee-AY-tus)

The urethra is a tubular canal that carries the flow of urine from the bladder to the outside of the body (see Figure 9.6 ■ for the male urethra). The external opening through which urine passes out of the body is called the **urinary meatus**. Mucous membrane also lines the urethra as it does other structures of the urinary system. This is one of the reasons that infection spreads up the urinary tract. The urethra is 1½ inches long in the female and 8 inches long in the male. In a woman it functions only as the outlet for urine and is in front of the vagina. In the male, however, it has two functions: an outlet for urine and the passageway for semen to leave the body.

Med Term Tip

Mucous membranes will carry infections up the urinary tract from the urinary meatus and urethra into the bladder and eventually up the ureters and the kidneys if not stopped. It is never wise to ignore a simple bladder infection or what is called *cystitis*.

Role of Kidneys in Homeostasis

electrolytes (ee-LEK-troh-lites) **homeostasis** (hoh-mee-oh-STAY-sis)

The kidneys are responsible for **homeostasis** or balance in your body. They continually adjust the chemical conditions in the body that allow you to survive. Because of its interaction with the bloodstream and its ability to excrete substances from the body, the urinary system maintains the body's proper balance of water and chemicals. If the body is low on water, the kidneys conserve it, or in the opposite case, if there is excess water in the body, the kidneys excrete the excess. In addition to water, the kidneys regulate the level of **electrolytes**—small biologically important molecules such as sodium (Na^+), potassium (K^+), chloride (Cl^-), and bicarbonate (HCO_3^-). Finally, the kidneys play an important role in maintaining the correct pH range within the body, making sure we do not become too acidic or too alkaline. The kidneys accomplish these important tasks through the production of urine.

Stages of Urine Production

filtration
glomerular filtrate
peritubular capillaries
reabsorption
secretion

As wastes and unnecessary substances are removed from the bloodstream by the nephrons, many desirable molecules are also removed initially. Waste products are eliminated from the body, but other substances such as water, electrolytes, and nutrients must be returned to the bloodstream. Urine, in its final form ready for elimination from the body, is the ultimate product of this entire process.

Med Term Tip

The amount of water and other fluids processed by the kidneys each day is astonishing. Approximately 190 quarts of fluid are filtered out of the glomerular blood every day. Most of this fluid returns to the body through the reabsorption process. About 99 percent of the water that leaves the blood each day through the filtration process returns to the blood by proximal tubule reabsorption.

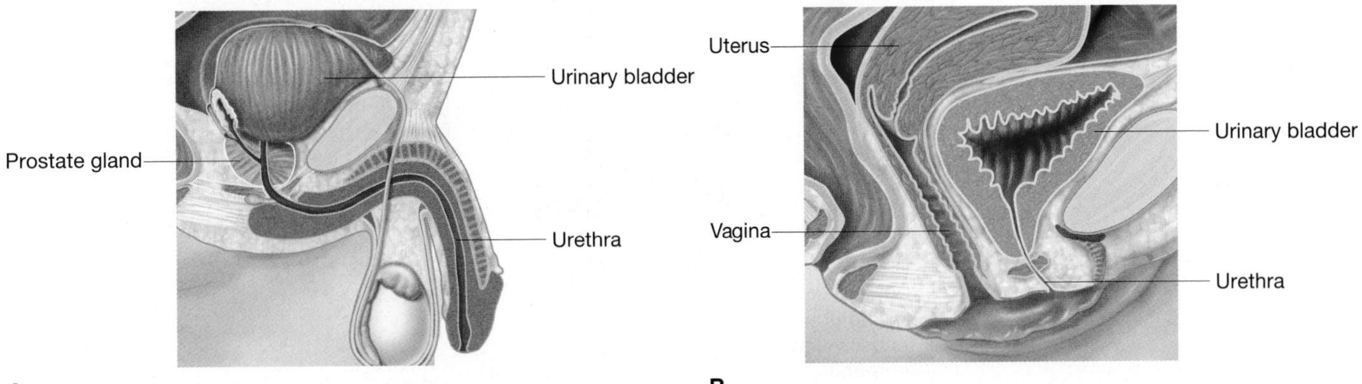

■ **Figure 9.6** A) The male urethra extends from the urinary bladder in the floor of the pelvis through the prostate gland and penis to the urinary meatus. B) The much shorter female urethra extends from the urinary bladder to the floor of the pelvis and exits just in front of the vaginal opening.

Urine production occurs in three stages: **filtration**, **reabsorption**, and **secretion**. Each of these steps is performed by a different section of the nephrons (see Figure 9.7 ■).

1. **Filtration.** The first stage is the filtering of particles, which occurs in the renal corpuscle. The pressure of blood flowing through the glomerulus forces material out of the bloodstream, through the wall of Bowman's capsule, and into the renal tubules. This fluid in the tubules is called the **glomerular filtrate** and consists of water, electrolytes, nutrients such as glucose and amino acids, wastes, and toxins.
2. **Reabsorption.** After filtration, the filtrate passes through the four sections of the tubule. As the filtrate moves along its twisted journey, most of the water and much of the electrolytes and nutrients are reabsorbed into the **peritubular capillaries**, a capillary bed that surrounds the renal tubules. They can then reenter the circulating blood.
3. **Secretion.** The final stage of urine production occurs when the special cells of the renal tubules secrete ammonia, uric acid, and other waste substances directly into the renal tubule. Urine formation is now finished; it passes into the collecting tubules, renal papilla, calyx, renal pelvis, and ultimately into the ureter.

Urine

albumin (al-BEW-min)
nitrogenous wastes (nigh-TROJ-eh-nus)
specific gravity
urinalysis (yoo-rih-NAL-ih-sis)

Urine is normally straw colored to clear, and sterile. Although it is 95 percent water, it also contains many dissolved substances, such as electrolytes, toxins, and **nitrogenous wastes**, the byproducts of muscle metabolism. At times the urine also contains substances that should not be there, such as glucose, blood, or **albumin**, a protein that should remain in the blood. This is the reason for performing a **urinalysis**, a physical and chemical analysis of urine, which gives medical personnel important information regarding disease processes occurring in a patient.

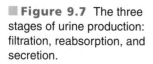

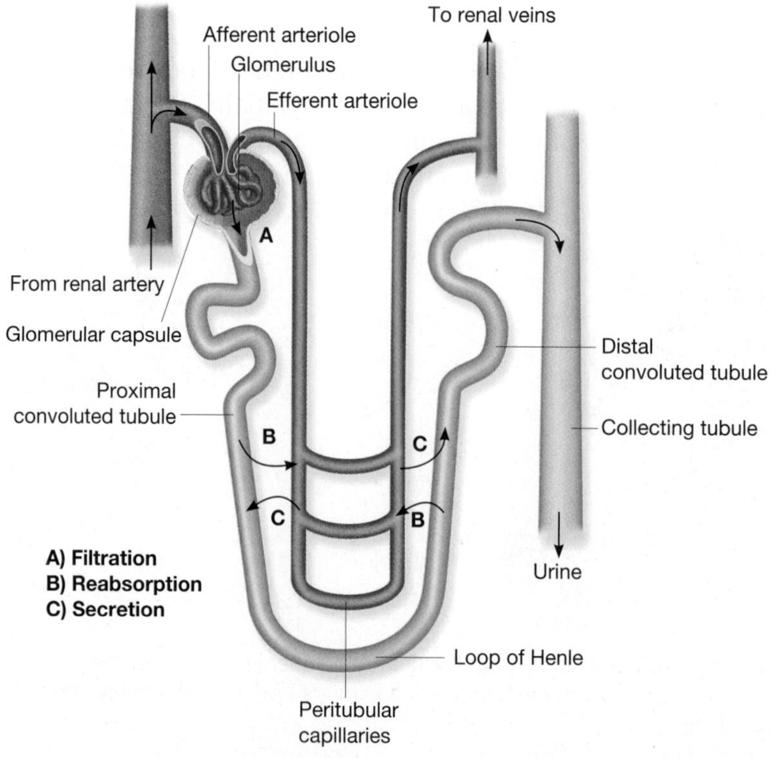

■ **Figure 9.7** The three stages of urine production: filtration, reabsorption, and secretion.

Normally, during a 24-hour period the output of urine will be 1,000 to 2,000 mL, depending on the amount of fluid consumed and the general health of the person. Normal urine is acidic because this is one way our bodies dispose of excess acids. **Specific gravity** indicates the amount of dissolved substances in urine. The specific gravity of pure water is 1.000. The specific gravity of urine varies from 1.001 to 1.030. Highly concentrated urine has a higher specific gravity, while the specific gravity of very dilute urine is close to that of water. See Table 9.1 ■ for the normal values for urine testing and Table 9.2 ■ for abnormal findings.

Med Term Tip

The color, odor, volume, and sugar content of urine have been examined for centuries. Color charts for urine were developed by 1140, and "taste testing" was common in the late seventeenth century. By the nineteenth century, urinalysis was a routine part of a physical examination.

Table 9.1 Values for Urinalysis Testing

ELEMENT	NORMAL FINDINGS
Color	Straw colored, pale yellow to deep gold
Odor	Aromatic
Appearance	Clear
Specific gravity	1.005–1.030
pH	5.0–8.0
Protein	Negative to trace
Glucose	None
Ketones	None
Blood	Negative

Table 9.2 Abnormal Urinalysis Findings

ELEMENT	IMPLICATIONS
Color	Color varies depending on the patient's fluid intake and output or medication. Brown or black urine color indicates a serious disease process.
Odor	A fetid or foul odor may indicate infection. For instance, a fruity odor may be found in diabetes mellitus, dehydration, or starvation. Other odors may be due to medication or foods.
Appearance	Cloudiness may mean that an infection is present.
Specific gravity	Concentrated urine has a higher specific gravity. Dilute urine, such as can be found with diabetes insipidus, acute tubular necrosis, or salt-restricted diets, has a lower specific gravity.
pH	A pH value below 7.0 (acidic) is common in urinary tract infections, metabolic or respiratory acidosis, diets high in fruits or vegetables, or administration of some drugs. A pH higher than 7.0 (basic or alkaline) is common in metabolic or respiratory alkalosis, fever, high-protein diets, and taking ascorbic acid.
Protein	Protein may indicate glomerulonephritis or preeclampsia in a pregnant woman.
Glucose	Small amounts of glucose may be present as the result of eating a high-carbohydrate meal, stress, pregnancy, and taking some medications, such as aspirin or corticosteroids. Higher levels may indicate poorly controlled diabetes, Cushing's syndrome, or infection.
Ketones	The presence of ketones may indicate poorly controlled diabetes, dehydration, starvation, or ingestion of large amounts of aspirin.
Blood	Blood may indicate some types of anemia, taking of some medications (such as blood thinners), arsenic poisoning, reactions to transfusion, trauma, burns, and convulsions.

Word Building

The following list contains examples of medical terms built directly from word parts. The definition for these terms can be determined by a straightforward translation of the word parts.

COMBINING FORM	COMBINED WITH	MEDICAL TERM	DEFINITION
cyst/o	-algia	**cystalgia** (sis-TAL-jee-ah)	bladder pain

Med Term Tip

Word watch—Be careful using the combining forms *cyst/o* meaning "bladder" and *cyt/o* meaning "cell."

COMBINING FORM	COMBINED WITH	MEDICAL TERM	DEFINITION
	-ectomy	**cystectomy** (sis-TEK-toh-me)	removal of the bladder
	-gram	**cystogram** (SIS-toh-gram)	record of the bladder
	-ic	**cystic** (SIS-tik)	pertaining to the bladder
	-itis	**cystitis** (sis-TYE-tis)	bladder inflammation
	-lith	**cystolith** (SIS-toh-lith)	bladder stone
	-ostomy	**cystostomy** (sis-TOSS-toh-mee)	create a new opening into the bladder
	-otomy	**cystotomy** (sis-TOT-oh-mee)	incision into the bladder
	-pexy	**cystopexy** (SIS-toh-pek-see)	surgical fixation of the bladder
	-plasty	**cystoplasty** (SIS-toh-plas-tee)	surgical repair of the bladder
	-rrhagia	**cystorrhagia** (sis-toh-RAH-jee-ah)	rapid bleeding from the bladder
	-scope	**cystoscope** (SIS-toh-scope)	instrument used to visually examine the bladder
lith/o	-tripsy	**lithotripsy** (LITH-oh-trip-see)	surgical crushing of a stone
	-otomy	**lithotomy** (lith-OT-oh-me)	incision to remove a stone
nephr/o	-ectomy	**nephrectomy** (ne-FREK-toh-mee)	removal of a kidney
	-gram	**nephrogram** (NEH-fro-gram)	x-ray of the kidney
	-itis	**nephritis** (neh-FRYE-tis)	kidney inflammation
	-lith	**nephrolith** (NEF-roh-lith)	kidney stone
	-logist	**nephrologist** (neh-FROL-oh-jist)	specialist in the kidney
	-malacia	**nephromalacia** (nef-roh-mah-LAY-she-ah)	softening of the kidney
	-megaly	**nephromegaly** (nef-roh-MEG-ah-lee)	enlarged kidney
	-oma	**nephroma** (neh-FROH-ma)	kidney tumor
	-osis	**nephrosis** (neh-FROH-sis)	abnormal kidney condition
	-ptosis	**nephroptosis** (nef-rop-TOH-sis)	drooping kidney
	-ostomy	**nephrostomy** (neh-FROS-toh-mee)	create a new opening into the kidney
	-otomy	**nephrotomy** (neh-FROT-oh-mee)	incision into a kidney

Word Building *(continued)*

COMBINING FORM	COMBINED WITH	MEDICAL TERM	DEFINITION
	-pathy	**nephropathy** (neh-FROP-ah-thee)	kidney disease
	-pexy	**nephropexy** (NEF-roh-pek-see)	surgical fixation of kidney
	-lithiasis	**nephrolithiasis** (nef-roh-lith-EE-a-sis)	condition of kidney stones
	-sclerosis	**nephrosclerosis** (nef-roh-skleh-ROH-sis)	hardening of the kidney
pyel/o	-gram	**pyelogram** (PYE-eh-loh-gram)	x-ray record of the renal pelvis
	-itis	**pyelitis** (pye-eh-LYE-tis)	renal pelvis inflammation
	-plasty	**pyeloplasty** (PIE-ah-loh-plas-tee)	surgical repair of the renal pelvis
ren/o	-al	**renal** (REE-nal)	pertaining to the kidney
ur/o	-logist	**urologist** (yoo-RALL-oh-jist)	specialist in urine
	-emia	**uremia** (yoo-REE-mee-ah)	blood condition of urine
ureter/o	-al	**ureteral** (yoo-REE-ter-all)	pertaining to the ureter

Med Term Tip

Word watch—Be particularly careful when using the three very similar combining forms: *uter/o* meaning "uterus," *ureter/o* meaning "ureter," and *urethr/o* meaning "urethra."

COMBINING FORM	COMBINED WITH	MEDICAL TERM	DEFINITION
	-ectasis	**ureterectasis** (yoo-ree-ter-EK-tah-sis)	ureter dilation
	-lith	**ureterolith** (yoo-REE-teh-roh-lith)	ureter stone
	-stenosis	**ureterostenosis** (yoo-ree-ter-oh-sten-OH-sis)	narrowing of a ureter
urethr/o	-al	**urethral** (yoo-REE-thral)	pertaining to the urethra
	-algia	**urethralgia** (yoo-ree-THRAL-jee-ah)	urethra pain
	-itis	**urethritis** (yoo-ree-THRIGH-tis)	urethra inflammation
	-rrhagia	**urethrorrhagia** (yoo-ree-throh-RAH-jee-ah)	rapid bleeding from the urethra
	-scope	**urethroscope** (yoo-REE-throh-scope)	instrument to visually examine the urethra
	-stenosis	**urethrostenosis** (yoo-ree-throh-steh-NOH-sis)	narrowing of the urethra
urin/o	-meter	**urinometer** (yoo-rin-OH-meter)	instrument to measure urine
	-ary	**urinary** (yoo-rih-NAIR-ee)	pertaining to urine

SUFFIX	COMBINED WITH	MEDICAL TERM	DEFINITION
-uria	an-	**anuria** (an-YOO-ree-ah)	condition of no urine
	bacteri/o	**bacteriuria** (back-teer-ree-YOO-ree-ah)	bacteria in the urine

Word Building *(continued)*

SUFFIX	COMBINED WITH	MEDICAL TERM	DEFINITION
	dys-	**dysuria** (dis-YOO-ree-ah)	condition of difficult or painful urination
	glycos/o	**glycosuria** (glye-kohs-YOO-ree-ah)	condition of sugar in the urine
	hemat/o	**hematuria** (hee-mah-TOO-ree-ah)	condition of blood in the urine
	keton/o	**ketonuria** (key-tone-YOO-ree-ah)	ketones in the urine
	noct/i	**nocturia** (nok-TOO-ree-ah)	condition of frequent nighttime urination
	olig/o	**oliguria** (ol-ig-YOO-ree-ah)	condition of scanty amount of urine
	poly-	**polyuria** (pol-ee-YOO-ree-ah)	condition of (too) much urine
	protein	**proteinuria** (pro-ten-YOO-ree-ah)	protein in the urine
	py/o	**pyuria** (pye-YOO-ree-ah)	condition of pus in the urine

Vocabulary

TERM	DEFINITION
anuria (an-YOO-ree-ah)	Complete suppression of urine formed by the kidneys and a complete lack of urine excretion.
azotemia (a-zo-TEE-mee-ah)	Accumulation of nitrogenous waste in the bloodstream. Occurs when the kidney fails to filter these wastes from the blood.
calculus (KAL-kew-lus)	Stone formed within an organ by an accumulation of mineral salts. Found in the kidney, renal pelvis, ureters, bladder, or urethra. Plural is *calculi* (see Figure 9.8 ■).
catheter (KATH-eh-ter)	Flexible tube inserted into the body for the purpose of moving fluids into or out of the body. Most commonly used to refer to a tube threaded through the urethra into the bladder to withdraw urine (see Figure 9.9 ■).

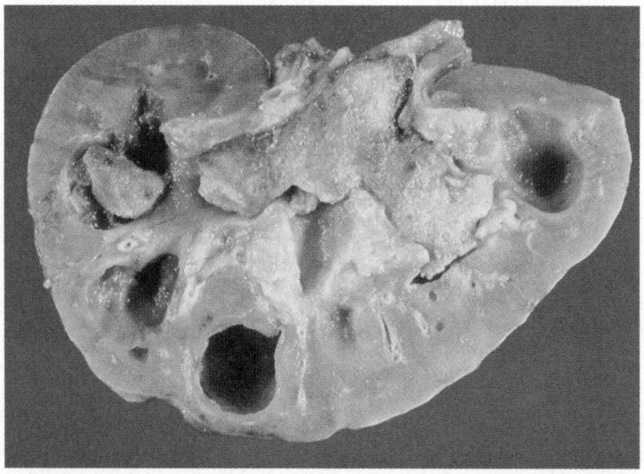

■ **Figure 9.8** Photograph of sectioned kidney specimen illustrating extensive renal calculi.
(Dr. E. Walker/Science Photo Library/Photo Researchers, Inc.)

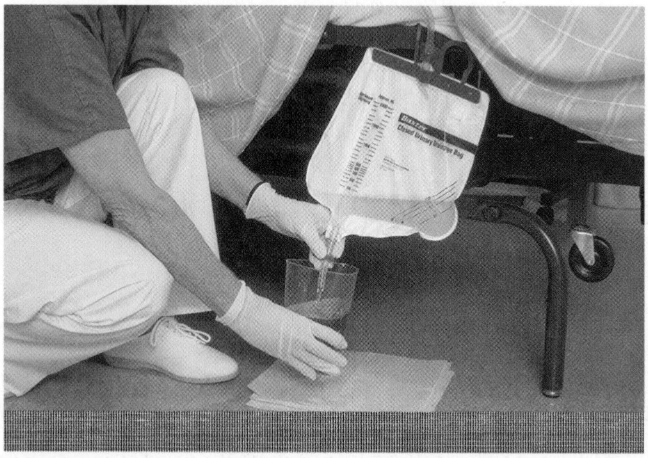

■ **Figure 9.9** Healthcare worker draining urine from a urinary catheter bag.

Vocabulary (*continued*)

TERM	DEFINITION
diuresis (dye-yoo-REE-sis)	Increased formation and secretion of urine.
enuresis (en-yoo-REE-sis)	Involuntary discharge of urine after the age by which bladder control should have been established. This usually occurs by the age of 5. *Nocturnal enuresis* refers to bed-wetting at night.
frequency	Greater-than-normal occurrence in the urge to urinate, without an increase in the total daily volume of urine. Frequency is an indication of inflammation of the bladder or urethra.
hesitancy	Decrease in the force of the urine stream, often with difficulty initiating the flow. It is often a symptom of a blockage along the urethra, such as an enlarged prostate gland.
micturition (mik-too-RIH-shun)	Another term for urination. **Med Term Tip** Terms such as *micturition*, *voiding*, and *urination* all mean basically the same thing—the process of releasing urine from the body.
nephrology (neh-FROL-oh-jee)	Branch of medicine involved in diagnosis and treatment of diseases and disorders of the kidney. Physician is a *nephrologist.*
renal colic (KOL-ik)	Pain caused by a kidney stone. Can be an excruciating pain and generally requires medical treatment.
stricture (STRIK-chur)	Narrowing of a passageway in the urinary system.
uremia (yoo-REE-me-ah)	Accumulation of waste products (especially nitrogenous wastes) in the bloodstream. Associated with renal failure.
urgency (ER-jen-see)	Feeling the need to urinate immediately.
urinary incontinence (in-CON-tin-ens)	Involuntary release of urine. In some patients an indwelling catheter is inserted into the bladder for continuous urine drainage (see Figure 9.9).
urinary retention	Inability to fully empty the bladder, often indicates a blockage in the urethra.
urology (yoo-RAL-oh-jee)	Branch of medicine involved in diagnosis and treatment of diseases and disorders of the urinary system (and male reproductive system). Physician is a *urologist.*
voiding	Another term for urination.

Pathology

TERM	DEFINITION
■ ***Kidney***	
acute tubular necrosis (ATN) (ne-KROH-sis)	Damage to the renal tubules due to presence of toxins in the urine or to ischemia. Results in oliguria.
diabetic nephropathy (ne-FROH-path-ee)	Accumulation of damage to the glomerulus capillaries due to the chronic high blood sugars of diabetes mellitus.

Pathology *(continued)*

TERM	DEFINITION
glomerulonephritis (gloh-mair-yoo-loh-neh-FRYE-tis)	Inflammation of the kidney (primarily of the glomerulus). Since the glomerular membrane is inflamed, it becomes more permeable and will allow protein and blood cells to enter the filtrate. Results in protein in the urine (proteinuria) and hematuria.
hydronephrosis (high-droh-neh-FROH-sis)	Distention of the renal pelvis due to urine collecting in the kidney; often a result of the obstruction of a ureter.
nephrolithiasis (nef-roh-lith-EE-a-sis)	Presence of calculi in the kidney. Usually begins with the solidification of salts present in the urine.
nephrotic syndrome (NS)	Damage to the glomerulus resulting in protein appearing in the urine, proteinuria, and the corresponding decrease in protein in the bloodstream.
nephroptosis (nef-rop-TOH-sis)	Downward displacement of the kidney out of its normal location; commonly called a *floating kidney*.
polycystic kidneys (POL-ee-sis-tik)	Formation of multiple cysts within the kidney tissue. Results in the destruction of normal kidney tissue and uremia.

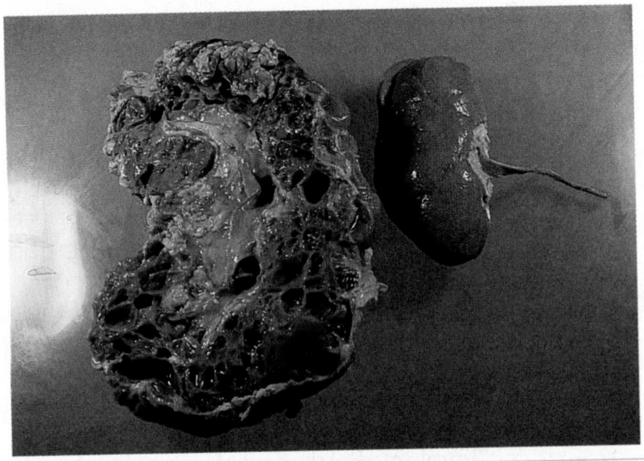

Figure 9.10 Photograph of a polycystic kidney on the left compared to a normal kidney on the right.

TERM	DEFINITION
pyelonephritis (pye-eh-loh-neh-FRYE-tis)	Inflammation of the renal pelvis and the kidney. One of the most common types of kidney disease. It may be the result of a lower urinary tract infection that moved up to the kidney by way of the ureters. There may be large quantities of white blood cells and bacteria in the urine. Blood (hematuria) may even be present in the urine in this condition. Can occur with any untreated or persistent case of cystitis.
renal cell carcinoma	Cancerous tumor that arises from kidney tubule cells.
renal failure	Inability of the kidneys to filter wastes from the blood resulting in uremia. May be acute or chronic. Major reason for a patient being placed on dialysis.
Wilm's tumor (VILMZ TOO-mor)	Malignant kidney tumor found most often in children.
Urinary Bladder	
bladder cancer	Cancerous tumor that arises from the cells lining the bladder; major sign is hematuria.
bladder neck obstruction (BNO)	Blockage of the bladder outlet. Often caused by an enlarged prostate gland in males.

Pathology *(continued)*

TERM	DEFINITION
cystocele (SIS-toh-seel)	Hernia or protrusion of the urinary bladder into the wall of the vagina.
interstitial cystitis (in-ter-STISH-al sis-TYE-tis)	Disease of unknown cause in which there is inflammation and irritation of the bladder. Most commonly seen in middle-aged women.
neurogenic bladder (noo-roh-JEN-ik)	Loss of nervous control that leads to retention; may be caused by spinal cord injury or multiple sclerosis.
urinary tract infection (UTI)	Infection, usually from bacteria, of any organ of the urinary system. Most often begins with cystitis and may ascend into the ureters and kidneys. Most common in women because of their shorter urethra.

Diagnostic Procedures

TERM	DEFINITION
■ ***Clinical Laboratory Tests***	
blood urea nitrogen (BUN) (BLUD yoo-REE-ah NIGH-troh-jen)	Blood test to measure kidney function by the level of nitrogenous waste (urea) that is in the blood.
clean catch specimen (CC)	Urine sample obtained after cleaning off the urinary opening and catching or collecting a urine sample in midstream (halfway through the urination process) to minimize contamination from the genitalia.
creatinine clearance (kree-AT-tih-neen)	Test of kidney function. Creatinine is a waste product cleared from the bloodstream by the kidneys. For this test, urine is collected for 24 hours, and the amount of creatinine in the urine is compared to the amount of creatinine that remains in the bloodstream.
urinalysis (U/A, UA) (yoo-rih-NAL-ih-sis)	Laboratory test that consists of the physical, chemical, and microscopic examination of urine.
urine culture and sensitivity (C&S)	Laboratory test of urine for bacterial infection. Attempt to grow bacteria on a culture medium in order to identify it and determine which antibiotics it is sensitive to.
■ ***Diagnostic Imaging***	
cystography (sis-TOG-rah-fee)	Process of instilling a contrast material or dye into the bladder by catheter to visualize the urinary bladder on x-ray.
excretory urography (EU) (EKS-kreh-tor-ee yoo-ROG-rah-fee)	Injecting dye into the bloodstream and then taking an x-ray to trace the action of the kidney as it excretes the dye.
intravenous pyelogram (IVP) (in-trah-VEE-nus PYE-eh-loh-gram)	Injecting a contrast medium into a vein and then taking an x-ray to visualize the renal pelvis.
kidneys, ureters, bladder (KUB)	X-ray taken of the abdomen demonstrating the kidneys, ureters, and bladder without using any contrast dye. Also called a *flat-plate abdomen.*

Diagnostic Prodedures *(continued)*

TERM	DEFINITION
retrograde pyelogram (RP) (RET-roh-grayd PYE-eh-loh-gram)	Diagnostic X-ray in which dye is inserted through the urethra to outline the bladder, ureters, and renal pelvis.
Figure 9.11 Color enhanced retrograde pyelogram X-ray. Radiopaque dye outlines urinary bladder, ureters, and renal pelves. *(Clinique Ste. Catherine/CNRI/Science Photo Library/Photo Researchers, Inc.)*	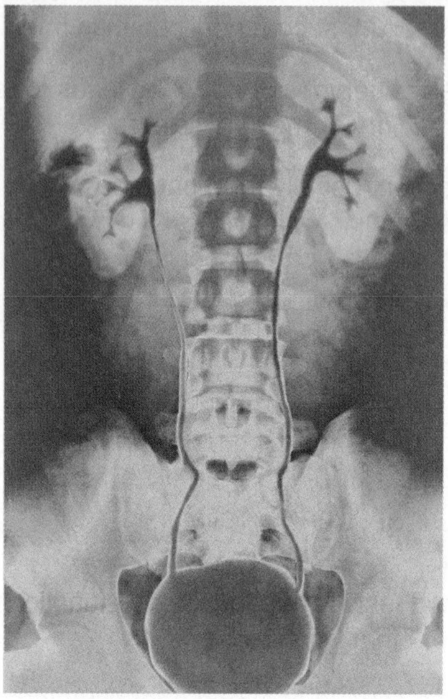
voiding cystourethrography (VCUG) (sis-toh-yoo-ree-THROG-rah-fee)	X-ray taken to visualize the urethra while the patient is voiding after a contrast dye has been placed in the bladder.
■ ***Endoscopic Procedure***	
cystoscopy (cysto) (sis-TOSS-koh-pee)	Visual examination of the urinary bladder using an instrument called a *cystoscope*.

Therapeutic Procedures

TERM	DEFINITION
■ ***Medical Treatments***	
catheterization (cath) (kath-eh-ter-ih-ZAY-shun)	Insertion of a tube through the urethra and into the urinary bladder for the purpose of withdrawing urine or inserting dye.
extracorporeal shockwave lithotripsy (ESWL) (eks-trah-cor-POR-ee-al shock-wave LITH-oh-trip-see)	Use of ultrasound waves to break up stones. Process does not require invasive surgery (see Figure 9.12 ■).
hemodialysis (HD) (hee-moh-dye-AL-ih-sis)	Use of an artificial kidney machine that filters the blood of a person to remove waste products. Use of this technique in patients who have defective kidneys is lifesaving (see Figure 9.13 ■).

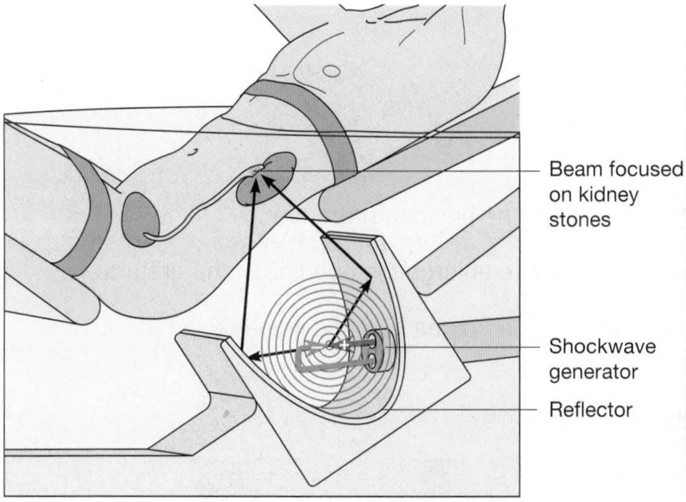

Figure 9.12 Extracorporeal shockwave lithotripsy, a non-invasive procedure using high frequency sound waves to shatter kidney stones.

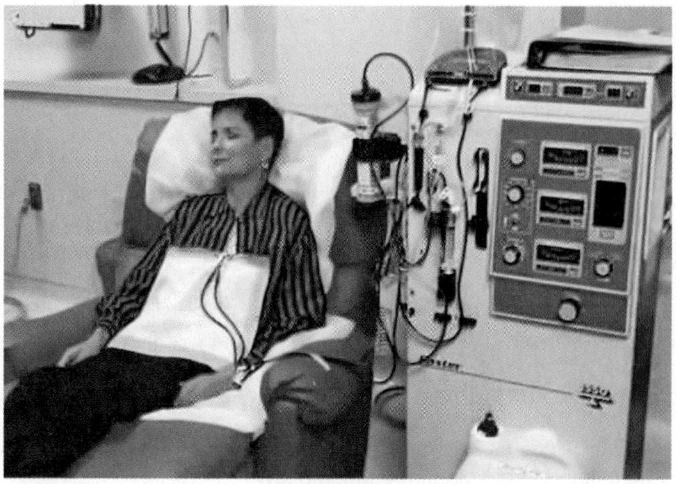

Figure 9.13 Patient undergoing hemodialysis. Patient's blood passes through hemodialysis machine for cleansing and is then returned to her body.

Therapeutic Procedures *(continued)*

TERM	DEFINITION
peritoneal dialysis (pair-ih-TOH-nee-al dye-AL-ih-sis)	Removal of toxic waste substances from the body by placing warm chemically balanced solutions into the peritoneal cavity. Wastes are filtered out of the blood across the peritoneum. Used in treating renal failure and certain poisonings.

Figure 9.14 Peritoneal dialysis. Chemically balanced solution is placed into the abdominal cavity to draw impurities out of the bloodstream. It is removed after several hours.

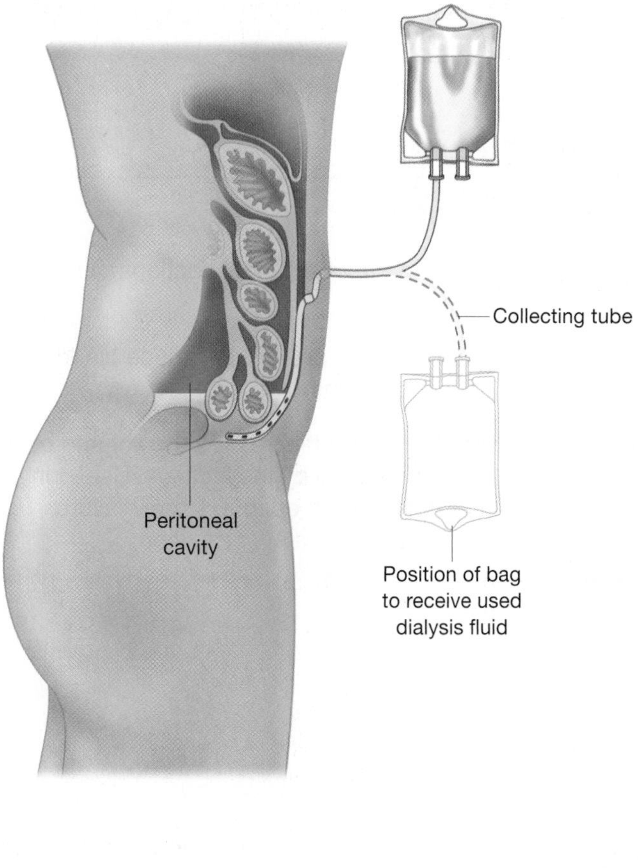

Therapeutic Procedures *(continued)*

TERM	DEFINITION
Surgical Treatments	
lithotripsy (LITH-oh-trip-see)	Destroying or crushing stones in the bladder or urethra.
meatotomy (mee-ah-TOT-oh-me)	Incision into the meatus in order to enlarge the opening of the urethra.
nephrolithotomy (nef-roh-lith-OT-oh-mee)	Surgical incision to directly remove stones from the kidney.
renal transplant	Surgical placement of a donor kidney.

Figure 9.15 Figure illustrates location of transplanted donor kidney.

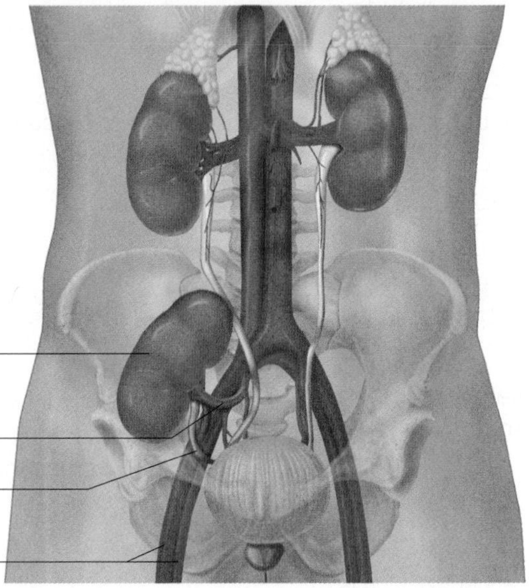

Pharmacology

CLASSIFICATION	ACTION	GENERIC AND BRAND NAMES
antibiotic	Used to treat bacterial infections of the urinary tract.	ciprofloxacin, Cipro; nitrofurantoin, Macrobid
antispasmodic (an-tye-spaz-MAH-dik)	Medication to prevent or reduce bladder muscle spasms.	oxybutynin, Ditropan; neostigmine, Prostigmine
diuretic (dye-yoo-REH-tiks)	Medication that increases the volume of urine produced by the kidneys. Useful in the treatment of edema, kidney failure, heart failure, and hypertension.	furosemide, Lasix; spironolactone, Aldactone

Abbreviations

AGN	acute glomerulonephritis	**HD**	hemodialysis
ARF	acute renal failure	**H_2O**	water
ATN	acute tubular necrosis	**I&O**	intake and output
BNO	bladder neck obstruction	**IPD**	intermittent peritoneal dialysis
BUN	blood urea nitrogen	**IVP**	intravenous pyelogram
CAPD	continuous ambulatory peritoneal dialysis	**K^+**	potassium
cath	catheterization	**KUB**	kidney, ureter, bladder
CC	clean catch urine specimen	**mL**	milliliter
Cl^-	chloride	**Na^+**	sodium
CRF	chronic renal failure	**NS**	nephrotic syndrome
C&S	culture and sensitivity	**pH**	acidity or alkalinity of urine
cysto	cystoscopy	**RP**	retrograde pyelogram
ESRD	end-stage renal disease	**SG, sp. gr.**	specific gravity
ESWL	extracorporeal shockwave lithotripsy	**U/A, UA**	urinalysis
EU	excretory urography	**UC**	urine culture
GU	genitourinary	**UTI**	urinary tract infection
HCO_3^-	bicarbonate	**VCUG**	voiding cystourethrography

Chapter Review

Terminology Checklist

Below are all Anatomy and Physiology key terms, Word Building, Vocabulary, Pathology, Diagnostic, Therapeutic, and Pharmacology terms presented in this chapter. Use this list as a study tool by placing a check in the box in front of each term as you master its meaning.

- ☐ acute tubular necrosis
- ☐ afferent arteriole
- ☐ albumin
- ☐ antibiotic
- ☐ antispasmodic
- ☐ anuria
- ☐ azotemia
- ☐ bacteriuria
- ☐ bladder cancer
- ☐ bladder neck obstruction
- ☐ blood urea nitrogen
- ☐ Bowman's capsule
- ☐ calculus
- ☐ calyx
- ☐ catheter
- ☐ catheterization
- ☐ clean catch specimen
- ☐ collecting tubule
- ☐ cortex
- ☐ creatinine clearance
- ☐ cystalgia
- ☐ cystectomy
- ☐ cystic
- ☐ cystitis
- ☐ cystocele
- ☐ cystogram
- ☐ cystography
- ☐ cystolith
- ☐ cystopexy
- ☐ cystoplasty
- ☐ cystorrhagia
- ☐ cystoscope
- ☐ cystoscopy
- ☐ cystostomy
- ☐ cystotomy
- ☐ diabetic nephropathy
- ☐ distal convoluted tubule
- ☐ diuresis
- ☐ diuretic
- ☐ dysuria
- ☐ efferent arteriole
- ☐ electrolyte
- ☐ enuresis
- ☐ excretory urography
- ☐ external sphincter
- ☐ extracorporeal shockwave lithotripsy
- ☐ filtration
- ☐ frequency
- ☐ genitourinary system
- ☐ glomerular capsule
- ☐ glomerular filtrate
- ☐ glomerulonephritis
- ☐ glomerulus
- ☐ glycosuria
- ☐ hematuria
- ☐ hemodialysis
- ☐ hesitancy
- ☐ hilum
- ☐ homeostasis
- ☐ hydronephrosis
- ☐ internal sphincter
- ☐ interstitial cystitis
- ☐ intravenous pyelogram
- ☐ ketonuria
- ☐ kidneys
- ☐ kidneys, ureters, bladder
- ☐ lithotomy
- ☐ lithotripsy
- ☐ loop of Henle
- ☐ meatotomy
- ☐ medulla
- ☐ micturition
- ☐ nephrectomy
- ☐ nephritis
- ☐ nephrogram
- ☐ nephrolith
- ☐ nephrolithiasis
- ☐ nephrolithotomy
- ☐ nephrologist
- ☐ nephrology
- ☐ nephroma
- ☐ nephromalacia
- ☐ nephromegaly
- ☐ nephron
- ☐ nephropathy
- ☐ nephropexy
- ☐ nephroptosis
- ☐ nephrosclerosis
- ☐ nephrosis
- ☐ nephrostomy
- ☐ nephrotic syndrome
- ☐ nephrotomy
- ☐ neurogenic bladder
- ☐ nitrogenous wastes
- ☐ nocturia
- ☐ oliguria
- ☐ peritoneal dialysis
- ☐ peritubular capillaries
- ☐ polycystic kidneys
- ☐ polyuria
- ☐ proteinuria
- ☐ proximal convoluted tubule
- ☐ pyelitis
- ☐ pyelogram
- ☐ pyelonephritis
- ☐ pyeloplasty
- ☐ pyuria
- ☐ reabsorption
- ☐ renal
- ☐ renal artery
- ☐ renal cell carcinoma
- ☐ renal colic
- ☐ renal corpuscle
- ☐ renal failure

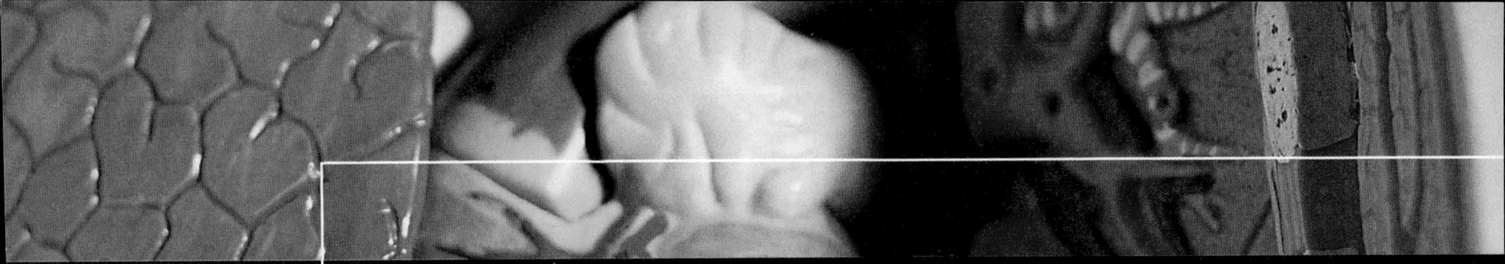

10 Reproductive System

Learning Objectives

Upon completion of this chapter, you will be able to:

- Identify and define the combining forms and suffixes introduced in this chapter.
- Correctly spell and pronounce medical terms and major anatomical structures relating to the reproductive systems.
- Locate and describe the major organs of the reproductive systems and their functions.
- Use medical terms to describe circumstances relating to pregnancy.
- Identify the symptoms and origin of sexually transmitted diseases.
- Build and define reproductive system medical terms from word parts.
- Identify and define reproductive system vocabulary terms.
- Identify and define selected reproductive system pathology terms.
- Identify and define selected reproductive system diagnostic procedures.
- Identify and define selected reproductive system therapeutic procedures.
- Identify and define selected medications relating to the reproductive systems.
- Define selected abbreviations associated with the reproductive systems.

Section I: Female Reproductive System at a Glance

Function

The female reproductive system produces ova (the female reproductive cell), provides a location for fertilization and growth of a baby, and secretes female sex hormones. In addition, the breasts produce milk to nourish the newborn.

Organs

breasts
fallopian tubes
ovaries
uterus
vagina
vulva

Combining Forms

amni/o	amnion
cervic/o	neck, cervix
chori/o	chorion
colp/o	vagina
culd/o	cul-de-sac
embry/o	embryo
episi/o	vulva
fet/o	fetus
gynec/o	woman, female
hymen/o	hymen
hyster/o	uterus
lact/o	milk
mamm/o	breast
mast/o	breast
men/o	menses, menstruation
metr/o	uterus
nat/o	birth
oophor/o	ovary
ov/o	egg
ovari/o	ovary
perine/o	perineum
salping/o	fallopian tubes, uterine tubes
uter/o	uterus
vagin/o	vagina
vulv/o	vulva

Suffixes Relating

-arche	beginning
-cyesis	state of pregnancy
-gravida	pregnancy
-para	to bear (offspring)
-partum	childbirth
-salpinx	fallopian tube
-tocia	labor, childbirth

Female Reproductive System Illustrated

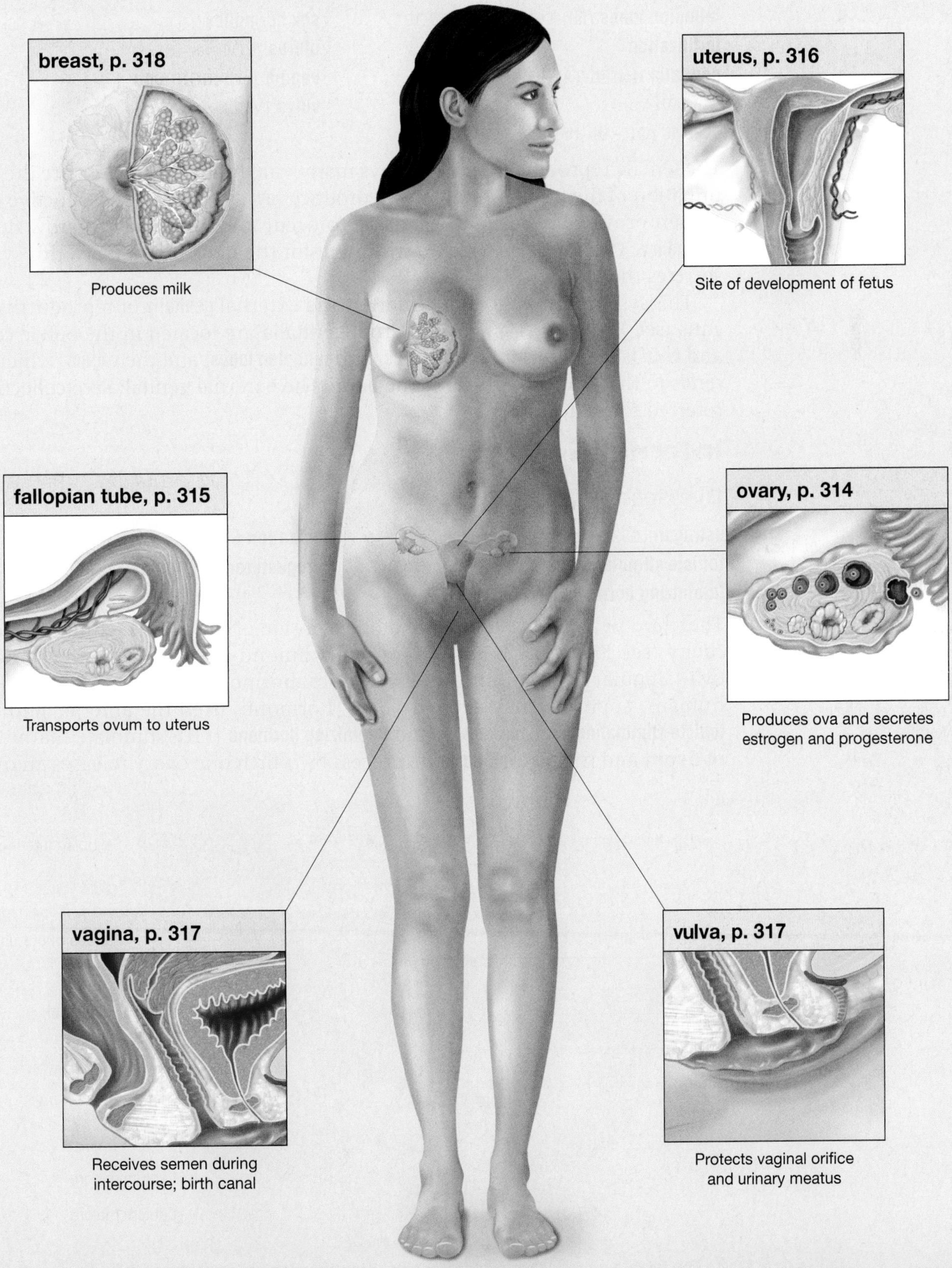

Anatomy and Physiology of the Female Reproductive System

breasts
fallopian tubes (fah-LOH-pee-an TOOBS)
fertilization
genitalia (jen-ih-TAY-lee-ah)
ova (OH-vah)
ovaries (OH-vah-reez)
pregnancy
sex hormones
uterus (YOO-ter-us)
vagina (vah-JIGH-nah)
vulva (VULL-vah)

The female reproductive system plays many vital functions that ensure the continuation of the human race. First, it produces **ova**, the female reproductive cells. It then provides a place for **fertilization** to occur and for a baby to grow during **pregnancy**. The **breasts** provide nourishment for the newborn. Finally, this system secretes the female **sex hormones**.

This system consists of both internal and external **genitalia** or reproductive organs (see Figure 10.1 ■). The internal genitalia are located in the pelvic cavity and consist of the **uterus**, two **ovaries**, two **fallopian tubes**, and the **vagina**, which extends to the external surface of the body. The external genitalia are collectively referred to as the **vulva**.

Internal Genitalia

Ovaries

Med Term Tip

The singular for egg is *ovum*. The plural term for many eggs is *ova*. The term *ova* is not used exclusively when discussing the human reproductive system. For instance, testing the stool for ova and parasites is used to detect the presence of parasites or their ova in the digestive tract, a common cause for severe diarrhea.

estrogen (ESS-troh-jen)
follicle stimulating hormone (FOLL-ih-kl)
luteinizing hormone (loo-teh-NIGH-zing)
ovulation (ov-yoo-LAY-shun)
progesterone (proh-JES-ter-ohn)

There are two ovaries, one located on each side of the uterus within the pelvic cavity (see Figure 10.1). These are small almond-shaped glands that produce ova (singular is *ovum*) and the female sex hormones (see Figure 10.2 ■). In humans, approximately every 28 days, hormones from the anterior pituitary, **follicle stimulating hormone** (FSH) and **luteinizing hormone** (LH), stimulate maturation of ovum and trigger **ovulation**, the process by which one ovary releases an ovum

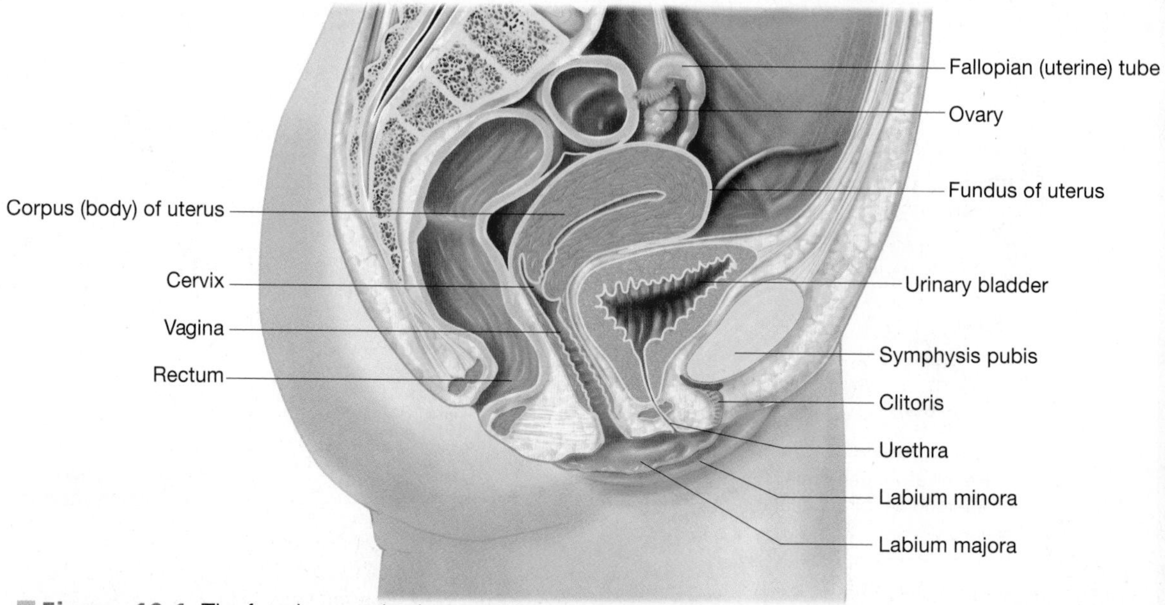

■ **Figure 10.1** The female reproductive system, sagittal view showing organs of the system in relation to the urinary bladder and rectum.

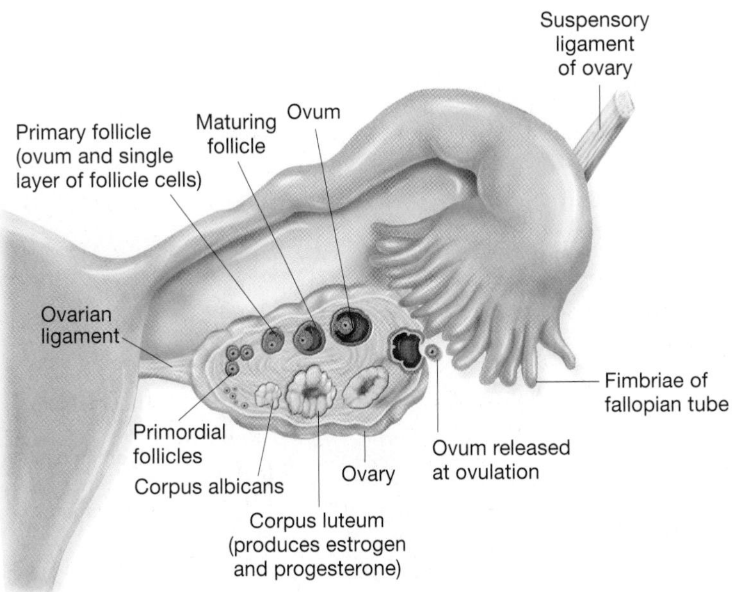

Figure 10.2 Structure of the ovary and fallopian (uterine) tube. Figure illustrates stages of ovum development and the relationship of the ovary to the fallopian tube.

(see Figure 10.3 ■). The principal female sex hormones produced by the ovaries, **estrogen** and **progesterone**, stimulate the lining of the uterus to be prepared to receive a fertilized ovum. These hormones are also responsible for the female secondary sexual characteristics.

Fallopian Tubes

conception (con-SEP-shun)
fimbriae (FIM-bree-ay)
oviducts (OH-vih-ducts)
uterine tubes (YOO-ter-in)

The fallopian tubes, also called the **uterine tubes** or **oviducts**, are approximately 5½ inches long and run from the area around each ovary to either side of the upper portion of the uterus (see Figures 10.4 ■ and 10.5 ■). As they near the ovaries, the unattached ends of these two tubes expand into finger-like projections called

Med Term Tip

When the fertilized egg adheres or implants to the fallopian tube instead of moving into the uterus, a condition called *tubal pregnancy* exists. There is not enough room in the fallopian tube for the fetus to grow normally. Implantation of the fertilized egg in any location other than the uterus is called an *ectopic pregnancy*. *Ectopic* is a general term meaning "in the wrong place."

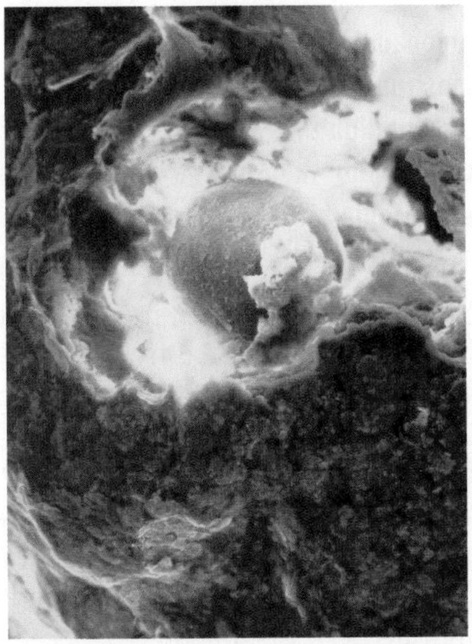

Figure 10.3 Enhanced color scanning electron micrograph showing an ovum (pink) released by the ovary at ovulation surrounded by follicle (white) tissue. The external surface of the ovary is brown in this photo. *(P.M. Motta and J. Van Blekrom/Science Photo Library/Photo Researchers, Inc.)*

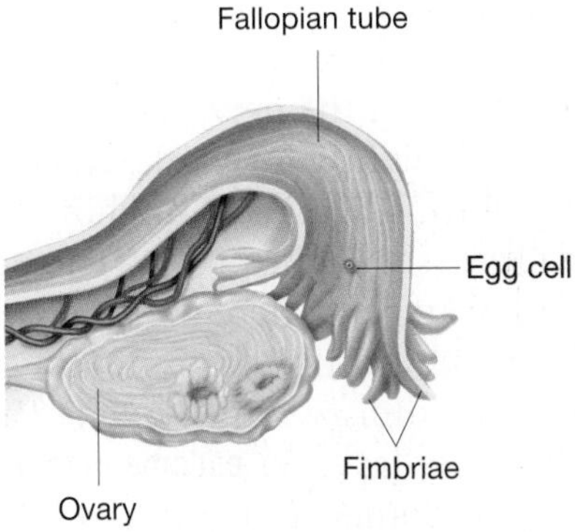

Figure 10.4 Fallopian (uterine) tube, longitudinal view showing released ovum within the fallopian tube.

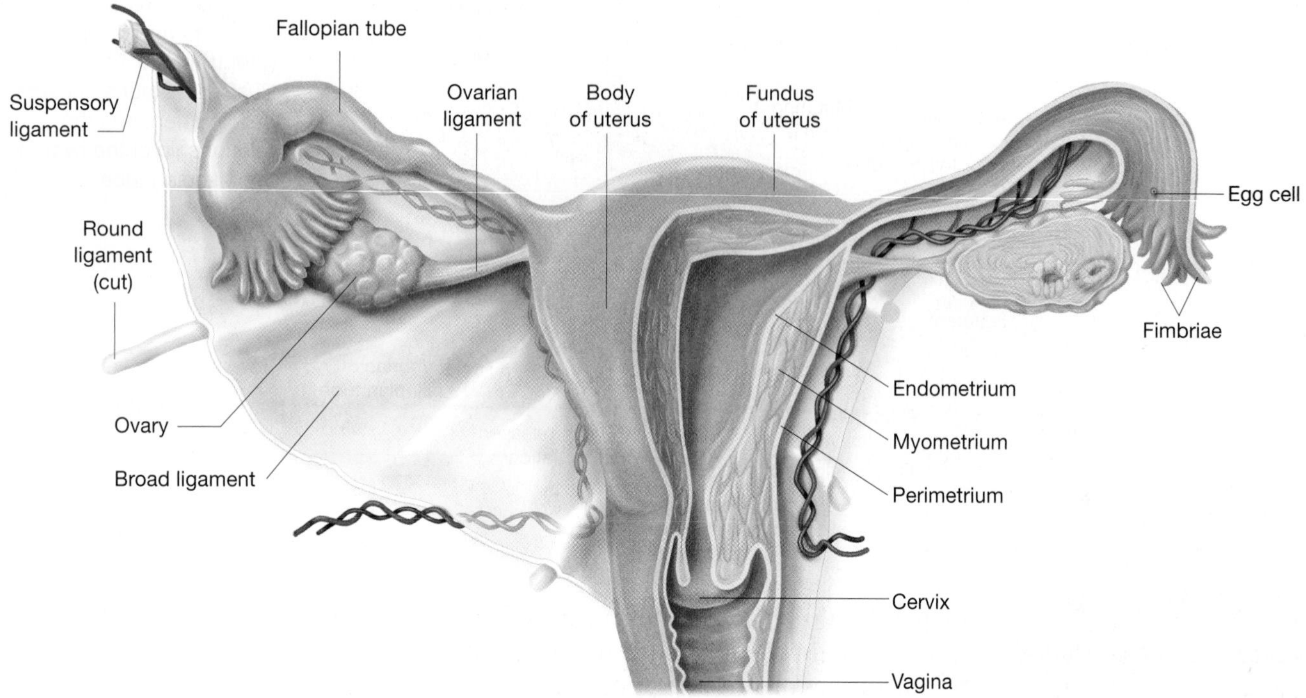

Figure 10.5 The uterus. Cutaway view shows regions of the uterus and cervix and its relationship to the fallopian (uterine) tubes and vagina.

fimbriae. The fimbriae catch an ovum after ovulation and direct it into the fallopian tube. The fallopian tube can then propel the ovum from the ovary to the uterus so that it can implant. The meeting of the egg and sperm, called fertilization or **conception**, normally takes place within the upper one-half of the fallopian tubes.

Uterus

anteflexion (an-tee-FLEK-shun)
cervix (SER-viks)
corpus (KOR-pus)
endometrium (en-doh-MEE-tre-um)
fundus (FUN-dus)
menarche (men-AR-kee)
menopause (MEN-oh-pawz)
menstrual period (MEN-stroo-all)
menstruation (men-stroo-AY-shun)
myometrium (my-oh-MEE-tre-um)
perimetrium (pear-ee-MEE-tre-um)

The uterus is a hollow, pear-shaped organ that contains a thick muscular wall, a mucous membrane lining, and a rich supply of blood (see Figure 10.5). It lies in the center of the pelvic cavity between the bladder and the rectum. It is normally bent slightly forward, which is called **anteflexion**, and is held in position by strong fibrous ligaments anchored in the outer layer of the uterus, called the **perimetrium** (see Figure 10.1). The uterus has three sections: the **fundus** or upper portion, between where the fallopian tubes connect to the uterus; **corpus** or body, which is the central portion; and **cervix** (Cx), or lower portion, also called the neck of the uterus, which opens into the vagina.

The inner layer, or **endometrium**, of the uterine wall contains a rich blood supply. The endometrium reacts to hormonal changes every month that prepare it to receive a fertilized ovum. In a normal pregnancy the fertilized ovum implants in the endometrium, which can then provide nourishment and protection for the developing baby. Contractions of the thick muscular walls of the uterus, called the **myometrium**, assist in propelling the fetus through the birth canal at delivery.

Med Term Tip

During pregnancy, the height of the fundus is an important measurement for estimating the stage of pregnancy and the size of the fetus. Following birth, massaging the fundus with pressure applied in a circular pattern stimulates the uterine muscle to contract to help stop bleeding. Patients may be more familiar with a common term for uterus, *womb*. However, the correct medical term is uterus.

If a pregnancy is not established, the endometrium is sloughed off, resulting in **menstruation** or the **menstrual period.** During a pregnancy, the lining of the uterus does not leave the body but remains to nourish the unborn child. A girl's first menstrual period (usually during her early teenage years) is called **menarche**, while the ending of menstrual activity and childbearing years is called **menopause**. This generally occurs between the ages of 40 and 55.

Med Term Tip

Word watch—Be careful using the combining forms *uter/o* meaning "uterus" and *ureter/o* meaning "ureter."

Vagina

Bartholin's glands (BAR-toh-linz)
hymen (HIGH-men)
vaginal orifice (VAJ-ih-nal OR-ih-fis)

The vagina is a muscular tube, lined with mucous membrane that extends from the cervix of the uterus to the outside of the body (see Figure 10.6 ■). The vagina allows for the passage of the menstrual flow. In addition, during intercourse, it receives the male's penis and semen, which is the fluid containing sperm. The vagina also serves as the birth canal through which the baby passes during a normal vaginal birth.

The **hymen** is a thin membranous tissue that partially covers the external vaginal opening or **vaginal orifice.** This membrane is broken by the use of tampons, during physical activity, or during sexual intercourse. A pair of glands, called **Bartholin's glands**, are located on either side of the vaginal orifice and secrete mucus for lubrication during intercourse.

Med Term Tip

Word watch—Be careful using the combining forms *colp/o* meaning "vagina" and *culd/o* meaning "cul-de-sac (rectouterine pouch)."

Vulva

clitoris (KLIT-oh-ris)
erectile tissue (ee-REK-tile)
labia majora (LAY-bee-ah mah-JOR-ah)
labia minora (LAY-bee-ah min-NOR-ah)
perineum (pair-ih-NEE-um)
urinary meatus (YOO-rih-nair-ee mee-AY-tus)

The vulva is a general term that refers to the group of structures that make up the female external genitalia. The **labia majora** and **labia minora** are folds of skin that serve as protection for the genitalia, the vaginal orifice, and the **urinary meatus** (see Figure 10.7 ■). Since the urinary tract and the reproductive organs are located in proximity to one another and each contains mucous membranes that can transport infection, there is a danger of infection entering the urinary tract. The **clitoris** is a small organ containing sensitive **erectile tissue** that is aroused during sexual stimulation and corresponds to the penis in the male. The region between the vaginal orifice and the anus is referred to as the **perineum**.

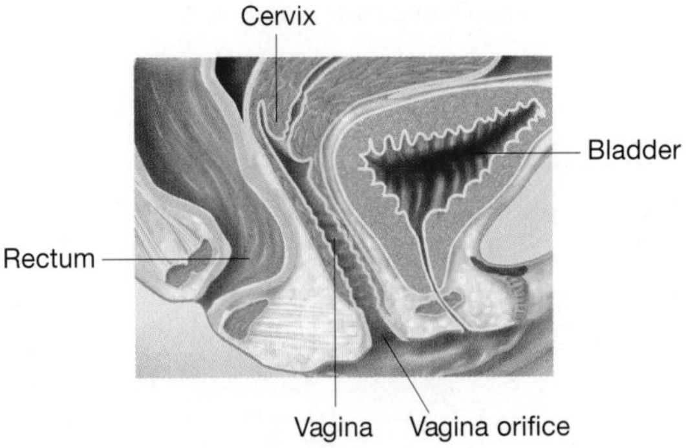

■ **Figure 10.6** The vagina, sagittal section showing the location of the vagina and its relationship to the cervix, uterus, rectum, and bladder.

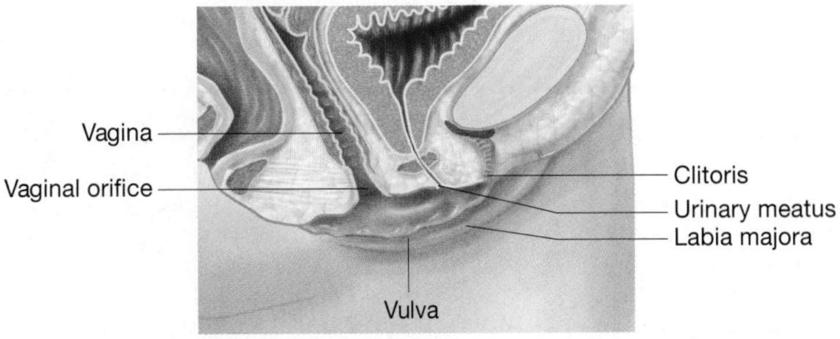

■ **Figure 10.7** The vulva, sagittal section illustrating how the labia major and labia minora cover and protect the vaginal orifice, clitoris, and urinary meatus.

Breast

areola (ah-REE-oh-la)
lactation (lak-TAY-shun)
lactiferous ducts (lak-TIF-er-us)
lactiferous glands (lak-TIF-er-us)
mammary glands (MAM-ah-ree)
nipple
nurse

The breasts, or **mammary glands**, play a vital role in the reproductive process because they produce milk, a process called **lactation**, to nourish the newborn. The size of the breasts, which varies greatly from woman to woman, has no bearing on the ability to **nurse** or feed a baby. Milk is produced by the **lactiferous glands** and is carried to the **nipple** by the **lactiferous ducts** (see Figure 10.8 ■). The **areola** is the pigmented area around the nipple. As long as the breast is stimulated by the nursing infant, the breast will continue to secrete milk.

Mid Term Tip

The term *abortion* (AB) has different meanings for medical professionals and the general population. The general population equates the term *abortion* specifically with the planned termination of a pregnancy. However, to the medical community, abortion is a broader medical term meaning that a pregnancy has ended before a fetus is *viable*, meaning before it can live on its own.

Pregnancy

amnion (AM-nee-on)
amniotic fluid (am-nee-OT-ik)
chorion (KOR-ree-on)
embryo (EM-bree-oh)
fetus (FEE-tus)
gestation (jess-TAY-shun)
placenta (plah-SEN-tah)
premature
umbilical cord (um-BILL-ih-kal KORD)

Pregnancy refers to the period of time during which a baby grows and develops in its mother's uterus (see Figure 10.9 ■). The normal length of time for a pregnancy, **gestation**, is 40 weeks. If a baby is born before completing at least 37 weeks of gestation, it is considered **premature**.

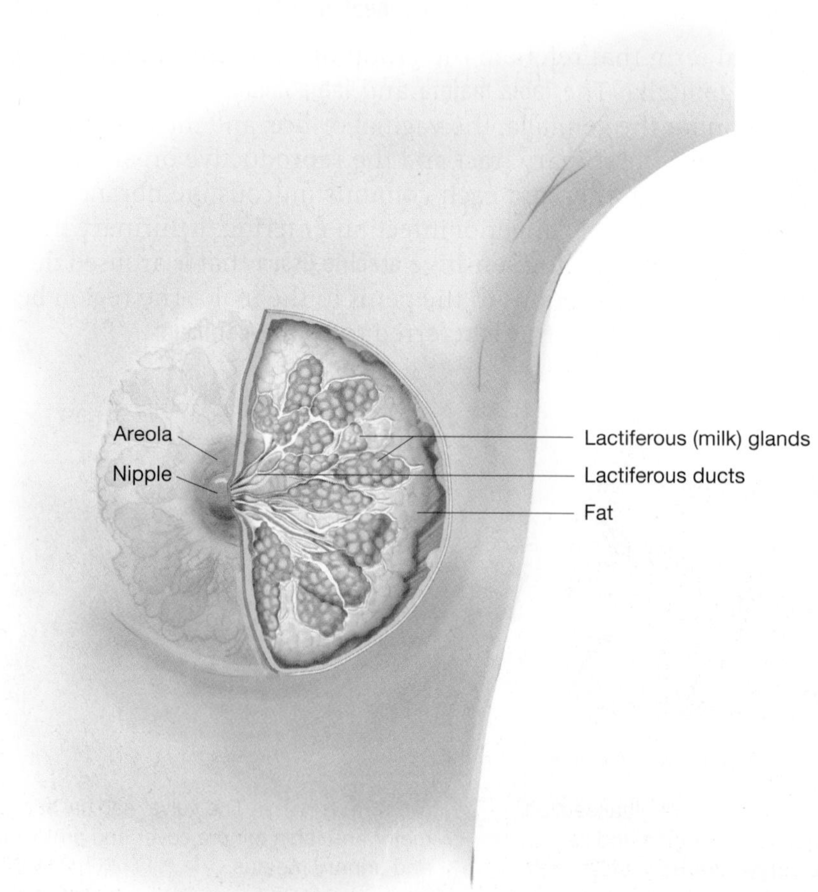

■ **Figure 10.8** The breast, cutaway view showing both internal and external features.

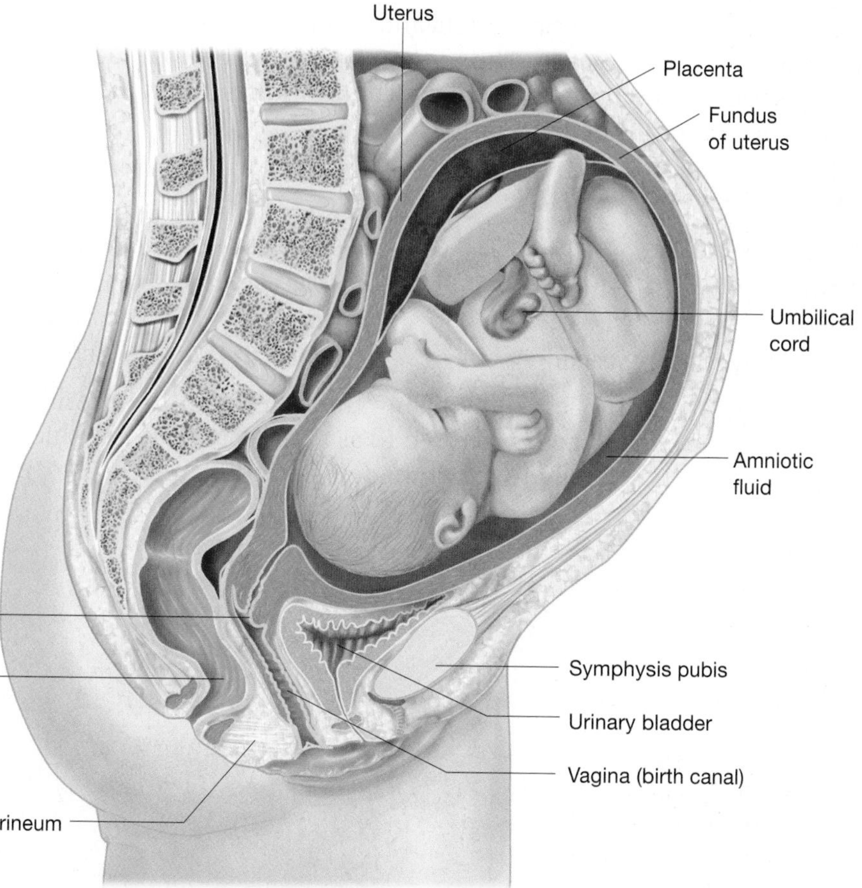

Uterus

Placenta

Fundus of uterus

Umbilical cord

Amniotic fluid

Cervix of uterus

Rectum

Symphysis pubis

Urinary bladder

Vagina (birth canal)

Perineum

During pregnancy the female body undergoes many changes. In fact, all of the body systems become involved in the development of a healthy infant. From the time the fertilized egg implants in the uterus until approximately the end of the eighth week, the infant is referred to as an **embryo** (see Figure 10.10 ■). During this period all the major organs and body systems are formed. Following the embryo stage and lasting until birth, the infant is called a **fetus** (see Figure 10.11 ■). During this time, the longest period of gestation, the organs mature and begin to function.

The fetus receives nourishment from its mother by way of the **placenta**, which is a spongy, blood-filled organ that forms in the uterus next to the fetus. The

Med Term Tip

During the embryo stage of gestation, the organs and organ systems of the body are formed. Therefore, this is a very common time for *congenital anomalies*, or birth defects, to occur. This may happen before the woman is even aware of being pregnant.

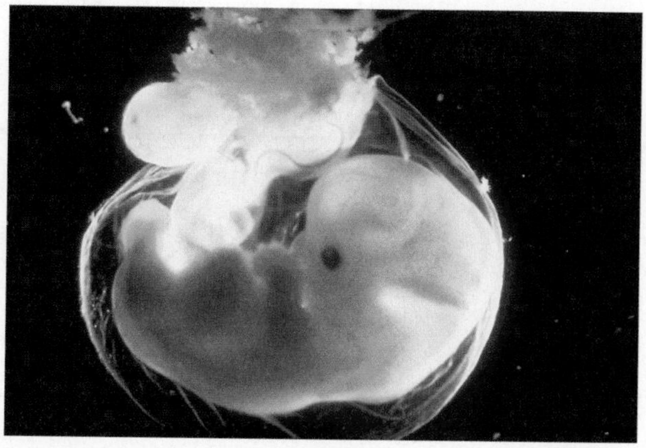

■ **Figure 10.10** Photograph illustrating the development of an embryo. *(Petit Format/Nestle/Photo Researchers, Inc.)*

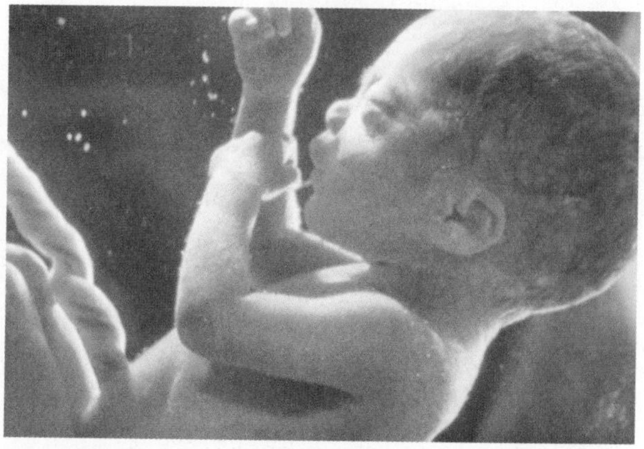

■ **Figure 10.11** Photograph illustrating the development of a fetus. *(Petit Format/Nestle/Photo Researchers, Inc.)*

placenta is commonly referred to as the afterbirth. The fetus is attached to the placenta by way of the **umbilical cord** and is surrounded by two membranous sacs, the **amnion** and the **chorion**. The amnion is the innermost sac, and it holds the **amniotic fluid** in which the fetus floats. The chorion is an outer, protective sac and also forms part of the placenta.

Labor and Delivery

breech presentation
crowning
delivery
dilation stage (dye-LAY-shun)
effacement (eh-FACE-ment)
expulsion stage (ex-PULL-shun)
labor
placental stage (plah-SEN-tal)

Labor is the actual process of expelling the fetus from the uterus and through the vagina. The first stage is referred to as the **dilation stage**, in which the uterine muscle contracts strongly to expel the fetus (see Figure 10.12A ■). During this

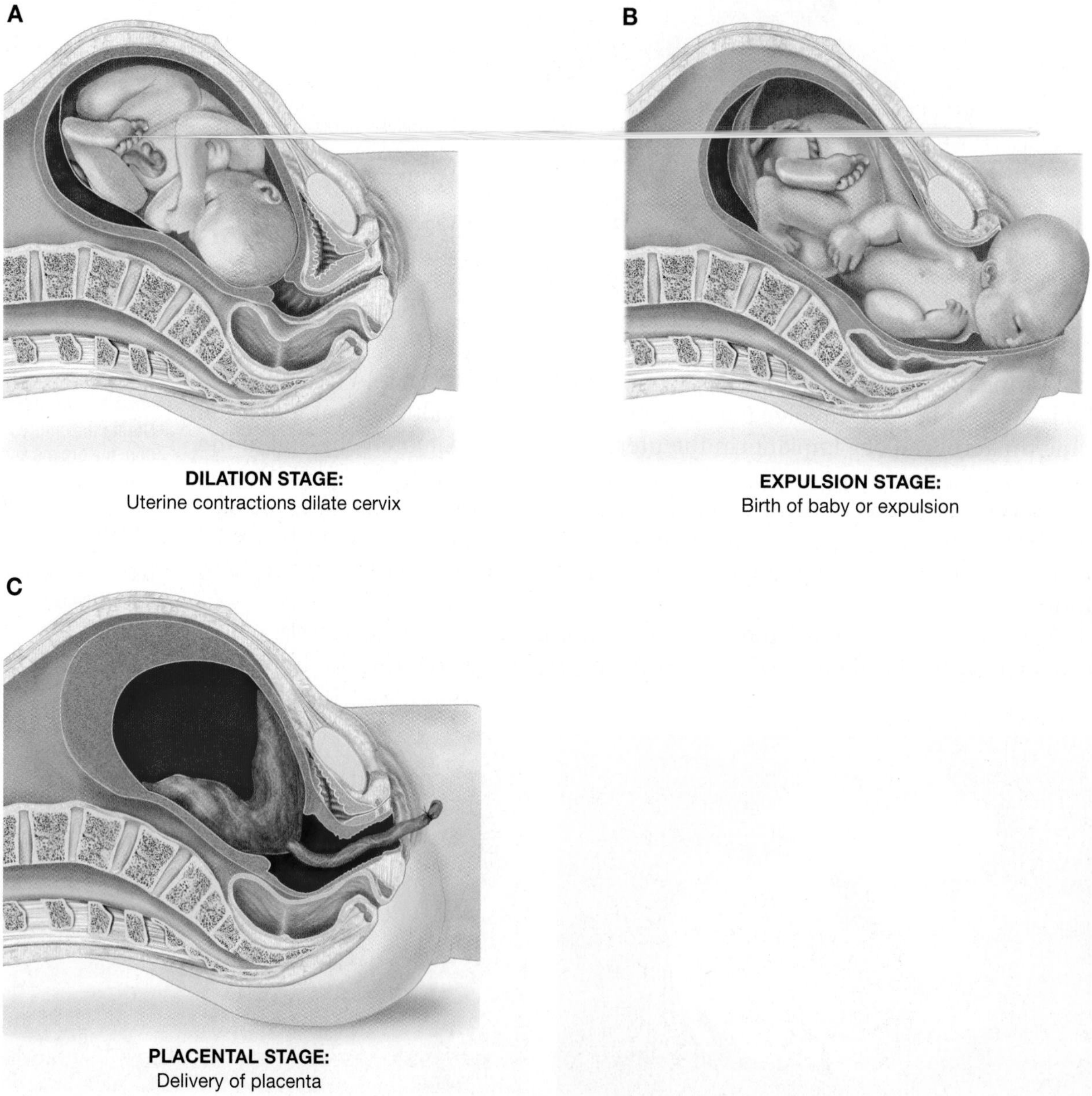

■ **Figure 10.12** The stages of labor and delivery. A) During the dilation stage the cervix thins and dilates to 10 cm. B) During the expulsion stage the infant is delivered. C) During the placental stage the placenta is delivered.

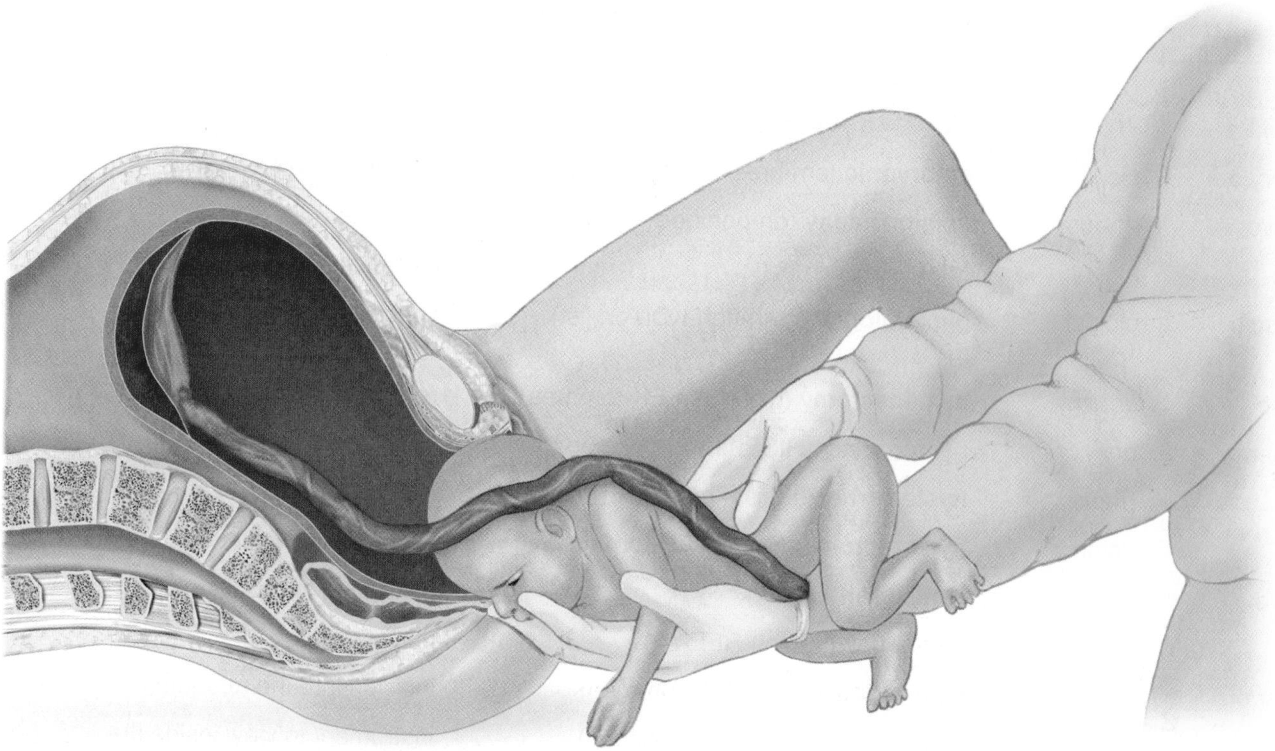

Figure 10.13 A breech birth. This image illustrates a newborn that has been delivered buttocks first.

process the fetus presses on the cervix and causes it to dilate or expand. As the cervix dilates, it also becomes thinner, referred to as **effacement.** When the cervix is completely dilated to 10 centimeters, the second stage of labor begins (see Figure 10.12B ■). This is the **expulsion stage** and ends with **delivery** of the baby. Generally, the head of the baby appears first, which is referred to as **crowning** (see Figure 10.10). In some cases the baby's buttocks will appear first, and this is referred to as a **breech presentation** (see Figure 10.13 ■). The last stage of labor is the **placental stage** (see Figure 10.12C ■). Immediately after childbirth, the uterus continues to contract, causing the placenta to be expelled through the vagina.

Word Building

The following list contains examples of medical terms built directly from word parts. The definition for these terms can be determined by a straightforward translation of the word parts.

COMBINING FORM	COMBINED WITH	MEDICAL TERM	DEFINITION
amni/o	-otomy	**amniotomy** (am-nee-OT-oh-mee)	incision into amnion
	-tic	**amniotic** (am-nee-OT-ik)	pertaining to the amnion
	-rrhea	**amniorrhea** (am-nee-oh-REE-ah)	flow of fluid from amnion
cervic/o	-ectomy	**cervicectomy** (ser-vih-SEK-toh-mee)	removal of cervix
	-al	**cervical** (SER-vih-kal)	pertaining to the cervix
	endo- -itis	**endocervicitis** (en-doh-ser-vih-SIGH-tis)	inflammation within cervix
chori/o	-nic	**chorionic** (koh-ree-ON-ik)	pertaining to the chorion
colp/o	-scope	**colposcope** (KOL-poh-scope)	instrument to view inside vagina

Word Building *(continued)*

COMBINING FORM	COMBINED WITH	MEDICAL TERM	DEFINITION
embry/o	-nic	**embryonic** (em-bree-ON-ik)	pertaining to the embryo
episi/o	-rrhaphy	**episiorrhaphy** (eh-peez-ee-OR-ah-fee)	suture of vulva
fet/o	-al	**fetal** (FEE-tall)	pertaining to the fetus
gynec/o	-ologist	**gynecologist** (gigh-neh-KOL-oh-jist)	specialist in female reproductive system
hymen/o	-ectomy	**hymenectomy** (high-men-EK-toh-mee)	removal of the hymen
hyster/o	-pexy	**hysteropexy** (HISS-ter-oh-pek-see)	surgical fixation of the uterus
	-rrhexis	**hysterorrhexis** (hiss-ter-oh-REK-sis)	ruptured uterus
	-ectomy	**hysterectomy** (hiss-ter-EK-toh-mee)	surgical removal of the uterus
lact/o	-ic	**lactic** (LAK-tik)	pertaining to milk
	-rrhea	**lactorrhea** (lak-toh-REE-ah)	milk discharge
lapar/o	-otomy	**laparotomy** (lap-ah-ROT-oh-mee)	incision into the abdomen
	-scope	**laparoscope** (LAP-ah-row-scope)	instrument to view inside the abdomen
mamm/o	-gram	**mammogram** (MAM-moh-gram)	record of the breast
	-ary	**mammary** (MAM-mah-ree)	pertaining to the breast
	-plasty	**mammoplasty** (MAM-moh-plas-tee)	surgical repair of breast
mast/o	-algia	**mastalgia** (mas-TAL-jee-ah)	breast pain
	-itis	**mastitis** (mas-TYE-tis)	inflammation of the breast
	-ectomy	**mastectomy** (mass-TEK-toh-mee)	removal of the breast
men/o	a- -rrhea	**amenorrhea** (ah-men-oh-REE-ah)	no menstrual flow
	dys- -rrhea	**dysmenorrhea** (dis-men-oh-REE-ah)	painful menstrual flow
	oligo- -rrhea	**oligomenorrhea** (ol-lih-goh-men-oh-REE-ah)	scanty menstrual flow
	-rrhagia	**menorrhagia** (men-oh-RAY-jee-ah)	abnormal, rapid menstrual flow
metr/o	endo- -itis	**endometritis** (en-doh-meh-TRY-tis)	inflammation within the uterus

Med Term Tip

Word watch—Be careful when using the combining form *metr/o* meaning "uterus" and the suffix *–metry* meaning "process of measuring."

	peri- -itis	**perimetritis** (pair-ih-meh-TRY-tis)	inflammation around the uterus
	-rrhea	**metrorrhea** (meh-troh-REE-ah)	flow from uterus
	-rrhagia	**metrorrhagia** (meh-troh-RAY-jee-ah)	rapid (menstrual) blood flow from uterus
nat/o	neo-	**neonate** (NEE-oh-nayt)	newborn
	neo- -ologist	**neonatologist** (nee-oh-nay-TALL-oh-jist)	specialist in the study of the newborn
oophor/o	-ectomy	**oophorectomy** (oh-off-oh-REK-toh-mee)	removal of the ovary
	-itis	**oophoritis** (oh-off-oh-RIGH-tis)	inflammation of the ovary

Word Building *(continued)*

COMBINING FORM	COMBINED WITH	MEDICAL TERM	DEFINITION
ovari/o	-an	**ovarian** (oh-VAIR-ee-an)	pertaining to the ovary
salping/o	-cyesis	**salpingocyesis** (sal-ping-goh-sigh-EE-sis)	tubal pregnancy
	-ectomy	**salpingectomy** (sal-ping-JECK-toh-mee)	removal of the fallopian tube
	-itis	**salpingitis** (sal-ping-JIGH-tis)	inflammation of the fallopian tubes
uter/o	-ine	**uterine** (YOO-ter-in)	pertaining to the uterus
vagin/o	-al	**vaginal** (VAJ-ih-nal)	pertaining to the vagina
	-itis	**vaginitis** (vaj-ih-NIGH-tis)	inflammation of the vagina
PREFIX	**SUFFIX**	**MEDICAL TERM**	**DEFINITION**
pseudo-	-cyesis	**pseudocyesis** (soo-doh-sigh-EE-sis)	false pregnancy
nulli-	-gravida	**nulligravida** (null-ih-GRAV-ih-dah)	no pregnancies
primi-		**primigravida** (prem-ih-GRAV-ih-dah)	first pregnancy
multi-		**multigravida** (mull-tih-GRAV-ih-dah)	multiple pregnancies
nulli-	-para	**nullipara** (null-IP-ah-rah)	no births
primi-		**primipara** (prem-IP-ah-rah)	first birth
multi-		**multipara** (mull-TIP-ah-rah)	multiple births
ante-	-partum	**antepartum** (an-tee-PAR-tum)	before birth
post-		**postpartum** (post-PAR-tum)	after birth
hemato-	-salpinx	**hematosalpinx** (hee-mah-toh-SAL-pinks)	blood in fallopian tube
pyo-		**pyosalpinx** (pie-oh-SAL-pinks)	pus in fallopian tube
dys-	-tocia	**dystocia** (dis-TOH-she-ah)	difficult labor and childbirth

Vocabulary

TERM	DEFINITION
atresia (ah-TREE-she-ah)	Congenital lack of a normal body opening.
barrier contraception (kon-trah-SEP-shun)	Prevention of a pregnancy using a device to prevent sperm from meeting an ovum. Examples include condoms, diaphragms, and cervical caps.
colostrum (kuh-LOS-trum)	Thin fluid first secreted by the breast after delivery. It does not contain much protein, but is rich in antibodies.
fraternal twins	Twins that develop from two different ova fertilized by two different sperm. Although twins, these siblings do not have identical DNA.
gynecology (GYN) (gigh-neh-KOL-oh-jee)	Branch of medicine specializing in the diagnosis and treatment of conditions of the female reproductive system. Physician is called a *gynecologist*.
hormonal contraception	Use of hormones to block ovulation and prevent contraception. May be in the form of a pill, a patch, an implant under the skin, or injection.
identical twins	Twins that develop from the splitting of one fertilized ovum. These siblings have identical DNA.

Vocabulary *(continued)*

TERM	DEFINITION
infertility	Inability to produce children. Generally defined as no pregnancy after properly timed intercourse for 1 year.
intrauterine device (IUD) (in-trah-YOO-ter-in)	Device that is inserted into the uterus by a physician for the purpose of contraception.

Figure 10.14 Photographs illustrating the shape of two different intrauterine devices (IUDs). *(Jules Selmes and Debi Treloar/Dorling Kindersley Media Library)*

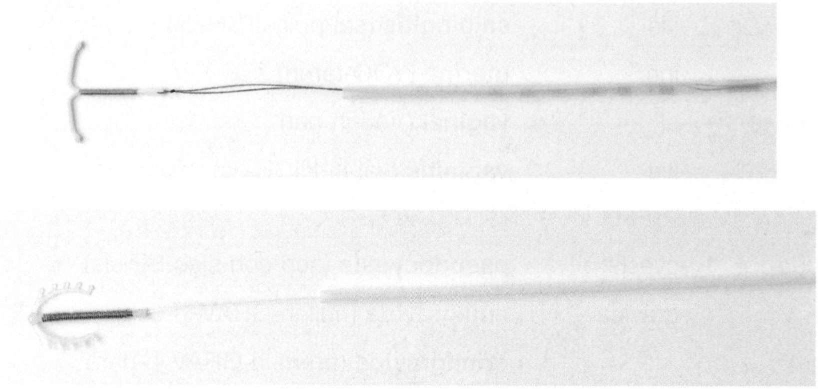

TERM	DEFINITION
meconium (meh-KOH-nee-um)	First bowel movement of a newborn. It is greenish-black in color and consists of mucus and bile.
neonatology (nee-oh-nay-TALL-oh-jee)	Branch of medicine specializing in the diagnosis and treatment of conditions involving newborns. Physician is called a *neonatologist.*
obstetrics (OB) (ob-STET-riks)	Branch of medicine specializing in the diagnosis and treatment of women during pregnancy and childbirth, and immediately after childbirth. Physician is called an *obstetrician.*
premenstrual syndrome (PMS) (pre-MEN-stroo-al SIN-drohm)	Symptoms that develop just prior to the onset of a menstrual period, which can include irritability, headache, tender breasts, and anxiety.
puberty (PEW-ber-tee)	Beginning of menstruation and the ability to reproduce.

Pathology

TERM	DEFINITION
■ ***Ovary***	
ovarian carcinoma (oh-VAY-ree-an kar-sih-NOH-mah)	Cancer of the ovary.
ovarian cyst (oh-VAY-ree-an SIST)	Cyst that develops within the ovary. These may be multiple cysts and may rupture, causing pain and bleeding.
■ ***Uterus***	
cervical cancer (SER-vih-kal CAN-ser)	Malignant growth in the cervix. Some cases are caused by the *human papilloma virus* (HPV), a sexually transmitted virus for which there is now a vaccine. An especially difficult type of cancer to treat that causes 5 percent of the cancer deaths in women. Pap smear tests have helped to detect early cervical cancer.
endometrial cancer (en-doh-MEE-tree-al CAN-ser)	Cancer of the endometrial lining of the uterus.

Pathology *(continued)*

TERM	DEFINITION
fibroid tumor (FIGH-broyd TOO-mor) **Figure 10.15** Common sites for the development of fibroid tumors.	Benign tumor or growth that contains fiber-like tissue. Uterine fibroid tumors are the most common tumors in women. 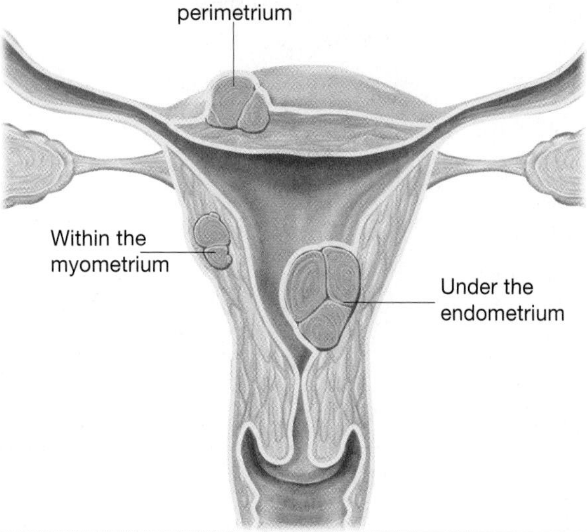
menometrorrhagia (men-oh-met-thro-RAY-jee-ah)	Excessive bleeding during the menstrual period and at intervals between menstrual periods.
prolapsed uterus (pro-LAPS'D YOO-ter-us)	Fallen uterus that can cause the cervix to protrude through the vaginal opening. Generally caused by weakened muscles from vaginal delivery or as the result of pelvic tumors pressing down.
■ ***Vagina***	
candidiasis (kan-dih-DYE-ah-sis)	Yeast infection of the skin and mucous membranes that can result in white plaques on the tongue and vagina. **Med Term Tip** The term *candida* comes from a Latin term meaning "dazzling white." Candida is the scientific name for yeast and refers to the very white discharge that is the hallmark of a yeast infection.
cystocele (SIS-toh-seel)	Hernia or outpouching of the bladder that protrudes into the vagina. This may cause urinary frequency and urgency.
rectocele (REK-toh-seel)	Protrusion or herniation of the rectum into the vagina.
toxic shock syndrome (TSS)	Rare and sometimes fatal staphylococcus infection that generally occurs in menstruating women. Initial infection of the vagina is associated with prolonged wearing of a super-absorbent tampon.
■ ***Pelvic Cavity***	
endometriosis (en-doh-mee-tree-OH-sis)	Abnormal condition of endometrium tissue appearing throughout the pelvis or on the abdominal wall. This tissue is normally found within the uterus.
pelvic inflammatory disease (PID) (PELL-vik in-FLAM-mah-toh-ree dih-ZEEZ)	Chronic or acute infection, usually bacterial, that has ascended through the female reproductive organs and out into the pelvic cavity. May result in scarring that interferes with fertility.
■ ***Breast***	
breast cancer	Malignant tumor of the breast. Usually forms in the milk-producing gland tissue or the lining of the milk ducts (see Figure 10.16A ■).

Figure 10.16 Comparison of breast cancer and fibrocystic disease. A) Breast with a malignant tumor growing in the lactiferous gland and duct. B) The location of a fibrocystic lump in the adipose tissue covering the breast.

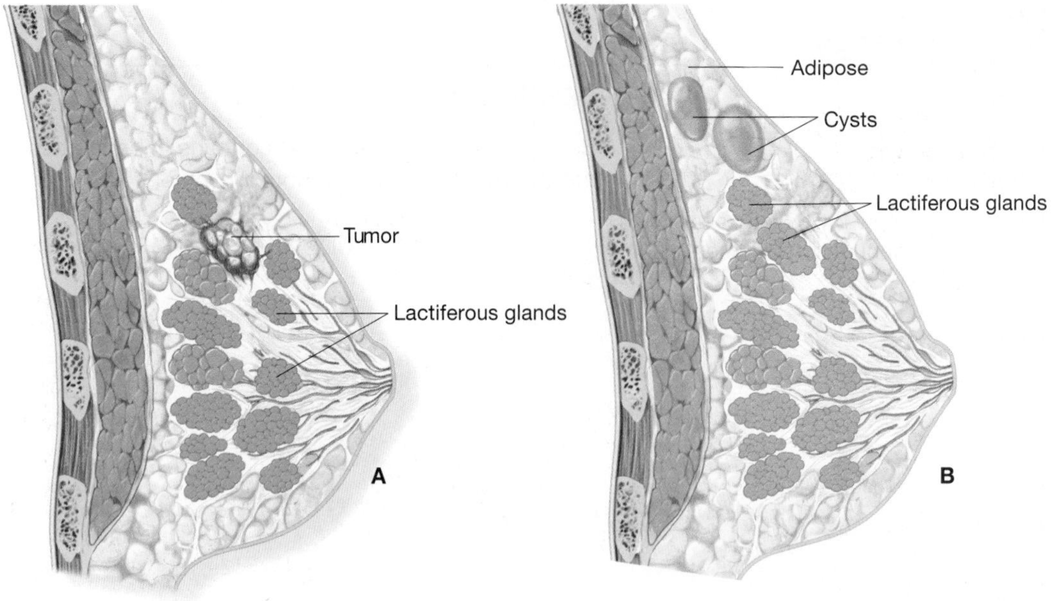

Pathology *(continued)*

TERM	DEFINITION
fibrocystic breast disease (figh-bro-SIS-tik)	Benign cysts forming in the breast (see Figure 10.16B).
■ ***Pregnancy***	
abruptio placentae (ah-BRUP-tee-oh plah-SEN-tee)	Emergency condition in which the placenta tears away from the uterine wall prior to delivery of the infant. Requires immediate delivery of the baby.
eclampsia (eh-KLAMP-see-ah)	Convulsive seizures and coma occurring in the woman between the twentieth week of pregnancy and the first week of postpartum. Preceded by preeclampsia.
hemolytic disease of the newborn (HDN) (hee-moh-LIT-ik)	Condition developing in the baby when the mother's blood type is Rh-negative and the baby's blood is Rh-positive. Antibodies in the mother's blood enter the fetus's bloodstream through the placenta and destroy fetus's red blood cells causing anemia, jaundice, and enlargement of the spleen. Treatment is early diagnosis and blood transfusion. Also called *erythroblastosis fetalis.*
placenta previa (plah-SEN-tah PREE-vee-ah)	A placenta that is implanted in the lower portion of the uterus and, in turn, blocks the birth canal.

Figure 10.17 Placenta previa, longitudinal section showing the placenta growing over the opening into the cervix.

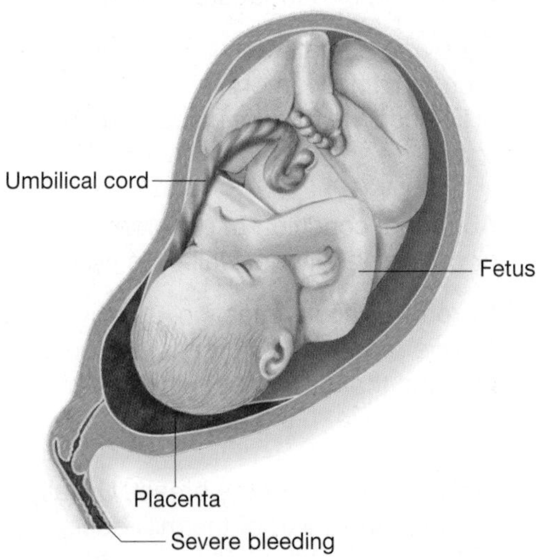

Pathology *(continued)*

TERM	DEFINITION
preeclampsia (pre-eh-KLAMP-see-ah)	Metabolic disease of pregnancy. If untreated, it may result in true eclampsia. Symptoms include hypertension, headaches, albumin in the urine, and edema. Also called *toxemia.*
prolapsed umbilical cord (pro-LAPS'D um-BILL-ih-kal)	When the umbilical cord of the baby is expelled first during delivery and is squeezed between the baby's head and the vaginal wall. This presents an emergency situation since the baby's circulation is compromised.
spontaneous abortion	Unplanned loss of a pregnancy due to the death of the embryo or fetus before the time it is viable, commonly referred to as a *miscarriage.*
stillbirth	Birth in which a viable-aged fetus dies shortly before or at the time of delivery.

Diagnostic Procedures

TERM	DEFINITION
■ ***Clinical Laboratory Tests***	
Pap (Papanicolaou) **smear** (pap-ah-NIK-oh-low)	Test for the early detection of cancer of the cervix named after the developer of the test, George Papanicolaou, a Greek physician. A scraping of cells is removed from the cervix for examination under a microscope.
pregnancy test (PREG-nan-see)	Chemical test that can determine a pregnancy during the first few weeks. Can be performed in a physician's office or with a home-testing kit.
■ ***Diagnostic Imaging***	
hysterosalpingography (HSG) (hiss-ter-oh-sal-pin-GOG-rah-fee)	Taking of an X-ray after injecting radiopaque material into the uterus and fallopian tubes.
mammography (mam-OG-rah-fee)	Using X-ray to diagnose breast disease, especially breast cancer.
pelvic ultrasonography (PELL-vik-ull-trah-son-OG-rah-fee)	Use of ultrasound waves to produce an image or photograph of an organ, such as the uterus, ovaries, or fetus.
■ ***Endoscopic Procedures***	
colposcopy	Examination of vagina using an instrument called a *colposcope.*
culdoscopy (kul-DOS-koh-pee)	Examination of the female pelvic cavity, particularly behind the uterus, by introducing an endoscope through the wall of the vagina.
laparoscopy (lap-ar-OS-koh-pee)	Examination of the peritoneal cavity using an instrument called a *laparoscope.* The instrument is passed through a small incision made by the surgeon into the abdominopelvic cavity.

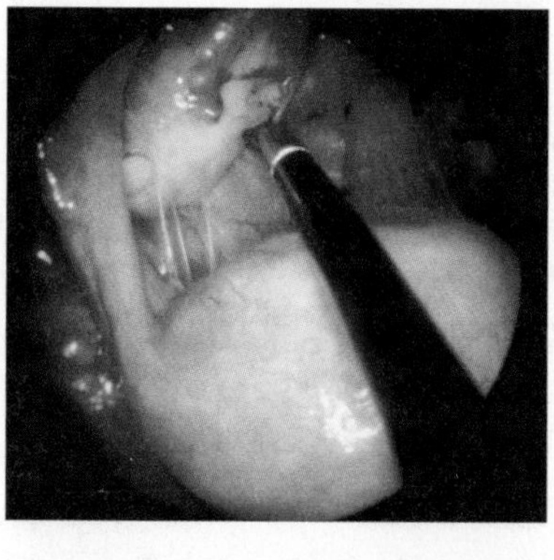

Figure 10.18 Photograph taken during a laparoscopic procedure. The fundus of the uterus is visible below the probe, the ovary is at the tip of the probe, and the fallopian tube extends along the left side of the photo. *(Southern Illinois University/Photo Researchers, Inc.)*

Diagnostic Procedures *(continued)*

TERM	DEFINITION
■ *Obstetrical Diagnostic Procedures*	
amniocentesis (am-nee-oh-sen-TEE-sis)	Puncturing of the amniotic sac using a needle and syringe for the purpose of withdrawing amniotic fluid for testing. Can assist in determining fetal maturity, development, and genetic disorders.
Apgar score (AP-gar)	Evaluation of a neonate's adjustment to the outside world. Observes color, heart rate, muscle tone, respiratory rate, and response to stimulus at one minute and five minutes after birth.
chorionic villus sampling (CVS) (kor-ree-ON-ik vill-us)	Removal of a small piece of the chorion for genetic analysis. May be done at an earlier stage of pregnancy than amniocentesis.
fetal monitoring (FEE-tal)	Using electronic equipment placed on the mother's abdomen or the fetus' scalp to check the fetal heart rate (FHR) and fetal heart tone (FHT) during labor. The normal heart rate of the fetus is rapid, ranging from 120 to 160 beats per minute. A drop in the fetal heart rate indicates the fetus is in distress.
■ *Additional Diagnostic Procedures*	
cervical biopsy (SER-vih-kal BYE-op-see)	Taking a sample of tissue from the cervix to test for the presence of cancer cells.
endometrial biopsy (EMB) (en-doh-MEE-tre-al BYE-op-see)	Taking a sample of tissue from the lining of the uterus to test for abnormalities.
pelvic examination (PELL-vik)	Physical examination of the vagina and adjacent organs performed by a physician placing the fingers of one hand into the vagina. An instrument called a *speculum* is used to open the vagina.

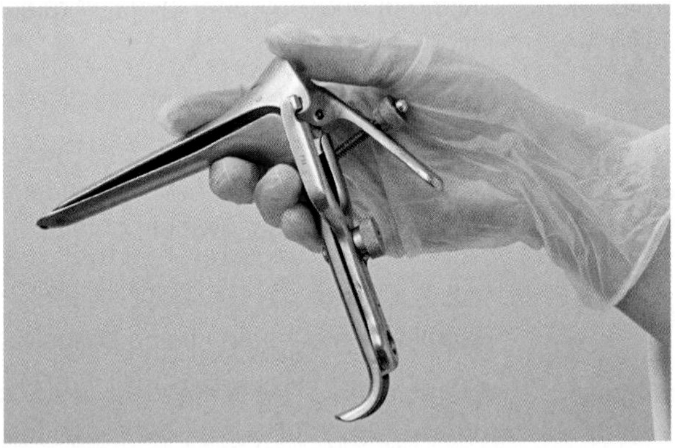

■ **Figure 10.19** A speculum used to hold the vagina open in order to visualize the cervix.

Therapeutic Procedures

TERM	DEFINITION
■ *Surgical Procedures*	
cesarean section (CS, C-section) (see-SAYR-ee-an)	Surgical delivery of a baby through an incision into the abdominal and uterine walls. Legend has it that the Roman emperor, Julius Caesar, was the first person born by this method.
conization (kon-ih-ZAY-shun)	Surgical removal of a core of cervical tissue. Also refers to partial removal of the cervix.

Therapeutic Procedures *(continued)*

TERM	DEFINITION
dilation and curettage (D & C) (dye-LAY-shun and koo-reh-TAHZ)	Surgical procedure in which the opening of the cervix is dilated and the uterus is scraped or suctioned of its lining or tissue. Often performed after a spontaneous abortion and to stop excessive bleeding from other causes.
elective abortion	Legal termination of a pregnancy for nonmedical reasons.
episiotomy (eh-peez-ee-OT-oh-mee)	Surgical incision of the perineum to facilitate the delivery process. Can prevent an irregular tearing of tissue during birth.
lumpectomy (lump-EK-toh-mee)	Removal of only a breast tumor and the tissue immediately surrounding it.
radical mastectomy (mast-EK-toh-mee)	Surgical removal of the breast tissue plus chest muscles and axillary lymph nodes.
simple mastectomy (mast-EK-toh-mee)	Surgical removal of the breast tissue.
therapeutic abortion	Termination of a pregnancy for the health of the mother or another medical reason.
total abdominal hysterectomy—bilateral salpingo-oophorectomy (TAH-BSO) (hiss-ter-EK-toh-me sal-ping-goh oh-oh-foe-REK-toh-mee)	Removal of the entire uterus, cervix, both ovaries, and both fallopian tubes.
tubal ligation (TOO-bal lye-GAY-shun)	Surgical tying off of the fallopian tubes to prevent conception from taking place. Results in sterilization of the female.
vaginal hysterectomy (VAJ-ih-nal hiss-ter-EK-toh-me)	Removal of the uterus through the vagina rather than through an abdominal incision.

Pharmacology

CLASSIFICATION	ACTION	GENERIC AND BRAND NAMES
abortifacient (ah-bore-tih-FAY-shee-ent)	Medication that terminates a pregnancy.	mifepristone, Mifeprex; dinoprostone, Prostin E2
fertility drug	Medication that triggers ovulation. Also called *ovulation stimulant.*	clomiphene, Clomid; follitropin alfa, Gonal-F
hormone replacement therapy (HRT)	Menopause or the surgical loss of the ovaries results in the lack of estrogen production. Replacing this hormone may prevent some of the consequences of menopause, especially in younger women who have surgically lost their ovaries.	conjugated estrogens, Cenestin, Premarin
oral contraceptive pills (OCPs) (kon-trah-SEP-tive)	Birth control medication that uses low doses of female hormones to prevent conception by blocking ovulation.	desogestrel/ethinyl estradiol, Ortho-Cept; ethinyl estradiol/norgestrel, Lo/Ovral
oxytocin (ox-ee-TOH-sin)	Oxytocin is a natural hormone that begins or improves uterine contractions during labor and delivery.	oxytocin, Pitocin, Syntocinon

Abbreviations

AB	abortion
AI	artificial insemination
BSE	breast self-examination
CS, C-section	cesarean section
CVS	chorionic villus sampling
Cx	cervix
D & C	dilation and curettage
EDC	estimated date of confinement
EMB	endometrial biopsy
ERT	estrogen replacement therapy
FEKG	fetal electrocardiogram
FHR	fetal heart rate
FHT	fetal heart tone
FSH	follicle-stimulating hormone
FTND	full-term normal delivery
GI, grav I	first pregnancy
GYN, gyn	gynecology
HCG, hCG	human chorionic gonadotropin
HDN	hemolytic disease of the newborn
HPV	human papilloma virus
HRT	hormone replacement therapy
HSG	hysterosalpingography
IUD	intrauterine device
IVF	*in vitro* fertilization
LBW	low birth weight
LH	luteinizing hormone
LMP	last menstrual period
NB	newborn
OB	obstetrics
OCPs	oral contraceptive pills
PAP	Papanicolaou test
PI, para I	first delivery
PID	pelvic inflammatory disease
PMS	premenstrual syndrome
TAH-BSO	total abdominal hysterectomy–bilateral salpingo-oophorectomy
TSS	toxic shock syndrome
UC	uterine contractions

Section II: Male Reproductive System at a Glance

Function

Similar to the female reproductive system, the male reproductive system is responsible for producing sperm, the male reproductive cell, secreting the male sex hormones, and delivering sperm to the female reproductive tract.

Organs

bulbourethral glands
epididymis
penis
prostate gland
seminal vesicles
testes
vas deferens

Combining Forms

andr/o	male	**prostat/o**	prostate
balan/o	glans penis	**spermat/o**	sperm
crypt/o	hidden	**testicul/o**	testes
epididym/o	epididymis	**varic/o**	varicose veins
orch/o	testes	**vas/o**	vas deferens
orchi/o	testes	**vesicul/o**	seminal vesicle
orchid/o	testes		

Suffixes Relating

-spermia	condition of sperm

Male Reproductive System Illustrated

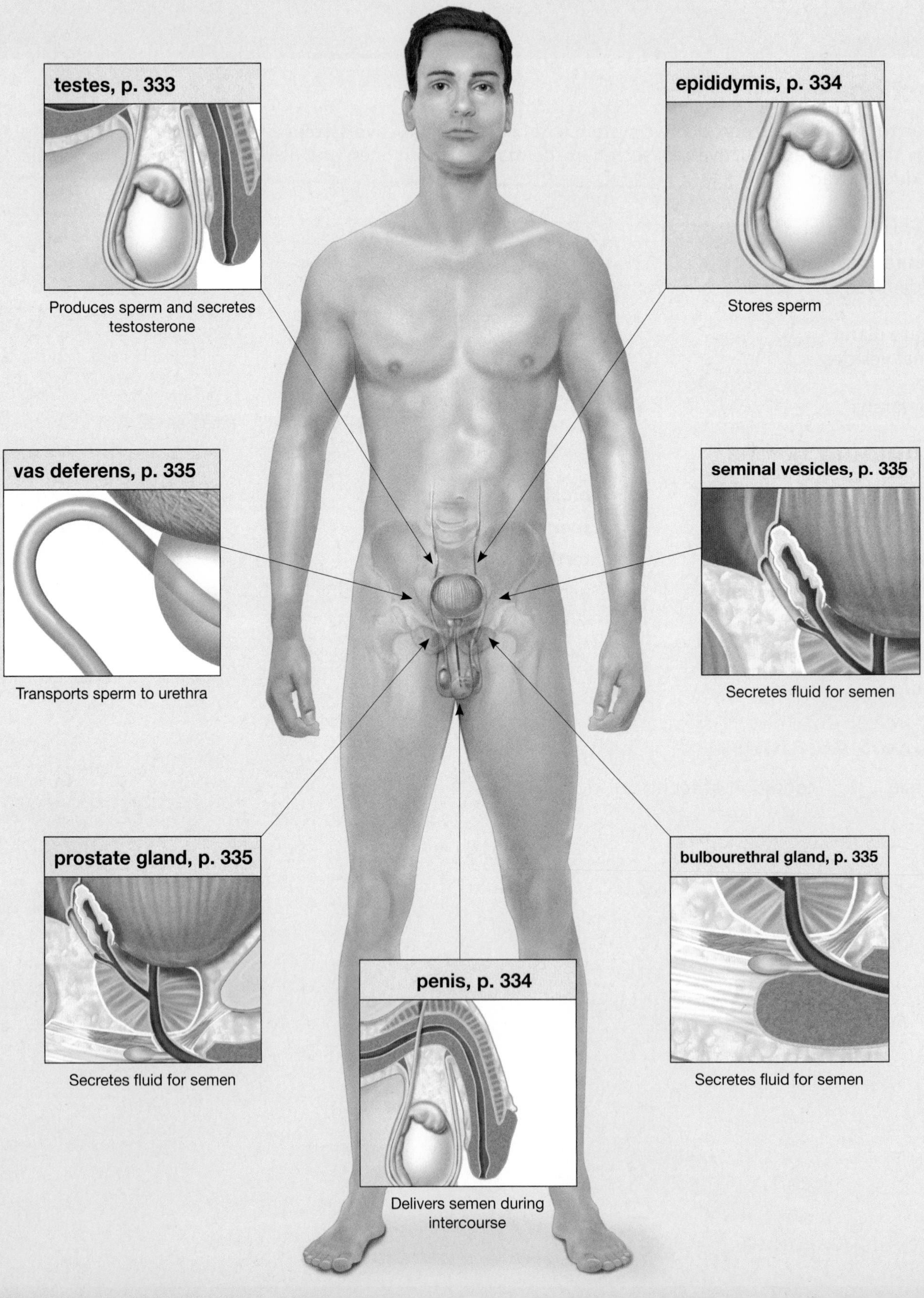

Anatomy and Physiology of the Male Reproductive System

bulbourethral glands (buhl-boh-yoo-REE-thral)
epididymis (ep-ih-DID-ih-mis)
genitourinary system (jen-ih-toh-YOO-rih-nair-ee)
penis (PEE-nis)
prostate gland (PROSS-tayt)
semen (SEE-men)
seminal vesicles (SEM-ih-nal VESS-ih-kls)
sex hormones
sperm
testes (TESS-teez)
vas deferens (VAS DEF-er-enz)

The male reproductive system has two main functions. The first is to produce **sperm**, the male reproductive cell. The second is to secrete the male **sex hormones**. In the male, the major organs of reproduction are located outside the body: the **penis**, and the two **testes**, each with an **epididymis** (see Figure 10.20 ■). The penis contains the urethra, which carries both urine and **semen** to the outside of the body. For this reason, this system is sometimes referred to as the **genitourinary system** (GU).

The internal organs of reproduction include two **seminal vesicles**, two **vas deferens**, the **prostate gland**, and two **bulbourethral glands.**

External Organs of Reproduction

Testes

perineum
scrotum (SKROH-tum)
seminiferous tubules (sem-ih-NIF-er-us TOO-byools)
spermatogenesis (sper-mat-oh-JEN-eh-sis)
testicles (test-IH-kles)
testosterone (tess-TOSS-ter-ohn)

The testes (singular is *testis*) or **testicles** are oval in shape and are responsible for the production of sperm (see Figure 10.20). This process, called **spermatogenesis,**

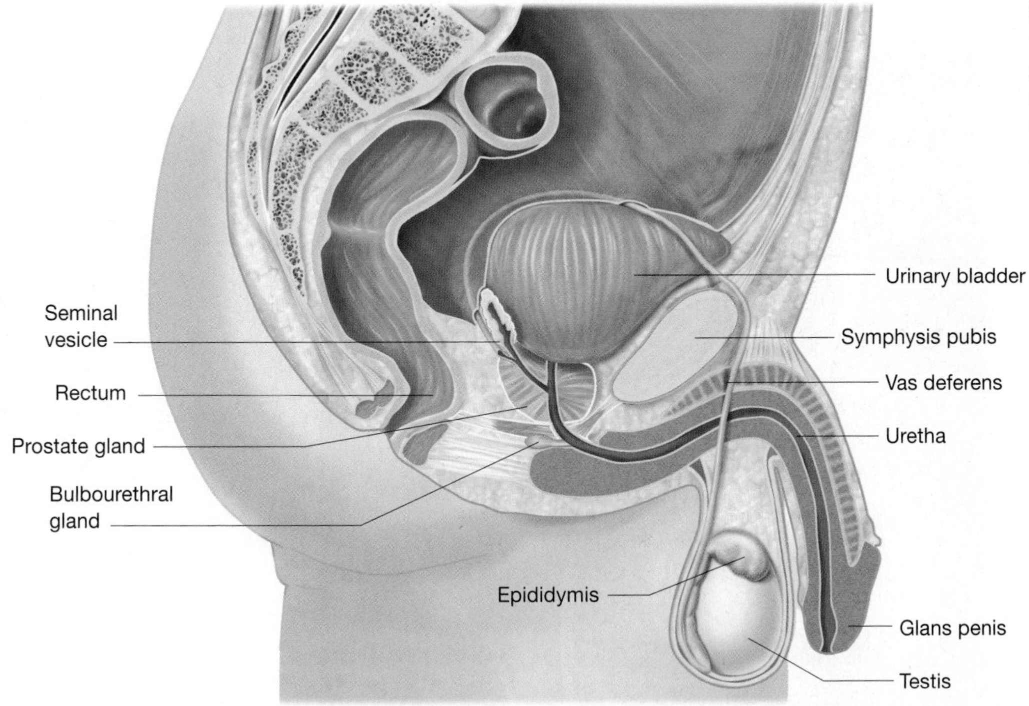

■ **Figure 10.20** The male reproductive system, sagittal section showing the organs of the system and their relation to the urinary bladder and rectum.

Med Term Tip

Spermatozoon and its plural form, *spermatozoa*, are other terms that mean "sperm." You have no doubt realized that there can be several terms with the same meaning in medical terminology. You must continue to remain flexible when working with these terms in your career. In some cases, one term will be more commonly used, depending on the type of medical specialty or even what part of the country you are in.

takes place within the **seminiferous tubules** that make up the insides of the testes (see Figure 10.21 ■). The testes must be maintained at the proper temperature for the sperm to survive. This lower temperature level is achieved by the placement of the testes suspended in the **scrotum**, a sac outside the body. The **perineum** of the male is similar to that in the female. It is the area between the scrotum and the anus. The male sex hormone **testosterone**, which is responsible for the development of the male reproductive organs, sperm, and secondary sex characteristics, is also produced by the testes.

Epididymis

Each epididymis is a coiled tubule that lies on top of the testes within the scrotum (see Figure 10.20). This elongated structure serves as the location for sperm maturation and storage until they are ready to be released into the vas deferens.

Penis

circumcision (ser-kum-SIH-zhun)
ejaculation (ee-jak-yoo-LAY-shun)
erectile tissue (ee-REK-tile)
glans penis (GLANS PEE-nis)
prepuce (PREE-pyoos)
sphincter (SFINGK-ter)
urinary meatus (YOO-rih-nair-ee me-AY-tus)

The penis is the male sex organ containing **erectile tissue** that is encased in skin (see Figure 10.20). This organ delivers semen into the female vagina. The soft tip of the penis is referred to as the **glans penis**. It is protected by a covering called the **prepuce** or foreskin. It is this covering of skin that is removed during the procedure known as **circumcision**. The penis becomes erect during sexual stimulation, which allows it to be placed within the female for the **ejaculation** of semen. The male urethra extends from the urinary bladder to the external opening in the penis, the **urinary meatus**, and serves a dual function: the elimination of urine and the ejaculation of semen. During the ejaculation process, a **sphincter** closes to keep urine from escaping.

Med Term Tip

During sexual intercourse, which is also referred to as *coitus*, the male can eject up to 100 million sperm cells. The adult male produces nearly 200 million sperm daily.

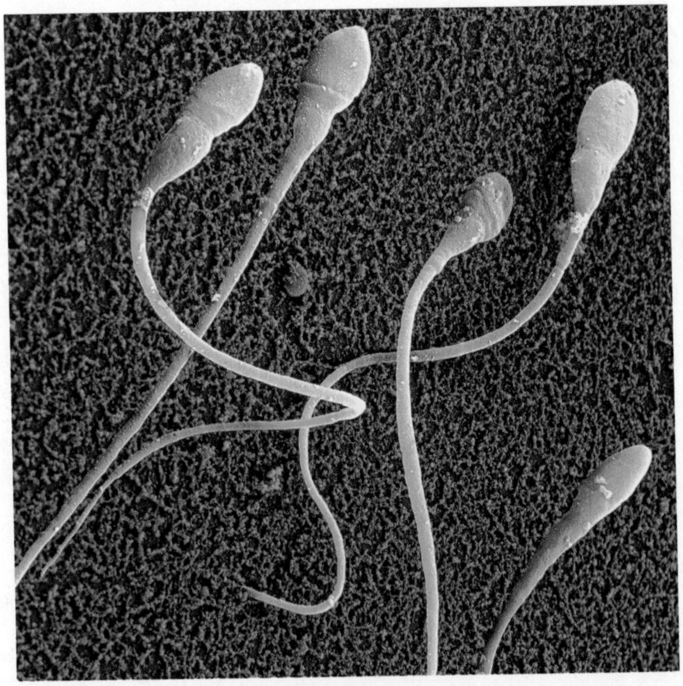

■ **Figure 10.21** Electronmicrograph of human sperm. *(Juergen Berger, Max-Planck Institute/Science Photo Library/Photo Researchers, Inc.)*

Internal Organs of Reproduction

Vas Deferens

spermatic cord (sper-MAT-ik)

Each vas deferens carries sperm from the epididymis up into the pelvic cavity. They travel up in front of the urinary bladder, over the top, and then back down the posterior side of the bladder to empty into the urethra (see Figure 10.20). They, along with nerves, arteries, veins, and lymphatic vessels running between the pelvic cavity and the testes, form the **spermatic cord**.

Seminal Vesicles

The two seminal vesicles are small glands located at the base of the urinary bladder (see Figure 10.20). These vesicles are connected to the vas deferens just before it empties into the urethra. The seminal vesicles secrete a glucose-rich fluid that nourishes the sperm. This liquid, along with the sperm, constitutes semen, the fluid that is eventually ejaculated during sexual intercourse.

Prostate Gland

The single prostate gland is located just below the urinary bladder (see Figure 10.20). It surrounds the urethra and when enlarged can cause difficulty in urination. The prostate is important for the reproductive process since it secretes an alkaline fluid that assists in keeping the sperm alive by neutralizing the pH of the urethra and vagina.

Bulbourethral Glands

Cowper's glands (KOW-perz)

The bulbourethral glands, also known as **Cowper's glands**, are two small glands located on either side of the urethra just below the prostate (see Figure 10.20). They produce a mucuslike lubricating fluid that joins with semen to become a part of the ejaculate.

Word Building

The following list contains examples of medical terms built directly from word parts. The definition for these terms can be determined by a straightforward translation of the word parts.

COMBINING FORM	COMBINED WITH	MEDICAL TERM	DEFINITION
andr/o	-gen	**androgen** (AN-droh-jen)	male producing
	-pathy	**andropathy** (an-DROP-ah-thee)	male disease
balan/o	-itis	**balanitis** (bal-ah-NYE-tis)	inflammation of glans penis
	-plasty	**balanoplasty** (BAL-ah-noh-plas-tee)	surgical repair of glans penis
	-rrhea	**balanorrhea** (bah-lah-noh-REE-ah)	discharge from glans penis
epididym/o	-ectomy	**epididymectomy** (ep-ih-did-ih-MEK-toh-mee)	removal of epididymis
	-al	**epididymal** (ep-ih-DID-ih-mal)	pertaining to the epididymis
	-itis	**epididymitis** (ep-ih-did-ih-MYE-tis)	inflammation of the epididymis

Word Building *(continued)*

COMBINING FORMS	COMBINED WITH	MEDICAL TERM	DEFINITION
orch/o	an- -ism	**anorchism** (an-OR-kizm)	condition of no testes
orchi/o	-ectomy	**orchiectomy** (or-kee-EK-toh-mee)	removal of testes
	-otomy	**orchiotomy** (or-kee-OT-oh-mee)	incision into testes
	-plasty	**orchioplasty** (OR-kee-oh-plas-tee)	surgical repair of testes
orchid/o	-ectomy	**orchidectomy** (or-kid-EK-toh-mee)	removal of the testes
	-pexy	**orchidopexy** (OR-kid-oh-peck-see)	surgical fixation of testes
prostat/o	-itis	**prostatitis** (pross-tah-TYE-tis)	prostate inflammation
	-ectomy	**prostatectomy** (pross-tah-TEK-toh-mee)	removal of prostate
	-ic	**prostatic** (pross-TAT-ik)	pertaining to the prostate
spermat/o	-ic	**spermatic** (sper-MAT-ik)	pertaining to sperm
	-lysis	**spermatolysis** (sper-mah-TOL-ih-sis)	sperm destruction
testicul/o	-ar	**testicular** (tes-TIK-yoo-lar)	pertaining to the testes
vesicul/o	-ar	**vesicular** (veh-SIC-yoo-lar)	pertaining to the seminal vesicle

Med Term Tip

Word watch—Be careful using the combining forms *vesic/o* meaning "bladder" and *vesicul/o* meaning "seminal vesicle."

PREFIX	SUFFIX	MEDICAL TERM	DEFINITION
a-	-spermia	**aspermia** (ah-SPER-mee-ah)	condition of no sperm
oligo-		**oligospermia** (ol-ih-goh-SPER-mee-ah)	condition of scanty (few) sperm

Vocabulary

TERM	DEFINITION
erectile dysfunction (ED) (ee-REK-tile)	Inability to engage in sexual intercourse due to inability to maintain an erection. Also called *impotence.*
sterility	Inability to father children due to a problem with spermatogenesis.

Pathology

TERM	DEFINITION
■ ***Testes***	
cryptorchidism (kript-OR-kid-izm)	Failure of the testes to descend into the scrotal sac before birth. Usually, the testes will descend before birth. A surgical procedure called orchidopexy may be required to bring the testes down into the scrotum permanently. Failure of the testes to descend could result in sterility in the male or an increased risk of testicular cancer.
hydrocele (HIGH-droh-seel)	Accumulation of fluid around the testes or along the spermatic cord. Common in infants.

Pathology *(continued)*

TERM	DEFINITION
testicular carcinoma (kar-sih-NOH-mah)	Cancer of one or both testicles; most common cancer in men under age 40.
testicular torsion	A twisting of the spermatic cord.
varicocele (VAIR-ih-koh-seel)	Enlargement of the veins of the spermatic cord that commonly occurs on the left side of adolescent males.
■ ***Prostate Gland***	
benign prostatic hypertrophy (BPH) (bee-NINE pross-TAT-ik high-PER-troh-fee)	Noncancerous enlargement of the prostate gland commonly seen in males over age 50.
prostate cancer (PROSS-tayt CAN-ser)	Slow-growing cancer that affects a large number of males after age 50. The prostate-specific antigen (PSA) test is used to assist in early detection of this disease.
■ ***Penis***	
epispadias (ep-ih-SPAY-dee-as)	Congenital opening of the urethra on the dorsal surface of the penis.
hypospadias (high-poh-SPAY-dee-as)	Congenital opening of the male urethra on the underside of the penis.
phimosis (fih-MOH-sis)	Narrowing of the foreskin over the glans penis resulting in difficulty with hygiene. This condition can lead to infection or difficulty with urination. The condition is treated with circumcision, the surgical removal of the foreskin.
priapism (pri-ah-pizm)	A persistent and painful erection due to pathological causes, not sexual arousal.
■ ***Sexually Transmitted Diseases***	
chancroid (SHANG-kroyd)	Highly infectious nonsyphilitic venereal ulcer.

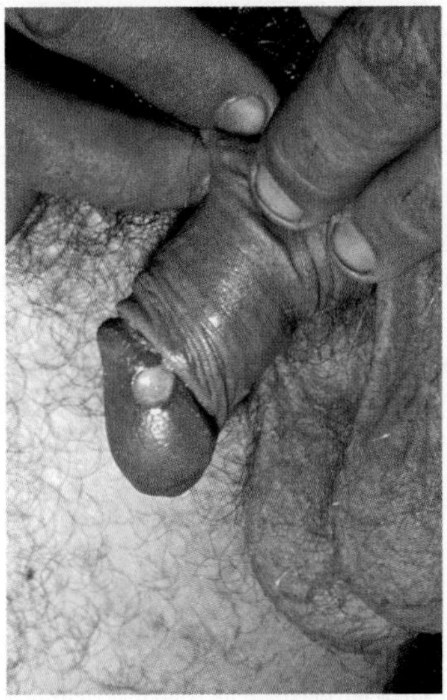

Figure 10.22 Photograph showing a chancroid on the glans penis. *(Joe Miller/Centers for Disease Control and Prevention [CDC])*

TERM	DEFINITION
chlamydia (klah-MID-ee-ah)	Bacterial infection causing genital inflammation in males and females. Can lead to pelvic inflammatory disease in females and eventual infertility.
genital herpes (JEN-ih-tal HER-peez)	Creeping skin disease that can appear like a blister or vesicle, caused by a sexually transmitted virus.

Pathology *(continued)*

TERM	DEFINITION
genital warts (JEN-ih-tal)	Growth of warts on the genitalia of both males and females that can lead to cancer of the cervix in females. Caused by the sexual transmission of the human papilloma virus (HPV).
gonorrhea (GC) (gon-oh-REE-ah)	Sexually transmitted bacterial infection of the mucous membranes of either sex. Can be passed on to an infant during the birth process.
human immunodeficiency virus (HIV)	Sexually transmitted virus that attacks the immune system.
sexually transmitted disease (STD)	Disease usually acquired as the result of sexual intercourse. Formerly referred to as *venereal disease* (VD).
syphilis (SIF-ih-lis)	Infectious, chronic, bacterial venereal disease that can involve any organ. May exist for years without symptoms, but is fatal if untreated. Treated with the antibiotic penicillin.
trichomoniasis (trik-oh-moh-NYE-ah-sis)	Genitourinary infection caused by a single-cell protist that is usually without symptoms (asymptomatic) in both males and females. In women the disease can produce itching and/or burning, a foul-smelling discharge, and result in vaginitis.

Diagnostic Procedures

TERM	DEFINITION
■ ***Clinical Laboratory Tests***	
prostate-specific antigen (PSA) (PROSS-tayt-specific AN-tih-jen)	A blood test to screen for prostate cancer. Elevated blood levels of PSA are associated with prostate cancer.
semen analysis (SEE-men ah-NAL-ih-sis)	Procedure used when performing a fertility workup to determine if the male is able to produce sperm. Semen is collected by the patient after abstaining from sexual intercourse for a period of three to five days. The sperm in the semen are analyzed for number, swimming strength, and shape. Also used to determine if a vasectomy has been successful. After a period of six weeks, no further sperm should be present in a sample from the patient.
■ ***Additional Diagnostic Procedures***	
digital rectal exam (DRE) (DIJ-ih-tal REK-tal)	Manual examination for an enlarged prostate gland performed by palpating (feeling) the prostate gland through the wall of the rectum.

Therapeutic Procedures

TERM	DEFINITION
■ ***Surgical Procedures***	
castration (kass-TRAY-shun)	Removal of the testicles in the male or the ovaries in the female.
circumcision (ser-kum-SIH-zhun)	Surgical removal of the end of the prepuce or foreskin of the penis. Generally performed on the newborn male at the request of the parents. The primary reason is for ease of hygiene. Circumcision is also a ritual practice in some religions.

Therapeutic Procedures *(continued)*

TERM	DEFINITION
orchidopexy (OR-kid-oh-peck-see)	Surgical fixation to move undescended testes into the scrotum and to attach them to prevent retraction. Used to treat cryptorchidism.
sterilization (ster-ih-lih-ZAY-shun)	Process of rendering a male or female sterile or unable to conceive children.
transurethral resection of the prostate (TUR, TURP) (trans-yoo-REE-thrall REE-sek-shun of the PROSS-tayt)	Surgical removal of the prostate gland by inserting a device through the urethra and removing prostate tissue.
vasectomy (vas-EK-toh-mee)	Removal of a segment or all of the vas deferens to prevent sperm from leaving the male body. Used for contraception purposes.

Med Term Tip

The vas deferens is the tubing that is severed during a procedure called a *vasectomy*. A vasectomy results in the sterilization of the male since the sperm are no longer able to travel into the urethra and out of the penis during sexual intercourse. The surgical procedure to reverse a vasectomy is a *vasovasostomy*. A new opening is created in order to reconnect one section of the vas deferens to another section of the vas deferens, thereby reestablishing an open tube for sperm to travel through.

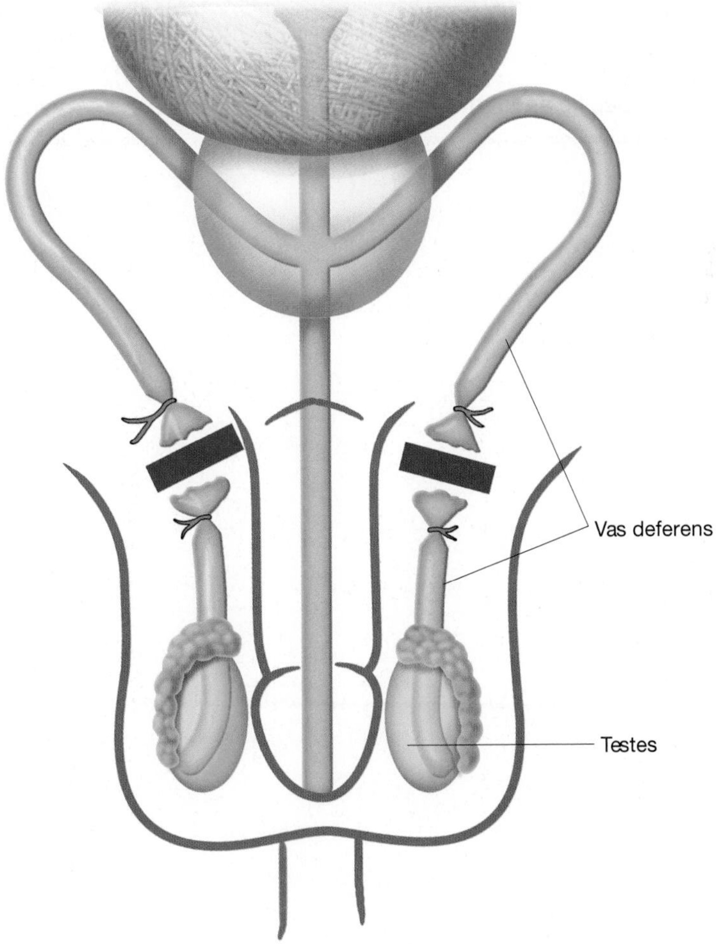

Figure 10.23 A vasectomy, showing how each vas deferens is tied off in two places and then a section is removed from the middle. This prevents sperm from traveling through the vas deferens during ejaculation.

TERM	DEFINITION
vasovasostomy (vas-oh-vay-ZOS-toh-mee)	Surgical procedure to reconnect the vas deferens to reverse a vasectomy.

Pharmacology

CLASSIFICATION	ACTION	GENERIC AND BRAND NAME
androgen therapy (AN-droh-jen)	Replacement of male hormones to treat patients who produce insufficient hormone naturally.	testosterone cypionate, Andronate, depAndro
antiprostatic agents (an-tye-pross-TAT-ik)	Medication to treat early cases of benign prostatic hypertrophy. May prevent surgery for mild cases.	finasteride, Proscar; dutasteride, Avodart
erectile dysfunction agents (ee-REK-tile)	Medication that temporarily produces an erection in patients with erectile dysfunction.	sildenafil citrate, Viagra; tadalafil, Cialis
spermatocide (sper-mah-toh-LIT-ik)	Destruction of sperm. One form of birth control is the use of spermatolytic creams.	nonoxynol 9, Semicid, Ortho-Gynol

Abbreviations

BPH	benign prostatic hypertrophy	**RPR**	rapid plasma reagin (test for syphilis)
DRE	digital rectal exam	**SPP**	suprapubic prostatectomy
ED	erectile dysfunction	**STD**	sexually transmitted disease
GC	gonorrhea	**TUR**	transurethral resection
GU	genitourinary	**TURP**	transurethral resection of the prostate
PSA	prostate-specific antigen	**VD**	venereal disease

Chapter Review

Terminology Checklist

Below are all Anatomy and Physiology key terms, Word Building, Vocabulary, Pathology, Diagnostic, Therapeutic, and Pharmacology terms presented in this chapter. Use this list as a study tool by placing a check in the box in front of each term as you master its meaning.

- ☐ abortifacient
- ☐ abruptio placentae
- ☐ amenorrhea
- ☐ amniocentesis
- ☐ amnion
- ☐ amniorrhea
- ☐ amniotic
- ☐ amniotic fluid
- ☐ amniotomy
- ☐ androgen
- ☐ androgen therapy
- ☐ andropathy
- ☐ anorchism
- ☐ anteflexion
- ☐ antepartum
- ☐ antiprostatic agents
- ☐ Apgar score
- ☐ areola
- ☐ aspermia
- ☐ atresia
- ☐ balanitis
- ☐ balanoplasty
- ☐ balanorrhea
- ☐ barrier contraception
- ☐ Bartholin's glands
- ☐ benign prostatic hypertrophy
- ☐ breast cancer
- ☐ breasts
- ☐ breech presentation
- ☐ bulbourethral gland
- ☐ candidiasis
- ☐ castration
- ☐ cervical
- ☐ cervical biopsy
- ☐ cervical cancer
- ☐ cervicectomy
- ☐ cervix
- ☐ cesarean section
- ☐ chancroid
- ☐ chlamydia
- ☐ chorion
- ☐ chorionic
- ☐ chorionic villus sampling
- ☐ circumcision
- ☐ clitoris
- ☐ colostrum
- ☐ colposcope
- ☐ colposcopy
- ☐ conception
- ☐ conization
- ☐ corpus
- ☐ Cowper's glands
- ☐ crowning
- ☐ cryptorchidism
- ☐ culdoscopy
- ☐ cystocele
- ☐ delivery
- ☐ digital rectal exam
- ☐ dilation and curettage
- ☐ dilation stage
- ☐ dysmenorrhea
- ☐ dystocia
- ☐ eclampsia
- ☐ effacement
- ☐ ejaculation
- ☐ elective abortion
- ☐ embryo
- ☐ embryonic
- ☐ endocervicitis
- ☐ endometrial biopsy
- ☐ endometrial cancer
- ☐ endometriosis
- ☐ endometritis
- ☐ endometrium
- ☐ epididymal
- ☐ epididymectomy
- ☐ epididymis
- ☐ epididymitis
- ☐ episiorrhaphy
- ☐ episiotomy
- ☐ epispadias
- ☐ erectile dysfunction
- ☐ erectile dysfunction agents
- ☐ erectile tissue
- ☐ estrogen
- ☐ expulsion stage
- ☐ fallopian tubes
- ☐ fertility drug
- ☐ fertilization
- ☐ fetal
- ☐ fetal monitoring
- ☐ fetus
- ☐ fibrocystic breast disease
- ☐ fibroid tumor
- ☐ fimbriae
- ☐ follicle stimulating hormone
- ☐ fraternal twins
- ☐ fundus
- ☐ genital herpes
- ☐ genitalia
- ☐ genital warts
- ☐ genitourinary system
- ☐ gestation
- ☐ glans penis
- ☐ gonorrhea
- ☐ gynecologist
- ☐ gynecology
- ☐ hematosalpinx
- ☐ hemolytic disease of the newborn
- ☐ hormonal contraception
- ☐ hormone replacement therapy
- ☐ human immunodeficiency virus
- ☐ hydrocele

- ☐ hymen
- ☐ hymenectomy
- ☐ hypospadias
- ☐ hysterectomy
- ☐ hysteropexy
- ☐ hysterorrhexis
- ☐ hysterosalpingography
- ☐ identical twins
- ☐ infertility
- ☐ intrauterine device
- ☐ labia majora
- ☐ labia minora
- ☐ labor
- ☐ lactation
- ☐ lactic
- ☐ lactiferous ducts
- ☐ lactiferous glands
- ☐ lactorrhea
- ☐ laparoscope
- ☐ laparoscopy
- ☐ laparotomy
- ☐ lumpectomy
- ☐ luteinizing hormone
- ☐ mammary
- ☐ mammary glands
- ☐ mammogram
- ☐ mammography
- ☐ mammoplasty
- ☐ mastalgia
- ☐ mastectomy
- ☐ mastitis
- ☐ meconium
- ☐ menarche
- ☐ menometrorrhagia
- ☐ menopause
- ☐ menorrhagia
- ☐ menstrual period
- ☐ menstruation
- ☐ metrorrhagia
- ☐ metrorrhea
- ☐ multigravida
- ☐ multipara
- ☐ myometrium
- ☐ neonate
- ☐ neonatologist
- ☐ neonatology
- ☐ nipple
- ☐ nulligravida
- ☐ nullipara
- ☐ nurse
- ☐ obstetrics
- ☐ oligomenorrhea
- ☐ oligospermia
- ☐ oophorectomy
- ☐ oophoritis
- ☐ oral contraceptive pills
- ☐ orchidectomy
- ☐ orchidopexy
- ☐ orchiectomy
- ☐ orchioplasty
- ☐ orchiotomy
- ☐ ova
- ☐ ovarian
- ☐ ovarian carcinoma
- ☐ ovarian cyst
- ☐ ovaries
- ☐ oviducts
- ☐ ovulation
- ☐ oxytocin
- ☐ Pap (Papanicolaou) smear
- ☐ pelvic examination
- ☐ pelvic inflammatory disease
- ☐ pelvic ultrasonography
- ☐ penis
- ☐ perimetritis
- ☐ perimetrium
- ☐ perineum
- ☐ phimosis
- ☐ placenta
- ☐ placenta previa
- ☐ placental stage
- ☐ postpartum
- ☐ preeclampsia
- ☐ pregnancy
- ☐ pregnancy test
- ☐ premature
- ☐ premenstrual syndrome
- ☐ prepuce
- ☐ priapism
- ☐ primigravida
- ☐ primipara
- ☐ progesterone
- ☐ prolapsed umbilical cord
- ☐ prolapsed uterus
- ☐ prostate cancer
- ☐ prostate gland
- ☐ prostatectomy
- ☐ prostate-specific antigen
- ☐ prostatic
- ☐ prostatitis
- ☐ pseudocyesis
- ☐ puberty
- ☐ pyosalpinx
- ☐ radical mastectomy
- ☐ rectocele
- ☐ salpingectomy
- ☐ salpingitis
- ☐ salpingocyesis
- ☐ scrotum
- ☐ semen
- ☐ semen analysis
- ☐ seminal vesicles
- ☐ seminiferous tubules
- ☐ sex hormones
- ☐ sexually transmitted disease
- ☐ simple mastectomy
- ☐ sperm
- ☐ spermatic
- ☐ spermatic cord
- ☐ spermatocide
- ☐ spermatogenesis
- ☐ spermatolysis
- ☐ sphincter
- ☐ spontaneous abortion
- ☐ sterility
- ☐ sterilization
- ☐ stillbirth
- ☐ syphilis
- ☐ testes
- ☐ testicles
- ☐ testicular
- ☐ testicular carcinoma
- ☐ testicular torsion
- ☐ testosterone
- ☐ therapeutic abortion

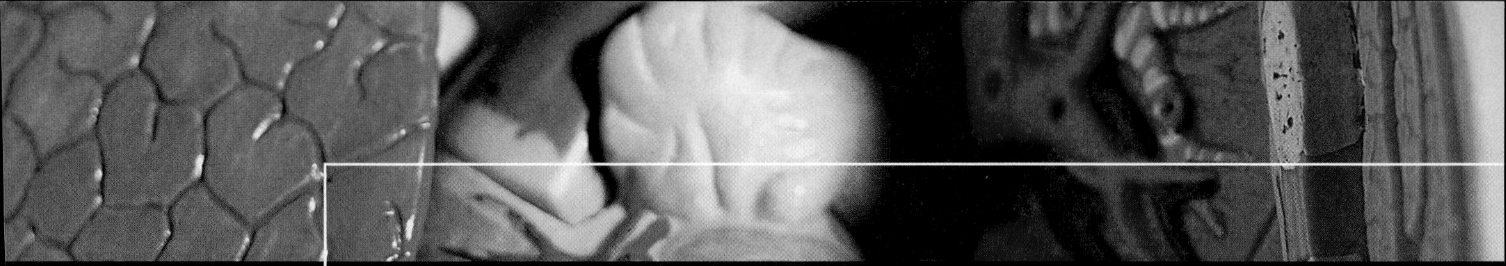

11

Endocrine System

Learning Objectives

Upon completion of this chapter, you will be able to:

- Identify and define the combining forms and suffixes introduced in this chapter.
- Correctly spell and pronounce medical terms and major anatomical structures relating to the endocrine system.
- Locate and describe the major organs of the endocrine system and their functions.
- List the major hormones secreted by each endocrine gland and describe their functions.
- Build and define endocrine system medical terms from word parts.
- Identify and define endocrine system vocabulary terms.
- Identify and define selected endocrine system pathology terms.
- Identify and define selected endocrine system diagnostic procedures.
- Identify and define selected endocrine system therapeutic procedures.
- Identify and define selected medications relating to the endocrine system.
- Define selected abbreviations associated with the endocrine system.

Endocrine System at a Glance

Function

Endocrine glands secrete hormones that regulate many body activities such as metabolic rate, water and mineral balance, immune system reactions, and sexual functioning.

Organs

adrenal glands
ovaries
pancreas (islets of Langerhans)
parathyroid glands
pineal gland
pituitary gland
testes
thymus gland
thyroid gland

Combining Forms

acr/o	extremities	**kal/i**	potassium
adren/o	adrenal glands	**natr/o**	sodium
adrenal/o	adrenal glands	**ophthalm/o**	eye
andr/o	male	**pancreat/o**	pancreas
calc/o	calcium	**parathyroid/o**	parathyroid gland
crin/o	secrete	**pineal/o**	pineal gland
estr/o	female	**pituitar/o**	pituitary gland
glyc/o	sugar	**thym/o**	thymus gland
glycos/o	sugar	**thyr/o**	thyroid gland
gonad/o	sex glands	**thyroid/o**	thyroid gland
home/o	sameness	**toxic/o**	poison

Suffixes

-crine	to secrete
-dipsia	thirst
-prandial	relating to a meal
-tropin	stimulate

Endocrine System Illustrated

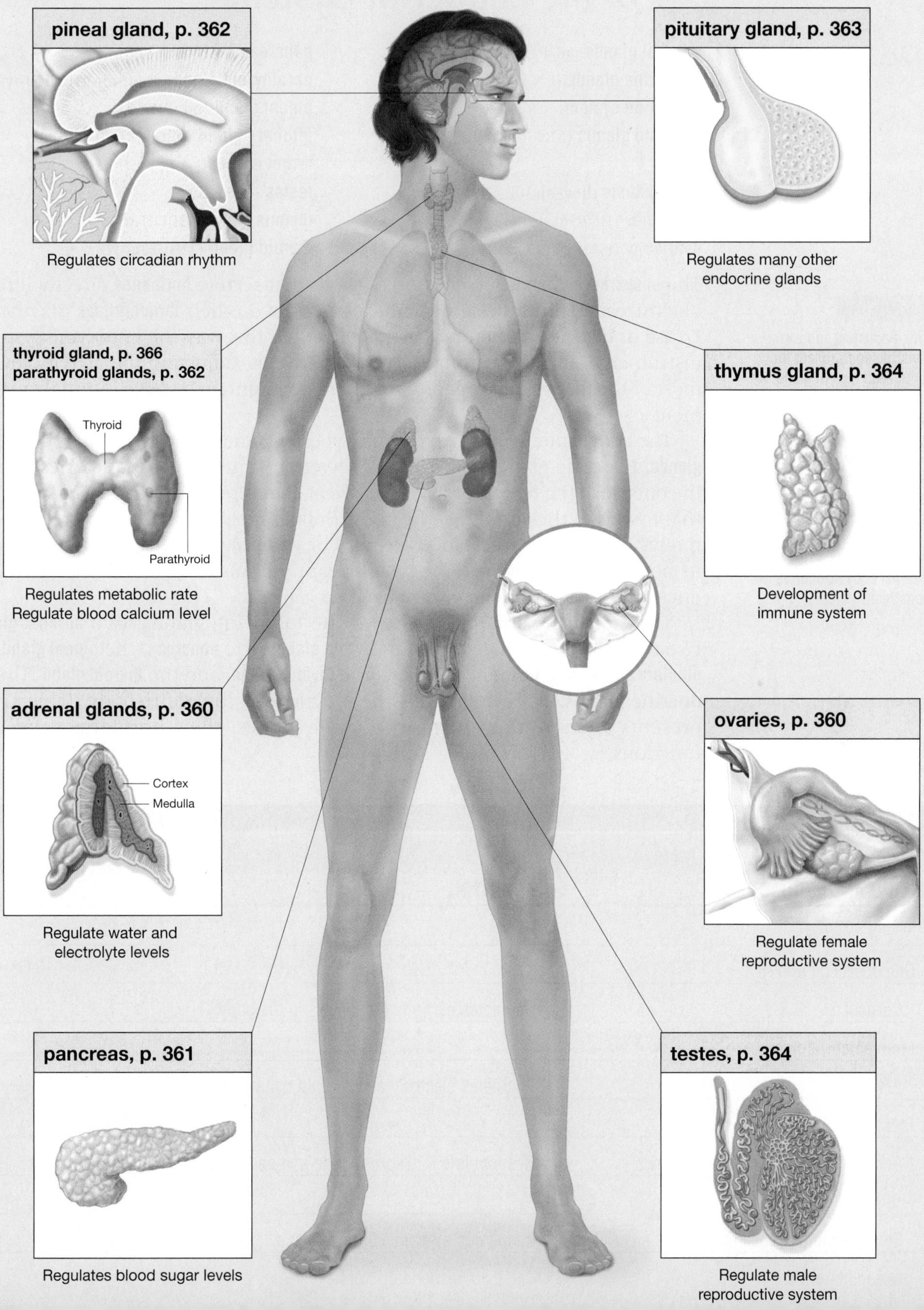

pineal gland, p. 362
Regulates circadian rhythm
pituitary gland, p. 363
Regulates many other endocrine glands
thyroid gland, p. 366
parathyroid glands, p. 362
Thyroid
Parathyroid
Regulates metabolic rate
Regulate blood calcium level
thymus gland, p. 364
Development of immune system
adrenal glands, p. 360
Cortex
Medulla
Regulate water and electrolyte levels
ovaries, p. 360
Regulate female reproductive system
pancreas, p. 361
Regulates blood sugar levels
testes, p. 364
Regulate male reproductive system

Anatomy and Physiology of the Endocrine System

adrenal glands (ad-REE-nal)
endocrine glands (EN-doh-krin)
endocrine system
exocrine glands (EKS-oh-krin)
glands
homeostasis (hoe-me-oh-STAY-sis)
hormones (HOR-mohnz)
ovaries (OH-vah-reez)
pancreas (PAN-kree-ass)
parathyroid glands (pair-ah-THIGH-royd)
pineal gland (pih-NEAL)
pituitary gland (pih-TOO-ih-tair-ee)
target organs
testes (TESS-teez)
thymus gland (THIGH-mus)
thyroid gland (THIGH-royd)

Med Term Tip

The terms *endocrine* and *exocrine* were constructed to reflect the function of each type of gland. As glands, they both secrete, indicated by the combining form *crin/o*. The prefix *exo-*, meaning "external" or "outward," tells us that exocrine gland secretions are carried to the outside of the body. However, the prefix *endo-*, meaning "within" or "internal," indicates that endocrine gland secretions are carried to other internal body structures by the bloodstream.

The **endocrine system** is a collection of **glands** that secrete **hormones** directly into the bloodstream. Hormones are chemicals that act on their **target organs** to either increase or decrease the target's activity level. In this way the endocrine system is instrumental in maintaining **homeostasis**—that is, adjusting the activity level of most of the tissues and organs of the body to maintain a stable internal environment.

The body actually has two distinct types of glands: **exocrine glands** and **endocrine glands**. Exocrine glands release their secretions into a duct that carries them to the outside of the body. For example, sweat glands release sweat into a sweat duct that travels to the surface of the body. Endocrine glands, however, release hormones directly into the bloodstream. For example, the thyroid gland secretes its hormones directly into the bloodstream. Because endocrine glands have no ducts, they are also referred to as *ductless glands*.

The endocrine system consists of the following glands: two **adrenal glands**, two **ovaries** in the female, four **parathyroid glands**, the **pancreas**, the **pineal gland**, the **pituitary gland**, two **testes** in the male, the **thymus gland**, and the **thyroid gland**. The endocrine glands as a whole affect the functions of the entire body. Table 11.1 ■ presents a description of the endocrine glands, their hormones, and their functions.

Table 11.1 Endocrine Glands and Their Hormones

GLAND AND HORMONE	FUNCTION
Adrenal cortex	
Glucocorticoids	
Cortisol	Regulates carbohydrate levels in the body
Mineralocorticoids	
Aldosterone	Regulates electrolytes and fluid volume in body
Steroid sex hormones	
Androgen, estrogen, progesterone	Responsible for reproduction and secondary sexual characteristics
Adrenal medulla	
Epinephrine (adrenaline)	Intensifies response during stress; "fight or flight" response
Norepinephrine	Chiefly a vasoconstrictor

Table 11.1 Endocrine Glands and Their Hormones *(continued)*

GLAND AND HORMONE	FUNCTION
Ovaries	
Estrogen	Stimulates development of secondary sex characteristics in females; regulates menstrual cycle
Progesterone	Prepares for conditions of pregnancy
Pancreas	
Glucagon	Stimulates liver to release glucose into the blood
Insulin	Regulates and promotes entry of glucose into cells
Parathyroid glands	
Parathyroid hormone (PTH)	Stimulates bone breakdown; regulates calcium level in the blood
Pituitary anterior lobe	
Adrenocorticotropin hormone (ACTH)	Regulates function of adrenal cortex
Follicle-stimulating hormone (FSH)	Stimulates growth of eggs in female and sperm in males
Growth hormone (GH)	Stimulates growth of the body
Luteinizing hormone (LH)	Regulates function of male and female gonads and plays a role in releasing ova in females
Melanocyte-stimulating hormone (MSH)	Stimulates pigment in skin
Prolactin	Stimulates milk production
Thyroid-stimulating hormone (TSH)	Regulates function of thyroid gland
Pituitary posterior lobe	
Antidiuretic hormone (ADH)	Stimulates reabsorption of water by the kidneys
Oxytocin	Stimulates uterine contractions and releases milk into ducts
Testes	
Testosterone	Promotes sperm production and development of secondary sex characteristics in males
Thymus	
Thymosin	Promotes development of cells in immune system
Thyroid gland	
Calcitonin	Stimulates deposition of calcium into bone
Thyroxine (T_4)	Stimulates metabolism in cells
Triiodothyronine (T_3)	Stimulates metabolism in cells

Adrenal Glands

adrenal cortex (KOR-tex)
adrenal medulla (meh-DOOL-lah)
adrenaline (ah-DREN-ah-lin)
aldosterone (al-DOSS-ter-ohn)
androgens (AN-druh-jenz)
corticosteroids (kor-tih-koh-STAIR-oydz)
cortisol (KOR-tih-sal)
epinephrine (ep-ih-NEF-rin)
estrogen (ESS-troh-jen)
glucocorticoids (gloo-koh-KOR-tih-koydz)
mineralocorticoids (min-er-al-oh-KOR-tih-koydz)
norepinephrine (nor-ep-ih-NEF-rin)
progesterone (proh-JESS-ter-ohn)
steroid sex hormones (STAIR-oyd)

The two adrenal glands are located above each of the kidneys (see Figure 11.1 ■). Each gland is composed of two sections: **adrenal cortex** and **adrenal medulla**.

The outer adrenal cortex manufactures several different families of hormones: **mineralocorticoids**, **glucocorticoids**, and **steroid sex hormones**. However, because they are all produced by the cortex, they are collectively referred to as **corticosteroids**. The mineralocorticoid hormone, **aldosterone**, regulates sodium (Na^+) and potassium (K^+) levels in the body. The glucocorticoid hormone, **cortisol**, regulates carbohydrates in the body. The adrenal cortex of both men and women secretes steroid sex hormones: **androgens**, **estrogen**, and **progesterone**. These hormones regulate secondary sexual characteristics. All hormones secreted by the adrenal cortex are steroid hormones.

The inner adrenal medulla is responsible for secreting the hormones **epinephrine**, also called **adrenaline**, and **norepinephrine**. These hormones are critical during emergency situations because they increase blood pressure, heart rate, and respiration levels. This helps the body perform better during emergencies or otherwise stressful times.

Med Term Tip

The term *cortex* is frequently used in anatomy to indicate the outer portion of an organ such as the adrenal gland or the kidney. The term *cortex* means "bark," as in the bark of a tree. The term *medulla* means "marrow." Because marrow is found in the inner cavity of bones, the term came to stand for the middle of an organ.

Ovaries

estrogen
gametes (gam-EATS)
gonads (GOH-nadz)
menstrual cycle (men-STROO-all)
ova
progesterone

The two ovaries are located in the lower abdominopelvic cavity of the female (see Figure 11.2 ■). They are the female **gonads**. Gonads are organs that produce **gametes** or the reproductive sex cells. In the case of females, the gametes are the **ova**. Of importance to the endocrine system, the ovaries produce the female sex hormones, **estrogen** and **progesterone**. Estrogen is responsible for the appearance of the female sexual characteristics and regulation of the **menstrual cycle**. Progesterone helps to maintain a suitable uterine environment for pregnancy.

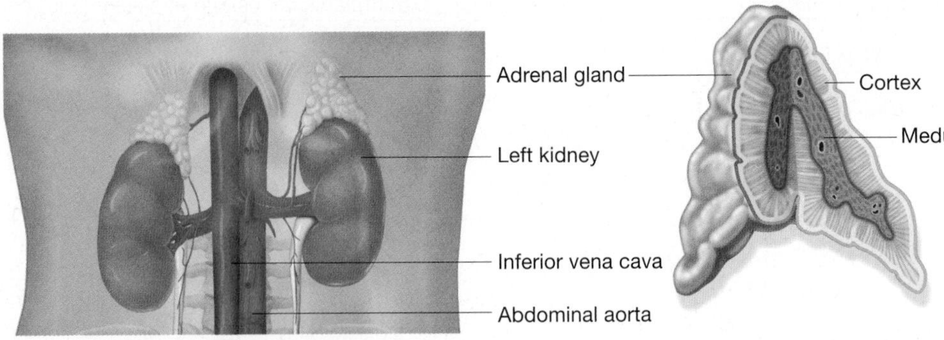

■ **Figure 11.1** The adrenal glands. These glands sit on top of each kidney. Each adrenal is subdivided into an outer cortex and an inner medulla. Each region secretes different hormones.

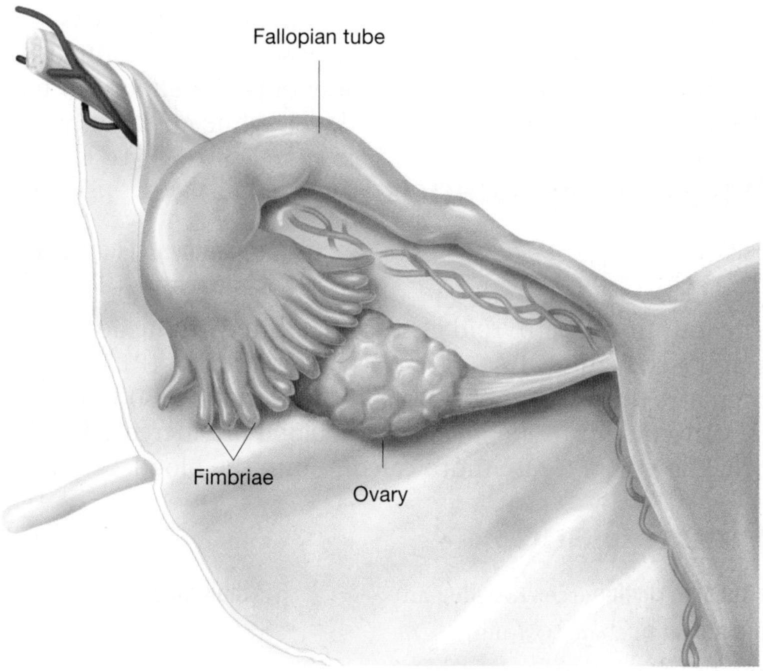

Figure 11.2 The ovaries. In addition to producing ova, the ovaries secrete the female sex hormones, estrogen and progesterone.

Pancreas

glucagon (GLOO-koh-gon)
insulin (IN-suh-lin)
islets of Langerhans (EYE-lets of LAHNG-er-hahnz)

The pancreas is located along the lower curvature of the stomach (see Figure 11.3A ■). It is the only organ in the body that has both endocrine and exocrine functions. The exocrine portion of the pancreas releases digestive enzymes through a duct into the duodenum of the small intestine. The endocrine sections of the pancreas, **islets of Langerhans**, are named after Dr. Paul Langerhans, a German anatomist. The islets cells produce two different hormones: **insulin** and **glucagon** (see Figure 11.3B ■). Insulin, produced by beta (β) islet cells, stimulates the cells of the body to take in glucose from the bloodstream, lowering your blood sugar level. This occurs after you have eaten a meal and absorbed the carbohydrates into your bloodstream. In this way the cells obtain the glucose they need for cellular respiration.

Another set of islet cells, the alpha (α) cells, secrete a different hormone, glucagon, which stimulates the liver to release glucose, thereby raising the blood

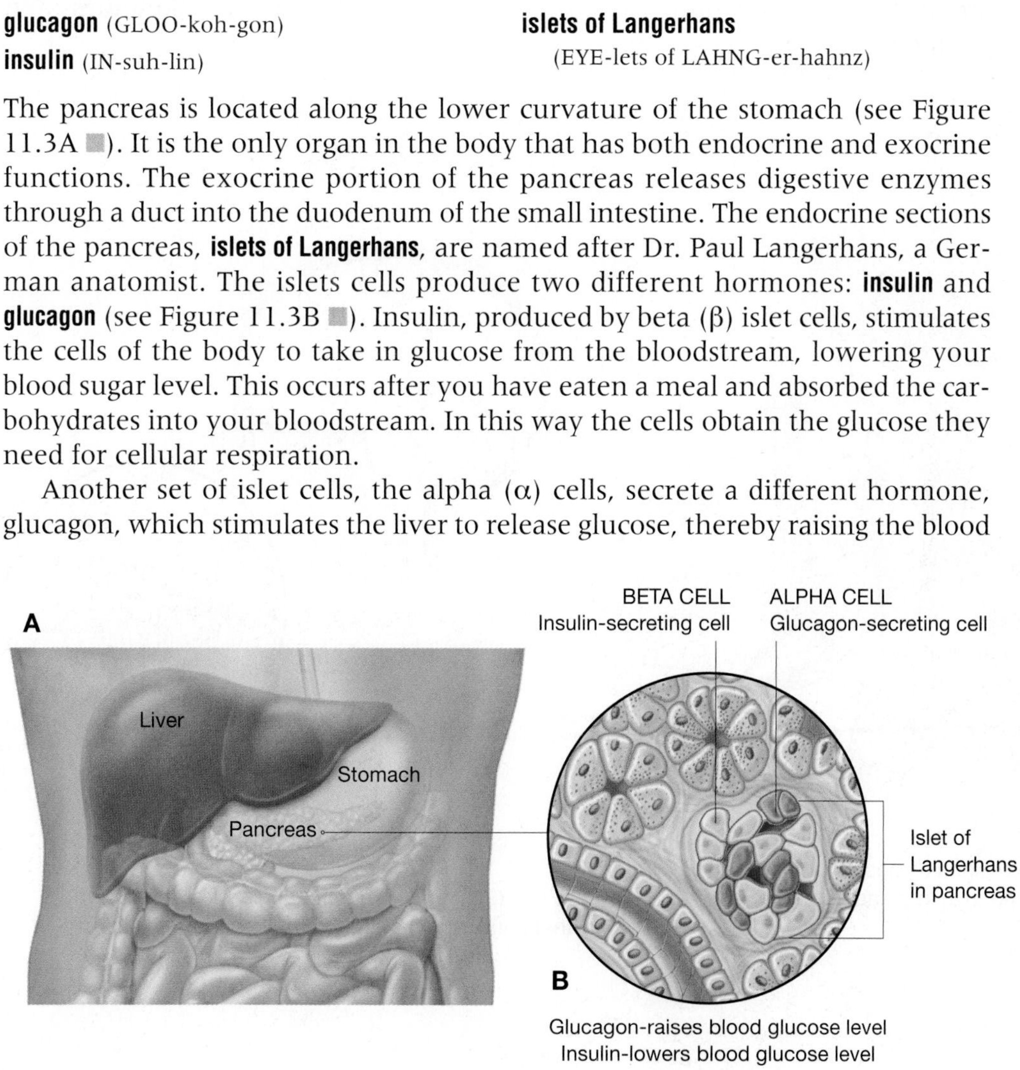

Figure 11.3 The pancreas. This organ sits just below the stomach and is both an exocrine and an endocrine gland. The endocrine regions of the pancreas are called the islets of Langerhans and they secrete insulin and glucagon.

glucose level. Glucagon is released when the body needs more sugar, such as at the beginning of strenuous activity or several hours after the last meal has been digested. Insulin and glucagon have opposite effects on blood sugar level. Insulin will reduce the blood sugar level, while glucagon will increase it.

Parathyroid Glands

calcium

parathyroid hormone (pair-ah-THIGH-royd HOR-mohn)

Med Term Tip

A calcium deficiency in the system can result in a condition called *tetany*, or muscle excitability and tremors. If the parathyroid glands are removed during thyroid surgery, calcium replacement in the body is often necessary.

The four tiny parathyroid glands are located on the dorsal surface of the thyroid gland (see Figure 11.4 ■). The **parathyroid hormone** (PTH) secreted by these glands regulates the amount of **calcium** in the blood. If blood calcium levels fall too low, parathyroid hormone levels in the blood are increased and will stimulate bone breakdown to release more calcium into the blood.

Pineal Gland

circadian rhythm (seer-KAY-dee-an)

melatonin (mel-ah-TOH-nin)

thalamus (THALL-mus)

Med Term Tip

The pineal gland is an example of an organ named for its shape. *Pineal* means "shaped like a pine cone."

The pineal gland is a small pine-cone-shaped gland that is part of the **thalamus** region of the brain (see Figure 11.5 ■). The pineal gland secretes **melatonin**, a hormone not well understood, but that plays a role in regulating the body's **circadian rhythm**. This is the 24-hour clock that governs our periods of wakefulness and sleepiness.

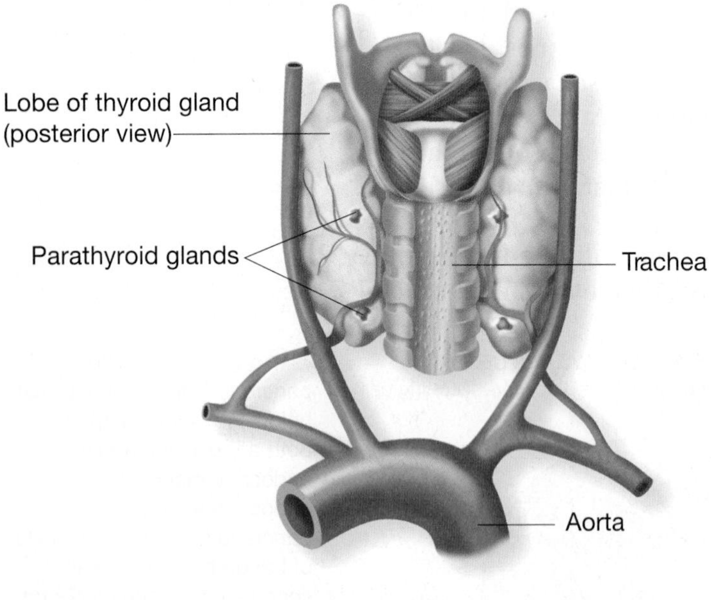

■ **Figure 11.4** The parathyroid glands. These four glands are located on the posterior side of the thyroid gland. They secrete parathyroid hormone.

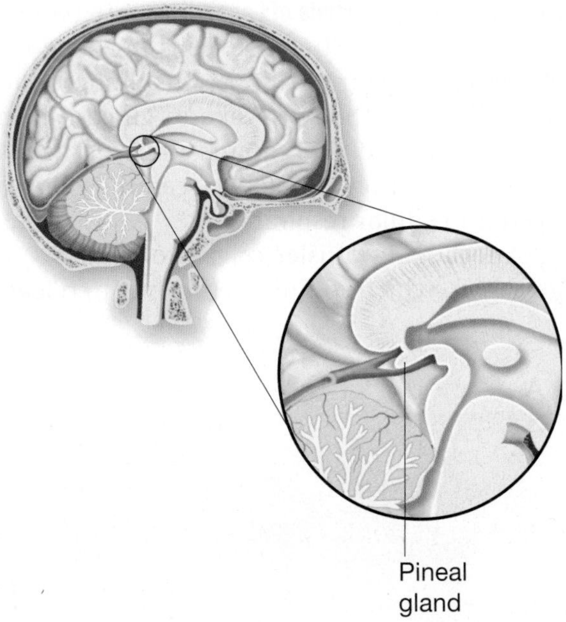

■ **Figure 11.5** The pineal gland is a part of the thalamus region of the brain. It secretes melatonin.

Pituitary Gland

adrenocorticotropin hormone (ah-dree-noh-kor-tih-koh-TROH-pin)
anterior lobe
antidiuretic hormone (an-tye-dye-yoo-RET-ik)
follicle-stimulating hormone (FOLL-ih-kl STIM-yoo-lay-ting)
gonadotropins (go-nad-oh-TROH-pins)
growth hormone
hypothalamus (high-poh-THAL-ah-mus)
luteinizing hormone (LOO-tee-in-eye-zing)
melanocyte-stimulating hormone
oxytocin (ok-see-TOH-sin)
posterior lobe
prolactin (proh-LAK-tin)
somatotropin (so-mat-oh-TROH-pin)
thyroid-stimulating hormone

The pituitary gland is located underneath the brain (see Figure 11.6 ■). The small marble-shaped gland is divided into an **anterior lobe** and a **posterior lobe**. Both lobes are controlled by the **hypothalamus**, a region of the brain active in regulating automatic body responses.

The anterior pituitary secretes several different hormones (see Figure 11.7 ■). **Growth hormone** (GH), also called **somatotropin**, promotes growth of the body by stimulating cells to rapidly increase in size and divide. **Thyroid-stimulating hormone** (TSH) regulates the function of the thyroid gland. **Adrenocorticotropin hormone** (ACTH) regulates the function of the adrenal cortex. **Prolactin** (PRL) stimulates milk production in the breast following pregnancy and birth. **Follicle-stimulating hormone** (FSH) and **luteinizing hormone** (LH) both exert their influence on the male and female gonads. Therefore, these two hormones together are referred to as the **gonadotropins**. Follicle-stimulating hormone is responsible for the develop-

Med Term Tip

The pituitary gland is sometimes referred to as the "master gland" because several of its secretions regulate other endocrine glands.

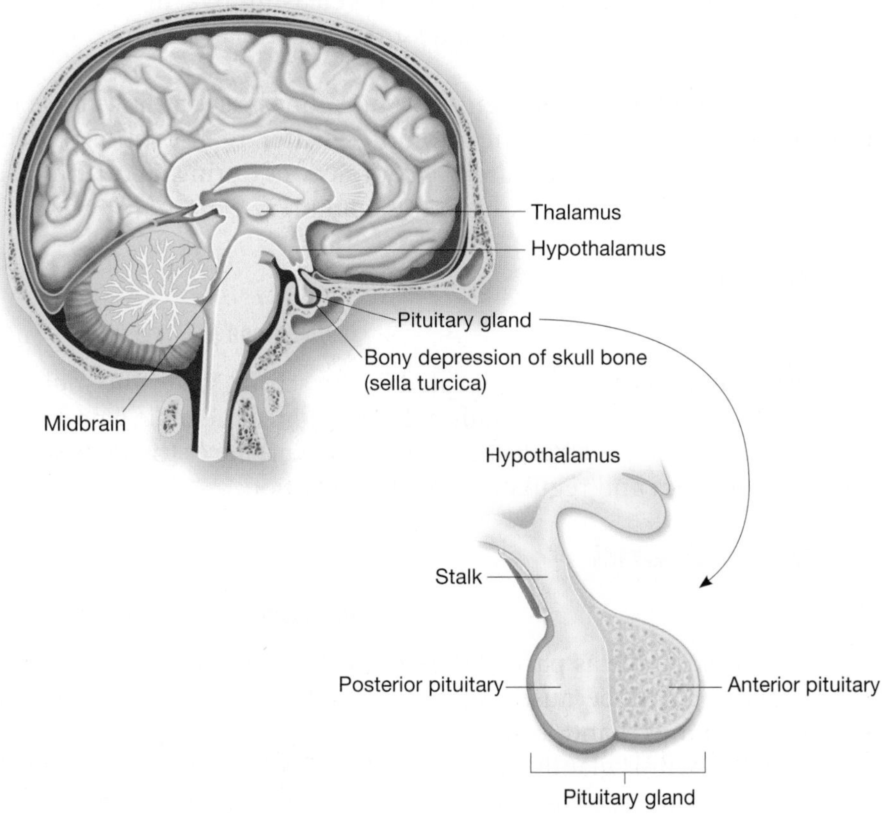

■ **Figure 11.6** The pituitary gland lies just underneath the brain. It is subdivided into anterior and posterior lobes. Each lobe secretes different hormones.

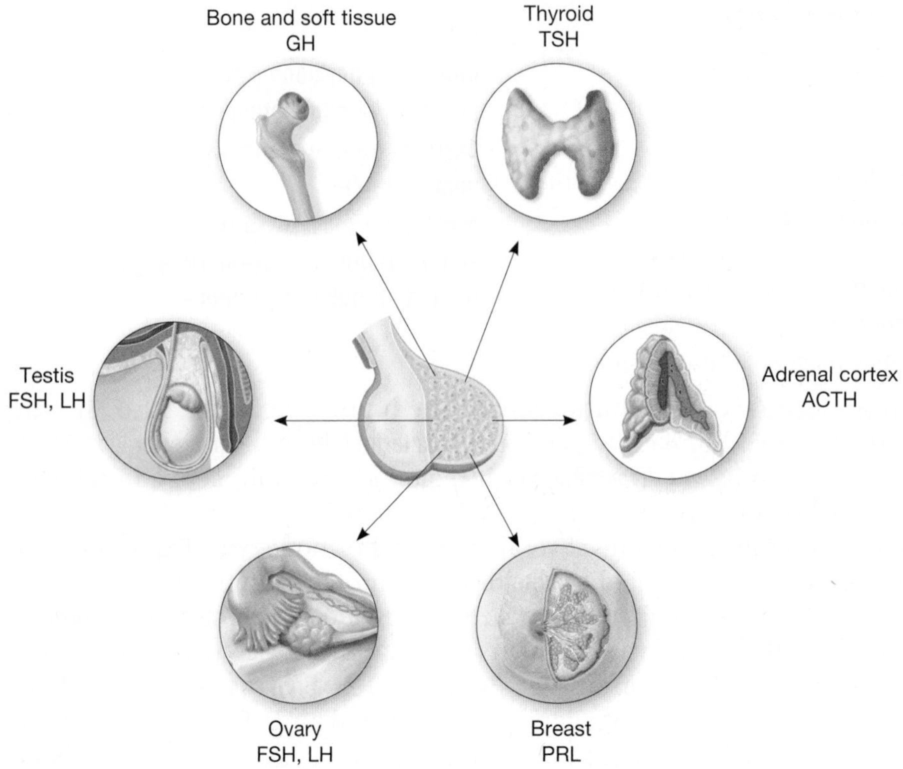

Figure 11.7 The anterior pituitary is sometimes called the master gland because it secretes many hormones that regulate other glands. This figure illustrates the different hormones and target tissues for the anterior pituitary.

Med Term Tip

Many people use the term *diabetes* to refer to diabetes mellitus (DM). But there is another type of diabetes, called *diabetes insipidus* (DI) that is a result of the inadequate secretion of the antidiuretic hormone (ADH) from the pituitary gland.

ment of ova in ovaries and sperm in testes. It also stimulates the ovary to secrete estrogen. Luteinizing hormone stimulates secretion of sex hormones in both males and females and plays a role in releasing ova in females. **Melanocyte-stimulating hormone** (MSH) stimulates melanocytes to produce more melanin, thereby darkening the skin.

The posterior pituitary secretes two hormones, **antidiuretic hormone** (ADH) and **oxytocin**. Antidiuretic hormone promotes water reabsorption by the kidney tubules. Oxytocin stimulates uterine contractions during labor and delivery, and after birth the release of milk from the mammary glands.

Testes

sperm **testosterone** (tess-TOSS-ter-own)

The testes are two oval glands located in the scrotal sac of the male (see Figure 11.8 ■). They are the male gonads, which produce the male gametes, **sperm**, and the male sex hormone, **testosterone**. Testosterone produces the male secondary sexual characteristics and regulates sperm production.

Thymus Gland

T cells **thymosin** (thigh-MOH-sin)

In addition to its role as part of the immune system, the thymus is also one of the endocrine glands because it secretes the hormone **thymosin**. Thymosin, like the rest of the thymus gland, is important for proper development of the immune system. The thymus gland is located in the mediastinal cavity anterior and superior to the heart (see Figure 11.9 ■). The thymus is present at birth and grows to its largest size during puberty. At puberty it begins to shrink and eventually is replaced with connective and adipose tissue.

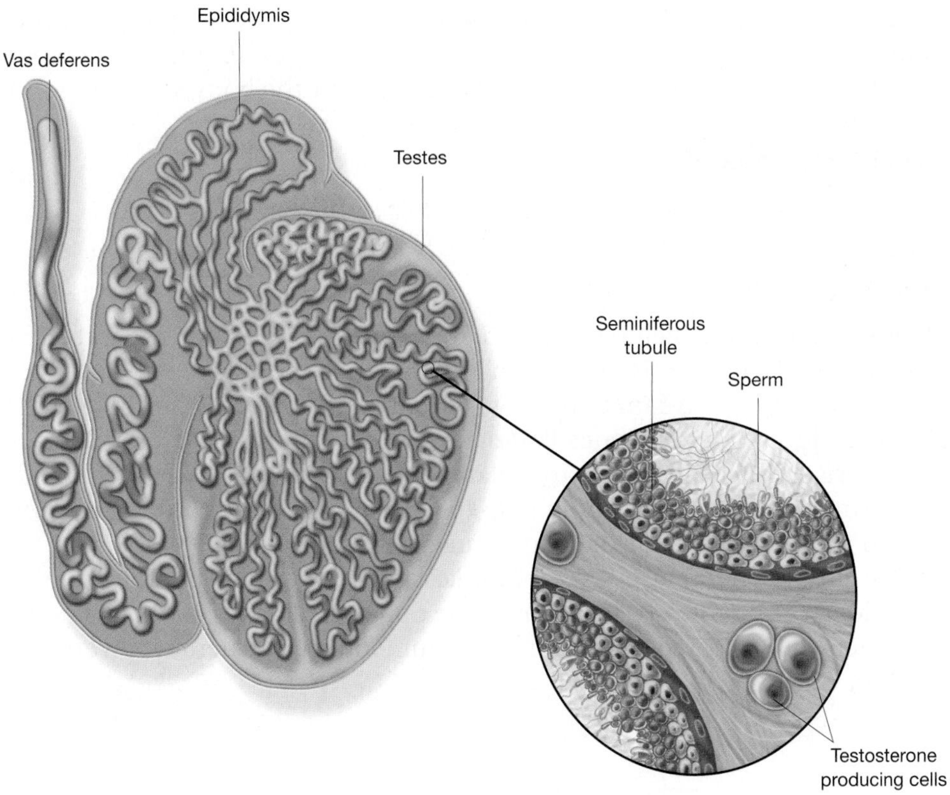

Figure 11.8 The testes. In addition to producing sperm, the testes secrete the male sex hormones, primarily testosterone.

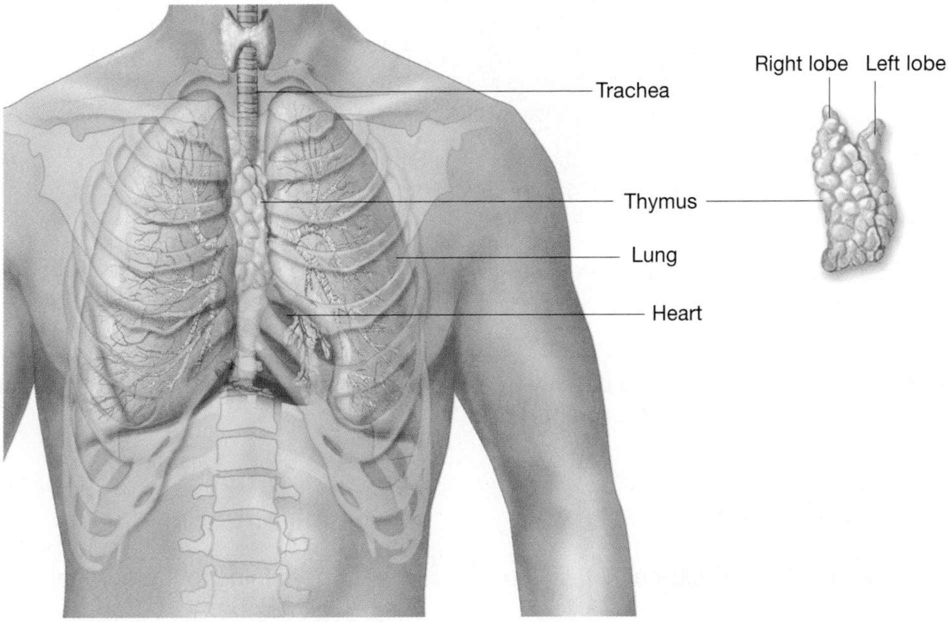

Figure 11.9 The thymus gland. This gland lies in the mediastinum of the thoracic cavity, just above the heart. It secretes thymosin.

The most important function of the thymus is the development of the immune system in the newborn. It is essential to the growth and development of thymic lymphocytes or **T cells**, which are critical for the body's immune system.

Thyroid Gland

calcitonin (kal-sih-TOH-nin)
iodine
thyroxine (thigh-ROKS-in)
triiodothyronine (try-eye-oh-doh-THIGH-roh-neen)

Med Term Tip

Iodine is found in many foods, including vegetables and seafood. It is also present in iodized salt, which is one of the best sources of iodine for people living in the goiter belt, composed of states located away from saltwater. A lack of iodine in the diet can lead to thyroid disorders, including *goiter*.

The thyroid gland, which resembles a butterfly in shape, has right and left lobes (see Figure 11.10 ■). It is located on either side of the trachea and larynx. The thyroid cartilage, or Adam's apple, is located just above the thyroid gland. This gland produces the hormones **thyroxine** (T_4) and **triiodothyronine** (T_3). These hormones are produced in the thyroid gland from the mineral **iodine** (**EYE** oh dine). Thyroxine and triiodothyronine help to regulate the production of energy and heat in the body to adjust the body's metabolic rate.

The thyroid gland also secretes **calcitonin** in response to hypercalcemia (too high blood calcium level). Its action is the opposite of parathyroid hormone and stimulates the increased deposition of calcium into bone, thereby lowering blood levels of calcium.

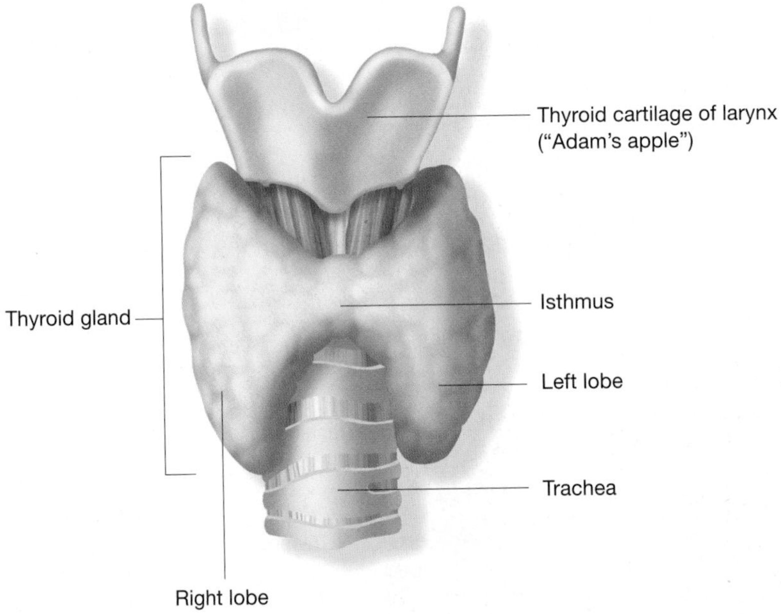

■ **Figure 11.10** The thyroid gland is subdivided into two lobes, one on each side of the trachea.

Word Building

The following list contains examples of medical terms built directly from word parts. The definitions of these terms can be determined by a straightforward translation of the word parts.

COMBINING FORM	COMBINED WITH	MEDICAL TERM	DEFINITION
adren/o	-al	**adrenal** (ah-DREE-nall)	pertaining to the adrenal glands
	-megaly	**adrenomegaly** (ad-ree-noh-MEG-ah-lee)	enlarged adrenal gland
	-pathy	**adrenopathy** (ad-ren-OP-ah-thee)	adrenal gland disease

Word Building *(continued)*

COMBINING FORM	COMBINED WITH	MEDICAL TERM	DEFINITION
adrenal/o	-ectomy	**adrenalectomy** (ad-ree-nal-EK-toh-mee)	removal of adrenal glands
	-itis	**adrenalitis** (ad-ree-nal-EYE-tis)	inflammation of an adrenal gland
calc/o	hyper- -emia	**hypercalcemia** (high-per-kal-SEE-mee-ah)	excessive calcium in the blood
	hypo- -emia	**hypocalcemia** (high-poh-kal-SEE-mee-ah)	low calcium in the blood
crin/o	endo- -ologist	**endocrinologist** (en-doh-krin-ALL-oh-jist)	specialist in the endocrine system
	endo- -pathy	**endocrinopathy** (en-doh-krin-OP-ah-thee)	endocrine system disease
glyc/o	hyper- -emia	**hyperglycemia** (high-per-glye-SEE-mee-ah)	excessive sugar in the blood
	hypo- -emia	**hypoglycemia** (high-poh-glye-SEE-mee-ah)	low sugar in the blood
kal/i	hyper- -emia	**hyperkalemia** (high-per-kal-EE-mee-ah)	excessive potassium in the blood
natr/o	hypo- -emia	**hyponatremia** (high-poh-nah-TREE-mee-ah)	low sodium in the blood
pancreat/o	-ic	**pancreatic** (pan-kree-AT-ik)	pertaining to the pancreas
parathyroid/o	-al	**parathyroidal** (pair-ah-THIGH-roy-dall)	pertaining to the parathyroid gland
	-ectomy	**parathyroidectomy** (pair-ah-thigh-royd-EK-toh-mee)	removal of the parathyroid gland
	hyper- -ism	**hyperparathyroidism** (HIGH-per-pair-ah-THIGH-royd-izm)	state of excessive parathyroid
	hypo- -ism	**hypoparathyroidism** (HIGH-poh-pair-ah-THIGH-royd-izm)	state of insufficient parathyroid
pituitar/o	-ary	**pituitary** (pih-TOO-ih-tair-ee)	pertaining to the pituitary gland
	hypo- -ism	**hypopituitarism** (HIGH-poh-pih-TOO-ih-tuh-rizm)	state of insufficient pituitary
	hyper- -ism	**hyperpituitarism** (HIGH-per-pih-TOO-ih-tuh-rizm)	state of excessive pituitary
thym/o	-ic	**thymic** (THIGH-mik)	pertaining to the thymus gland
	-ectomy	**thymectomy** (thigh-MEK-toh-mee)	removal of the thymus
	-itis	**thymitis** (thigh-MY-tis)	thymus inflammation
	-oma	**thymoma** (thigh-MOH-mah)	thymus tumor
thyr/o	-megaly	**thyromegaly** (thigh-roh-MEG-ah-lee)	enlarged thyroid
thyroid/o	-al	**thyroidal** (thigh-ROYD-all)	pertaining to the thyroid gland

Word Building *(continued)*

COMBINING FORM	COMBINED WITH	MEDICAL TERM	DEFINITION
	-ectomy	**thyroidectomy** (thigh-royd-EK-toh-mee)	removal of the thyroid
	hyper- -ism	**hyperthyroidism** (hi-per-THIGH-royd-izm)	state of excessive thyroid
	hypo- -ism	**hypothyroidism** (high-poh-THIGH-royd-izm)	state of insufficient thyroid
SUFFIX	**COMBINED WITH**	**MEDICAL TERM**	**DEFINITION**
-dipsia	poly-	**polydipsia** (pall-ee-DIP-see-ah)	many (excessive) thirst
-uria	poly-	**polyuria** (pall-ee-YOO-ree-ah)	condition of (too) much urine
	glycos/o	**glycosuria** (glye-kohs-YOO-ree-ah)	sugar in the urine

Vocabulary

TERM	DEFINITION
acidosis (as-ih-DOH-sis)	Excessive acidity of body fluids due to the accumulation of acids, as in diabetic acidosis.
edema (eh-DEE-mah)	Condition in which the body tissues contain excessive amounts of fluid.
endocrinology (en-doh-krin-ALL-oh-jee)	Branch of medicine involving diagnosis and treatment of conditions and diseases of endocrine glands. Physician is an *endocrinologist*.
exophthalmos (eks-off-THAL-mohs)	Condition in which the eyeballs protrude, such as in Graves' disease. This is generally caused by an overproduction of thyroid hormone.

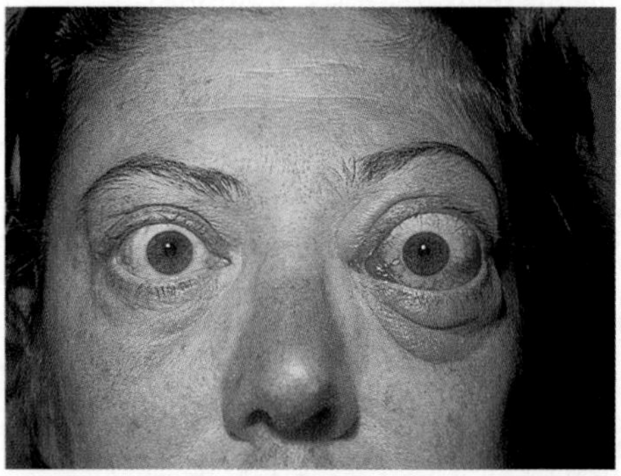

Figure 11.11 A photograph of a woman with exophthalmos. This condition is associated with hypersecretion of the thyroid gland. *(Custom Medical Stock Photo, Inc.)*

TERM	DEFINITION
gynecomastia (gigh-neh-koh-MAST-ee-ah)	Development of breast tissue in males. May be a symptom of adrenal feminization (see Pathology table).
hirsutism (HER-soot-izm)	Condition of having an excessive amount of hair. Term generally used to describe females who have the adult male pattern of hair growth. Can be the result of a hormonal imbalance.
hypersecretion	Excessive hormone production by an endocrine gland.
hyposecretion	Deficient hormone production by an endocrine gland.
obesity (oh-BEE-sih-tee)	Having an abnormal amount of fat in the body.
syndrome (SIN-drohm)	Group of symptoms and signs that, when combined, present a clinical picture of a disease or condition.

Pathology

TERM	DEFINITION
■ *Adrenal Glands*	
Addison's disease (AD-ih-sons dih-ZEEZ)	Disease named for British physician Thomas Addison that results from a deficiency in adrenocortical hormones. There may be an increased pigmentation of the skin, generalized weakness, and weight loss.
adrenal feminization (ad-REE-nal fem-ih-nigh-ZAY-shun)	Development of female secondary sexual characteristics (such as breasts) in a male. Often as a result of increased estrogen secretion by the adrenal cortex.
adrenal virilism (ad-REE-nal VIR-ill-izm)	Development of male secondary sexual characteristics (such as deeper voice and facial hair) in a female. Often as a result of increased androgen secretion by the adrenal cortex.
Cushing's syndrome (CUSH-ings SIN-drohm)	Set of symptoms, named after U.S. neurosurgeon Harvey Cushing, that result from hypersecretion of the adrenal cortex. This may be the result of a tumor of the adrenal glands. The syndrome may present symptoms of weakness, edema, excess hair growth, skin discoloration, and osteoporosis.

Figure 11.12 Cushing's syndrome. A photograph of a woman with the characteristic facial features of Cushing's syndrome. *(Biophoto Associates/ Science Source/Photo Researchers, Inc.)*

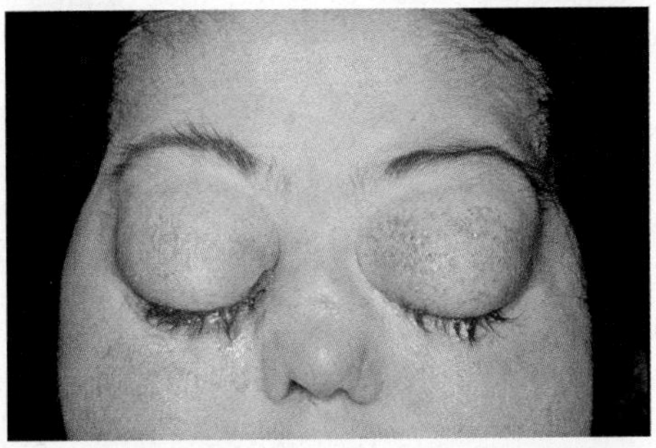

TERM	DEFINITION
pheochromocytoma (fee-oh-kroh-moh-sigh-TOH-ma)	Usually benign tumor of the adrenal medulla that secretes epinephrine. Symptoms include anxiety, heart palpitations, dyspnea, profuse sweating, headache, and nausea.
■ *Pancreas*	
diabetes mellitus (DM) (dye-ah-BEE-teez MELL-ih-tus)	Chronic disorder of carbohydrate metabolism that results in hyperglycemia and glycosuria. There are two distinct forms of diabetes mellitus: *insulin-dependent diabetes mellitus* (IDDM) or *type 1*, and *non–insulin-dependent diabetes mellitus* (NIDDM) or *type 2*.
diabetic retinopathy (dye-ah-BET-ik ret-in-OP-ah-thee)	Secondary complication of diabetes that affects the blood vessels of the retina, resulting in visual changes and even blindness.
insulin-dependent diabetes mellitus (IDDM) (dye-ah-BEE-teez MELL-ih-tus)	Also called *type 1 diabetes mellitus.* It develops early in life when the pancreas stops insulin production. Patient must take daily insulin injections.
insulinoma (in-sue-lin-OH-mah)	Tumor of the islets of Langerhans cells of the pancreas that secretes an excessive amount of insulin.
ketoacidosis (kee-toh-ass-ih-DOH-sis)	Acidosis due to an excess of acidic ketone bodies (waste products). A serious condition requiring immediate treatment that can result in death for the diabetic patient if not reversed. Also called *diabetic acidosis.*

Pathology *(continued)*

TERM	DEFINITION
non–insulin-dependent diabetes mellitus (dye-ah-BEE-teez MELL-ih-tus)	Also called *type 2 diabetes mellitus.* It typically develops later in life. The pancreas produces normal to high levels of insulin, but the cells fail to respond to it. Patients may take oral hypoglycemics to improve insulin function, or may eventually have to take insulin.
peripheral neuropathy (per-IF-eh-rall new-ROP-ah-thee)	Damage to the nerves in the lower legs and hands as a result of diabetes mellitus. Symptoms include either extreme sensitivity or numbness and tingling.
■ ***Parathyroid Glands***	
tetany (TET-ah-nee)	Nerve irritability and painful muscle cramps resulting from hypocalcemia. Hypoparathyroidism is one cause of tetany.
Recklinghausen disease (REK-ling-how-zenz)	Excessive production of parathyroid hormone, which results in degeneration of the bones. Named for German histologist Friedrich von Recklinghausen.
■ ***Pituitary Gland***	
acromegaly (ak-roh-MEG-ah-lee)	Chronic disease of adults that results in an elongation and enlargement of the bones of the head and extremities. There can also be mood changes. Due to an excessive amount of growth hormone in an adult.

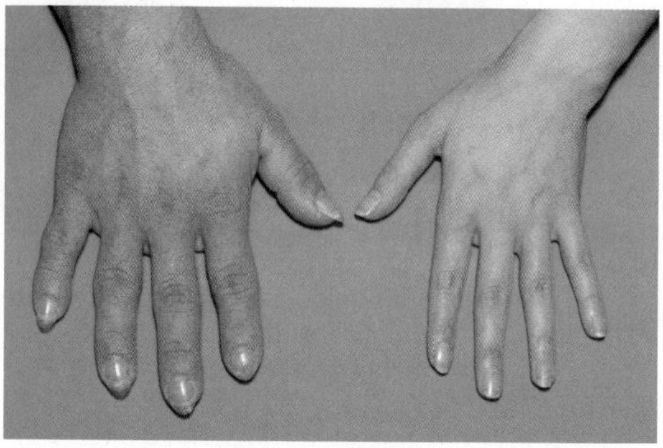

Figure 11.13 Acromegaly. The hand on the right is from an adult with normal levels of growth hormone. The hand on the left is from an adult with excessive levels of growth hormone. This results in an increase in the size of the hands, feet, and jaw. *(Bart's Medical Library/Phototake NYC)*

TERM	DEFINITION
diabetes insipidus (DI) (dye-ah-BEE-teez in-SIP-ih-dus)	Disorder caused by the inadequate secretion of antidiuretic hormone by the posterior lobe of the pituitary gland. There may be polyuria and polydipsia.
dwarfism (DWARF-izm)	Condition of being abnormally short in height. It may be the result of a hereditary condition or a lack of growth hormone.
gigantism (JYE-gan-tizm)	Excessive development of the body due to the overproduction of the growth hormone by the pituitary gland in a child or teenager. The opposite of *dwarfism.*
panhypopituitarism (pan-high-poh-pih-TOO-ih-tair-izm)	Deficiency in all the hormones secreted by the pituitary gland. Often recognized because of problems with the glands regulated by the pituitary–adrenal cortex, thyroid, ovaries, and testes.
■ ***Thyroid Gland***	
cretinism (KREE-tin-izm)	Congenital condition in which a lack of thyroid hormones may result in arrested physical and mental development.

Pathology *(continued)*

TERM	DEFINITION
goiter (GOY-ter) **Figure 11.14** Goiter. A photograph of a male with an extreme goiter or enlarged thyroid gland.	Enlargement of the thyroid gland. 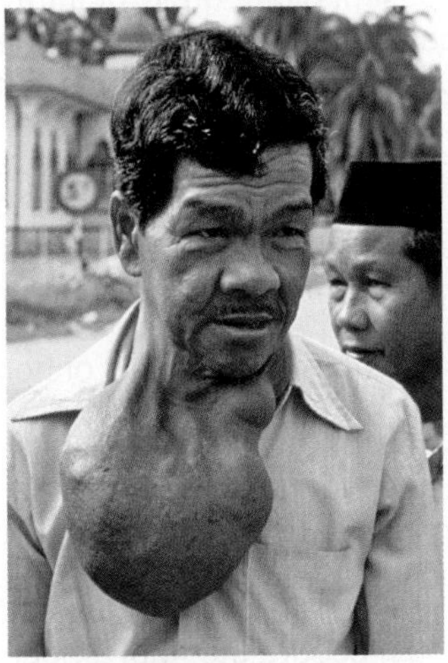
Graves' disease	Condition named for Irish physician Robert Graves that results in overactivity of the thyroid gland and can cause a crisis situation. Symptoms include exophthalmos and goiter. A type of *hyperthyroidism.*
Hashimoto's disease (hash-ee-MOH-tohz dih-ZEEZ)	Chronic autoimmune form of thyroiditis, results in hyposecretion of thyroid hormones.
myxedema (miks-eh-DEE-mah)	Condition resulting from a hyposecretion of the thyroid gland in an adult. Symptoms can include anemia, slow speech, swollen facial features, edematous skin, drowsiness, and mental lethargy.
thyrotoxicosis (thigh-roh-toks-ih-KOH-sis)	Condition resulting from marked overproduction of the thyroid gland. Symptoms include rapid heart action, tremors, enlarged thyroid gland, exophthalmos, and weight loss.
■ ***All Glands***	
adenocarcinoma (ad-eh-no-car-sih-NO-mah)	Cancerous tumor in a gland that is capable of producing the hormones secreted by that gland. One cause of hypersecretion pathologies.

Diagnostic Procedures

TERM	DEFINITION
■ ***Clinical Laboratory Tests***	
blood serum test	Blood test to measure the level of substances such as calcium, electrolytes, testosterone, insulin, and glucose. Used to assist in determining the function of various endocrine glands.
fasting blood sugar (FBS)	Blood test to measure the amount of sugar circulating throughout the body after a 12-hour fast.

Diagnostic Procedures *(continued)*

TERM	DEFINITION
glucose tolerance test (GTT) (GLOO-kohs)	Test to determine the blood sugar level. A measured dose of glucose is given to a patient either orally or intravenously. Blood samples are then drawn at certain intervals to determine the ability of the patient to use glucose. Used for diabetic patients to determine their insulin response to glucose.
protein-bound iodine test (PBI)	Blood test to measure the concentration of thyroxine (T_4) circulating in the bloodstream. The iodine becomes bound to the protein in the blood and can be measured. Useful in establishing thyroid function.
radioimmunoassay (RIA) (ray-dee-oh-im-yoo-noh-ASS-ay)	Test used to measure the levels of hormones in the plasma of the blood.
thyroid function test (TFT) (THIGH-royd)	Blood test used to measure the levels of thyroxine, triiodothyronine, and thyroid-stimulating hormone in the bloodstream to assist in determining thyroid function.
total calcium	Blood test to measure the total amount of calcium to assist in detecting parathyroid and bone disorders.
two-hour postprandial glucose tolerance test (post-PRAN-dee-al)	Blood test to assist in evaluating glucose metabolism. The patient eats a high carbohydrate diet and then fasts overnight before the test. Then the blood sample is taken two hours after a meal.
■ ***Diagnostic Imaging***	
thyroid echogram (THIGH-royd EK-oh-gram)	Ultrasound examination of the thyroid that can assist in distinguishing a thyroid nodule from a cyst.
thyroid scan (THIGH-royd)	Test in which radioactive iodine is administered that localizes in the thyroid gland. The gland can then be visualized with a scanning device to detect pathology such as tumors.

Therapeutic Procedures

TERM	DEFINITION
■ ***Medical Procedures***	
chemical thyroidectomy (thigh-royd-EK-toh-mee)	Large dose of radioactive iodine is given in order to kill thyroid gland cells without having to actually do surgery.
hormone replacement therapy	Artificial replacement of hormones in patients with hyposecretion disorders. May be oral pills, injections, or adhesive skin patches.
■ ***Surgical Procedures***	
laparoscopic adrenalectomy (lap-row-SKOP-ik ad-ree-nal-EK-toh-mee)	Removal of the adrenal gland through a small incision in the abdomen and using endoscopic instruments.
lobectomy (lobe-EK-toh-mee)	Removal of a lobe from an organ. In this case, one lobe of the thyroid gland.

Pharmacology

CLASSIFICATION	ACTION	GENERIC AND BRAND NAMES
antithyroid agents	Medication given to block production of thyroid hormones in patients with hypersecretion disorders.	methimazole, Tapazole; propylthiouracil
corticosteroids (kor-tih-koh-STAIR-oydz)	Although the function of these hormones in the body is to regulate carbohydrate metabolism, they also have a strong anti-inflammatory action. Therefore they are used to treat severe chronic inflammatory diseases such as rheumatoid arthritis. Long-term use of corticosteroids has adverse side effects such as osteoporosis and the symptoms of Cushing's disease. Also used to treat adrenal cortex hyposecretion disorders such as Addison's disease.	prednisone, Deltasone
human growth hormone therapy	Hormone replacement therapy with human growth hormone in order to stimulate skeletal growth. Used to treat children with abnormally short stature.	somatropin, Genotropin; somatrem, Protropin
insulin (IN-suh-lin)	Administered to replace insulin for type 1 diabetics or to treat severe type 2 diabetics.	human insulin, Humulin L
oral hypoglycemic agents (high-poh-glye-SEE-mik)	Medications taken by mouth that cause a decrease in blood sugar; not used for insulin-dependent patients.	metformin, Glucophage; glipizide, Glucotrol
thyroid replacement hormone	Hormone replacement therapy for patients with hypothyroidism or who have had a thyroidectomy.	levothyroxine, Levo-T; liothyronine, Cytomel
vasopressin (vaz-oh-PRESS-in)	Given to control diabetes insipidus and promote reabsorption of water in the kidney tubules.	desmopressin acetate, Desmopressin; conivaptan, Vaprisol

Abbreviations

α	alpha
ACTH	adrenocorticotropin hormone
ADH	antidiuretic hormone
β	beta
BMR	basal metabolic rate
DI	diabetes insipidus
DM	diabetes mellitus
FBS	fasting blood sugar
FSH	follicle-stimulating hormone
GH	growth hormone
GTT	glucose tolerance test
IDDM	insulin-dependent diabetes mellitus
K^+	potassium
LH	luteinizing hormone
MSH	melanocyte-stimulating hormone
Na^+	sodium
NIDDM	non–insulin-dependent diabetes mellitus
NPH	neutral protamine Hagedorn (insulin)
PBI	protein-bound iodine
PRL	prolactin
PTH	parathyroid hormone
RAI	radioactive iodine
RIA	radioimmunoassay
T_3	triiodothyronine
T_4	thyroxine
TFT	thyroid function test
TSH	thyroid-stimulating hormone

Chapter Review

Terminology Checklist

Below are all Anatomy and Physiology key terms, Word Building, Vocabulary, Pathology, Diagnostic, Therapeutic, and Pharmacology terms presented in this chapter. Use this list as a study tool by placing a check in the box in front of each term as you master its meaning.

- ☐ acidosis
- ☐ acromegaly
- ☐ Addison's disease
- ☐ adenocarcinoma
- ☐ adrenal
- ☐ adrenal cortex
- ☐ adrenalectomy
- ☐ adrenal feminization
- ☐ adrenal glands
- ☐ adrenaline
- ☐ adrenalitis
- ☐ adrenal medulla
- ☐ adrenal virilism
- ☐ adrenocorticotropin hormone
- ☐ adrenomegaly
- ☐ adrenopathy
- ☐ aldosterone
- ☐ androgen
- ☐ anterior lobe
- ☐ antidiuretic hormone
- ☐ antithyroid agents
- ☐ blood serum test
- ☐ calcitonin
- ☐ calcium
- ☐ chemical thyroidectomy
- ☐ circadian rhythm
- ☐ corticosteroids
- ☐ cortisol
- ☐ cretinism
- ☐ Cushing's syndrome
- ☐ diabetes insipidus
- ☐ diabetes mellitus
- ☐ diabetic retinopathy
- ☐ dwarfism
- ☐ edema
- ☐ endocrine glands
- ☐ endocrine system
- ☐ endocrinologist
- ☐ endocrinology
- ☐ endocrinopathy
- ☐ epinephrine
- ☐ estrogen
- ☐ exocrine glands
- ☐ exophthalmos
- ☐ fasting blood sugar
- ☐ follicle-stimulating hormone
- ☐ gametes
- ☐ gigantism
- ☐ glands
- ☐ glucagon
- ☐ glucocorticoids
- ☐ glucose tolerance test
- ☐ glycosuria
- ☐ goiter
- ☐ gonadotropins
- ☐ gonads
- ☐ Graves' disease
- ☐ growth hormone
- ☐ gynecomastia
- ☐ Hashimoto's disease
- ☐ hirsutism
- ☐ homeostasis
- ☐ hormone
- ☐ hormone replacement therapy
- ☐ human growth hormone therapy
- ☐ hypercalcemia
- ☐ hyperglycemia
- ☐ hyperkalemia
- ☐ hyperparathyroidism
- ☐ hyperpituitarism
- ☐ hypersecretion
- ☐ hyperthyroidism
- ☐ hypocalcemia
- ☐ hypoglycemia
- ☐ hyponatremia
- ☐ hypoparathyroidism
- ☐ hypopituitarism
- ☐ hyposecretion
- ☐ hypothalamus
- ☐ hypothyroidism
- ☐ insulin
- ☐ insulin-dependent diabetes mellitus
- ☐ insulinoma
- ☐ iodine
- ☐ islets of Langerhans
- ☐ ketoacidosis
- ☐ laparoscopic adrenalectomy
- ☐ lobectomy
- ☐ luteinizing hormone
- ☐ melanocyte-stimulating hormone
- ☐ melatonin
- ☐ menstrual cycle
- ☐ mineralocorticoids
- ☐ myxedema
- ☐ non–insulin-dependent diabetes mellitus
- ☐ norepinephrine
- ☐ obesity
- ☐ oral hypoglycemic agent
- ☐ ova
- ☐ ovaries
- ☐ oxytocin
- ☐ pancreas
- ☐ pancreatic
- ☐ panhypopituitarism
- ☐ parathyroid glands
- ☐ parathyroidal
- ☐ parathyroidectomy
- ☐ parathyroid hormone
- ☐ peripheral neuropathy
- ☐ pheochromocytoma
- ☐ pineal gland
- ☐ pituitary
- ☐ pituitary gland
- ☐ polydipsia

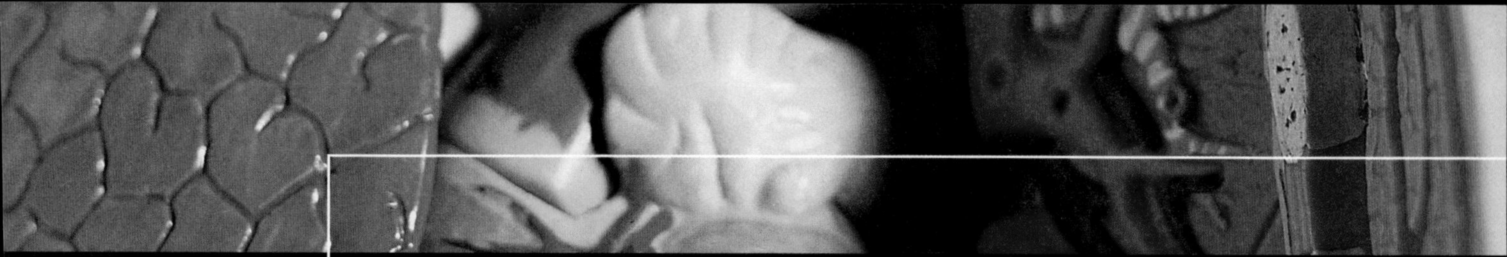

12 Nervous System

Learning Objectives

Upon completion of this chapter, you will be able to:

- Identify and define the combining forms and suffixes introduced in this chapter.
- Correctly spell and pronounce medical terms and major anatomical structures relating to the nervous system.
- Locate and describe the major organs of the nervous system and their functions.
- Describe the components of a neuron.
- Distinguish between the central nervous system, peripheral nervous system, and autonomic nervous system.
- Build and define nervous system medical terms from word parts.
- Identify and define nervous system vocabulary terms.
- Identify and define selected nervous system pathology terms.
- Identify and define selected nervous system diagnostic procedures.
- Identify and define selected nervous system therapeutic procedures.
- Identify and define selected medications relating to the nervous system.
- Define selected abbreviations associated with the nervous system.

Nervous System at a Glance

Function

The nervous system coordinates and controls body function. It receives sensory input, makes decisions, and then orders body responses.

Organs

brain
nerves
spinal cord

Combining Forms

cephal/o	head
cerebell/o	cerebellum
cerebr/o	cerebrum
encephal/o	brain
gli/o	glue
medull/o	medulla oblongata
mening/o	meninges
meningi/o	meninges
myel/o	spinal cord
neur/o	nerve
phas/o	speech
poli/o	gray matter
pont/o	pons
radicul/o	nerve root
thalam/o	thalamus
thec/o	sheath (meninges)
ventricul/o	brain ventricle

Suffixes

-algesia	pain, sensitivity
-esthesia	feeling, sensation
-paresis	weakness
-phasia	speech
-plegia	paralysis
-taxia	muscle coordination

Nervous System Illustrated

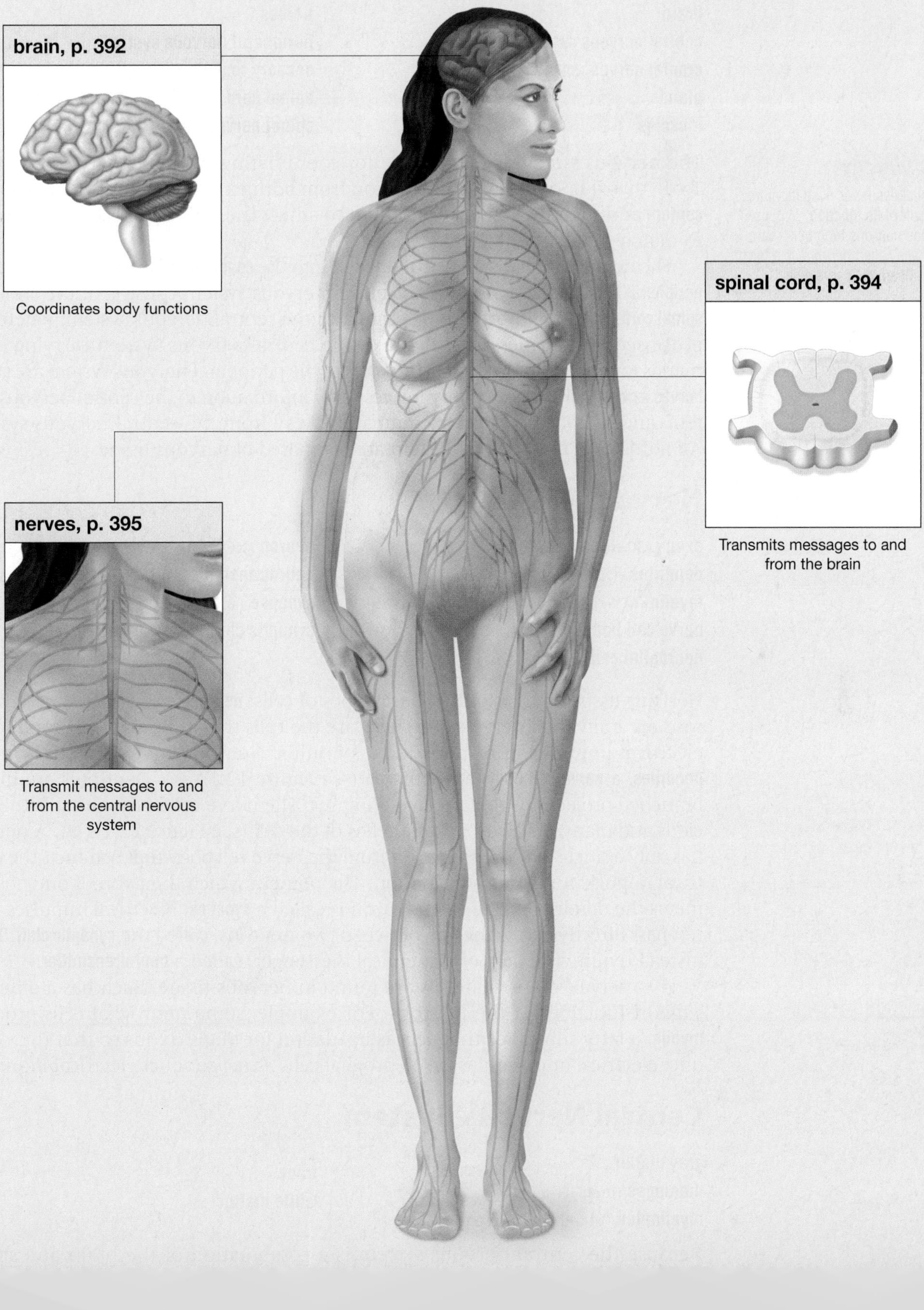

Anatomy and Physiology of the Nervous System

brain
central nervous system
cranial nerves (KRAY-nee-al)
glands
muscles
nerves
peripheral nervous system (per-IF-er-al)
sensory receptors
spinal cord
spinal nerves

Med Term Tip

Neuroglial tissue received its name as a result of its function. This tissue holds neurons together. Therefore, it was called *neuroglial*, a term literally meaning "nerve glue."

The nervous system is responsible for coordinating all the activity of the body. To do this, it first receives information from both external and internal **sensory receptors** and then uses that information to adjust the activity of **muscles** and **glands** to match the needs of the body.

The nervous system can be subdivided into the **central nervous system** (CNS) and the **peripheral nervous system** (PNS). The central nervous system consists of the **brain** and **spinal cord**. Sensory information comes into the central nervous system, where it is processed. Motor messages then exit the central nervous system carrying commands to muscles and glands. The **nerves** of the peripheral nervous system are **cranial nerves** and **spinal nerves**. Sensory nerves carry information to the central nervous system, and motor nerves carry commands away from the central nervous system. All portions of the nervous system are composed of nervous tissue.

Nervous Tissue

axon (AK-son)
dendrites (DEN-drights)
myelin (MY-eh-lin)
nerve cell body
neuroglial cells (noo-ROH-glee-all)
neuron (NOO-ron)
neurotransmitter (noo-roh-TRANS-mit-ter)
synapse (sih-NAPSE)
synaptic cleft (sih-NAP-tik)

Nervous tissue consists of two basic types of cells: **neurons** and **neuroglial cells**. Neurons are individual nerve cells. These are the cells that are capable of conducting electrical impulses in response to a stimulus. Neurons have three basic parts: **dendrites**, a **nerve cell body**, and an **axon** (see Figure 12.1A ■). Dendrites are highly branched projections that receive impulses. The nerve cell body contains the nucleus and many of the other organelles of the cell (see Figure 12.1B ■). A neuron has only a single axon, a projection from the nerve cell body that conducts the electrical impulse toward its destination. The point at which the axon of one neuron meets the dendrite of the next neuron is called a **synapse**. Electrical impulses cannot pass directly across the gap between two neurons, called the **synaptic cleft**. They instead require the help of a chemical messenger, called a **neurotransmitter**.

A variety of neuroglial cells are found in nervous tissue. Each has a different support function for the neurons. For example, some neuroglial cells produce **myelin**, a fatty substance that acts as insulation for many axons so that they conduct electrical impulses faster. Neuroglial cells *do not* conduct electrical impulses.

Central Nervous System

gray matter
meninges (men-IN-jeez)
myelinated (MY-eh-lih-nayt-ed)
tract
white matter

Because the central nervous system is a combination of the brain and spinal cord, it is able to receive impulses from all over the body, process this informa-

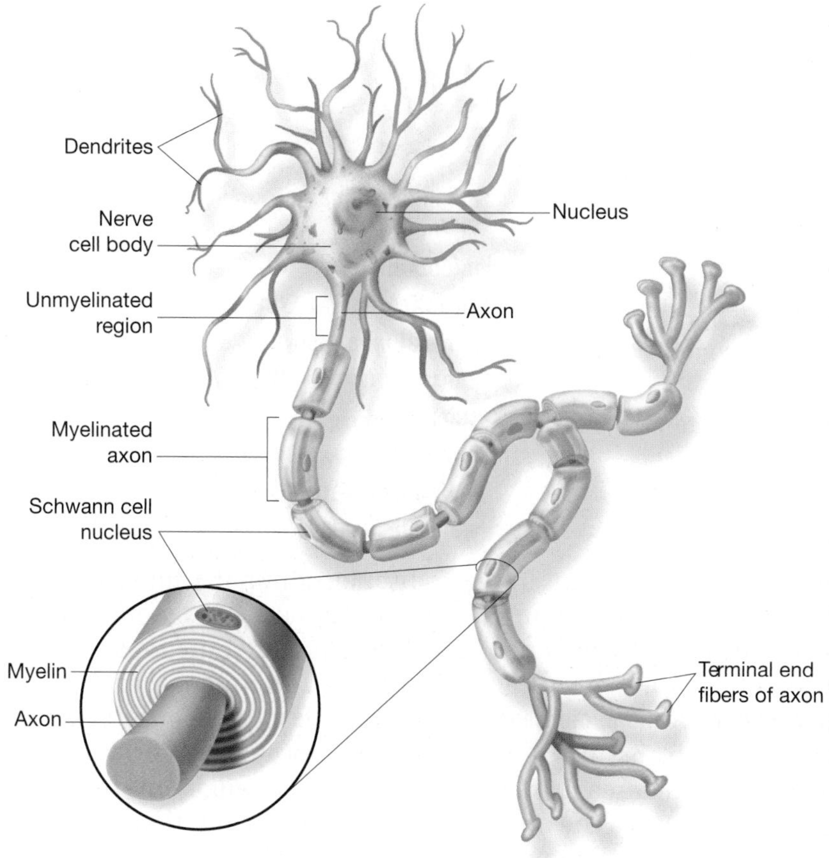

A

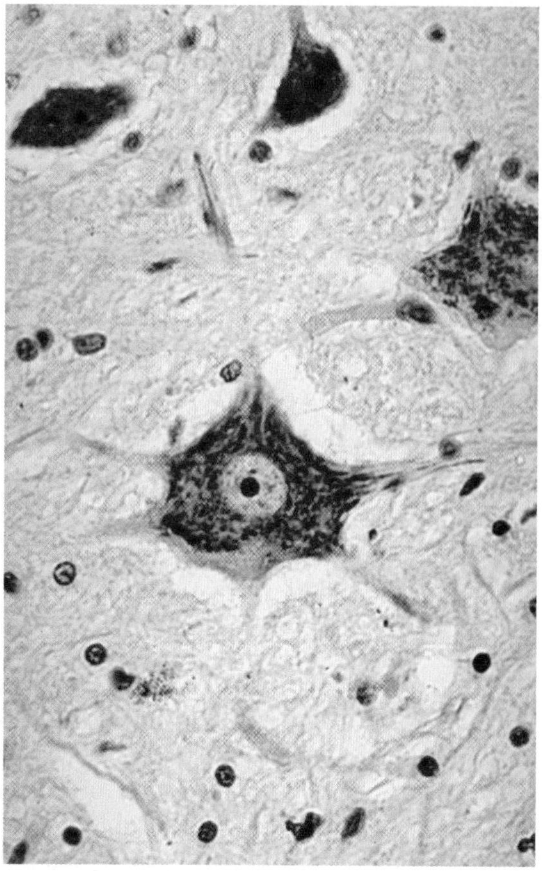

B

Figure 12.1 A) The structure of a neuron, showing the dendrites, nerve cell body, and axon. B) Photomicrograph of typical neuron showing the nerve cell body, nucleus, and dendrites.

tion, and then respond with an action. This system consists of both **gray** and **white matter.** Gray matter is comprised of unsheathed or uncovered cell bodies and dendrites. White matter is **myelinated** nerve fibers (see Figure 12.2 ■). The myelin sheath makes the nervous tissue appear white. Bundles of nerve fibers inter-

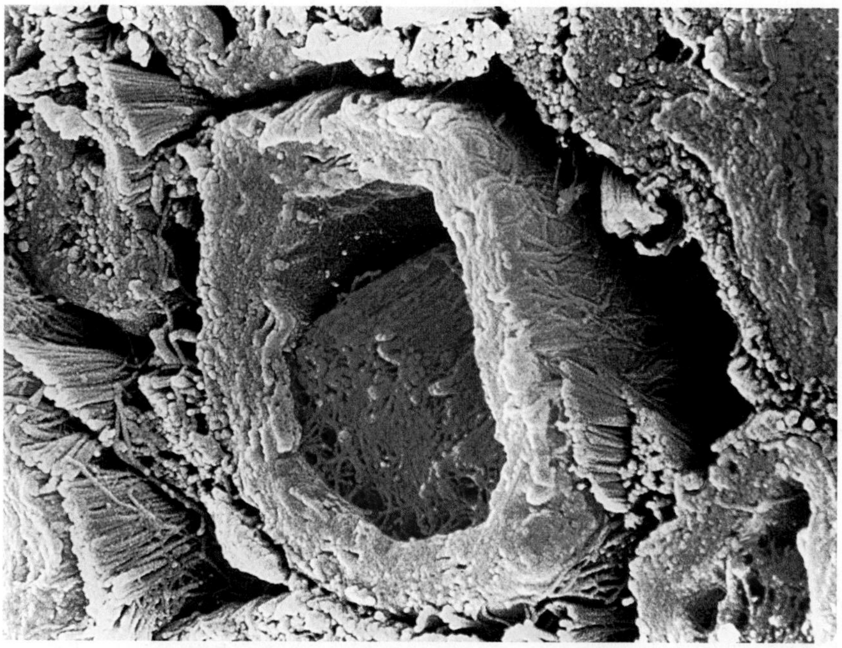

Figure 12.2 Electronmicrograph illustrating an axon (red) wrapped in its myelin sheath (blue). *(Quest/Science Photo Library/Photo Researchers, Inc.)*

Med Term Tip

Myelin is a lipid and a very white molecule. This is why myelinated neurons are called *white matter.*

connecting different parts of the central nervous system are called **tracts**. The central nervous system is encased and protected by three membranes known as the **meninges**.

The Brain

brain stem
cerebellum (ser-eh-BELL-um)
cerebral cortex (seh-REE-bral KOR-teks)
cerebral hemisphere
cerebrospinal fluid (ser-eh-broh-SPY-nal)
cerebrum (SER-eh-brum)
diencephalon (dye-en-SEFF-ah-lon)
frontal lobe
gyri (JYE-rye)
hypothalamus (high-poh-THAL-ah-mus)
medulla oblongata (meh-DULL-ah ob-long-GAH-tah)
midbrain
occipital lobe (ock-SIP-ih-tal)
parietal lobe (pah-RYE-eh-tal)
pons (PONZ)
sulci (SULL-kye)
temporal lobe (TEM-por-al)
thalamus (THAL-ah-mus)
ventricles (VEN-trik-lz)

The brain is one of the largest organs in the body and coordinates most body activities. It is the center for all thought, memory, judgment, and emotion. Each part of the brain is responsible for controlling different body functions, such as temperature regulation, blood pressure, and breathing. There are four sections to the brain: **cerebrum**, **cerebellum**, **diencephalon**, and **brain stem** (see Figure 12.3 ■).

The largest section of the brain is the cerebrum. It is located in the upper portion of the brain and is the area that processes thoughts, judgment, memory, problem solving, and language. The outer layer of the cerebrum is the **cerebral cortex**, which is composed of folds of gray matter. The elevated portions of the cerebrum, or convolutions, are called **gyri** and are separated by fissures, or valleys, called **sulci**. The cerebrum is subdivided into left and right halves called **cerebral hemispheres**. Each hemisphere has four lobes. The lobes and their locations and functions are as follows (see Figure 12.4 ■):

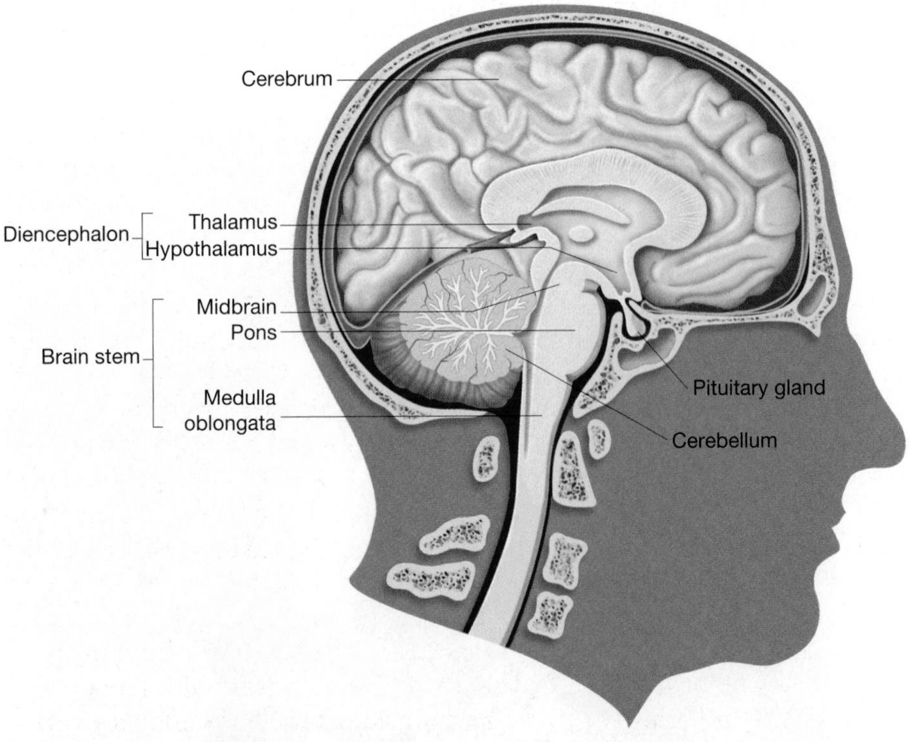

■ **Figure 12.3** The regions of the brain.

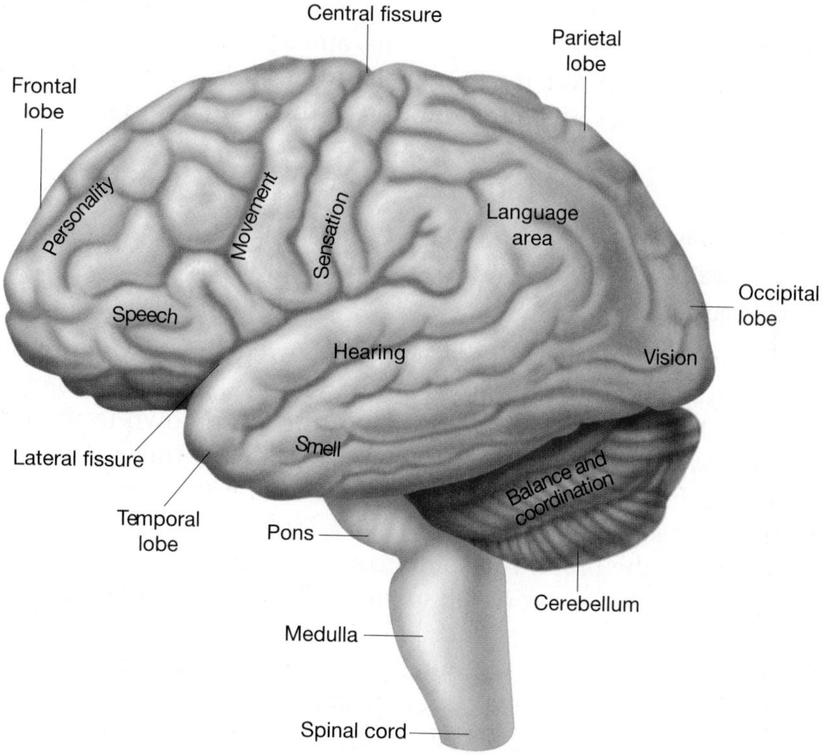

Figure 12.4 The functional regions of the cerebrum.

1. **Frontal lobe:** Most anterior portion of the cerebrum; controls motor function, personality, and speech
2. **Parietal lobe:** Most superior portion of the cerebrum; receives and interprets nerve impulses from sensory receptors and interprets language
3. **Occipital lobe:** Most posterior portion of the cerebrum; controls vision
4. **Temporal lobe:** Left and right lateral portion of the cerebrum; controls hearing and smell

The diencephalon, located below the cerebrum, contains two of the most critical areas of the brain, the **thalamus** and the **hypothalamus**. The thalamus is composed of gray matter and acts as a center for relaying impulses from the eyes, ears, and skin to the cerebrum. Our pain perception is controlled by the thalamus. The hypothalamus located just below the thalamus controls body temperature, appetite, sleep, sexual desire, and emotions. The hypothalamus is actually responsible for controlling the autonomic nervous system, cardiovascular system, digestive system, and the release of hormones from the pituitary gland.

The cerebellum, the second largest portion of the brain, is located beneath the posterior part of the cerebrum. This part of the brain aids in coordinating voluntary body movements and maintaining balance and equilibrium. The cerebellum refines the muscular movement that is initiated in the cerebrum.

The final portion of the brain is the brain stem. This area has three components: **midbrain**, **pons**, and **medulla oblongata**. The midbrain acts as a pathway for impulses to be conducted between the brain and the spinal cord. The pons—a term meaning bridge—connects the cerebellum to the rest of the brain. The medulla oblongata is the most inferior positioned portion of the brain; it connects the brain to the spinal cord. However, this vital area contains the centers that control respiration, heart rate, temperature, and blood pressure. Additionally, this is the site where nerve tracts cross from one side of the brain to control functions and movement on the other side of the body. In other words, with few exceptions, the left side of the brain controls the right side of the body and vice versa.

The brain has four interconnected cavities called **ventricles**: one in each cerebral hemisphere, one in the thalamus, and one in front of the cerebellum. These contain **cerebrospinal fluid** (CSF), which is the watery, clear fluid that provides protection from shock or sudden motion to the brain and spinal cord.

Spinal Cord

ascending tracts
central canal
descending tracts
spinal cavity
vertebral canal
vertebral column

The function of the spinal cord is to provide a pathway for impulses traveling to and from the brain. The spinal cord is actually a column of nervous tissue that extends from the medulla oblongata of the brain down to the level of the second lumbar vertebra within the **vertebral column**. The thirty-three vertebrae of the backbone line up to form a continuous canal for the spinal cord called the **spinal cavity** or **vertebral canal** (see Figure 12.5 ■).

Similar to the brain, the spinal cord is also protected by cerebrospinal fluid. It flows down the center of the spinal cord within the **central canal**. The inner core of the spinal cord consists of cell bodies and dendrites of peripheral nerves and therefore is gray matter. The outer portion of the spinal cord is myelinated white matter. The white matter is either **ascending tracts** carrying sensory information up to the brain or **descending tracts** carrying motor commands down from the brain to a peripheral nerve.

Med Term Tip

Certain disease processes attack the gray matter and the white matter of the central nervous system. For instance, *poliomyelitis* is a viral infection of the gray matter of the spinal cord. The combining term *poli/o* means "gray matter." This disease has almost been eradicated, due to the polio vaccine.

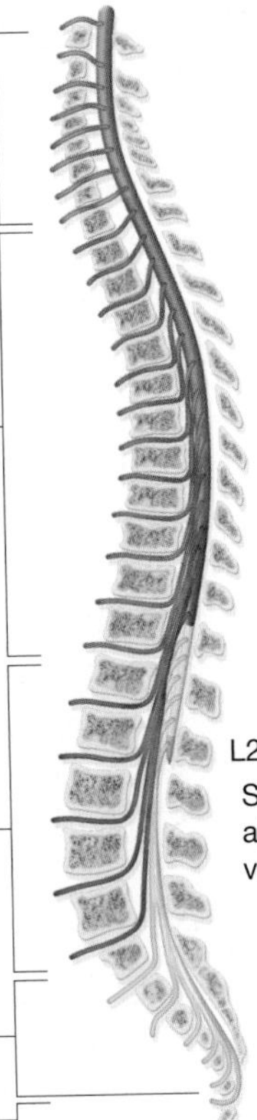

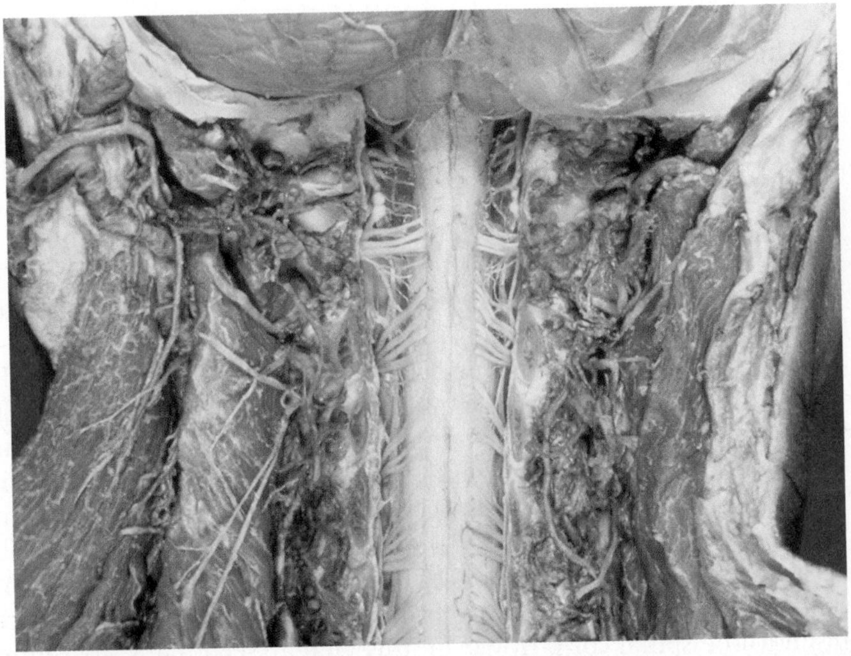

■ **Figure 12.5** A) The levels of the spinal cord and spinal nerves. B) Photograph of the spinal cord as it descends from the brain. The spinal nerve roots are clearly visible branching off from the spinal cord. *(Video Surgery/Photo Researchers, Inc.)*

Meninges

arachnoid layer (ah-RAK-noyd)
dura mater (DOO-rah MATE-er)
pia mater (PEE-ah MATE-er)
subarachnoid space (sub-ah-RAK-noyd)
subdural space (sub-DOO-ral)

The meninges are three layers of connective tissue membranes that surround the brain and spinal cord (see Figure 12.6 ■). Moving from external to internal, the meninges are:

1. **Dura mater**: Meaning *tough mother*; it forms a tough, fibrous sac around the central nervous system
2. **Subdural space**: Actual space between the dura mater and arachnoid layers
3. **Arachnoid layer**: Meaning *spiderlike*; it is a thin, delicate layer attached to the pia mater by weblike filaments
4. **Subarachnoid space**: Space between the arachnoid layer and the pia mater; it contains cerebrospinal fluid that cushions the brain from the outside
5. **Pia mater**: Meaning *soft mother*; it is the innermost membrane layer and is applied directly to the surface of the brain and spinal cord

Peripheral Nervous System

afferent neurons (AFF-er-ent)
autonomic nervous system (aw-toh-NOM-ik)
efferent neurons (EFF-er-ent)
ganglion (GANG-lee-on)
motor neurons
nerve root
sensory neurons
somatic nerves

The peripheral nervous system (PNS) includes both the twelve pairs of cranial nerves and the thirty-one pairs of spinal nerves. A nerve is a group or bundle of axon fibers located outside the central nervous system that carries messages between the central nervous system and the various parts of the body. Whether a nerve is cranial or spinal is determined by where the nerve originates. Cranial nerves arise from the brain, mainly at the medulla oblongata. Spinal nerves split off from the spinal cord, and one pair (a left and a right) exits between each pair of vertebrae. The point where either type of nerve is attached to the central nervous system is called the **nerve root**. The names of most nerves reflect either

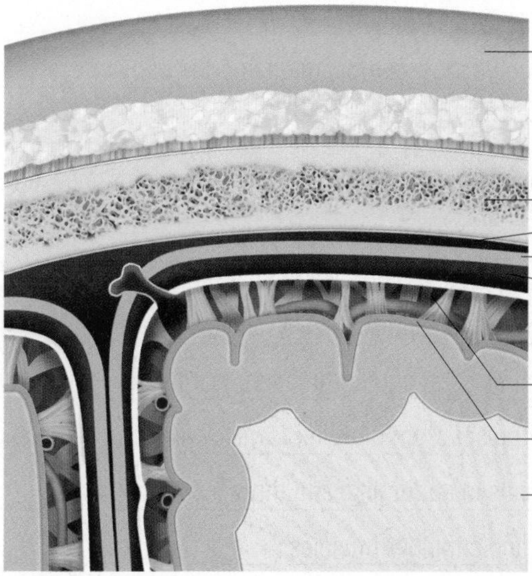

■ **Figure 12.6** The meninges. This figure illustrates the location and structure of each layer of the meninges and their relationship to the skull and brain.

Med Term Tip

Because nerve tracts cross from one side of the body to the other side of the brain, damage to one side of the brain results in symptoms appearing on the opposite side of the body. Since nerve cells that control the movement of the right side of the body are located in the left side of the medulla oblongata, a stroke that paralyzed the right side of the body would actually have occurred in the left side of the brain.

the organ the nerve serves or the portion of the body the nerve is traveling through. The entire list of cranial nerves is found in Table 12.1 ■. Figure 12.7 ■ illustrates some of the major spinal nerves in the human body.

Although most nerves carry information to and from the central nervous system, individual neurons carry information in only one direction. **Afferent neurons**, also called **sensory neurons**, carry sensory information from a sensory receptor to the central nervous system. **Efferent neurons**, also called **motor neurons**, carry activity instructions from the central nervous system to muscles or glands out in the body (see Figure 12.8 ■). The nerve cell bodies of the neurons forming the nerve are grouped together in a knot-like mass, called a **ganglion**, located outside the central nervous system.

The nerves of the peripheral nervous system are subdivided into two divisions, the **autonomic nervous system** (ANS) and **somatic nerves**, each serving a different area of the body.

Autonomic Nervous System

parasympathetic branch (pair-ah-sim-pah-THET-ik)

sympathetic branch (sim-pah-THET-ik)

The autonomic nervous system is involved with the control of involuntary or unconscious bodily functions. It may increase or decrease the activity of the smooth muscle found in viscera and blood vessels, cardiac muscle, and glands. The autonomic nervous system is divided into two branches: **sympathetic branch** and **parasympathetic branch**. The sympathetic nerves control the "fight or flight" reaction during times of stress and crisis. These nerves increase heart rate, dilate airways, increase blood pressure, inhibit digestion, and stimulate the production of adrenaline during a crisis. The parasympathetic nerves serve as a counterbalance for the sympathetic nerves, the "rest and digest" reaction. Therefore, they cause heart rate to slow down, lower blood pressure, and stimulate digestion.

Table 12.1 Cranial Nerves

NUMBER	NAME	FUNCTION
I	Olfactory	Transports impulses for sense of smell
II	Optic	Carries impulses for sense of sight
III	Oculomotor	Motor impulses for eye muscle movement and the pupil of eye
IV	Trochlear	Controls oblique muscle of eye on each side
V	Trigeminal	Carries sensory facial impulses and controls muscles for chewing; branches into eyes, forehead, upper and lower jaw
VI	Abducens	Controls an eyeball muscle to turn eye to side
VII	Facial	Controls facial muscles for expression, salivation, and taste on two-thirds of tongue (anterior)
VIII	Vestibulocochlear	Responsible for impulses of equilibrium and hearing; also called auditory nerve
IX	Glossopharyngeal	Carries sensory impulses from pharynx (swallowing) and taste on one-third of tongue
X	Vagus	Supplies most organs in abdominal and thoracic cavities
XI	Accessory	Controls the neck and shoulder muscles
XII	Hypoglossal	Controls tongue muscles

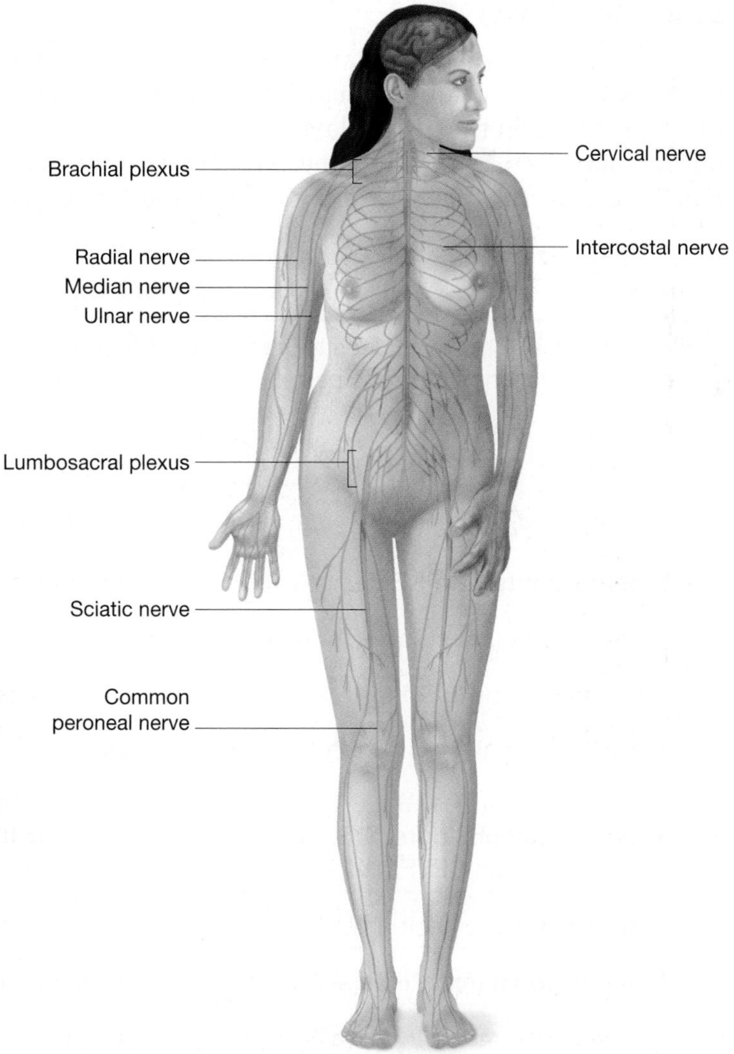

Figure 12.7 The major spinal nerves.

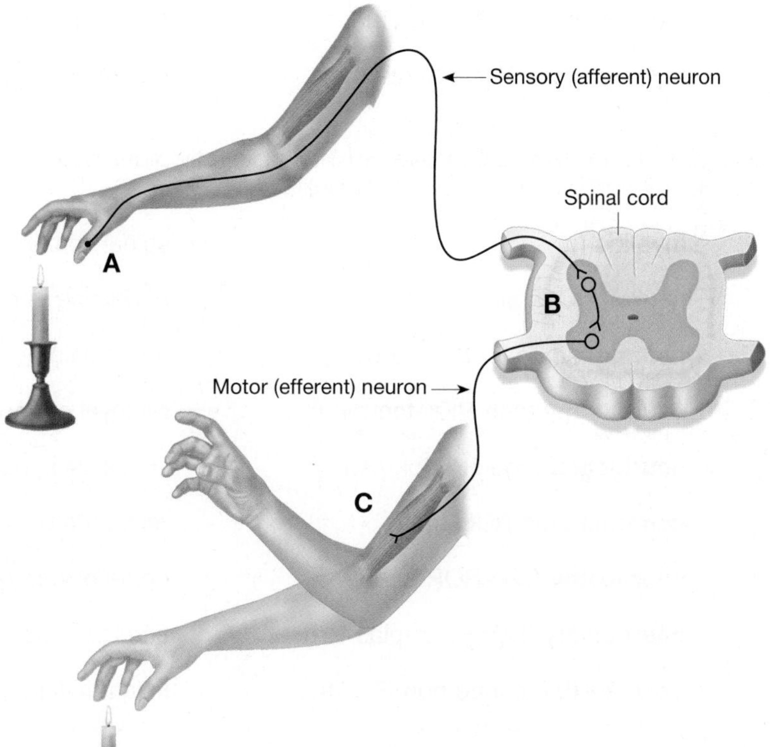

Figure 12.8 The functional structure of the peripheral nervous system. A) Afferent or sensory neurons carry sensory information to the spinal cord. B) The spinal cord receives incoming sensory information and delivers motor messages. C) Efferent or motor neurons deliver motor commands to muscles and glands.

Somatic Nerves

Somatic nerves serve the skin and skeletal muscles and are mainly involved with the conscious and voluntary activities of the body. The large variety of sensory receptors found in the dermis layer of the skin use somatic nerves to send their information, such as touch, temperature, pressure, and pain, to the brain. These are also the nerves that carry motor commands to skeletal muscles.

Word Building

The following list contains examples of medical terms built directly from word parts. The definition for these terms can be determined by a straightforward translation of the word parts.

COMBINING FORM	COMBINED WITH	MEDICAL TERM	DEFINITION
cephal/o	-algia	**cephalalgia** (seff-al-AL-jee-ah)	head pain (headache)
cerebell/o	-ar	**cerebellar** (ser-eh-BELL-ar)	pertaining to the cerebellum
	-itis	**cerebellitis** (ser-eh-bell-EYE-tis)	cerebellum inflammation
cerebr/o	-al	**cerebral** (seh-REE-bral)	pertaining to the cerebrum
	spin/o -al	**cerebrospinal** (ser-eh-broh-SPY-nal)	pertaining to the cerebrum and spine
encephal/o	electr/o -gram	**electroencephalogram** (EEG) (ee-lek-troh-en-SEFF-ah-loh-gram)	record of brain's electricity
	-itis	**encephalitis** (en-seff-ah-LYE-tis)	brain inflammation
meningi/o	-oma	**meningioma** (meh-nin-jee-OH-mah)	meninges tumor
mening/o	-eal	**meningeal** (meh-NIN-jee-all)	pertaining to the meninges
	-itis	**meningitis** (men-in-JYE-tis)	meninges inflammation
myel/o	-gram	**myelogram** (MY-eh-loh-gram)	record of spinal cord

Med Term Tip

The combining form *myel/o* means "marrow" and is used for both the spinal cord and bone marrow. To the ancient Greek philosophers and physicians, the spinal cord appeared to be much like the marrow found in the medullary cavity of a long bone.

COMBINING FORM	COMBINED WITH	MEDICAL TERM	DEFINITION
	-itis	**myelitis** (my-eh-LYE-tis)	spinal cord inflammation
neur/o	-al	**neural** (NOO-rall)	pertaining to nerves
	-algia	**neuralgia** (noo-RAL-jee-ah)	nerve pain
	-ectomy	**neurectomy** (noo-REK-toh-mee)	removal of nerve
	-ologist	**neurologist** (noo-RAL-oh-jist)	specialist in nerves
	-oma	**neuroma** (noo-ROH-mah)	nerve tumor
	-pathy	**neuropathy** (noo-ROP-ah-thee)	nerve disease
	-plasty	**neuroplasty** (NOOR-oh-plas-tee)s	surgical repair of nerves
	poly- -itis	**polyneuritis** (pol-ee-noo-RYE-tis)	inflammation of many nerves

Word Building *(continued)*

COMBINING FORM	COMBINED WITH	MEDICAL TERM	DEFINITION
	-rrhaphy	**neurorrhaphy** (noo-ROR-ah-fee)	suture of nerve
pont/o	-ine	**pontine** (pon-TEEN)	pertaining to the pons
radicul/o	-itis	**radiculitis** (rah-dick-yoo-LYE-tis)	nerve root inflammation
	-pathy	**radiculopathy** (rah-dick-yoo-LOP-ah-thee)	nerve root disease
thalam/o	-ic	**thalamic** (tha-LAM-ik)	pertaining to the thalamus
thec/o	intra- -al	**intrathecal** (in-tra-THEE-kal)	pertaining to within the meninges

SUFFIX	COMBINED WITH	MEDICAL TERM	DEFINITION
-algesia	an-	**analgesia** (an-al-JEE-zee-ah)	absence of pain or sensation
-esthesia	an-	**anesthesia** (an-ess-THEE-zee-ah)	lack of sensations
	hyper-	**hyperesthesia** (high-per-ess-THEE-zee-ah)	excessive sensations
-paresis	mono-	**monoparesis** (mon-oh-pah-REE-sis)	weakness of one
-phasia	a-	**aphasia** (ah-FAY-zee-ah)	lack of speech
	dys-	**dysphasia** (dis-FAY-zee-ah)	difficult speech
-plegia	mono-	**monoplegia** (mon-oh-PLEE-jee-ah)	paralysis of one
	quadri-	**quadriplegia** (kwod-rih-PLEE-jee-ah)	paralysis of four
-taxia	a-	**ataxia** (ah-TAK-see-ah)	lack of muscle coordination

Vocabulary

TERM	DEFINITION
anesthesiology (an-es-thee-zee-ol-oh-jee)	Branch of medicine specializing in all aspects of anesthesia, including for surgical procedures, resuscitation measures, and the management of acute and chronic pain. Physician is an *anesthesiologist*.
aura (AW-ruh)	Sensations, such as seeing colors or smelling an unusual odor, that occur just prior to an epileptic seizure or migraine headache.
coma (COH-mah)	Profound unconsciousness or stupor resulting from an illness or injury.
conscious (KON-shus)	Condition of being awake and aware of surroundings.
convulsion (kon-VULL-shun)	Severe involuntary muscle contractions and relaxations. These have a variety of causes, such as epilepsy, fever, and toxic conditions.
delirium (dee-LEER-ee-um)	Abnormal mental state characterized by confusion, disorientation, and agitation.

Vocabulary (continued)

TERM	DEFINITION
dementia (dee-MEN-she-ah)	Progressive impairment of intellectual function that interferes with performing activities of daily living. Patients have little awareness of their condition. Found in disorders such as Alzheimer's.
focal seizure (FOE-kal)	Localized seizure often affecting one limb.
hemiparesis (hem-ee-par-EE-sis)	Weakness or loss of motion on one side of the body.
hemiplegia (hem-ee-PLEE-jee-ah)	Paralysis on only one side of the body.
neurology (noo-rol-oh-jee)	Branch of medicine concerned with diagnosis and treatment of diseases and conditions of the nervous system. Physician is a *neurologist*.
neurosurgery (noo-roh-SIR-jury)	Branch of medicine concerned with treating conditions and diseases of the nervous systems by surgical means. Physician is a *neurosurgeon*.
palsy (PAWL-zee)	Temporary or permanent loss of the ability to control movement.
paralysis (pah-RAL-ih-sis)	Temporary or permanent loss of function or voluntary movement.
paraplegia (pair-ah-PLEE-jee-ah)	Paralysis of the lower portion of the body and both legs.
paresthesia (par-es-THEE-zee-ah)	Abnormal sensation such as burning or tingling.
seizure (SEE-zyoor)	Sudden, uncontrollable onset of symptoms; such as in an epileptic seizure.
syncope (SIN-koh-pee)	Fainting.
tremor (TREM-or)	Involuntary repetitive alternating movement of a part of the body.
unconscious (un-KON-shus)	Condition or state of being unaware of surroundings, with the inability to respond to stimuli.

Pathology

TERM	DEFINITION
Brain	
absence seizure	Type of epileptic seizure that lasts only a few seconds to half a minute, characterized by a loss of awareness and an absence of activity. It is also called a *petit mal seizure*.
Alzheimer's disease (ALTS-high-merz)	Chronic, organic mental disorder consisting of dementia, which is more prevalent in adults between ages 40 and 60. Involves progressive disorientation, apathy, speech and gait disturbances, and loss of memory. Named for German neurologist Alois Alzheimer.
astrocytoma (ass-troh-sigh-TOH-mah)	Tumor of the brain or spinal cord that is composed of astrocytes, one of the types of neuroglial cells.

Pathology *(continued)*

TERM	DEFINITION
brain tumor	Intracranial mass, either benign or malignant. A benign tumor of the brain can still be fatal since it will grow and cause pressure on normal brain tissue.

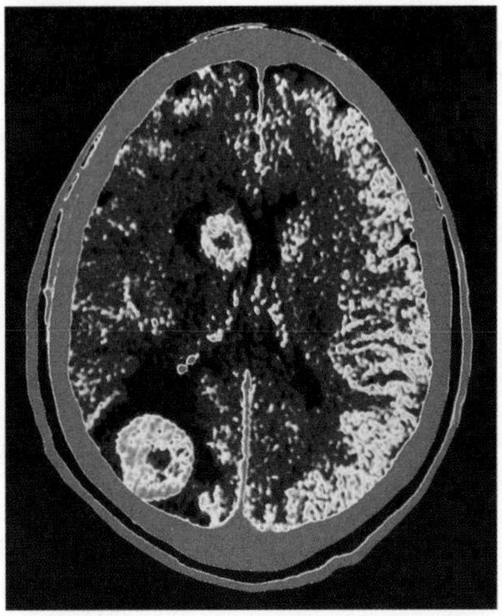

Figure 12.9 Color enhanced CT-scan showing two malignant tumors in the brain. *(Scott Camazine/Photo Researchers, Inc.)*

TERM	DEFINITION
cerebral aneurysm (AN-yoo-rizm)	Localized abnormal dilation of a blood vessel, usually an artery; the result of a congenital defect or weakness in the wall of the vessel. A ruptured aneurysm is a common cause of a hemorrhagic cerebrovascular accident.

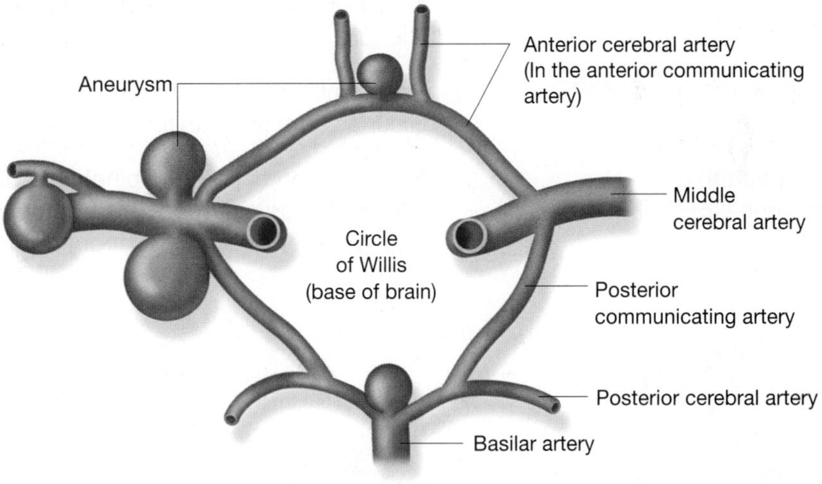

Figure 12.10 Common locations for cerebral artery aneurysms in the Circle of Willis.

TERM	DEFINITION
cerebral contusion (kon-TOO-shun)	Bruising of the brain from a blow or impact. Symptoms last longer than 24 hours and include unconsciousness, dizziness, vomiting, unequal pupil size, and shock.
cerebral palsy (CP) (ser-REE-bral PAWL-zee)	Nonprogressive brain damage resulting from a defect, trauma, or oxygen deprivation at the time of birth.
cerebrovascular accident (CVA) (ser-eh-broh-VASS-kyoo-lar AK-sih-dent)	The development of an infarct due to loss in the blood supply to an area of the brain. Blood flow can be interrupted by a ruptured blood vessel (hemorrhage), a floating clot (embolus), a stationary clot (thrombosis), or compression (see Figure 12.11). The extent of damage depends on the size and location of the infarct and often includes dysphasia and hemiplegia. Commonly called a *stroke.*

Figure 12.11 The four common causes for cerebrovascular accidents.

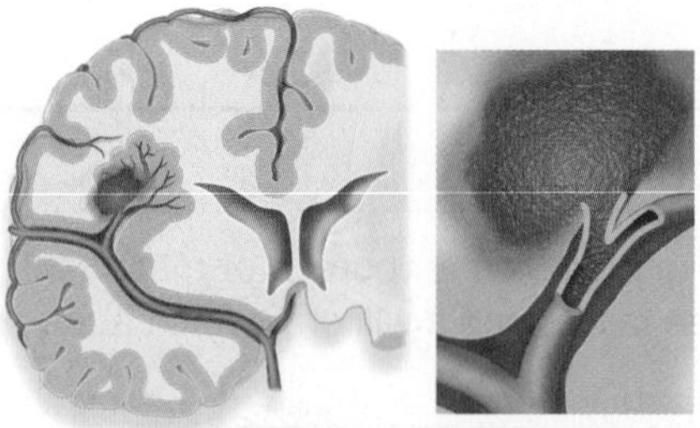

Cerebral hemorrhage: Cerebral artery ruptures and bleeds into brain tissue.

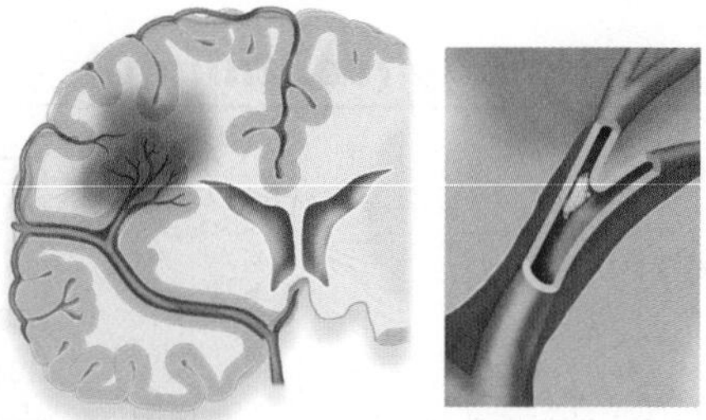

Cerebral embolism: Embolus from another area lodges in cerebral artery and blocks blood flow.

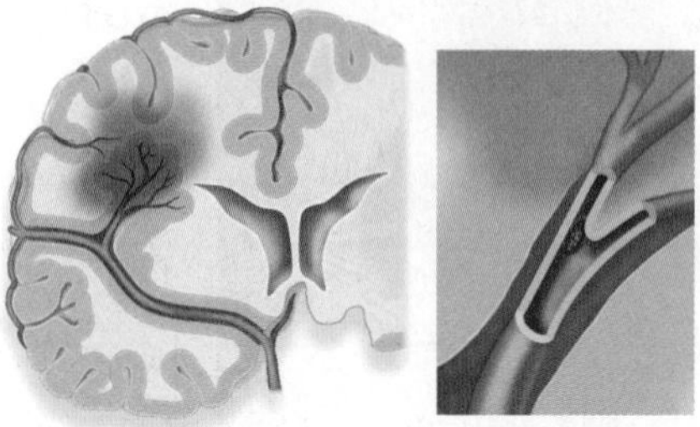

Cerebral thrombosis: Blood clot forms in cerebral artery and blocks blood flow.

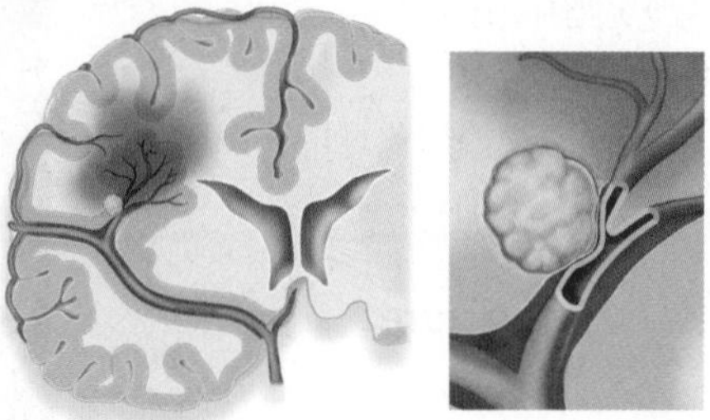

Compression: Pressure from tumor squeezes adjacent blood vessel and blocks blood flow.

Pathology *(continued)*

TERM	DEFINITION
concussion (kon-KUSH-un)	Injury to the brain resulting from the brain being shaken inside the skull from a blow or impact. Can result in unconsciousness, dizziness, vomiting, unequal pupil size, and shock. Symptoms last 24 hours or less.
epilepsy (EP-ih-lep-see)	Recurrent disorder of the brain in which seizures and loss of consciousness occur as a result of uncontrolled electrical activity of the neurons in the brain.
hydrocephalus (high-droh-SEFF-ah-lus)	Accumulation of cerebrospinal fluid within the ventricles of the brain, causing the head to be enlarged. It is treated by creating an artificial shunt for the fluid to leave the brain. If left untreated, it may lead to seizures and mental retardation.

Figure 12.12 Hydrocephalus. The figure on the left is a child with the enlarged ventricles of hydrocephalus. The figure on the right is the same child with a shunt to send the excess cerebrospinal fluid to the abdominal cavity.

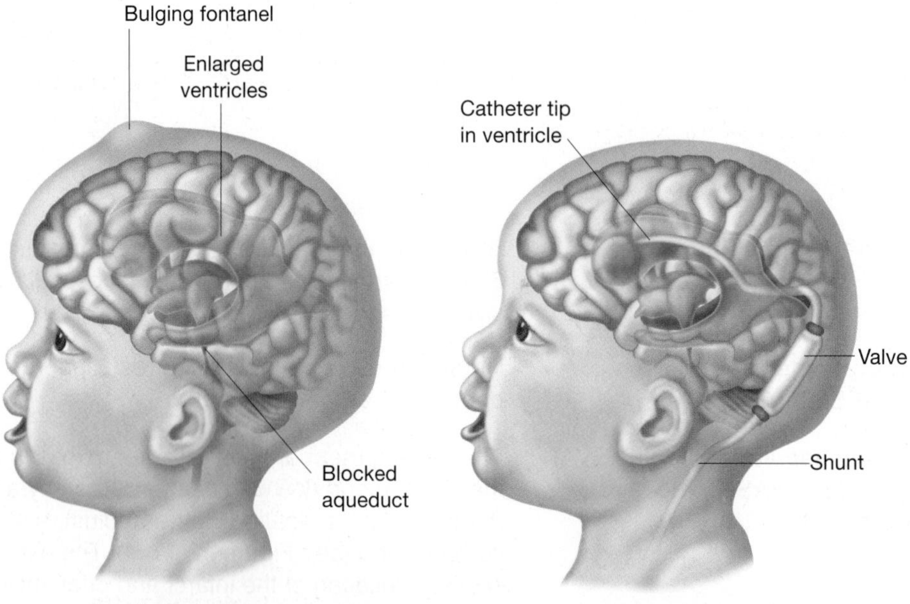

Pathology *(continued)*

TERM	DEFINITION
migraine (MY-grain)	Specific type of headache characterized by severe head pain, sensitivity to light, dizziness, and nausea.
Parkinson's disease (PARK-in-sons dih-ZEEZ)	Chronic disorder of the nervous system with fine tremors, muscular weakness, rigidity, and a shuffling gait. Named for British physician Sir James Parkinson.
Reye syndrome (RISE SIN-drohm)	Combination of symptoms first recognized by Australian pathologist R. D. K. Reye that includes acute encephalopathy and damage to various organs, especially the liver. This occurs in children under age 15 who have had a viral infection. It is also associated with taking aspirin. For this reason, it's not recommended for children to use aspirin.
tonic-clonic seizure	Type of severe epileptic seizure characterized by a loss of consciousness and convulsions. The seizure alternates between strong continuous muscle spasms (tonic) and rhythmic muscle contraction and relaxation (clonic). It is also called a *grand mal seizure*.
transient ischemic attack (TIA) (TRAN-shent iss-KEM-ik)	Temporary interference with blood supply to the brain, causing neurological symptoms such as dizziness, numbness, and hemiparesis. May eventually lead to a full-blown stroke (cerebrovascular accident).
■ ***Spinal Cord***	
amyotrophic lateral sclerosis (ALS) (ah-my-oh-TROFF-ik LAT-er-al skleh-ROH-sis)	Disease with muscular weakness and atrophy due to degeneration of motor neurons of the spinal cord. Also called *Lou Gehrig's disease,* after the New York Yankees baseball player who died from the disease.
meningocele (men-IN-goh-seel)	Congenital condition in which the meninges protrude through an opening in the vertebral column (see Figure 12.13B ■). See *spina bifida.*

■ Figure 12.13 Spina bifida. A) Spina bifica occulta, the vertebra is not complete, but there is not protrusion of nervous system structures. B) Meningocele, the meninges sac protrudes through the opening in the vertebra. C) Myelomeningocele, the meninges sac and spinal cord protrude through the opening in the vertebra.

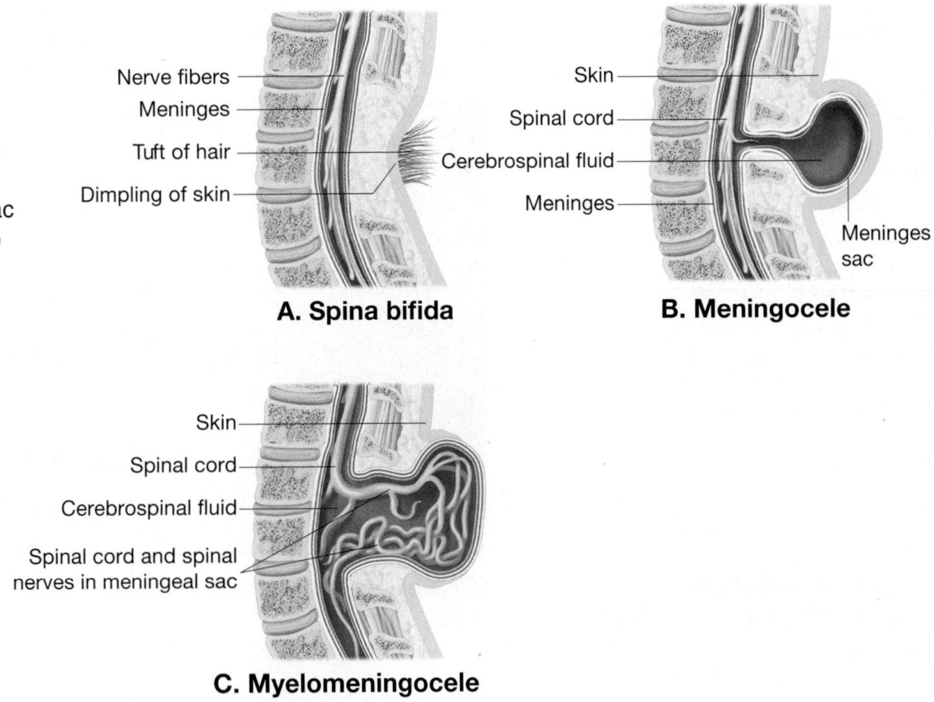

Pathology *(continued)*

TERM	DEFINITION
myelomeningocele (my-eh-loh-meh-NIN-goh-seel)	Congenital condition in which the meninges and spinal cord protrude through an opening in the vertebral column (see Figure 12.13C ■). See *spina bifida.*
poliomyelitis (poh-lee-oh-my-eh-lye-tis)	Viral inflammation of the gray matter of the spinal cord. Results in varying degrees of paralysis, may be mild and reversible or may be severe and permanent. This disease has been almost eliminated due to the discovery of a vaccine in the 1950s.
spina bifida (SPY-nah BIFF-ih-dah)	Congenital defect in the walls of the spinal canal in which the laminae of the vertebra do not meet or close (see Figure 12.13A ■). May result in a meningocele or a myelomeningocele—meninges or the spinal cord being pushed through the opening.
spinal cord injury (SCI)	Damage to the spinal cord as a result of trauma. Spinal cord may be bruised or completely severed.
■ ***Nerves***	
Bell's palsy (BELLZ PAWL-zee)	One-sided facial paralysis due to inflammation of the facial nerve, probably viral in nature. The patient cannot control salivation, tearing of the eyes, or expression, but most will eventually recover.
Guillain-Barré syndrome (GHEE-yan bah-RAY)	Disease of the nervous system in which nerves lose their myelin covering. May be caused by an autoimmune reaction. Characterized by loss of sensation and/or muscle control starting in the legs. Symptoms then move toward the trunk and may even result in paralysis of the diaphragm.
multiple sclerosis (MS) (MULL-tih-pl skleh-ROH-sis)	Inflammatory disease of the central nervous system in which there is extreme weakness and numbness due to loss of myelin insulation from nerves.
myasthenia gravis (my-ass-THEE-nee-ah GRAV-iss)	Disease with severe muscular weakness and fatigue due to insufficient neurotransmitter at a synapse.
shingles (SHING-lz)	Eruption of painful blisters on the body along a nerve path. Thought to be caused by a *Herpes zoster* virus infection of the nerve root.

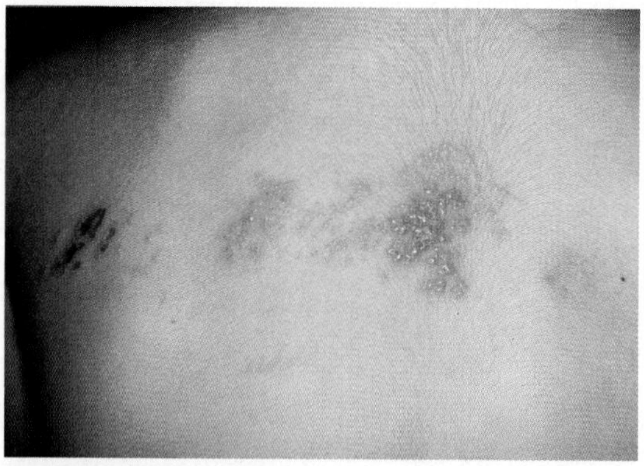

■ **Figure 12.14** Photograph of the skin eruptions associated with shingles.

TERM	DEFINITION
■ ***Meninges***	
epidural hematoma (ep-ih-DOO-ral hee-mah-TOH-mah)	Mass of blood in the space outside the dura mater of the brain and spinal cord.

Pathology *(continued)*

TERM	DEFINITION
subdural hematoma (sub-DOO-ral hee-mah-TOH-mah)	Mass of blood forming beneath the dura mater if the meninges are torn by trauma. May exert fatal pressure on the brain if the hematoma is not drained by surgery.

Figure 12.15 A subdural hematoma. A meningeal vein is ruptured and blood has accumulated in the subdural space producing pressure on the brain.

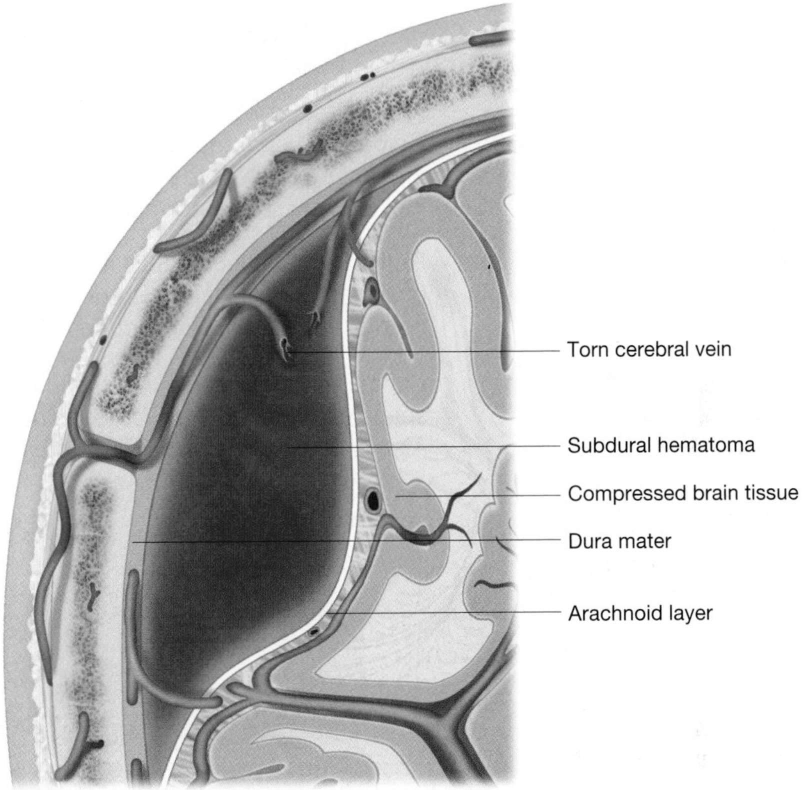

Diagnostic Procedures

TERM	DEFINITION
Clinical Laboratory Tests	
cerebrospinal fluid analysis (ser-eh-broh-SPY-nal FLOO-id an-NAL-ih-sis)	Laboratory examination of the clear, watery, colorless fluid from within the brain and spinal cord. Infections and the abnormal presence of blood can be detected in this test.
Diagnostic Imaging	
brain scan	Image of the brain taken after injection of radioactive isotopes into the circulation.
cerebral angiography (seh-REE-bral-an-jee-OG-rah-fee)	X-ray of the blood vessels of the brain after the injection of radiopaque dye.
echoencephalography (ek-oh-en-SEFF-ah-log-rah-fee)	Recording of the ultrasonic echoes of the brain. Useful in determining abnormal patterns of shifting in the brain.
myelography (my-eh-LOG-rah-fee)	Injection of radiopaque dye into the spinal canal. An X-ray is then taken to examine the normal and abnormal outlines made by the dye.

Diagnostic Procedures *(continued)*

TERM	DEFINITION
positron emission tomography (PET) (PAHZ-ih-tron ee-MISH-un toh-MOG-rah-fee)	Use of positive radionuclides to reconstruct brain sections. Measurement can be taken of oxygen and glucose uptake, cerebral blood flow, and blood volume. The amount of glucose the brain uses indicates how metabolically active the tissue is.
■ ***Additional Diagnostic Tests***	
Babinski reflex (bah-BIN-skeez)	Reflex test developed by French neurologist Joseph Babinski to determine lesions and abnormalities in the nervous system. The Babinski reflex is present if the great toe extends instead of flexes when the lateral sole of the foot is stroked. The normal response to this stimulation is flexion of the toe.
electroencephalography (EEG) (ee-lek-troh-en-SEFF-ah-LOG-rah-fee)	Recording the electrical activity of the brain by placing electrodes at various positions on the scalp. Also used in sleep studies to determine if there is a normal pattern of activity during sleep.
lumbar puncture (LP) (LUM-bar PUNK-chur)	Puncture with a needle into the lumbar area (usually the fourth intervertebral space) to withdraw fluid for examination and for the injection of anesthesia. Also called *spinal puncture* or *spinal tap.*
nerve conduction velocity	Test that measures how fast an impulse travels along a nerve. Can pinpoint an area of nerve damage.

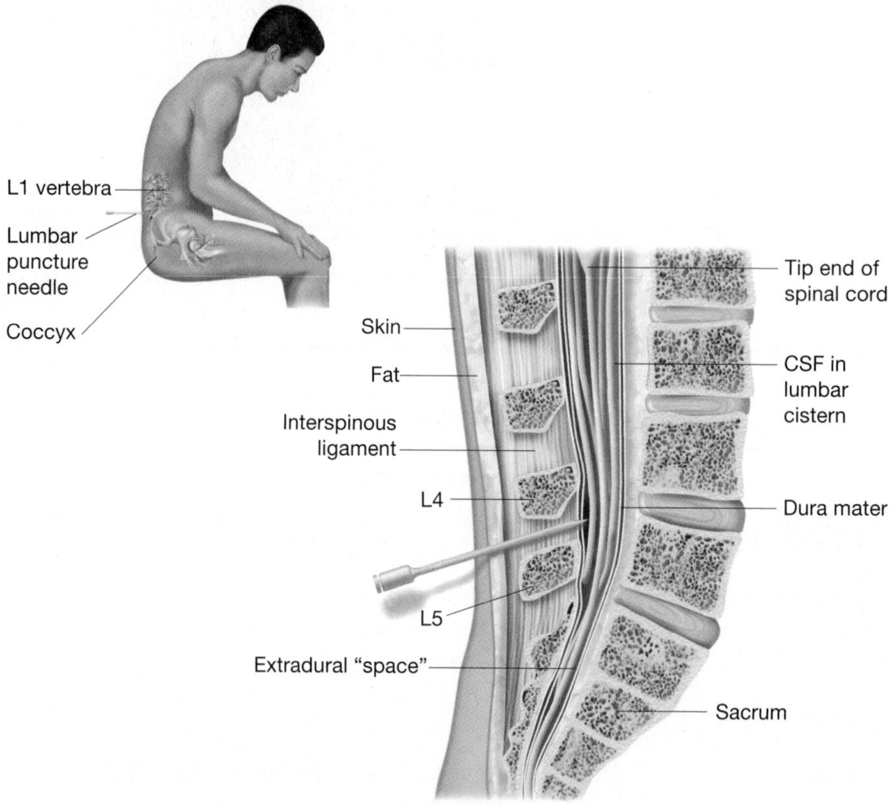

■ **Figure 12.16** A lumbar puncture. The needle is inserted between the lumbar vertebrae and into the spinal canal.

Therapeutic Procedures

TERM	DEFINITION
Medical Procedures	
nerve block	Injection of regional anesthetic to stop the passage of sensory or pain impulses along a nerve path.
Surgical Procedures	
carotid endarterectomy (kah-ROT-id end-ar-ter-EK-toh-mee)	Surgical procedure for removing an obstruction within the carotid artery, a major artery in the neck that carries oxygenated blood to the brain. Developed to prevent strokes, but is found to be useful only in severe stenosis with transient ischemic attack.
cerebrospinal fluid shunts (ser-eh-broh SPY-nal FLOO-id)	Surgical procedure in which a bypass is created to drain cerebrospinal fluid. It is used to treat hydrocephalus by draining the excess cerebrospinal fluid from the brain and diverting it to the abdominal cavity.
laminectomy (lam-ih-NEK-toh-mee)	Removal of a portion of a vertebra in order to relieve pressure on the spinal nerve.
tractotomy (track-OT-oh-mee)	Surgical interruption of a nerve tract in the spinal cord. Used to treat intractable pain or muscle spasms.

Pharmacology

CLASSIFICATION	ACTION	GENERIC AND BRAND NAMES
analgesic (an-al-JEE-zik)	Non-narcotic medication to treat minor to moderate pain. Includes aspirin, acetaminophen, and ibuprofen.	aspirin, Bayer, Ecotrin; acetaminophen, Tylenol; ibuprofen, Aleve
anesthetic (an-ess-THET-ik)	Drug that produces a loss of sensation or a loss of consciousness.	lidocaine, Xylocaine; pentobarbital, Nembutal; propofol, Diprivan; procaine, Novocain
anticonvulsant (an-tye-kon-VULL-sant)	Substance that reduces the excitability of neurons and therefore prevents the uncontrolled neuron activity associated with seizures.	carbamazepine, Tegretol; phenobarbital, Nembutal
dopaminergic drugs (dope-ah-men-ER-gik)	Group of medications to treat Parkinson's disease by either replacing the dopamine that is lacking or increasing the strength of the dopamine that is present.	levodopa; L-dopa, Larodopa; levodopa/carbidopa, Sinemet
hypnotic (hip-NOT-tik)	Drug that promotes sleep.	secobarbital, Seconal; temazepam, Restoril
narcotic analgesic (nar-KOT-tik)	Drug used to treat severe pain; has the potential to be habit forming if taken for a prolonged time. Also called *opiates*.	morphine, MS Contin; oxycodone, OxyContin; meperidine, Demerol
sedative (SED-ah-tiv)	Drug that has a relaxing or calming effect.	amobarbital, Amytal; butabarbital, Butisol

Abbreviations

ALS	amyotrophic lateral sclerosis	**HA**	headache
ANS	autonomic nervous system	**ICP**	intracranial pressure
CNS	central nervous system	**LP**	lumbar puncture
CP	cerebral palsy	**MS**	multiple sclerosis
CSF	cerebrospinal fluid	**PET**	positron emission tomography
CVA	cerebrovascular accident	**PNS**	peripheral nervous system
CVD	cerebrovascular disease	**SCI**	spinal cord injury
EEG	electroencephalogram, electroencephalography	**TIA**	transient ischemic attack

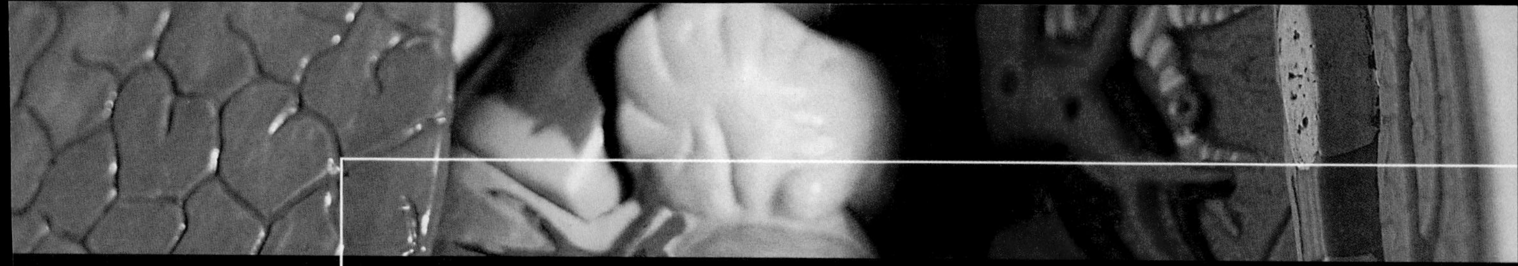

13 Special Senses: The Eye and Ear

Learning Objectives

Upon completion of this chapter, you will be able to:

- Identify and define the combining forms and suffixes introduced in this chapter.
- Correctly spell and pronounce medical terms and major anatomical structures relating to the eye and ear.
- Locate and describe the major structures of the eye and ear and their functions.
- Describe how we see.
- Describe the path of sound vibration.
- Build and define eye and ear medical terms from word parts.
- Identify and define eye and ear vocabulary terms.
- Identify and define selected eye and ear pathology terms.
- Identify and define selected eye and ear diagnostic procedures.
- Identify and define selected eye and ear therapeutic procedures.
- Identify and define selected medications relating to the eye and ear.
- Define selected abbreviations associated with the eye and ear.

Section I: The Eye at a Glance

Function

The eye contains the sensory receptor cells for vision.

Structures

choroid
conjunctiva
eye muscles
eyeball
eyelids
lacrimal apparatus
retina
sclera

Combining Forms

ambly/o	dull, dim	**ocul/o**	eye
aque/o	water	**ophthalm/o**	eye
blephar/o	eyelid	**opt/o**	eye, vision
chrom/o	color	**optic/o**	eye
conjunctiv/o	conjunctiva	**nyctal/o**	night
core/o	pupil	**papill/o**	optic disk
corne/o	cornea	**phac/o**	lens
cycl/o	ciliary muscle	**phot/o**	light
dacry/o	tear, tear duct	**presby/o**	old age
dipl/o	double	**pupill/o**	pupil
glauc/o	gray	**retin/o**	retina
ir/o	iris	**scler/o**	sclera
irid/o	iris	**uve/o**	choroid
kerat/o	cornea	**vitre/o**	glassy
lacrim/o	tears		

Suffixes

-metrist	one who measures
-opia	vision
-tropia	to turn

The Eye Illustrated

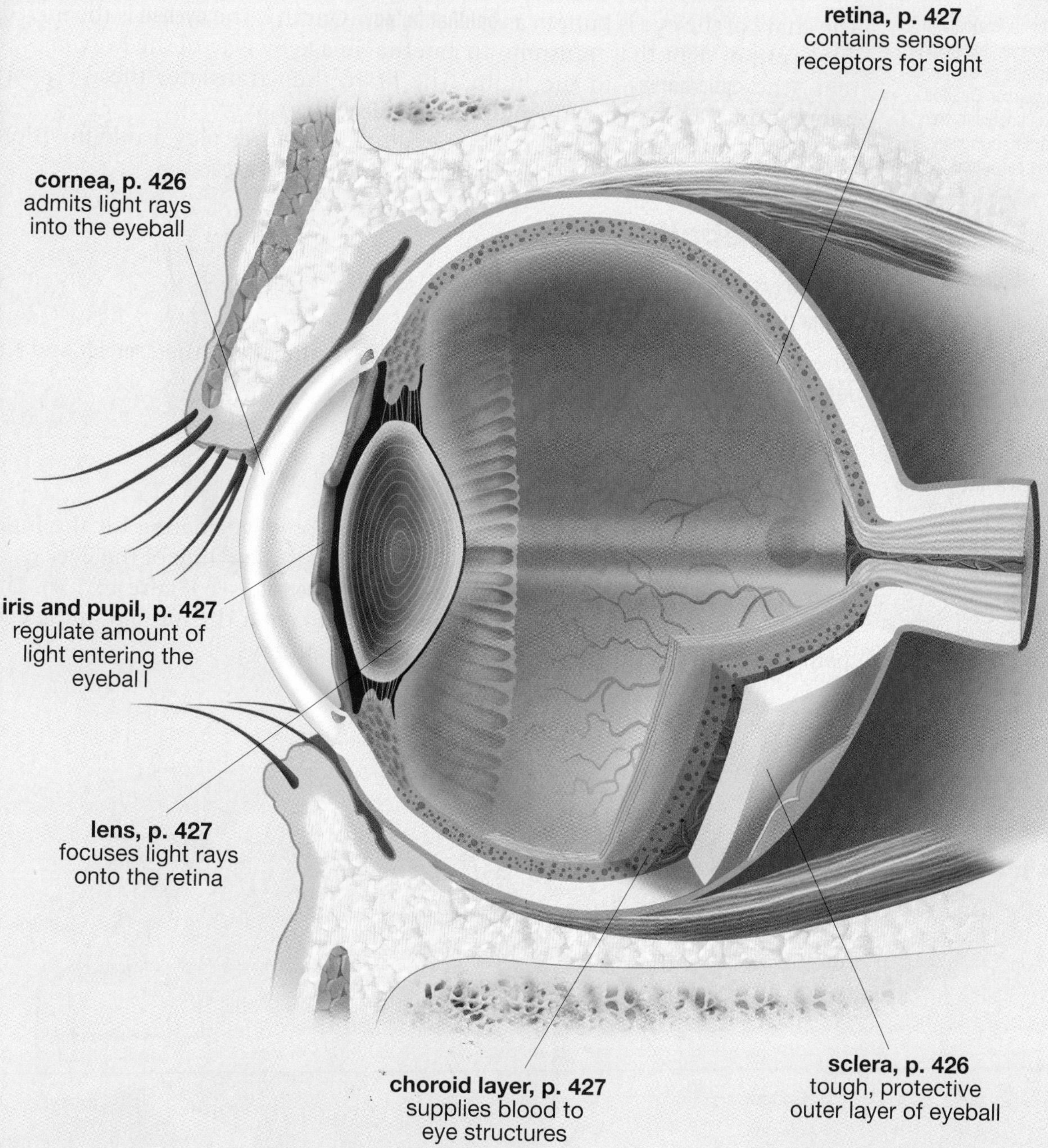

retina, p. 427
contains sensory receptors for sight
cornea, p. 426
admits light rays into the eyeball
iris and pupil, p. 427
regulate amount of light entering the eyebal l
lens, p. 427
focuses light rays onto the retina
choroid layer, p. 427
supplies blood to eye structures
sclera, p. 426
tough, protective outer layer of eyeball

Anatomy and Physiology of the Eye

conjunctiva (kon-JUNK-tih-vah)
eyeball
eyelids
eye muscles
lacrimal apparatus (LAK-rim-al)
ophthalmology (off-thal-MALL-oh-gee)
optic nerve (OP-tik)

Med Term Tip

When studying the functions and terminology of the eye, it is helpful to know the meanings of the terms *opaque* and *transparent*. Opaque means that light is unable to pass through. Transparent, however, means that light is permitted through.

The study of the eye is known as **ophthalmology** (Ophth). The **eyeball** is the incredible organ of sight that transmits an external image by way of the nervous system—the **optic nerve**—to the brain. The brain then translates these sensory impulses into an image with computerlike accuracy.

In addition to the eyeball, several external structures play a role in vision. These are the **eye muscles**, **eyelids**, **conjunctiva**, and **lacrimal apparatus**.

The Eyeball

choroid (KOR-oyd)
retina (RET-in-ah)
sclera (SKLAIR-ah)

The actual eyeball is composed of three layers: the **sclera**, the **choroid**, and the **retina**.

Med Term Tip

The color of the sclera may indicate the presence of disease. For instance, a yellowish cast to the sclera can be present in liver disease and certain anemias.

Sclera

cornea (COR-nee-ah)
refracts

The outer layer, the sclera, provides a tough protective coating for the inner structures of the eye. Another term for the sclera is the white of the eye.

The anterior portion of the sclera is called the **cornea** (see Figure 13.1 ■). This clear, transparent area of the sclera allows light to enter the interior of the eyeball. The cornea actually bends, or **refracts**, the light rays.

■ **Figure 13.1** The internal structures of the eye.

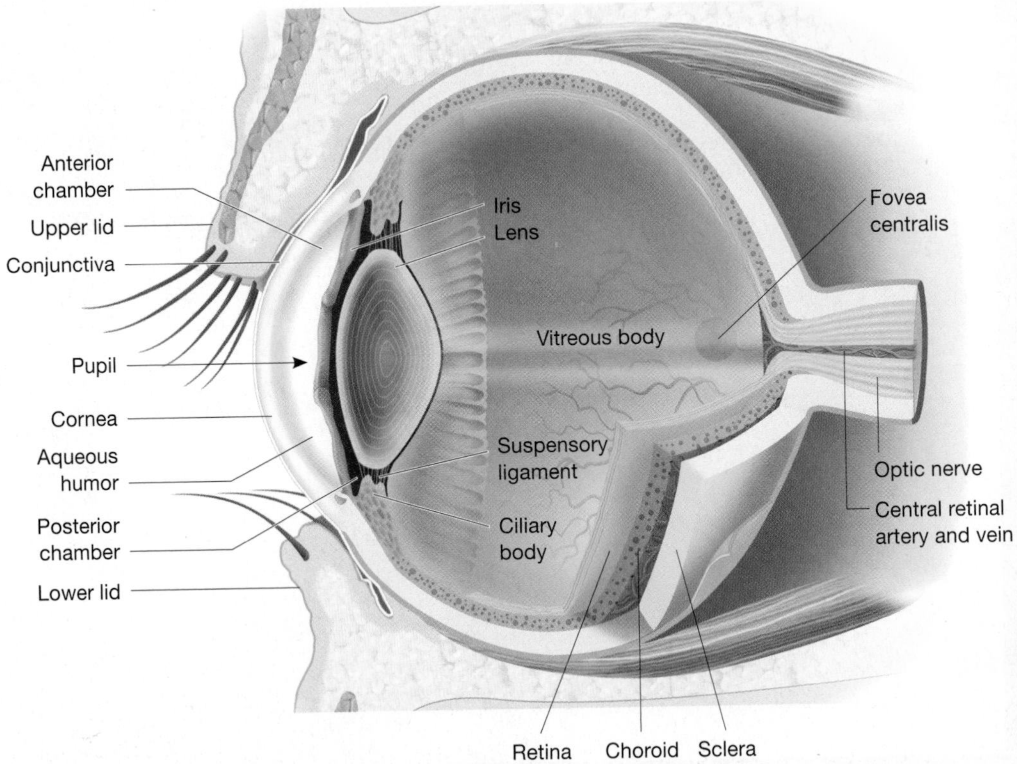

Choroid

ciliary body (SIL-ee-ar-ee)
iris
lens
pupil

The second or middle layer of the eyeball is called the choroid. This opaque layer provides the blood supply for the eye.

The anterior portion of the choroid layer consists of the **iris**, **pupil**, and **ciliary body** (see Figure 13.1). The iris is the colored portion of the eye and contains smooth muscle. The pupil is the opening in the center of the iris that allows light rays to enter the eyeball. The iris muscle contracts or relaxes to change the size of the pupil, thereby controlling how much light enters the interior of the eyeball. Behind the iris is the **lens.** The lens is not actually part of the choroid layer, but it is attached to the muscular ciliary body. By pulling on the edge of the lens, these muscles change the shape of the lens so it can focus incoming light onto the retina.

Med Term Tip

The function of the choroid, to provide the rest of the eyeball with blood, is responsible for an alternate name for this layer—*uvea*. The combining form *uve/o* means "vascular."

Retina

aqueous humor (AY-kwee-us)
cones
fovea centralis (FOH-vee-ah sen-TRAH-lis)
macula lutea (MAK-yoo-lah loo-TEE-ah)
optic disk
retinal blood vessels (RET-in-al)
rods
vitreous humor (VIT-ree-us)

The third and innermost layer of the eyeball is the retina. It contains the sensory receptor cells, **rods** and **cones**, that respond to light rays. Rods are active in dim light and help us to see in gray tones. Cones are active only in bright light and are responsible for color vision. When the lens projects an image onto the retina, it strikes an area called the **macula lutea**, or yellow spot (see Figure 13.1). In the center of the macula lutea is a depression called the **fovea centralis**, meaning central pit. This pit contains a high concentration of sensory receptor cells and, therefore, is the point of clearest vision. Also visible on the retina is the **optic disk**. This is the point where the **retinal blood vessels** enter and exit the eyeball and where the optic nerve leaves the eyeball (see Figure 13.2 ■). There are no sensory receptor cells in the optic disk and therefore it causes a blind spot in each eye's field of vision. The interior spaces of the eyeball are not empty. The spaces between the cornea and lens are filled with **aqueous humor**, a watery fluid, and the large open area between the lens and retina contains **vitreous humor**, a semisolid gel.

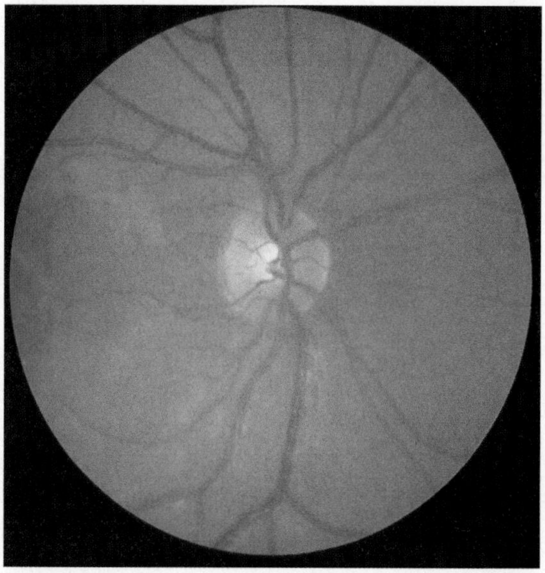

■ **Figure 13.2** Photograph of the retina of the eye. The optic disk appears yellow and the retinal arteries are clearly visible radiating out from it.

■ **Figure 13.3** The arrangement of the external eye muscles, A) lateral and B) anterior views.

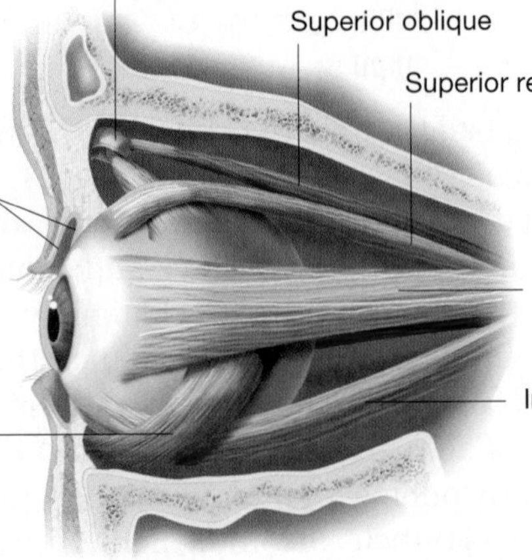

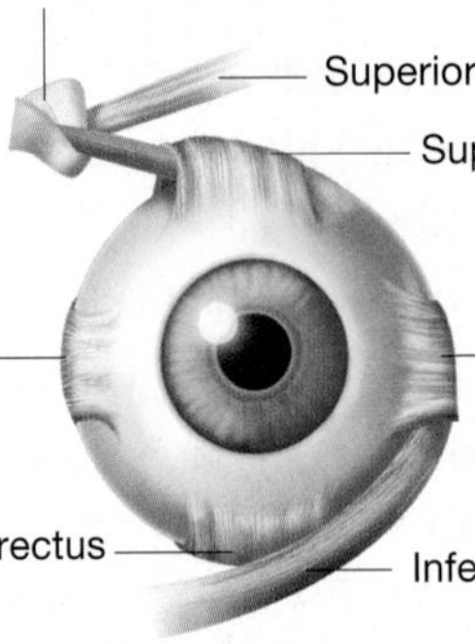

Muscles of the Eye

oblique muscles (oh-BLEEK)   **rectus muscles** (REK-tus)

Six muscles connect the actual eyeball to the skull (see Figure 13.3 ■). These muscles allow for change in the direction of each eye's sightline. In addition, they provide support for the eyeball in the eye socket. Children may be born with a weakness in some of these muscles and may require treatments such as eye exercises or even surgery to correct this problem commonly referred to as crossed eyes or *strabismus* (see Figure 13.4 ■). The muscles involved are the four **rectus** and two **oblique muscles**. Rectus muscles (meaning straight) pull the eye up, down, left, or right in a straight line. Oblique muscles are on an angle and produce diagonal eye movement.

Med Term Tip

Like many other muscles, the names *rectus* and *oblique* provide clues regarding the direction of their fibers, or their *line of pull.* Rectus means straight and oblique means slanted. Rectus muscles have a straight line of pull. Since the fibers of an oblique muscle are slanted on an angle, they produce rotation.

■ **Figure 13.4** Photograph of an infant with strabismus. The left eye is turned inward, called esotropia. *(Bart's Medical Library/Phototake NYC)*

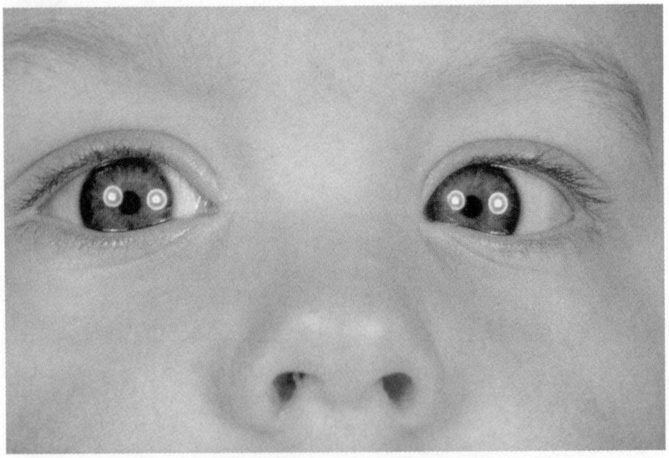

The Eyelids

cilia (SIL-ee-ah)
eyelashes
sebaceous glands (see-BAY-shus)

A pair of eyelids over each eyeball provides protection from foreign particles, injury from the sun and intense light, and trauma (see Figure 13.1). Both the upper and lower edges of the eyelids have **eyelashes** or **cilia** that protect the eye from foreign particles. In addition, **sebaceous glands** located in the eyelids secrete lubricating oil onto the eyeball.

Conjunctiva

mucous membrane

The conjunctiva of the eye is a **mucous membrane** lining. It forms a continuous covering on the underside of each eyelid and across the anterior surface of each eyeball (see Figure 13.1). This serves as protection for the eye by sealing off the eyeball in the socket.

Lacrimal Apparatus

lacrimal ducts
lacrimal gland
nasal cavity
nasolacrimal duct (naz-oh-LAK-rim-al)
tears

The **lacrimal gland** is located under the outer upper corner of each eyelid. These glands produce **tears**. Tears serve the important function of washing and lubricating the anterior surface of the eyeball. **Lacrimal ducts** located in the inner corner of the eye socket then collect the tears and drain them into the **nasolacrimal duct**. This duct ultimately drains the tears into the **nasal cavity** (see Figure 13.5 ■).

How We See

When light rays strike the eye, they first pass through the cornea, pupil, aqueous humor, lens, and vitreous humor (see Figure 13.6 ■). They then strike the retina and stimulate the rods and cones. When the light rays hit the retina, an upside-down image is sent along nerve impulses to the optic nerve (see

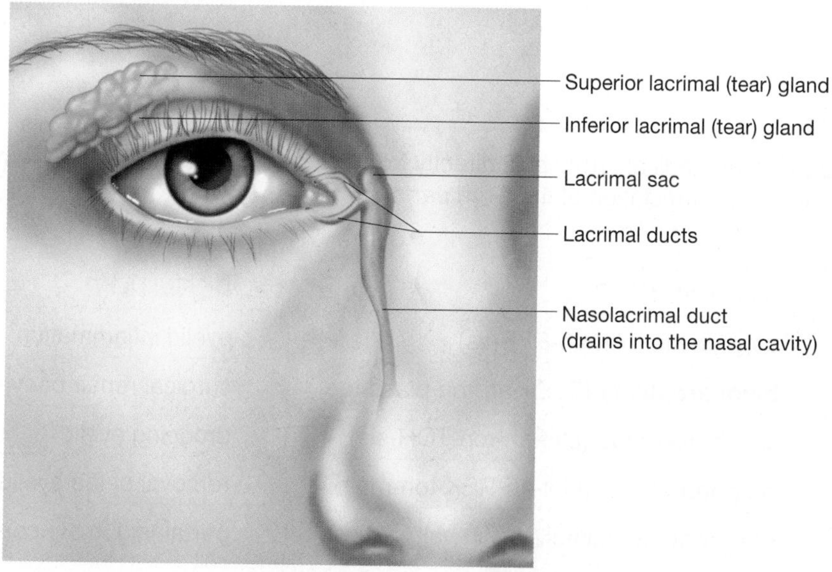

■ **Figure 13.5** The structure of the lacrimal apparatus.

Figure 13.6 The path of light through the cornea, pupil, lens, and striking the retina.

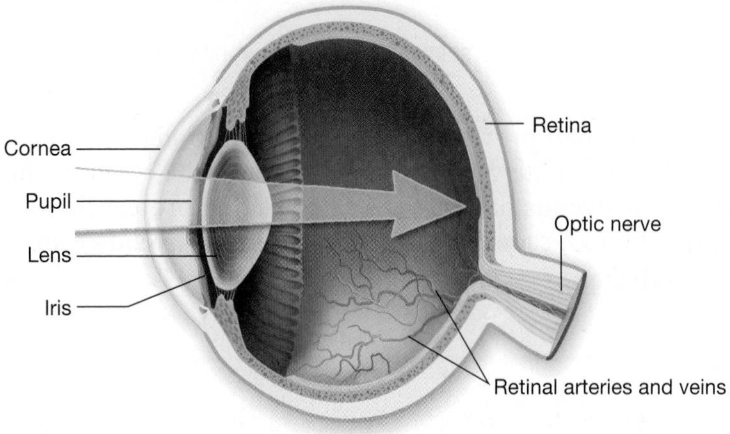

Figure 13.7 ■). The optic nerve transmits these impulses to the brain, where the upside-down image is translated into the right-side-up image we are looking at.

Vision requires proper functioning of four mechanisms:

1. Coordination of the external eye muscles so that both eyes move together.
2. The correct amount of light admitted by the pupil.
3. The correct focus of light on the retina by the lens.
4. The optic nerve transmitting sensory images to the brain.

Figure 13.7 The image formed on the retina is inverted. The brain rights the image as part of the interpretation process.

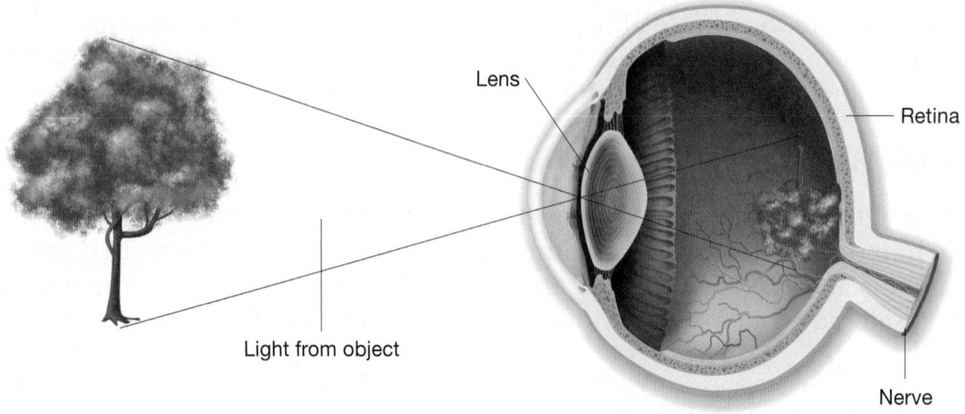

Word Building

The following list contains examples of medical terms built directly from word parts. The definitions of these terms can be determined by a straightforward translation of the word parts.

COMBINING FORM	COMBINED WITH	MEDICAL TERM	DEFINITION
blephar/o	-itis	**blepharitis** (blef-ah-RYE-tis)	eyelid inflammation
	-plasty	**blepharoplasty** (BLEF-ah-roh-plass-tee)	surgical repair of eyelid
	-ptosis	**blepharoptosis** (blef-ah-rop-TOH-sis)	drooping eyelid
	-ectomy	**blepharectomy** (blef-ah-REK-toh-mee)	removal of the eyelid
conjuctiv/o	-al	**conjunctival** (kon-JUNK-tih-vall)	pertaining to the conjunctiva

Word Building (continued)

COMBINING FORM	COMBINED WITH	MEDICAL TERM	DEFINITION
	-itis	**conjunctivitis** (kon-junk-tih-VYE-tis)	conjunctiva inflammation (pink eye)
	-plasty	**conjunctivoplasty** (kon-junk-tih-VOH-plas-tee)	surgical repair of the conjunctiva
corne/o	-al	**corneal** (KOR-nee-all)	pertaining to the cornea

Med Term Tip

Word watch — Be careful using the combining forms *core/o* meaning "pupil" and *corne/o* meaning "cornea."

COMBINING FORM	COMBINED WITH	MEDICAL TERM	DEFINITION
cycl/o	-plegia	**cycloplegia** (sigh-kloh-PLEE-jee-ah)	paralysis of the ciliary body
dacry/o	cyst/o -itis	**dacryocystitis** (dak-ree-oh-sis-TYE-tis)	tear bladder inflammation
dipl/o	-opia	**diplopia** (dip-LOH-pee-ah)	double vision
ir/o	-itis	**iritis** (eye-RYE-tis)	iris inflammation
irid/o	-al	**iridal** (ir-id-all)	pertaining to the iris
	-ectomy	**iridectomy** (ir-id-EK-toh-mee)	removal of iris
	-plegia	**iridoplegia** (ir-id-oh-PLEE-jee-ah)	paralysis of iris
	scler/o -otomy	**iridosclerotomy** (ir-ih-doh-skleh-ROT-oh-mee)	incision into iris and sclera
kerat/o	-itis	**keratitis** (kair-ah-TYE-tis)	cornea inflammation

Med Term Tip

Word watch — Be careful using the combining form *kerat/o*, which means both "cornea" and "hard protein keratin."

COMBINING FORM	COMBINED WITH	MEDICAL TERM	DEFINITION
	-meter	**keratometer** (KAIR-ah-toh-mee-ter)	instrument to measure (curve of) cornea
	-otomy	**keratotomy** (kair-ah-TOT-oh-mee)	incision into the cornea
lacrim/o	-al	**lacrimal** (LAK-rim-al)	pertaining to tears
ocul/o	-ar	**ocular** (OCK-yoo-lar)	pertaining to the eye
	intra- -ar	**intraocular** (in-trah-OCK-yoo-lar)	pertaining to within the eye
	myc/o -osis	**oculomycosis** (ok-yoo-loh-my-KOH-sis)	abnormal condition of eye fungus
ophthalm/o	-algia	**ophthalmalgia** (off-thal-MAL-jee-ah)	eye pain
	-ic	**ophthalmic** (off-THAL-mik)	pertaining to the eye
	-ologist	**ophthalmologist** (off-thal-MALL-oh-jist)	specialist in the eye
	-plegia	**ophthalmoplegia** (off-thal-moh-PLEE-jee-ah)	eye paralysis
	-rrhagia	**ophthalmorrhagia** (off-thal-moh-RAH-jee-ah)	rapid bleeding from the eye
	-scope	**ophthalmoscope** (off-THAL-moh-scope)	instrument to view inside the eye
opt/o	-ic	**optic** (OP-tik)	pertaining to the eye or vision
	-meter	**optometer** (op-TOM-eh-ter)	instrument to measure vision
	-metrist	**optometrist** (op-TOM-eh-trist)	one who measures vision

Word Building *(continued)*

COMBINING FORM	COMBINED WITH	MEDICAL TERM	DEFINITION
pupill/o	-ary	**pupillary** (PYOO-pih-lair-ee)	pertaining to the pupil
retin/o	-al	**retinal** (RET-in-al)	pertaining to the retina
	-pathy	**retinopathy** (ret-in-OP-ah-thee)	retina disease
	-pexy	**retinopexy** (ret-ih-noh-PEX-ee)	surgical fixation of the retina
scler/o	-al	**scleral** (SKLAIR-all)	pertaining to the sclera
	-malacia	**scleromalacia** (sklair-oh-mah-LAY-she-ah)	softening of the sclera
	-otomy	**sclerotomy** (skleh-ROT-oh-mee)	incision into the sclera
	-itis	**scleritis** (skler-EYE-tis)	inflammation of the sclera
uve/o	-itis	**uveitis** (yoo-vee-EYE-tis)	inflammation of the choroid

Vocabulary

TERM	DEFINITION
emmetropia (EM) (em-eh-TROH-pee-ah)	State of normal vision.
legally blind	Describes a person who has severely impaired vision. Usually defined as having visual acuity of 20/200 that cannot be improved with corrective lenses or having a visual field of less then 20 degrees.
nyctalopia (nik-tah-LOH-pee-ah)	Difficulty seeing in dim light; also called *night-blindness*. Usually due to damaged rods. **Med Term Tip** The simple translation of *nyctalopia* is "night vision." However, it is used to mean "night blindness."
ophthalmology (opf-thal-MOLL-oh-jee)	Branch of medicine involving the diagnosis and treatment of conditions and diseases of the eye and surrounding structures. The physician is an *ophthalmologist*.
optician (op-TISH-an)	Specialist in grinding corrective lenses.
optometry (op-TOM-eh-tree)	Medical profession specializing in examining the eyes, testing visual acuity, and prescribing corrective lenses. A doctor of optometry is an *optometrist*.
papilledema (pah-pill-eh-DEEM-ah)	Swelling of the optic disk. Often as a result of increased intraocular pressure. Also called *choked disk*.
photophobia (foh-toh-FOH-bee-ah)	Although the term translates into *fear of light,* it actually means a strong sensitivity to bright light.
presbyopia (prez-bee-OH-pee-ah)	Visual loss due to old age, resulting in difficulty in focusing for near vision (such as reading).
xerophthalmia (zee-ROP-thal-mee-ah)	Dry eyes.

Pathology

TERM	DEFINITION
■ ***Eyeball***	
achromatopsia (ah-kroh-mah-TOP-see-ah)	Condition of color blindness—unable to perceive one or more colors; more common in males.
amblyopia (am-blee-OH-pee-ah)	Loss of vision not as a result of eye pathology. Usually occurs in patients who see two images. In order to see only one image, the brain will no longer recognize the image being sent to it by one of the eyes. May occur if strabismus is not corrected. This condition is not treatable with a prescription lens. Commonly referred to as *lazy eye.*
astigmatism (Astigm) (ah-STIG-mah-tizm)	Condition in which light rays are focused unevenly on the retina, causing a distorted image, due to an abnormal curvature of the cornea.
cataract (KAT-ah-rakt)	Damage to the lens causing it to become opaque or cloudy, resulting in diminished vision. Treatment is usually surgical removal of the cataract or replacement of the lens.

Med Term Tip

The term *cataract* comes from the Latin word meaning "waterfall." This refers to how a person with a cataract sees the world—as if looking through a waterfall.

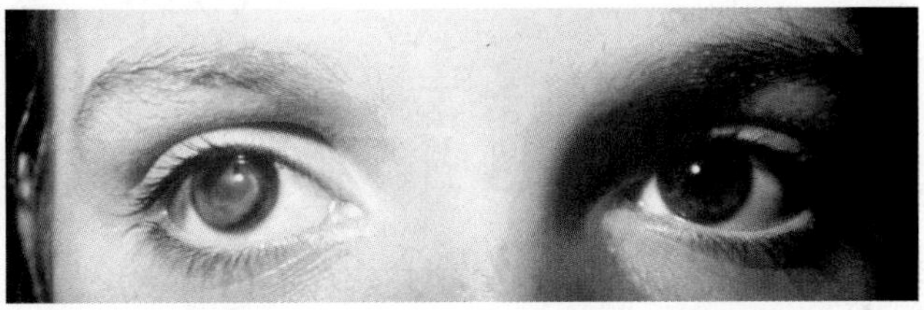

Figure 13.8 Photograph of a person with a cataract in the right eye.

TERM	DEFINITION
corneal abrasion	Scraping injury to the cornea. If it does not heal, it may develop into an ulcer.
glaucoma (glau-KOH-mah)	Increase in intraocular pressure, which, if untreated, may result in atrophy (wasting away) of the optic nerve and blindness. Glaucoma is treated with medication and surgery. There is an increased risk of developing glaucoma in persons over age 60, of African ancestry, who have sustained a serious eye injury, and in anyone with a family history of diabetes or glaucoma.
hyperopia (high-per-OH-pee-ah)	With this condition a person can see things in the distance but has trouble reading material at close range. Also known as *farsightedness.* This condition is corrected with converging or biconvex lenses.

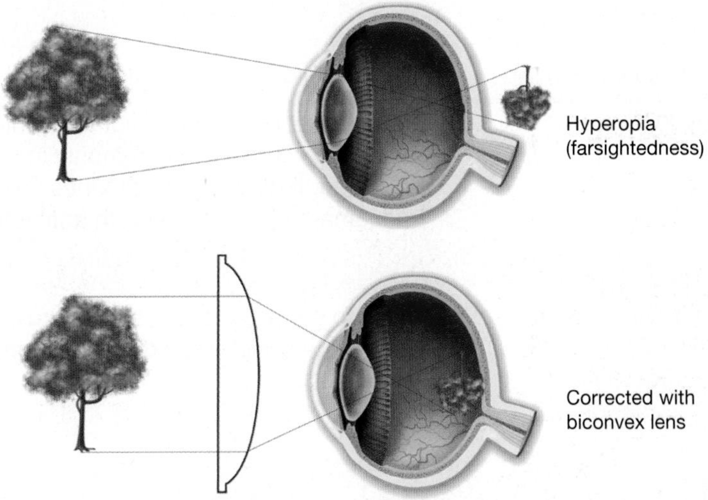

Figure 13.9 Hyperopia (farsightedness). In the uncorrected top figure, the image would come into focus behind the retina, making the image on the retina blurry. The bottom image shows how a biconvex lens corrects this condition.

Pathology (continued)

TERM	DEFINITION
macular degeneration (MAK-yoo-lar)	Deterioration of the macular area of the retina of the eye. May be treated with laser surgery to destroy the blood vessels beneath the macula.
monochromatism (mon-oh-KROH-mah-tizm)	Unable to perceive one color.
myopia (MY) (my-OH-pee-ah)	With this condition a person can see things close up but distance vision is blurred. Also known as *nearsightedness.* This condition is corrected with diverging or biconcave lenses.

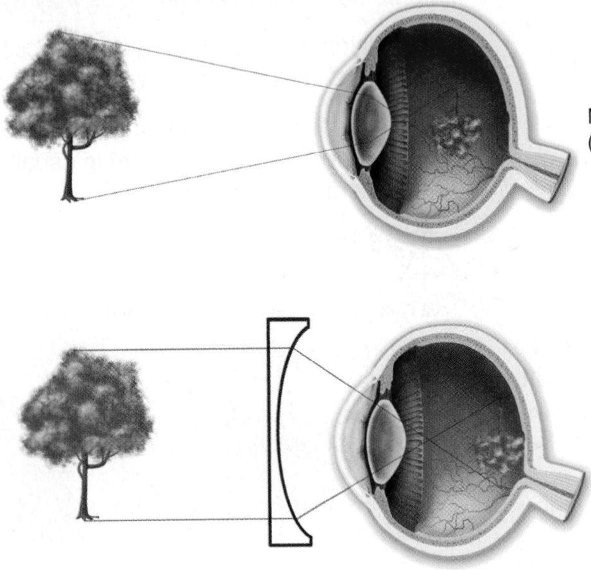

Figure 13.10 Myopia (nearsightedness). In the uncorrected top figure, the image comes into focus in front of the lens, making the image on the retina blurry. The bottom image shows how a biconcave lens corrects this condition.

TERM	DEFINITION
retinal detachment (RET-in-al)	Occurs when the retina becomes separated from the choroid layer. This separation seriously damages blood vessels and nerves, resulting in blindness. May be treated with surgical or medical procedures to stabilize the retina and prevent separation.
retinitis pigmentosa (ret-in-EYE-tis pig-men-TOH-sah)	Progressive disease of the eye resulting in the retina becoming hard (sclerosed), pigmented (colored), and atrophying (wasting away). There is no known cure for this condition.
retinoblastoma (RET-in-noh-blast-OH-mah)	Malignant eye tumor occurring in children, usually under the age of 3. Requires enucleation.
■ ***Conjunctiva***	
pterygium (the-RIJ-ee-um)	Hypertrophied conjunctival tissue in the inner corner of the eye.
trachoma (tray-KOH-mah)	Chronic infectious disease of the conjunctiva and cornea caused by bacteria. Occurs more commonly in those living in hot, dry climates. Untreated, it may lead to blindness when the scarring invades the cornea. Trachoma can be treated with antibiotics.
■ ***Eyelids***	
hordeolum (hor-DEE-oh-lum)	Refers to a *stye* (or *sty*), a small purulent inflammatory infection of a sebaceous gland of the eyelid; treated with hot compresses and/or surgical incision.

Pathology *(continued)*

TERM	DEFINITION
■ ***Eye Muscles***	
esotropia (ST) (ess-oh-TROH-pee-ah)	Inward turning of the eye; also called *cross-eyed.* An example of a form of strabismus (muscle weakness of the eye).
exotropia (XT) (eks-oh-TROH-pee-ah)	Outward turning of the eye; also called *wall-eyed.* Also an example of strabismus (muscle weakness of the eye).
strabismus (strah-BIZ-mus)	Eye muscle weakness commonly seen in children resulting in the eyes looking in different directions at the same time. May be corrected with glasses, eye exercises, and/or surgery.
■ ***Brain-Related Vision Pathologies***	
hemianopia (hem-ee-ah-NOP-ee-ah)	Loss of vision in half of the visual field. A stroke patient may suffer from this disorder.
nystagmus (niss-TAG-mus)	Jerky-appearing involuntary eye movements, usually left and right. Often an indication of brain injury.

Diagnostic Procedures

TERM	DEFINITION
■ ***Eye Examination Tests***	
color vision tests	Use of polychromic (multicolored) charts to determine the ability of the patient to recognize color.

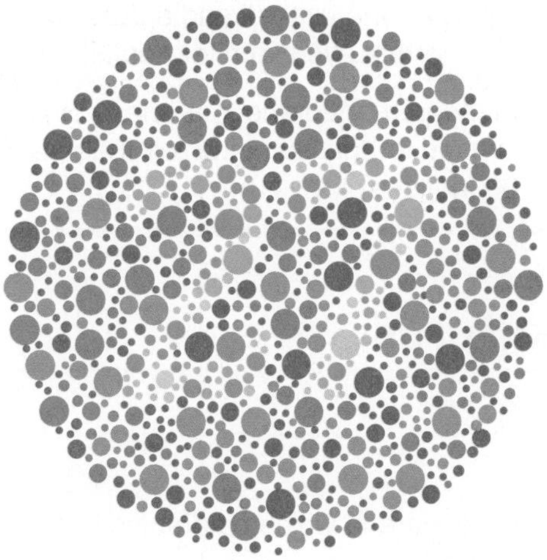

■ **Figure 13.11** An example of color blindness test. A person with red-green color blindness would not be able to distinguish the green 27 from the surrounding red circles.

TERM	DEFINITION
fluorescein angiography (floo-oh-RESS-ee-in an-jee-OG-rah-fee)	Process of injecting a dye (fluorescein) to observe the movement of blood and detect lesions in the macular area of the retina. Used to determine if there is a detachment of the retina.
fluorescein staining (floo-oh-RESS-ee-in)	Applying dye eye drops that are a bright green fluorescent color. Used to look for corneal abrasions or ulcers.
keratometry (kair-ah-TOM-eh-tree)	Measurement of the curvature of the cornea using an instrument called a *keratometer.*
ophthalmoscopy (off-thal-MOSS-koh-pee)	Examination of the interior of the eyes using an instrument called an *ophthalmoscope* (see Figure 13.12 ■). The physician dilates the pupil in order to see the cornea, lens, and retina. Used to identify abnormalities in the blood vessels of the eye and some systemic diseases.

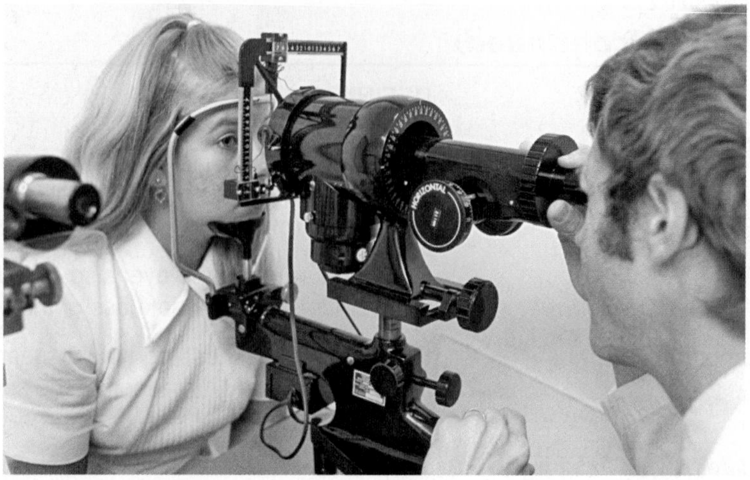

■ **Figure 13.12** Examination of the interior of the eye using an ophthalmoscope.

Diagnostic Procedures *(continued)*

TERM	DEFINITION
refractive error test (ree-FRAK-tiv)	Vision test for a defect in the ability of the eye to accurately focus the image that is hitting it. Refractive errors result in myopia and hyperopia.
slit lamp microscopy	Examining the posterior surface of the cornea.
Snellen chart (SNEL-enz)	Chart used for testing distance vision named for Dutch ophthalmologist Hermann Snellen. It contains letters of varying size and is administered from a distance of 20 feet. A person who can read at 20 feet what the average person can read at this distance is said to have 20/20 vision.
tonometry (tohn-OM-eh-tree)	Measurement of the intraocular pressure of the eye using a *tonometer* to check for the condition of glaucoma. The physician places the tonometer lightly on the eyeball and a pressure measurement is taken. Generally part of a normal eye exam for adults.
visual acuity (VA) **test** (VIZH-oo-al ah-KYOO-ih-tee)	Measurement of the sharpness of a patient's vision. Usually, a Snellen chart is used for this test in which the patient identifies letters from a distance of 20 feet.

Therapeutic Procedures

TERMS	DEFINITION
■ ***Surgical Procedures***	
cryoextraction (cry-oh-eks-TRAK-shun)	Procedure in which cataract is lifted from the lens with an extremely cold probe.
cryoretinopexy (cry-oh-RET-ih-noh-pek-see)	Surgical fixation of the retina by using extreme cold.
enucleation (ee-new-klee-AH-shun)	Surgical removal of an eyeball.
keratoplasty (KAIR-ah-toh-plass-tee)	Surgical repair of the cornea is the simple translation of this term that is utilized to mean corneal transplant.
laser-assisted in-situ keratomileusis (LASIK) (in-SIH-tyoo kair-ah-toh-mih-LOO-sis)	Correction of myopia using laser surgery to remove corneal tissue (see Figure 13.13 ■).

Figure 13.13 LASIK surgery. The cornea has been lifted in order to reshape it. *(Chris Barry/Phototake NYC)*

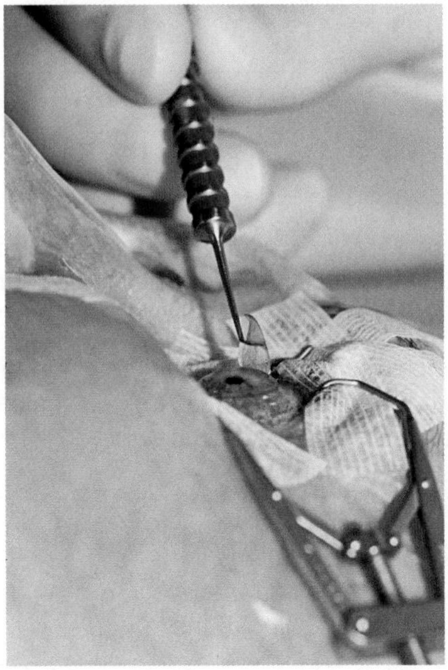

Therapeutic Procedures *(continued)*

TERM	DEFINITION
laser photocoagulation (LAY-zer foh-toh-koh-ag-yoo-LAY-shun)	Use of a laser beam to destroy very small precise areas of the retina. May be used to treat retinal detachment or macular degeneration.
phacoemulsification (fak-oh-ee-mull-sih-fih-KAY-shun)	Use of high-frequency sound waves to emulsify (liquefy) a lens with a cataract, which is then aspirated (removed by suction) with a needle.
photorefractive keratectomy (PRK) (foh-toh-ree-FRAK-tiv kair-ah-TEK-toh-mee)	Use of a laser to reshape the cornea and correct errors of refraction.
radial keratotomy (RK) (RAY-dee-all kair-ah-TOT-oh-mee)	Spokelike incisions around the cornea that result in it becoming flatter. A surgical treatment for myopia.
scleral buckling (SKLAIR-al)	Placing a band of silicone around the outside of the sclera that stabilizes a detaching retina.
strabotomy (strah-BOT-oh-mee)	Incision into the eye muscles in order to correct strabismus.

Pharmacology

CLASSIFICATION	ACTION	GENERIC AND BRAND NAMES
anesthetic ophthalmic solution (off-THAL-mik)	Eye drops for pain relief associated with eye infections, corneal abrasions, or surgery.	proparacain, Ak-Taine, Ocu-Caine; tetracaine, Opticaine, Pontocaine
antibiotic ophthalmic solution (off-THAL-mik)	Eye drops for the treatment of bacterial eye infections.	erythromycin, Del-Mycin, Ilotycin Ophthalmic
antiglaucoma medications (an-tye-glau-KOH-mah)	Group of drugs that reduce intraocular pressure by lowering the amount of aqueous humor in the eyeball. May achieve this by either reducing the production of aqueous humor or increasing its outflow.	timolol, Betimol, Timoptic; acetazolamide, Ak-Zol, Dazamide; prostaglandin analogs, Lumigan, Xalatan

Pharmacology *(continued)*

CLASSIFICATION	ACTION	GENERIC AND BRAND NAMES
artificial tears	Medications, many of them over the counter, to treat dry eyes.	buffered isotonic solutions, Akwa Tears, Refresh Plus, Moisture Eyes
miotic (my-OT-ik)	Any substance that causes the pupil to constrict. These medications may also be used to treat glaucoma.	physostigmine, Eserine Sulfate, Isopto Eserine; carbachol, Carbastat, Miostat
mydriatic (mid-ree-AT-ik)	Any substance that causes the pupil to dilate by paralyzing the iris and/or ciliary body muscles. Particularly useful during eye examinations and eye surgery.	atropine sulfate, Atropine-Care Ophthalmic, Atropisol Ophthalmic
ophthalmic decongestants	Over-the-counter medications that constrict the arterioles of the eye, reduce redness and itching of the conjunctiva.	tetrahydrozoline, Visine, Murine

Abbreviations

ARMD	age-related macular degeneration
Astigm	astigmatism
c.gl.	correction with glasses
D	diopter (lens strength)
DVA	distance visual acuity
ECCE	extracapsular cataract extraction
EENT	eye, ear, nose, and throat
EM	emmetropia
EOM	extraocular movement
ICCE	intracapsular cataract extraction
IOP	intraocular pressure
LASIK	laser-assisted in-situ keratomileusis
OD	right eye
Ophth.	ophthalmology
OS	left eye
OU	each eye/both eyes
PERRLA	pupils equal, round, react to light and accommodation
PRK	photorefractive keratectomy
REM	rapid eye movement
s.gl.	without correction or glasses
SMD	senile macular degeneration
ST	esotropia
VA	visual acuity
VF	visual field
XT	exotropia

Med Term Tip

The abbreviations for right eye (OD) and left eye (OS) are easy to remember when we know their origins. OD stands for *oculus* (eye) *dexter* (right). OS has its origin in *oculus* (eye) *sinister* (left). At one time in history it was considered to be sinister if a person looked at another from only the left side. Hence the term *oculus sinister* (OS) means left eye.

Section II: The Ear at a Glance

Function

The ear contains the sensory receptors for hearing and equilibrium (balance).

Structures

auricle
external ear
inner ear
middle ear

Combining Forms

acous/o	hearing
audi/o	hearing
audit/o	hearing
aur/o	ear
auricul/o	ear
cerumin/o	cerumen
cochle/o	cochlea
labyrinth/o	labyrinth (inner ear)
myring/o	eardrum
ot/o	ear
salping/o	eustachian tube
staped/o	stapes
tympan/o	eardrum, middle ear

Suffixes

-cusis	hearing
-otia	ear condition

The Ear Illustrated

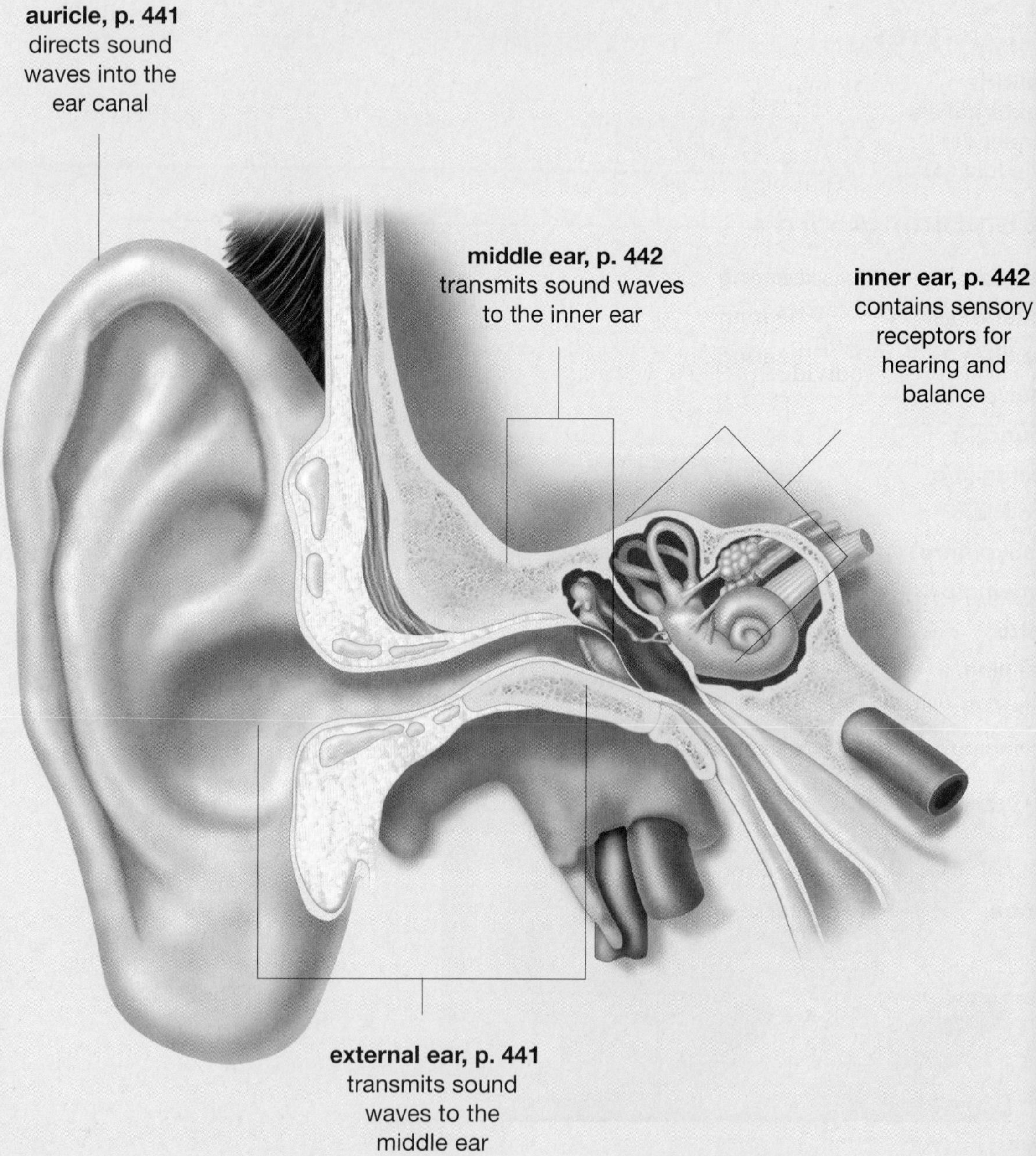

auricle, p. 441
directs sound waves into the ear canal
middle ear, p. 442
transmits sound waves to the inner ear
inner ear, p. 442
contains sensory receptors for hearing and balance
external ear, p. 441
transmits sound waves to the middle ear

Anatomy and Physiology of the Ear

audiology (aw-dee-OL-oh-jee)
cochlear nerve (KOK-lee-ar)
equilibrium (ee-kwih-LIB-ree-um)
external ear
hearing
inner ear
middle ear
otology (oh-TOL-oh-jee)
vestibular nerve (ves-TIB-yoo-lar)
vestibulocochlear nerve (ves-tib-yoo-loh-KOK-lee-ar)

The study of the ear is referred to as **otology** (Oto), and the study of hearing disorders is called **audiology**. While there is a large amount of overlap between these two areas, there are also examples of ear problems that do not affect hearing. The ear is responsible for two senses: **hearing** and **equilibrium**, or our sense of balance. Hearing and equilibrium sensory information is carried to the brain by cranial nerve VIII, the **vestibulocochlear nerve**. This nerve is divided into two major branches. The **cochlear nerve** carries hearing information, and the **vestibular nerve** carries equilibrium information.

The ear is subdivided into three areas:

1. **external ear**
2. **middle ear**
3. **inner ear**

External Ear

auditory canal (AW-dih-tor-ee)
auricle (AW-rih-k'l)
cerumen (seh-ROO-men)
external auditory meatus (AW-dih-tor-ee me-A-tus)
pinna (PIN-ah)
tympanic membrane (tim-PAN-ik)

The external ear consists of three parts: the **auricle**, the **auditory canal**, and the **tympanic membrane** (see Figure 13.14 ■). The auricle or **pinna** is what is commonly referred to as *the ear* because this is the only visible portion. The auricle with its

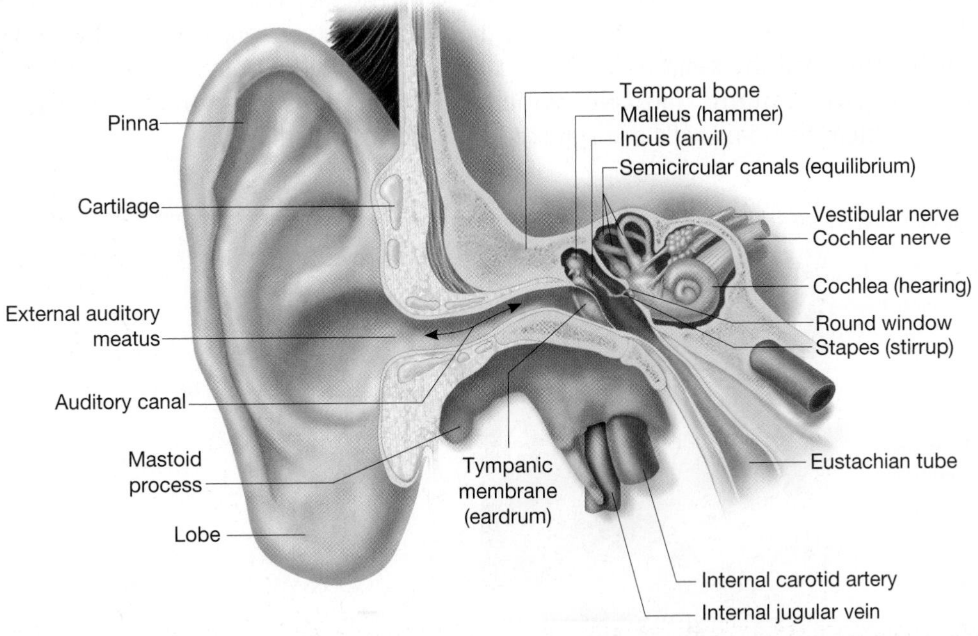

■ **Figure 13.14** The internal structures of the outer, middle, and inner ear.

earlobe has a unique shape in each person and functions like a funnel to capture sound waves as they go past the outer ear and channel them through the **external auditory meatus**. The sound then moves along the auditory canal and causes the tympanic membrane (eardrum) to vibrate. The tympanic membrane actually separates the external ear from the middle ear. Ear wax or **cerumen** is produced in oil glands in the auditory canal. This wax helps to protect and lubricate the ear. It is also just barely liquid at body temperature. This causes cerumen to slowly flow out of the auditory canal, carrying dirt and dust with it. Therefore, the auditory canal is self-cleaning.

Med Term Tip

The term *tympanic membrane* comes from the Greek word for "drumhead." The tympanic membrane or eardrum vibrates to sound waves like a drum head.

Middle Ear

auditory tube (AW-dih-tor-ee)
eustachian tube (yoo-STAY-she-en)
incus (ING-kus)
malleus (MAL-ee-us)
ossicles (OSS-ih-kls)
oval window
stapes (STAY-peez)

The middle ear is located in a small cavity in the temporal bone of the skull. This air-filled cavity contains three tiny bones called **ossicles** (see Figure 13.15 ■). These three bones, the **malleus**, **incus**, and **stapes**, are vital to the hearing process. They amplify the vibrations in the middle ear and transmit them to the inner ear from the malleus to the incus and finally to the stapes. The stapes, the last of the three ossicles, is attached to a very thin membrane that covers the opening to the inner ear called the **oval window**.

The **eustachian tube** or **auditory tube** connects the nasopharynx with the middle ear (see Figure 13.14). Each time you swallow the eustachian tube opens. This connection allows pressure to equalize between the middle ear cavity and the atmospheric pressure.

Med Term Tip

The three bones in the middle ear are referred to by terms that are similar to their shape. Thus, the malleus is called the hammer, the incus is the anvil, and the stapes is the stirrup (see Figure 13.15).

Inner Ear

cochlea (KOK-lee-ah)
labyrinth (LAB-ih-rinth)
organs of Corti (KOR-tee)
saccule (SAK-yool)
semicircular canals
utricle (YOO-trih-k'l)

The inner ear is also located in a cavity within the temporal bone (see Figure 13.14). This fluid-filled cavity is referred to as the **labyrinth** because of its shape. The labyrinth contains the hearing and equilibrium sensory organs: the **cochlea** for hearing and the **semicircular canals**, **utricle**, and **saccule** for equilibrium. Each of these organs contains hair cells, which are the actual sensory receptor cells. In the cochlea, the hair cells are referred to as **organs of Corti**.

Med Term Tip

Frequently, children will twirl in circles and fall or stumble from dizziness when they stop. This is caused from a temporary imbalance in the inner ear.

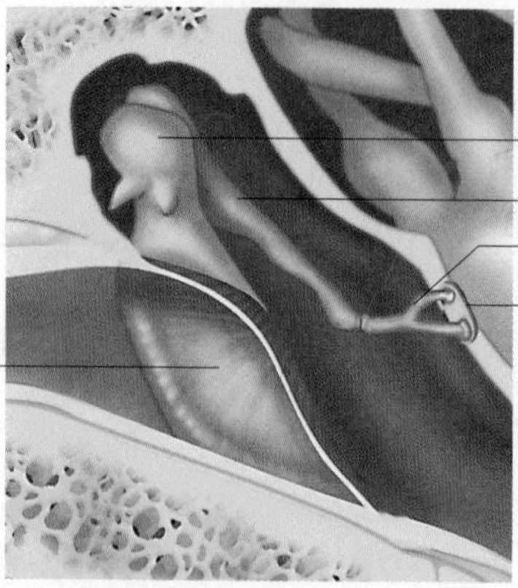

■ **Figure 13.15** Close-up view of the ossicles within the middle ear. These three bones extend from the tympanic membrane to the oval window.

How We Hear

conductive hearing loss (kon-DUK-tiv)

sensorineural hearing loss (sen-soh-ree-NOO-ral)

Figure 13.16 outlines the path of sound through the outer ear and middle ear and into the cochlea of the inner ear. Sound waves traveling down the external auditory canal strike the eardrum, causing it to vibrate. The ossicles conduct these vibrations across the middle ear from the eardrum to the oval window. Oval window movements initiate vibrations in the fluid that fills the cochlea. As the fluid vibrations strike a hair cell, they bend the small hairs and stimulate the nerve ending. The nerve ending then sends an electrical impulse to the brain on the cochlear portion of the vestibulocochlear nerve.

Hearing loss can be divided into two main categories: **conductive hearing loss** and **sensorineural hearing loss.** Conductive refers to disease or malformation of the outer or middle ear. All sound is weaker and muffled in conductive hearing loss since it is not conducted correctly to the inner ear. Sensorineural hearing loss is the result of damage or malformation of the inner ear (cochlea) or the cochlear nerve. In this hearing loss, some sounds are distorted and heard incorrectly. There can also be a combination of both conductive and sensorineural hearing loss.

Med Term Tip

Hearing impairment is becoming a greater problem for the general population for several reasons. First, people are living longer. Hearing loss can accompany old age, and there are a greater number of people over 50 years of age requiring hearing assistance. In addition, sound technology has produced music quality that was never available before. However, listening to loud music either naturally or through earphones can cause gradual damage to the hearing mechanism.

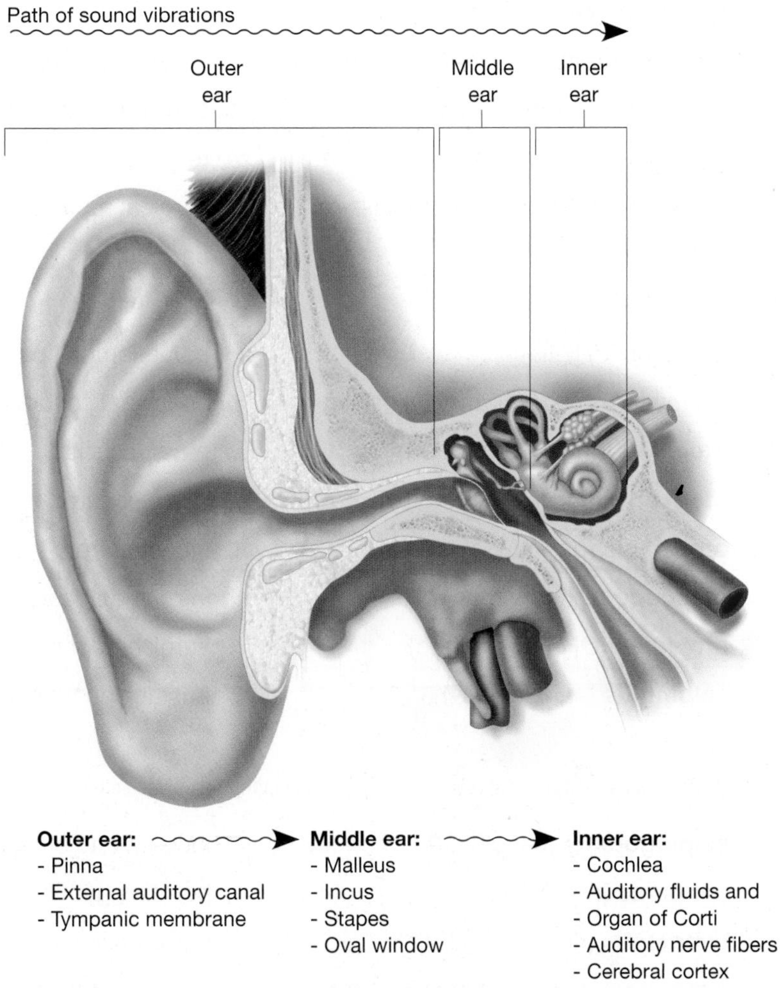

Figure 13.16 The path of sound waves through the outer, middle, and inner ear.

Word Building

The following list contains examples of medical terms built directly from word parts. The definitions of these terms can be determined by a straightforward translation of the word parts.

COMBINING FORM	COMBINED WITH	MEDICAL TERM	DEFINITION
acous/o	-tic	**acoustic** (ah-KOOS-tik)	pertaining to hearing
audi/o	-gram	**audiogram** (AW-dee-oh-gram)	record of hearing
	-meter	**audiometer** (aw-dee-OM-eh-ter)	instrument to measure hearing
	-ologist	**audiologist** (aw-dee-OL-oh-jist)	hearing specialist
audit/o	-ory	**auditory** (AW-dih-tor-ee)	pertaining to hearing
aur/o	-al	**aural** (AW-ral)	pertaining to the ear

Med Term Tip

Word watch—Be careful when using two terms that sound the same — *aural* meaning "pertaining to the ear" and *oral* meaning "pertaining to the mouth."

auricul/o	-ar	**auricular** (aw-RIK-cu-lar)	pertaining to the ear
cochle/o	-ar	**cochlear** (KOK-lee-ar)	pertaining to the cochlea
labyrinth/o	-ectomy	**labyrinthectomy** (lab-ih-rin-THEK-toh-mee)	removal of the labyrinth
	-otomy	**labyrinthotomy** (lab-ih-rinth-OT-oh-mee)	incision into the labyrinth
myring/o	-itis	**myringitis** (mir-ing-JYE-tis)	eardrum inflammation
	-ectomy	**myringectomy** (mir-in-GEK-toh-mee)	removal of the eardrum
	-plasty	**myringoplasty** (mir-IN-goh-plass-tee)	surgical repair of eardrum
ot/o	-algia	**otalgia** (oh-TAL-jee-ah)	ear pain
	-ic	**otic** (OH-tik)	pertaining to the ear
	-itis	**otitis** (oh-TYE-tis)	ear inflammation
	myc/o -osis	**otomycosis** (oh-toh-my-KOH-sis)	abnormal condition of ear fungus
	-ologist	**otologist** (oh-TOL-oh-jist)	ear specialist
	py/o -rrhea	**otopyorrhea** (oh-toh-pye-oh-REE-ah)	pus discharge from ear
	-rrhagia	**otorrhagia** (oh-toh-RAH-jee-ah)	bleeding from the ear
	-scope	**otoscope** (OH-toh-scope)	instrument to view inside the ear
	-plasty	**otoplasty** (OH-toh-plas-tee)	surgical repair of the (external) ear
salping/o	-itis	**salpingitis** (sal-pin-JIH-tis)	eustachian tube inflammation

Med Term Tip

Word watch—Be careful using the combining form *salping/o*, which can mean either "Eustachian tube" or "fallopian tube."

	-otomy	**salpingotomy** (sal-pin-GOT-oh-mee)	incision into eustachian tube
tympan/o	-ic	**tympanic** (tim-PAN-ik)	pertaining to the eardrum
	-itis	**tympanitis** (tim-pan-EYE-tis)	eardrum inflammation
	-meter	**tympanometer** (tim-pah-NOM-eh-ter)	instrument to measure eardrum
	-plasty	**tympanoplasty** (tim-pan-oh-PLASS-tee)	surgical repair of eardrum

Word Building *(continued)*

COMBINING FORM	COMBINED WITH	MEDICAL TERM	DEFINITION
	-rrhexis	**tympanorrhexis** (tim-pan-oh-REK-sis)	eardrum rupture
	-otomy	**tympanotomy** (tim-pan-OT-oh-mee)	incision into the eardrum
	-ectomy	**tympanectomy** (tim-pan-EK-toh-mee)	removal of the eardrum
SUFFIX	**COMBINED WITH**	**MEDICAL TERM**	**DEFINITION**
-otia	micro-	**microtia** (my-KROH-she-ah)	(abnormally) small ears
	macro-	**macrotia** (mah-KROH-she-ah)	(abnormally) large ears

Vocabulary

TERM	DEFINITION
American Sign Language (ASL)	Nonverbal method of communicating in which the hands and fingers are used to indicate words and concepts. Used by both persons who are deaf and persons with speech impairments.

Figure 13.17 Photograph of a teacher and student communicating using American Sign Language.
(Trevon Baker/Baker Consulting and Design)

TERM	DEFINITION
binaural (bin-AW-rall)	Referring to both ears.
decibel (dB) (DES-ih-bel)	Measures the intensity or loudness of a sound. Zero decibels is the quietest sound measured and 120 dB is the loudest sound commonly measured.
hertz (Hz)	Measurement of the frequency or pitch of sound. The lowest pitch on an audiogram is 250 Hz. The measurement can go as high as 8000 Hz, which is the highest pitch measured.
monaural (mon-AW-rall)	Referring to one ear.
otorhinolaryngology (ENT) (oh-toh-rye-rye-noh-lair-in-GOL-oh-jee)	Branch of medicine involving the diagnosis and treatment of conditions and diseases of the ear, nose, and throat. Also referred to as *ENT*. Physician is an *otorhinolaryngologist*.
presbycusis (pres-bih-KOO-sis)	Normal loss of hearing that can accompany the aging process.
residual hearing (rih-ZID-yoo-al)	Amount of hearing that is still present after damage has occurred to the auditory mechanism.
tinnitus (tin-EYE-tus)	Ringing in the ears.
vertigo (VER-tih-goh)	Dizziness.

Pathology

TERM	DEFINITION
■ *Hearing Loss*	
anacusis (an-ah-KOO-sis)	Total absence of hearing; inability to perceive sound. Also called *deafness.*
deafness	Inability to hear or having some degree of hearing impairment.
■ *External Ear*	
ceruminoma (seh-roo-men-oh-ma)	Excessive accumulation of ear wax resulting in a hard wax plug. Sound becomes muffled.
otitis externa (OE) (oh-TYE-tis ex-TERN-ah)	External ear infection. Most commonly caused by fungus. Also called *otomycosis* and commonly referred to as *swimmer's ear.*
■ *Middle Ear*	
otitis media (OM) (oh-TYE-tis MEE-dee-ah)	Seen frequently in children; commonly referred to as a *middle ear infection.* Often preceded by an upper respiratory infection during which pathogens move from the pharynx to the middle ear via the eustachian tube. Fluid accumulates in the middle ear cavity. The fluid may be watery, *serous otitis media,* or full of pus, *purulent otitis media.*
otosclerosis (oh-toh-sklair-OH-sis)	Loss of mobility of the stapes bone, leading to progressive hearing loss.
■ *Inner Ear*	
acoustic neuroma (ah-KOOS-tik noor-OH-mah)	Benign tumor of the eighth cranial nerve sheath. The pressure causes symptoms such as tinnitus, headache, dizziness, and progressive hearing loss.
labyrinthitis (lab-ih-rin-THIGH-tis)	May affect both the hearing and equilibrium portions of the inner ear. Also referred to as an *inner ear infection.*
Ménière's disease (may-nee-ARZ dih-ZEEZ)	Abnormal condition within the labyrinth of the inner ear that can lead to a progressive loss of hearing. The symptoms are dizziness or vertigo, hearing loss, and tinnitus (ringing in the ears). Named for French physician Prosper Ménière.

Diagnostic Procedures

TERM	DEFINITION
■ *Audiology Tests*	
audiometry (aw-dee-OM-eh-tree)	Test of hearing ability by determining the lowest and highest intensity (decibels) and frequencies (hertz) that a person can distinguish. The patient may sit in a soundproof booth and receive sounds through earphones as the technician decreases the sound or lowers the tones.

Figure 13.18 Audiometry exam. Photograph of a young person holding up his hand to indicate in which ear he is able to hear the sound. *(Jorgen Shytte/Peter Arnold, Inc.)*

Diagnostic Procedures (*continued*)

TERM	DEFINITION
Rinne and Weber tuning-fork tests (RIN-eh)	These tests assess both nerve and bone conduction of sound. The physician holds a tuning fork, an instrument that produces a constant pitch when it is struck, against or near the bones on the side of the head. Friedrich Rinne was a German otologist, and Ernst Weber was a German physiologist.
■ ***Otology Tests***	
otoscopy (oh-TOSS-koh-pee)	Examination of the ear canal, eardrum, and outer ear using an *otoscope*. **Med Term Tip** Small children are prone to placing objects in their ears. In some cases, as with peas and beans, these become moist in the ear canal and swell, which makes removal difficult. *Otoscopy*, or the examination of the ear using an *otoscope*, can aid in identifying and removing the cause of hearing loss if it is due to foreign bodies (see Figure 13.14).
■ **Figure 13.19** An otoscope, used to visually examine the external auditory ear canal and tympanic membrane.	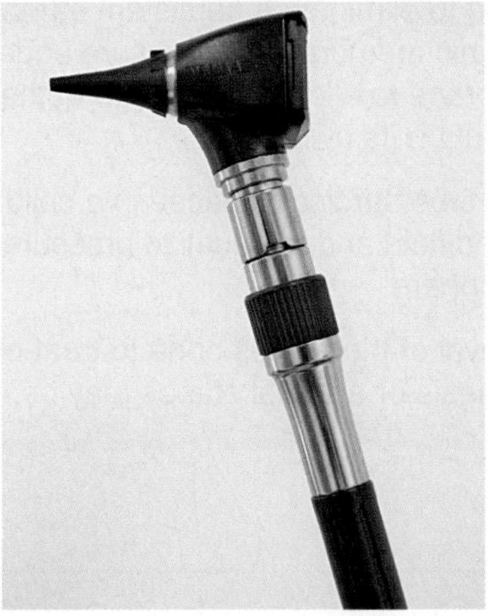
tympanometry (tim-pah-NOM-eh-tree)	Measurement of the movement of the tympanic membrane. Can indicate the presence of pressure in the middle ear.
■ ***Balance Tests***	
falling test	Test used to observe balance and equilibrium. The patient is observed balancing on one foot, then with one foot in front of the other, and then walking forward with eyes open. The same test is conducted with the patient's eyes closed. Swaying and falling with the eyes closed can indicate an ear and equilibrium malfunction.

Therapeutic Procedures

TERM	DEFINITION
■ ***Audiology Procedures***	
hearing aid	Apparatus or mechanical device used by persons with impaired hearing to amplify sound. Also called an *amplification device*.
■ ***Surgical Procedures***	
cochlear implant (KOK-lee-ar)	Mechanical device surgically placed under the skin behind the outer ear (pinna) that converts sound signals into magnetic impulses to stimulate the auditory nerve (see Figure 13.20 ■). Can be beneficial for those with profound sensorineural hearing loss.

Figure 13.20 Photograph of a child with a cochlear implant. This device sends electrical impulses directly to the brain.

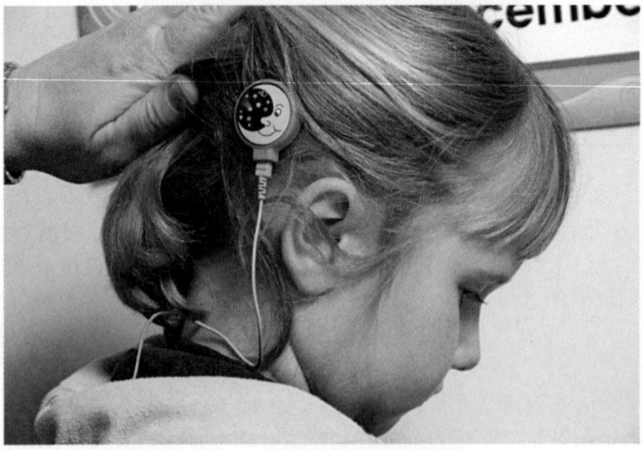

Therapeutic Procedures *(continued)*

TERM	DEFINITION
myringotomy (mir-in-GOT-oh-mee)	Surgical puncture of the eardrum with removal of fluid and pus from the middle ear to eliminate a persistent ear infection and excessive pressure on the tympanic membrane. A pressure equalizing tube is placed in the tympanic membrane to allow for drainage of the middle ear cavity; this tube typically falls out on its own.
pressure equalizing tube (PE tube)	Small tube surgically placed in a child's eardrum to assist in drainage of trapped fluid and to equalize pressure between the middle ear cavity and the atmosphere.
stapedectomy (stay-pee-DEK-toh-mee)	Removal of the stapes bone to treat otosclerosis (hardening of the bone). A prosthesis or artificial stapes may be implanted.

Pharmacology

CLASSIFICATION	ACTION	GENERIC AND BRAND NAMES
antibiotic otic solution (OH-tik)	Eardrops to treat otitis externa.	Neomycin, polymyxin B, and hydrocortisone solution, Otocort, Cortisporin, Otic Care
antiemetics (an-tye-ee-mit-tiks)	Medications that are effective in treating the nausea associated with vertigo.	meclizine, Antivert, Meni-D; phenothiazine, Compazine
anti-inflammatory otic solution (OH-tik)	Reduces inflammation, itching, and edema associated with otitis externa.	antipyrine & benzoaine, Allergan Ear Drops, A/B Otic
wax emulsifiers	Substances used to soften ear wax to prevent buildup within the external ear canal.	carbamide peroxide, Debrox Drops, Murine Ear Drops

Abbreviations

AD	right ear
AS	left ear
ASL	American Sign Language
AU	both ears
BC	bone conduction
dB	decibel
EENT	eyes, ears, nose, throat
ENT	ear, nose, and throat
HEENT	head, ears, eyes, nose, throat
Hz	hertz
OM	otitis media
Oto	otology
PE tube	pressure tube equalizing
PORP	partial ossicular replacement prosthesis
SOM	serous otitis media
TORP	total ossicular replacement prosthesis

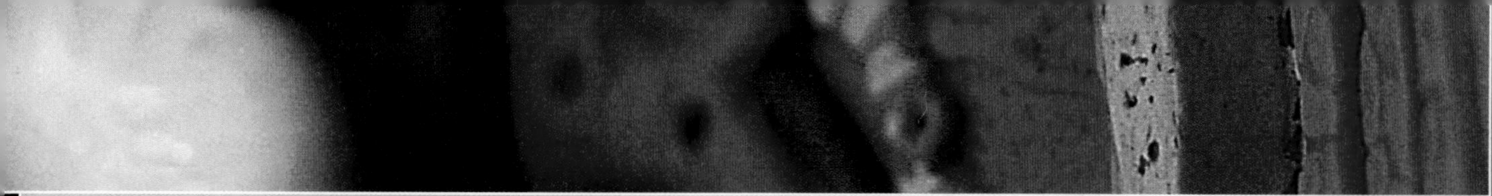

Appendices

Appendix I

Abbreviations

Abbreviation	Meaning
@	at
5-FU	5-fluorouracil
^{67}Ga	radioactive gallium
^{99m}Tc	radioactive technetium
^{131}I	radioactive iodine
^{133}Xe	radioactive xenon
^{201}Tl	radioactive thallium
α	alpha
$\bar{a}$	before
AAROM	active-assisted range of motion
AB	abortion
ABGs	arterial blood gases
ac	before meals
ACTH	adrenocorticotropic hormone
AD	right ear, Alzheimer's disease
ad lib	as desired
ADD	attention deficit disorder
ADH	antidiuretic hormone
ADHD	attention-deficit hyperactivity disorder
ADL	activities of daily living
AE	above elbow
AF	atrial fibrillation
AGN	acute glomerulonephritis
AI	artificial insemination
AIDS	acquired immunodeficiency syndrome
AK	above knee
ALL	acute lymphocytic leukemia
ALS	amyotropic lateral sclerosis
ALT	alanine transaminase
AMI	acute myocardial infarction
AML	acute myelogenous leukemia
Angio	angiography
ANS	autonomic nervous system
ante	before
AP	anteroposterior
APAP	acetaminophen (Tylenol)
aq	aqueous (water)
ARC	AIDS-related complex
ARDS	adult respiratory distress syndrome

Abbreviation	Meaning
ARF	acute renal failure
ARMD	age-related macular degeneration
AROM	active range of motion
AS	arteriosclerosis, left ear
ASA	aspirin
ASD	atrial septal defect
ASHD	arteriosclerotic heart disease
ASL	American Sign Language
AST	aspartate transaminase
Astigm	astigmatism
ATN	acute tubulor necrosis
AU	both ears
AuD	doctor of audiology
AV, A-V	atrioventricular
β	beta
Ba	barium
BaE	barium enema
basos	basophil
BBB	bundle branch block (L for left; R for right)
BC	bone conduction
BCC	basal cell carcinoma
BDT	bone density testing
BE	barium enema, below elbow
bid	twice a day
BK	below knee
BM	bowel movement
BMD	bone mineral density
BMR	basal metabolic rate
BMT	bone marrow transplant
BNO	bladder neck obstruction
BP	blood pressure
BPD	bipolar disorder
BPH	benign prostatic hypertrophy
bpm	beats per minute
Bronch	bronchoscopy
BS	bowel sounds
BSE	breast self-examination
BSN	bachelor of science in nursing
BUN	blood urea nitrogen
BX, bx	biopsy

Abbreviation	Meaning
$\bar{c}$	with
C1, C2, etc.	first cervical vertebra, second cervical vertebra, etc.
Ca^{2+}	calcium
CA	cancer, chronological age
CABG	coronary artery bypass graft
CAD	coronary artery disease
cap(s)	capsule(s)
CAPD	continuous ambulatory peritoneal dialysis
CAT	computerized axial tomography
cath	catheterization
CBC	complete blood count
CBD	common bile duct
cc	cubic centimeter
CC	clean catch urine specimen, cardiac catheterization, chief complaint
CCS	certified coding specialist
CCU	cardiac care unit, coronary care unit
c.gl.	correction with glasses
chemo	chemotherapy
CHF	congestive heart failure
CIS	carcinoma in situ
Cl^-	chloride
CLL	chronic lymphocytic leukemia
CLS	clinical laboratory scientist
CLT	clinical laboratory technician
CMA	certified medical assistant
CML	chronic myelogenous leukemia
CNA	certified nurse aide
CNS	central nervous system
CO_2	carbon dioxide
CoA	coarctation of the aorta
COPD	chronic obstructive pulmonary disease
COTA	certified occupational therapy assistant
CP	cerebral palsy, chest pain
CPK	creatine phosphokinase
CPR	cardiopulmonary resuscitation
CRF	chronic renal failure
crit	hematocrit
CRT	certified respiratory therapist
C & S	culture and sensitivity test
CS, CS-section	cesarean section
CSD	congenital septal defect
CSF	cerebrospinal fluid
CT	computerized tomography, cytotechnologist
CTA	clear to auscultation
CTS	carpal tunnel syndrome
CV	cardiovascular
CVA	cerebrovascular accident
CVD	cerebrovascular disease
CVS	chorionic villus biopsy
Cx	cervix
CXR	chest x-ray
cysto	cystoscopic exam
d	day
D	diopter (lens strength)
D & C	dilation and curettage
D/C, d/c	discontinue
dB	decibel
DC	doctor of chiropractic
DDM	doctor of dental medicine
DDS	doctor of dental surgery
DEA	Drug Enforcement Agency
decub	lying down, decubitus ulcer
Derm, derm	dermatology
DI	diabetes insipidus, diagnostic imaging
diff	differential
dil	dilute
disc	discontinue
disp	dispense
DJD	degenerative joint disease
DM	diabetes mellitus
DO	doctor of osteopathy
DOE	dyspnea on exertion
DPT	diphtheria, pertussis, tetanus; doctor of physical therapy
DRE	digital rectal exam
DSA	digital subtraction angiography
DSM-IV	*Diagnostic and Statistical Manual for Mental Disorders,* Fourth edition
dtd	give of such a dose
DTR	deep tendon reflex; dietetic technician, registered
DVA	distance visual acuity
DVT	deep vein thrombosis
Dx	diagnosis
DXA	dual-energy absorptiometry
ECC	extracorporeal circulation
ECCE	extracapsular cataract extraction
ECG	electrocardiogram
Echo	echocardiogram
ECT	electroconvulsive therapy
ED	erectile dysfunction
EDC	estimated date of confinement
EEG	electroencephalogram, electroencephalography
EENT	eyes, ears, nose, throat

Abbreviation	Meaning
EGD	esophagogastroduodenoscopy
EKG	electrocardiogram
ELISA	enzyme-linked immunosorbent assay
EM	emmetropia
EMB	endometrial biopsy
EMG	electromyogram
EMT-B	emergency medical technician–basic
EMT-I	emergency medical technician–intermediate
EMT-P	emergency medical technician–paramedic
Endo	endoscopy
ENT	ear, nose, and throat
EOM	extraocular movement
eosins, eos	eosinophil
ER	emergency room
ERCP	endoscopic retrograde cholangiopancreatography
ERT	estrogen replacement therapy
ERV	expiratory reserve volume
ESR	erythrocyte sedimentation rate
ESRD	end-stage renal disease
e-stim	electrical stimulation
ESWL	extracorporeal shock-wave lithotripsy
et	and
EU	excretory urography
EUA	exam under anesthesia
FBS	fasting blood sugar
FDA	Federal Drug Administration
FEKG	fetal electrocardiogram
FHR	fetal heart rate
FHT	fetal heart tone
FOBT	fecal occult blood test
FRC	functional residual capacity
FS	frozen section
FSH	follicle-stimulating hormone
FTND	full-term normal delivery
FVC	forced vital capacity
Fx, FX	fracture
GI	first pregnancy
GA	general anesthesia
GB	gallbladder
GC	gonorrhea
GERD	gastroesophageal reflux disease
GH	growth hormone
GI	gastrointestinal
gm	gram
GOT	glutamic oxaloacetic transaminase
gr	grain

Abbreviation	Meaning
grav I	first pregnancy
gt	drop
gtt	drops
GTT	glucose tolerance test
GU	genitourinary
GVHD	graft vs. host disease
GYN, gyn	gynecology
H_2O	water
HA	headache
HAV	hepatitis A virus
Hb	hemoglobin
HBV	hepatitis B virus
HCG, hCG	human chorionic gonadotropin
HCl	hydrochloric acid
HCO_3^-	bicarbonate
HCT, Hct	hematocrit
HCV	hepatitis C virus
HD	Hodgkin's disease, hemodialysis
HDN	hemolytic disease of the newborn
HDV	hepatitis D virus
HEENT	head, ears, eyes, nose, throat
HEV	hepatitis E virus
Hgb, HGB	hemoglobin
HIV	human immunodeficieny virus
HMD	hyaline membrane disease
HNP	herniated nucleus pulposus
HPV	human papilloma virus
HRT	hormone replacement therapy
hs	at bed time
HSG	hysterosalpingography
HSV	*Herpes simplex* virus
HSV-1	*Herpes simplex* virus type 1
HTN	hypertension
Hz	hertz
i̅	one
IBD	inflammatory bowel disease
IBS	irritable bowel syndrome
IC	inspiratory capacity
ICCE	intracapsular cataract cryoextraction
ICP	intracranial pressure
ICU	intensive care unit
I & D	incision and drainage
ID	intradermal
IDDM	insulin-dependent diabetes mellitus
Ig	immunoglobins (IgA, IgD, IgE, IgG, IgM)
i̅i̅	two
i̅i̅i̅	three
IM	intramuscular
inj	injection

Abbreviation	Meaning
I & O	intake and output
IOP	intraocular pressure
IPD	intermittent peritoneal dialysis
IPPB	intermittent positive pressure breathing
IRDS	infant respiratory distress syndrome
IRV	inspiratory reserve volume
IU	international unit
IUD	intrauterine device
IV	intravenous
IVC	intravenous cholangiogram
IVF	*in vitro* fertilization
IVP	intravenous pyelogram
JRA	juvenile rheumatoid arthritis
K^+	potassium
kg	kilogram
KS	Kaposi's sarcoma
KUB	kidney, ureter, bladder
L	left, liter
L1, L2, etc.	first lumbar vertebra, second lumbar vertebra, etc.
LASIK	laser-assisted in-situ keratomileusis
LAT, lat	lateral
LBW	low birth weight
LDH	lactate dehydrogenase
LE	lower extremity
LGI	lower gastrointestinal series
LH	luteinizing hormone
LL	left lateral
LLE	left lower extremity
LLL	left lower lobe
LLQ	left lower quadrant
LMP	last menstrual period
LP	lumbar puncture
LPN	licensed practical nurse
LUE	left upper extremity
LUL	left upper lobe
LUQ	left upper quadrant
LVAD	left ventricular assist device
LVH	left ventricular hypertrophy
lymphs	lymphocyte
LVN	licensed vocational nurse
MA	mental age
MAO	monoamine oxidase
mcg	microgram
MD	doctor of medicine, muscular dystrophy
MDI	metered dose inhaler
mEq	milliequivalent
mets	metastases
mg	milligram
MI	myocardial infarction, mitral insufficiency
mL	milliliter
MLT	medical laboratory technician
MM	malignant melanoma
mm Hg	millimeters of mercury
MMPI	Minnesota Multiphasic Personality Inventory
mono	mononucleosis
monos	monocyte
MR	mitral regurgitation
MRA	magnetic resonance angiography
MRI	magnetic resonance imaging
MS	mitral stenosis, multiple sclerosis, musculoskeletal
MSH	melanocyte-stimulating hormone
MSN	master of science in nursing
MT	medical technologist
MTX	methotrexate
MUA	manipulation under anesthesia
MVP	mitral valve prolapse
n & v	nausea and vomiting
Na^+	sodium
NB	newborn
NG	nasogastric (tube)
NHL	non-Hodgkin's lymphoma
NIDDM	non–insulin-dependent diabetes mellitus
NK	natural killer cells
NMR	nuclear magnetic resonance
no sub	no substitute
noc	night
non rep	do not repeat
NP	nurse practitioner
NPH	neutral protamine Hagedorn (insulin)
NPO	nothing by mouth
NS	normal saline, nephrotic syndrome
NSAID	nonsteroidal anti-inflammatory drug
O_2	oxygen
OA	osteoarthritis
OB	obstetrics
OCD	obsessive-compulsive disorder
OCPs	oral contraceptive pills
OD	overdose, right eye, doctor of optometry
oint	ointment
OM	otitis media
O & P	ova and parasites
Ophth.	ophthalmology
OR	operating room
ORIF	open reduction–internal fixation

Abbreviation	Meaning
Orth, ortho	orthopedics
OS	left eye
OT	occupational therapy
OTC	over the counter
Oto	otology
OTR	occupational therapist
OU	each eye
oz	ounce
p̄	after
P	pulse
PI	first delivery
PA	posteroanterior, physician assistant, pernicious anemia
PAC	premature atrial contraction
PAP	Papanicolaou test, pulmonary arterial pressure
para I	first delivery
PARR	postanesthetic recovery room
PBI	protein-bound iodine
pc	after meals
PCA	patient-controlled administration
PCP	*Pneumocystis carinii* pneumonia
PCV	packed cell volume
PDA	patent ductus arteriosus
PDR	*Physician's Desk Reference*
PE tube	pressure equalizing tube
PEG	pneumoencephalogram, percutaneous endoscopic gastrostomy
per	with
PERRLA	pupils equal, round, react to light and accommodation
PET	positron emission tomography
PFT	pulmonary function test
pH	acidity or alkalinity of urine
PharmD	doctor of pharmacy
PID	pelvic inflammatory disease
PMNs	polymorphonuclear neutrophil
PMS	premenstrual syndrome
PNS	peripheral nervous system
PO, po	by mouth
polys	polymorphonuclear neutrophil
PORP	partial ossicular replacement prosthesis
pp	postprandial
PPD	purified protein derivative (tuberculin test)
preop, pre-op	preoperative
prep	preparation, prepared
PRK	photo refractive keratectomy
PRL	prolactin
prn	as needed
pro-time	prothrombin time
PROM	passive range of motion
prot	protocol
PSA	prostate specific antigen
pt	patient
PT	prothrombin time, physical therapy, physical therapist
PTA	physical therapy assistant
PTC	percutaneous transhepatic cholangiography
PTCA	percutaneous transluminal coronary angioplasty
PTH	parathyroid hormone
PUD	peptic ulcer disease
PVC	premature ventricular contraction
q	every
qam	every morning
qd	once a day, every day
qh	every hour
qhs	every night
qid	four times a day
qod	every other day
qs	quantity sufficient
R	respiration, right, roentgen
Ra	radium
RA	rheumatoid arthritis, room air
rad	radiation absorbed dose
RBC	red blood cell
RD	registered dietitian
RDH	registered dental hygienist
RDS	respiratory distress syndrome
REEGT	registered electroencephalography technologist
REM	rapid eye movement
REPT	registered evoked potential technologist
Rh−	Rh-negative
Rh+	Rh-positive
RHIA	registered health information administrator
RHIT	registered health information technician
RIA	radioimmunoassay
RL	right lateral
RLE	right lower extremity
RLL	right lower lobe
RLQ	right lower quadrant
RML	right mediolateral, right middle lobe
RN	registered nurse
ROM	range of motion
RP	retrograde pyelogram
RPh	registered pharmacist
RPR	rapid plasma reagin (test for syphilis)

Abbreviation	Meaning
RPSGT	registered polysomnographic technologist
RRT	registered radiologic technologist, registered respiratory therapist
RUE	right upper extremity
RUL	right upper lobe
RUQ	right upper quadrant
RV	reserve volume
Rx	take
s̄	without
S1	first heart sound
S2	second heart sound
SA, S-A	sinoatrial
SAD	seasonal affective disorder
SARS	severe acute respiratory syndrome
SC, sc	subcutaneous
SCC	squamous cell carcinoma
SCI	spinal cord injury
SCIDS	severe combined immunodeficiency syndrome
sed-rate	erythrocyte sedimentation rate
segs	segmented neutrophils
SG	skin graft, specific gravity
s.gl.	without correction or glasses
SGOT	serum glutamic oxaloacetic transaminase
SIDS	sudden infant death syndrome
Sig	label as follows/directions
SK	streptokinase
sl	under the tongue
SLE	systemic lupus erythematosus
SMAC	sequential multiple analyzer computer
SMD	senile macular degeneration
SOB	shortness of breath
sol	solution
SOM	serous otitis media
sp. gr.	specific gravity
SPP	suprapubic prostatectomy
SR	erythrocyte sedimentation rate
s̄s̄	one-half
st	stage
ST	esotropia
stat, STAT	at once, immediately
STD	skin test done, sexually transmitted disease
STSG	split-thickness skin graft
subcu	subcutaneous
subq	subcutaneous
supp.	suppository
suppos	suppository

Abbreviation	Meaning
susp	suspension
syr	syrup
T	tablespoon
t	teaspoon
T & A	tonsillectomy and adenoidectomy
T1, T2, etc.	first thoracic vertebra, second thoracic vertebra, etc.
T_3	triiodothyronine
T_4	thyroxine
tab	tablet
TAH	total abdominal hysterectomy
TAH-BSO	total abdominal hysterectomy–bilateral salpingo-ophorectomy
TB	tuberculosis
tbsp	tablespoon
TENS	transcutaneous electrical nerve stimulation
TFT	thyroid function test
THA	total hip arthroplasty
THR	total hip replacement
TIA	transient ischemic attack
tid	three times a day
TKA	total knee arthroplasty
TKR	total knee replacement
TLC	total lung capacity
TNM	tumor, nodes, metastases
TO	telephone order
top	apply topically
TORP	total ossicular replacement prosthesis
tPA	tissue-type plasminogen activator
TPN	total parenteral nutrition
TPR	temperature, pulse, and respiration
TSH	thyroid-stimulating hormone
tsp	teaspoon
TSS	toxic shock syndrome
TUR	transurethral resection
TURP	transurethral resection of prostate
TV	tidal volume
TX, Tx	traction, treatment
u	unit
U/A, UA	urinalysis
UC	uterine contractions, urine culture
UE	upper extremity
UGI	upper gastrointestinal series
ung	ointment
URI	upper respiratory infection
US	ultrasound
UTI	urinary tract infection

Abbreviation	Meaning
UV	ultraviolet
VA	visual acuity
VC	vital capacity
VCUG	voiding cystourethrography
VD	venereal disease
VF	visual field
VFib	ventricular fibrillation
VO	verbal order

Abbreviation	Meaning
VS	vital signs
VSD	ventricular septal defect
VT	ventricular tachycardia
WBC	white blood cell
wt	weight
x	times
XT	exotropia

Appendix II

Combining Forms

Combining Form	Meaning
abdomin/o	abdomen
acous/o	hearing
acr/o	extremities
aden/o	gland
adenoid/o	adenoids
adip/o	fat
adren/o	adrenal glands
adrenal/o	adrenal glands
aer/o	air
agglutin/o	clumping
albin/o	white
alveol/o	alveolus; air sac
ambly/o	dull or dim
amni/o	amnion
an/o	anus
andr/o	male
angi/o	vessel
ankyl/o	stiff joint
anter/o	front
anthrac/o	coal
anxi/o	anxiety
aort/o	aorta
append/o	appendix
appendic/o	appendix
aque/o	water
arteri/o	artery
arthr/o	joint
articul/o	joint
atel/o	incomplete
ather/o	fatty substance, plaque
atri/o	atrium
audi/o	hearing
audit/o	hearing
aur/o	ear
auricul/o	ear
azot/o	nitrogenous waste
bacteri/o	bacteria
balan/o	glans penis
bar/o	weight
bas/o	base
bi/o	life
blast/o	primitive cell
blephar/o	eyelid
brachi/o	arm
bronch/o	bronchus
bronchi/o	bronchiole
bronchiol/o	bronchiole
bucc/o	cheek
burs/o	sac
calc/o	calcium

Combining Form	Meaning
carcin/o	cancer
cardi/o	heart
carp/o	wrist
caud/o	tail
cec/o	cecum
cephal/o	head
cerebell/o	cerebellum
cerebr/o	cerebrum
cerumin/o	cerumen
cervic/o	neck, cervix
chem/o	chemical, drug
chol/e	bile, gall
cholangi/o	bile duct
cholecyst/o	gallbladder
choledoch/o	common bile duct
chondr/o	cartilage
chori/o	chorion
chrom/o	color
cis/o	to cut
clavicul/o	clavicle
coagul/o	clotting
coccyg/o	coccyx
cochle/o	cochlea
col/o	colon
colon/o	colon
colp/o	vagina
coni/o	dust
conjunctiv/o	conjunctiva
core/o	pupil
corne/o	cornea
coron/o	heart
cortic/o	outer portion
cost/o	rib
crani/o	skull
crin/o	secrete
crur/o	leg
cry/o	cold
crypt/o	hidden
culd/o	cul-de-sac
cutane/o	skin
cyan/o	blue
cycl/o	ciliary muscle
cyst/o	urinary bladder
cyt/o	cell
dacry/o	tear; tear duct
dent/o	tooth
derm/o	skin
dermat/o	skin
diaphor/o	profuse sweating
diaphragmat/o	diaphragm

Combining Form	Meaning
dipl/o	double
dist/o	away from
dors/o	back of body
duoden/o	duodenum
electr/o	electricity
embry/o	embryo
encephal/o	brain
enter/o	small intestine
eosin/o	rosy red
epididym/o	epididymis
epiglott/o	epiglottis
episi/o	vulva
epitheli/o	epithelium
erg/o	work
erythr/o	red
esophag/o	esophagus
esthesi/o	feeling, sensation
estr/o	female
fasci/o	fibrous band
femor/o	femur
fet/o	fetus
fibr/o	fibers
fibrin/o	fibers, fibrous
fibul/o	fibula
fluor/o	fluorescence, luminous
gastr/o	stomach
gingiv/o	gums
glauc/o	gray
gli/o	glue
glomerul/o	glomerulus
gloss/o	tongue
glute/o	buttock
glyc/o	sugar
glycos/o	sugar, glucose
gonad/o	sex glands
granul/o	granules
gynec/o	female
hem/o	blood
hemangi/o	blood vessel
hemat/o	blood
hepat/o	liver
hidr/o	sweat
hist/o	tissue
home/o	sameness
humer/o	humerus
hydr/o	water
hymen/o	hymen
hyster/o	uterus
ichthy/o	scaly, dry
ile/o	ileum
ili/o	ilium
immun/o	immune, protection
infer/o	below
ir/o	iris
irid/o	iris

Combining Form	Meaning
ischi/o	ischium
jejun/o	jejunum
kal/i	potassium
kerat/o	cornea, hard, horny
keton/o	ketone
kinesi/o	movement
kyph/o	hump
labi/o	lip
labyrinth/o	labyrinth
lacrim/o	tears
lact/o	milk
lamin/o	lamina, part of vertebra
lapar/o	abdomen
laryng/o	larynx, voice box
later/o	side
leuk/o	white
lingu/o	tongue
lip/o	fat
lith/o	stone
lob/o	lobe
lord/o	bent backwards
lumb/o	loin
lymph/o	lymph
lymphaden/o	lymph node
lymphangi/o	lymph vessel
mamm/o	breast
mandibul/o	mandible
mast/o	breast
maxill/o	maxilla
meat/o	meatus
medi/o	middle
medull/o	medulla oblongata, inner portion
melan/o	black
men/o	menses, menstruation
mening/o	meninges
meningi/o	meninges
ment/o	mind
metacarp/o	metacarpals
metatars/o	metatarsals
metr/o	uterus
morph/o	shape
muscul/o	muscle
mut/a	genetic change, mutation
my/o	muscle
myc/o	fungus
myel/o	spinal cord, bone marrow
myocardi/o	heart muscle
myos/o	muscle
myring/o	eardrum
nas/o	nose
nat/o	birth
natr/o	sodium
necr/o	death
nephr/o	kidney

Combining Form	Meaning
neur/o	nerve
neutr/o	neutral
noct/i	night
nyctal/o	night
ocul/o	eye
odont/o	tooth
olig/o	scanty
onc/o	tumor
onych/o	nail
oophor/o	ovary
ophthalm/o	eye
opt/o	eye, vision
optic/o	eye
or/o	mouth
orch/o	testes
orchi/o	testes
orchid/o	testes
organ/o	organ
orth/o	straight, upright
oste/o	bone
ot/o	ear
ov/o	egg
ovari/o	ovary
ox/i	oxygen
ox/o	oxygen
palat/o	palate
pancreat/o	pancreas
papill/o	optic disk
parathyroid/o	parathyroid gland
patell/o	patella
path/o	disease
ped/o	foot, child
pelv/o	pelvis
perine/o	perineum
peritone/o	peritoneum
phac/o	lens
phag/o	eat, swallow
phalang/o	phalanges
pharmac/o	drug
pharyng/o	throat, pharynx
phas/o	speech
phleb/o	vein
phon/o	sound
phot/o	light
phren/o	mind
pil/o	hair
pineal/o	pineal gland
pituitar/o	pituitary gland
plant/o	sole of the foot
pleur/o	pleura
pneum/o	lung, air
pneumon/o	lung, air
pod/o	foot
poli/o	gray matter
pont/o	pons

Combining Form	Meaning
poster/o	back
presby/o	old age
proct/o	anus and rectum
prostat/o	prostate
prosth/o	addition
proxim/o	near to
psych/o	mind
pub/o	pubis, genital region
pulmon/o	lung
pupill/o	pupil
py/o	pus
pyel/o	renal pelvis
pylor/o	pylorus
radi/o	x-ray, radius
radicul/o	nerve root
rect/o	rectum
ren/o	kidney
retin/o	retina
rhin/o	nose
rhytid/o	wrinkle
roentgen/o	X-ray
sacr/o	sacrum
salping/o	fallopian tubes, uterine tubes, eustachian tubes
sanguin/o	blood
scapul/o	scapula
schiz/o	divided
scler/o	hard, sclera
scoli/o	crooked, bent
seb/o	oil
sect/o	cut
sialaden/o	salivary gland
sigmoid/o	sigmoid colon
sinus/o	sinus, cavity
somat/o	body
somn/o	sleep
son/o	sound
spermat/o	sperm
sphygm/o	pulse
spin/o	spine
spir/o	breathing
splen/o	spleen
spondyl/o	vertebrae
staped/o	stapes
stern/o	sternum
steth/o	chest
super/o	above
synovi/o	synovial membrane
synov/o	synovial membrane
system/o	system
tars/o	ankle
ten/o	tendon
tend/o	tendon
tendin/o	tendon
testicul/o	testes

Combining Form	Meaning
thalam/o	thalamus
thec/o	sheath (meninges)
therm/o	heat
thorac/o	chest
thromb/o	clot
thym/o	thymus
thyr/o	thyroid gland
thyroid/o	thyroid gland
tibi/o	tibia
tom/o	to cut
tonsill/o	tonsils
tox/o	poison
toxic/o	poison
trache/o	trachea, windpipe
trich/o	hair
tympan/o	eardrum
uln/o	ulna
ungu/o	nail
ur/o	urine, urinary tract
ureter/o	ureter

Combining Form	Meaning
urethr/o	urethra
urin/o	urine
uter/o	uterus
uve/o	vascular
vagin/o	vagina
valv/o	valve
valvul/o	valve
varic/o	varicose veins
vascul/o	blood vessel
vas/o	vas deferens, vessel, duct
ven/o	vein
ventr/o	belly
ventricul/o	ventricle
vertebr/o	vertebra
vesic/o	bladder
vesicul/o	seminal vesicle
viscer/o	internal organ
vitre/o	glassy
vulv/o	vulva
xer/o	dry

Appendix III

Prefixes

Prefix	Meaning	Prefix	Meaning
a-	without, away from	**micro-**	small
ab-	away from	**mono-**	one
ad-	towards	**multi-**	many
allo-	other, different from usual	**neo-**	new
an-	without	**nulli-**	none
ante-	before, in front of	**pan-**	all
anti-	against	**para-**	beside, beyond, near
auto-	self	**per-**	through
bi-	two	**peri-**	around, about
brady-	slow	**poly-**	many
circum-	around	**post-**	behind, after
dys-	painful, difficult	**pre-**	before, in front of
endo-	within, inner	**pseudo-**	false
epi-	upon, over, above	**quad-**	four
eu-	normal, good	**retro-**	backward, behind
hemi-	half	**semi-**	partial, half
hetero-	different	**sub-**	below, under
homo-	same	**super-**	above, excess
hydro-	water	**supra-**	above
hyper-	over, above	**tachy-**	rapid, fast
hypo-	under, below	**trans-**	through, across
infra-	under, beneath, below	**tri-**	three
inter-	among, between	**ultra-**	beyond, excess
intra-	within, inside	**uni-**	one
macro-	large	**xeno-**	strange, foreign

Appendix IV

Suffixes

Suffix	Meaning
-ac	pertaining to
-al	pertaining to
-algesia	pain, sensitivity
-algia	pain
-an	pertaining to
-apheresis	removal, carry away
-ar	pertaining to
-arche	beginning
-ary	pertaining to
-asthenia	weakness
-blast	immature, embryonic
-capnia	carbon dioxide
-cele	hernia, protrusion
-centesis	puncture to withdraw fluid
-cise	cut
-clasia	to surgically break
-crine	to secrete
-cusis	hearing
-cyesis	state of pregnancy
-cyte	cell
-cytosis	more than the normal number of cells
-derma	skin
-desis	stabilize, fuse
-dipsia	thirst
-dynia	pain
-eal	pertaining to
-ectasia	dilation
-ectasis	dilation, expansion
-ectomy	surgical removal, excision
-emesis	vomit
-emia	blood condition
-esthesia	feeling, sensation
-gen	that which produces
-genesis	produces, generates
-genic	producing, produced by
-globin	protein
-globulin	protein
-gram	record, picture
-graph	instrument for recording
-graphy	process of recording
-gravida	pregnancy
-ia	state, condition
-iac	pertaining to
-iasis	abnormal condition
-iatrist	physician
-ic	pertaining to
-ical	pertaining to
-ile	pertaining to
-ior	pertaining to
-ism	state of
-itis	inflammation
-kinesia	movement
-listhesis	slipping
-lith	stone
-lithiasis	condition of stones
-logist	one who studies
-logy	study of
-lucent	to shine through
-lysis	destruction
-malacia	abnormal softening
-mania	excessive excitement
-manometer	instrument to measure pressure
-megaly	enlargement, large
-meter	instrument for measuring
-metrist	one who measures
-metry	process of measuring
-ole	small
-oma	tumor, mass
-opaque	nontransparent
-opia	vision
-opsy	view of
-orexia	appetite
-ory	pertaining to
-ose	pertaining to
-osis	abnormal condition
-osmia	smell
-ostomy	surgically create an opening
-otia	ear condition
-otomy	cutting into, incision
-ous	pertaining to
-para	to bear (offspring)
-paresis	weakness
-partum	childbirth
-pathy	disease
-penia	abnormal decrease, too few
-pepsia	digestion
-pexy	surgical fixation
-phage	eat, swallow
-phagia	eat, swallow
-phasia	speech
-phil	attracted to
-philia	to have an attraction for
-phobia	irrational fear
-phonia	voice
-phoresis	carrying
-plasia	growth, formation, development
-plasm	growth, formation, development

Suffix	Meaning
-plasty	surgical repair
-plegia	paralysis
-pnea	breathing
-poiesis	formation
-porosis	porous
-prandial	pertaining to a meal
-ptosis	drooping
-ptysis	spitting
-rrhage	excessive, abnormal flow
-rrhaphy	suture
-rrhea	discharge, flow
-rrhexis	rupture
-salpinx	fallopian tube
-sclerosis	hardening
-scope	instrument for viewing
-scopy	process of visually examining
-spermia	condition of sperm

Suffix	Meaning
-stasis	standing still
-stenosis	narrowing
-taxia	muscular coordination
-tension	pressure
-therapy	treatment
-thorax	chest
-tic	pertaining to
-tocia	labor, childbirth
-tome	instrument used to cut
-tonia	tone
-tripsy	surgical crushing
-trophy	nourishment, development
-tropia	to turn
-tropin	stimulate
-ule	small
-uria	condition of the urine

Chapter Review Answers

Chapter 1 Answers

Practice Exercises

A. 1. combining form 2. o 3. suffix 4. prefix 5. spelling 6. word root, combining vowel, prefix, suffix

B. 1. gland 2. cancer 3. heart 4. chemical 5. to cut 6. skin 7. small intestines 8. stomach 9. female 10. blood 11. water 12. immune 13. voice box 14. shape 15. kidney 16. nerve 17. eye 18. ear 19. lung 20. nose 21. urine, urinary tract

C. 1. surgical repair 2. narrowing 3. inflammation of 4. pertaining to 5. pain 6. cutting into 7. enlargement 8. surgical removal of 9. excessive, abnormal flow 10. puncture to remove fluid 11. record or picture 12. pertaining to 13. abnormal softening 14. state of 15. to suture 16. surgical creation of opening 17. surgical fixation 18. discharge or flow 19. process of visually examining 20. tumor, mass

D. 1. pulmonology 2. neuralgia or neurodynia 3. rhinorrhea 4. nephromalacia 5. cardiomegaly 6. gastrotomy 7. dermatitis 8. laryngectomy 9. arthroplasty 10. adenopathy

E. 1. intra-/endo- 2. macro- 3. pre-/ante- 4. peri- 5. neo- 6. a-/an- 7. hemi-/semi- 8. dys- 9. supra-/super-/hyper- 10. hyper-/ super- 11. poly-/multi- 12. brady- 13. auto- 14. trans- 15. bi-

F. 1. tachy-, fast 2. pseudo-, false 3. hypo-, under/below 4. inter-, among/between 5. eu-, normal/good 6. post-, after 7. mono-, one 8. sub-, below/under

G. 1. metastases 2. ova 3. diverticula 4. atria 5. diagnoses 6. vertebrae

H. 1. cardiology 2. gastrology 3. dermatology 4. ophthalmology 5. urology 6. nephrology 7. hematology 8. gynecology 9. neurology 10. pathology

I. 1. cardiomalacia 2. gastrostomy 3. rhinoplasty 4. hypertrophy 5. pathology 6. adenoma 7. gastroenterology 8. otitis 9. hydrotherapy 10. carcinogen

J. 1. l 2. e 3. j 4. f 5. d 6. k 7. m 8. o 9. g 10. n 11. b 12. h 13. a 14. c 15. i

Chapter 2 Answers

Practice Exercises

A. 1. cells, tissues, organs, systems, body 2. cell membrane, cytoplasm, nucleus 3. histology 4. epithelial 5. anatomical 6. right lower 7. cranial, spinal 8. nine 9. right iliac 10. pleural, pericardial

B. 1. c 2. a 3. b

C. 1. n 2. f 3. k 4. d 5. a 6. e 7. m 8. i 9. b 10. j 11. h 12. l 13. c 14. g

D. 1. epi-; above 2. inter-; between 3. intra-; within 4. peri-; around or about 5. hypo-; under or below 6. retro-; behind or backward 7. sub-; under or below 8. trans-; through or across

E. 1. dorsal 2. thoracic 3. superior 4. caudal 5. visceral 6. lateral 7. distal 8. neural 9. systemic 10. muscular 11. ventral 12. anterior 13. cephalic 14. medial

F. 1. MS 2. lat 3. RUQ 4. CV 5. GI 6. AP 7. GU 8. LLQ

G. 1. internal organ 2. back 3. abdomen 4. chest 5. middle 6. belly 7. front 8. tissues 9. epithelium 10. skull 11. body 12. near to 13. head

H. 1. integumentary, d 2. cardiovascular, i 3. digestive, g 4. female reproductive, b 5. musculoskeletal (skeletal), a 6. respiratory, j 7. urinary, c 8. male reproductive, f 9. nervous, h 10. musculoskeletal (muscular), e

I. 1. a 2. c 3. f 4. e 5. a 6. d 7. b 8. e 9. c 10. b

J. 1. cephalic 2. pubic 3. crural 4. gluteal 5. cervical 6. brachial 7. dorsum 8. thoracic

K. 1. otorhinolaryngology 2. cardiology 3. gynecology 4. orthopedics 5. ophthalmology 6. urology 7. dermatology 8. gastroenterology

Labeling Exercise

A. 1. cell 2. tissue 3. organ 4. system 5. whole body

B1. 1. frontal or coronal plane 2. sagittal or median plane 3. transverse or horizontal plane

B2. 1. cephalic 2. cervical 3. thoracic 4. brachial 5. abdominal 6. pelvic 7. pubic 8. crural 9. trunk 10. vertebral 11. dorsum 12. gluteal

Chapter 3 Answers

Practice Exercises

A. 1. epidermis, dermis, subcutaneous layer 2. basal cell 3. adipose 4. dermis 5. keratin 6. melanin 7. corium 8. nail bed 9. sebaceous, sweat 10. apocrine

B. 1. dermatitis 2. dermatosis 3. dermatome 4. dermatologist 5. dermatoplasty 6. dermatology 7. melanoma 8. melanocyte 9. ichthyoderma 10. leukoderma 11. erythroderma 12. onychomalacia 13. paronychia 14. onychophagia 15. onychectomy

C. 1. cold 2. skin 3. profuse sweating 4. pus 5. blue 6. nail 7. fat 8. sweat 9. wrinkles 10. oil 11. hair 12. death

D. 1. flat, discolored area 2. small solid raised spot less than 0.5 cm 3. fluid filled sac 4. crack-like lesion 5. raised spot containing pus 6. small, round swollen area 7. fluid-filled blister 8. open sore 9. firm, solid mass larger than 0.5 cm 10. torn or jagged wound

E. 1. redness involving superficial layer of skin 2. burn damage through epidermis and into dermis causing vesicles 3. burn damage to full thickness of epidermis and dermis

F. 1. e 2. f 3. i 4. j 5. a 6. c 7. l 8. g 9. k 10. h 11. d 12. b

G. 1. h 2. i 3. j 4. e 5. c 6. a 7. f 8. g 9. b 10. d

H. 1. FS 2. I & D 3. ID 4. subq, subcu, SC, sc 5. UV 6. BX, bx

I. 1. culture and sensitivity 2. basal cell carcinoma 3. dermatology 4. skin graft 5. decubitus ulcer 6. malignant melanoma

J. 1. xeroderma 2. petechiae 3. tinea 4. scabies 5. paronychia 6. Kaposi's sarcoma 7. impetigo 8. keloid 9. exfoliative cytology 10. frozen section

K. 1. hypodermic, or subcutaneous 2. intradermal 3. epidermis

L. 1. graft from another human 2. graft from another species 3. graft from self 4. graft from another species

M. 1. antifungal, f 2. antipruritic, d 3. antiparasitic, a 4. anti-viral, c 5. corticosteroid cream, b 6. anesthetic, g 7. antibiotic, e

Medical Record Analysis

1. c—intense itching (urticaria) 2. translated into student's own words: size of 10 × 14 mm; left cheek 20 mm anterior to the ear; erythema; poorly defined borders, depigmentation, vesicles 3. wear sunscreen and a hat 4. congestive heart failure; CHF; dyspnea, lower extremity edema, cyanosis 5. biopsy 6. excision; dermatoplasty

Chart Note Transcription

1. ulcer 2. dermatologist 3. pruritus 4. erythema 5. pustules 6. dermis 7. necrosis 8. culture and sensitivity 9. cellulitis 10. debridement

Labeling Exercise

A. 1. epidermis 2. dermis 3. subcutaneous layer 4. sweat gland 5. sweat duct 6. hair 7. sebaceous gland 8. arrector pili muscle 9. sensory receptors

B1. 1. epidermis 2. dermis 3. subcutaneous layer 4. sebaceous gland 5. arrector pili muscle 6. hair shaft 7. hair follicle 8. hair root 9. papilla

B2. 1. free edge 2. lateral nail groove 3. lunula 4. nail bed 5. nail body 6. cuticle 7. nail root

Chapter 4 Answers

Practice Exercises

A. 1. axial, appendicular 2. smooth 3. frame, protect vital organs, work with muscles for movement, store minerals, red blood cell production 4. myoneural 5. short 6. periosteum 7. wrist 8. cancellous 9. synovial 10. skeletal, smooth, cardiac 11. foramen 12. diaphysis

B. 1. osteocyte 2. osteoblast 3. osteoporosis 4. osteopathy 5. osteotomy 6. osteotome 7. osteomyelitis 8. osteomalacia 9. osteochondroma 10. myopathy 11. myoplasty 12. myorrhaphy 13. electromyogram 14. myasthenia 15. tenodynia 16. tenorrhaphy 17. arthrodesis 18. arthroplasty 19. arthrotomy 20. arthritis 21. arthrocentesis 22. arthralgia 23. chondrectomy 24. chondroma 25. chondromalacia

C. 1. -desis 2. -asthenia 3. -listhesis 4. -clasia 5. -kinesia 6. -porosis

D. 1. femoral 2. sternal 3. clavicular 4. coccygeal 5. maxillary 6. tibial 7. patellar 8. phalangeal 9. humeral 10. pubic

E. 1. lamina, part of vertebra 2. stiff joint 3. cartilage 4. vertebrae 5. muscle 6. straight 7. hump 8. tendon 9. bone marrow 10. joint

F. 1. surgical repair of cartilage 2. slow movement 3. porous bone 4. abnormal increase in lumbar spine curve (swayback) 5. lack of development/nourishment 6. bone marrow tumor 7. artificial substitute for a body part 8. skull incision 9. puncture of a joint to withdraw fluid 10. bursa inflammation

G. 1. cervical, 7 2. thoracic, 12 3. lumbar, 5 4. sacrum, 1 (5 fused) 5. coccyx, 1 (3–5 fused)

H. 1. S = -scopy; visual examination of inside of a joint 2. P = inter-, S = -al; pertaining to between vertebrae 3. S = -malacia; softening of cartilage 4. S = -ectomy; surgical removal of disk 5. P = intra- S = -al; pertaining to inside the skull 6. P = sub-, -ar = pertaining to; pertaining to under the scapula

I. 1. e 2. d 3. b 4. c 5. a 6. h 7. g 8. f

J. 1. c 2. h 3. f 4. g 5. d 6. e 7. a 8. b

K. 1. medical doctor who treats musculoskeletal system 2. uses manipulation of vertebral column 3. specialty that treats disorders of feet 4. fitting of braces and splints 5. fabricates and fits artificial limbs

L. 1. patella 2. tarsals 3. clavicle 4. femur 5. phalanges 6. carpals 7. tibia 8. scapula 9. phalanges

M. 1. degenerative joint disease 2. electromyogram 3. first cervical vertebra 4. sixth thoracic vertebra 5. intramuscular 6. range of motion 7. juvenile rheumatoid arthritis 8. left lower extremity 9. orthopedics 10. carpal tunnel syndrome

N. 1. CDH 2. TKR 3. HNP 4. DTR 5. UE 6. L5 7. BDT 8. AK 9. fx/FX 10. NSAID

O. 1. osteoporosis 2. rickets 3. lateral epicondylitis 4. whiplash 5. osteogenic sarcoma 6. scoliosis 7. pseudotrophic muscular dystrophy 8. systemic lupus erythematosus 9. spondylolisthesis 10. carpal tunnel syndrome

P. 1. nonsteroidal anti-inflammatory drugs, b 2. corticosteroids, e 3. skeletal muscle relaxants, a 4. bone reabsorption inhibitors, c 5. calcium supplements, d

Medical Record Analysis

1. rehabilitation specialist; Motrin (a nonsteroidal anti-inflammatory medication), physical therapy for range of motion and strengthening exercises, and low-fat, low-calorie diet 2. arthroscopy; torn lateral meniscus and chondromalacia; arthroscopic meniscectomy 3. a—nonsurgical treatments, such as medicine and therapy; b—a patient who has not been admitted to the hospital 4. physical therapy for lower extremity ROM and strengthening exercises, and gait training with a walker; occupational therapy for ADL instruction, especially dressing and personal care 5. patient was able to bend knee to 90° but lacked 5° of being able to straighten it back out; 6. a—blockage of arteries to the heart muscle; b—high blood pressure

Chart Note Transcription

1. Colles' fracture (fx) 2. cast 3. fracture 4. orthopedist 5. osteoporosis 6. computerized axial tomography (CT or CAT scan) 7. flexion 8. extension 9. comminuted fracture (fx) 10. femur 11. total hip arthroplasty (THA)

Labeling Exercise

A. 1. skull 2. cervical vertebrae 3. sternum 4. ribs 5. thoracic vertebrae 6. lumbar vertebrae 7. ilium 8. pubis 9. ischium 10. femur 11. patella 12. tibia 13. fibula 14. tarsals 15. metatarsals 16. phalanges 17. maxilla 18. mandible 19. scapula 20. humerus 21. ulna 22. radius 23. sacrum 24. coccyx 25. carpals 26. metacarpals 27. phalanges

B1. 1. proximal epiphysis 2. diaphysis 3. distal epiphysis 4. articular cartilage 5. epiphyseal line 6. spongy or cancellous bone 7. compact or cortical bone 8. medullary cavity

B2. 1. periosteum 2. synovial membrane 3. articular cartilage 4. joint cavity 5. joint capsule

Chapter 5 Answers

Practice Exercises

A. 1. cardiology 2. endocardium, myocardium, epicardium 3. sinoatrial node 4. away from 5. tricuspid, pulmonary, mitral (bicuspid), aortic 6. atria, ventricles 7. pulmonary 8. apex 9. septum 10. systole, diastole

B. 1. cardiac 2. cardiomyopathy 3. cardiomegaly 4. tachycardia 5. bradycardia 6. cardiorrhexis 7. angiostenosis 8. angiitis 9. angiospasm 10. arterial 11. arteriosclerosis 12. arteriole

C. 1. endocarditis 2. epicarditis 3. myocarditis

D. 1. heart 2. valve 3. chest 4. artery 5. vein 6. vessel 7. ventricle 8. clot 9. atrium 10. fatty substance

E. 1. venous 2. cardiology 3. venogram 4. electrocardiography 5. hypertension 6. hypotension 7. valvoplasty 8. interventricular 9. atherectomy 10. arteriostenosis

F. 1. -tension 2. -stenosis 3. -manometer 4. -ule, -ole 5. –sclerosis 6. –lytic

G. 1. blood pressure 2. congestive heart failure 3. myocardial infarction 4. coronary care unit 5. premature ventricular contraction 6. cardiopulmonary resuscitation 7. coronary artery disease 8. chest pain 9. electrocardiogram 10. first heart sound

H. 1. MVP 2. VSD 3. PTCA 4. Vfib 5. DVT 6. LDH 7. CoA 8. tPA 9. CV 10. ECC

I. 1. f 2. h 3. d 4. g 5. b 6. i 7. a 8. c 9. e 10. j

J. 1. thin flexible tube 2. an area of dead tissue 3. a blood clot 4. pounding heartbeat 5. backflow 6. weakened and ballooning arterial wall 7. complete stoppage of heart activity 8. serious cardiac arrhythmia 9. heart attack 10. varicose veins in anal region

K. 1. c 2. g 3. j 4. a 5. d 6. b 7. i 8. e 9. f 10. h

L. 1. antiarrhythmic, e 2. antilipidemic, g 3. cardiotonic, f 4. diuretic, h 5. anticoagulant, b 6. thrombolytic, a 7. vasodilator, d 8. calcium channel blocker, c

M. 1. murmur 2. defibrillation 3. hypertension 4. pacemaker 5. varicose veins 6. angina pectoris 7. CCU 8. MI 9. angiography 10. echocardiogram 11. hemangioma 12. Holter monitor 13. CHF

Medical Record Analysis

1. Lopressor to control blood pressure, Norpace to slow down the heart rate, Valium to reduce anxiety, Lasix to reduce swelling 2. EKG, cardiac enzymes blood test; myocardial infarction 3. patient developed dyspnea and cyanosis 4. b—dizziness 5. mitral valve replacement 6. compare: both conditions allow blood to flow backwards; contrast: prolapse—too floppy, valve droops down, and stenosis—too stiff, preventing it from opening all the way or closing all the way

Chart Note Transcription

1. angina pectoris 2. bradycardia 3. hypertension 4. myocardial infarction (MI) 5. electrocardiogram (EKG, ECG) 6. cardiac enzymes 7. coronary artery disease (CAD) 8. cardiac catheterization 9. stress test (treadmill test) 10. percutaneous transluminal coronary angioplasty (PTCA) 11. coronary artery bypass graft (CABG)

Labeling Exercise

A. 1. heart 2. artery 3. vein 4. capillary

B1. 1. right atrium 2. right ventricle 3. pulmonary arteries 4. capillary bed lungs 5. pulmonary veins 6. left atrium 7. left ventricle 8. aorta 9. systemic arteries 10. systemic capillary beds 11. systemic veins 12. vena cavae

B2. 1. right atrium 2. tricuspid valve 3. right ventricle 4. pulmonary valve 5. pulmonary trunk 6. pulmonary artery 7. pulmonary vein 8. left atrium 9. mitral or bicuspid valve 10. left ventricle 11. aortic valve 12. aorta 13. superior vena cava 14. inferior vena cava 15. endocardium 16. myocardium 17. pericardium

Chapter 6 Answers

Practice Exercises

A. 1. hematology 2. spleen, tonsils, thymus 3. thoracic duct, right lymphatic duct 4. axillary, cervical, mediastinal, inguinal 5. phagocytosis 6. erythrocytes (red blood cells), leukocytes (white blood cells), platelets (thrombocytes) 7. plasma 8. active acquired 9. antibody-mediated 10. hemostasis

B. 1. splenomegaly 2. splenectomy 3. splenotomy 4. lymphocytes 5. lymphoma 6. lymphadenopathy 7. lymphadenoma 8. lymphadenitis 9. immunologist 10. immunoglobulin 11. immunology 12. hematic 13. hematoma 14. hematopoiesis 15. hemolytic 16. hemolysis

C. 1. leukopenia 2. erythropenia 3. thrombopenia 4. pancytopenia 5. leukocytosis 6. erythrocytosis 7. thrombocytosis 8. hemoglobin 9. immunoglobulin 10. erythrocyte 11. leukocyte 12. lymphocyte

D. 1. lymphaden/o 2. thromb/o 3. sanguin/o, hem/o, hemat/o 4. tonsill/o 5. tox/o 6. phag/o 7. lymphangi/o 8. tonsill/o 9. splen/o 10. lymph/o

E. 1. basophil 2. complete blood count 3. hemoglobin 4. prothrombin time 5. graft vs. host disease 6. red blood count/red blood cell 7. packed cell volume 8. erythrocyte sedimentation rate 9. differential 10. lymphocyte

F. 1. AIDS 2. ARC 3. HIV 4. ALL 5. BMT 6. mono 7. KS 8. eosins, eos 9. IG 10. SCIDS

G. 1. g 2. i 3. e 4. a 5. h 6. d 7. c 8. j 9. b 10. f

H. 1. c 2. h 3. d 4. a 5. e 6. b 7. f 8. g 9. j 10. i

I. 1. d 2. f 3. b 4. g 5. a 6. e 7. c

J. 1. reverse transcriptase inhibitor, e 2. anticoagulant, a 3. antihemorrhagic, d 4. blocks effects of histamine, h 5. immunosuppresant, f 6. thrombolytic, b 7. hematinic, g 8. corticosteroid, c 9. antiplatelet, i

K. 1. polycythemia vera 2. mononucleosis 3. anaphylactic shock 4. HIV 5. Kaposi's sarcoma 6. AIDS 7. Hodgkin's disease 8. *Pneumocystis carinii* 9. peritonsillar abscess

Medical Record Analysis

1. feeling "run down," intermittent diarrhea, weight loss, dry cough 2. negative means absence; there was no evidence of pneumonia in the X-ray 3. a—the original or critical reaction; b—contained within a capsule; c—fluid collecting within the abdominal cavity; d—spread to a dis-

tant site 4. ultrasound 5. d—an enlarged spleen (splenomegaly) 6. magnetic resonance image (MRI); brain, liver 7. resolved: ascites, diarrhea; persisted: dry cough

Chart Note Transcription

1. hematologist 2. ELISA 3. prothrombin time 4. complete blood count (CBC) 5. erythropenia 6. thrombopenia 7. leukocytosis 8. bone marrow aspiration 9. leukemia 10. homologous transfusion

Labeling Exercise

A. 1. plasma 2. red blood cells or erythrocytes 3. platelets or thrombocytes 4. white blood cells or leukocytes

B1. 1. thymus gland 2. lymph node 3. tonsil 4. spleen 5. lymphatic vessels

B2. 1. cervical nodes 2. mediastinal nodes 3. axillary nodes 4. inguinal nodes

Chapter 7 Answers

Practice Exercises

A. 1. exchange of O_2 and CO_2 2. ventilation 3. exchange of O_2 and CO_2 in the lungs 4. exchange of O_2 and CO_2 at cellular level 5. nasal cavity, pharynx, larynx, trachea, bronchial tubes, lungs 6. pharynx 7. epiglottis 8. filter out dust 9. diaphragm 10. 12–20 11. 30–60 12. 3; 2 13. alveoli 14. pleura 15. palate 16. bronchioles

B. 1. rhinitis 2. rhinorrhagia 3. rhinorrhea 4. rhinoplasty 5. laryngitis 6. laryngospasm 7. laryngoscopy 8. laryngeal 9. laryngotomy 10. laryngectomy 11. laryngoplasty 12. laryngoplegia 13. bronchial 14. bronchitis 15. bronchoscopy 16. bronchogenic 17. bronchospasm 18. thoracoplasty 19. thoracotomy 20. thoracalgia 21. thoracic 22. tracheotomy 23. tracheoplasty 24. tracheostenosis 25. endotracheal 26. tracheitis 27. tracheostomy

C. 1. trachea or windpipe 2. larynx 3. bronchus 4. breathing 5. lung or air 6. nose 7. dust 8. pleura 9. epiglottis 10. alveolus or air sac 11. lung 12. oxygen 13. sinus 14. lobe 15. nose

D. 1. dilation 2. carbon dioxide 3. voice 4. chest 5. breathing 6. spitting 7. smell

E. 1. eupnea 2. dyspnea 3. tachypnea 4. orthopnea 5. apnea

F. 1. volume of air in the lungs after a maximal inhalation or inspiration 2. amount of air entering lungs in a single inspiration or leaving air in single expiration of quiet breathing 3. air remaining in the lungs after a forced expiration

G. 1. inhalation or inspiration 2. hemoptysis 3. pulmonary emboli 4. sinusitis 5. pharyngitis 6. pneumothorax 7. pertussis 8. pleurotomy 9. pleurisy 10. nasopharyngitis

H. 1. URI 2. PFT 3. LLL 4. O_2 5. CO_2 6. IPPB 7. COPD 8. Bronch 9. TLC 10. TB 11. IRDS

I. 1. chest X-ray 2. tidal volume 3. temperature, pulse, respirations 4. arterial blood gases 5. dyspnea on exertion 6. right upper lobe 7. sudden infant death syndrome 8. total lung capacity 9. adult respiratory distress syndrome 10. metered dose inhaler 11. clear to auscultation 12. severe acute respiratory syndrome

J. 1. e 2. k 3. h 4. a 5. j 6. l 7. c 8. g 9. f 10. b 11. d 12. i

K. 1. cardiopulmonary resuscitation 2. thoracentesis 3. respirator 4. supplemental oxygen 5. patent 6. ventilation-perfusion scan 7. sputum cytology 8. hyperventilation 9. rhonchi 10. anthracosis

L. 1. decongestant, f 2. antitussive, a 3. antibiotic, c 4. expectorant, g 5. mucolytic, h 6. bronchodilator, d 7. antihistamine, e 8. corticosteroid, b

Medical Record Analysis

1. sudden attack 2. intravenous, immediately, arterial blood gases 3. steroid to reduce inflammation; Alupent to relax bronchospasms 4. what triggers his attacks; referred patient to an allergist 5. hacking and producing thick, nonpurulent phlegm 6. a—crackling lung sounds

Chart Note Transcription

1. dyspnea 2. tachypnea 3. arterial blood gases (ABGs) 4. hypoxemia 5. auscultation 6. rales 7. purulent 8. sputum 9. CXR 10. pneumonia 11. endotracheal intubation

Labeling Exercise

A. 1. pharynx and larynx 2. trachea 3. nasal cavity 4. bronchial tubes 5. lungs

B1. 1. nares 2. paranasal sinuses 3. nasal cavity 4. pharyngeal tonsil 5. Eustachian tube 6. hard palate 7. soft palate 8. palatine tonsil 9. epiglottis 10. vocal cords 11. esophagus 12. trachea

B2. 1. trachea 2. right upper lobe 3. right middle lobe 4. right lower lobe 5. apex of lung 6. left upper lobe 7. left lower lobe 8. diaphragm

Chapter 8 Answers

Practice Exercises

A. 1. gastrointestinal 2. gut, alimentary canal, mouth, anus 3. salivary glands, liver, gallbladder, pancreas 4. digesting food, absorbing nutrients, eliminating waste 5. cutting, grinding 6. peristalsis 7. hydrochloric acid, chyme 8. duodenum, jejunum, ileum 9. sigmoid 10. bile, eumulsification

B. 1. esophagus 2. liver 3. ileum 4. anus and rectum 5. tongue 6. lip 7. jejunum 8. sigmoid colon 9. rectum 10. gum 11. gallbladder 12. duodenum 13. anus 14. small intestine 15. teeth

C. 1. gastritis 2. gastroenterology 3. gastrectomy 4. gastroscopy 5. gastralgia 6. gastromegaly 7. gastrotomy 8. esophagitis 9. esophagoscopy 10. esophagoplasty 11. esophageal 12. esophagectasis 13. proctopexy 14. proctoptosis 15. proctitis 16. proctologist 17. cholecystectomy 18. cholecystolithiasis 19. cholecystolithotripsy 20. cholecystitis 21. laparoscope 22. laparotomy 23. laparoscopy 24. hepatoma 25. hepatomegaly 26. hepatic 27. hepatitis 28. pancreatitis 29. pancreatic 30. colostomy 31. colitis

D. 1. postprandial 2. cholelithiasis 3. anorexia 4. dysphagia 5. hematemesis 6. bradypepsia

E. 1. bowel movement 2. upper gastrointestinal series 3. barium enema 4. bowel sounds 5. nausea and vomiting 6. ova and parasites 7. by mouth 8. common bile duct 9. nothing by mouth 10. postprandial

F. 1. NG 2. GI 3. HBV 4. FOBT 5. IBD 6. HSV-1 7. AST 8. pc 9. PUD 10. GERD

G. 1. visual exam of the colon 2. tooth x-ray 3. bright red blood in the stools 4. blood test to determine amount of waste product in the bloodstream 5. weight loss and wasting from a chronic illness 6. use NG tube to wash out stomach 7. surgical repair of hernia 8. pulling teeth 9. surgical crushing of common bile duct stone 10. surgically create a connection between two organs

H. 1. h 2. i 3. f 4. c 5. a 6. j 7. l 8. e 9. b 10. k 11. d 12. g 13. o 14. p 15. n 16. m

I. 1. liver biopsy 2. colostomy 3. barium swallow 4. lower GI series 5. colectomy 6. fecal occult blood test 7. choledocholithotripsy 8. total parenteral nutrition 9. gastric stapling 10. cholecystography 11. colonoscopy 12. ileostomy

J. 1. d 2. g 3. h 4. e 5. f 6. b 7. c 8. a

K. 1. antidiarrheal, g 2. proton pump inhibitor, h 3. emetic, f 4. antiemetic, d 5. H_2-receptor antagonist, a 6. anorexiant, b 7. laxative, c 8. antacid, e

Medical Record Analysis

1. left upper quadrant, stomach, spleen 2. complete blood count (CBC), occult blood test 3. gastroscopy; a deep ulcer 1.5 cm in diameter, evidence of bleeding 4. gastric carcinoma 5. d—a blood transfusion 6. tonsillectomy, compound fracture, BPH, and TUR

Chart Note Transcription

1. gastroenterologist 2. constipation 3. cholelithiasis 4. cholecystectomy 5. gastroesophageal reflux disease 6. ascites 7. lower gastrointestinal series 8. polyposis 9. colonoscopy 10. sigmoid colon 11. colectomy 12. colostomy

Labeling Exercise

A. 1. salivary glands 2. esophagus 3. pancreas 4. small intestine 5. oral cavity 6. stomach 7. liver and gallbladder 8. colon

B1. 1. esophagus 2. cardiac or lower esophageal sphincter 3. pyloric sphincter 4. duodenum 5. antrum 6. fundus of stomach 7. rugae 8. body of stomach

B2. 1. cystic duct 2. common bile duct 3. gallbladder 4. duodenum 5. liver 6. hepatic duct 7. pancreas 8. pancreatic duct

Chapter 9 Answers

Practice Exercises

A. 1. nephrons 2. filtration, reabsorption, secretion 3. electrolytes 4. retroperitoneal 5. hilum 6. glomerulus 7. calyx 8. two, one 9. micturition, voiding 10. urinalysis

B. 1. nephropexy 2. nephrogram 3. nephrolithiasis 4. nephrectomy 5. nephritis 6. nephropathy 7. nephrosclerosis 8. cystitis 9. cystorrhagia 10. cystoplasty 11. cystoscope 12. cystalgia 13. pyeloplasty 14. pyelitis 15. pyelogram 16. ureterolith 17. ureterectasis 18. ureterostenosis 19. urethritis 20. urethroscope

C. 1. urine 2. meatus 3. urinary bladder 4. kidney 5. renal pelvis 6. sugar 7. night 8. scanty 9. ureter 10. glomerulus

D. 1. drooping 2. condition of the urine 3. stone 4. surgical crushing 5. condition of stones

E. 1. urination, voiding 2. increases urine production 3. pain associated with kidney stone 4. inserting a tube through urethra into the bladder 5. inflammation of renal pelvis 6. inflammation of glomeruli in the kidney 7. incision to remove stone

8. bedwetting 9. enlargement of uretheral opening 10. damage to glomerulus secondary to diabetes mellitus 11. lab test of chemical composition of urine 12. decrease in force of urine stream

F. 1. anuria 2. hematuria 3. calculus/nephrolith 4. lithotripsy 5. urethritis 6. pyuria 7. bacteriuria 8. dysuria 9. ketonuria 10. proteinuria 11. polyuria

G. 1. K^+ 2. Na^+ 3. UA 4. BUN 5. SG, sp.gr. 6. IVP 7. BNO 8. I & O 9. ATN 10. ESRD

H. 1. kidneys, ureters, bladder 2. catheter/catheterization 3. cystoscopy 4. genitourinary 5. extracorporeal shockwave lithotripsy 6. urinary tract infection 7. urine culture 8. retrograde pyelogram 9. acute renal failure 10. blood urea nitrogen 11. chronic renal failure 12. water

I. 1. c 2. g 3. h 4. i 5. f 6. e 7. d 8. b 9. a 10. j

J. 1. renal transplant 2. nephropexy 3. urinary tract infection 4. pyelolithectomy 5. renal biopsy 6. ureterectomy 7. cystostomy 8. cystoscopy 9. IVP

K. 1. antispasmodic, b 2. antibiotic, c 3. diuretic, a

Medical Record Analysis

1. bladder neck obstruction 2. severe right side pain, unable to stand fully erect, 101°F temperature, sweaty, and flushed skin 3. large enough to be visible with the naked eye 4. a—present from birth; b—of long duration; c—disease-causing; d—by mouth 5. a—protein 6. alike: both are infections of kidney tissue; different: glomerulonephritis—infection is in the glomerulus and it allows protein to leak into the urine; pyelonephritis—infection is in the renal pelvis portion of the kidney, more common, often caused by bladder infection moving up the ureters to the kidney

Chart Note Transcription

1. urologist 2. hematuria 3. cystitis 4. clean-catch specimen 5. urinalysis (U/A, UA) 6. pyuria 7. retrograde pyelogram 8. ureter 9. ureterolith 10. extracorporeal shockwave lithotripsy (ESWL) 11. calculi

Labeling Exercise

A. 1. kidney 2. urinary bladder 3. ureter 4. male urethra 5. female urethra

B1. 1. cortex 2. medulla 3. calyx 4. renal pelvis 5. renal papilla 6. renal pyramid 7. ureter

B2. 1. efferent arteriole 2. glomerular (Bowman's) capsule 3. glomerulus 4. afferent arteriole 5. proximal convoluted tubule 6. descending loop of Henle 7. distal convoluted tubule 8. collecting tubule 9. ascending loop of Henle 10. peritubular capillaries

Chapter 10 Answers

Practice Exercises

A. 1. gynecology 2. gynecologist 3. dilation, expulsion, placental 4. gestation 5. menopause 6. ovum 7. endometrium 8. uterus 9. fallopian tubes 10. total abdominal hysterectomy–bilateral salpingo-oophorectomy

B. 1. colposcopy 2. colposcope 3. cervicectomy 4. cervicitis 5. cervical 6. hysteropexy 7. hysterectomy 8. hysterorrhexis 9. oophoritis 10. oophorectomy 11. mammary 12. mammogram 13. mammoplasty 14. amniotic 15. amniotomy 16. amniorrhea

C. 1. cervix 2. last menstrual period 3. fetal heart rate 4. pelvic inflammatory disease 5. date of birth 6. cesarean section 7. newborn 8. premenstrual syndrome 9. toxic shock syndrome 10. low birth weight

D. 1. GI, grav I 2. AI 3. UC 4. FTND 5. IUD 6. D & C 7. DUB 8. gyn/GYN 9. AB 10. OCPs

E. 1. uterus 2. uterus 3. female 4. vulva 5. ovary 6. ovary 7. fallopian tube 8. menstruation or menses 9. vagina 10. breast

F. 1. b 2. e 3. h 4. c 5. i 6. j 7. d 8. n 9. l 10. f 11. o 12. g 13. k 14. m 15. a

G. 1. conization 2. stillbirth 3. puberty 4. premenstrual syndrome 5. laparoscopy 6. fibroid tumor 7. D & C 8. eclampsia 9. endometriosis 10. cesarean section

H. 1. labor, childbirth 2. pregnancy 3. beginning 4. pregnancy 5. childbirth 6. to bear (offspring) 7. fallopian tube 8. sperm condition

I. 1. e 2. i 3. h 4. c 5. a 6. d 7. g 8. b 9. f

J. 1. urinary, reproductive 2. testes, epididymis, penis 3. foreskin 4. testes 5. bulbourethral glands 6. testosterone 7. perineum

K. 1. prostatectomy 2. prostatic 3. prostatitis 4. orchiectomy 5. orchioplasty 6. orchiotomy 7. andropathy 8. androgen 9. spermatogenesis 10. spermatolysis

L. 1. suprapubic prostatectomy 2. transurethral resection 3. genitourinary 4. benign prostatic hypertrophy 5. digital rectal exam 6. prostate-specific antigen

M. 1. the formation of mature sperm 2. accumulation of fluid within the testes 3. surgical removal of the prostate gland by inserting a device through the urethra and removing prostate tissue 4. failure to produce sperm 5. surgical removal of the testes 6. surgical removal of part or all of the vas deferens 7. destruction of tissue with an electric current, caustic agent, hot iron, or by freezing

N. 1. androgen therapy, f 2. oxytocin, a 3. antiprostatic agent, b 4. birth control pills, g 5. kills sperm, d

6. erectile dysfunction agent, h 7. hormone replacement therapy, i 8. abortifacient, e 9. fertility drug, c

Medical Record Analysis

1. oophorectomy and chemotherapy; full body CT scan 2. menarche at 13, menorrhagia with chronic anemia 3. c—nullipara and d—multigravida 4. pelvic ultrasound; because the placenta overlies the cervix, it will detach before the baby can physically be born 5. size consistent with 25 weeks of gestation, turned head down, umbilical cord is not around the neck, fetal heart tones are strong, male, no evidence of developmental or genetic disorders 6. a—a greater than normal level of risk of problems developing or fetal death with this pregnancy; b—she looks like she is 8 months pregnant (her abdomen is not too small or too large)

Chart Note Transcription

1. ejaculation 2. cryptorchidism 3. orchidopexy 4. vasectomy 5. ejaculation 6. digital rectal exam (DRE) 7. prostate cancer 8. prostate-specific antigen (PSA) 9. benign prostatic hypertrophy (BPH) 10. transurethral resection (TUR)

Labeling Exercise

A1. 1. fallopian tube 2. ovary 3. fundus of uterus 4. corpus (body) of uterus 5. cervix 6. vagina 7. clitoris 8. labium majora 9. labia minora

A2. 1. seminal vesicles 2. vas deferens 3. prostate gland 4. bulbourethral gland 5. urethra 6. epididymis 7. glans penis 8. testis

B. 1. areola 2. nipple 3. lactiferous gland 4. lactiferous duct 5. fat

Chapter 11 Answers

Practice Exercises

A. 1. endocrinology 2. pituitary 3. gonads 4. corticosteroids 5. testosterone 6. estrogen, progesterone 7. antidiuretic hormone (ADH) 8. thymus gland 9. exophthalmos 10. adenocarcinoma

B. 1. thyroidectomy 2. thyroidal 3. hyperthyroidism 4. pancreatic 5. pancreatitis 6. pancreatectomy 7. pancreatotomy 8. adrenal 9. adrenomegaly 10. adrenopathy 11. thymoma 12. thymectomy 13. thymic 14. thymitis

C. 1. b 2. a 3. e 4. k 5. h 6. j 7. i 8. f 9. g 10. c 11. d

D. 1. protein-bound iodine 2. potassium 3. thyroxine 4. glucose tolerance test 5. diabetes mellitus 6. basal metabolic rate 7. sodium 8. antidiuretic hormone

E. 1. NIDDM 2. IDDM 3. ACTH 4. PTH 5. T_3 6. TSH 7. FBS 8. PRL

F. 1. glycosuria 2. endocrine 3. polyuria 4. hypercalcemia 5. polydipsia 6. adrenocorticotropin 7. postprandial

G. 1. hormone obtained from cortex of adrenal gland 2. having excessive hair 3. a nerve condition characterized with spasms of extremities; can occur from imbalance of pH and calcium or disorder of parathyroid gland 4. disorder of the retina occurring with diabetes mellitus 5. increase in blood sugar level 6. decrease in blood sugar level 7. another term for epinephrine; produced by inner portion of adrenal gland 8. hormone produced by pancreas; essential for metabolism of blood sugar 9. toxic condition due to hyperactivity of thyroid gland 10. a condition resulting when the endocrine gland secretes more hormone than is needed by the body

H. 1. sodium 2. female 3. pineal gland 4. pituitary gland 5. potassium 6. calcium 7. parathyroid glands 8. extremities 9. sugar 10. sex glands

I. 1. e 2. d 3. a 4. f 5. c 6. b

J. 1. insulinoma 2. ketoacidosis 3. panhypopituitarinism 4. pheochromocytoma 5. Hashimoto's disease 6. gynecomastia

K. 1. corticosteroids, e 2. human growth hormone therapy, a 3. oral hypoglycemic agent, d 4. antithyroid agent, c 5. insulin, f 6. vasopressin, b

Medical Record Analysis

1. hyperglycemia; ketoacidosis; glycosuria 2. student answers will vary 3. a—damage to the retina as a result of diabetes; b—a therapeutic plan; c—state of profound unconsciousness; d—twice a day 4. fasting blood sugar, serum glucose level, 2-hour postprandial glucose tolerance test 5. abdominal X-ray, pancreas CT scan 6. 2,000-calorie ADA diet with three meals and two snacks, may engage in any activity, return to school next Monday, check serum glucose level b.i.d., and call office for insulin dosage

Chart Note Transcription

1. endocrinologist 2. obesity 3. hirsutism 4. radioimmunoassay (RIA) 5. cortisol 6. adenoma 7. adrenal cortex 8. Cushing's syndrome 9. adenoma 10. adrenal cortex 11. adrenalectomy

Labeling Exercise

A. 1. pineal gland 2. thyroid and parathyroid glands 3. adrenal glands 4. pancreas 5. pituitary gland 6. thymus gland 7. ovary 8. testis

B1. 1. pituitary gland 2. bone and soft tissue 3. GH 4. testes 5. FSH, LH 6. ovary 7. FSH, LH 8. thyroid gland 9. TSH 10. adrenal cortex 11. ACTH 12. breast 13. PRL

B2. 1. liver 2. stomach 3. pancreas 4. beta cell 5. alpha cell 6. islet of Langerhans

Chapter 12 Answers

Practice Exercises

A. 1. neurology 2. brain, spinal cord, nerves 3. peripheral nervous system, central nervous system 4. efferent or motor 5. afferent or sensory 6. cerebrum 7. cerebellum 8. eyesight 9. hearing, smell 10. parasympathetic, sympathetic

B. 1. neuritis 2. neurologist 3. neuralgia 4. polyneuritis 5. neurectomy 6. neuroplasty 7. neuroma 8. neurorrhaphy 9. meningitis 10. meningocele 11. myelomeningocele 12. encephalogram 13. encephalopathy 14. encephalitis 15. encephalocele 16. cerebrospinal 17. cerebral

C. 1. b 2. f 3. g 4. h 5. i 6. a 7. e 8. c 9. d

D. 1. transient ischemic attack 2. multiple sclerosis 3. spinal cord injury 4. central nervous system 5. peripheral nervous system 6. headache 7. cerebral palsy 8. lumbar puncture 9. amyotrophic lateral sclerosis

E. 1. CSF 2. CVD 3. EEG 4. ICP 5. PET 6. CVA 7. SAH 8. ANS

F. 1. h 2. k 3. d 4. g 5. a 6. b 7. f 8. j 9. e 10. l 11. i 12. c

G. 1. injecting radiopaque dye into spinal canal to examine under X-ray the outlines made by the dye 2. X-ray of the blood vessels of the brain after the injection of radiopaque dye 3. reflex test on bottom of foot to detect lesion and abnormalities of nervous system 4. test of balance to determine neurological function 5. laboratory examination of fluid taken from the brain and spinal cord 6. positron emission tomography to measure cerebral blood flow, blood volume, oxygen, and glucose uptake 7. recording the ultrasonic echoes of the brain 8. needle puncture into the spinal cavity to withdraw fluid

H. 1. paralysis 2. muscular coordination 3. pain, sensitivity 4. weakness 5. speech 6. feeling, sensation

I. 1. meninges 2. brain 3. cerebellum 4. spinal cord 5. head 6. thalamus 7. nerve 8. nerve root 9. cerebrum 10. pons

J. 1. tumor of astrocyte cells 2. seizure 3. without sensation 4. paralysis of one-half of body 5. physician that treats nervous system with surgery 6. without pain, sensitivity 7. localized seizure of one limb 8. paralysis of all four limbs 9. accumulation of blood in the subdural space 10. within the meninges

K. 1. d 2. e 3. f 4. g 5. b 6. a 7. c 8. j 9. h 10. i

L. 1. delirium 2. amyotrophic lateral sclerosis 3. Bell's palsy 4. cerebral aneurysm 5. Parkinson's disease 6. cerebrospinal fluid shunt 7. transient ischemic attack 8. subdural hematoma 9. cerebral palsy 10. nerve conduction velocity

M. 1. anesthetic, e 2. dopaminergic drugs, a 3. hypnotic, d 4. analgesic, g 5. sedative, b 6. narcotic analgesic, c 7. anticonvulsant, f

Medical Record Analysis

1. the muscles that receive nerve supply from or below the 2nd lumbar vertebra are paralyzed 2. no, the spinal cord was completely severed 3. a—comminuted—shattered bone; b—sanguinous—bloody; c—decubitus ulcer—pressure sore; d—catheterization—thin, flexible tube inserted into the bladder 4. d—leg strengthening 5. independent transfers, independent wheelchair mobility, independent ADLs 6. lumbar laminectomy with spinal fusion; stabilize the fracture and remove the epidural hematoma

Chart Note Transcription

1. neurologist 2. dysphasia 3. hemiparesis 4. convulsions 5. electroencephalography (EEG) 6. lumbar puncture (LP) 7. brain scan 8. cerebral cortex 9. astrocytoma 10. craniotomy 11. cryosurgery

Labeling Exercise

A. 1. brain 2. spinal nerves 3. spinal cord

B1. 1. dendrites 2. nerve cell body 3. unmyelinated region 4. myelinated axon 5. nucleus 6. axon 7. terminal end fibers

B2. 1. cerebrum 2. diencephalon 3. thalamus 4. hypothalamus 5. brain stem 6. midbrain 7. pons 8. cerebellum 9. medulla oblongata

Chapter 13 Answers

Practice Exercises

A. 1. ophthalmology 2. cilia 3. lacrimal 4. cornea 5. retina 6. iris 7. malleus, incus, stapes 8. otology 9. tympanic membrane 10. cerumen 11. eustachian or auditory 12. vestibulocochlear nerve

B. 1. blepharitis 2. blepharoplasty 3. blepharoptosis 4. retinopathy 5. retinopexy 6. ophthalmology 7. ophthalmic 8. ophthalmoscopy 9. iridoplegia 10. iridectomy 11. otoplasty 12. otopyorrhea 13. otalgia 14. otitis 15. tympanorrhexis 16. tympanotomy 17. tympanitis 18. audiogram 19. audiometer 20. audiology

C. 1. conductive—problem with outer or middle ear, muffles sound; sensorineural—damage of inner ear or nerve 2. cornea, pupil, lens, retina 3. mucous membrane that covers and protects front of eyeball 4. incus, malleus, stapes, vibrate to amplify and conduct sound waves from outer ear to inner ear

D. 1. -tropia 2. -opia 3. -itis 4. -logy 5. -otomy 6. -plasty 7. -pexy 8. -algia 9. -otia 10. -cusis

E. 1. tear or tear duct 2. choroid 3. water 4. light 5. cornea 6. glassy 7. double 8. gray 9. old age 10. dull or dim 11. ear 12. stapes 13. hearing 14. eustachian or auditory tube 15. eardrum or tympanic membrane

F. 1. dull/dim vision 2. double vision 3. enlarge or widen pupil 4. constrict pupil 5. diminished vision of old age 6. ringing in the ears 7. middle ear bone 8. measure movement in eardrum 9. auditory tube 10. inner ear 11. results of hearing test 12. middle ear infection

G. 1. h 2. g 3. a 4. d 5. b 6. i 7. c 8. f 9. e 10. j

H. 1. c 2. b 3. d 4. a 5. e 6. j 7. i 8. f 9. h 10. g

I. 1. otology 2. both eyes 3. rapid eye movement 4. hertz 5. senile macular degeneration 6. pupils equal, round, react to light and accommodation 7. intraocular pressure 8. decibel 9. right eye 10. visual field

J. 1. PE tube 2. EENT 3. BC 4. AU 5. OM 6. EM 7. XT 8. OS 9. Acc 10. VA

K. 1. tonometry 2. emmetropia 3. conjunctivitis 4. myopia 5. cataract 6. hordeolum 7. entropion 8. strabismus 9. hyperopia 10. presbycusis 11. otorhinolaryngologist 12. inner ear 13. Ménière's disease 14. acoustic neuroma

L. 1. artificial tears, h 2. antiglaucoma medication, c 3. antibiotic otic solution, i 4. mydriatic, a 5. antiemetic, g 6. antibiotic ophthalmic solution, j 7. anti-inflammatory otic solution, b 8. miotic, f 9. wax emulsifier, e 10. anesthetic ophthalmic solution, d

Medical Record Analysis

1. pupils open and close correctly when the physician shines a light into the eye; pupils become smaller in bright light and larger in dim light; it is important to prevent too much light from reaching the inside of the eyeball 2. eye muscles, conjunctiva, iris/pupil, retina, macular area of the retina, cornea 3. breast cancer with a mastectomy, cholelithiasis with a cholecystectomy 4. dilate the pupil, miotic drops 5. a—farsightedness (hyperopia) 6. cryoextraction

Chart Note Transcription

1. otorhinolaryngologist (ENT) 2. otitis media (OM) 3. AU, binaural 4. otoscopy 5. tympanic membrane 6. cerumen 7. tympanometry 8. audiometric test 9. conductive hearing loss 10. myringotomy

Labeling Exercise

A1. 1. iris 2. lens 3. conjunctiva 4. pupil 5. cornea 6. suspensory ligaments 7. ciliary body 8. fovea centralis 9. optic nerve 10. retina 11. choroid 12. sclera

A2. 1. pinna 2. external auditory meatus 3. auditory canal 4. tympanic membrane 5. malleus 6. incus 7. semicircular canals 8. vestibular nerve 9. cochlear nerve 10. cochlea 11. round window 12. stapes 13. Eustachian tube

B. 1. superior lacrimal gland 2. inferior lacrimal gland 3. lacrimal sac 4. lacrimal ducts 5. nasolacrimal duct

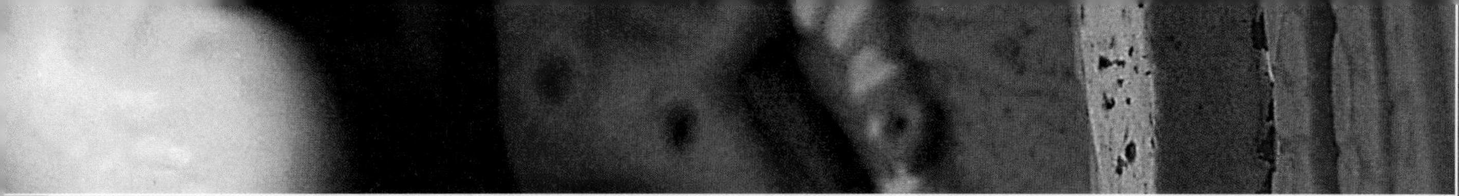

Glossary/Index

A

AB, 330

Abbreviations, 10, 37. *See also* individual subject headings

Abdomen
- anatomical divisions of, 34*t*
- clinical divisions of, 34*t*

abdominal, pertaining to the abdomen, 31, 36

Abdominal aorta, 360*f*

Abdominal cavity, the superior portion of the abdominopelvic cavity. 31, 32, 32*f*, 33*t*

Abdominal region, 31, 32*f*

Abdominopelvic cavity, a ventral cavity consisting of the abdominal and pelvic cavities. It contains digestive, urinary, and reproductive organs, 31, 32, 33*t*

Abducens nerve, 396*t*

Abduction, directional term meaning to move away from the median or middle line of the body, 8, 108, 108*f*

ABG, 227

ABO system, the major system of blood typing, 172

Abortifacient, Medication that terminates a pregnancy, 329

Abortion (AB), 318

Abrasion, scraping away a portion of the surface of the skin. Performed to remove acne scars, tattoos, and scar tissue, 55

Abruptio placentae, emergency condition in which the placenta tears away from the uterine wall before the twentieth week of pregnancy. Requires immediate delivery of the baby, 326

Abscess, a collection of pus in the skin, 59

Absence seizure, type of epileptic seizure that lasts only a few seconds to half a minute, characterized by a loss of awareness and an absence of activity. It is also called a *petit mal seizure,* 400

Acapnia, lack of carbon dioxide, 218

Accessory nerve, 396*t*

Accessory organs, the accessory organs to the digestive system consist of the organs that are part of the system, but not part of the continuous tube from mouth to anus. The accessory organs are the liver, pancreas, gallbladder, and salivary glands, 244, 250–51

ACE inhibitor drugs, medication that produces vasodilation and decreases blood pressure, 151

Achromatopsia, condition of color blindness; more common in males, 433

Acidosis, excessive acidity of body fluids due to the accumulation of acids, as in diabetic acidosis, 368

Acne, inflammatory disease of the sebaceous glands and hair follicles that results in papules and pustules, 59

Acne rosacea, hypertrophy of sebaceous glands causing thickened skin generally on the nose, forehead, and cheeks, 59

Acne vulgaris, a common form of acne occurring in adolescence from an oversecretion of the oil glands. It is characterized by papules, pustules, blackheads, and whiteheads, 59

Acoustic, pertaining to hearing, 444

Acoustic neuroma, benign tumor of the eighth cranial nerve sheath, which can cause symptoms from pressure being exerted on tissues, 446

Acquired immunity, the protective response of the body to a specific pathogen, 184

Acquired immunodeficiency syndrome (AIDS), disease that involves a defect in the cell-mediated immunity system. A syndrome of opportunistic infections that occur in the final stages of infection with the human immunodeficiency virus (HIV). This virus attacks T_4 lymphocytes and destroys them, which reduces the person's ability to fight infection, 62, 189

Acromegaly, chronic disease of adults that results in an elongation and enlargement of the bones of the head and extremities, 370, 370*f*

ACTH, 373

Action, the type of movement a muscle produces, 107

Active acquired immunity, immunity developing after direct exposure to a pathogen, 184, 185

Acute care hospitals, hospitals that typically provide services to diagnose (laboratory, diagnostic imaging) and treat (surgery, medications, therapy) diseases for a short period of time. In addition, they usually provide emergency and obstetrical care. Also called general hospital, 11

Acute respiratory distress syndrome, 221

Acute tubular necrosis (ATN), damage to the renal tubules due to presence of toxins in the urine or to ischemia; results in oliguria, 291

Adam's apple, 212, 366*f*
Addison's disease, disease that results from a deficiency in adrenocortical hormones. There may be an increased pigmentation of the skin, generalized weakness, and weight loss, 369
Adduction, directional term meaning to move toward the median or middle line of the body, 8, 108, 108*f*
Adenocarcinoma, malignant adenoma in a glandular organ, 371
Adenoidectomy, excision of the adenoids, 187
Adenoiditis, inflammation of the adenoid tissue, 187
Adenoids, another term for pharyngeal tonsils. The tonsils are a collection of lymphatic tissue found in the nasopharynx to combat microorganisms entering the body through the nose or mouth, 184, 211, 212
ADH, 373
Adhesion, scar tissue forming in the fascia surrounding a muscle making it difficult to stretch the muscle, 111
Adipose, a type of connective tissue. Also called fat. It stores energy and provides protective padding for underlying structures, 23
Adjective suffixes, 7
Adrenal, pertaining to the adrenal gland, 366
Adrenal cortex, the outer portion of the adrenal glands; secretes several families of hormones: mineralocorticoids, glucocorticoids, and steroid sex hormones, 358*t,* 360, 360*f*
Adrenal feminization, development of female secondary sexual characteristics (such as breasts) in a male; often as a result of increased estrogen secretion by the adrenal cortex, 369
Adrenal glands, a pair of glands in the endocrine system located just above each kidney. These glands are composed of two sections, the cortex and the medulla, that function independently of each other. The cortex secretes steroids, such as aldosterone, cortisol, androgens, estrogens, and progestins. The medulla secretes epinephrine and norepinephrine. The adrenal glands are regulated by adrenocorticotropin hormone, which is secreted by the pituitary gland, 28*t,* 357*f,* 358, 358*t,* 360, 360*f*
Adrenal medulla, the inner portion of the adrenal gland. It secretes epinephrine and norepinephrine, 358*t,* 360, 360*f*
Adrenal virilism, development of male secondary sexual characteristics (such as deeper voice and facial hair) in a female; often as a result of increased androgen secretion by the adrenal cortex, 369
Adrenalectomy, excision of the adrenal gland, 367
Adrenaline, a hormone produced by the adrenal medulla. Also known as epinephrine. Some of its actions include increasing heart rate and force of contraction, bronchodilation, and relaxation of intestinal muscles, 358*t,* 360
Adrenalitis, inflammation of an adrenal gland, 367
Adrenocorticotropin hormone (ACTH), a hormone secreted by anterior pituitary. It regulates function of the adrenal gland cortex, 359*t,* 363–64
Adrenomegaly, enlarged adrenal gland, 366
Adrenopathy, adrenal gland disease, 366
Adult respiratory distress syndrome (ARDS), acute respiratory failure in adults characterized by tachypnea, dyspnea, cyanosis, tachycardia, and hypoxemia, 221
Aerosol therapy, medication suspended in a mist that is intended to be inhaled. Delivered by a *nebulizer,* which delivers the mist for a period of time while the patient breathes, or a *metered dose inhaler* (MDI), which delivers a single puff of mist, 225
Afferent, 283
Afferent arteriole, arteriole that carries blood into the glomerulus, 283, 284*f,* 286*f*
Afferent neurons, nerve that carries impulses to the brain and spinal cord from the skin and sense organs. Also called sensory neurons, 395, 396
Agglutinate, clumping together to form small clusters. Platelets agglutinate to start the clotting process, 172
Agranulocytes, nongranular leukocyte. This is one of the two types of leukocytes found in plasma that are classified as either monocytes or lymphocytes, 171, 171*t,* 173
AIDS, 192
AIDS-related complex (ARC), early stage of AIDS. There is a positive test for the virus but only mild symptoms of weight loss, fatigue, skin rash, and anorexia, 189
Alanine transaminase (ALT), an enzyme normally present in the blood. Blood levels are increased in persons with liver disease, 260
Albinism, a condition in which the person is not able to produce melanin. An albino person has white hair and skin and the pupils of the eye are red, 59
Albumin, a protein that is normally found circulating in the bloodstream. It is abnormal for albumin to be in the urine, 170, 286
Aldosterone, a hormone produced by the adrenal cortex. It regulates the levels of sodium and potassium in the body and as a side effect the volume of water lost in urine, 358*t,* 360

Alimentary canal, also known as the gastrointestinal system or digestive system. This system covers the area between the mouth and the anus and includes 30 feet of intestinal tubing. It has a wide range of functions. This system serves to store and digest food, absorb nutrients, and eliminate waste. The major organs of this system are the mouth, pharynx, esophagus, stomach, small intestine, colon, rectum, and anus, 244

Allergen, antigen capable of causing a hypersensitivity or allergy in the body, 187

Allergist, a physician who specializes in testing for and treating allergies, 187

Allergy, hypersensitivity to a substance in the environment or a medication, 187

Allograft, skin graft from one person to another; donor is usually a cadaver, 64

Alopecia, absence or loss of hair, especially of the head, 63

ALS, 408

ALT, 264

Alveoli, the tiny air sacs at the end of each bronchiole. The alveoli are surrounded by a capillary network. Gas exchange takes place as oxygen and carbon dioxide diffuse across the alveolar and capillary walls, 212, 213, 213*f*

Alzheimer's disease, chronic, organic mental disorder consisting of dementia that is more prevalent in adults between 40 and 60. Involves progressive disorientation, apathy, speech and gait disturbances, and loss of memory, 400

Amblyopia, loss of vision not as a result of eye pathology; usually occurs in patients who see two images. In order to see only one image, the brain will no longer recognize the image being sent to it by one of the eyes; may occur if strabismus is not corrected; commonly referred to as lazy eye, 433

Ambulatory care center, a facility that provides services that do not require overnight hospitalization. The services range from simple surgeries, to diagnostic testing, to therapy. Also called a surgical center or an outpatient clinic, 11

Amenorrhea, absence of menstruation, which can be the result of many factors, including pregnancy, menopause, and dieting, 322

American Sign Language (ASL), nonverbal method of communicating in which the hands and fingers are used to indicate words and concepts. Used by people who are deaf and speech impaired, 445, 445*f*

Amino acids, organic substances found in plasma, used by cells to build proteins, 170

Amniocentesis, puncturing of the amniotic sac using a needle and syringe for the purpose of withdrawing amniotic fluid for testing. Can assist in determining fetal maturity, development, and genetic disorders, 328

Amnion, the inner of two membranous sacs surrouding the fetus. The amniotic sac contains amniotic fluid in which the baby floats, 318, 320

Amniorrhea, discharge of amniotic fluid, 321

Amniotic, pertaining to the amnion, 321

Amniotic fluid, the fluid inside the amniotic sac, 318, 319*f*, 320

Amniotomy, incision into the amniotic sac, 321

Amplification device, 446

Amputation, partial or complete removal of a limb for a variety of reasons, including tumors, gangrene, intractable pain, crushing injury, or uncontrollable infection, 100

Amylase, digestive enzyme found in saliva that begins the digestion of carbohydrates, 250

Amyotrophic lateral sclerosis (ALS), disease with muscular weakness and atrophy due to degeneration of motor neurons of the spinal cord. Also called *Lou Gehrig's disease,* after the New York Yankees' baseball player who died from the disease, 403

Anacusis, total absence of hearing; unable to perceive sound. Also called *deafness,* 446

Anal, pertaining to the anus, 252

Anal fistula, abnormal tubelike passage from the surface around the anal opening directly into the rectum, 257

Anal sphincter, ring of muscle that controls anal opening, 249, 250

Analgesia, a reduction in the perception of pain or sensation due to a neurological condition or medication, 399

Analgesic, substance that relieves pain without the loss of consciousness. May be either narcotic or non-narcotic. Narcotic drugs are derived from the opium poppy and act on the brain to cause pain relief and drowsiness, 407

Anaphylactic shock, life-threatening condition resulting from the ingestion of food or medications that produce a severe allergic response. Circulatory and respiratory problems occur, including respiratory distress, hypotension, edema, tachycardia, and convulsions, 189

Anaphylaxis, severe reaction to an antigen, 189

Anastomosis, creating a passageway or opening between two organs or vessels, 262

Anatomical position, used to describe the positions and relationships of a structure in the human body. For descriptive purposes the assumption is always that the person is in the anatomical position. The body is standing erect with the arms at the side of the body, the palms of the hands facing forward, and the eyes looking straight ahead. The legs are parallel with the feet and toes pointing forward, 29–30, 30*f*

Ancillary reports, report in a patient's medical record from various treatments and therapies the patient has received, such as rehabilitation, social services, respiratory therapy, or from the dietician, 11

Androgen, a class of steroid hormones secreted by the adrenal cortex. These hormones, such as testosterone, produce a masculinizing effect, 335, 358*t*, 360

Androgen therapy, replacement male hormones to treat patients who produce insufficient hormone naturally, 340

Andropathy, male disease, 335

Anemia, reduction in the number of red blood cells (RBCs) or amount of hemoglobin in the blood; results in less oxygen reaching the tissues, 175

Anesthesia, partial or complete loss of sensation with or without a loss of consciousness as a result of a drug, disease, or injury, 399

Anesthesiologist, a physician who has a specialization in the practice of administering anesthetics, 399

Anesthesiologist's report, a medical record document that relates the details regarding the drugs given to a patient and the patient's response to anesthesia and vital signs during surgery, 11

Anesthesiology, branch of medicine specializing in all aspects of anesthesia, including for surgical procedures, resuscitation measures, and the management of acute and chronic pain. Physician is an *anesthesiologist*, 399

Anesthetic, substance that produces a lack of feeling that may be of local or general effect, depending on the type of administration, 65, 407

Anesthetic ophthalmic solution, eyedrops for pain relief associated with eye infections and corneal abrasions, 437

Aneurysm, weakness in the wall of an artery that results in localized widening of the artery, 146, 147*f*

Aneurysmectomy, surgical removal of an aneurysm, 150

Angiitis, inflammation of vessels, 141

Angina pectoris, severe chest pain with a sensation of constriction around the heart. Caused by a deficiency of oxygen to the heart muscle, 144, 145*f*

Angiogram, record of a vessel, 141

Angiography, process of taking an X-ray of blood or lymphatic vessels after injection of a radiopaque substance, 149

Angioplasty, surgical repair of blood vessels, 141, 151*f*

Angiospasm, involuntary muscle contraction of a vessel, 141

Angiostenosis, narrowing of a vessel, 141

Anhidrosis, abnormal condition of no sweat, 54

Ankylosing spondylitis, inflammatory spinal condition that resembles rheumatoid arthritis; results in gradual stiffening and fusion of the vertebrae; more common in men than women, 98

Anorchism, congenital absence of one or both testes, 336

Anorexia, loss of appetite that can accompany other conditions such as a gastrointestinal (GI) upset, 254

Anorexiant, substance that treats obesity by suppressing appetite, 264

Anosmia, loss of the sense of smell, 218

Anoxia, lack of oxygen, 217

ANS, 408

Antacid, substance that neutralizes acid in the stomach, 264

Antagonistic pairs, pair of muscles arranged around a joint that produce opposite actions, 107

Anteflexion, while the uterus is normally in this position, an exaggeration of the forward bend of the uterus is abnormal. The forward bend is near the neck of the uterus. The position of cervix, or opening of the uterus, remains normal, 316

Antepartum, before birth, 323

Anterior, directional term meaning near or on the front or belly side of the body, 35*f*, 35*t*

Anterior lobe, the anterior portion of the pituitary gland. It secretes adrenocorticotropin hormone, follicle-stimulating hormone, growth hormone, luteinizing hormone, melanocyte-stimulating hormone, prolactin, and thyroid-stimulating hormone, 363

Anterior pituitary gland, 363*f*, 364*f*

Anterior tibial artery, 140*f*

Anterior tibial vein, 142*f*

Anthracosis, A type of pneumoconiosis that develops from the collection of coal dust in the lung. Also called black lung or miner's lung, 221

Anti-virals, substance that weakens a viral infection in the body, often by interfering with the virus's ability to replicate, 65

Antiarrhythmic, controls cardiac arrhythmias by altering nerve impulses within the heart, 151

Antibiotic, substance that destroys or prohibits the growth of microorganisms. Used to treat bacterial infections. Not found effective in treating viral infections. To be effective, it must be taken regularly for a specified period, 65, 227, 296

Antibiotic ophthalmic solution, eyedrops for the treatment of bacterial eye infections, 437

Antibiotic otic solution, Eardrops to treat otitis externa, 448

Antibody, protein material produced in the body as a response to the invasion of a foreign substance, 183*f,* 185–86

Antibody-mediated immunity, the production of antibodies by B cells in response to an antigen. Also called *humoral immunity.* 185

Anticoagulant, substance that prevents or delays the clotting or coagulation of blood, 151, 178

Anticonvulsant, prevents or relieves convulsions. Drugs such as phenobarbital reduce excessive stimulation in the brain to control seizures and other symptoms of epilepsy, 407

Antidiarrheal, prevents or relieves diarrhea, 264

Antidiuretic hormone (ADH), a hormone secreted by the posterior pituitary. It promotes water reabsorption by the kidney tubules, 359*t,* 363, 364

Antiemetic, substance that controls nausea and vomiting, 264, 448

Antifungal, substance that kills fungi infecting the skin, 65

Antigen, substance that is capable of inducing the formation of an antibody. The antibody then intereacts with the antigen in the antigen–antibody reaction, 185

Antigen-antibody complex, combination of the antigen with its specific antibody; increases susceptibility to phagocytosis and immunity, 185, 186

Antiglaucoma medications, a group of drugs that reduce intraocular pressure by lowering the amount of aqueous humor in the eyeball; may achieve this by either reducing the production of aqueous humor or increasing its outflow, 437

Antihemorrhagic, substance that prevents or stops hemorrhaging, 178

Antihistamine, substance that acts to control allergic symptoms by counteracting histamine, which exists naturally in the body, and which is released in allergic reactions, 192, 227

Antilipidemic, substance that reduces amount of cholesterol and lipids in the bloodstream; treats hyperlipidemia, 151

Antiparasitic, substance that kills mites or lice, 65

Antiplatelet agent, substance that interferes with the action of platelets; prolongs bleeding time; commonly referred to as blood thinner. Used to prevent heart attacks and strokes, 178

Antiprostatic agents, medications to treat early cases of benign prostatic hypertrophy; may prevent surgery for mild cases, 340

Antipruritic, substance that reduces severe itching, 65

Antiseptic, substance used to kill bacteria in skin cuts and wounds or at a surgical site, 65

Antispasmodic, medication to prevent or reduce bladder muscle spasms, 296

Antithyroid agents, medication given to block production of thyroid hormones in patients with hypersecretion disorders, 373

Antitussive, substance that controls or relieves coughing. Codeine is an ingredient in many prescription cough medicines that acts upon the brain to control coughing, 227

Antrum, the tapered distal end of the stomach, 248, 248*f*

Anuria, complete suppression of urine formed by the kidneys and a complete lack of urine excretion, 289, 290

Anus, the terminal opening of the digestive tube, 249, 250*f*

Anvil, 441*f,* 442

Aorta, the largest artery in the body. It is located in the mediastinum and carries oxygenated blood away from the left side of the heart, 33*t,* 132*f,* 133*f,* 134*f,* 135, 135*f,* 136, 183*f,* 362*f*

Aortic, pertaining to the aorta, 141

Aortic arch, 140*f*

Aortic semilunar valve, 135*f*

Aortic valve, the semilunar valve between the left ventricle of the heart and the aorta in the heart. It prevents blood from flowing backwards into the ventricle, 134*f,* 135, 136*f,* 137*f*

Apex, directional term meaning tip or summit. An area of the lungs and heart, 35*t,* 133, 137*f,* 139*f,* 214, 214*f*

Apgar score, evaluation of a neonate's adjustment to the outside world; observes color, heart rate, muscle tone, respiratory rate, and response to stimulus, 328

Aphagia, not eating, 254

Aphasia, inability to communicate through speech. Often an after effect of a stroke (CVA), 399

Aphonia, no voice, 218

Aphthous ulcers, painful ulcers in the mouth of unknown cause. Commonly called *canker sores,* 256

Aplastic anemia, severe form of anemia that develops as a consequence of loss of functioning red bone marrow; results in a decrease in the number of all the formed elements; treatment may eventually require a bone marrow transplant, 175

Apnea, the condition of not breathing, 218

Apocrine gland, type of sweat gland that opens into hair follicles located in the pubic, anal, and mammary areas. These glands secrete a substance that can produce an odor when it comes into contact with bacteria on the skin causing what is commonly referred to as body odor, 53, 54
Appendectomy, surgical removal of the appendix, 252
Appendicitis, inflammation of the appendix, 252
Appendicular skeleton, the appendicular skeleton consists of the bones of the upper and lower extremities, shoulder, and pelvis, 84, 88–90, 89*f*
Appendix, 34*t*, 249*f*, 250*f*
Aqueous humor, a watery fluid filling the spaces between the cornea and lens, 426*f*, 427
Arachnoid layer, the delicate middle layer of the meninges, 395, 395*f*
ARC, 192
ARDS, 227
Areola, the pigmented area around the nipple of the breast, 318, 318*f*
Arrector pili, a small slip of smooth muscle attached to hairs; when this muscle contracts the hair shaft stands up and results in "goose bumps." 51*f*, 52, 53*f*
Arrhythmia, irregularity in the heartbeat or action, 145
Arterial, pertaining to the artery, 141
Arterial anastomosis, surgical joining together of two arteries; performed if an artery is severed or if a damaged section of an artery is removed, 150
Arterial blood gases (ABG), lab test that measures the amount of oxygen, carbon dioxide, and nitrogen in the blood, and the pH, 223
Arteries, the blood vessels that carry blood away from the heart, 26*t*, 51*f*, 83*f*, 131*f*, 132, 138, 139*f*, 140*f*, 181*f*
Arterioles, the smallest branches of the arteries. They carry blood to the capillaries, 138, 141, 181*f*
Arteriorrhexis, a ruptured artery, 141
Arteriosclerosis, condition with thickening, hardening, and loss of elasticity of the walls of the arteries, 146
Arthralgia, pain in a joint, 93
Arthritis, inflammation of a joint that is usually accompanied by pain and swelling. A chronic disease, 3, 93
Arthrocentesis, removal of synovial fluid with a needle from a joint space, such as in the knee, for examination, 93
Arthroclasia, surgically breaking loose a stiffened joint, 93
Arthrodesis, surgical fusion or stiffening of a joint to provide stability. This is sometimes done to relieve the pain of arthritis, 93
Arthrogram, record of a joint, 93
Arthrography, visualization of a joint by radiographic study after injection of a contrast medium into the joint space, 100
Arthroscope, instrument to view inside a joint, 3, 93
Arthroscopic surgery, use of an arthroscope to facilitate performing surgery on a joint, 100
Arthroscopy, examination of the interior of a joint by entering the joint with an arthroscope. The arthroscope contains a small television camera that allows the physician to view the interior of the joint on a monitor during the procedure, 100
Arthrotomy, surgically cutting into a joint, 93
Articular cartilage, layer of cartilage covering the ends of bones forming a synovial joint, 82, 83*f*
Articulation, another term for a joint, the point where two bones meet, 91, 92
Artificial tears, medications, many of them over the counter, to treat dry eyes, 438
Asbestosis, a type of pneumoconiosis that develops from collection of asbestos fibers in the lungs; may lead to the development of lung cancer, 221
Ascending colon, the section of the colon following the cecum. It ascends the right side of the abdomen, 249, 249*f*, 250*f*
Ascending tracts, nerve tracts carrying sensory information up the spinal cord to the brain, 394
Ascites, collection or accumulation of fluid in the peritoneal cavity, 254
ASL, 448
Aspartate transaminase (AST), an enzyme normally present in the blood. Blood levels are increased in persons with liver disease, 260
Aspermia, lack of, or failure to ejaculate, sperm, 336
Asphyxia, lack of oxygen that can lead to unconsciousness and death if not corrected immediately. Some of the common causes are drowning, foreign body in the respiratory tract, poisoning, and electric shock, 218
Asphyxiation, 218
Aspiration, for respiratory system, refers to inhaling food, liquid, or a foreign object into the airways; term also refers to withdrawing fluid from a body cavity using suction, 219
AST, 264
Asthma, disease caused by various conditions, such as allergens, and resulting in constriction of the bronchial airways and labored respirations. Can cause violent spasms of the bronchi (bronchospasms) but is generally not a life-threatening condition. Medication can be very effective, 220
Astigm, 438

Astigmatism (Astigm), a condition in which light rays are focused unevenly on the eye, which causes a distorted image due to an abnormal curvature of the cornea, 433

Astrocytoma, tumor of the brain or spinal cord that is composed of astrocytes, 400

Ataxia, having a lack of muscle coordination as a result of a disorder or disease, 399

Atelectasis, condition in which lung tissue collapses, which prevents the respiratory exchange of oxygen and carbon dioxide. Can be caused by a variety of conditions, including pressure upon the lung from a tumor or other object, 221

Atherectomy, excision of fatty substance, 141

Atheroma, tumor-like collection of fatty substances, 143

Atherosclerosis, the most common form of arteriosclerosis. Caused by the formation of yellowish plaques of cholesterol buildup on the inner walls of the arteries, 147

Atherosclerotic plaque, 147*f*

Atonia, lack of tone, 110

Atresia, congenital lack of a normal body opening, 323

Atria, the two upper chambers of the heart. The left atrium receives blood returning from the lungs, and the right atrium receives blood returning from the body, 134

Atrial, pertaining to the atrium, 143

Atrial septal defect (ASD), 145

Atrioventricular bundle, in the heart, conducts the electrical impulse from the atrioventricular node into the ventricles, 136, 137*f,* 138

Atrioventricular node, this area at the junction of the right atrium and ventricle receives the stimulus from the sinoatrial node and sends the impulse to the ventricles through the bundle of His, 136, 137*f,* 138

Atrioventricular valve (AV), the heart valves located between an atrium and a ventricle. Includes the tricuspid valve in the right side of the heart and the bicuspid or mitral valve in the left side of the heart, 135

Atrophy, lack or loss of normal development, 111

Audiogram, chart that shows the faintest sounds a patient can hear during audiometry testing, 444

Audiologist, provides a comprehensive array of services related to prevention, diagnosis, and treatment of hearing impairment and its associated communication disorders, 444

Audiology, study of hearing, 441

Audiometer, instrument to measure hearing, 444

Audiometry, process of measuring hearing, 446, 446*f*

Auditory, pertaining to hearing, 444

Auditory canal, the canal that leads from the external opening of the ear to the eardrum, 441, 441*f*

Auditory tube, another name for the eustachian tube connecting the middle ear and pharynx, 211, 212, 442

Aura, sensations, such as seeing colors or smelling an unusual odor, that occur just prior to an epileptic seizure or a migraine headache, 399

Aural, pertaining to the ear, 444

Auricle, also called the pinna. The external ear. It functions to capture sound waves as they go past the outer ear, 440*f,* 441

Auricular, pertaining to the ear, 444

Auscultation, listening to the sounds within the body by using a stethoscope, 143

Autograft, skin graft from a person's own body, 64, 64*f*

Autoimmune disease, a disease that results from the body's immune system attacking its own cells as if they were pathogens; examples include systemic lupus erythematosus, rheumatoid arthritis, and multiple sclerosis, 187

Autologous transfusion, procedure for collecting and storing a patient's own blood several weeks prior to the actual need. It can then be used to replace blood lost during a surgical procedure, 177

Autonomic nervous system, the portion of the nervous system that consists of nerves to the internal organs that function involuntarily. It regulates the functions of glands (especially the salivary, gastric, and sweat glands), the adrenal medulla, heart, and smooth muscle tissue. This system is divided into two parts: sympathetic and parasympathetic, 136, 137, 395, 396–98

Axial skeleton, the axial skeleton includes the bones in the head, spine, chest, and trunk, 84–86, 86*f*

Axillary, pertaining to the armpit. There is a collection of lymph nodes in this area that drains each arm, 182*t,* 183*f*

Axon, single projection of a neuron that conducts impulse away from nerve cell body, 390, 391*f*

Azotemia, accumulation of nitrogenous waste in the bloodstream. Occurs when the kidney fails to filter these wastes from the blood, 290

B

B cells, common name for B lymphocytes, responds to foreign antigens by producing protective antibodies, 185, 186

B lymphocytes, the humoral immunity cells, which respond to foreign antigens by producing protective antibodies. Simply referred to as *B cells.* 185, 186

Bradycardia, abnormally slow heart rate, below 60 bpm, 143
Bradykinesia, slow movement, commonly seen with the rigidity of Parkinson's disease, 110
Bradypepsia, slow digestion rate, 254
Bradypnea, slow breathing, 218
Brain, the brain is one of the largest organs in the body and coordinates most body activities. It is the center for all thought, memory, judgment, and emotion. Each part of the brain is responsible for controlling different body functions, such as temperature regulation and breathing. The four sections to the brain are the cerebrum, cerebellum, diencephalon, and brain stem, 23, 29*t*, 33*t*, 389*f*, 390, 392–94, 395*f*
Brain scan, injection of radioactive isotopes into the circulation to determine the function and abnormality of the brain, 405
Brain stem, this area of the brain has three components: medulla oblongata, pons, and the midbrain. The brain stem is a pathway for impulses to be conducted between the brain and the spinal cord. It also contains the centers that control respiration, heart rate, and blood pressure. In addition, the twelve pairs of cranial nerves begin in the brain stem, 392
Brain tumor, intracranial mass, either benign or malignant. A benign tumor of the brain can be fatal since it will grow and cause pressure on normal brain tissue. The most malignant brain tumors in children are gliomas, 401, 401*f*
Breast cancer, malignant tumor of the breast; usually forms in the milk-producing gland tissue or the lining of the milk ducts, 325
Breasts, milk-producing glands to provide nutrition for newborn. Also called *mammary glands.* 28*t*, 313*f*, 314, 318, 318*f*, 364*f*
Breech presentation, placement of the fetus in which the buttocks or feet are presented first for delivery rather than the head, 320, 321, 321*f*
Bridge, dental appliance that is attached to adjacent teeth for support to replace missing teeth, 254
Bronch, 227
Bronchial, pertaining to the bronchi, 217
Bronchial tree, 213*f*
Bronchial tube, an organ of the respiratory system that carries air into each lung, 27*t*, 209*f*, 210, 212–13
Bronchiectasis, results from a dilation of a bronchus or the bronchi that can be the result of infection. This abnormal stretching can be irreversible and result in destruction of the bronchial walls. The major symptom is a large amount of purulent (pus-filled) sputum. Rales (bubbling chest sound) and hemoptysis may be present, 217, 221
Bronchioles, the narrowest air tubes in the lungs. Each bronchiole terminates in tiny air sacs called alveoli, 212, 213, 213*f*
Bronchitis, an acute or chronic inflammation of the lower respiratory tract that often occurs after other childhood infections such as measles, 217
Bronchodilator, dilates or opens the bronchi (airways in the lungs) to improve breathing, 227
Bronchogenic, originating in the bronchi, 217
Bronchogenic carcinoma, malignant lung tumor that originates in the bronchi. Usually associated with a history of cigarette smoking, 221, 221*f*
Bronchogram, an X-ray record of the lungs and bronchial tubes, 217, 223
Bronchography, process of taking an X-ray of the lung after a radiopaque substance has been placed into the trachea or bronchial tree, 223
Bronchoplasty, surgical repair of a bronchial defect, 217
Bronchoscope, an instrument to view inside a bronchus, 217, 224
Bronchoscopy (Broncho), using the bronchoscope to visualize the bronchi. The instrument can also be used to obtain tissue for biopsy and to remove foreign objects, 224, 224*f*
Bronchospasm, an involuntary muscle spasm in the bronchi, 217
Bronchus, the distal end of the trachea splits into a left and right main bronchi as it enters each lung. Each main bronchus is subdivided into smaller branches. The smallest bronchi are the bronchioles. Each bronchiole ends in tiny air sacs called alveoli, 212, 213
Bruit, 144
Buccal, (1) Pertaining to the cheeks. (2) Drugs that are placed under the lip or between the cheek and gum, 252
Buccolabial, pertaining to cheeks and lips, 252
Buffers, chemicals that neutralize acid, particularly stomach acid, 251
Bulbourethral gland, also called *Cowper's gland.* These two small male reproductive system glands are located on either side of the urethra just distal to the prostate. The secretion from these glands neutralizes the acidity in the urethra and the vagina, 28*t*, 332*f*, 333, 333*f*, 335
BUN, 297
Bundle branch block (BBB), occurs when the electrical impulse is blocked from travelling down the bundle of His or bundle branches. Results in the ventricles beating at a different rate than the atria. Also called a *heart block,* 145
Bundle branches, part of the conduction system of the heart; the electrical signal travels down the interventricular septum, 136, 137*f*, 138

Bundle of His, the bundle of His is located in the interventricular septum. It receives the electrical impulse from the atrioventricular node and distributes it through the ventricular walls, causing them to contract simultaneously, 136, 137*f,* 138
Bunion, inflammation of the bursa of the great toe, 99
Bunionectomy, removal of the bursa at the joint of the great toe, 100
Burn, a full-thickness burn exists when all the layers are burned; also called a *third-degree burn.* A partial-thickness burn exists when the first layer of skin, the epidermis, is burned, and the second layer of skin, dermis, is damaged; also called a *second-degree burn.* A *first-degree burn* damages only the epidermis, 60, 60*f*
Bursa, a saclike connective tissue structure found in some joints. It protects moving parts from friction. Some common bursa locations are the elbow, knee, and shoulder joints, 91, 92
Bursectomy, excision of a bursa, 93
Bursitis, inflammation of a bursa between bony prominences and muscles or tendons. Common in the shoulder and knee, 92, 93
Bx, bx, 65

C
C&S, 65, 227, 297
CABG, 152
Cachexia, loss of weight and generalized wasting that occurs during a chronic disease, 254
CAD, 152
Calcitonin, a hormone secreted by the thyroid gland. It stimulates deposition of calcium into bone, 359*t,* 366
Calcium, an inorganic substance found in plasma. It is important for bones, muscles, and nerves, 170, 362
Calcium channel blocker drugs, medication that treats hypertension, angina pectoris, and congestive heart failure by causing the heart to beat less forcefully and less often, 152
Calcium supplements, maintaining high blood levels of calcium in association with vitamin D helps maintain bone density and treats osteomalacia, osteoporosis, and rickets, 101
Calculus, a stone formed within an organ by an accumulation of mineral salts. Found in the kidney, renal pelvis, bladder, or urethra. Plural is *calculi,* 290, 290*f*
Callus, the mass of bone tissue that forms at a fracture site during its healing, 95
Calyx, a duct that connects the renal papilla to the renal pelvis. Urine flows from the collecting tubule through the calyx and into the renal pelvis, 282, 283*f*
Cancellous bone, the bony tissue found inside a bone. It contains cavities that hold red bone marrow. Also called *spongy bone,* 82, 83, 83*f*
Cancerous tumors, malignant growths in the body, 184
Candidiasis, yeastlike infection of the skin and mucous membranes that can result in white plaques on the tongue and vagina, 325
Canines, also called the cuspid teeth or eyeteeth. Permanent teeth located between the incisors and the biscuspids that assist in biting and cutting food. Humans have four canine teeth, 246, 246*f*
Canker sores, 256
Capillaries, the smallest blood or lymphatic vessels. Blood capillaries are very thin to allow gas, nutrient, and waste exchange between the blood and the tissues. Lymph capillaries collect lymph fluid from the tissues and carry it to the larger lymph vessels, 131*f,* 132, 132*f,* 138–39, 139*f,* 182, 213*f*
Capillary bed, the network of capillaries found in a given tissue or organ, 138
Carbon dioxide, a waste product of cellular energy production. It is removed from the cells by the blood and eliminated from the body by the lungs, 132, 133, 210
Carbuncle, inflammation and infection of the skin and hair follicle that may result from several untreated boils. Most commonly found on neck, upper back, or head, 63
Cardiac, pertaining to the heart, 143
Cardiac arrest, when the heart stops beating and circulation ceases, 145
Cardiac catheterization, passage of a thin tube (catheter) through an arm vein and the blood vessel leading into the heart. Done to detect abnormalities, to collect cardiac blood samples, and to determine the pressure within the cardiac area, 149
Cardiac enzymes, complex protein molecules found only in heart muscle. Cardiac enzymes are taken by blood sample to determine the amount of the heart disease or damage, 148
Cardiac muscle, the involuntary muscle found in the heart, 23, 105, 105*f,* 106, 106*f,* 133
Cardiac scan, patient is given radioactive thallium intravenously and then scanning equipment is used to visualize the heart; it is especially useful in determining myocardial damage, 149
Cardiac sphincter, also called the *lower esophageal sphincter.* Prevents food and gastric juices from backing up into the esophagus, 248, 248*f*
Cardiologist, a physician specializing in treating diseases and conditions of the cardiovascular system, 143

Cardiology, the branch of medicine specializing in conditions of the cardiovascular system, 26*t*, 143
Cardiomegaly, abnormally enlarged heart, 143
Cardiomyopathy, general term for a disease of the myocardium that may be caused by alcohol abuse, parasites, viral infection, and congestive heart failure, 145
Cardiopulmonary resuscitation (CPR), emergency treatment provided by persons trained in CPR and given to patients when their respirations and heart stop. CPR provides oxygen to the brain, heart, and other vital organs until medical treatment can restore a normal heart and pulmonary function, 150, 152, 226
Cardiorrhexis, ruptured heart, 143
Cardiotonic, substance that strengthens the heart muscle, 152
Cardiovascular system (CV), system that transports blood to all areas of the body. Organs of the cardiovascular system include the heart and blood vessels (arteries, veins, and capillaries). Also called the *circulatory system,* 26*t*, 129–66
  abbreviations, 152
  anatomy and physiology, 132–41
  diagnostic procedures, 148–49
  pathology, 144–48
  pharmacology, 151–52
  therapeutic procedures, 150–51
  vocabulary, 143–44
  word building, 141, 143
Cardioversion, 150
Carditis, 6
Carotid artery, 140*f*, 441*f*
Carotid endarterectomy, surgical procedure for removing an obstruction within the carotid artery, a major artery in the neck that carries oxygenated blood to the brain. Developed to prevent strokes but found to be useful only in severe stenosis with TIA, 407
Carpal, pertaining to the wrist, 94
Carpal tunnel release, surgical cutting of the ligament in the wrist to relieve nerve pressure caused by carpal tunnel disease, which can be caused by repetitive motion such as typing, 112
Carpal tunnel syndrome, a painful disorder of the wrist and hand, induced by compression of the median nerve as it passes under ligaments on the palm side of the wrist. Symptoms include weakness, pain, burning, tingling, and aching in the forearm, wrist, and hand, 111
Carpals, the wrist bones in the upper extremity, 88, 89*f*, 90, 90*f*
Cartilage, strong, flexible connective tissue found in several locations in the body, such as covering the ends of bones in a synovial joint, nasal septum, external ear, eustachian tube, larynx, trachea, bronchi, and the intervertebral discs, 23, 82, 441*f*
Cartilaginous joints, a joint that allows slight movement but holds bones firmly in place by a solid piece of cartilage. The public symphysis is an example of a cartilaginous joint. The fetal skeleton is composed of cartilaginous tissue, 91, 92
Cast, application of a solid material to immobilize an extremity or portion of the body as a result of a fracture, dislocation, or severe injury. It is most often made of plaster of Paris, 95
Castration, excision of the testicles in the male or the ovaries in the female, 338
Cataract, diminished vision resulting from the lens of the eye becoming opaque or cloudy. Treatment is usually surgical removal of the cataract, 433, 433*f*
cath, 297
Catheter, a flexible tube inserted into the body for the purpose of moving fluids into or out of the body. In the cardiovascular system used to place dye into blood vessels so they may be visualized on X-rays. In the urinary system used to drain urine from the bladder, 143, 290, 290*f*
Catheterization, insertion of a tube through the urethra and into the urinary bladder for the purpose of withdrawing urine or inserting dye, 294
Caudal, directional term meaning toward the feet or tail, or below, 35*f*, 35*t*
Cauterization, destruction of tissue using an electric current, a caustic product, or a hot iron, or by freezing, 64
CC, 297
Cecum, first portion of the colon. It is a blind pouch off the beginning of the large intestine. The appendix grows out of the end of the cecum, 249, 249*f*, 250*f*
Cell, the basic unit of all living things. All tissues and organs in the body are composed of cells. They perform survival functions such as reproduction, respiration, metabolism, and excretion. Some cells are also able to carry on specialized functions, such as contraction by muscle cells and electrical impulse transmission by nerve cells, 22
Cell membrane, the outermost boundary of the cell, 22
Cell-mediated immunity, immunity that results from the activation of sensitized T lymphocytes. The immune response causes antigens to be destroyed by the direct action of cells. Also called *cellular immunity,* 185

Cellular immunity, also called cell-mediated immunity. This process results in the production of T cells and natural killer, NK, cells that directly attach to foreign cells. This immune response fights invasion by viruses, bacteria, fungi, and cancer, 185
Cellulitis, inflammation of the cellular or connective tissues, 61
Cementum, anchors the root of a tooth into the socket of the jaw, 246, 247, 247*f*
Central canal, canal that extends down the length of the spinal cord; contains cerebrospinal fluid, 394
Central fissure, 393*f*
Central nervous system, the portion of the nervous system that consists of the brain and spinal cord. It receives impulses from all over the body, processes this information, and then responds with an action. It consists of both gray matter and white matter, 390–95
  brain, 392–94
  meninges, 395
  spinal cord, 394
Centrifuge, 169*f*
Cephalalgia, a headache, 398
Cephalic, Directional term meaning toward the head, or above, 35*t*
Cephalic region, the head region of the body, 31, 32*f*
Cephalic vein, 142*f*
Cerebellar, pertaining to the cerebellum, 398
Cerebellitis, inflammation of the cerebellum, 398
Cerebellum, the second largest portion of the brain, located beneath the posterior portion of the cerebrum. This part of the brain aids in coordinating voluntary body movements and maintaining balance and equilibrium. It is attached to the brain stem by the pons. The cerebellum refines the muscular movement that is initiated in the cerebrum, 392, 392*f*, 393*f*
Cerebral, pertaining to the cerebrum, 398
Cerebral aneurysm, localized abnormal dilatation of a blood vessel, usually an artery; the result of a congenital defect or weakness in the wall of the vessel; a ruptured aneurysm is a common cause for a hemorrhagic CVA, 401, 401*f*
Cerebral angiography, x-ray of the blood vessels of the brain after the injection of a radiopaque dye, 405
Cerebral contusion, bruising of the brain from a blow or impact; symptoms last longer than 24 hours and include unconsciousness, dizziness, vomiting, unequal pupil size, and shock, 401
Cerebral cortex, the outer layer of the cerebrum. It is composed of folds of gray matter called gyri, which are separated by sulci, 392
Cerebral hemispheres, the division of the cerebrum into right and left halves, 392
Cerebral palsy (CP), a group of disabilities caused by injury to the brain either before or during birth or very early in infancy. This is the most common permanent disability in childhood, 401
Cerebrospinal, pertaining to the cerebrum and spine, 398
Cerebrospinal fluid (CSF), watery, clear fluid found in the ventricles of the brain. It provides protection from shock or sudden motion to the brain, 392, 394
Cerebrospinal fluid analysis, laboratory examination of the clear, watery, colorless fluid from within the brain and spinal cord. Infections and the abnormal presence of blood can be detected in this test, 405
Cerebrospinal fluid shunts, a surgical procedure in which a bypass is created to drain cerebrospinal fluid. It is used to treat hydrocephalus by draining the excess cerebrospinal fluid from the brain and diverting it to the abdominal cavity, 407
Cerebrovascular accident (CVA), also called a *stroke.* The development of an infarct due to loss in the blood supply to an area of the brain. Blood flow can be interrupted by a ruptured blood vessel (hemorrhage), a floating clot (embolus), a stationary clot (thrombosis), or compression. The extent of damage depends on the size and location of the infarct and often includes speech problems and muscle paralysis, 401, 402*f*
Cerebrum, the largest section of the brain. It is located in the upper portion and is the area that possesses our thoughts, judgment, memory, association skills, and the ability to discriminate between items. The outer layer of the cerebrum is the cerebral cortex, which is composed of folds of gray matter. The elevated portions of the cerebrum, or convolutions, are called gyri and are separated by fissures or sulci. The cerebrum has both a left and right division or hemisphere. Each hemisphere has four lobes: frontal, parietal, occipital, and temporal, 392, 392*f*
Cerumen, also called ear wax. A thick, waxy substance produced by oil glands in the auditory canal. This wax helps to protect and lubricate the ear, 441, 442
Ceruminoma, a hard accumulation of ear wax in the ear canal, 446
Cervical, (1) Pertaining to the neck. (2) Pertaining to the cervix, 94, 321

Cervical biopsy, taking a sample of tissue from the cervix to test for the presence of cancer cells, 328
Cervical cancer, malignant growth in the cervix. An especially difficult type of cancer to treat, it causes 5% of the cancer deaths in women. Pap tests have helped to detect early cervical cancer, 324
Cervical nerve, 397*f*
Cervical nodes, 182*t*, 183*f*
Cervical region, the neck region of the body, 31, 32*f*
Cervical vertebrae, the seven vertebrae in the neck region, 84, 85, 88*t*
Cervicectomy, excision of the cervix, 321
Cervix, the narrow, distal portion of the uterus that joins to the vagina, 314*f*, 316, 316*f*, 317*f*, 319*f*
Cesarean section (CS, C-section), surgical delivery of a baby through an incision into the abdominal and uterine walls. Legend has it that the Roman emperor Julius Caesar was the first person born by this method, 328
Chancroid, highly infectious nonsyphilitic venereal ulcer, 337, 337*f*
Cheeks, form the lateral walls of the oral cavity, 244
Chemabrasion, abrasion using chemicals; also called a *chemical peel*. 64
Chemical thyroidectomy, large dose of radioactive iodine is given in order to kill thyroid gland cells without having to actually do surgery, 372
Chest tube, 226
Chest x-ray (CXR), taking a radiograhic picture of the lungs and heart from the back and sides, 223
Cheyne-Stokes respiration, abnormal breathing pattern in which there are long periods (10 to 60 seconds) of apnea followed by deeper, more rapid breathing, 219
Chicken pox, 63, 63*f*
Chiropractic, healthcare profession concerned with diagnosis and treatment of the spine and musculoskeletal system with the intention of affecting the nervous system and improving health. Healthcare practitioner is a *chiropractor*, 95
Chiropractor, 95
Chlamydia, parasitic microorganism causing genital infections in males and females; can lead to pelvic inflammatory disease in females and eventual infertility, 337
Choked disk, 432
Cholecystalgia, gallbladder pain, 252
Cholecystectomy, surgical excision of the gallbladder. Removal of the gallbladder through the laparoscope is a newer procedure with fewer complications than the more invasive abdominal surgery. The laparoscope requires a small incision into the abdominal cavity, 252
Cholecystic, pertaining to the gallbladder, 252
Cholecystitis, inflammation of the gallbladder, 260
Cholecystogram, dye given orally to the patient is absorbed and enters the gallbladder. An X-ray is then taken, 252
Choledocholithotripsy, crushing of a gallstone in the common bile duct, 263
Cholelithiasis, formation or presence of stones or calculi in the gallbladder or common bile duct, 260, 260*f*
Chondrectomy, excision of cartilage, 93
Chondroma, cartilage tumor, 93
Chondromalacia, softening of cartilage, 93
Chondroplasty, surgical repair of cartilage, 93
Chordae tendineae, 135*f*
Chorion, the outer of two membranous sacs surrounding the fetus. It helps to form the placenta, 318, 320
Chorionic, pertaining to the chorion, 321
Chorionic villus sampling (CVS), removal of a small piece of the chorion for genetic analysis; may be done at an earlier stage of pregnancy than amniocentesis, 328
Choroid, the middle layer of the eyeball. This layer provides the blood supply for the eye, 426, 426*f*, 427
Choroid layer, 425*f*
Chronic obstructive pulmonary disease (COPD), progressive, chronic, and usually irreversible condition in which the lungs have a diminished capacity for inspiration (inhalation) and expiration (exhalation). The person may have difficulty breathing on exertion (dyspnea) and a cough. Also called *chronic obstructive lung disease (COLD)*, 221
Chyme, semisoft mixture of food and digestive fluids that pass from the stomach into the small intestines, 248
Cicatrix, a scar, 55
Cilia, a term for eyelashes that protect the eye from foreign particles or for nasal hairs that help filter dust and bacteria out of inhaled air, 210, 429
Ciliary body, the intraocular eye muscles that change the shape of the lens, 426*f*, 427
Circadian rhythm, the 24-hour clock that governs our periods of wakefulness and sleepiness, 362, 363
Circulatory system, system that transports blood to all areas of the body. The organs of the circulatory system include the heart and blood vessels (arteries, veins, and capillaries). Also called the *cardiovascular system*, 132, 132*f*

Circumcision, surgical removal of the end of the prepuce or foreskin of the penis. Generally performed on the newborn male at the request of the parents. The primary reason is for ease of hygiene. Circumcision is also a ritual practice in some religions, 334, 338
Circumduction, movement in a circular direction from a central point, 109
Cirrhosis, chronic disease of the liver, 260
Clavicle, also called the collar bone. A bone of the pectoral girdle, 88, 89*f*, 90, 90*f*
Clavicular, pertaining to the clavicle or collar bone, 94
Clean catch specimen (CC), urine sample obtained after cleaning off the urinary opening and catching or collecting a sample in midstream (halfway through the urination process) to minimize contamination from the genitalia, 293
Cleft lip, congenital anomaly in which the upper lip fails to come together. Often seen along with a cleft palate. Corrected with surgery, 256
Cleft palate, congenital anomaly in which the roof of the mouth has a split or fissure. Corrected with surgery, 256
Clitoris, a small organ containing erectile tissue that is covered by the labia minora. It contains sensitive tissue that is aroused during sexual stimulation and is similar to the penis in the male, 314*f*, 317
Closed fracture, a simple fracture with no open skin or wound, 96, 96*f*
Clubbing, the abnormal widening and thickening of the ends of the fingers and toes associated with chronic oxygen deficiency. Seen in patients with chronic respiratory conditions or circulatory problems, 219
CNS, 408
Coagulate, convert liquid to a gel or solid, as in blood coagulation, 174
Coarctation of the aorta (CoA), severe congenital narrowing of the aorta, 147
Coccygeal, pertaining to the coccyx or tailbone, 94
Coccyx, the tailbone, the four small fused vertebrae at the distal end of the vertebral column, 84, 85, 86*f*, 88*t*
Cochlea, a portion of the labyrinth associated with hearing. It is rolled in the shape of a snail shell. The organs of Corti line the cochlea, 441*f*, 442
Cochlear, pertaining to the cochlea, 444
Cochlear implant, mechanical device that is surgically placed under the skin behind the outer ear (pinna). It converts sound signals into magnetic impulses to stimulate the auditory nerve. Can be beneficial for those with profound sensorineural hearing loss, 447, 448*f*
Cochlear nerve, the branch of the vestibulocochlear nerve that carries hearing information to the brain, 441, 441*f*
Coitus, 334
Cold sores, 256
Colectomy, surgical removal of the colon, 252
Collagen fibers, fibers made up of an insoluble fibrous protein present in connective tissue that forms a flexible mat to protect the skin and other parts of the body, 52
Collecting tubule, a portion of the renal tubule, 283, 284*f*, 286*f*
Colles' fracture, a specific type of wrist fracture, 97, 97*f*
Colon, also called the *large intestine*. Functions to reabsorb most of the fluid in the digested food. The material that remains after water reabsorption is the feces. The sections of the colon are the cecum, ascending colon, transverse colon, descending colon, and sigmoid colon, 27*t*, 33*t*, 34*t*, 243*f*, 244, 249–50
Colonic, pertaining to the colon, 252
Colonoscope, instrument to view inside the colon, 252, 261
Colonoscopy, a flexible fiberscope passed through the anus, rectum, and colon is used to examine the upper portion of the colon. Polyps and small growths can be removed during this procedure, 261
Color vision tests, use of polychromic (multicolored) charts to determine the ability of the patient to recognize color, 435, 435*f*
Colorectal, pertaining to the colon and rectum, 252
Colorectal carcinoma, cancerous tumor along the length of the colon and rectum, 257
Colostomy, surgical creation of an opening in some portion of the colon through the abdominal wall to the outside surface. The fecal material (stool) drains into a bag worn on the abdomen, 252, 263, 263*f*
Colostrum, a thin fluid first secreted by the breast after delivery; it does not contain much protein, but is rich in antibodies, 323
Colposcope, instrument to view inside the vagina, 321, 327
Colposcopy, visual examination of the cervix and vagina using a colposcope or instrument with a magnifying lens, 327
Coma, profound unconsciousness resulting from an illness or injury, 399
Combining form, the word root plus the combining vowel. It is always written with a / between the word root and the combining vowel. For example, in the combining form *cardi/o, cardi* is the word root and */o* is the combining vowel, 4

Combining vowel, a vowel inserted between word parts that makes it possible to pronounce long medical terms. It is usually the vowel *o,* 2, 3–4
Comedo, medical term for a blackhead. It is an accumulation of sebum in a sebaceous gland that has become blackened, 55
Comminuted fracture, a fracture in which the bone is shattered, splintered, or crushed into many pieces or fragments. The fracture is completely through the bone, 97
Common bile duct, a duct that carries bile from the gallbladder to the duodenum, 251
Common iliac artery, 140*f*
Common iliac vein, 142*f*
Compact bone, the hard exterior surface bone. Also called *cortical bone,* 82, 83*f*
Complemental air, 215*t*
Complete blood count (CBC), blood test that consists of five tests; red blood cell count (RBC), white blood count (WBC), hemoglobin (Hg), hematocrit (Hct), and white blood cell differential, 176
Compound fracture, an open fracture in which the skin has been broken through by the fracture, 96, 96*f,* 97
Compression fracture, fracture involving loss of height of a vertebral body, 97
Conception, fertilization of an ovum by a sperm, 315, 316
Concussion, injury to the brain that results from a blow or impact from an object. Can result in unconsciousness, dizziness, vomiting, unequal pupil size, and shock, 402
Conductive hearing loss, loss of hearing as a result of the blocking of sound transmission in the middle ear and outer ear, 443
Condyle, refers to the rounded portion at the end of a bone, 83, 84, 85*f*
Cones, the sensory receptors of the retina that are active in bright light and see in color, 427
Confidentiality, 12
Congenital anomalies, 319
Congenital septal defect (CSD), defect, present at birth, in the wall separating two chambers of the heart. Results in a mixture of oxygenated and deoxygenated blood being carried to the surrounding tissues. There can be an atrial septal defect (ASD) and a ventricular septal defect (VSD), 145
Congestive heart failure (CHF), pathological condition of the heart in which there is a reduced outflow of blood from the left side of the heart. Results in weakness, breathlessness, and edema, 145
Conization, surgical removal of a core of cervical tissue. Also refers to partial removal of the cervix, 328
Conjunctiva, a protective mucous membrane lining on the underside of each eyelid and across the anterior surface of each eyeball, 426, 426*f,* 428*f,* 429
Conjunctival, pertaining to the conjunctiva, 430
Conjunctivitis, also referred to as *pink eye* or an inflammation of the conjunctiva, 431
Conjunctivoplasty, surgical repair of the conjunctiva, 431
Connective tissue, the supporting and protecting tissue in body structures. Examples are fat or adipose tissue, cartilage, and bone, 23, 24*f*
Conscious, condition of being awake and aware of surroundings, 399
Constipation, experiencing difficulty in defecation or infrequent defecation, 254
Consultation reports, document in a patient's medical record. They are the reports given by specialists who the physician has requested to evaluate the patient, 11
Contracture, an abnormal shortening of a muscle, making it difficult to stretch the muscle, 99, 99*f,* 111
Contusion, injury caused by a blow to the body; causes swelling, pain, and bruising; the skin is not broken, 55
Convulsions, severe involuntary muscle contractions and relaxations. These have a variety of causes, such as epilepsy, fever, and toxic conditions, 399
COPD, 227
Corium, the living layer of skin located between the epidermis and the subcutaneous tissue. Also referred to as the *dermis,* it contains hair follicles, sweat glands, sebaceous glands, blood vessels, lymph vessels, nerve fibers, and muscle fibers, 52
Cornea, a portion of the sclera that is clear and transparent and allows light to enter the interior of the eye. It also plays a role in bending light rays, 425*f,* 426*f,* 430*f*
Corneal, pertaining to the cornea, 431
Corneal abrasion, scraping injury to the cornea; if it does not heal, it may develop into an ulcer, 433
Coronal plane, a vertical plane that divides the body into front (anterior or ventral) and back (posterior or dorsal) sections. Also called the *frontal plane,* 30, 31
Coronal section, sectional view of the body produced by a cut along the frontal plane; also called a *frontal section.* 30, 31
Coronary, pertaining to the heart, 143

Coronary arteries, a group of three arteries that branch off the aorta and carry blood to the myocardium, 138, 139*f*
Coronary artery bypass graft (CABG), open-heart surgery in which a blood vessel is grafted to route blood around the point of constriction in a diseased coronary artery, 150
Coronary artery disease (CAD), insufficient blood supply to the heart muscle due to an obstruction of one or more coronary arteries; may be caused by atherosclerosis and may cause angina pectoris and myocardial infarction, 145
Corpus, the body or central portion of the uterus, 316
Corpus (uterus), 314*f*
Corpus albicans, 315*f*
Corpus luteum, 315*f*
Cortex, the outer layer of an organ. In the endocrine system, it refers to the outer layer of the adrenal glands; in the urinary system, the outer layer of the kidney, 282, 283*f*
Cortical, pertaining to the cortex, 93
Cortical bone, the hard exterior surface bone. Also called *compact bone,* 82, 83*f*
Corticosteroid cream, a powerful anti-inflammatory cream, 65
Corticosteroids, general term for the group of hormones secreted by the adrenal contex. They include mineralocorticoid hormones, glucocorticoid hormones, and steroid sex hormones. Used as a medication for its strong anti-inflammatory properties, 101, 192, 227, 360, 373
Cortisol, a steroid hormone secreted by the adrenal cortex. It regulates carbohydrate metabolism, 358*t,* 360
Costal, pertaining to the ribs, 94
Cowper's glands, also called *bulbourethral glands.* These two small male reproductive system glands are located on either side of the urethra just distal to the prostate. The secretion from these glands neutralizes the acidity in the urethra and the vagina, 335
CP, 408
CPK, 112, 152
CPR, 152, 227
Cranial, Pertaining to the skull, 94
Cranial bones, 87*t*
Cranial cavity, a dorsal body cavity. It is within the skull and contains the brain, 31, 32, 32*f,* 33*t*
Cranial nerves, nerves that arise from the brain, 390, 396*t*
Craniotomy, incision into the skull, 93
Cranium, the skull; bones that form a protective covering over the brain, 84, 85, 86*f*
Creatine phosphokinase (CPK), a muscle enzyme found in skeletal muscle and cardiac muscle; blood test becomes elevated in disorders such as heart attack, muscular dystrophy, and other skeletal muscle pathologies, 112, 148
Creatinine, a waste product of muscle metabolism, 170
Creatinine clearance, test of kidney function. Creatinine is a waste product cleared from the bloodstream by the kidneys. For this test, urine is collected for 24 hours and the amount of creatinine in the urine is compared to the amount of creatinine that remains in the bloodstream, 293
Crepitation, sound of broken bones rubbing together, 95
Cretinism, congenital condition due to a lack of thyroid that may result in arrested physical and mental development, 370
CRF, 297
Crick in the neck, 111
Cricoid cartilage, 211*f*
Crohn's disease, form of chronic inflammatory bowel disease affecting the ileum and/or colon. Also called *regional ileitis,* 257
Cross infection, occurs when a person, either a patient or healthcare worker, acquires a pathogen from another patient or healthcare worker, 186
Cross-eyed, 435
Cross-section, an internal view of the body produced by a slice perpendicular to the long axis of the structure, 30, 31
Croup, acute viral respiratory infection common in infants and young children and characterized by a hoarse cough, 220
Crown, portion of a tooth that is covered by enamel. Also an artificial covering for the tooth created to replace the original enamel, 246, 247*f,* 254
Crowning, when the head of the baby is visible through the vaginal opening. A sign that birth is imminent, 320, 321
Crural, pertaining to the leg, 36
Crural region, the lower extremity region of the body, 31, 32*f*
Cryoextraction, procedure in which cataract is lifted from the lens with an extremely cold probe, 436
Cryoretinopexy, surgical fixation of the retina by using extreme cold, 436
Cryosurgery, exposing tissues to extreme cold in order to destroy them. Used in treating malignant tumors and to control pain and bleeding, 64

Cryptorchidism, failure of the testes to descend into the scrotal sac before birth. Generally, the testes will descend before the boy is 1 year old. A surgical procedure called orchidopexy may be required to bring the testes down into the scrotum permanently. Failure of the testes to descend could result in sterility in the male, 336
CS, C-section, 330
CSD, 152
CSF, 408
CTS, 112
Culdoscopy, examination of the female pelvic cavity by introducing an endoscope through the wall of the vagina, 327
Culture and sensitivity (C&S), a laboratory test in which a colony of pathogens that have been removed from an infected area are grown to identify the pathogen and then determine its sensitivity to a variety of antibiotics, 63
Curettage, removal of superficial skin lesions with a curette (surgical instrument shaped like a spoon) or scraper, 64
Cushing's syndrome, set of symptoms that result from hypersecretion of the adrenal cortex. This may be the result of a tumor of the adrenal glands. The syndrome may present symptoms of weakness, edema, excess hair growth, skin discoloration, and osteoporosis, 369, 369*f*
Cuspids, permanent teeth located between the incisors and the bicuspids that assist in biting and cutting food. Humans have four cuspids. Also called canine teeth or eyeteeth, 245*f*, 246, 246*f*
Cusps, the leaflets or flaps of a heart valve, 135
Cutaneous membrane, this is another term for the skin, 50
Cuticle, the thin skinlike layer overlapping the base of a nail, 52
CVA, 408
CVS, 330
Cyanosis, slightly bluish color of the skin due to a deficiency of oxygen and an excess of carbon dioxide in the blood. It is caused by a variety of disorders, ranging from chronic lung disease to congenital and chronic heart problems, 52, 55, 219
Cycloplegia, Paralysis of the ciliary body, 431
Cyst, fluid-filled sac under the skin, 58, 58*f*
Cystalgia, bladder pain, 288
Cystectomy, excision of the bladder, 288
Cystic, pertaining to the bladder, 288
Cystic duct, duct leading from the gallbladder to the common bile duct; carries bile, 251*f*, 260*f*
Cystic fibrosis (CF), hereditary condition causing the exocrine glands to malfunction. The patient produces very thick mucus that causes severe congestion within the lungs and digestive system. Through more advanced treatment, many children are now living into adulthood with this disease, 221
Cystitis, inflammation of the bladder, 285, 288
cysto, 297
Cystocele, hernia or outpouching of the bladder that protrudes into the vagina. This may cause urinary frequency and urgency, 293, 325
Cystogram, record of the bladder, 288
Cystography, process of instilling a contrast material or dye into the bladder by catheter to visualize the urinary bladder on X-ray, 293
Cystolith, bladder stone, 288
Cystopexy, surgical fixation of the bladder, 288
Cystoplasty, surgical repair of the bladder, 288
Cystorrhagia, rapid bleeding from the bladder, 288
Cystoscope, instrument used to visually examine the bladder, 288
Cystoscopy (cysto), visual examination of the urinary bladder using an instrument called a cystoscope, 294
Cystostomy, creation of an opening through the body wall and into the bladder, 288
Cystotomy, incision into the bladder, 288
Cytology, the study of cells, 22
Cytoplasm, the watery internal environment of a cell, 22
Cytotoxic, pertaining to poisoning cells, 185, 186

D

D&C, 330
Dacryocystitis, inflammation of tear sac, 431
Deafness, the inability to hear or having some degree of hearing impairment, 446
Decibel (dB), measures the intensity or loudness of a sound. Zero decibels is the quietest sound measured and 120 dB is the loudest sound commonly measured, 445
Deciduous teeth, the twenty teeth that begin to erupt around the age of 6 months. Eventually pushed out by the permanent teeth, 246, 247
Decongestant, substance that reduces nasal congestion and swelling, 227
decub, 65
Decubitus ulcer, bedsore or pressure sore caused by pressure over bony prominences on the body; caused by a lack of blood flow, 61
Deep, directional term meaning away from the surface of the body, 36*t*
Deep tendon reflex (DTR), muscle contraction in response to a stretch caused by striking the muscle tendon with a reflex hammer; test used to determine if muscles are responding properly, 112

Defecation, evacuation of feces from the rectum, 249, 250
Defibrillation, a procedure that converts serious irregular heartbeats, such as fibrillation, by giving electric shocks to the heart, 150, 150*f*
Delirium, state of mental confusion with a lack of orientation to time and place, 399
Delivery, the emergence of the baby from the birth canal, 320, 321
Dementia, progressive impairment of intellectual function that interferes with performing the activities of daily living. Patients have little awareness of their condition. Found in disorders such as Alzheimer's, 400
Dendrite, branched process off a neuron that receives impulses and carries them to the cell body, 390, 391*f*
Dental, pertaining to teeth 252
Dental caries, gradual decay and disintegration of teeth caused by bacteria that can result in inflamed tissue and abscessed teeth. Commonly called a *tooth cavity*, 254
Dentalgia, tooth pain, 252
Dentin, the main bulk of the tooth. It is covered by enamel, 246, 247, 247*f*
Dentist, 254
Dentistry, branch of healthcare involved with the prevention, diagnosis, and treatment of conditions involving the teeth, jaw, and mouth. Dentistry is practiced by a *dentist* or *oral surgeon*, 254
Denture, partial or complete set of artificial teeth that are set in plastic materials. Substitute for the natural teeth and related structures, 254
Deoxygenated, blood in the veins that is low in oxygen content, 132
Depigmentation, loss of normal skin color or pigment, 55
Depression, 109
Derm, derm, 65
Dermabrasion, abrasion or rubbing using wire brushes or sandpaper, 64
Dermatitis, inflammation of the skin, 54
Dermatologist, a physician specialized in the diagnosis and treatment of diseases of the integumentary system, 54
Dermatology, the branch of medicine specializing in conditions of the integumentary system, 25*t*, 55
Dermatome, instrument for cutting the skin or thin transplants of skin, 64
Dermatopathy, general term for skin disease, 54
Dermatoplasty, the surgical repair of the skin, 54, 64
Dermatosis, abnormal condition of the skin, 54
Dermis, the living layer of skin located between the epidermis and the subcutaneous tissue. It is also referred to as the corium or the *true skin*. It contains hair follicles, sweat glands, sebaceous glands, blood vessels, lymph vessels, nerve fibers, and muscle fibers, 51*f*, 52, 53*f*
Descending aorta, 137*f*
Descending colon, the section of the colon that descends the left side of the abdomen, 249, 249*f*, 250*f*
Descending tracts, nerve tracts carrying motor signals down the spinal cord to the muscles, 394
Diabetes insipidus (DI), disorder caused by the inadequate secretion of a hormone by the posterior lobe of the pituitary gland. There may be polyuria and polydipsia. This is more common in the young, 370
Diabetes mellitus (DM), a serious disease in which the pancreas fails to produce insulin or the insulin does not work properly. Consequently, the patient has very high blood sugar. The kidney will attempt to lower the high blood sugar level by excreting excess sugar in the urine, 364, 369
Diabetic acidosis, 369
Diabetic nephropathy, accumulation of damage to the glomerulus capillaries due to the chronic high blood sugars of diabetes mellitus, 291
Diabetic retinopathy, secondary complication of diabetes that affects the blood vessels of the retina, resulting in visual changes and even blindness, 369
Diagnostic reports, found in a patient's medical record, it consists of the results of all diagnostic tests performed on the patient, principally from the lab and medical imaging (for example, X-ray and ultrasound), 11
Diaphoresis, excessive or profuse sweating, 55
Diaphragm, The major muscle of inspiration. It separates the thoracic from the abdominal cavity, 31, 32, 32*f*, 133*f*, 214*f*, 215
Diaphragmatic, pertaining to the diaphragm, 217
Diaphragmatocele, 256
Diaphysis, the shaft portion of a long bone, 82, 83*f*
Diarrhea, passing of frequent, watery bowel movements. Usually accompanies gastrointestinal (GI) disorders, 254
Diastole, the period of time during which a heart chamber is relaxed, 135, 136
Diastolic pressure, the lower pressure within blood vessels during the relaxation phase of the heart beat, 141
Diencephalon, the portion of the brain that contains two of the most critical areas of the brain, the thalamus and the hypothalamus, 392

Digestive system, system that digests food and absorbs nutrients. Organs include the mouth, pharynx, esophagus, stomach, small and large intestines, liver, gallbladder, and anus. Also called the gastrointestinal system, 27*t*, 241–78, 243*f*
- abbreviations, 264
- accessory organs of, 250–51
- anatomy and physiology, 245–51
- colon, 249–50
- diagnostic procedures, 260–62
- esophagus, 247–48
- gallbladder, 251
- liver, 250
- oral cavity, 244–47
- pancreas, 251
- pathology, 256–60
- pharmacology, 264
- pharynx, 247
- salivary glands, 250
- small intestine, 248–49
- stomach, 248
- teeth, 246–47
- therapeutic procedures, 262–63
- vocabulary, 254–55
- word building, 252–54

Digital rectal exam (DRE), manual examination for an enlarged prostate gland performed by palpating (feeling) the prostate gland through the wall of the rectum, 338

Digital veins, 142*f*

Dilation and curettage (D&C), surgical procedure in which the opening of the cervix is dilated and the uterus is scraped or suctioned of its lining or tissue. Often performed after a spontaneous abortion and to stop excessive bleeding from other causes, 329

Dilation stage, the first stage of labor. It begins with uterine contractions that press the fetus against the cervix causing it to dilate to 10 cm and become thin. The thinning of the cervix is called effacement, 320, 320*f*

Diphtheria, a bacterial infection of the respiratory system characterized by severe inflammation that can form a membrane coating in the upper respiratory tract that can cause marked difficulty breathing, 220

Diplopia, double vision, 431

Directional/positional terms, 33

Discharge summary, part of a patient's medical record. It is a comprehensive outline of the patient's entire hospital stay. It includes condition at time of admission, admitting diagnosis, test results, treatments and patient's response, final diagnosis, and follow-up plans, 11

Dislocation, occurs when the bones in a joint are displaced from their normal alignment, 99

Distal, directional term meaning located farthest from the point of attachment to the body, 35*f*, 36*t*

Distal convoluted tubule, a portion of the renal tubule, 283, 284*f*, 286*f*

Diuresis, abnormal secretion of large amounts of urine, 291

Diuretic, substance that increases the excretion of urine, which promotes the loss of water and salt from the body. Can assist in lowering blood pressure; therefore, these drugs are used to treat hypertension. Potassium in the body may be depleted with continued use of diuretics. Potassium-rich foods such as bananas, kiwi, and orange juice can help correct this deficiency, 152, 296

Diverticulectomy, surgical removal of a diverticulum, 263

Diverticulitis, inflammation of a diverticulum or sac in the intestinal tract, especially in the colon, 257, 257*f*, 258

Diverticulosis, abnormal condition of having diverticula (out pouches off the gut), 258

Diverticulum, 257

DM, 373

Dopaminergic drugs, group of medications to treat Parkinson's disease by either replacing the dopamine that is lacking or increasing the strength of the dopamine that is present, 407

Doppler ultrasonography, measurement of sound-wave echos as they bounce off tissues and organs to produce an image. In cardiovascular system, used to measure velocity of blood moving through blood vessels to look for blood clots, 149

Dorsal, directional term meaning near or on the back or spinal cord side of the body, 35*f*, 35*t*

Dorsal cavities, 33*t*

Dorsiflexion, backward bending, as of hand or foot, 108, 108*f*

Dorsum, refers to the posterior region of back of the body, 31, 32*f*

DPT, 220, 227

DRE, 340

Dry gangrene, late stages of gangrene characterized by the affected area becoming black and leathery, 61

DTR, 112

Dual-energy absorptiometry, measurement of bone density using low dose X-ray for the purpose of detecting osteoporosis, 100

Duchenne's muscular dystrophy, 111

Duodenal, pertaining to the duodenum, 252

Duodenum, the first section of small intestines. Digestion is completed in the duodenum after the chyme mixes with digestive juices from the pancreas and gallbladder, 248, *248f,* 249, *249f, 250f, 251f, 260f*
Dura mater, the term means tough mother. It is the fibrous outermost meninges layer that forms a tough protective layer, 395, *395f*
Dwarfism, condition of being abnormally small. It may be the result of a hereditary condition or an endocrine dysfunction, 370
Dyscrasia, a general term indicating the presence of a disease affecting blood, 174
Dysentery, disease characterized by diarrhea, often with mucus and blood, severe abdominal pain, fever, and dehydration, 258
Dyskinesia, difficult or painful movement, 110
Dysmenorrhea, painful cramping that is associated with menstruation, 322
Dysorexia, abnormal appetite, 254
Dyspepsia, indigestion, 254
Dysphagia, having difficulty eating, 254
Dysphasia, impairment of speech as a result of a brain lesion, 399
Dysphonia, abnormal voice, 218
Dyspnea, difficult, labored breathing, 218, 220
Dystocia, abnormal or difficult labor and childbirth, 323
Dystonia, abnormal tone, 110
Dystrophy, 6
Dysuria, painful or difficult urination. This is a symptom in many disorders, such as cystitis, urethritis, enlarged prostate in the male, and prolapsed uterus in the female, 290

E

Ear, 29*t,* 439–61, *440f, 441f*
- abbreviations, 448
- anatomy and physiology, 441–43
- diagnostic procedures, 446–47
- external, 441–42
- hearing, 443
- inner, 442
- middle, 442
- pathology, 446
- pharmacology, 448
- therapeutic procedures, 447–48
- vocabulary, 445
- word building, 444–45

Ecchymosis, skin discoloration or bruise caused by blood collecting under the skin, 56, *56f*
ECG, 152
Echocardiography (ECHO), noninvasive diagnostic method using ultrasound to visualize internal cardiac structures; cardiac valve activity can be evaluated using this method, 149
Echoencephalography, recording of the ultrasonic echoes of the brain; useful in determining abnormal patterns of shifting in the brain, 405
Eclampsia, convulsive seizures and coma that can occur in a woman between the twentieth week of pregnancy and the first week of postpartum. Often associated with hypertension, 326
\Ectopic pregnancy, 316
Eczema, superficial dermatitis accompanied by papules, vesicles, and crusting, 61
ED, 340
Edema, condition in which the body tissues contain excessive amounts of fluid, 368
EEG, 408
Effacement, the thinning of the cervix during labor, 320, 321
Efferent, 283
Efferent arteriole, arteriole that carries blood away from the glomerulus, 283, *284f, 286f*
Efferent neurons, nerves that carry impulses away from the brain and spinal cord to the muscles and glands. Also called *motor neurons.* 395, 396, *397f*
EGD, 264
Egg cell, *316f*
Ejaculation, the impulse of forcing seminal fluid from the male urethra, 334
EKG, 152
Elastin fibers, *213f*
Elbow, 83
Elective abortion, the legal termination of a pregnancy for nonmedical reasons, 329
Electrocardiogram (ECG,EKG), record of the electrical activity of the heart. Useful in the diagnosis of abnormal cardiac rhythm and heart muscle (myocardium) damage, *138f,* 143
Electrocardiography, process of recording the electrical activity of the heart, 149
Electrocautery, to destroy tissue with an electric current, 64
Electroencephalogram (EEG), a record of the brain's electrical activity, 398
Electroencephalography (EEG), recording the electrical activity of the brain by placing electrodes at various positions on the scalp. Also used in sleep studies to determine if there is a normal pattern of activity during sleep, 406
Electrolyte, chemical compound that separates into charged particles, or ionizes, in a solution. Sodium chloride (NaCl) and potassium (K) are examples of electrolytes, 286
Electromyogram (EMG), record of muscle electricity, 110
Electromyography, recording of the electrical patterns of a muscle in order to diagnose diseases, 112

Elephantiasis, inflammation, obstruction, and destruction of the lymph vessels that results in enlarged tissues due to edema, 189
Elevation, a muscle action that raises a body part, as in shrug the shoulders, 109
ELISA, 192
Embolectomy, surgical removal of an embolus or clot from a blood vessel, 150
Embolus, obstruction of a blood vessel by a blood clot that moves from another area, 147, 148*f*
Embryo, the term to describe the developing infant from fertilization until the end of the eighth week, 318, 319, 319*f*
Embryonic, pertaining to the embryo, 322
Emesis, vomiting, usually with some force, 255
Emetic, substance that induces vomiting, 264
EMG, 112
Emmetropia (EM), state of normal vision, 432
Emphysema, pulmonary condition that can occur as a result of long-term heavy smoking. Air pollution also worsens this disease. The patient may not be able to breathe except in a sitting or standing position, 221
Empyema, pus within the pleural space, usually the result of infection, 223
Emulsification, to make fats and lipids more soluble in water, 250
Enamel, the hardest substance in the body. Covers the outer surface of teeth, 246, 247, 247*f*
Encephalitis, inflammation of the brain due to disease factors such as rabies, influenza, measles, or smallpox, 398
Endarterectomy, removal of the inside layer of an artery, 150
Endings
  plural, 9
  singular, 9
Endocarditis, inflammation of the inner lining layer of the heart. May be due to microorganisms or to an abnormal immunological response, 134, 145
Endocardium, the inner layer of the heart, which is very smooth and lines the chambers of the heart, 133, 134, 134*f*
Endocervicitis, inflammation of the inner aspect of the cervix, 321
Endocrine glands, a glandular system that secretes hormones directly into the bloodstream rather than into a duct. Endocrine glands are frequently referred to as ductless glands. The endocrine system includes the thyroid gland, adrenal glands, parathyroid glands, pituitary gland, pancreas (islets of Langerhans), testes, ovaries, and thymus gland, 358, 358*t*–359*t*
Endocrine system, the body system that consists of glands that secrete hormones directly into the blood stream. The endocrine glands include the adrenal glands, parathyroid glands, pancreas, pituitary gland, testes, ovaries, thymus gland, and thyroid gland, 28*t*, 355–86, 357*f*, 358
  abbreviations, 373
  adrenal glands, 360
  anatomy and physiology, 358–66
  diagnostic procedures, 371–72
  ovaries, 360
  pancreas, 361–62
  parathyroid glands, 362
  pathology, 369–71
  pharmacology, 373
  pineal gland, 362–63
  pituitary gland, 363–64
  testes, 364
  therapeutic procedures, 372
  thymus gland, 364–66
  thyroid gland, 366
  vocabulary, 368
  word building, 366–68
Endocrinologist, physician who specializes in the treatment of endocrine glands, including diabetes, 367, 368
Endocrinology, the branch of medicine specializing in conditions of the endocrine system, 28*t*, 368
Endocrinopathy, a disease of the endocrine system, 367
Endometrial biopsy (EMB), taking a sample of tissue from the lining of the uterus to test for abnormalities, 328
Endometrial cancer, cancer of the endometrial lining of the uterus, 324
Endometriosis, abnormal condition of endometrium tissue appearing throughout the pelvis or on the abdominal wall. This tissue is usually found within the uterus, 322, 325
Endometritis, inflammation of the endometrial lining of the uterus, 325
Endometrium, the inner lining of the uterus. It contains a rich blood supply and reacts to hormonal changes every month, which results in menstruation. During a pregnancy, the lining of the uterus does not leave the body but remains to nourish the unborn child, 316, 316*f*
Endoscopic retrograde cholanglopancreatography (ERCP), using an endoscope to X-ray the bile and pancreatic ducts, 261
Endothelium, 139*f*
Endotracheal, pertaining to inside the trachea, 218
Endotracheal intubation, placing a tube through the mouth to create an airway, 225, 225*f*

ENT, 448
Enteric, pertaining to the small intestines, 252
Enteritis, inflammation of only the small intestine, 252
Enucleated, the loss of a cell's nucleus, 170
Enucleation, surgical removal of an eyeball, 436
Enuresis, involuntary discharge of urine after the age by which bladder control should have been established. This usually occurs by age 5. Also called bedwetting at night, 291
Enzyme-linked immunosorbent assay (ELISA), a blood test for an antibody to the AIDS virus. A positive test means that the person has been exposed to the virus. In the case of a false-positive reading, the Western blot test would be used to verify the results, 190
Eosinophils, granulocyte white blood cells that destroy parasites and increase during allergic reactions, 169*f*, 171*f*, 171*t*
eosins, eos, 178
Epicardium, the outer layer of the heart. It forms part of the pericardium, 133, 134
Epicondyle, a projection located above or on a condyle, 83, 84, 85*f*
Epidermal, pertaining to upon the skin, 54
Epidermis, the superficial layer of skin. It is composed of squamous epithelium cells. These are flat scalelike cells that are arranged in layers, called stratified squamous epithelium. The many layers of the epidermis create a barrier to infection. The epidermis does not have a blood supply, so it is dependent on the deeper layers of skin for nourishment. However, the deepest epidermis layer is called the basal layer. These cells are alive and constantly dividing. Older cells are pushed out toward the surface by new cells forming beneath. During this process, they shrink and die, becoming filled with a protein called keratin. The keratin-filled cells are sloughed off as dead cells, 50–51, 51*f*, 53*f*
Epididymal, pertaining to the epididymis, 335
Epididymectomy, surgical excision of the epididymis, 335
Epididymis, a coiled tubule that lies on top of the testes within the scrotum. This tube stores sperm as they are produced and turns into the vas deferens, 28*t*, 332*f*, 333, 334, 365*f*
Epididymitis, inflammation of the epididymis that causes pain and swelling in the inguinal area, 335
Epidural hematoma, mass of blood in the space outside the dura mater of the brain and spinal cord, 404
Epidural space, 395*f*
Epigastric, pertaining to above the stomach. An anatomical division of the abdomen, the middle section of the upper row, 34
Epigastric region, 34*t*
Epiglottis, a flap of cartilage that covers the larynx when a person swallows. This prevents food and drink from entering the larynx and trachea, 211*f*, 212, 245*f*, 247
Epilepsy, recurrent disorder of the brain in which convulsive seizures and loss of consciousness occur, 402
Epinephrine, a hormone produced by the adrenal medulla. Also known as *adrenaline*. Some of its actions include increased heart rate and force of contraction, bronchodilation, and relaxation of intestinal muscles, 358*t*, 360
Epiphyseal line, 83*f*
Epiphysis, the wide ends of a long bone, 82
Episiorrhaphy, suture the perineum, 322
Episiotomy, surgical incision of the perineum to facilitate the delivery process. Can prevent an irregular tearing of tissue during birth, 329
Epispadias, congenital opening of the urethra on the dorsal surface of the penis, 337
Epistaxis, nosebleed, 210, 219
Epithelial tissue, tissue found throughout the body as the skin, the outer covering of organs, and the inner lining for tubular or hollow structures, 23, 24*f*
Epithelium, epithelial tissue composed of close-packed cells that form the covering for and lining of body structures, 23
Equilibrium, The sense of balance, 441, 441*f*
ERCP, 264
Erectile dysfunction (ED), inability to copulate due to inability to maintain an erection; also called *impotence*, 336
Erectile dysfunction agents, medications that temporarily produce an erection in patients with erectile dysfunction, 340
Erectile tissue, tissue with numerous blood vessels and nerve endings. It becomes filled with blood and enlarges in size in response to sexual stimulation, 317, 334
ERT, 330
Erythema, redness or flushing of the skin, 56
Erythroblastosis fetalis, 326
Erythrocyte sedimentation rate (ESR, sed rate), blood test to determine the rate at which mature red blood cells settle out of the blood after the addition of an anticoagulant. An indicator of the presence of an inflammatory disease, 176
Erythrocytes, also called red blood cells or RBCs. Cells that contain hemoglobin, an iron-containing pigment that binds oxygen in order to transport it to the cells of the body, 26*t*, 170, 171*f*, 173, 175
Erythrocytosis, too many red cells, 173

Erythroderma, red skin, 55
Erythropenia, too few red cells, 173
Erythropoiesis, the process of forming erythrocytes, 173
Eschar, a thick layer of dead tissue and tissue fluid that develops over a deep burn area, 56
Esophageal, pertaining to the esophagus, 252
Esophageal varices, enlarged and swollen varicose veins in the lower end of the esophagus; they can rupture and result in serious hemorrhage, 256
Esophagectasis, stretched out or dilated esophagus, 252
Esophagogastroduodenoscopy (EGD), use of a flexible fiberoptic scope to visually examine the esophagus, stomach, and beginning of the duodenum, 262
Esophagus, the tube that carries food from the pharynx to the stomach, 27*t*, 33*t*, 211*f*, 243*f*, 244, 245*f*, 247–48, 248*f*
Esotropia, inward turning of the eye. An example of a form of strabismus (muscle weakness of the eye), 428*f*, 435
ESR, SR, sed rate, 178
ESRD, 297
Estrogen, one of the hormones produced by the ovaries. It works with progesterone to control the menstrual cycle and it is responsible for producing the secondary sexual characteristics, 314, 358*t*, 359*t*, 360
ESWL, 297
Ethmoid bone, a cranial bone, 84, 85, 87*t*
Eupnea, normal breathing, 218
Eustachian tube, tube or canal that connects the middle ear with the nasopharynx and allows for a balance of pressure between the outer and middle ear. Infection can travel via the mucous membranes of the eustachian tube, resulting in middle ear infections, 211, 211*f*, 212, 245*f*, 441*f*, 442
Eversion, directional term meaning turning outward, 109, 109*f*
Ewing's sarcoma, malignant growth found in the shaft of long bones that spreads through the periosteum. Removal is treatment of choice, as this tumor will metastasize or spread to other organs, 98
Excretory urography (EU), injection of dye into the bloodstream followed by taking an X-ray to trace the action of the kidney as it excretes the dye, 293
Exfoliative cytology, scraping cells from tissue and then examining them under a microscope, 63
Exhalation, to breathe air out of the lungs. Also called expiration, 210
Exocrine, 358
Exocrine glands, glands that secrete substances into a duct. Tears and tear ducts are examples of an exocrine gland, 358
Exophthalmos, condition in which the eyeballs protrude, such as in Graves' disease. This is generally caused by an overproduction of thyroid hormone, 368, 368*f*
Exostosis, a bone spur, 95
Exotropia, outward turning of the eye. Also an example of strabismus (muscle weakness of the eye), 435
Expectorant, substance that assists in the removal of secretions from the bronchopulmonary membranes, 227
Expiration, 210, 216*f*
Expiratory reserve volume (ERV), the amount of air that can be forcibly exhaled after a normal quiet respiration. This is also called *supplemental air*, 215*t*
Exploratory laparotomy, abdominal operation for the purpose of examining the abdominal organs and tissues for signs of disease or other abnormalities, 263
Expulsion stage, stage of labor and delivery during which the baby is delivered, 320, 320*f*, 321
Extension, movement that brings limb into or toward a straight condition, 108, 108*f*
Extensor capri, a muscle named for its action, extension, 107
External auditory meatus, the opening into the external ear canal, 441, 441*f*, 442
External ear, the outermost portion of the ear. It consists of the auricle, auditory canal, and eardrum, 440*f*, 441–42
External iliac artery, 140*f*
External iliac vein, 142*f*
External oblique, a muscle named for the direction of its fibers, on an oblique angle, 107
External respiration, the exchange of oxygen and carbon dioxide that takes place in the lungs, 210
External sphincter, ring of voluntary muscle that controls the emptying of urine from the bladder, 284
Extracorporeal circulation (ECC), during open heart surgery, the routing of blood to a heart-lung machine so it can be oxygenated and pumped to the rest of the body, 150
Extracorporeal shockwave lithotripsy (ESWL), use of ultrasound waves to break up stones. Process does not require surgery, 294, 295*f*
Extraction, removing or pulling teeth, 262
Eye, 29*t*, 425*f*, 426*f*
- abbreviations, 438
- anatomy and physiology, 426–30
- conjunctiva, 429

diagnostic procedures, 435–36
eyeball, 426–27
eyelids, 429
lacrimal apparatus, 429
muscles, 428
pathology, 433–35
pharmacology, 437–38
retina, 427
therapeutic procedures, 436–37
vision, 429–30
vocabulary, 432
word building, 430–32
Eye muscles, there are six muscles that connect the eyeball to the orbit cavity. These muscles allow for rotation of the eyeball, 426
Eyeball, the eye by itself, without any appendages such as the eye muscles or tear ducts, 426–27
Eyelashes, along the upper and lower edges of the eyelids; protect the eye from foreign particles; also called *cilia.* 429
Eyelids, an upper and lower fold of skin that provides protection from foreign particles, injury from the sun and intense light, and trauma. Both the upper and lower edges of the eyelids have small hairs or cilia. In addition, sebaceous or oil glands are located in the eyelids. These secrete a lubricating oil, 426, 426*f,* 429

F
Facial bones, the skull bones that surround the mouth, nose, and eyes; muscles for chewing are attached to the facial bones, 84, 85, 86*f,* 87*t*
Facial nerve, 396*t*
Falling test, test used to observe balance and equilibrium. The patient is observed balancing on one foot, then with one foot in front of the other, and then walking forward with eyes open. The same test is conducted with the patient's eyes closed. Swaying and falling with the eyes closed can indicate an ear and equilibrium malfunction, 447
Fallopian tubes, organs in the female reproductive system that transport eggs from the ovary to the uterus, 28*t,* 33*t,* 34*t,* 313*f,* 314, 314*f,* 315–16, 315*f,* 316*f,* 361*f*
Farsightedness, 433
Fascia, connective tissue that wraps muscles. It tapers at each end of a skeletal muscle to form tendons, 106
Fascial, pertaining to fascia, 110
Fasciitis, inflammation of fascia, 110
Fasciotomy, incision into fascia, 110
Fasting blood sugar (FBS), blood test to measure the amount of sugar circulating throughout the body after a 12-hour fast, 371
Fats, lipid molecules transported throughout the body dissolved in the blood, 170
FBS, 373
FDA, 471
Fecal occult blood test (FOBT), laboratory test on the feces to determine if microscopic amounts of blood are present; also called *hemoccult* or *stool guaiac.* 260
Feces, food that cannot be digested becomes a waste product and is expelled or defecated as feces, 249
Female reproductive system, system responsible for producing eggs for reproduction and provides place for growing baby. Organs include ovaries, fallopian tubes, uterus, vagina, and mammary glands, 28*t,* 313*f,* 314*f*
abbreviations, 330
anatomy and physiology, 314–21
breast, 318
diagnostic procedures, 327–28
internal genitalia, 314–17
pathology, 324–27
pharmacology, 329
therapeutic procedures, 328–29
vocabulary, 323–24
vulva, 317
word building, 321–23
Female urethra, 281*f*
Femoral, pertaining to the femur or thigh bone, 94
Femoral artery, 140*f*
Femoral vein, 142*f*
Femur, also called the *thigh bone.* It is a lower extremity bone, 82, 85*f,* 88, 89*f,* 90, 91*f,* 91*t*
Fertility drug, medication that triggers ovulation. Also called *ovulation stimulant,* 329
Fertilization, also called *impregnation.* The fusion of an ova and sperm to produce an embryo, 314
Fetal, pertaining to the fetus, 322
Fetal monitoring, using electronic equipment placed on the mother's abdomen to check the baby's heart rate and strength during labor, 328
Fetus, the term to describe the developing newborn from the end of the eighth week until birth, 318, 319, 319*f*
Fever blisters, 256
Fibrillation, abnormal quivering or contractions of heart fibers. When this occurs within the fibers of the ventricle of the heart, arrest and death can occur. Emergency equipment to defibrillate, or convert the heart to a normal beat, is necessary, 145
Fibrin, whitish protein formed by the action of thrombin and fibrinogen, which is the basis for the clotting of blood, 172
Fibrinogen, blood protein that is essential for clotting to take place, 170, 173

Fibrinolysis, destruction of fibers, 173
Fibrinous, pertaining to being fibrous, 173
Fibrocystic breast disease, benign cysts forming in the breast, 326, 326*f*
Fibroid tumor, benign tumor or growth that contains fiberlike tissue. Uterine fibroid tumors are the most common tumors in women, 325, 325*f*
Fibromyalgia, a condition with widespread aching and pain in the muscles and soft tissue, 111
Fibrous joints, a joint that has almost no movement because the ends of the bones are joined together by thick fibrous tissue. The sutures of the skull are an example of a fibrous joint, 91, 92
Fibula, one of the lower leg bones in the lower extremity, 89*f*, 90, 91*f*, 91*t*
Fibular, pertaining to the fibula, a lower leg bone, 94
Fibular vein, 142*f*
Filtration, first stage of urine production during which waste products are filtered from the blood, 286, 287
Fimbriae, the fingerlike extensions on the end of the fallopian tubes. The fimbriae drape over each ovary in order to direct the ovum into the fallopian tube after it is expelled by the ovary, 315, 316, 316*f*, 361*f*
First-degree burn, 60, 60*f*
Fissure, a deep groove or slit-type opening, 58, 58*f*, 83, 84
Fistulectomy, excision of a fistula, 263
Fixation, a procedure to stabilize a fractured bone while it heals. *External fixation* includes casts, splints, and pins inserted through the skin. *Internal fixation* includes pins, plates, rods, screws, and wires that are applied during an *open reduction*, 101
Flat bone, a type of bone with a thin flattened shape. Examples include the scapula, ribs, and pelvic bones, 82, 83
Flexion, act of bending or being bent, 108, 108*f*
Flexor carpi, a muscle named for its action, flexion, 107
Floating kidney, 292
Fluorescein angiography, process of injecting a dye (fluorescein) to observe the movement of blood for detecting lesions in the macular area of the retina. Used to determine if there is a detachment of the retina, 434
Fluorescein staining, applying dye eyedrops that are a bright green fluorescent color; used to look for corneal abrasions or ulcers, 434
Flutter, an arrhythmia in which the atria beat too rapidly, but in a regular pattern, 146
Focal seizure, a localized epileptic seizure often affecting one limb, 400
Follicle-stimulating hormone (FSH), a hormone secreted by the anterior pituitary gland. It stimulates growth of eggs in females and sperm in males, 314, 359*t*, 363
Foramen, a passage or opening through a bone for nerves and blood vessels, 83, 84
Formed elements, the solid, cellular portion of blood. It consists of erythrocytes, leukocytes, and platelets, 170
Fossa, a shallow cavity or depression within or on the surface of a bone, 83, 84
Fovea capitis, 85*f*
Fovea centralis, the area of the retina that has the sharpest vision, 427
Fracture, an injury to a bone that causes it to break. Fractures are named to describe the type of damage to the bone, 96–98, 97
Fraternal twins, twins that develop from two different ova fertilized by two different sperm; although twins, these siblings do not have identical DNA, 323
Free edge, the exposed edge of a nail that is trimmed when nails become too long, 52
Frequency, a greater than normal occurrence in the urge to urinate, without an increase in the total daily volume of urine. Frequency is an indication of inflammation of the bladder or urethra, 291
Frontal bone, the forehead bone of the skull, 84, 85, 87*f*, 87*t*
Frontal lobe, one of the four cerebral hemisphere lobes. It controls motor functions, 392, 393, 393*f*
Frontal plane, a vertical plane that divides the body into front (anterior or ventral) and back (posterior or dorsal) sections. Also called the *coronal plane*, 30, 30*f*, 31
Frontal section, sectional view of the body produced by a cut along the frontal plane; also called a *coronal section.* 30, 31
Frozen section (FS), a thin piece of tissue is cut from a frozen specimen for rapid examination under a microscope, 63
FS, 65
FSH, 373
Full-term pregnancy, 319*f*
Functional bowel syndrome, 259
Functional residual capacity (FRC), the air that remains in the lungs after a normal exhalation has taken place, 215*t*
Fundus, the domed upper portion of an organ such as the stomach or uterus, 248, 248*f*
Fundus (uterus), 314*f*, 316, 316*f*, 319*f*
Fungal scrapings, scrapings, taken with a curette or scraper, of tissue from lesions are placed on a growth medium and examined under a microscope to identify fungal growth, 63

Fungi, organisms found in the Kingdom Fungi. Some are capable of causing disease in humans, such as yeast infections or histoplasmosis, 184

Funny bone, 83

Furuncle, staphylococcal skin abscess with redness, pain, and swelling. Also called a *boil,* 63

G

Gallbladder (GB), small organ located just under the liver. It functions to store the bile produced by the liver. The gallbladder releases bile into the duodenum through the common bile duct, 27*t*, 33*t*, 34*t*, 243*f*, 244, 251, 251*f*, 260*f*

Gametes, the reproductive sex cells—ova and sperm, 360

Gamma globulin, protein component of blood containing antibodies that help to resist infection, 170

Ganglion, knotlike mass of nerve tissue located outside the brain and spinal cord, 395, 396

Ganglion cyst, cyst that forms on tendon sheath, usually on hand, wrist, or ankle, 111

Gangrene, necrosis of the skin usually due to deficient blood supply, 61

Gastralgia, stomach pain, 252

Gastrectomy, surgical removal of the stomach, 253

Gastric, pertaining to the stomach, 252

Gastric carcinoma, cancerous tumor of the stomach, 256

Gastric stapling, procedure that closes off a large section of the stomach with rows of staples. Results in a much smaller stomach to assist very obese patients to lose weight, 263

Gastritis, inflammation of the stomach that can result in pain, tenderness, nausea, and vomiting, 253

Gastroenteritis, inflammation of the stomach and small intestines, 3, 252

Gastroenterologist, a physician specialized in treating diseases and conditions of the gastrointestinal tract, 252

Gastroenterology, branch of medicine specializing in conditions of the gastrointestinal system, 27*t*, 255

Gastroesophageal reflux disease (GERD), acid from the stomach backs up into the esophagus, causing inflammation and pain, 256

Gastrointestinal, 27*t*

Gastrointestinal system (GI), system that digests food and absorbs nutrients. Organs include the mouth, pharynx, esophagus, stomach, small and large intestines, liver, gallbladder, and anus. Also called the digestive system, 244

Gastrointestinal tract, the continuous tube that extends from mouth to anus; also called *gut* or *alimentary canal,* 244

Gastromalacia, softening of the stomach, 252

Gastroscope, instrument to view inside the stomach, 253, 262

Gastroscopy, a flexible gastroscope is passed through the mouth and down the esophagus in order to visualize inside the stomach; used to diagnose peptic ulcers and gastric carcinoma, 262

Gastrostomy, surgical creation of a gastric fistula or opening through the abdominal wall. The opening is used to place food into the stomach when the esophagus is not entirely open (esophageal stricture), 252

Gavage, using a nasogastric tube to place liquid nourishment directly into the stomach, 262

General hospital, hospitals that typically provide services to diagnose (laboratory, diagnostic imaging) and treat (surgery, medications, therapy) diseases for a short period of time. In addition, they usually provide emergency and obstetrical care. Also called an *acute care hospital,* 11

Genital herpes, creeping skin disease that can appear like a blister or vesicle, caused by a sexually transmitted virus, 337

Genital warts, growths and elevations of warts on the genitalia of both males and females that can lead to cancer of the cervix in females, 338

Genitalia, the male and female reproductive organs, 314

Genitourinary system (GU), the organs of the urinary system and the female or male sexual organs, 282, 333

GERD, 264

Gestation, length of time from conception to birth, generally nine months. Calculated from the first day of the last menstrual period, with a range of from 259 days to 280 days, 318

GH, 373

Gigantism, excessive development of the body due to the overproduction of the growth hormone by the pituitary gland. The opposite of dwarfism, 370

Gingiva, the tissue around the teeth; also called *gums.* 244, 245*f*, 246, 247*f*

Gingival, pertaining to the gums, 253

Gingivitis, inflammation of the gums characterized by swelling, redness, and a tendency to bleed, 253

Girdle, 88

Glands, the organs of the body that release secretions. Exocrine glands, like sweat glands, release their secretions into ducts. Endocrine glands, such as the thyroid gland, release their hormones directly into the blood stream, 358, 390
adrenal, 28*t*
apocrine, 53, 54
bulbourethral, 28*t*
lymph, 182
parathyroid, 28*t*
pineal, 28*t*
pituitary, 28*t*
prostate, 28*t*, 33*t*
salivary, 27*t*
sebaceous, 25*t*, 50, 51*f*, 52–53
sudoriferous, 53
sweat, 25*t*, 50, 51*f*, 53–54
thymus, 26*t*, 28*t*, 33*t*, 181, 184
thyroid, 28*t*, 211*f*
Glans penis, the larger and softer tip of the penis. It is protected by a covering called the prepuce or foreskin, 333*f*, 334
Glaucoma, increase in intraocular pressure that, if untreated, may result in atrophy (wasting away) of the optic nerve and blindness. Glaucoma is treated with medication and surgery. There is an increased risk of developing glaucoma in persons over 60 years of age, people of African ancestry, persons who have sustained a serious eye injury, and anyone with a family history of diabetes or glaucoma, 433
Globulins, one type of protein found dissolved in the plasma, 170
Glomerular, 284*f*
Glomerular capsule, also called Bowman's capsule. Part of the renal corpuscle. It is a double-walled cuplike structure that encircles the glomerulus. In the filtration stage of urine production, waste products filtered from the blood enter Bowman's capsule as the glomerular filtrate, 283, 286*f*
Glomerular filtrate, the product of the filtration stage of urine production. Water, electrolytes, nutrients, wastes, and toxins that are filtered from blood passing through the glomerulus. The filtrate enters Bowman's capsule, 286
Glomerulonephritis, inflammation of the kidney (primarily of the glomerulus). Since the glomerular membrane is inflamed, it becomes more permeable and will allow protein and blood cells to enter the filtrate. Results in protein in the urine (proteinuria) and hematuria, 292
Glomerulus, ball of capillaries encased by Bowman's capsule. In the filtration stage of urine production, wastes filtered from the blood leave the glomerulus capillaries and enter Bowman's capsule, 283, 284*f*, 286*f*
Glossal, pertaining to the tongue, 253
Glossopharyngeal nerve, 396*t*
Glottis, the opening between the vocal cords. Air passes through the glottis as it moves through the larynx. Changing the tension of the vocal cords changes the size of the opening, 212
Glucagon, a hormone secreted by the pancreas. It stimulates the liver to release glucose into the blood, 359*t*, 361
Glucocorticoids, a group of hormones secreted by the adrenal cortex. They regulate carbohydrate levels in the body. Cortisol is an example of a glucocorticoid, 358*t*, 360
Glucose, the form of sugar used by the cells of the body to make energy. It is transported to the cells in the blood, 170
Glucose tolerance test (GTT), test to determine the blood sugar level. A measured dose of glucose is given to a patient either orally or intravenously. Blood samples are then drawn at certain intervals to determine the ability of the patient to utilize glucose. Used for diabetic patients to determine their insulin response to glucose, 372
Glutamic oxaloacetic transaminase (GOT), 148
Gluteal, pertaining to the buttocks, 31, 36
Gluteal region, refers to the buttock region of the body, 31, 32*f*
Gluteus maximus, a muscle named for its size and location: Gluteus means *rump area* and maximus means *large*. 107
Glycosuria, presence of an excess of sugar in the urine, 290, 368
Goiter, enlargement of the thyroid gland, 371, 371*f*
Gonadotropins, common name for follicle-stimulating hormone and luteinizing hormone, 363
Gonads, the organs responsible for producing sex cells. The female gonads are the ovaries, and they produce ova. The male gonads are the testes, and they produce sperm, 360
Gonorrhea, sexually transmitted inflammation of the mucous membranes of either sex. Can be passed on to an infant during the birth process, 338
GOT, 152
Graft *versus* host disease (GVHD), serious complication of bone marrow transplant; immune cells from the donor bone marrow (graft) attack the recipient's (host's) tissues. 189
Grand mal seizure, 403
Granulocytes, granular polymorphonuclear leukocyte. There are three types: neutrophil, eosinophil, and basophil, 171, 171*t*, 173

Graves' disease, condition, named for Robert Graves, an Irish physician, that results in overactivity of the thyroid gland and can result in a crisis situation. Also called *hyperthyroidism,* 368, 371

Gray matter, tissue within the central nervous system. It consists of unsheathed or uncovered nerve cell bodies and dendrites, 390, 391

Great saphenous vein, 142*f*

Greenstick fracture, fracture in which there is an incomplete break; one side of the bone is broken and the other side is bent. This type of fracture is commonly found in children due to their softer and more pliable bone structure, 97

Growth hormone (GH), a hormone secreted by the anterior pituitary that stimulates growth of the body, 359*t,* 363

GTT, 373

Guillain-Barré syndrome, disease of the nervous system in which nerves lose their myelin covering; may be caused by an autoimmune reaction; characterized by loss of sensation and/or muscle control in the arms and legs; symptoms then move toward the trunk and may even result in paralysis of the diaphragm, 404

Gums, the tissue around the teeth; also called *gingiva.* 244, 246

Gut, name for the continuous muscular tube that stretches between the mouth and anus; also called the *alimentary canal,* 244

GVHD, 192

GYN, gyn, 330

Gynecologist, a physician specialized in treating conditions and diseases of the female reproductive system, 322, 323

Gynecology, branch of medicine specializing in conditions of the female reproductive system, 28*t,* 323

Gynecomastia, the development of breast tissue in males; may be a symptom of adrenal feminization, 368

Gyri, the convoluted, elevated portions of the cerebral cortex. They are separated by fissures or sulci. Singular is gyrus, 392

H

H_2-receptor antagonist, blocks the production of stomach acids, 264

Hair, a structure in the integumentary system, 25*t,* 49, 50, 51*f,* 52

Hair follicle, cavities in the dermis that contain the hair root. Hair grows longer from the root, 52, 53*f*

Hair root, deeper cells that divide to grow a hair longer, 52, 53*f*

Hair shaft, older keratinized cells that form most of the length of a hair, 52, 53*f*

Hammer, 441*f,* 442

Hand, 92*f*

Hard palate, 211*f,* 245*f*

Hashimoto's disease, chronic form of thyroiditis, named for a Japanese surgeon, 371

HCT, Hct, crit, 178

HD, 192, 297

HDN, 330

Head, the large ball-shaped end of a bone. It may be separated from the shaft of the bone by an area called the neck, 83, 84, 85*f*

Health Insurance Portability and Accountability Act (HIPAA), 12

Health maintenance organization (HMO), an organization that contracts with a group of physicians and other healthcare workers to provide care exclusively for its members. The HMO pays the healthcare workers a prepaid fixed amount per member, called capitation, whether that member requires medical attention or not, 12

Healthcare settings, 11–12

Hearing, one of the special senses; sound waves detected by the ear, 441, 443

Hearing aid, apparatus or mechanical device used by persons with impaired hearing to amplify sound. Same as amplification device, 447

Hearing impairment, 443

Heart, organ of the cardiovascular system that contracts to pump blood through the blood vessels, 26*t,* 33*t,* 131*f,* 132, 133–38, 181*f,* 214*f,* 365*f*

- chambers, 134
- conduction system of, 136–38
- layers, 133–34
- valves, 135–36

Heart attack, 146

Heart transplantation, replacement of a diseased or malfunctioning heart with a donor's heart, 151

Heart valve prolapse, the cusps or flaps of the heart valve are too loose and fail to shut tightly, allowing blood to flow backwards through the valve when the heart chamber contracts. Most commonly occurs in the mitral valve, but may affect any of the heart valves, 146

Heart valve stenosis, the cusps or flaps of the heart valve are too stiff. Therefore, they are unable to open fully, making it difficult for blood to flow through, or to shut tightly, allowing blood to flow backwards. This condition may affect any of the heart valves, 146

Heartburn, 255

Heimlich maneuver, technique for removing a foreign body or food from the trachea or pharynx when it is choking a person. The maneuver consists of applying pressure just under the diaphragm to pop the obstruction out, 226
Hematemesis, to vomit blood from the gastrointestinal tract, often looks like coffee grounds, 254
Hematic, pertaining to blood, 173
Hematic system, the system that consists of plasma and blood cells—erythrocytes, leukocytes, and platelets; responsible for transporting oxygen, protecting against pathogens, and controlling bleeding, 26*t*
Hematinic, substance that increases the number of erythrocytes or the amount of hemoglobin in the blood, 178
Hematochezia, passing bright red blood in the stools, 255
Hematocrit (Hct, Hct, crit), blood test to measure the volume of red blood cells (erythrocytes) within the total volume of blood, 176
Hematologist, a physician who specializes in treating diseases and conditions of the blood, 173, 174
Hematology, branch of medicine specializing in conditions of the hematic system, 26*t*, 174
Hematoma, swelling or mass of blood caused by a break in a vessel in an organ or tissue, or beneath the skin, 174
Hematopoiesis, the process of forming blood, 170, 173
Hematosalpinx, condition of having blood in the fallopian tubes, 323
Hematuria, condition of blood in the urine, 290
Hemianopia, loss of vision in half of the visual field. A stroke patient may suffer from this disorder, 435
Hemiparesis, weakness or loss of motion on one side of the body, 400
Hemiplegia, paralysis on only one side of the body, 400
Hemoccult, 260
Hemodialysis (HD), use of an artificial kidney machine that filters the blood of a person to remove waste products. Use of this technique in patients who have defective kidneys is lifesaving, 294, 295*f*
Hemoglobin (Hg), iron-containing pigment of red blood cells that carries oxygen from the lungs to the tissue, 170, 173, 176
Hemolysis, the destruction of blood cells, 173
Hemolytic, destruction of blood, 173
Hemolytic anemia, an anemia that develops as the result of the excessive loss of erythrocytes, 175
Hemolytic disease of the newborn (HDN), condition in which antibodies in the mother's blood enter the fetus's blood and cause anemia, jaundice, edema, and enlargement of the liver and spleen. Also called *erythroblastosis fetalis,* 326
Hemolytic reaction, the destruction of a patient's erythrocytes that occurs when receiving a transfusion of an incompatible blood type. Also called a *transfusion reaction*, 175
Hemophilia, hereditary blood disease in which there is a prolonged blood clotting time. It is transmitted by a sex-linked trait from females to males. It appears almost exclusively in males, 174
Hemoptysis, coughing up blood or blood-stained sputum, 219
Hemorrhage, blood flow, the escape of blood from a blood vessel, 173
Hemorrhoid, varicose veins in the rectum, 147, 258
Hemorrhoidectomy, surgical excision of hemorrhoids from the anorectal area, 263
Hemostasis, to stop bleeding or the stagnation of the circulating blood, 172, 174
Hemostatic agent, 178
Hemothorax, condition of having blood in the chest cavity, 218
Hepatic, pertaining to the liver, 253
Hepatic duct, the duct that leads from the liver to the common bile duct; transports bile, 251, 251*f*, 260*f*
Hepatic portal vein, 142*f*
Hepatitis, infectious, inflammatory disease of the liver. Hepatitis B and C types are spread by contact with blood and bodily fluids of an infected person, 253, 260
Hepatoma, liver tumor, 253
Herniated nucleus pulposus (HNP), a rupture of the fibrocartilage disk between two vertebrae. This results in pressure on a spinal nerve and causes pain, weakness, and nerve damage. Also called a slipped disk, 98, 98*f*
Hernioplasty, surgical repair of a hernia; also called herniorrhaphy, 263
Herniorrhaphy, 263
Herpes labialis, infection of the lip by the herpes simplex virus type 1 (HSV-1). Also called *fever blisters* or *cold sores*, 256
Herpes simplex virus (HSV), 65
Herpes zoster virus, 404
Hertz (Hz), measurement of the frequency or pitch of sound. The lowest pitch on an audiogram is 250 Hz. The measurement can go as high as 8000 Hz, which is the highest pitch measured, 445
Hesitancy, a decrease in the force of the urine stream, often with difficulty initiating the flow. It is often a symptom of a blockage along the urethra, such as an enlarged prostate gland, 291

Hymenectomy, surgical removal of the hymen. Performed when the hymen tissue is particularly tough, 322

Hyoid bone, a single, U-shaped bone suspended in the neck between the mandible and larynx. It is a point of attachment for swallowing and speech muscles, 84, 85, 211*f*

Hypercalcemia, condition of having an excessive amount of calcium in the blood, 367

Hypercapnia, excessive carbon dioxide, 218

Hyperemesis, excessive vomiting, 254

Hyperemia, redness of the skin caused by increased blood flow to the skin, 56

Hyperesthesia, having excessive sensation, 399

Hyperglycemia, having an excessive amount of glucose (sugar) in the blood, 367

Hyperhidrosis, abnormal condition of excessive sweat, 54

Hyperkalemia, condition of having an excessive amount of potassium in the blood, 367

Hyperkinesia, an excessive amount of movement, 110

Hyperlipidemia, condition of having too high a level of lipids such as cholesterol in the bloodstream; a risk factor for developing atherosclerosis and coronary artery disease, 174

Hyperopia, with this condition a person can see things in the distance but has trouble reading material at close vision. Also known as *farsightedness,* 433, 433f

Hyperparathyroidism, state of excessive thyroid, 367

Hyperpigmentation, abnormal amount of pigmentation in the skin, which is seen in diseases such as acromegaly and adrenal insufficiency, 56

Hyperpituitarism, state of excessive pituitary gland, 367

Hyperpnea, excessive deep breathing, 218

Hypersecretion, excessive hormone production by an endocrine gland, 368

Hypertension, high blood pressure, 148

Hyperthyroidism, condition resulting from overactivity of the thyroid gland that can result in a crisis situation. Also called *Graves' disease,* 368, 371

Hypertonia, excessive tone, 110

Hypertrophy, an increase in the bulk or size of a tissue or structure, 111

Hyperventilation, to breathe both fast (tachypnea) and deep (hyperpnea), 219

Hypnotic, substance used to produce sleep or hypnosis, 407

Hypocalcemia, condition of having a low calcium level in the blood, 367

Hypochondriac, 34*t*

Hypochromic anemia, anemia resulting from having insufficient hemoglobin in the erythrocytes; named because the hemoglobin molecule is responsible for the dark red color of the erythrocytes, 175

Hypodermic, pertaining to under the skin, 54

Hypodermis, the deepest layer of skin; composed primarily of adipose, 52

Hypogastric, pertaining to below the stomach. An anatomical division of the abdomen, the middle section of the bottom row, 34*t*

Hypogastric region, 34*t*

Hypoglossal, pertaining to under the tongue, 253

Hypoglossal nerve, 396*t*

Hypoglycemia, condition of having a low sugar level in the blood, 367

Hypokinesia, insufficient movement, 110

Hyponatremia, condition of having a low sodium level in the blood, 367

Hypoparathyroidism, state of insufficient thyroid, 367

Hypopituitarism, state of insufficient pituitary gland, 367

Hypopnea, insufficient or shallow breathing, 218

Hyposecretion, deficient hormone production by an endocrine gland, 368

Hypospadias, congenital opening of the male urethra on the underside of the penis, 337

Hypotension, low blood pressure, 148

Hypothalamus, a portion of the diencephalon that lies just below the thalamus. It controls body temperature, appetite, sleep, sexual desire, and emotions such as fear. It also regulates the release of hormones from the pituitary gland and regulates the parasympathetic and sympathetic nervous systems, 363, 363*f,* 392, 392*f,* 393

Hypothyroidism, result of a deficiency in secretion by the thyroid gland. This results in a lowered basal metabolism rate with obesity, dry skin, slow pulse, low blood pressure, sluggishness, and goiter. Treatment is replacement with synthetic thyroid hormone, 368

Hypotonia, insufficient tone, 110

Hypoventilation, to breathe both slow (bradypnea) and shallow (hypopnea), 219

Hypoxemia, deficiency of oxygen in the blood, 217

Hypoxia, absence of oxygen in the tissues, 217

Hysterectomy, removal of the uterus, 322

Hysteropexy, surgical fixation of the uterus, 322

Hysterorrhexis, rupture of the uterus, 322

Hysterosalpingectomy, 8

Hysterosalpingography, process of taking an X-ray of the uterus and oviducts after a radiopaque material is injected into the organs, 327

Hz, 448

I
I&D, 65
Ichthyoderma, dry and scaly skin condition, 55
Ichthyosis, condition in which the skin becomes dry, scaly, and keratinized, 61
ID, 65
IDDM, 373
Identical twins, twins that develop from the splitting of one fertilized ovum; these siblings have identical DNA, 323
Ileal, pertaining to the ileum, 253
Ileocecal valve, sphincter between the ileum and the cecum, 248, 249, 250*f*
Ileostomy, surgical creation of a passage through the abdominal wall into the ileum, 253
Ileum, the third portion of the small intestines. Joins the colon at the cecum. The ileum and cecum are separated by the ileocecal valve, 9, 248, 249, 249*f*
Ileus, severe abdominal pain, inability to pass stools, vomiting, and abdominal distention as a result of an intestinal blockage; may require surgery to reverse the blockage, 258
Iliac, pertaining to the ilium; one of the pelvic bones, 94
Ilium, one of three bones that form the os coxae or innominate bone of the pelvis, 9, 88, 89*f*, 90, 91*f*, 91*t*
IM, 112
Immune response, ability of lymphocytes to respond to specific antigens, 184, 185–86
Immunity, the body's ability to defend itself against pathogens, 184–86
  immune response, 185–86
  standard precautions, 186
Immunization, providing protection against communicable diseases by stimulating the immune system to produce antibodies against that disease. Children can now be immunized for the following diseases; hepatitis B, diphtheria, tetanus, pertussis, tetanus, *Haemophilus influenzae* type b, polio, measles, mumps, rubella, and chickenpox. Also called *vaccination,* 184, 185, 192
Immunocompromised, having an immune system that is unable to respond properly to pathogens, 188
Immunodeficiency disorder, 188
Immunoglobulins (Ig), antibodies secreted by the B cells. All antibodies are immunoglobulins. They assist in protecting the body and its surfaces from the invasion of bacteria. For example, the immunoglobulin IgA in colostrum, the first milk from the mother, helps to protect the newborn from infection, 188
Immunologist, a physician who specializes in treating infectious diseases and other disorders of the immune system, 187, 188
Immunology, branch of medicine specializing in conditions of the lymphatic and immune systems, 26*t*, 188
Immunosuppressants, substances that block certain actions of the immune system; required to prevent rejection of a transplanted organ, 192
Immunotherapy, the production or strengthening of a patient's immune system in order to treat a disease, 192
Impacted fracture, fracture in which bone fragments are pushed into each other, 97
Impetigo, a highly contagious staphylococcal skin infection, most commonly occurring on the faces of children. It begins as blisters that then rupture and dry into a thick, yellow crust, 61, 61*f*
Implant, prosthetic device placed in the jaw to which a tooth or denture may be anchored, 255
Implantable cardiovert-defibrillator, a device implanted in the heart that delivers an electrical shock to restore a normal heart rhythm. Particularly useful for persons who experience ventricular fibrillation, 150
Incision and drainage (I&D), making an incision to create an opening for the drainage of material such as pus, 64
Incisors, biting teeth in the very front of the mouth that function to cut food into smaller pieces. Humans have eight incisors, 245*f*, 246, 246*f*
Incus, one of the three ossicles of the middle ear. Also called the *anvil,* 441*f*, 442, 442*f*
Infant respiratory distress syndrome (IRDS), a lung condition most commonly found in premature infants that is characterized by tachypnea and respiratory grunting. Also called *hyaline membrane disease* (HMD) and *respiratory distress syndrome of the newborn,* 222
Infarct, area of tissue within an organ that undergoes necrosis (death) following the loss of blood supply, 143
Inferior, directional term meaning toward the feet or tail, or below, 35*f*, 35*t*
Inferior vena cava, the branch of the vena cava that drains blood from the abdomen and lower body, 134*f*, 135, 136, 137*f*, 142*f*, 360*f*
Infertility, inability to produce children; generally defined as no pregnancy after properly timed intercourse for one year, 324
Inflammation, the tissue response to injury from pathogens or physical agents; characterized by redness, pain, swelling, and feeling hot to touch, 188, 188*f*

Inflammatory bowel disease (IBD), 259
Influenza, viral infection of the respiratory system characterized by chills, fever, body aches, and fatigue. Commonly called the *flu,* 222
Informed consent, a medical record document, voluntarily signed by the patient or a responsible party, that clearly describes the purpose, methods, procedures, benefits, and risks of a diagnostic or treatment procedure, 11
Inguinal, pertaining to the groin area. There is a collection of lymph nodes in this region that drain each leg, 182
Inguinal hernia, hernia or outpouching of intestines into the inguinal region of the body, 258, 258*f*
Inguinal nodes, 182*t,* 183*f*
Inhalation, (1) To breathe air into the lungs. Also called *inspiration.* (2) To introduce drugs into the body by inhaling them, 210
Innate immunity, 184
Inner ear, the innermost section of the ear. It contains the cochlea, semicircular canals, saccule, and utricle, 440*f,* 441, 441*f,* 442, 443*f*
Inner ear infection, 446
Innominate bone, also called the os coxae or hip bone. It is the pelvis portion of the lower extremity. It consists of the ilium, ischium, and pubis and unites with the sacrum and coccyx to form the pelvis, 88, 90
Insertion, the attachment of a skeletal muscle to the more movable bone in the joint, 107
Inspiration, 210, 216*f*
Inspiratory capacity (IC), the volume of air inhaled after a normal exhale, 215*t*
Inspiratory reserve volume (IRV), the air that can be forcibly inhaled after a normal respiration has taken place. Also called *complemental air,* 215*t*
Insulin, the hormone secreted by the pancreas. It regulates the level of sugar in the blood stream. The more insulin present in the blood, the lower the blood sugar will be, 359*t,* 361, 373
Insulin-dependent diabetes mellitus (IDDM), also called type 1 diabetes mellitus; it develops early in life when the pancreas stops insulin production. Persons with IDDM must take daily insulin injections, 369
Insulinoma, tumor of the islets of Langerhans cells of the pancreas that secretes an excessive amount of insulin, 369
Integument, another term for skin, 50
Integumentary system, the skin and its appendages including sweat glands, oil glands, hair, and nails. Sense organs that allow us to respond to changes in temperature, pain, touch, and pressure are located in the skin. It is the largest organ in the body, 25*t,* 48–77
abbreviations, 65
accessory organs, 52–54
anatomy and physiology of, 50
diagnostic procedures, 63
pathology, 58–63
pharmacology, 65
skin, 50–52
therapeutic procedures, 64
vocabulary, 55–57
word building, 54–55
Interatrial, pertaining to between the atria, 143
Interatrial septum, the wall or septum that divides the left and right atria, 134
Intercostal muscles, muscles between the ribs. When they contract, they raise the ribs, which helps to enlarge the thoracic cavity, 215
Intercostal nerve, 397*f*
Intermittent claudication, attacks of severe pain and lameness caused by ischemia of the muscles, typically the calf muscles; brought on by walking even very short distances, 111
Intermittent positive pressure breathing (IPPB), method for assisting patients to breathe using a mask connected to a machine that produces an increased pressure, 225
Internal genitalia, 314–17
Internal iliac artery, 140*f*
Internal iliac vein, 142*f*
Internal medicine, branch of medicine involving the diagnosis and treatment of diseases and conditions of internal organs such as the respiratory system. The physician is an *internist,* 219, 255
Internal respiration, the process of oxygen and carbon dioxide exchange at the cellular level when oxygen leaves the bloodstream and is delivered to the tissues, 210
Internal sphincter, ring of involuntary muscle that keeps urine within the bladder, 284
Internist, a physician specialized in treating diseases and conditions of internal organs such as the respiratory system, 219, 255
Internodal pathway, 137*f*
Interstitial cystitis, disease of unknown cause in which there is inflammation and irritation of the bladder. Most commonly seen in middle-aged women, 293
Interventricular, pertaining to between the ventricles, 143
Interventricular septum, the wall or septum that divides the left and right ventricles, 134, 135*f,* 137*f*
Intervertebral, pertaining to between vertebrae, 93
Intervertebral disk, fibrous cartilage cushion between vertebrae, 84, 85

Intracoronary artery stent, placing a stent within a coronary artery to treat coronary ischemia due to atherosclerosis, 151
Intracranial, pertaining to inside the skull, 93
Intradermal (ID), (1) Pertaining to within the skin. (2) Injection of medication into the skin, 54, 65
Intramuscular (IM), injection of medication into the muscle, 112
Intraocular, pertaining to within the eye, 431
Intrathecal, (1) Pertaining to within the meninges. (2) Injection into the meninges space surrounding the brain and spinal cord, 399
Intrauterine device (IUD), device that is inserted into the uterus by a physician for the purpose of contraception, 324, 324*f*
Intravenous cholecystography, a dye is administered intravenously to the patient that allows for X-ray visualization of the gallbladder, 261
Intravenous pyelogram (IVP), injecting a contrast medium into a vein and then taking an X-ray to visualize the renal pelvis, 293
Intussusception, an intestinal condition in which one portion of the intestine telescopes into an adjacent portion causing an obstruction and gangrene if untreated, 258, 258*f*
Inversion, directional term meaning turning inward or inside out, 109, 109*f*
Involuntary muscles, muscles under the control of the subconscious regions of the brain. The smooth muscles found in internal organs and cardiac muscles are examples of involuntary muscle tissue, 105
Iodine, a mineral required by the thyroid to produce its hormones, 366
IPPB, 227
IRDS, 227
Iridal, pertaining to the iris, 431
Iridectomy, excision of the iris, 431
Iridoplegia, paralysis of the iris, 431
Iridosclerotomy, incision into the iris and sclera, 431
Iris, the colored portion of the eye. It can dilate or constrict to change the size of the pupil and control the amount of light entering the interior of the eye, 425*f*, 426*f*, 427, 430*f*
Iritis, inflammation of the iris, 431
Iron-deficiency anemia, anemia that results from having insufficient iron to manufacture hemoglobin, 175
Irregular bones, a type of bone having an irregular shape. Vertebrae are irregular bones, 82
Irritable bowel syndrome (IBS), disturbance in the functions of the intestine from unknown causes. Symptoms generally include abdominal discomfort and an alteration in bowel activity. Also called *functional bowel syndrome* or *spastic colon,* 259
Ischemia, localized and temporary deficiency of blood supply due to an obstruction of the circulation, 143
Ischial, pertaining to the ischium, one of the pelvic bones, 94
Ischium, one of the three bones that form the os coxae or innominate bone of the pelvis, 88, 89*f*, 90, 91*f*, 91*t*
Islets of Langerhans, the regions within the pancreas that secrete insulin and glucagon, 361, 361*f*
Isthmus, 366*f*
IVF, 330
IVP, 297

J
Jaundice, yellow cast to the skin, mucous membranes, and the whites of the eyes caused by the deposit of bile pigment from too much bilirubin in the blood. Bilirubin is a waste product produced when worn-out red blood cells are broken down. May be a symptom of disorders such as gallstones blocking the common bile duct or carcinoma of the liver, 255
Jaw bone, 247*f*
Jejunal, pertaining to the jejunum, 253
Jejunostomy, 249
Jejunum, the middle portion of the small intestines. Site of nutrient absorption, 248, 249, 249*f*
Joint, the point at which two bones meet. It provides flexibility, 25*t*, 82, 91–92
Joint capsule, elastic capsule that encloses synovial joints, 91, 92
Jugular vein, 142*f*, 441*f*

K
Kaposi's sarcoma (KS), form of skin cancer frequently seen in acquired immunodeficiency syndrome (AIDS) patients. Consists of brownish-purple papules that spread from the skin and metastasize to internal organs, 62, 189
Keloid, formation of a scar after an injury or surgery that results in a raised, thickened red area, 56
Keratin, a hard protein substance produced by the body. It is found in hair and nails, and filling the inside of epidermal cells, 50, 51
Keratitis, inflammation of the cornea, 431
Keratometer, instrument to measure the cornea, 431, 435
Keratometry, measurement of the curvature of the cornea using an instrument called a keratometer, 435
Keratoplasty, surgical repair of the cornea (corneal transplant), 436
Keratosis, overgrowth and thickening of the epithelium, 56

Keratotomy, incision into the cornea, 431
Ketoacidosis, acidosis due to an excess of ketone bodies (waste products). A serious condition that requires immediate treatment and can result in death for the diabetic patient if not reversed, 369
Ketones, 287*t*
Ketonuria, ketones in the urine, 290
Kidneys, the two kidneys are located in the lumbar region of the back behind the parietal peritoneum. They are under the muscles of the back, just a little above the waist. The kidneys have a concave or depressed area that gives them a bean-shaped appearance. The center of this concavity is called the hilum, 27*t,* 33, 34*t,* 281*f,* 282–83, 283*f,* 284*f,* 360*f*
Kidneys, ureters, bladder (KUD), x-ray taken of the abdomen demonstrating the kidneys, ureters, and bladder without using any contrast dye; also called a flat-plate abdomen, 293
Kinesiology, the study of movement, 110
KS, 192
KUB, 297
Kyphosis, abnormal increase in the outward curvature of the thoracic spine. Also known as hunchback or humpback, 95, 95*f*

L

Labia majora, the outer folds of skin that serves as protection for the female external genitalia and urethral meatus, 314*f,* 317, 317*f*
Labia minora, the inner folds of skin that serves as protection for the female external genitalia and urethral meatus, 314*f,* 317
Labor, the period of time beginning with uterine contractions and ending with the birth of the baby. There are three stages: the dilation stage, the expulsion stage, and the placental stage, 320, 321
Labor and delivery, 320–21
Labyrinth, the term that refers to the inner ear. It is several fluid-filled cavities within the temporal bone. The labyrinth consists of the cochlea, vestibule, and three semicircular canals. Hair cells called the organs of Corti line the inner ear. These hair cells change the sound vibrations to electrical impulses and send the impulses to the brain via the vestibulocochlear nerve, 442
Labyrinthectomy, excision of the labyrinth, 444
Labyrinthitis, labyrinth inflammation, 446
Labyrinthotomy, incision in the labyrinth, 444
Laceration, a torn or jagged wound; incorrectly used to describe a cut, 58, 58*f*
Lacrimal, pertaining to tears, 431
Lacrimal apparatus, consists of the lacrimal gland, lacrimal ducts, and the nasolacrimal duct, 426, 429
Lacrimal bone, a facial bone, 84, 85, 87*f,* 87*t*
Lacrimal ducts, tear ducts located in the inner corner of the eye socket. They collect the tears and drain them into the lacrimal sac, 429, 429*f*
Lacrimal gland, a gland located in the outer corner of each eyelid. It washes the anterior surface of the eye with fluid called tears, 429, 429*f*
Lactate dehydrogenase (LDH), 148
Lactation, the function of secreting milk after childbirth from the breasts or mammary glands, 318
Lacteals, lymphatic vessels in the intestines that serve to absorb fats from the diet, 181
Lactic, pertaining to milk, 322
Lactiferous ducts, carry milk from the milk-producing glands to the nipple, 318, 318*f*
Lactiferous glands, milk-producing glands in the breast, 318, 318*f*
Lactorrhea, discharge of milk, 322
Laminectomy, removal of a portion of a vertebra in order to relieve pressure on the spinal nerve, 100, 407
Laparoscope, instrument to view inside the abdomen, 253, 322, 327
Laparoscopic adrenalectomy, excision of the adrenal gland through a small incision in the abdomen and using endoscopic instruments, 372
Laparoscopic cholecystectomy, excision of the gallbladder using a laparoscope, 263
Laparoscopy, an instrument or scope is passed into the abdominal wall through a small incision. The abdominal cavity is then examined for tumors and other conditions with this lighted instrument. Also called *peritoneoscopy,* 262, 327, 327*f*
Laparotomy, incision into the abdomen, 253, 322
Laryngeal, pertaining to the larynx, 217
Laryngectomy, surgical removal of the larynx. This procedure is most frequently performed for excision of cancer, 217
Laryngitis, inflammation of the larynx causing difficulty in speaking, 217
Laryngopharynx, the inferior section of the pharynx. It lies at the same level in the neck as the larynx. Air has already entered the larynx, therefore the laryngopharynx carries food and drink to the esophagus, 211, 211*f,* 247
Laryngoplasty, surgical repair of the larynx, 217
Laryngoplegia, paralysis of the voice box, 217
Laryngoscope, instrument to view the larynx, 217, 224
Laryngoscopy, examination of the interior of the larynx with a lighted instrument called a *laryngoscope,* 224

Larynx, also called the *voice box.* Respiratory system organ responsible for producing speech. It is located just below the pharynx, 27*t,* 209*f,* 210, 212
Laser photocoagulation, the use of a laser beam to destroy very small precise areas of the retina; may be used to treat retinal detachment or macular degeneration, 437
Laser therapy, removal of skin lesions and birthmarks using a laser beam that emits intense heat and power at a close range. The laser converts frequencies of light into one small, powerful beam, 64
Laser-assisted in-situ keratomileusis (LASIK), correction of myopia using laser surgery to remove corneal tissue, 436, 437*f*
LASIK, 438
Lateral (lat), directional term meaning to the side, 35*f,* 35*t*
Lateral epicondylitis, inflammation of the muscle attachment to the lateral epicondyle of the elbow; often caused by strongly gripping. Commonly called tennis elbow, 111
Lateral fissure, 393*f*
Lavage, using an NG tube to wash out the stomach, 262
Laxative, a mild cathartic, 264
Lazy eye, 433
LDH, 152
Left atrium, 132*f,* 134*f,* 135*f,* 137*f*
Left coronary artery, 139*f*
Left hypochondriac, an anatomical division of the abdomen, the left side of the upper row, 34*t*
Left iliac, an anatomical division of the abdomen, the left side of the upper row, 34*t*
Left lower quadrant (LLQ), a clinical division of the abdomen. It contains portions of small and large intestines, left ovary and fallopian tube, and left ureter, 34*t*
Left lumbar, an anatomical division of the abdomen, the left side of the middle row, 34*t*
Left upper quadrant (LUQ), a clinical division of the abdomen. It contains the left lobe of the liver, spleen, stomach, portion of the pancreas, and portion of small and large intestines, 34*t*
Left ventricle, 132*f,* 134*f,* 135*f,* 137*f*
Legally blind, describes a person who has severely impaired vision. Usually defined as having visual acuity of 20/200, 432
Legionnaire's disease, severe, often fatal disease characterized by pneumonia and gastrointestinal symptoms. Caused by a gram-negative bacillus and named after people who came down with it at an American Legion convention in 1976, 222
Lens, the transparent structure behind the pupil and iris. It functions to bend light rays so they land on the retina, 425*f,* 426*f,* 427, 430*f*
Lesion, a general term for a wound, injury, or abnormality, 56
Leukemia, cancer of the WBC-forming bone marrow; results in a large number of abnormal WBCs circulating in the blood, 175
Leukocytes, also called *white blood cells* or WBCs. A group of several different types of cells that provide protection against the invasion of bacteria and other foreign material. They are able to leave the bloodstream and search out the foreign invaders (bacteria, virus, and toxins), where they perform phagocytosis, 26*t,* 170, 171, 171*t,* 173, 175
Leukocytosis, too many white cells, 173
Leukoderma, disappearance of pigment from the skin in patches, causing a milk-white appearance. Also called *vitiligo,* 55
Leukopenia, too few white (cells), 173
Leukopoiesis, white (cell) producing, 173
LH, 373
Ligaments, very strong bands of connective tissue that bind bones together at a joint, 82
Ligation and stripping, surgical treatment for varicose veins; the damaged vein is tied off (ligation) and removed (stripping), 151
Lingual tonsils, tonsils located on the very posterior section of the tongue as it joins with the pharynx, 184, 211, 212, 245*f*
Lipectomy, surgical removal of fat, 54
Lipocytes, medical term for cells that contain fat molecules, 52
Lipoma, fatty tumor that generally does not metastasize, 54
Liposuction, removal of fat beneath the skin by means of suction, 64
Lips, the anterior opening of the oral cavity, 244, 245*f*
Lithotomy, surgical incision to remove kidney stones, 288
Lithotripsy, destroying or crushing kidney stones in the bladder or urethra with a device called a lithotriptor, 288, 296
Liver, a large organ located in the right upper quadrant of the abdomen. It serves many functions in the body. Its digestive system role includes producing bile, processing the absorbed nutrients, and detoxifying harmful substances, 27*t,* 33*t,* 34*t,* 243*f,* 244, 250, 251*f*
Liver transplant, transplant of a liver from a donor, 263
LLQ, 34*t*
Lobe, ear, 441*f*

Lobectomy, surgical removal of a lobe from an organ, such as a lung. Often the treatment of choice for lung cancer; may also be the removal of one lobe of the thyroid gland, 217, 372

Lobes, subdivisions of an organ such as the lungs or brain, 214

Long bone, a type of bone that is longer than it is wide. Examples include the femur, humerus, and phalanges, 82, 83

Long-term care facility, a facility that provides long-term care for patients who need extra time to recover from an illness or accident before they return home or for persons who can no longer care for themselves. Also called a *nursing home*, 11

Longitudinal section, an internal view of the body produced by a lengthwise slice along the long axis of a structure, 30, 31

Loop of Henle, a portion of the renal tubule, 283, 284*f*, 286*f*

Lordosis, abnormal increase in the forward curvature of the lumbar spine. Also known as *swayback*, 95*f*, 96

Lower esophageal sphincter, also called the cardiac sphincter. Prevents food and gastric juices from backing up into the esophagus, 248

Lower extremity (LE), the leg, 31, 88, 89*f*, 91*t*

Lower gastrointestinal series (lower GI series), x-ray image of the colon and rectum is taken after the administration of barium by enema; also called a *barium enema*, 261, 261*f*

Lumbar, pertaining to the five low back vertebrae, 94

Lumbar puncture (LP), puncture with a needle into the lumbar area (usually the fourth intervertebral space) to withdraw fluid for examination and for the injection of anesthesia. Also called *spinal puncture* or *spinal tap*, 406, 406*f*

Lumbar vertebrae, the five vertebrae in the low back region, 84, 85, 88*t*

Lumbosacral plexus, 397*f*

Lumen, the space, cavity, or channel within a tube or tubular organ or structure in the body, 138, 139*f*

Lumpectomy, excision of only a breast tumor and the tissue immediately surrounding it, 329

Lung volumes/capacities, 214–15, 215*t*

Lungs, the major organs of respiration. The lungs consist of air passageways, the bronchi and bronchioles, and the air sacs, alveoli. Gas exchange takes place within the alveoli, 27*t*, 33*t*, 132*f*, 133*f*, 209*f*, 210, 214, 214*f*, 365*f*

Lunula, the lighter-colored, half-moon region at the base of a nail, 52

LUQ, 34*t*

Luteinizing hormone (LH), a hormone secreted by the anterior pituitary. It regulates function of male and female gonads and plays a role in releasing ova in females, 314, 359*t*, 363

Lymph, clear, transparent, colorless fluid found in the lymphatic vessels and the cisterna chyli, 181

Lymph glands, another name for *lymph nodes;* small organs composed of lymphatic tissue located along the route of the lymphatic vessels; remove impurities from the lymph and manufacture lymphocytes and antibodies, 182

Lymph nodes, small organs in the lymphatic system that filter bacteria and other foreign organisms from the body fluids, 26*t*, 180*f*, 181, 182, 182*t*, 183*f*

Lymphadenectomy, excision of the lymph node. This is usually done to test for malignancy, 187, 192

Lymphadenitis, inflammation of the lympth glands. Referred to as swollen glands, 189

Lymphadenopathy, disease of the lymph nodes, 187

Lymphangiogram, x-ray taken of the lymph vessels after the injection of dye. The lymph flow through the chest is traced, 187

Lymphangiography, process of taking an X-ray of the lymph vessels after the injection of a radiopaque material, 190

Lymphangioma, lymph vessel tumor, 187

Lymphatic, pertaining to lymph, 187

Lymphatic and immune system, 26*t*, 180*f*
- abbreviations, 191
- anatomy and physiology, 181–86
- diagnostic procedures, 190
- immunity, 184–86
- lymph nodes, 182
- pathology, 189
- pharmacology, 191
- spleen, 184, 184*f*
- therapeutic procedures, 191
- thymus gland, 184, 184*f*
- tonsils, 184, 184*f*
- vocabulary, 187–88
- word building, 187

Lymphatic capillaries, the smallest lymph vessels; they collect excessive tissue fluid, 181, 182

Lymphatic ducts, the two largest vessels in the lymphatic system, the right lymphatic duct and the thoracic duct, 181, 182, 183*f*

Lymphatic system, system that helps the body fight infection. Organs include the spleen, lymph vessels, and lymph nodes, 26*t*, 180*f*

Lymphatic vessels, extensive network of vessels throughout the entire body; conduct lymph from the tissue toward the thoracic cavity, 26*t*, 180*f*, 181–82, 181*f*, 182*f*, 183*f*

Lymphedema, edema appearing in the extremities due to an obstruction of the lymph flow through the lymphatic vessels, 188

Lymphocytes, an agranulocyte white blood cell that provides protection through the immune response, 169*f,* 171*f,* 171*t,* 183*f*
Lymphoma, a tumor of lymphatic tissue, 187
lymphs, 178

M

Macrophage, phagocytic cells that are found in large quantities in the lymph nodes. They engulf foreign particles, 184, 185*f*
Macrotia, abnormally large ears, 445
Macula lutea, images are projected onto the area of the retina, 427
Macular degeneration, deterioration of the macular area of the retina of the eye. May be treated with laser surgery to destroy the blood vessels beneath the macula, 434
Macule, flat, discolored area that is flush with the skin surface. An example would be a freckle or a birthmark, 58, 58*f*
Magnetic resonance imaging (MRI), medical imaging that uses radio-frequency radiation as its source of energy. It does not require the injection of contrast medium or exposure to ionizing radiation. The technique is useful for visualizing large blood vessels, the heart, the brain, and soft tissues, 98
Male reproductive system, system responsible for producing sperm for reproduction; organs include testes, vas deferens, urethra, prostate gland, and penis, 28*t,* 331–54, 332*f,* 333*f*
- abbreviations, 340
- anatomy and physiology, 333–35
- bulbourethral glands, 335
- diagnostic procedures, 338
- epididymis, 334
- external organs of, 333–34
- internal organs of, 335
- pathology, 336–38
- penis, 334
- pharmacology, 340
- prostate gland, 335
- seminal vesicles, 335
- testes, 333–34
- therapeutic procedures, 338–39
- vas deferens, 335
- vocabulary, 336
- word building, 335–36

Male urethra, 281*f,* 286*f*
Malignant melanoma (MM), malignant, darkly pigmented tumor or mole of the skin, 62, 62*f*
Malleus, one of the three ossicles of the middle ear. Also called the *hammer,* 441*f,* 442, 442*f*
Mammary, pertaining to the breast, 322
Mammary glands, the breasts; milk-producing glands to provide nutrition for newborn, 318
Mammogram, x-ray record of the breast, 322
Mammography, process of X-raying the breast, 327
Mammoplasty, surgical repair of the breast, 322
Mandible, the lower jawbone, 84, 85, 87*f,* 87*t,* 211*f,* 246*f*
Mandibular, pertaining to the mandible or lower jaw, 94
Mastalgia, breast pain, 322
Mastectomy, excision of the breast, 322
Mastitis, inflammation of the breast, which is common during lactation but can occur at any age, 322
Mastoid process, 441*f*
Maxilla, the upper jawbone, 84, 85, 87*f,* 87*t*
Maxillary, pertaining to the maxilla or upper jaw, 94
MD, 112
MDI, 227
Meatotomy, surgical enlargement of the urinary opening (meatus), 296
Meconium, a substance that collects in the intestines of a fetus and becomes the first stool of a newborn, 324
Medial, directional term meaning to the middle or near the middle of the body or the structure, 35*f,* 35*t*
Median cubital vein, 142*f*
Median nerve, 397*f*
Median plane, plane that runs lengthwise from front to back and divides the body or any of its parts into right and left portions; also called the *sagittal plane,* 30, 31
Mediastinal, there is a collection of lymph nodes located in the mediastinum (central chest area) that drain the chest, 182*t,* 183*f*
Mediastinum, the central region of the chest cavity. It contains the organs between the lungs, including the heart, aorta, esophagus, and trachea, 31, 32, 33*t,* 133*f,* 214, 214*f*
Medical record, documents the details of a patient's hospital stay. Each health care professional that has contact with the patient in any capacity completes the appropriate report of that contact and adds it to the medical chart. This results in a permanent physical record of the patient's day-to-day condition, when and what services he or she receives, and the response to treatment. Also called a chart, 10–11
Medical terms, interpreting, 8–9
- pronunciation, 8–9
- spelling, 9

Medulla, the central area of an organ. In the endocrine system it refers to the adrenal medulla; in the urinary system, it refers to the inner portion of the kidney, 282, 283*f,* 393*f*
Medulla oblongata, a portion of the brain stem that connects the spinal cord with the brain. It contains the respiratory, cardiac, and blood pressure control centers, 392, 392*f,* 393

Medullary, pertaining to the medulla, 93
Medullary cavity, the large open cavity that extends the length of the shaft of a long bone; contains yellow bone marrow, 82, 83
Melanin, the black color pigment in the skin. It helps to prevent the sun's ultraviolet rays from entering the body, 50, 51
Melanocyte-stimulating hormone (MSH), a hormone secreted by the anterior pituitary. It stimulates pigment production in the skin, 359*t,* 363–64
Melanocytes, special cells in the basal layer of the epidermis. They contain the black pigment melanin that gives skin its color and protects against the ultraviolet rays of the sun, 50, 51, 54
Melanoma, also called *malignant melanoma.* A dangerous form of skin cancer caused by an overgrowth of melanin in a melanocyte. It may metastasize or spread. Exposure to ultraviolet light is a risk factor for developing melanoma, 54
Melatonin, hormone secreted by the pineal gland; plays a role in regulating the body's circadian rhythm, 362
Melena, passage of dark tarry stools; color is the result of digestive enzymes working on blood in the stool, 255
Menarche, the first menstrual period, 316, 317
Ménière's disease, abnormal condition within the labyrinth of the inner ear that can lead to a progressive loss of hearing. The symptoms are dizziness or vertigo, hearing loss, and tinnitus (ringing in the ears), 446
Meningeal, pertaining to the meninges, 398
Meninges, three connective tissue membrane layers that surround the brain and spinal cord. The three layers are dura mater, arachnoid layer, and pia mater. The dura mater and arachnoid layer are separated by the subdural space. The arachnoid layer and pia mater are separated by the subarachnoid space, 390, 392, 395
Meningioma, slow-growing tumor in the meninges of the brain, 398
Meningitis, inflammation of the membranes of the spinal cord and brain that is caused by a microorganism, 398
Meningocele, congenital hernia in which the meninges, or membranes, protrude through an opening in the spinal column or brain, 403, 403*f*
Menometrorrhagia, excessive bleeding during the menstrual period and at intervals between menstrual periods, 325
Menopause, cessation or ending of menstrual activity. This is generally between the ages of 40 and 55, 316, 317
Menorrhagia, excessive bleeding during the menstrual period. Can be either in the total number of days or the amount of blood or both, 322
Menstrual cycle, the 28-day fertility cycle in women; includes ovulation and sloughing off the endometrium if a pregnancy does not occur, 360
Menstrual period, another name for the menstrual cycle, 316, 317
Menstruation, the loss of blood and tissue as the endometrium is shed by the uterus. The flow exits the body through the cervix and vagina. The flow occurs approximately every 28 days, 316, 317
Metacarpal, pertaining to the hand bones, 94
Metacarpals, the hand bones in the upper extremity, 88, 89*f,* 90, 90*f*
Metastacized, 182
Metastasize, when cancerous cells migrate away from a tumor site. They commonly move through the lymphatic system and become trapped in lymph nodes, 182
Metatarsal, pertaining to the foot bones, 94
Metatarsals, the ankle bones in the lower extremity, 88, 89*f,* 90, 91*f,* 91*t*
Metered dose inhaler (MDI), 225
Metrorrhagia, rapid (menstrual) blood flow from the uterus, 322
Metrorrhea, discharge from the uterus, 322
MI, 152
Microtia, abnormally small ears, 445
Micturition, another term for urination, 291
Midbrain, a portion of the brain stem, 363*f,* 392, 392*f,* 393
Middle ear, the middle section of the ear. It contains the ossicles, 440*f,* 441, 441*f,* 442, 443*f*
Middle ear infection, 446
Midline organs, 34*t*
Migraine, a specific type of headache characterized by severe head pain, photophobia, vertigo, and nausea, 403
Miner's lung, 221
Mineralocorticoids, a group of hormones secreted by the adrenal cortex. They regulate electrolytes and fluid volume in the body. Aldosterone is an example of a mineralocorticoid, 358*t,* 360
Miotic, substance that causes the pupil to constrict, 438
Miscarriage, 327
Mitral valve, a valve between the left atrium and ventricle in the heart. It prevents blood from flowing backwards into the atrium. It is also

Myelinated, nerve fibers covered with a layer of myelin, 390
Myelitis, inflammation of the spinal cord, 398
Myelogram, x-ray record of the spinal cord following injection of meninges with radiopaque dye, 398
Myelography, injection of a radiopaque dye into the spinal canal. An X-ray is then taken to examine the normal and abnormal outlines made by the dye, 100, 405
Myeloma, malignant neoplasm originating in plasma cells in the bone, 93
Myelomeningocele, a hernia composed of meninges and spinal cord, 403*f*, 404
Myocardial, pertaining to heart muscle, 110, 143
Myocardial infarction (MI), condition caused by the partial or complete occlusion or closing of one or more of the coronary arteries. Symptoms include severe chest pain or heavy pressure in the middle of the chest. A delay in treatment could result in death. Also referred to as *MI* or *heart attack,* 145*f*, 146, 146*f*
Myocarditis, inflammation of heart muscle, 146
Myocardium, the middle layer of the muscle. It is thick and composed of cardiac muscle. This layer produces the heart contraction, 106, 133, 134, 134*f*, 137*f*
Myometrium, the middle muscle layer of the uterus, 316, 316*f*
Myoneural junction, the point at which a nerve contacts a muscle fiber, 106
Myopathy, any disease of muscles, 110
Myopia, with this condition a person can see things that are close up but distance vision is blurred. Also known as *nearsightedness,* 434, 434*f*
Myoplasty, surgical repair of muscle, 110
Myorrhaphy, suture a muscle, 110
Myorrhexis, muscle ruptured, 110
Myotonia, muscle tone, 110
Myringectomy, excision of the eardrum, 444
Myringitis, eardrum inflammation, 444
Myringoplasty, surgical reconstruction of the eardrum. Also called *tympanoplasty,* 444
Myringotomy, surgical puncture of the eardrum with removal of fluid and pus from the middle ear, to eliminate a persistent ear infection and excessive pressure on the tympanic membrane. A polyethylene tube is placed in the tympanic membrane to allow for drainage of the middle ear cavity, 448
Myxedema, condition resulting from a hypofunction of the thyroid gland. Symptoms can include anemia, slow speech, enlarged tongue and facial features, edematous skin, drowsiness, and mental apathy, 371

N

Nail bed, connects nail body to connective tissue underneath, 52
Nail body, flat plate of keratin that forms most of the nails, 52
Nail root, base of a nail; nails grow longer from the root, 52
Nails, a structure in the integumentary system, 25*t*, 49, 50, 52, 53*f*
Narcotic analgesic, drug used to treat severe pain; has the potential to be habit forming if taken for a prolonged time. Also called opiates, 407
Nares, external openings of the nose that open into the nasal cavity, 210, 211*f*
Nasal bone, a facial bone, 84, 85, 87*f*, 87*t*
Nasal cannula, two-pronged plastic device for delivering oxygen into the nose; one prong is inserted into each naris, 219
Nasal cavity, large cavity just behind the external nose that receives the outside air. It is covered with mucous membrane to cleanse the air. The nasal septum divides the nasal cavity into left and right halves, 27*t*, 209*f*, 210–11, 211*f*, 245*f*, 429
Nasal septum, a flexible cartilage wall that divides the nasal cavity into left and right halves. It is covered by mucous membrane, 210
Nasogastric, pertaining to the nose and stomach, 252
Nasogastric intubation (NG tube), a flexible catheter is inserted into the nose and down the esophagus to the stomach; may be used for feeding or to suction out stomach fluids, 262
Nasolacrimal duct, duct that collects tears from the inner corner of the eye socket and drains them into the nasal cavity, 429, 429*f*
Nasopharyngitis, inflammation of nasal cavity and throat, 217
Nasopharynx, the superior section of the pharynx that receives air from the nose, 211, 211*f*
Natural immunity, immunity that is not specific to a particular disease and does not require prior exposure to the pathogen. Also called innate immunity, 184
Natural killer (NK) cells, t cells that can kill by entrapping foreign cells, tumor cells, and bacteria. Also called T8 cells, 185, 186
Nausea, a feeling of needing to vomit, 255
Nearsightedness, 434
Nebulizer, 225
Neck, a narrow length of bone that connects the ball of a ball-and-socket joint to the diaphysis of a long bone, 83, 84, 85*f*
Necrosis, dead tissue, 54
Neonate, term used to describe the newborn infant during the first four weeks of life, 322
Neonatologist, specialist in the treatment of the newborn, 322, 324

Neonatology, study of the newborn, 324
Nephrectomy, excision of a kidney, 288
Nephritis, inflammation of the kidney, 288
Nephrogram, x-ray of the kidney, 288
Nephrolith, kidney stone, 288
Nephrolithiasis, the presence of calculi in the kidney, 289, 292
Nephrolithotomy, incision into the kidney to remove a stone, 296
Nephrologist, specialist in the treatment of kidney disorders, 288, 291
Nephrology, branch of medicine specializing in conditions of the urinary system, 27*t,* 291
Nephroma, kidney tumor, 288
Nephromalacia, softening of the kidney, 288
Nephromegaly, enlarged kidney, 288
Nephron, the functional or working unit of the kidney that filters the blood and produces the urine. There are more than 1 million nephrons in an adult kidney. Each nephron consists of a renal corpuscle and the renal tubules, 282, 283, 284*f*
Nephropathy, kidney disease, 289
Nephropexy, surgical fixation of a kidney, 289
Nephroptosis, drooping kidney, 288, 292
Nephrosclerosis, hardening of the kidney, 289
Nephrosis, abnormal condition (degeneration) of the kidney, 288
Nephrostomy, creating a new opening across the body wall into the kidney, 288
Nephrotic syndrome (NS), damage to the glomerulus resulting in protein appearing in the urine, proteinuria, and the corresponding decrease in protein in the bloodstream, 292
Nephrotomy, incision into a kidney, 288
Nerve block, also referred to as regional anesthesia. This anesthetic interrupts a patient's pain sensation in a particular region of the body. The anesthetic is injected near the nerve that will be blocked from sensation. The patient usually remains conscious, 407
Nerve cell body, the portion of the nerve cell that includes the nucleus, 390, 391*f*
Nerve cells, 22*f*
Nerve conduction velocity, a test to determine if nerves have been damaged by recording the rate at which an electrical impulse travels along a nerve. If the nerve is damaged, the velocity will be decreased, 406
Nerve root, the point where a spinal or cranial nerve is attached to the CNS, 395
Nerves, structures in the nervous system that conduct electrical impulses from the brain and spinal cord to muscles and other organs, 23, 29*t,* 51*f,* 389*f,* 390
Nervous system, system that coordinates all the conscious and subconscious activities of the body. Organs include the brain, spinal cord, and nerves, 29*t,* 387–421, 389*f*
abbreviations, 408
anatomy and physiology, 390–98
central, 390–95
diagnostic procedures, 405–6
nervous tissue, 390
pathology, 400–405
peripheral, 395–98
pharmacology, 407
therapeutic procedures, 407
vocabulary, 399–400
word building, 398–99
Nervous tissue, nervous tissue conducts electrical impulses to and from the brain and the rest of the body, 23, 24*f,* 390
Neural, pertaining to nerves, 398
Neuralgia, nerve pain, 398
Neurectomy, excision of a nerve, 398
Neurogenic bladder, loss of nervous control that leads to retention; may be caused by spinal cord injury or multiple sclerosis, 293
Neuroglial cells, cells that perform support functions for neurons, 390
Neurologist, physician who specializes in disorders of the nervous system, 398, 400
Neurology, branch of medicine specializing in conditions of the nervous system, 29*t,* 400
Neuroma, nerve tumor, 398
Neuron, the name for an individual nerve cell. Neurons group together to form nerves and other nervous tissue, 23, 390
Neuropathy, disease of the nerves, 398
Neuroplasty, surgical repair of nerves, 398
Neurorrhaphy, suture a nerve, 399
Neurosurgery, branch of medicine specializing in surgery on the nervous system, 29*t,* 400
Neurotransmitter, chemical messenger that carries an electrical impulse across the gap between two neurons, 390
Neutrophils, granulocyte white blood cells that are important for phagocytosis. They are also the most numerous of the leukocytes, 169*f,* 171*f,* 171*t*
Nevus, pigmented (colored) congenital skin blemish, birthmark, or mole. Usually benign but may become cancerous, 56
NHL, 192
NIDDM, 373
Night-blindness, 432
Nipple, point at which milk is released from the breast, 318, 318*f*
Nitrogenous wastes, waste products that contain nitrogen. These products, such as ammonia and urea, are produced during protein metabolism, 286
NK, 192

Nocturia, excessive urination during the night. May or may not be abnormal, 290
Nocturnal enuresis, 291
Nodule, solid, raised group of cells, 58, 58*f*
Non-Hodgkins's lymphoma (NHL), cancer of the lymphatic tissues other than Hodgkin's lymphoma, 189
Non-insulin-dependent diabetes mellitus (NIDDM), also called type 2 diabetes mellitus. It develops later in life when the pancreas produces insufficient insulin; persons may take oral hypoglycemics to stimulate insulin secretion, or may eventually have to take insulin, 369, 370
Nonsteroidal antiinflammatory drugs (NSAIDs), a large group of drugs including aspirin and ibuprofen that provide mild pain relief and anti-inflammatory benefits for conditions such as arthritis, 101
Norepinephrine, a hormone secreted by the adrenal medulla. It is a strong vasoconstrictor, 358*t*, 360
Nosocomial infection, an infection acquired as a result of hospital exposure, 186
Nucleus, organelle of the cell that contains the DNA, 22, 391*f*
Nulligravida, woman who has never been pregnant, 323
Nullipara, woman who has never produced a viable baby, 323
Number prefixes, 5–6
Nurse, to breastfeed a baby, 318
Nurse's notes, medical record document that records the patient's care throughout the day. It includes vital signs, treatment specifics, patient's response to treatment, and patient's condition, 10
Nursing home, a facility that provides long-term care for patients who need extra time to recover from all illness or accident before they return home or for persons who can no longer care for themselves. Also called a *long-term care facility,* 11
Nyctalopia, difficulty seeing in dim light; usually due to damaged rods, 432
Nystagmus, jerky-appearing involuntary eye movement, 435

O

O&P, 264
Obesity, having an abnormal amount of fat in the body, 255, 368
Oblique fracture, fracture at an angle to the bone, 97, 97*f*
Oblique muscles, oblique means slanted. Two of the eye muscles are oblique muscles, 428, 428*f*
Obstetrician, 324
Obstetrics (OB), branch of medicine that treats women during pregnancy and childbirth, and immediately after childbirth, 28*t*, 324
Occipital bone, a cranial bone, 84, 85, 87*f*, 87*t*
Occipital lobe, one of the four cerebral hemisphere lobes. It controls eyesight, 392, 393, 393*f*
Occupational Safety and Health Administration (OSHA), federal agency that issued mandatory guidelines to ensure that all employees at risk of exposure to body fluids are provided with personal protective equipment, 186
Ocular, pertaining to the eye, 431
Oculomotor nerve, 396*t*
Oculomycosis, condition of eye fungus, 431
Olfactory nerve, 396*t*
Oligomenorrhea, scanty menstrual flow, 322
Oligospermia, condition of having few sperm, 336
Oliguria, condition of scanty amount of urine, 290
OM, 448
Onychectomy, excision of a nail, 54
Onychia, infected nailbed, 63
Onychomalacia, softening of nails, 54
Onychomycosis, abnormal condition of nail fungus, 54
Onychophagia, nail biting, 54
Oophorectomy, removal of an ovary, 322
Oophoritis, inflammation of an ovary, 322
Open fracture, 96, 96*f*
Operative report, a medical record report from the surgeon detailing an operation. It includes a pre- and postprocedure itself, and how the patient tolerated the procedure, 11
Ophthalmalgia, eye pain, 431
Ophthalmic, pertaining to the eyes, 431
Ophthalmic decongestants, over-the-counter medications that constrict the arterioles of the eye, reduce redness and itching of the conjunctiva, 438
Ophthalmologist, a physician specialized in treating conditions and diseases of the eye, 431, 432
Ophthalmology (Ophth), branch of medicine specializing in condition of the eye, 29*t*, 426, 432
Ophthalmoplegia, paralysis of the eye, 431
Ophthalmorrhagia, rapid bleeding from the eye, 431
Ophthalmoscope, instrument to view inside the eye, 431, 435, 436*f*
Ophthalmoscopy, examination of the interior of the eyes using an instrument called an ophthalmoscope. The physician will dilate the pupil in order to see the cornea, lens, and retina. Identifies abnormalities in the blood vessels of the eye and some systemic diseases, 435
Opiates, 407
Opportunistic infections, infectious diseases that are associated with AIDS since they occur as a

result of the lowered immune system and resistance of the body to infections and parasites, 188

Opposition, moves thumb away from palm; the ability to move the thumb into contact with the other fingers, 109

Optic, pertaining to the eye, 431

Optic disk, the area of the retina associated with the optic nerve. Also called the blind spot, 427

Optic nerve, the second cranial nerve that carries impulses from the retinas to the brain, 396*t*, 426, 426*f*, 430*f*

Optician, grinds and fits prescription lenses and contacts as prescribed by a physician or optometrist, 432

Optometer, instrument to measure vision, 431

Optometrist (OD), doctor of optometry; provides care for the eyes including examining the eyes for diseases, assessing visual acuity, prescribing corrective lenses and eye treatments, and educating patients, 431, 432

Optometry, process of measuring vision, 432

Oral, (1) Pertaining to the mouth. (2) Administration of medication through the mouth, 253

Oral cavity, the mouth, 27*t*, 243*f*, 244–47, 245*f*

Oral contraceptive pills (OCPs), birth control medication that uses low doses of female hormones to prevent conception by blocking ovulation, 329

Oral hypoglycemic agents, medication taken by mouth that causes a decrease in blood sugar. This is not used for insulin-dependent patients. There is no proof that this medication will prevent the long-term complications of diabetes mellitus, 373

Oral surgeon, 254

Orbit, 87*f*

Orchidectomy, excision of the testes, 336

Orchidopexy, surgical fixation to move undescended testes into the scrotum and attaching to prevent retraction, 336, 339

Orchiectomy, surgical removal of the testes, 336

Orchioplasty, surgical repair of the testes, 336

Orchiotomy, incision into the testes, 336

Organic, pertaining to organs, 37

Organs, group of different types of tissue coming together to perform special functions. For example, the heart contains muscular fibers, nerve tissue, and blood vessels, 25–29, 33*t*–36*t*

Organs of Corti, the sensory receptor hair cells lining the cochlea. These cells change the sound vibrations to electrical impulses and send the impulses to the brain via the vestibulocochlear nerve, 442

Origin, the attachment of a skeletal muscle to the less movable bone in the joint, 107

Oropharynx, the middle section of the pharynx that receives food and drink from the mouth, 211, 211*f*, 247

Orthodontic, pertaining to straight teeth, 253

Orthodontics, the dental specialty concerned with straightening teeth, 247, 255

Orthodontist, 255

Orthopedic surgeon, 96

Orthopedic surgery, the branch of medicine specializing in surgical treatments of the musculoskeletal system, 25*t*, 96

Orthopedics (Ortho), branch of medicine specializing in the diagnosis and treatment of conditions of the musculoskeletal system, 25*t*, 96

Orthopedist, 96

Orthopnea, term to describe a patient who needs to sit up straight in order to breathe comfortably, 218, 219

Orthostatic hypotension, the sudden drop in blood pressure a person experiences when standing up suddenly, 144

Orthotics, the use of equipment, such as splints and braces, to support a paralyzed muscle, promote a specific motion, or correct musculoskeletal deformities, 96

Os coxae, also called the innominate bone or hip bone. It is the pelvis portion of the lower extremity. It consists of the ilium, ischium, and pubis and unites with the sacrum and coccyx to form the pelvis, 88, 90, 91*t*

Osseous tissue, bony tissue. One of the hardest tissues in the body, 82

Ossicles, the three small bones in the middle ear. The bones are the incus, malleus, and stapes. The ossicles amplify and conduct the sound waves to the inner ear, 442, 442*f*

Ossification, the process of bone formation, 82

Ostealgia, bone pain, 93

Osteoarthritis (OA), noninflammatory type of arthritis resulting in degeneration of the bones and joints, especially those bearing weight, 3, 99

Osteoblast, an embryonic bone cell, 82

Osteochondroma, tumor composed of both cartilage and bony substance, 93

Osteoclasia, intentional breaking of a bone in order to correct a deformity, 93

Osteocyte, mature bone cells, 82

Osteogenic sarcoma, the most common type of bone cancer; usually begins in osteocytes found at the ends of long bones, 98

Osteomalacia, softening of the bones caused by a deficiency of phosphorus or calcium. It is thought that in children the cause is insufficient sunlight and vitamin D, 98

Osteomyelitis, inflammation of the bone and bone marrow due to infection; can be difficult to treat, 93
Osteopathy, form of medicine that places great emphasis on the musculoskeletal system and the body system as a whole. Manipulation is also used as part of the treatment, 93
Osteoporosis, decrease in bone mass that results in a thinning and weakening of the bone with resulting fractures. The bone becomes more porous, especially in the spine and pelvis, 98
Osteotome, an instrument to cut bone, 93
Osteotomy, incision into a bone, 93
Otalgia, ear pain, 444
Otic, pertaining to the ear, 444
Otitis, ear inflammation, 444
Otitis externa (OE), external ear infection; most commonly caused by fungus. Also called *otomycosis* and commonly referred to as *swimmer's ear,* 446
Otitis media (OM), commonly referred to as middle ear infection; seen frequently in children. Often preceded by an upper respiratory infection, 446
Oto, 448
Otolaryngology, 219
Otologist, a physician specialized in the diagnosis and treatment of diseases of the ear, 444
Otology (Oto), study of the ear, 441
Otomycosis, fungal infection of the ear, usually in the auditory canal, 444
Otoplasty, corrective surgery to change the size of the external ear or pinna. The surgery can either enlarge or lessen the size of the pinna, 444
Otopyorrhea, pus discharge from the ear, 444
Otorhinolaryngologist, 219, 445
Otorhinolaryngology (ENT), branch of medicine that treats diseases of the ears, nose, and throat. Also referred to as *ENT,* 27*t*, 29*t*, 219, 445
Otorrhagia, bleeding from the ear, 444
Otosclerosis, progressive hearing loss caused by immobility of the stapes bone, 446
Otoscope, instrument to view inside the ear, 444, 447*f*
Otoscopy, examination of the ear canal, eardrum, and outer ear using the otoscope. Foreign material can be removed from the ear canal with this procedure, 447
Outer ear, 441*f*, 443*f*
Outpatient clinic, a facility that provides services that do not require overnight hospitalization. The services range from simple surgeries to diagnostic testing to therapy. Also called an ambulatory care center or a surgical center, 11
Ova, female sex cells or gametes produced in the ovary. An ovum fuses with a sperm to produce an embryo. Singular is ovum, 314, 315*f*, 360
Ova and parasites, laboratory examination of feces with a microscope for the presence of parasites or their eggs, 260
Oval window, the division between the middle and inner ear, 442, 442*f*
Ovarian, pertaining to the ovaries, 323
Ovarian carcinoma, cancer of the ovary, 324
Ovarian cyst, sac that develops within the ovary, 324
Ovaries, the female gonads. These two glands are located on either side of the lower abdominopelvic region of the female. They are responsible for the production of the sex cells, ova, and the hormones estrogen and progesterone, 28*t*, 33*t*, 34*t*, 313*f*, 314–15, 314*f*, 315*f*, 357*f*, 358, 359*t*, 360, 361*f*, 364*f*
Oviducts, tubes that carry the ovum from the ovary to the uterus; also called fallopian tubes or uterine tubes, 315
Ovulation, the release of an ovum from the ovary, 314
Ovulation stimulant, 329
Oximeter, instrument to measure oxygen, 217, 224
Oximetry, process of measuring oxygen, 224
Oxygen (O_2), gaseous element absorbed by the blood from the air sacs in the lungs. It is necessary for cells to make energy, 132, 133, 210
Oxygenated, term for blood with a high oxygen level, 132
Oxytocin, a hormone secreted by the posterior pituitary. It stimulates uterine contractions during labor and delivery, 329, 359*t*, 363, 364

P

Pacemaker, another name for the sinoatrial node of the heart, 136, 138
Pacemaker implantation, electrical device that substitutes for the natural pacemaker of the heart. It controls the beating of the heart by a series of rhythmic electrical impulses. An external pacemaker has the electrodes on the outside of the body; an internal pacemaker has the electrodes surgically implanted within the chest wall, 150, 151*f*
Packed cells, a transfusion of only the formed elements and without plasma, 174
Paget's disease, a fairly common metabolic disease of the bone from unknown causes. It usually attacks middle-aged and elderly people and is characterized by bone destruction and deformity, 98
Palate, the roof of the mouth. The anterior portion is hard or bony, and the posterior portion is soft or flexible, 210, 244
Palatine bone, a facial bone, 84, 85, 87*t*
Palatine tonsils, tonsils located in the lateral wall of the pharynx close to the mouth, 184, 211, 211*f*, 212, 245*f*

Palatoplasty, surgical repair of the palate, 253
Pallor, abnormal paleness of the skin, 56
Palpitations, pounding, racing heartbeat, 144
Palsy, temporary or permanent loss of the ability to control movement, 400
Pancreas, organ in the digestive system that produces digestive enzymes. Also a gland in the endocrine system that produces two hormones, insulin and glucagon, 27*t*, 28*t*, 33*t*, 34*t*, 243*f*, 244, 251, 251*f*, 260*f*, 357*f*, 358, 359*t*, 361–62, 361*f*
Pancreatic, pertaining to the pancreas, 253, 367
Pancreatic duct, duct carrying pancreatic juices from the pancreas to the duodenum, 251, 251*f*, 260*f*
Pancreatic enzymes, digestive enzymes produced by the pancreas and added to the chyme in the duodenum, 251
Pancreatitis, inflammation of the pancreas, 253
Pancytopenia, too few of all types of blood cells, 173
Panhypopituitarism, deficiency in all the hormones secreted by the pituitary gland; often recognized because of problems with the glands regulated by the pituitary—adrenal cortex, thyroid, ovaries, and testes, 370
Pansinusitis, inflammation of all the sinuses, 218
PAP, 330
Pap (Papanicolaou) smear, test for the early detection of cancer of the cervix named after the developer of the test, George Papanicolaou, a Greek physician. A scraping of cells is removed from the cervix for examination under a microscope, 327
Papilla, 53*f*
Papillary muscle, 135*f*
Papilledema, swelling of the optic disk, often as a result of increased intraocular pressure. Also called *choked disk,* 432
Papule, small, solid, circular raised spot on the surface of the skin, often as a result of an inflammation in an oil gland, 58, 58*f*
Paracentesis, insertion of a needle into the abdominal cavity to withdraw fluid; tests to diagnose disease may be conducted on the fluid, 262
Paralysis, temporary or permanent loss of function or voluntary movement, 400
Paranasal sinuses, air-filled cavities within the facial bones that open into the nasal cavity; act as an echo chamber during sound production, 210, 211*f*
Paraplegia, paralysis of the lower portion of the body and both legs, 400
Parasympathetic branch, a branch of the autonomic nervous system. This system serves as a counterbalance for the sympathetic nerves. Therefore, it causes the heart rate to slow down, lower the blood pressure, constrict eye pupils, and increase digestion, 396
Parathyroid gland, 357*f*
Parathyroid glands, four small glands located on the back surface of the thyroid gland. The parathyroid hormone secreted by these glands regulates the amount of calcium in the blood, 28*t*, 358, 359*t*, 362, 362*f*
Parathyroid hormone (PTH), the hormone secreted by the parathyroid glands. The more hormone, the higher the calcium level in the blood and the lower the level stored in bone. A low hormone level will cause tetany, 359*t*, 362
Parathyroidal, pertaining to the parathyroid glands, 367
Parathyroidectomy, excision of one or more of the parathyroid glands. This is performed to halt the progress of hyperparathyroidism, 367
Paresthesia, an abnormal sensation such as burning or tingling, 400
Parietal bone, a cranial bone, 84, 85, 87*f*, 87*t*
Parietal layer, the outer pleural layer around the lungs. It lines the inside of the chest cavity, 31, 33
Parietal lobe, one of the four cerebral hemisphere lobes. It receives and interprets nerve impulses from sensory receptors, 392, 393, 393*f*
Parietal pericardium, the outer layer of the pericardium surrounding the heart, 133, 134
Parietal peritoneum, the outer layer of the serous membrane sac lining the abdominopelvic cavity, 31, 33
Parietal pleura, the outer layer of the serous membrane sac lining the thoracic cavity, 31, 33, 214
Parkinson's disease, chronic disorder of the nervous system with fine tremors, muscular weakness, rigidity, and a shuffling gait, 403
Paronychia, infection around a nail, 63
Parotid duct, 251*f*
Parotid glands, a pair of salivary glands located in front of the ears, 250, 251*f*
Passive acquired immunity, immunity that results when a person receives protective substances produced by another human or animal. This may take the form of maternal antibodies crossing the placenta to a baby or an antitoxin injection, 184, 185
Patella, also called the *kneecap.* It is a lower extremity bone, 88, 89*f*, 90, 91*f*, 91*t*
Patellar, pertaining to the patella or kneecap, 94
Patent, open or unblocked, such as a patent airway, 219
Patent ductus arteriosus (PDA), congenital heart anomaly in which the opening between the pulmonary artery and the aorta fails to close at birth. This condition requires surgery, 148

Pathogenic, pertaining to microscopic organisms, such as bacteria, that are capable of causing disease, 187

Pathogens, disease-bearing organisms, 50, 171

Pathologic fracture, fracture caused by diseased or weakened bone, 97

Pathologist's report, a medical record report given by a pathologist who studies tissue removed from the patient (for example: bone marrow, blood, or tissue biopsy), 11

Pathology, the branch of medicine specializing in studying how disease affects the body, 187

PCP, 192, 227

PDA, 152

Pectoral girdle, consists of the clavicle and scapula; functions to attach the upper extremity to the axial skeleton, 88, 89*f*, 90, 90*f*

Pediculosis, infestation with lice, 62, 62*f*

Pelvic, pertaining to the pelvis, 94

Pelvic cavity, the inferior portion of the abdominopelvic cavity, 31, 32, 32*f*, 33*t*

Pelvic examination, physical examination of the vagina and adjacent organs performed by a physician placing the fingers of one hand into the vagina, A visual examination is performed using a speculum, 328

Pelvic girdle, consists of the ilium, ischium, and pubis; functions to attach the lower extremity to the axial skeleton, 88, 89*f*, 91*f*, 91*t*

Pelvic inflammatory disease (PID), any inflammation of the female reproductive organs, generally bacterial in nature, 325

Pelvic region, lowest anterior region of the trunk, 31, 32*f*

Pelvic ultrasonography, use of ultrasound waves to produce an image or photograph of an organ, such as the uterus, ovaries, or fetus, 327

Pelvis, 92*f*

Penis, the male sex organ. It is composed of erectile tissue that becomes erect during sexual stimulation, allowing it to be placed within the female vagina for ejaculation of semen. The larger, soft tip is referred to as the glans penis, 28*t*, 332*f*, 333, 334

Peptic ulcer disease (PUD), ulcer occurring in the lower portion of the esophagus, stomach, and duodenum and thought to be caused by the acid of gastric juices, 257, 257*f*

Percussion, use of the fingertips to tap the body lightly and sharply. Aids in determining the size, position, and consistency of the underlying body part, 219

Percutaneous diskectomy, a thin catheter tube is inserted into the intervertebral disk through the skin and the herniated or ruptured disk material is sucked out or a laser is used to vaporize it, 100

Percutaneous transhepatic cholangiography (PTC), a contrast medium is injected directly into the liver to visualize the bile ducts. Used to detect obstructions, 261

Percutaneous transluminal coronary angioplasty (PTCA), method for treating localized coronary artery narrowing. A balloon catheter is inserted through the skin into the coronary artery and inflated to dilate the narrow blood vessel, 151

Perforated ulcer, 257

Pericardial cavity, cavity formed by the serous membrane sac surrounding the heart, 31, 33, 33*t*

Pericarditis, inflammatory process or disease of the pericardium, 9, 146

Pericardium, the double-walled outer sac around the heart. The inner layer of the pericardium is called the epicardium, the outer layer is the heart itself. This sac contains pericardial fluid that reduces friction caused by the heart beating, 133, 133*f*, 134, 134*f*

Perimetritis, inflammation around the uterus, 322

Perimetrium, the outer layer of the uterus, 316, 316*f*

Perineum, in the male, the external region between the scrotum and anus. In the female, the external region between the vagina and anus, 317, 319*f*, 333, 334

Periodontal disease, disease of the supporting structures of the teeth, including the gums and bones, 256

Periodontal ligaments, small ligaments that anchor the root of a tooth in the socket of the jaw, 246, 247, 247*f*

Periodontic, pertaining to around the teeth, 253

Periodontics, branch of dentistry concerned with treating conditions involving the gums and tissues surrounding the teeth. A specialist is a *periodontist,* 255

Periodontist, 255

Periosteum, the membrane that covers most bones. It contains numerous nerves and lymphatic vessels, 82, 83*f*

Peripheral nervous system (PNS), the portion of the nervous system that contains the cranial nerves and spinal nerves. These nerves are mainly responsible for voluntary muscle movement, smell, taste, sight, and hearing, 390, 395–98

Peripheral neuropathy, damage to the nerves in the lower legs and hands as a result of diabetes mellitus; symptoms include either extreme sensitivity or numbness and tingling, 370

Peripheral vascular disease (PVD), any abnormal condition affecting blood vessels outside the heart; symptoms may include pain, pallor, numbness, and loss of circulation and pulses, 148

Peristalsis, the wavelike muscular movements in the wall of the digestive system tube—esophagus, stomach, small intestines, and colon—that function to move food along the tube, 247, 248
Peritoneal, pertaining to the peritoneum, 37
Peritoneal dialysis, removal of toxic waste substances from the body by placing warm chemically balanced solutions into the peritoneal cavity. Used in treating renal failure and certain poisonings, 295, 295*f*
Peritoneoscopy, 262
Peritoneum, membranous sac that lines the abdominal cavity and encases the abdominopelvic organs. The kidneys are an exception since they lay outside the peritoneum and alongside the vertebral column, 31, 33
Peritubular capillaries, capillary bed surrounding the renal tubules, 284*f,* 286, 286*f*
Permanent teeth, the thirty-two permanent teeth begin to erupt at about the age of 6. Generally complete by the age of 16, 246, 247
Pernicious anemia, anemia associated with insufficient absorption of vitamin B_{12} by the digestive system, 175
Peroneal artery, 140*f*
Peroneal nerve, 397*f*
Perspiration, another term for sweating, 53, 54
Pertussis, a contagious bacterial infection of the larynx, trachea, and bronchi characterized by coughing attacks that end with a whooping sound. Also called *whooping cough,* 220
PET, 408
Petechiae, flat, pinpoint, purplish spots from bleeding under the skin, 56, 56*f*
Petit mal seizure, 400
pH, 297
Phacoemulsification, use of high-frequency sound waves to emulsify (liquefy) a lens with a cataract, which is then aspirated (removed by suction) with a needle, 437
Phagocyte, neutrophil component of the blood; has the ability to ingest and destroy bacteria, 171
Phagocytosis, the process of engulfing or ingesting material. Several types of white blood cells function by engulfing bacteria, 171*t*
Phalangeal, pertaining to the phalanges or finger and toe bones, 94
Phalanges, the finger bones in the upper extremities and the toe bones in the lower extremities, 88, 89*f,* 90, 90*f,* 91*f,* 91*t*
Pharyngeal, pertaining to the pharynx, 217, 253
Pharyngeal tonsils, another term for *adenoids.* The tonsils are a collection of lymphatic tissue found in the nasopharynx to combat microorganisms entering the body through the nose, 184, 211, 211*f,* 212
Pharyngitis, inflammation of the mucous membrane of the pharynx, usually caused by a viral or bacterial infection. Commonly called a *sore throat,* 217
Pharyngoplasty, surgical repair of the pharynx, 253
Pharyngoplegia, paralysis of the pharynx, 253
Pharynx, medical term for the throat. The passageway that conducts air from the nasal cavity to the trachea and also carries food and drink from the mouth to the esophagus. The pharynx is divided into three sections: the nasopharynx, oropharynx, and laryngopharynx, 27*t,* 184, 209*f,* 210, 211–12, 244, 247
Pheochromocytoma, usually benign tumor of the adrenal medulla that secretes epinephrine; symptoms include anxiety, heart palpitations, dyspnea, profuse sweating, headache, and nausea, 369
Phimosis, narrowing of the foreskin over the glans penis that results in difficulty with hygiene. This condition can lead to infection or difficulty with urination. It is treated with circumcision, the surgical removal of the foreskin, 337
Phlebitis, inflammation of a vein, 143
Phlebogram, record of veins, 154
Phlebography, 149
Phlebotomist, 177, 177*f*
Phlebotomy, creating an opening into a vein to withdraw blood, 177, 177*f*
Phlegm, thick mucus secreted by the membranes that line the respiratory tract. When phlegm is coughed through the mouth, it is called *sputum.* Phlegm is examined for color, odor, and consistency, 219
Photophobia, strong sensitivity to bright light, 432
Photosensitivity, condition in which the skin reacts abnormally when exposed to light such as the ultraviolet rays of the sun, 57
Physician's offices, individual or groups of physicians providing diagnostic and treatment services in a private office setting rather than a hospital, 12
Physician's orders, medical record document that contains a complete list of the care, medications, tests, and treatments the physician orders for the patient, 10
Physician's progress notes, part of a patient's medical record. It is the physician's daily record of the patient's condition, results of the physician's examinations, summary of test results, updated assessment and diagnoses, and further plans for the patient's care, 11
Pia mater, the term means soft mother. This thin innermost meninges layer is applied directly to the surface of the brain, 395, 395*f*
PID, 330

Pineal gland, a gland in the endocrine system that produces a hormone called melatonin, 28*t,* 357*f,* 358, 362–63, 362*f*
Pinna, also called the *auricle*. The external ear, which functions to capture sound waves as they go past the outer ear, 441, 441*f*
Pisse prophets, 282
Pituitary, pertaining to the pituitary gland, 367
Pituitary anterior lobe, 359*t*
Pituitary gland, an endocrine gland located behind the optic nerve in the brain. It is also called the master gland since it controls the functions of many other endocrine glands. It is divided into two lobes: anterior and posterior. The anterior pituitary gland secretes hormones that aid in controlling growth and stimulating the thyroid gland, sexual glands, and adrenal cortex. The posterior pituitary is responsible for the antidiuretic hormone and oxytocin, 28*t,* 357*f,* 358, 363–64, 363*f,* 392*f*
Pituitary posterior lobe, 359*t*
Placenta, also called afterbirth. An organ attached to the uterine wall that is composed of maternal and fetal tissues. Oxygen, nutrients, carbon dioxide, and wastes are exchanged between the mother and baby through the placenta. The baby is attached to the placenta by way of the umbilical cord, 318, 319, 319*f*
Placenta previa, occurs when the placenta is in the lower portion of the uterus and thus blocks the birth canal, 326, 326*f*
Placental stage, the third stage of labor, which takes place after delivery of the infant. The uterus resumes strong contractions and the placenta detaches from the uterine wall and is delivered through the vagina, 320, 320*f,* 321
Plantar flexion, bend sole of foot; point toes downward, 108, 108*f*
Plaque, a yellow, fatty deposit of lipids in an artery, 144, 145*f,* 147*f*
Plasma, the liquid portion of blood containing 90% water. The remaining 10% consists of plasma proteins (serum albumin, serum globulin, fibrinogen, and prothrombin), inorganic substances (calcium, potassium, and sodium), organic components (glucose, amino acids, cholesterol), and waste products (urea, uric acid, ammonia, and creatinine), 26*t,* 169*f,* 170
Plasma proteins, proteins that are found in plasma. Includes serum albumin, serum globulin, fibrinogen, and prothrombin, 170
Plasmapheresis, method of removing plasma from the body without depleting the formed elements; whole blood is removed and the cells and plasma are separated; the cells are returned to the patient along with a donor plasma transfusion, 177
Plastic surgery, surgical specialty involved in repair, reconstruction, or improvement of body structures such as the skin that are damaged, missing, or misshapen. Physician is a plastic surgeon, 57
Platelet count, blood test to determine the number of platelets in a given volume of blood, 176
Platelets, cells responsible for the coagulation of blood. These are also called thrombocytes and contain no hemoglobin, 26*t,* 169*f,* 170, 172*f*
Pleura, a protective double layer of serous membrane around the lungs. The parietal membrane is the outer layer and the visceral layer is the inner membrane. It secretes a thin, watery fluid to reduce friction associated with lung movement, 31, 33, 214
Pleural, pertaining to the pleura, 37
Pleural cavity, cavity formed by the serous membrane sac surrounding the lungs, 31, 33, 33*t,* 214
Pleural effusion, abnormal presence of fluid or gas in the pleural cavity. Physicians can detect the presence of fluid by tapping the chest (percussion) or listening with a stethoscope (auscultation), 223
Pleural rub, grating sound made when two surfaces, such as the pleural surfaces, rub together during respiration. It is caused when one of the surfaces becomes thicker as a result of inflammation or other disease conditions. This rub can be felt through the fingertips when they are placed on the chest wall or heard through the stethoscope, 219
Pleurectomy, excision of the pleura, 217
Pleurisy, inflammation of the pleura, 223
Pleuritis, 223
Pleurocentesis, a puncture of the pleura to withdraw fluid from the thoracic cavity in order to diagnose disease, 217
Pleurodynia, Pleural pain, 217
Plural endings, 9
Pneumoconiosis, condition resulting from inhaling environmental particles that become toxic, such as coal dust (anthracosis) or asbestos (asbestosis), 222
***Pneumocystis carinii* pneumonia (PCP),** pneumonia with a nonproductive cough, very little fever, and dyspnea. Seen in persons with weakened immune systems, such as patients with AIDS, 189, 222
Pneumonia, inflammatory condition of the lung, which can be caused by bacterial and viral infections, diseases, and chemicals, 222
Pneumothorax, collection of air or gas in the pleural cavity, which can result in the collapse of a lung, 218, 223, 223*f*
PNS, 408

Podiatrist, 96
Podiatry, healthcare profession specializing in diagnosis and treatment of disorders of the feet and lower legs. Healthcare professional is a *podiatrist*, 96
Poliomyelitis, acute viral disease that causes an inflammation of the gray matter of the spinal cord, resulting in paralysis in some cases. Has been brought under almost total control through vaccinations, 404
Polyarteritis, inflammation of many arteries, 148
Polycystic kidneys, formation of multiple cysts within the kidney tissue; results in the destruction of normal kidney tissue and uremia, 292, 292*f*
Polycythemia vera, production of too many red blood cells in the bone marrow, 175
Polydipsia, condition of having an excessive amount of thirst, such as in diabetes, 368
Polymyositis, disease involving muscle inflammation and weakness from an unknown cause, 110
Polyneuritis, inflammation of many nerves, 398
Polyp, small tumor with a pedicle or stem attachment. Commonly found in vascular organs such as the nose, uterus, and rectum, 255
Polyphagia, to eat excessively, 254
Polyposis, small tumors that contain a pedicle or footlike attachment in the mucous membranes of the large intestine (colon), 259, 259*f*
Polysomnography, monitoring a patient while sleeping to identify sleep apnea. Also called *sleep apnea study*, 224
Polyuria, condition of having excessive urine production. This can be a symptom of disease conditions such as diabetes, 290, 368
Pons, this portion of the brain stem forms a bridge between the cerebellum and cerebrum. It is also where nerve fibers cross from one side of the brain to control functions and movement on the other side of the brain, 392, 392*f*, 393, 393*f*
Pontine, pertaining to the pons, 399
Popliteal artery, 140*f*
Popliteal vein, 142*f*
Positron emission tomography (PET), use of positive radionuclides to reconstruct brain sections. Measurements can be taken of oxygen and glucose uptake, cerebral blood flow, and blood volume, 406
Posterior, directional term meaning near or on the back or spinal cord side of the body, 35*f*, 35*t*
Posterior lobe, the posterior portion of the pituitary gland. It secretes antidiuretic hormone and oxytocin, 363
Posterior pituitary gland, 363*f*
Posterior tibial artery, 140*f*
Posterior tibial vein, 142*f*
Postpartum, period immediately after delivery or childbirth, 323
Postprandial, pertaining to after a meal, 254
Postural drainage, draining secretions from the bronchi by placing the patient in a position that uses gravity to promote drainage. Used for the treatment of cystic fibrosis and bronchiectasis, and before lobectomy surgery, 225
Potassium (K+), an inorganic substance found in plasma. It is important for bones and muscles, 170
PPD, 227
Preeclampsia, toxemia of pregnancy that, if untreated, can result in true eclampsia. Symptoms include hypertension, headaches, albumin in the urine, and edema, 327
Prefix, a word part added in front of the word root. It frequently gives information about the location of the organ, the number of parts or the time (frequency). Not all medical terms have a prefix, 2, 3, 4–6
  number, 5–6
Pregnancy, the time from fertilization of an ovum to the birth of the newborn, 314, 318–21
  labor and delivery, 320–21
Pregnancy test, chemical test that can determine a pregnancy during the first few weeks. Can be performed in a physician's office or with a home-testing kit, 327
Premature, infant born prior to thirty-seven weeks of gestation, 318
Premenstrual syndrome (PMS), symptoms that develop just prior to the onset of a menstrual period, which can include irritability, headache, tender breasts, and anxiety, 324
Premolar, another term for the bicuspid teeth, 246, 246*f*
Prepatellar bursitis, 92
Prepuce, also called the foreskin. A protective covering over the glans penis. It is this covering of the skin that is removed during circumcision, 334
Presbycusis, loss of hearing that can accompany the aging process, 445
Presbyopia, visual loss due to old age, resulting in difficulty in focusing for near vision (such as reading), 432
Pressure equalizing tube (PE tube), small tube surgically placed in a child's ear to assist in drainage of infection, 448
Priapism, a persistent and painful erection due to pathological causes, not sexual arousal, 337
Primigravida, woman who has been pregnant once, 323
Primipara, woman who has given birth once, 323

PRK, 438
PRL, 373
Procedural suffixes, 8
Process, a projection from the surface of a bone, 83, 84
Proctologist, specialist in the rectum, 253, 255
Proctology, branch of medicine specializing in conditions of the lower gastrointestinal system, 27*t*, 255
Proctopexy, surgical fixation of the rectum, 253
Proctoptosis, drooping rectum, 253
Progesterone, one of the hormones produced by the ovaries. It works with estrogen to control the menstrual cycle, 314, 358*t*, 359*t*, 360
Prolactin (PRL), a hormone secreted by the anterior pituitary. It stimulates milk production, 359*t*, 363
Prolapsed umbilical cord, when the umbilical cord of the baby is expelled first during delivery and is squeezed between the baby's head and the vaginal wall. This presents an emergency situation since the baby's circulation is compromised, 327
Prolapsed uterus, fallen uterus that can cause the cervix to protrude through the vaginal opening. Generally caused by weakened muscles from vaginal delivery or as the result of pelvic tumors pressing down, 325
Pronation, to turn downward or backward, as with the hand or foot, 109, 109*f*
Prone, directional term meaning lying horizontally facing downward, 36*f*, 36*t*
Pronunciation, of medical terms, 8–9
Prostate cancer, slow-growing cancer that affects a large number of males after age 50. The PSA (prostate-specific antigen) test is used to assist in early detection of this disease, 337
Prostate gland, a gland in the male reproductive system that produces fluids that nourish the sperm, 28*t*, 33*t*, 284*f*, 286*f*, 332*f*, 333, 333*f*, 335
Prostate-specific antigen (PSA), a blood test to screen for prostate cancer. Elevated blood levels of PSA are associated with prostate cancer, 338
Prostatectomy, surgical removal of the prostate gland, 336
Prostatic, pertaining to the prostate gland, 336
Prostatitis, inflamed condition of the prostate gland that may be a result of an infection, 336
Prosthesis, artificial device used as a substitute for a body part that is either congenitally missing or absent as a result of accident or disease; for instance, an artificial leg or hip prosthesis, 96
Prosthetic hip joint, 101*f*
Prosthetics, artificial devices, such as limbs and joints, that replace a missing body part, 96
Prosthetist, 96
Protease inhibitor drugs, medications that inhibit protease, an enzyme viruses need to reproduce, 192
Protein-bound iodine test (PBI), blood test to measure the concentration of thyroxine (T_4) circulating in the blood stream. The iodine becomes bound to the protein in the blood and can be measured. Useful in establishing thyroid function, 372
Proteinuria, protein in the urine, 290
Prothrombin, protein element within the blood that interacts with calcium salts to form thrombin, 172
Prothrombin time (Pro time), measurement of the time it takes for a sample of blood to coagulate, 176
Proton pump inhibitor, blocks the stomach's ability to secrete acid. Used to treat peptic ulcers and gastroesophageal reflux disease, 264
Protozoans, single-celled organisms that can infect the body, 184
Proximal, directional term meaning located closest to the point of attachment to the body, 35*f*, 35*t*
Proximal convoluted tubule, a portion of the renal tubule, 283, 284*f*, 286*f*
Pruritus, severe itching, 57
PSA, 340
Pseudocyesis, false pregnancy, 323
Pseudohypertrophic muscular dystrophy, one type of inherited muscular dystrophy in which the muscle tissue is gradually replaced by fatty tissue, making the muscle look strong, 111
Psoriasis, chronic inflammatory condition consisting of crusty papules forming patches with circular borders, 62, 62*f*
PTCA, 152
Pterygium, hypertrophied conjunctival tissue in the inner corner of the eye, 434
PTH, 373
Puberty, beginning of menstruation and the ability to reproduce. Usually occurs around 16 years of age, 324
Pubic, pertaining to the pubis; one of the pelvic bones, 94
Pubic region, the genital region of the body, 31, 32*f*
Pubis, one of the three bones that form the os coxae or innominate bone, 88, 89*f*, 90, 91*f*, 91*t*
PUD, 264
Pulmonary, pertaining to the lung, 217, 220
Pulmonary angiography, injecting dye into a blood vessel for the purpose of taking an X-ray of the arteries and veins of the lungs, 224
Pulmonary artery, the large artery that carries deoxygenated blood from the right ventricle to the lung, 132*f*, 135, 136, 137*f*

Pulmonary capillaries, network of capillaries in the lungs that tightly encase each alveolus; site of gas exchange, 212, 213
Pulmonary circulation, the pulmonary circulation transports deoxygenated blood from the right side of the heart to the lungs where oxygen and carbon dioxide are exchanged. Then it carries oxygenated blood back to the left side of the heart, 132
Pulmonary edema, condition in which lung tissue retains an excessive amount of fluid. Results in labored breathing, 222
Pulmonary embolism, blood clot or air bubble in the pulmonary artery or one of its branches, 222
Pulmonary fibrosis, formation of fibrous scar tissue in the lungs, which leads to decreased ability to expand the lungs. May be caused by infections, pneumoconiosis, autoimmune diseases, and toxin exposure, 222
Pulmonary function test (PFT), breathing equipment used to determine respiratory function and measure lung volumes and gas exchange, 214, 215, 224
Pulmonary semilunar valve, 135*f*
Pulmonary trunk, 133*f*, 134*f*
Pulmonary valve, the semilunar valve between the right ventricle and pulmonary artery in the heart. It prevents blood from flowing backwards into the ventricle, 134*f*, 135, 136*f*, 137*f*
Pulmonary vein, large vein that returns oxygenated blood from the lungs to the left atrium, 132*f*, 135, 136, 137*f*
Pulmonologist, a physician specialized in treating diseases and disorders of the respiratory system, 217, 220
Pulmonology, branch of medicine specializing in conditions of the respiratory system, 27*t*
Pulp cavity, the hollow interior of a tooth; contains soft tissue made up of blood vessels, nerves, and lymph vessels, 246, 247, 247*f*
Pulse (P), expansion and contraction produced by blood as it moves through an artery. The pulse can be taken at several pulse points throughout the body where an artery is close to the surface, 141
Pupil, the hole in the center of the iris. The size of the pupil is changed by the iris dilating or constricting, 425*f*, 426*f*, 427, 430*f*
Pupillary, pertaining to the pupil, 432
Purified protein derivative (PPD), 224
Purkinje fibers, part of the conduction system of the heart; found in the ventricular myocardium, 136, 137*f*, 138
Purpura, hemorrhages into the skin and mucous membranes, 56*f*, 57
Purulent, pus-filled sputum, which can be the result of infection, 57
Pustule, raised spot on the skin containing pus, 58, 58*f*
Pyelitis, inflammation of the renal pelvis, 289
Pyelogram, x-ray record of the renal pelvis after injection of a radiopaque dye, 289
Pyelonephritis, inflammation of the renal pelvis and the kidney. One of the most common types of kidney disease. It may be the result of a lower urinary tract infection that moved up to the kidney by way of the ureters. There may be large quantities of white blood cells and bacteria in the urine, and blood (hematuria) may even be present in the urine in this condition. Can occur with any untreated or persistent case of cystitis, 292
Pyeloplasty, surgical repair of the renal pelvis, 289
Pyloric, pertaining to the pylorus, 253
Pyloric sphincter, sphincter at the distal end of the stomach. Controls the passage of food into the duodenum, 248, 248*f*, 249*f*, 251*f*
Pyoderma, pus producing skin infection, 55
Pyogenic, pus-forming, 54
Pyosalpinx, condition of having pus in the fallopian tubes, 323
Pyothorax, condition of having pus in the chest cavity, 218, 223
Pyrosis, heartburn, 255
Pyuria, presence of pus in the urine, 290

Q
Quadriplegia, paralysis of all four extremities. Same as tetraplegia, 399

R
Radial, pertaining to the radius; a lower arm bone, 94
Radial artery, 140*f*
Radial keratotomy, spokelike incisions around the cornea that result in it becoming flatter; a surgical treatment for myopia, 437
Radial nerve, 397*f*
Radial vein, 142*f*
Radical mastectomy, surgical removal of the breast tissue plus chest muscles and axillary lymph nodes, 329
Radiculitis, nerve root inflammation, 399
Radiculopathy, disease of the nerve root, 399
Radiography, making of X-ray pictures, 100
Radioimmunoassay (RIA), test used to measure the levels of hormones in the plasma of the blood, 372
Radius, one of the forearm bones in the upper extremity, 88, 89*f*, 90, 90*f*
Rales, abnormal crackling sound made during inspiration. Usually indicates the presence of moisture and can indicate a pneumonia condition, 220

Raynaud's phenomenon, periodic ischemic attacks affecting the extremities of the body, especially the fingers, toes, ears, and nose. The affected extremities become cyanotic and very painful. These attacks are brought on by arterial constriction due to extreme cold or emotional stress, 148

RBC, 178

RDS, 227

Reabsorption, second phase of urine production; substances needed by the body are reabsorbed as the filtrate passes through the kidney tubules, 286, 287

Recklinghausen disease, excessive production of parathyroid hormone, which results in degeneration of the bones, 370

Rectal, (1) Pertaining to the rectum. (2) Substances introduced directly into the rectal cavity in the form of suppositories or solution. Drugs may have to be administered by this route if the patient is unable to take them by mouth due to nausea, vomiting, and surgery, 253

Rectocele, protrusion or herniation of the rectum into the vagina, 325

Rectum, an area at the end of the digestive tube for storage of feces that leads to the anus, 249, 249*f*, 250, 250*f*, 314*f*, 317*f*, 319*f*, 333*f*

Rectus abdominis, a muscle named for its location and the direction of its fibers: rectus means straight and abdominis means abdominal, 107

Rectus muscles, rectus means straight. Four of the eye muscles are rectus muscles, 428, 428*f*

Red blood cell count (RBC), blood test to determine the number of erythrocytes in a volume of blood; a decrease in red blood cells may indicate anemia; an increase may indicate polycythemia, 176

Red blood cell morphology, examination of blood for abnormalities in the shape (morphology) of the erythrocytes. Used to determine diseases like sickle-cell anemia, 176

Red blood cells (RBC), also called erythrocytes or RBCs. Cells that contain hemoglobin and iron-containing pigment that binds oxygen in order to transport it to the cells of the body, 169*f*, 170

Red bone marrow, tissue that manufactures most of the blood cells. It is found in cancellous bone cavities, 82, 83

Reduction, correcting a fracture by realigning the bone fragments. *Closed reduction* is doing this without entering the body. *Open reduction* is making a surgical incision at the site of the fracture to do the reduction, often necessary where there are bony fragments to be removed, 101

Refractive error test, eye examination performed by a physician to determine and correct refractive errors in the eye, 436

Refracts, the bending of light rays as they enter the eye, 426

Regional ileitis, 257

Regurgitation, to flow backwards. In cardiovascular system refers to blood flowing backwards through valve. In digestive system refers to food flowing backwards from stomach to mouth, 144, 255

Rehabilitation centers, facilities that provide intensive physical and occupational therapy. They include inpatient and outpatient treatment, 12

Reinfection, an infection that occurs when a person becomes infected again with the same pathogen that originally brought him or her to the hospital, 186

Renal, pertaining to the kidney, 289

Renal artery, artery that originates from the abdominal aorta and carries blood to the nephrons of the kidney, 140*f*, 282, 283*f*, 286*f*

Renal cell carcinoma, cancerous tumor that arises from kidney tubule cells, 292

Renal colic, pain caused by a kidney stone, which can be excruciating and generally requires medical treatment, 291

Renal corpuscle, part of a nephron. It is a double-walled cuplike structure called the glomerular capsule or Bowman's capsule and contains a capillary network called the glomerulus. An afferent arteriole carries blood to the glomerulus and an efferent arteriole carries blood away from the glomerulus. The filtration stage of urine production occurs in the renal corpuscle as wastes are filtered from the blood in the glomerulus and enter Bowman's capsule, 283

Renal failure, inability of the kidneys to filter wastes from the blood resulting in uremia; may be acute or chronic; major reason for a patient being placed on dialysis, 292

Renal papilla, tip of a renal pyramid, 282, 283*f*

Renal pelvis, large collecting site for urine within the kidney. Collects urine from each calyx. Urine leaves the renal pelvis via the ureter, 282, 283*f*

Renal pyramid, triangular-shaped region of the renal medulla, 282, 283*f*

Renal transplant, surgical replacement with a donor kidney, 296, 296*f*

Renal tubule, network of tubes found in a nephron. It consists of the proximal convoluted tubule, the loop of Henle, the distal tubule, and the collecting tubule. The reabsorption and secretion stages of urine production occur within the renal tubule. As the glomerular filtrate

passes through the renal tubule, most of the water and some of the dissolved substances, such as amino acids and electrolytes, are reabsorbed. At the same time, substances that are too large to filter into Bowman's capsule, such as urea, are secreted directly from the bloodstream into the renal tubule. The filtrate that reaches the collecting tubule becomes urine, 283
Renal vein, vein that carries blood away from the kidneys, 142*f*, 282, 283*f*, 286*f*
Repetitive motion disorder, group of chronic disorders involving the tendon, muscle, joint, and nerve damage, resulting from the tissue being subjected to pressure, vibration, or repetitive movements for prolonged periods, 111
Reproductive system, 311–54
Residual volume (RV), the air remaining in the lungs after a forced exhalation, 215*t*
Respirator, 225, 225*f*
Respiratory membrane, formed by the tight association of the walls of alveoli and capillaries; gas exchange between lungs and blood occurs across this membrane, 212, 213
Respiratory muscles, 215
Respiratory rate, 215–16, 216*t*
Respiratory system, system that brings oxygen into the lungs and expels carbon dioxide. Organs include the nose, pharynx, larynx, trachea, bronchial tubes, and lungs, 27*t*, 207–40, 209*f*
  abbreviations, 227
  anatomy and physiology, 210–16
  bronchial tubes, 212–13
  diagnostic procedures, 223–24
  larynx, 212
  lung volumes/capacities, 214–15
  lungs, 214
  muscles, 215
  nasal cavity, 210–11
  pathology, 220–23
  pharmacology, 227
  pharynx, 211–12
  rate, 215–16
  therapeutic procedures, 225–26
  trachea, 212
  vocabulary, 218–20
  word building, 217–18
Respiratory therapist (RT), allied health professional whose duties include conducting pulmonary function tests, monitoring oxygen and carbon dioxide levels in the blood, and administering breathing treatments, 214, 215, 220
Respiratory therapy, allied health specialty that assists patients with respiratory and cardiopulmonary disorders, 220
Retina, the innermost layer of the eye. It contains the visual receptors called rods and cones. The rods and cones receive the light impulses and transmit them to the brain via the optic nerve, 425*f*, 426, 426*f*, 427, 427*f*, 430*f*
Retinal, pertaining to the retina, 432
Retinal arteries, 430*f*
Retinal blood vessels, the blood vessels that supply oxygen to the rods and cones of the retina, 427
Retinal detachment, occurs when the retina becomes separated from the choroid layer. This separation seriously damages blood vessels and nerves, resulting in blindness, 434
Retinal veins, 430*f*
Retinitis pigmentosa, progressive disease of the eye that results in the retina becoming hard (sclerosed), pigmented (colored), and atrophied (wasting away). There is no known cure for this condition, 434
Retinoblastoma, malignant glioma of the retina, 434
Retinopathy, retinal disease, 432
Retinopexy, surgical fixation of the retina, 432
Retrograde pyelogram (RP), a diagnostic X-ray in which dye is inserted through the urethra to outline the bladder, ureters, and renal pelvis, 294, 294*f*
Retroperitoneal, pertaining to behind the peritoneum. Used to describe the position of the kidneys, which is outside of the peritoneal sac alongside the spine, 33, 282
Retrovirus, 188
Reverse transcriptase inhibitor drugs, medication that inhibits reverse transcriptase, an enzyme needed to viruses to reproduce, 192
Reye's syndrome, a brain inflammation that occurs in children following a viral infection, usually the flu or chickenpox. It is characterized by vomiting and lethargy and may lead to coma and death, 403
Rh factor, an antigen marker found on erythrocytes of persons with Rh+ blood, 172–73
Rh-negative (Rh-), a person with Rh– blood type. The person's RBCs do not have the Rh marker and will make antibodies against Rh+ blood, 172, 173
Rh-positive (Rh+), a person with Rh+ blood type. The person's RBCs have the Rh marker, 172
Rheumatoid arthritis (RA), chronic form of arthritis with inflammation of the joints, swelling, stiffness, pain, and changes in the cartilage that can result in crippling deformities, 99, 99*f*
Rhinitis, inflammation of the nose, 217
Rhinomycosis, condition of having a fungal infection in the nose, 217

Rhinoplasty, plastic surgery of the nose, 217
Rhinorrhagia, rapid and excessive flow of blood from the nose, 218
Rhinorrhea, watery discharge from the nose, especially with allergies or a cold, runny nose, 218
Rhonchi, somewhat musical sound during expiration, often found in asthma or infection, and caused by spasms of the bronchial tubes. Also called *wheezing,* 220
Rhytidectomy, surgical removal of excess skin to eliminate wrinkles. Commonly referred to as a *facelift,* 54, 64
Rhytidoplasty, excision of wrinkles, 54
RIA, 373
Rib cage, also called the chest cavity. It is the cavity formed by the curved ribs extending from the vertebral column around the sides and attaching to the sternum. The ribs are part of the axial skeleton, 84, 85, 88*f*
Ribs, 86*f*
Rickets, deficiency in calcium and vitamin D found in early childhood that results in bone deformities, especially bowed legs, 98
Right atrium, 132*f,* 134*f,* 135*f,* 137*f*
Right coronary artery, 139*f*
Right hypochondriac, an anatomical division of the abdomen; the right upper row, 34*t*
Right iliac, an anatomical division of the abdomen; the right lower row. Also called the *right inguinal,* 34*t*
Right lower quadrant (RLQ), a clinical division of the abdomen. It contains portions of small and large intestines, right ovary and fallopian tube, appendix, right ureter, 34*t*
Right lumbar, an anatomical division of the abdomen, the right middle row, 34*t*
Right lymphatic duct, one of two large lymphatic ducts. It drains right arm and the right side of the neck and chest; empties lymph into the right subclavian vein, 181, 182
Right upper quadrant (RUQ), a clinical division of the abdomen. It contains the right lobe of the liver, the gallbladder, a portion of the pancreas, and portions of small and large intestine, 34*t*
Right ventricle, 132*f,* 134*f,* 135*f,* 137*f*
Rinne and Weber tuning-fork tests, the physician holds a tuning fork, an instrument that produces a constant pitch when it is struck against or near the bones on the side of the head. These tests assess both nerve and bone conduction of sound, 447
RLQ, 34*t*
Rods, the sensory receptors of the retina that are active in dim light and do not perceive color, 427
Root, the portion of a tooth below the gum line, 246, 247*f*
Root canal, dental treatment involving the pulp cavity of the root of a tooth. Procedure is used to save a tooth that is badly infected or abscessed, 246, 247, 247*f,* 262
Rotation, moving around a central axis, 109
Rotator cuff injury, the rotator cuff consists of the joint capsule of the shoulder joint that is reinforced by the tendons from several shoulder muscles; at high risk for strain or tearing injuries, 111
Round window, 441*f*
Rubella, contagious viral skin infection; commonly called *German measles.* 62
Rugae, the prominent folds in the mucosa of the stomach. They smooth out and almost disappear allowing the stomach to expand when it is full of food. Also found in the urinary bladder, 248, 248*f,* 284
Rule of nines, 61*f*
RUQ, 34*t*

S

Saccule, found in the inner ear. It plays a role in equilibrium, 442
Sacral, pertaining to the sacrum, 94
Sacrum, the five fused vertebrae that form a large flat bone in the upper buttock region, 84, 85, 86*f,* 88*t*
Sagittal plane, a vertical plane that divides the body into left and right sections, 30, 30*f,* 31
Sagittal section, sectional view of the body produced by a cut along the sagittal plane, 30, 31
Saliva, watery fluid secreted into the mouth from the salivary glands; contains digestive enzymes that break down carbohydrates and lubricants that make it easier to swallow food, 244
Salivary glands, exocrine glands with ducts that open into the mouth. They produce saliva, which makes the bolus of food easier to swallow and begins the digestive process. There are three pairs of salivary glands: parotid, submandibular, and sublingual, 27*t,* 243*f,* 244, 250
Salpingectomy, excision of the fallopian tubes, 323
Salpingitis, inflammation of the fallopian tube or tubes; also, inflammation of the eustachian tube, 323, 444
Salpingocyesis, tubal pregnancy, 323
Salpingotomy, incision into the fallopian tubes, 444
Sanguinous, pertaining to blood, 173
Sarcoidosis, inflammatory disease of the lymph system in which lesions may appear in the liver, skin, lungs, lymph nodes, spleen, eyes, and small bones of the hands and feet, 189
SARS, 227

Scabies, contagious skin disease caused by an egg-laying mite that causes intense itching; often seen in children, 62
Scapula, also called the shoulder blade. An upper extremity bone, 88, 89*f*, 90, 90*f*
Scapular, pertaining to the scapula or shoulder blade, 94
SCC, 65
Schwann cell, 391*f*
Sciatic nerve, 397*f*
SCIDS, 191
Sclera, the tough protective outer layer of the eyeball. It is commonly referred to as the white of the eye, 425*f*, 426, 426*f*
Scleral, pertaining to the sclera, 432
Scleral buckling, placing a band of silicone around the outside of the sclera to stabilize a detaching retina, 437
Scleritis, inflammation of the sclera, 432
Scleroderma, disorder in which the skin becomes taut, thick, and leatherlike, 55
Scleromalacia, softening of the sclera, 432
Sclerotomy, incision into the sclera, 432
Scoliosis, abnormal lateral curvature of the spine, 95*f*, 99
Scratch test, form of allergy testing in which the body is exposed to an allergen through a light scratch in the skin, 190, 190*f*
Scrotum, a sac that serves as a container for the testes. This sac, which is divided by a septum, supports the testicles and lies between the legs and behind the penis, 333, 334
Sebaceous cyst, sac under the skin filled with sebum or oil from a sebaceous gland. This can grow to a large size and may need to be excised, 62
Sebaceous glands, also called oil glands. They produce a substance called sebum that lubricates the skin surface, 25*t*, 50, 51*f*, 52–53, 53*f*, 429
Seborrhea, excessive discharge of sebum, 54
Sebum, thick, oily substance secreted by sebaceous glands that lubricates the skin to prevent drying out. When sebum accumulates, it can cause congestion in the sebaceous glands and whiteheads or pimples may form. When the sebum becomes dark it is referred to as a comedo or blackhead, 52
Second-degree burn, 60, 60*f*
Secretion, third phase of urine production; additional waste products are added to the filtrate as it passes through the kidney tubules, 286, 287
Sedative, produces relaxation without causing sleep, 407
Seizure, sudden attack of severe muscular contractions associated with a loss of consciousness. This is seen in grand mal epilepsy, 400
Self-innoculation, infection that occurs when a person becomes infected in a different part of the body by a pathogen from another part of his or her own body, such as intestinal bacteria spreading to the urethra, 186
Semen, semen contains sperm and fluids secreted by male reproductive system glands. It leaves the body through the urethra, 333
Semen analysis, this procedure is used when performing a fertility workup to determine if the male is able to produce sperm. Semen is collected by the patient afer abstaining from sexual intercourse for a period of three to five days. The sperm in the semen are analyzed for number, swimming strength, and shape. This is also used to determine if a vasectomy has been successful. After a period of six weeks, no sperm should be present in a sample from the patient, 338
Semicircular canals, a portion of the labyrinth associated with balance and equilibrium, 442
Semilunar valve, the heart valves located between the ventricles and the great arteries leaving the heart. The pulmonary valve is located between the right ventricle, and the pulmonary artery and the aortic valve are located between the left ventricle and the aorta, 135
Seminal vesicles, two male reproductive system glands located at the base of the bladder. They secrete a fluid that nourishes the sperm into the vas deferens. This fluid plus the sperm constitutes much of the semen, 28*t*, 33*t*, 332*f*, 333, 333*f*, 335
Seminiferous tubules, network of coiled tubes that make up the bulk of the testes. Sperm development takes place in the walls of the tubules and the mature sperm are released into the tubule in order to leave the testes, 333, 334, 365*f*
Sensorineural hearing loss, type of hearing loss in which the sound is conducted normally through the external and middle ear but there is a defect in the inner ear or with the cochlear nerve, resulting in the inability to hear. A hearing aid may help, 443
Sensory neurons, nerves that carry sensory information from sensory receptors to the brain; also called *afferent neurons,* 395, 396, 397*f*
Sensory receptors, nerve fibers that are located directly under the surface of the skin. These receptors detect temperature, pain, touch, and pressure. The messages for these sensations are conveyed to the brain and spinal cord from the nerve endings in the skin, 50, 51*f*, 390
Sepsis, 175

Septicemia, having bacteria in the blood stream; commonly referred to as *blood poisoning,* 175
Sequential multiple analyzer computer (SMAC), machine for doing multiple blood chemistry tests automatically, 176
Serous fluid, watery secretion of serous membranes, 214
Serum, clear, sticky fluid that remains after the blood has clotted, 170
Serum bilirubin, blood test to determine the amount of the waste product bilirubin in the bloodstream; elevated levels indicate liver disease, 260
Serum lipoprotein, a laboratory test to measure the amount of cholesterol and triglycerides in the blood, 148
Severe acute respiratory syndrome (SARS), acute viral respiratory infection that begins like the flu but quickly progresses to severe dyspnea; high fatality rate. First appeared in China in 2003, 222
Severe combined immunodeficiency syndrome (SCIDS), disease seen in children born with a nonfunctioning immune system; often forced to live in sealed sterile rooms, 189
Sex hormones, hormones secreted by the gonads and the adrenal cortex; estrogen and progesterone in females and testosterone in males, 314, 333
Sexually transmitted disease (STD), disease usually acquired as the result of sexual intercourse; formerly more commonly referred to as venereal disease, 338
SG, 65
Shingles, eruption of vesicles along a nerve, causing a rash and pain. Caused by the same virus as chickenpox, 404, 404*f*
Short bone, a type of bone that is roughly cube shaped. The carpals are short bones, 82, 83
Shortness of breath (SOB), term used to indicate that a patient is having some difficulty breathing. The cause can range from mild SOB after exercise to SOB associated with heart disease, 216, 220
Sialadenitis, inflammation of a salivary gland, 253
Sickle cell anemia, severe, chronic, incurable disorder that results in anemia and causes joint pain, chronic weakness, and infections. It is more common in people of Mediterranean and African heritage. The actual blood cell is crescent shaped, 175, 175*f*
SIDS, 227
Sigmoid colon, the final section of colon. It follows an S-shaped path and terminates in the rectum, 249, 249*f*, 250*f*
Sigmoidal, pertaining to the sigmoid colon, 253
Sigmoidoscope, instrument to view inside the sigmoid colon, 253, 262
Sigmoidoscopy, using a flexible sigmoidoscope to visually examine the sigmoid colon; commonly done to diagnose cancer and polyps, 262
Silicosis, form of respiratory disease resulting from the inhalation of silica (quartz) dust. Considered an occupational disease, 222
Simple fracture, 96
Simple mastectomy, surgical removal of the breast tissue, 329
Singular endings, 9
Sinoatrial node (SA), also called the pacemaker of the heart. It is an area of the right atria that initiates the electrical pulse that causes the heart to contract, 136, 137*f*, 138
Sinus, a hollow cavity within a bone, 83, 84
Skeletal muscle, a voluntary muscle that is attached to bones by a tendon, 105, 105*f*, 106, 106*f*
Skeletal muscle relaxant, produces the relaxation of skeletal muscle, 112
Skeletal muscle tissue, 23
Skeletal system, 25*t*, 79–103, 81*f*
- abbreviations, 102
- anatomy and physiology, 82–92
- appendicular skeleton, 88–90, 89*f*
- axial skeleton, 84–86
- bones, 82–84
- diagnostic procedures, 100
- joints, 91–92
- pathology, 96–99
- pharmacology, 101
- therapeutic procedures, 100–101
- vocabulary, 95–96
- word building, 93–94

Skeleton, bones forming the framework for the body; site for skeletal muscle attachments, 82
- appendicular, 84, 88–90
- axial, 84–86

Skin, the major organ of the integumentary system. It forms a barrier between the external and internal environments, 25*t*, 49, 50–52, 395*f*
Skin graft, the transfer of skin from a normal area to cover another site. Used to treat burn victims and after some surgical procedures, 64
Skull, 85, 86*f*, 87*f*, 87*t*, 92*f*, 395*f*
SLE, 65
Sleep apnea, condition in which breathing stops repeatedly during sleep long enough to cause a drop in oxygen levels in the blood, 222
Sleep apnea study, 224
Slit lamp microscopy, in ophthalmology, examining the posterior surface of the cornea, 436
SMAC, 178
Small intestine, the portion of the digestive tube between the stomach and colon, and the

Spongy bone, the bony tissue found inside a bone. It contains cavities that hold red bone marrow. Also called *cancellous bone,* 82, 83, 83*f*

Spontaneous abortion, loss of a fetus without any artificial aid. Also called a *miscarriage,* 327

Sprain, pain and disability caused by trauma to a joint. A ligament may be torn in severe sprains, 99

Sputum, mucus or phlegm that is coughed up from the lining of the respiratory tract. Tested to determine what type of bacteria of virus is present as an aid in selecting the proper antibiotic treatment, 219, 220

Sputum culture and sensitivity (C&S), testing sputum by placing it on a culture medium and observing any bacterial growth. The specimen is then tested to determine antibiotic effectiveness, 223

Sputum cytology, testing for malignant cells in sputum, 223

Squamous cell carcinoma (SCC), epidermal cancer that may go into deeper tissue but does not generally metastasize, 62

Standard precautions, 186

Stapedectomy, removal of the stapes bone to treat otosclerosis (hardening of the bone). A prosthesis or artificial stapes may be implanted, 448

Stapes, one of the three ossicles of the middle ear. It is attached to the oval window leading to the inner ear. Also called the *stirrup,* 441*f,* 442, 442*f*

STD, 340

Stent, a stainless steel tube placed within a blood vessel or a duct to widen the lumen, 144, 144*f*

Sterility, inability to father children due to a problem with spermatogenesis, 336

Sterilization, process of rendering a male or female sterile or unable to conceive children, 339

Sternal, pertaining to the sternum or breast bone, 94

Sternocleidomastoid, muscle named for its attachments, the sternum, clavicle, and mastoid process, 107

Sternum, also called the *breast bone.* It is part of the axial skeleton and the anterior attachment for ribs, 84, 85, 86*f*

Steroid sex hormones, a class of hormones secreted by the adrenal cortex. It includes aldosterone, cortisol, androgens, estrogens, and progestins, 358*t,* 360

Stethoscope, instrument for listening to body sounds, such as the chest, heart, or intestines, 144

Stillbirth, viable-aged fetus dies before or at the time of delivery, 327

Stirrup, 441*f,* 442

Stomach, a J-shaped muscular organ that acts as a sac to collect, churn, digest, and store food. It is composed of three parts: the fundus, body, and antrum. Hydrochloric acid is secreted by glands in the mucous membrane lining of the stomach. Food mixes with other gastric juices and the hydrochloric acid to form a semisoft mixture called chyme, which then passes into the duodenum, 27*t,* 33*t,* 243*f,* 244, 248, 248*f,* 250*f*

Stool culture, a laboratory test of feces to determine if there are any pathogenic bacteria present, 261

Stool guaiac, 260

Strabismus, an eye muscle weakness resulting in each eye looking in a different direction at the same time. May be corrected with glasses, eye exercises, and/or surgery. Also called *lazy eye* or *crossed eyes,* 428*f,* 435

Strabotomy, incision into the eye muscles in order to correct strabismus, 437

Strain, trauma to muscle from excessive stretching or pulling, 111

Stratified squamous epithelium, the layers of flat or scalelike cells found in the epidermis. *Stratified* means multiple layers and *squamous* means flat, 50

Strawberry hemangioma, congenital collection of dilated blood vessels causing a red birthmark that fades a few months after birth, 57, 57*f*

Stress fracture, a slight fracture caused by repetitive low-impact forces, like running, rather than a single forceful impact, 97

Stress testing, method for evaluating cardiovascular fitness. The patient is placed on a treadmill or a bicycle and then subjected to steadily increasing levels of work. An EKG and oxygen levels are taken while the patient exercises, 149, 149*f*

Striated muscle, another name for skeletal muscle, referring to its striped appearance under the microscope, 106, 106*f*

Stricture, narrowing of a passageway in the urinary system, 291

Stridor, harsh, high-pitched, noisy breathing sound that is made when there is an obstruction of the bronchus or larynx. Found in conditions such as croup in children, 220

Stroke, 401

STSG, 65

Stye (sty), 434

Subarachnoid space, the space located between the arachnoid layer and pia mater. It contains cerebrospinal fluid, 395, 395*f*

Subcutaneous (SC, sc, sub-q, subcu), (1) Pertaining to under the skin. (2) Injection of medication under the skin, 54, 65

Subclavian artery, 140*f*

Subclavian vein, 142*f*, 183*f*
Subcutaneous layer, this is the deepest layer of the skin where fat is formed. This layer of fatty tissue protects the deeper tissues of the body and acts as an insulation for heat and cold, 51*f*, 52, 53*f*
Subdural hematoma, mass of blood forming beneath the dura mater of the brain, 405, 405*f*
Subdural space, the space located between the dura mater and the arachnoid layer, 395, 395*f*
Sublingual (SL), (1) Pertaining to under the tongue. (2) Administration of medicine by placing it under the tongue, 253
Sublingual duct, 251*f*
Sublingual glands, a pair of salivary glands in the floor of the mouth, 250, 251*f*
Subluxation, an incomplete dislocation, the joint alignment is disrupted, but the ends of the bones remain in contact, 99
Submandibular ducts, 245*f*, 251*f*
Submandibular glands, a pair of salivary glands in the floor of the mouth, 250, 251*f*
subq, 65
Sudden infant death syndrome (SIDS), the sudden, unexplained death of an infant in which a postmortem examination fails to determine the cause of death, 222
Sudoriferous glands, the typical sweat glands of the skin, 53
Suffix, a word part attached to the end of a word. It frequently indicates a condition, disease, or procedure. Almost all medical terms have a suffix, 2, 3, 6–8
  adjective, 7
  procedural, 8
  surgical, 7
Suffocation, 218
Sulci, also called *fissures.* The grooves that separate the gyri of the cerebral cortex. Singular is sulcus, 392
Superficial, directional term meaning toward the surface of the body, 36*t*
Superior, directional term meaning toward the head, or above, 35*f*, 35*t*
Superior mesenteric vein, 142*f*
Superior vena cava, the branch of the vena cava that drains blood from the chest and upper body, 134*f*, 135, 136, 137*f*, 142*f*
Supination, turn the palm or foot upward, 109, 109*f*
Supine, directional term meaning lying horizontally and facing upward, 36*f*, 36*t*
Supplemental air, 215*t*
Supplemental oxygen therapy, providing a patient with additional concentration of oxygen to improve oxygen levels in the bloodstream.Oxygen may be provided by a mask or nasal cannula, 225
Suppurative, containing or producing pus, 57
Surgical center, a facility that provides services that range from simple surgeries to diagnostic testing to therapy and do not require overnight hospitalization. Also called an *ambulatory care center* or an *outpatient clinic,* 11
Surgical suffixes, 7
Suspensory ligament, 426*f*
Suture, 87*f*
Sweat duct, duct leading from a sweat gland to the surface of the skin; carries sweat, 53
Sweat glands, glands that produce sweat, which assists the body in maintaining its internal temperature by creating a cooling effect when it evaporates, 25*t*, 50, 51*f*, 53–54
Sweat pore, the surface opening of a sweat duct, 53
Sweat test, test performed on sweat to determine the level of chloride. There is an increase in skin chloride in the disease cystic fibrosis, 224
Swimmer's ear, 446
Sympathetic branch, a branch of the autonomic nervous system. This system stimulates the body in times of stress and crisis by increasing heart rate, dilating airways to allow for more oxygen, increasing blood pressure, inhibiting digestion, and stimulating the production of adrenaline during a crisis, 396
Symphysis pubis, 314*f*, 319*f*, 333*f*
Synapse, the point at which the axon of one neuron meets the dendrite of the next neuron, 390
Synaptic cleft, the gap between two neurons, 390
Syncope, fainting, 400
Syndrome, group of symptoms and signs that when combined present a clinical picture of a disease or condition, 368
Synovectomy, excision of the synovial membrane, 93
Synovial fluid, the fluid secreted by a synovial membrane in a synovial joint. It lubricates the joint and reduces friction, 91, 92
Synovial joint, a freely moving joint that is lubricated by synovial fluid, 91, 92, 92*f*
Synovial membrane, the membrane that lines a synovial joint. It secretes a lubricating fluid called *synovial fluid,* 91, 92
Synovitis, inflammation of the synovial membrane, 93
Syphilis, infectious, chronic, venereal disease that can involve any organ. May exist for years without symptoms. Treated with the antibiotic pencillin, 338
System, several organs working in a compatible manner to perform a complex function or functions. Examples include the digestive system, the cardiovascular system, and the respiratory system, 25–29, 33*t*–36*t*

Systematic, pertaining to a system, 37
Systemic circulation, the systematic circulation transports oxygenated blood from the left side of the heart to the cells of the body and then back to the right side of the heart, 132
Systemic lupus erythematosus (SLE), chronic disease of the connective tissue that injures the skin, joints, kidneys, nervous system, and mucous membranes. May produce a characteristic butterfly rash across the cheeks and nose, 62, 65, 99
Systemic veins, 132*f*
Systole, the period of time during which a heart chamber is contracting, 135, 136
Systolic pressure, the maximum pressure within blood vessels during a heart contraction, 141

T

T cells, lymphocytes active in cellular immunity, 184, 364, 366
T lymphocytes, a type of lymphocyte involved with producing cells that physically attack and destroy pathogens, 184
Tachycardia, abnormally fast heart rate, over 100 bpm, 143
Tachypnea, rapid breathing rate, 218
TAH-BSO, 330
Talipes, congenital deformity of the foot. Also referred to as a *clubfoot,* 99
Target organs, the organs that hormones act on to either increase or decrease the organ's activity level, 358
Tarsal, pertaining to the ankle, 94
Tarsals, the ankle bones in the lower extremity, 88, 89*f*, 90, 91*f*, 91*t*
Taste buds, found on the surface of the tongue; designed to detect bitter, sweet, sour, and salty flavors in our food, 244
TB, 227
Tears, fluid that washes and lubricates the anterior surface of the eyeball, 429
Teeth, structures in mouth that mechanically break up food into smaller pieces during chewing, 244, 245*f*, 246–47
Temporal bone, a cranial bone, 84, 85, 87*f*, 87*t*, 441*f*
Temporal lobe, one of the four cerebral hemisphere lobes. It controls hearing and smell, 392, 393, 393*f*
Tendinitis, inflammation of tendon, 110
Tendinous, pertaining to a tendon, 110
Tendons, the strong connective tissue cords that attach skeletal muscles to bones, 23, 106
Tendoplasty, surgical repair of a tendon, 110
Tendotomy, incision into a tendon, 110
Tennis elbow, 111
Tenodesis, surgical procedure to stabilize a joint by anchoring down the tendons of the muscles that move the joint, 112
Tenodynia, pain in a tendon, 110
Tenoplasty, surgical repair of a tendon, 110
Tenorrhaphy, suture a tendon, 110
Testes, the male gonads. The testes are oval glands located in the scrotum that produce sperm and the male hormone, testosterone, 28*t*, 332*f*, 333–34, 333*f*, 339*f*, 358, 359*t*, 364, 365*f*
Testicles, also called *testes* (singular is testis). These oval-shaped organs are responsible for the development of sperm within the seminiferous tubules. The testes must be maintained at the proper temperature for the sperm to survive. This lower temperature level is controlled by the placement of the scrotum outside the body. The hormone testosterone, which is responsible for the growth and development of the male reproductive organs, is also produced by the testes, 333
Testicular, pertaining to the testes, 336
Testicular carcinoma, cancer of one or both testicles, 337
Testicular torsion, a twisting of the spermatic cord, 337
Testis, 357*f*, 364*f*
Testosterone, male hormone produced in the testes. It is responsible for the growth and development of the male reproductive organs, 333, 334, 359*t*, 364, 365*f*
Tetany, a condition that results from a calcium deficiency in the blood. It is characterized by muscle twitches, cramps, and spasms, 370
Tetralogy of Fallot, combination of four congenital anomalies: pulmonary stenosis, an interventricular septal defect, abnormal blood supply to the aorta, and hypertrophy of the right ventricle. Needs immediate surgery to correct, 146
TFT, 373
THA, 102
Thalamic, pertaining to the thalamus, 399
Thalamus, a portion of the diencephalon. It is composed of gray matter and acts as a center for relaying impulses from the eyes, ears, and skin to the cerebrum. Pain perception is also controlled by the thalamus, 362, 363*f*, 392, 392*f*, 393
Thalassemia, a genetic disorder in which the person is unable to make functioning hemoglobin; results in anemia, 175
Therapeutic abortion, the termination of a pregnancy for the health of the mother, 329
Third-degree burn, 60, 60*f*
Thoracalgia, chest pain, 218

Thoracentesis, surgical puncture of the chest wall for the removal of fluids, 226, 226*f*
Thoracic, pertaining to the chest, 94, 218
Thoracic cavity, a ventral body cavity in the chest area that contains the lungs and heart, 31, 32, 32*f*, 33*t*
Thoracic duct, the largest lymph vessel. It drains the entire body except for the right arm, chest wall, and both lungs. It empties lymph into the left subclavian vein, 181, 182, 183*f*
Thoracic region, the chest region of the body, 31, 32*f*
Thoracic surgeon, a physician specialized in treating conditions and diseases of the respiratory system by surgical teams, 220
Thoracic surgery, branch of medicine specializing in surgery on the respiratory system and thoracic cavity, 27*t*, 220
Thoracic vertebrae, the twelve vertebrae in the chest region, 84, 85, 88*t*
Thoracostomy, insertion of a tube into the chest for the purpose of draining off fluid or air, 226
Thoracotomy, incision into the chest, 218
THR, 102
Thrombin, a clotting enzyme that converts fibrinogen to fibrin, 172
Thrombocytes, also called *platelets.* Platelets play a critical part in the blood-clotting process by agglutinating into small clusters and releasing thrombokinase, 172, 173
Thrombocytosis, too many clotting cells (platelets), 173
Thrombolytic, able to dissolve existing blood clots, 152, 178
Thrombolytic therapy, drugs, such as streptokinase or tissue-type plasminogen activator, are injected into a blood vessel to dissolve clots and restore blood flow, 150
Thrombopenia, too few clotting (cells), 173
Thrombophlebitis, inflammation of a vein that results in the formation of blood clots within the vein, 148
Thromboplastin, substance released by platelets; reacts with prothrombin to form thrombin, 172
Thrombopoiesis, producing clotting (cells), 173
Thrombus, a blood clot, 148
Thymectomy, removal of the thymus gland, 187, 367
Thymic, pertaining to the thymus gland, 367
Thymitis, inflammation of the thymus gland, 367
Thymoma, malignant tumor of the thymus gland, 187, 367
Thymosin, hormone secreted by thymus gland. It causes lymphocytes to change into T lymphocytes, 184, 359*t*, 364
Thymus gland, an endocrine gland located in the upper mediastinum that assists the body with the immune function and the development of antibodies. As part of the immune response it secretes a hormone, thymosin, that changes lymphocytes to T cells, 26*t*, 28*t*, 33*t*, 180*f*, 181, 184, 214*f*, 357*f*, 358, 359*t*, 364–66, 365*f*
Thyroid cartilage, a piece of cartilage associated with the larynx. It is also commonly called the Adam's apple and is larger in males, 211*f*, 212
Thyroid echogram, ultrasound examination of the thyroid that can assist in distinguishing a thyroid nodule from a cyst, 372
Thyroid function test (TFT), blood tests used to measure the levels of T_3, T_4, and TSH in the blood stream to assist in determining thyroid function, 372
Thyroid gland, this endocrine gland is located on either side of the trachea. Its shape resembles a butterfly with a large left and right lobe connected by a narrow isthmus. This gland produces the hormones thyroxine (also known as T_4) and triiodothyronine (also known as T_3), 28*t*, 211*f*, 357*f*, 358, 359*t*, 362*f*, 366, 366*f*
Thyroid replacement hormone, given to replace thyroid in patients with hypothyroidism or who have had a thyroidectomy, 373
Thyroid replacement therapy, 373
Thyroid scan, test in which a radioactive element is administered that localizes in the thyroid gland. The gland can then be visualized with a scanning device to detect pathology such as tumors, 372
Thyroid-stimulating hormone (TSH), a hormone secreted by the anterior pituitary. It regulates function of the thyroid gland, 359*t*, 363, 364*f*
Thyroidal, pertaining to the thyroid gland, 367
Thyroidectomy, removal of the entire thyroid or a portion (partial thyroidectomy) to treat a variety of conditions, including nodes, cancer, and hyperthyroidism, 368
Thyromegaly, enlarged thyroid, 367
Thyrotoxicosis, condition that results from overproduction of the thyroid glands. Symptoms include a rapid heart action, tremors, enlarged thyroid gland, exophthalmos, and weight loss, 371
Thyroxine (T_4), a hormone produced by the thyroid gland. It is also known as T_4 and requires iodine for its production. This hormone regulates the level of cell metabolism. The greater the level of hormone in the bloodstream, the higher cell metabolism will be, 359*t*, 366
TIA, 408
Tibia, also called the *shin bone.* It is a lower extremity bone, 88, 89*f*, 90, 91*f*, 91*t*
Tibial, pertaining to the tibia or shin bone, 94
Tidal volume (TV), the amount of air that enters the lungs in a single inhalation or leaves the lungs in a single exhalation of quiet breathing, 215*t*

Tinea, fungal skin disease resulting in itching, scaling lesions, 62
Tinea capitis, fungal infection of the scalp; commonly called *ringworm.* 62
Tinea pedis, fungal infection of the foot; commonly called *athlete's foot.* 62
Tinnitus, ringing in the ears, 445
Tissues, tissues are formed when cells of the same type are grouped to perform one activity. For example, nerve cells combine to form nerve fibers. There are four types of tissue: nerve, muscle, epithelial, and connective, 23
connective, 23
epithelial, Pertaining to the epithelium, 23
muscle, 23
nervous, 23
TKR, 102
TLC, 227
Tongue, a muscular organ in the floor of the mouth. Works to move food around inside the mouth and is also necessary for speech, 211*f*, 244, 245*f*, 251*f*
Tonic-clonic seizure, type of severe epileptic seizure characterized by a loss of consciousness and convulsions. The seizure alternates between strong continuous muscle spasms (tonic) and rhythmic muscle contraction and relaxation (clonic). It is also called a *grand mal seizure*, 403
Tonometry, measurement of the intraocular pressure of the eye using a tonometer to check for the condition of glaucoma. After a local anesthetic is applied, the physician places the tonometer lightly upon the eyeball and a pressure measurement is taken. Generally part of a normal eye exam for adults, 436
Tonsillar, pertaining to the tonsils, 187
Tonsillectomy, surgical removal of the tonsils, 187
Tonsillitis, inflammation of the tonsils, 187
Tonsils, the collections of lymphatic tissue located in the pharynx to combat microorganisms entering the body through the nose or mouth. The tonsils are the pharyngeal tonsils, the palatine tonsils, and the lingual tonsils, 26*t*, 180*f*, 181, 184, 184*f*
Tooth cavity, 254
Torticollis, severe neck spasms pulling the head to one side; commonly called *wryneck* or a *crick in the neck.* 111
Total abdominal hysterectomy - bilateral salpingo-oophorectomy (TAH-BSO), removal of the entire uterus, cervix, both ovaries, and both fallopian tubes, 329
Total calcium, blood test to measure the total amount of calcium to assist in detecting parathyroid and bone disorders, 372
Total hip arthroplasty (THA), surgical reconstruction of a hip by implanting a prosthetic or artificial hip joint; also called *total hip replacement.* 100
Total hip replacement (THR), 100
Total knee arthroplasty (TKA), surgical reconstruction of a knee joint by implanting a prosthetic knee joint; also called *total knee replacement.* 101
Total lung capacity (TLC), the volume of air in the lungs after a maximal inhalation, 215*t*
Total parenteral nutrition (TPN), providing 100% of a patient's nutrition intravenously. Used when a patient is unable to eat, 262
Toxemia, 327
Toxic shock syndrome (TSS), rare and sometimes fatal staphylococcus infection that generally occurs in menstruating women, 325
Toxins, substances poisonous to the body. Many are filtered out of the blood by the kidney, 184
TPN, 264
Trachea, also called the *windpipe*. It conducts air from the larynx down to the main bronchi in the chest, 27*t*, 33*t*, 209*f*, 210, 211*f*, 212, 212*f*, 214*f*, 245*f*, 362*f*, 365*f*, 366*f*
Tracheostenosis, narrowing and stenosis of the lumen or opening into the trachea, 218
Tracheostomy, surgical procedure used to make an opening in the trachea to create an airway. A tracheostomy tube can be inserted to keep the opening patent, 226, 226*f*
Tracheotomy, surgical incision into the trachea to provide an airway, 218, 226
Trachoma, chronic infectious disease of the conjunctiva and cornea caused by bacteria. Occurs more commonly in people living in hot, dry climates. Untreated, it may lead to blindness when the scarring invades the cornea. Trachoma can be treated with antibiotics, 434
Tract, a bundle of fibers located within the central nervous system, 390, 392
Traction, process of pulling or drawing, usually with a mechanical device. Used in treating orthopedic (bone and joint) problems and injuries, 101
Tractotomy, incision into a spinal cord tract, 407
Transfusion reaction, 175
Transient ischemic attack (TIA), temporary interference with blood supply to the brain, causing neurological symptoms such as dizziness, numbness, and hemiparesis. May lead eventually to a full-blown stroke (CVA), 403
Transurethral resection of the prostate (TUR), surgical removal of the prostate gland by inserting a device through the urethra and removing prostate tissue, 339

Transverse colon, the section of colon that crosses the upper abdomen from the right side of the body to the left, 249, 249*f*, 250*f*
Transverse fracture, complete fracture that is straight across the bone at right angles to the long axis of the bone, 98, 98*f*
Transverse plane, a horizontal plane that divides the body into upper (superior) and lower (inferior) sections. Also called the *horizontal plane*, 30, 30*f*, 31
Transverse section, sectional view of the body produced by a cut along the transverse plane, 30, 31
Treadmill test, 149, 149*f*
Tremor, involuntary quivering movement of a part of the body, 400
Trichomoniasis, genitourinary infection that is usually without symptoms (asymptomatic) in both males and females. In women the disease can produce itching and/or burning and a foul-smelling discharge, and can result in vaginitis, 338
Trichomycosis, abnormal condition of hair fungus, 55
Tricuspid valve, a valve between the right atrium and ventricle of the heart. It prevents blood from flowing backwards into the atrium. A tricuspid valve has three cusps or flaps, 135, 136*f*, 137*f*
Trigeminal nerve, 396*t*
Triiodothyronine (T_3), a hormone produced by the thyroid gland known as T_3 that requires iodine for its production. This hormone regulates the level of cell metabolism. The greater the level of hormone in the blood stream, the higher cell metabolism will be, 359*t*, 366
Trochanter, the large blunt process that provides the attachment for tendons and muscles, 83, 84, 85*f*
Trochlear nerve, 396*t*
Trunk, the torso region of the body, 31, 32*f*
TSH, 373
Tubal ligation, surgical tying off of the fallopian tubes to prevent conception from taking place. Results in sterilization of the female, 329
Tubal pregnancy, 316
Tubercle, a small, rounded process that provides the attachment for tendons and muscles, 83, 84
Tuberculin skin tests (TB test), applying a chemical agent (Tine or Mantoux tests) under the surface of the skin to determine if the patient has been exposed to tuberculosis, 224
Tuberculosis (TB), infectious disease caused by the tubercle bacillus, *Myocobacterium tuberculosis*. Most commonly affects the respiratory system and causes inflammation and calcification of the system. Tuberculosis is again on the uprise and is seen in many patients who have AIDS, 222
Tuberosity, a large, rounded process that provides the attachment to tendons and muscles, 83, 84
TV, 227
Two-hour postprandial glucose tolerance test, blood test to assist in evaluating glucose metabolism. The patient eats a high-carbohydrate diet and fasts overnight before the test. A blood sample is then taken two hours after a meal, 372
Tympanectomy, excision of the eardrum, 445
Tympanic, pertaining to the eardrum, 444
Tympanic membrane, also called the eardrum. As sound moves along the auditory canal, it strikes the tympanic membrane causing it to vibrate. This conducts the sound wave into the middle ear, 441, 442*f*
Tympanitis, eardrum inflammation, 444
Tympanometer, instrument to measure the eardrum, 444
Tympanometry, measurement of the movement of the tympanic membrane. Can indicate the presence of pressure in the middle ear, 447
Tympanoplasty, another term for the surgical reconstruction of the eardrum. Also called *myringoplasty*, 444
Tympanorrhexis, ruptured eardrum, 445
Tympanotomy, incision into the eardrum, 445
Type A blood, one of the ABO blood types. A person with type A markers on his or her RBCs. Type A blood will make anti-B antibodies, 172
Type AB blood, one of the ABO blood types. A person with both type A and type B markers on his or her RBCs. Since it has both markers, it will not make antibodies against either A or B blood, 172
Type B blood, one of the ABO blood types. A person with type B markers on his or her RBCs. Type B blood will make anti-A antibodies, 172
Type O blood, one of the ABO blood types. A person with no markers on his or her RBCs. Type O blood will not react with anti-A or anti-B antibodies. Therefore, it is considered the universal donor, 172
Type and crossmatch, lab test performed before a person receives a blood transfusion; double checks the blood type of both the donor's and recipient's blood, 177

U

U/A, UA, 297
Ulcer, open sore or lesion in skin or mucous membrane, 59, 59*f*

Ulcerative colitis, ulceration of unknown origin of the mucous membranes of the colon. Also known as *inflammatory bowel disease* (IBD), 259
Ulna, one of the forearm bones in the upper extremity, 88, 89*f,* 90, 90*f*
Ulnar, pertaining to the ulna, one of the lower arm bones, 94
Ulnar artery, 140*f*
Ulnar nerve, 397*f*
Ulnar vein, 142*f*
Ultraviolet (UV), 65
Umbilical, an anatomical division of the abdomen; the middle section of the middle row, 34*t*
Umbilical cord, a cord extending from the baby's umbilicus (navel) to the placenta. It contains blood vessels that carry oxygen and nutrients from the mother to the baby and carbon dioxide and wastes from the baby to the mother, 318, 319*f,* 320
Unconscious, condition or state of being unaware of surroundings with the inability to respond to stimuli, 400
Ungual, 55
Universal donor, type O blood is considered the universal donor. Since it has no markers on the RBC surface, it will not trigger a reaction with anti-A or anti-B antibodies, 172
Universal recipient, a person with type AB blood has no antibodies against the other blood types and therefore, in an emergency, can receive any type of blood, 172
Upper extremity (UE), the arm, 31, 88, 89*f,* 90, 90*f*
Upper gastrointestinal (UGI) series, administering a barium contrast material orally and then taking an X-ray to visualize the esophagus, stomach, and duodenum, 261
Urea, a waste product of protein metabolism. It diffuses through the tissues in lymph and is returned to the circulatory system for transport to the kidneys, 170
Uremia, an excess of urea and other nitrogenous waste in the blood, 282, 289, 291
Ureteral, pertaining to the ureter, 289
Ureterectasis, dilation of the ureter, 289
Ureterolith, a calculus in the ureter, 289
Ureterostenosis, narrowing of the ureter, 289
Ureters, organs in the urinary system that transport urine from the kidney to the bladder, 27*t,* 33*t,* 34*t,* 281*f,* 282, 283, 283*f,* 284*f*
Urethra, the tube that leads from the urinary bladder to the outside of the body. In the male it is also used by the reproductive system to release semen, 27*t,* 33*t,* 281*f,* 282, 284*f,* 285, 286*f,* 314*f,* 333*f*
Urethral, pertaining to the urethra, 289
Urethralgia, urethral pain, 289
Urethritis, inflammation of the urethra, 289
Urethrorrhagia, rapid bleeding from the urethra, 289
Urethroscope, instrument to view inside the urethra, 289
Urethrostenosis, narrowing of the urethra, 289
Urgency, Feeling the need to urinate immediately, 291
Urinalysis (U/A, UA), laboratory test that consists of the physical, chemical, and microscopic examination of urine, 287, 287*t,* 293
Urinary, pertaining to urine, 289
Urinary bladder, organ in the urinary system that stores urine, 27*t,* 33*t,* 281*f,* 282, 284, 284*f,* 286*f,* 314*f,* 319*f,* 333*f*
Urinary incontinence, involuntary release of urine. In some patients an indwelling catheter is inserted into the bladder for continuous urine drainage, 291
Urinary meatus, the external opening of the urethra, 285, 317, 317*f,* 334
Urinary retention, an inability to fully empty the bladder, often indicates a blockage in the urethra, 291
Urinary system, system that filters wastes from the blood and excretes the waste products in the form of urine. Organs include the kidneys, ureters, urinary bladder, and urethra, 27*t,* 279–309, 281*f*
- abbreviations, 297
- anatomy and physiology, 282–87
- diagnostic procedures, 293–94
- homeostasis, kidneys and, 285
- kidneys, 282–83
- pathology, 291–93
- pharmacology, 296
- therapeutic procedures, 294–96
- ureters, 283
- urethra, 285
- urinary bladder, 284
- urinary production stages, 285–86
- urine, 286–87
- vocabulary, 290–91
- word building, 288–90

Urinary tract infection (UTI), infection, usually from bacteria such as *E. coli,* of any organ of the urinary system; most often begins with cystitis and may ascend into the ureters and kidneys; most common in women because of their shorter urethra, 293
Urination, the release of urine from the urinary bladder, 284
Urine, the fluid that remains in the urinary system following the three stages of urine production: filtration, reabsorption, and secretion, 282, 285–87, 286*f*
- production, 286–87, 286*f*

Urine culture and sensitivity (C&S), laboratory test of urine for bacterial infection; attempt to grow bacteria on a culture medium in order to identify it and determine which antibiotics it is sensitive to, 293
Urinometer, instrument to measure urine, 289
Urologist, a physician specialized in treating conditions and diseases of the urinary system and male reproductive system, 289, 291
Urology, branch of medicine specializing in conditions of the urinary system and male reproductive system, 27*t,* 28*t,* 291
Urticaria, hives, a skin eruption of pale reddish wheals (circular elevations of the skin) with severe itching. Usually associated with food allergy, stress, or drug reactions, 57, 188
Uterine, pertaining to the uterus, 323
Uterine tubes, tubes that carry the ovum from the ovary to the uterus; also called *fallopian tubes* or *oviducts,* 315
Uterus, also called the *womb.* An internal organ of the female reproductive system. This hollow, pear-shaped organ is located in the lower pelvic cavity between the urinary bladder and rectum. The uterus receives the fertilized ovum and it becomes implanted in the uterine wall, which provides nourishment and protection for the developing fetus. The uterus is divided into three regions: fundus, corpus, and cervix, 28*t,* 33*t,* 286*f,* 313*f,* 314, 314*f,* 316–17, 316*f,* 319*f*
UTI, 297
Utricle, found in the inner ear. It plays a role in equilibrium, 442
UV, 65
Uveitis, inflammation of the uvea of the eye, 432
Uvula, structure that hangs down from the posterior edge of the soft palate, helps in the production of speech, and is the location of the gag reflex, 244, 245*f*

V
Vaccination, providing protection against communicable diseases by stimulating the immune system to produce antibodies against that disease. Children can now be immunized for the following diseases: hepatitis B, diphtheria, tetanus, pertussis, *Haemophilus influenzae* type b, polio, measles, mumps, rubella, and chickenpox. Also called *immunization,* 184, 185, 192
Vagina, organ in the female reproductive system that receives the penis and semen, 28*t,* 33*t,* 286*f,* 313*f,* 314, 314*f,* 316*f,* 317, 317*f,* 319*f*
Vaginal, (1) Pertaining to the vagina. (2) Tablets and suppositories inserted vaginally and used to treat vaginal yeast infections and other irritations, 323
Vaginal hysterectomy, removal of the uterus through the vagina rather than through an abdominal incision, 329
Vaginal orifice, the external vaginal opening. It may be covered by a hymen, 317, 317*f*
Vaginitis, inflammation of the vagina, 323
Vagus nerve, 396*t*
Valve replacement, excision of a diseased heart valve and replacement with an artificial valve, 151
Valves, flaplike structures found within the tubular organs such as lymph vessels, veins, and the heart. They function to prevent the backflow of fluid, 181, 181*f,* 182
Valvoplasty, surgical repair of a valve, 143
Valvular, pertaining to a valve, 143
Valvulitis, inflammation of a valve, 143
Varicella, contagious viral skin infection; commonly called *chickenpox,* 63, 63*f*
Varicocele, enlargement of the veins of the spermatic cord, which commonly occurs on the left side of adolescent males. Seldom needs treatment, 337
Varicose veins, swollen and distended veins, usually in the legs, 148
Vas deferens, also called ductus deferens. The vas deferens is a long, straight tube that carries sperm from the epididymis up into the pelvic cavity, where it continues around the bladder and empties into the urethra. It is one of the components, along with nerves and blood vessels, of the spermatic cord, 28*t,* 33*t,* 332*f,* 333, 333*f,* 335, 339*f,* 365*f*
Vascular, pertaining to vessels, 143
Vasectomy, removal of a segment or all of the vas deferens to prevent sperm from leaving the male body. Used for contraception purposes, 339, 339*f*
Vasoconstrictor, contracts smooth muscle in walls of blood vessels; raises blood pressure, 152
Vasodilator, produces a relaxation of blood vessels to lower blood pressure, 152
Vasopressin, substance given to control diabetes insipidus and promote reabsorption of water in the kidney tubules, 373
Vasovasostomy, creation of a new opening between two sections of vas deferens. Used to reverse a vasectomy, 339
VCUG, 297
VD, 340
Vegetation, 145
Veins, blood vessels of the cardiovascular system that carry blood toward the heart, 26*t,* 51*f,* 131*f,* 132, 139*f,* 141, 142*f,* 181*f*
Vena cava, 132*f,* 133*f*
Venereal disease (VD), 338
Venipuncture, 177
Venogram, 143

Venography, process of taking an X-ray tracing of a vein, 149
Venous, pertaining to a vein, 143
Ventilation, the movement of air in and out of the lungs, 210
Ventilation-perfusion scan, a nuclear medicine diagnostic test that is especially useful in identifying pulmonary emboli. Radioactive air is inhaled for the ventilation portion to determine if air is filling the entire lung. Radioactive intravenous injection shows whether blood is flowing to all parts of the lung, 224
Ventilator, a machine that provides artificial ventilation for a patient unable to breath on his or her own. Also called a *respirator*, 225, 225*f*
Ventral, directional term meaning near or on the front or belly side of the body, 35*f*, 35*t*
Ventral cavities, 33*t*
Ventricles, the two lower chambers of the heart that receive blood from the atria and pump it back out of the heart. The left ventricle pumps blood to the body, and the right ventricle pumps blood to the lungs. Also fluid-filled spaces within the cerebrum. These contain cerebrospinal fluid, which is the watery, clear fluid that provides a protection from shock or sudden motion to the brain, 134, 392, 394
Ventricular, pertaining to a ventricle, 143
Ventricular septal defect (VSD), 145
Venules, the smallest veins. Venules receive deoxygenated blood leaving the capillaries, 141, 143, 181*f*
Vermiform appendix, a small outgrowth at the end of the cecum. Its function or purpose is unknown, 249
Verruca, warts; a benign neoplasm (tumor) caused by a virus. Has a rough surface that is removed by chemicals and/or laser therapy, 57
Vertebrae, 86*f*
Vertebral, pertaining to the vertebrae, 37
Vertebral canal, the bony canal through the vertebrae that contains the spinal cord, 394
Vertebral column, part of the axial skeleton. It is a column of twenty-six vertebrae that forms the backbone and protects the spinal cord. It is divided into five sections: cervical, thoracic, and lumbar vertebrae, sacrum, and coccyx. Also called *spinal column*, 84, 85, 88*f*, 88*t*, 394
Vertebral region, the spinal column region of the body, 31, 32*f*
Vertigo, dizziness, 445
Vesicle, small, fluid-filled raised spot on the skin, 59, 59*f*
Vesicular, pertaining to the seminal vesicle, 336
Vestibular nerve, the branch of the vestibulocochlear nerve responsible for sending equilibrium information to the brain, 441, 441*f*
Vestibulocochlear nerve, the eighth cranial nerve. It is responsible for hearing and balance, 396*t*, 441
Viruses, a group of infectious particles that cause disease, 184
Viscera, the name for the internal organs of the body, such as the lungs, stomach, and liver, 31, 33
Visceral, pertaining to the viscera or internal organs, 37
Visceral layer, the inner pleural layer. It adheres to the surface of the lung, 31, 33
Visceral muscle, the muscle found in the walls of internal organs such as the stomach, 106, 106*f*
Visceral pericardium, the inner layer of the pericardium surrounding the heart, 133, 134
Visceral peritoneum, the inner layer of the serous membrane sac encasing the abdominopelvic viscera, 31, 33
Visceral pleura, the inner layer of the serous membrane sac encasing the thoracic viscera, 31, 33, 214
Vision, 429–30
Visual acuity (VA) test, measurement of the sharpness of a patient's vision. Usually, a Snellen chart is used for this test and the patient identifies letters from a distance of 20 feet, 436
Vital capacity (VC), the total volume of air that can be exhaled after a maximum inhalation. This amount will be equal to the sum of tidal volume, inspiratory reserve volume, and expiratory reserve volume, 215*t*
Vital signs (VS), respiration, pulse, temperature, skin color, blood pressure, and reaction of pupils. These are signs of the condition of body functions, 215
Vitamin D therapy, maintaining high blood levels of calcium in association with vitamin D helps maintain bone density and treats osteomalacia, osteoporosis, and rickets, 101
Vitiligo, disappearance of pigment from the skin in patches, causing a milk-white appearance. Also called *leukoderma*, 63
Vitreous body, 426*f*
Vitreous humor, the transparent jellylike substance inside the eyeball, 427
Vocal cords, the structures within the larynx that vibrate to produce sound and speech, 211*f*, 212, 212*f*
Voiding, another term for urination, 291

Voiding cystourethrography (VCUG), x-ray taken to visualize the urethra while the patient is voiding after a contrast dye has been placed in the bladder, 294
Voluntary muscles, muscles that a person can consciously choose to contract. The skeletal muscles of the arm and leg are examples of this type of muscle, 105
Volvulus, condition in which the bowel twists upon itself and causes a painful obstruction that requires immediate surgery, 259, 259*f*
Vomer bone, a facial bone, 84, 85, 87*t*
von Recklinghausen's disease, 370
VSD, 152
Vulva, a general term meaning the external female genitalia. It consists of the Bartholin's glands, labia major, labia minora, and clitoris, 28*t*, 313*f*, 314, 317

W

Walking pneumonia, 222
Wall-eyed, 435
Warts, 57
Wax emulsifiers, substances used to soften ear wax to prevent buildup within the external ear canal, 448
WBC, 178
Western blot, test used as a backup to the ELISA blood test to detect the presence of the antibody to HIV (AIDS virus) in the blood, 190
Wet gangrene, area of gangrene becoming infected by pus-producing bacteria, 63
Wheal, small, round raised area on the skin that may be accompanied by itching, 59, 59*f*
Whiplash, 99
White blood cell count (WBC), blood test to measure the number of leukocytes in a volume of blood. An increase may indicate the presence of infection or a disease such as leukemia. A decrease in WBCs is caused by X-ray therapy and chemotherapy, 176
White blood cell differential (diff), blood test to determine the number of each variety of leukocyte, 176
White blood cells (WBC), blood cells that provide protection against the invasion of bacteria and other foreign material, 22*f*, 170
White matter, tissue in the central nervous system. It consists of myelinated nerve fibers, 390, 391
Whole blood, refers to the mixture of both plasma and formed elements, 169*f*, 174
Whooping cough, 220
Wilm's tumor, malignant kidney tumor found most often in children, 292
Windpipe, 212
Wisdom teeth, 246
Womb, 316
Word building, 8, 36–37, 54–55
Word root, the foundation of a medical term that provides the basic meaning of the word. In general, the word root will indicate the body system or part of the body that is being discussed. A word may have more than one word root, 2, 3
Wryneck, 111

X

Xenograft, skin graft from an animal of another species (usually pig); also called *heterograft.* 64
Xeroderma, dry skin, 55
Xerophthalmia, dry eyes, 432

Y

Yellow bone marrow, yellow bone marrow is located mainly in the center of the diaphysis of long bones. It contains mainly fat cells, 82, 83, 83*f*

Z

Zygomatic bone, a facial bone, 84, 85, 87*f*, 87*t*

Pearson Education, Inc.

YOU SHOULD CAREFULLY READ THE TERMS AND CONDITIONS BEFORE USING THE CD-ROM PACKAGE. USING THIS CD-ROM PACKAGE INDICATES YOUR ACCEPTANCE OF THESE TERMS AND CONDITIONS.

Pearson Education, Inc. provides this program and licenses its use. You assume responsibility for the selection of the program to achieve your intended results, and for the installation, use, and results obtained from the program. This license extends only to use of the program in the United States or countries in which the program is marketed by authorized distributors.

LICENSE GRANT

You hereby accept a nonexclusive, nontransferable, permanent license to install and use the program ON A SINGLE COMPUTER at any given time. You may copy the program solely for backup or archival purposes in support of your use of the program on the single computer. You may not modify, translate, disassemble, decompile, or reverse engineer the program, in whole or in part.

TERM

The License is effective until terminated. Pearson Education, Inc. reserves the right to terminate this License automatically if any provision of the License is violated. You may terminate the License at any time. To terminate this License, you must return the program, including documentation, along with a written warranty stating that all copies in your possession have been returned or destroyed.

LIMITED WARRANTY

THE PROGRAM IS PROVIDED "AS IS" WITHOUT WARRANTY OF ANY KIND, EITHER EXPRESSED OR IMPLIED, INCLUDING, BUT NOT LIMITED TO, THE IMPLIED WARRANTIES OR MERCHANTABILITY AND FITNESS FOR A PARTICULAR PURPOSE. THE ENTIRE RISK AS TO THE QUALITY AND PERFORMANCE OF THE PROGRAM IS WITH YOU. SHOULD THE PROGRAM PROVE DEFECTIVE, YOU (AND NOT PRENTICE-HALL, INC. OR ANY AUTHORIZED DEALER) ASSUME THE ENTIRE COST OF ALL NECESSARY SERVICING, REPAIR, OR CORRECTION. NO ORAL OR WRITTEN INFORMATION OR ADVICE GIVEN BY PRENTICE-HALL, INC., ITS DEALERS, DISTRIBUTORS, OR AGENTS SHALL CREATE A WARRANTY OR INCREASE THE SCOPE OF THIS WARRANTY.

SOME STATES DO NOT ALLOW THE EXCLUSION OF IMPLIED WARRANTIES, SO THE ABOVE EXCLUSION MAY NOT APPLY TO YOU. THIS WARRANTY GIVES YOU SPECIFIC LEGAL RIGHTS AND YOU MAY ALSO HAVE OTHER LEGAL RIGHTS THAT VARY FROM STATE TO STATE.

Pearson Education, Inc. does not warrant that the functions contained in the program will meet your requirements or that the operation of the program will be uninterrupted or error-free.

However, Pearson Education, Inc. warrants the diskette(s) or CD-ROM(s) on which the program is furnished to be free from defects in material and workmanship under normal use for a period of ninety (90) days from the date of delivery to you as evidenced by a copy of your receipt.

The program should not be relied on as the sole basis to solve a problem whose incorrect solution could result in injury to person or property. If the program is employed in such a manner, it is at the user's own risk and Pearson Education, Inc. explicitly disclaims all liability for such misuse.

LIMITATION OF REMEDIES

Pearson Education, Inc.'s entire liability and your exclusive remedy shall be:

1. the replacement of any diskette(s) or CD-ROM(s) not meeting Pearson Education, Inc.'s "LIMITED WARRANTY" and that is returned to Pearson Education, or
2. if Pearson Education is unable to deliver a replacement diskette(s) or CD-ROM(s) that is free of defects in materials or workmanship, you may terminate this agreement by returning the program.

IN NO EVENT WILL PRENTICE-HALL, INC. BE LIABLE TO YOU FOR ANY DAMAGES, INCLUDING ANY LOST PROFITS, LOST SAVINGS, OR OTHER INCIDENTAL OR CONSEQUENTIAL DAMAGES ARISING OUT OF THE USE OR INABILITY TO USE SUCH PROGRAM EVEN IF PRENTICE-HALL, INC. OR AN AUTHORIZED DISTRIBUTOR HAS BEEN ADVISED OF THE POSSIBILITY OF SUCH DAMAGES, OR FOR ANY CLAIM BY ANY OTHER PARTY.

SOME STATES DO NOT ALLOW FOR THE LIMITATION OR EXCLUSION OF LIABILITY FOR INCIDENTAL OR CONSEQUENTIAL DAMAGES, SO THE ABOVE LIMITATION OR EXCLUSION MAY NOT APPLY TO YOU.

GENERAL

You may not sublicense, assign, or transfer the license of the program. Any attempt to sublicense, assign or transfer any of the rights, duties, or obligations hereunder is void.

This Agreement will be governed by the laws of the State of New York.

Should you have any questions concerning this Agreement, you may contact Pearson Education, Inc. by writing to:

Director of New Media
Higher Education Division
Pearson Education, Inc.
One Lake Street
Upper Saddle River, NJ 07458

Should you have any questions concerning technical support, you may contact:

Product Support Department: Monday–Friday 8:00 A.M. –8:00 P.M. and Sunday 5:00 P.M.-12:00 A.M. (All times listed are Eastern). 1-800-677-6337

You can also get support by filling out the web form located at http://247.prenhall.com

YOU ACKNOWLEDGE THAT YOU HAVE READ THIS AGREEMENT, UNDERSTAND IT, AND AGREE TO BE BOUND BY ITS TERMS AND CONDITIONS. YOU FURTHER AGREE THAT IT IS THE COMPLETE AND EXCLUSIVE STATEMENT OF THE AGREEMENT BETWEEN US THAT SUPERSEDES ANY PROPOSAL OR PRIOR AGREEMENT, ORAL OR WRITTEN, AND ANY OTHER COMMUNICATIONS BETWEEN US RELATING TO THE SUBJECT MATTER OF THIS AGREEMENT.

Become a medical professional in months!

Yes! I am interested in finding out how I can have a rewarding career in medicine. Please send me information on the following programs:

- ❑ Dental Assistant
- ❑ Expanded Duties Dental Assistant
- ❑ Health Unit Coordinator
- ❑ Massage Therapy
- ❑ Medical Administrative Assistant
- ❑ Medical Assistant
- ❑ Nursing
- ❑ Nursing Assistant
- ❑ Ophthalmic Medical Assistant
- ❑ Ophthalmic Medical Technician
- ❑ Occupational Therapy Assistant
- ❑ Pharmacy Technician
- ❑ Phlebotomy Technician
- ❑ Physical Therapist Assistant
- ❑ Physical Therapy Technician
- ❑ Radiography
- ❑ Respiratory Therapy
- ❑ Veterinary Assistant
- ❑ Veterinary Technician

Name ____________________
Address ____________________
City ____________ State ________ Zip ________
Phone ____________ Day or Evening (circle one)
Email address ____________________

PIMA MEDICAL INSTITUTE

Mail this card today!
Or, call us at 888-635-5206.

Arizona California Colorado Nevada New Mexico Washington

Become a medical professional in months!

Yes! I am interested in finding out how I can have a rewarding career in medicine. Please send me information on the following programs:

- ❑ Dental Assistant
- ❑ Expanded Duties Dental Assistant
- ❑ Health Unit Coordinator
- ❑ Massage Therapy
- ❑ Medical Administrative Assistant
- ❑ Medical Assistant
- ❑ Nursing
- ❑ Nursing Assistant
- ❑ Ophthalmic Medical Assistant
- ❑ Ophthalmic Medical Technician
- ❑ Occupational Therapy Assistant
- ❑ Pharmacy Technician
- ❑ Phlebotomy Technician
- ❑ Physical Therapist Assistant
- ❑ Physical Therapy Technician
- ❑ Radiography
- ❑ Respiratory Therapy
- ❑ Veterinary Assistant
- ❑ Veterinary Technician

Name ____________________
Address ____________________
City ____________ State ________ Zip ________
Phone ____________ Day or Evening (circle one)
Email address ____________________

PIMA MEDICAL INSTITUTE

Mail this card today!
Or, call us at 888-635-5206.

Arizona California Colorado Nevada New Mexico Washington

NO POSTAGE
NECESSARY
IF MAILED
IN THE
UNITED STATES

BUSINESS REPLY MAIL

FIRST-CLASS MAIL PERMIT NO. 704 Tucson AZ

POSTAGE WILL BE PAID BY ADDRESSEE

Pima Medical Institute
941 S. Dobson Rd., Suite #302
Attn: Admission Support Center
Mesa, AZ 85202-9900

NO POSTAGE
NECESSARY
IF MAILED
IN THE
UNITED STATES

BUSINESS REPLY MAIL

FIRST-CLASS MAIL PERMIT NO. 704 Tucson AZ

POSTAGE WILL BE PAID BY ADDRESSEE

Pima Medical Institute
941 S. Dobson Rd., Suite #302
Attn: Admission Support Center
Mesa, AZ 85202-9900

NO POSTAGE
NECESSARY
IF MAILED
IN THE
UNITED STATES

BUSINESS REPLY MAIL

FIRST-CLASS MAIL PERMIT NO. 704 Tucson AZ

POSTAGE WILL BE PAID BY ADDRESSEE

Pima Medical Institute
941 S. Dobson Rd., Suite #302
Attn: Admission Support Center
Mesa, AZ 85202-9900

NO POSTAGE
NECESSARY
IF MAILED
IN THE
UNITED STATES

BUSINESS REPLY MAIL

FIRST-CLASS MAIL PERMIT NO. 704 Tucson AZ

POSTAGE WILL BE PAID BY ADDRESSEE

Pima Medical Institute
941 S. Dobson Rd., Suite #302
Attn: Admission Support Center
Mesa, AZ 85202-9900